CONTENTS

NOTES

General

1. The Army List is divided into three parts as follows:

   a. *Part I.* Contains details of major appointments, headquarters and establishments, and regimental and corps lists of officers of the active Army and the Territoral Army.

   b. *Part II.* Contains an alphabetical list of non-effective officers in receipt of retired pay.

   c. *Part III.* Contains the biographical list of serving officers. (Restricted sale).

Part I

2. Communications on officers' personal entries in the Army List should be addressed to the Ministry of Defence MS(AODO), Stanmore, Middlesex, HA7 4PZ. Communications from officers about their personal entries should be sent through commanding officers. Officers who succeed to peerages, baronetcies or courtesy titles, or who change their names are to notify the Ministry of Defence MS(AODO), Stanmore so that official records and the Army List may be corrected.

3. Communications on other matters should be addressed to the Ministry of Defence, MS(AODO)(AL), Room D3, F Block, Government Buildings, Stanmore, Middlesex, HA7 4PZ.

4. This edition of the Army List Part I is corrected to include promotions, appointments, etc. promulgated on or before 1 May 1986.

5. **The Gradation List.** This shows general officers down to and including major generals, under their substantive rank and in order of their seniority. All brigadiers and colonels are shown at the heads of their respective late regimental or corps lists. Lieutenant colonels and below are shown under their parent regimental or corps lists. The Gradation Lists for officers of the Royal Marines and for Warrant Officers (Class I) have been discontinued.

6. **Royal Armoured Corps and Infantry.**

   a. For corps and regiments bearing standards, guidons and regimental Colours the badges, devices, distinctions and mottoes borne thereon are shown after the titles of regiments, the "centre" badge being printed in bold type. In the case of other regiments and corps the badge, etc. shown after the title is the cap badge or shoulder belt badge.

   b. The honorary distinctions and battle honours awarded to regiments of the Royal Armoured Corps and infantry regiments are listed on the regimental pages. Those printed in bold type are borne on the standards, guidons or colours of existing regiments or, in the case of regiments having no standards, guidons or colours, on their appointments. Such battle honours of the Great War and Second World War are borne on the The Queen's Colour, the remaining battle honours shown in bold type being borne on the Regimental Colour. Foot Guards bear all battle honours shown in bold type on The Queen's and Regimental Colours.

   c. Notes on amalgamated Royal Armoured Corps regiments are shown at the beginning of the Royal Armoured Corps section. Notes on the amalgamated infantry regiments are shown at the beginning of each division.

   d. The figures in brackets after the titles of infantry regiments denote the former regiments of Foot to which the regiments belonged.

7. **Symbols, degrees and professional qualifications.** All entries include honours and awards. All symbols, degrees and professional qualifications are shown in regimental and corps lists except that honorary degrees are shown only in respect of general officers. Symbols are shown in entries relating to civilians throughout the Army List.

8. **Indian Army Associations.** A list of addresses of secretaries or representatives of associations connected with the Indian Army (pre-1947) and auxiliary Force (India) is maintained at the National Army Museum, the official museum of the Indian Army. Correspondence should be addressed to:

The Director, National Army Museum, Royal Hospital Road, Chelsea, London SW3 4HT
(*Tel No:* 01-730 0717)

SYMBOLS AND ABBREVIATIONS

SYMBOLS - BRIEF CURRENT MEANING

Symbol	*Short title*
adp	Advanced Automatic Data Processing Course
ae	Long Aeronautical Engineering Course
aic	Long Armour/Infantry Course
ato	Ammunition Technical Officer
aws	Air Warfare Course
C	Long Civil Engineering Course
cl	Post-Graduate Personnel Management Course
df	Defence Fellow
dis	Design of Information Systems Course
E	Long Electrical Course
ee	Long Electronic Engineering Course
ENG	Long Engineering Course
EM	Long Electrical and Mechanical Course
G†	Instructor-in-Gunnery(AA)
G	Instructor-in-Gunnery(Field)
G(a)	Instructor-in-Gunnery(AD)
G(gw)	Instructor-in-Gunnery(GW)
G(s)	Instructor-in-Gunnery(SSGW)
G(ss)	Instructor-in-Gunnery(SSGW)
G(y)	Instructor-in-Gunnery(Locating)
gsd	Gun System Design Course
gw	Guided Weapons Systems Course
hp	Half Pay
I*	Interpreter First Class
I	Interpreter Second Class
idc	Imperial Defence College Course
im	Industrial Administration Course
jsc	WRAC Staff College Course
jsdc	Joint Services Defence College
jssc	Joint Services Staff College Course
lc	Long Civil Catering Course
lcc	LCL Command Certificate(Ocean Going)
M	Long Mechanical Course
me	Long Mechanical Engineering Course
mvt	Military Vehicles Technology Course
nadc	NATO Defence College Course
ndc	National Defence College Course
oaws(US)	US Air War College
ocds()	Overseas College of Defence Studies
odc()	Overseas Defence College Course
o	Ordnance Officers Course
osc()	Overseas Staff College
owc	LCL Watch-Keeping Certificate (Ocean Going)
P	Officers Long Plant Course
pfc	Long Finance and Accountancy Course
ph	Rotary Wing Pilot
ph(i)	Rotary Wing B1 Flying Instructor
ph(cfs)	Rotary Wing A2 Flying Instructor
ph(cfs*)	Rotary Wing A1 Flying Instructor
pi	Long Petroleum Installation Course
pl	Fixed Wing Pilot
pl(i)	Fixed Wing B1 Flying Instructor
pl(cfs)	Fixed Wing A2 Flying Instructor
pl(cfs*)	Fixed Wing A1 Flying Instructor
psc†	Army Staff Course (Division I or II at RMCS followed by Staff College Camberley)
psc( )†	Army Staff Course (Division I or II at RMCS followed by Staff College in Australia, India, or Pakistan)
psc	Army Staff Course (Division III at RMCS followed by Staff College Camberley)
psc( )	Army Staff Course (Division III at RMCS followed by Staff College in Australia, India or Pakistan. Alternatively Staff College in Canada or Germany without attending RMCS)
psc(n)†	Naval Staff Course(preceded by Divisions I or II at RMCS)
psc(n)	Naval Staff Course(preceded by Division III at RMCS)
psc(a)†	Air Force Staff Course(preceded by Divisions I or II at RMCS)
psc(a)	Air Force Staff Course(preceded by Division III at RMCS)
psm	Advanced Certificate of Royal Military School of Music
ptsc	Technical Staff Course
qs	RAF Staff College
rcds	Royal College of Defence Studies Course
RLY	Railway Course
s	Food Technology Course
sowc	Senior Officers' War Course
sq	Staff qualified(other than at a Staff College)
sq(V)	Staff qualified(TA)
SVY	Army Survey Course
SVY(cg)	Advanced Cartography Course
SVY(gy)	Advanced Geodesy Course
SVY(pg)	Advanced Photogrammetry Course
SVY(pr)	Advanced Printing Course
t	Advanced Transport Course
t*	Advanced Transportation Course(US)
TE	Telecommunications Engineering Course
TEM	Telecommunication Engineering Management Course
TN	Long Transportation Course
tp	Empire Test Pilots'Course
tt	Tank Technology Course
Y	Instructor in Counter-Bombardment
†	On probation
††	University Medical or Dental Cadets
ø	Denotes a female officer (not QARANC or WRAC)
¶	Non-regular Permanent Staff (TA only)

ORDERS, DECORATIONS AND MEDALS

𝔙ℭ	Victoria Cross	
𝔊ℭ	George Cross	
KG	Knight of the Order of the Garter	
KT	Knight of the Order of the Thistle	
KP	Knight of the Order of St. Patrick	
GCB	Knight Grand Cross or Dame Grand Cross of the Order of the Bath	
OM	Member of the Order of Merit	
KCB	Knight Commander	of the Order of the Bath
CB	Companion	of the Order of the Bath
GCSI	Knight Grand Commander	of the Order of the Star of India
KCSI	Knight Commander	of the Order of the Star of India
CSI	Companion	of the Order of the Star of India
GCMG	Knight Grand Cross	of the Order of St Michael and St George
KCMG	Knight Commander	of the Order of St Michael and St George
CMG	Companion	of the Order of St Michael and St George
GCIE	Knight Grand Commander	of the Order of the Indian Empire
KCIE	Knight Commander	of the Order of the Indian Empire
CIE	Companion	of the Order of the Indian Empire
CI	Lady of the Imperial Order of the Crown of India	
GCVO	Knight Grand Cross or Dame Grand Cross	of the Royal Victorian Order
KCVO	Knight Commander	of the Royal Victorian Order
DCVO	Dame Commander	of the Royal Victorian Order
CVO	Commander	of the Royal Victorian Order
GBE	Knight Grand Cross or Dame Grand Cross of the Order of the British Empire	
CH	Member of the Order of the Companions of Honour	
KBE	Knight Commander	of the Order of the British Empire
DBE	Dame Commander	of the Order of the British Empire
CBE	Commander	of the Order of the British Empire
DSO	Companion of the Distinguished Service Order	
LVO	Lieutenant of the Royal Victorian Order	
OBE	Officer of the Order of the British Empire	
ISO	Companion of the Imperial Service Order	
MVO	Member of the Royal Victorian Order	
MBE	Member of the Order of the British Empire	
RRC	Member of the Royal Red Cross	
DSC	Distinguished Service Cross	
MC	Military Cross	
DFC	Distinguished Flying Cross	
AFC	Air Force Cross	
ARRC	Associate of the Royal Red Cross	
DCM	Distinguished Conduct Medal	
CGM	Conspicuous Gallantry Medal	
GM	George Medal	
DSM	Distinguished Service Medal	
MM	Military Medal	
DFM	Distinguished Flying Medal	
AFM	Air Force Medal	
QGM	The Queen's Gallantry Medal	
BEM	British Empire Medal	
ERD	Army Emergency Reserve Decoration	
VD	Volunteer Officers' Decoration or Colonial Auxiliary Forces Officers Decoration	
TD	Territorial Decoration or Efficiency Decoration	
AK	Knight of Australia	
QSO	Queen's Service Order (New Zealand)	
▪	Denotes the award of a bar to a decoration or medal for valour. The award of additional bars is indicated by the addition of a further similar symbol for each award.	

APPOINTMENTS TO THE QUEEN

ADC Gen	Aide de Camp General
ADC	Aide de Camp
Eq	Equerry
QHC	Honorary Chaplain
QHDS	Honorary Dental Surgeon
QHNS	Honorary Nursing Sister
QHP	Honorary Physician
QHS	Honorary Surgeon
QHVS	Honorary Veterinary Surgeon

REGIMENT AND CORPS ABBREVIATIONS

A and SH	The Argyll and Sutherland Highlanders (Princess Louise's) - Scottish Division
AAC	Army Air Corps
ACC	Army Catering Corps
ALC	Army Legal Corps
APTC	Army Physical Training Corps
BW	The Black Watch (Royal Highland Regiment - Scottish Division)
RHG/D	The Blues and Royals (Royal Horse Guards and 1st Dragoons) - Household Cavalry
CAMERONIANS	The Cameronians (Scottish Rifles) - Scottish Division
CHESHIRE	The Cheshire Regiment - Prince of Wales's Division
COLDM GDS	Coldstream Guards - Guards Division
REME	Corps of Royal Electrical and Mechanical Engineers
RE	Corps of Royal Engineers
RMP	Corps of Royal Military Police
D and D	The Devonshire and Dorset Regiment - Prince of Wales's Division
DERR	The Duke of Edinburgh's Royal Regiment (Berkshire and Wiltshire) - Prince of Wales's Division
DWR	The Duke of Wellington's Regiment (West Riding) - King's Division
GSC	General Service Corps
GLOSTERS	The Gloucestershire Regiment - Prince of Wales's Division
GORDONS	The Gordon Highlanders - Scottish Division
GREEN HOWARDS	The Green Howards (Alexandra Princess of Wales's Own Yorkshire Regiment) - King's Division
GREN GDS	Grenadier Guards - Guards Division
2 GR	2nd King Edward VIIs Own Gurkha Rifles (The Sirmoor Rifles) - Bde of Gurkhas
6 GR	6th Queen Elizabeth's Own Gurkha Rifles - Bde of Gurkhas
7 GR	7th Duke of Edinburgh's Own Gurkha Rifles - Bde of Gurkhas
10 GR	10th Princess Mary's Own Gurkha Rifles - Bde of Gurkhas
GTR	Gurkha Transport Regiment - Bde of Gurkhas
INT CORPS	Intelligence Corps
IG	Irish Guards - Guards Division
14/20 H	14th/20th King's Hussars - RAC
KINGS OWN BORDER	The King's Own Royal Border Regiment - King's Division
KOSB	The King's Own Scottish Borderers - Scottish Division
KINGS	The King's Regiment - King's Division
15/19 H	15th/19th The King's Royal Hussars - RAC
17/21 L	17th/21st Lancers
LG	The Life Guards - Household Cavalry
LI	The Light Infantry - Light Division
MPSC	Military Provost Staff Corps
OTC	Officers Training Corps
PARA	The Parachute Regiment
PWO	The Prince of Wales's Own Regiment of Yorkshire - King's Division
QARANC	Queen Alexandra's Royal Army Nursing Corps
QDG	1st The Queen's Dragoon Guards - RAC
QGE	The Queen's Gurkha Engineers - Bde of Gurkhas
QG SIGNALS	Queens Gurkha Signals - Bde of Gurkhas
QO HLDRS	Queen's Own Highlanders (Seaforth and Camerons) - Scottish Division
QLR	The Queen's Lancashire Regiment - King's Division
QOH	The Queen's Own Hussars - RAC
QUEENS	The Queen's Regiment - Queen's Division
QRIH	The Queen's Royal Irish Hussars - RAC
16/5 L	16th/5th The Queen's Royal Lancers - RAC
R ANGLIAN	The Royal Anglian Regiment - Queen's Division
RAC	Royal Armoured Corps
RACHD	Royal Army Chaplain's Department
RADC	Royal Army Dental Corps
RAEC	Royal Army Educational Corps
RAMC	Royal Army Medical Corps
RAOC	Royal Army Ordnance Corps
RAPC	Royal Army Pay Corps
RAVC	Royal Army Veterinary Corps
R SIGNALS	Royal Corps of Signals

RCT	Royal Corps of Transport
4/7 DG	4th/7th Royal Dragoon Guards - RAC
RGJ	The Royal Green Jackets - Light Division
R HAMPS	The Royal Hampshire Regiment - Prince of Wales's Division
RHF	The Royal Highland Fusiliers (Princess Margaret's Own Glasgow and Ayrshire Regiment) - Scottish Division
RHA	Royal Horse Artillery
RH	The Royal Hussars (Prince of Wales's Own) - RAC
13/18 H	13th/18th Royal Hussars (Queen Mary's Own) - RAC
5 INNIS DG	5th Royal Inniskilling Dragoon Guards - RAC
R IRISH	The Royal Irish Rangers (27th (Inniskilling) 83rd and 87th) - King's Division
9/12th L	9th/12th Royal Lancers (Prince of Wales's) - RAC
RPC	Royal Pioneer Corps
RA	Royal Regiment of Artillery
RRF	The Royal Regiment of Fusiliers - Queen's Division
RRW	The Royal Regiment of Wales - Prince of Wales's Division
RS	The Royal Scots (The Royal Regiment) - Scottish Division
SCOTS DG	The Royal Scots Dragoon Guards (Carabiniers and Greys) - RAC
RTR	Royal Tank Regiment - RAC
RWF	The Royal Welch Fusiliers - Prince of Wales's Division
SG	Scots Guards - Guards Division
SASC	Small Arms School Corps
SAS	Special Air Service Regiment
STAFFORDS	The Staffordshire Regiment (The Prince of Wales's) - Prince of Wales's Division
WG	Welsh Guards - Guards Division
WRAC	Women's Royal Army Corps
WFR	The Worcestershire and Sherwood Foresters Regiment - Prince of Wales's Division
Y and L	The York and Lancaster Regiment - King's Division

TA

UNIT TITLES WHICH DIFFER FROM THOSE OF REGULAR UNITS

R MON RE (M)	Royal Monmouthshire Royal Engineers (Militia)
HAC	The Honourable Artillery Company
RY	The Royal Yeomanry - RAC
R WX Y	The Royal Wessex Yeomanry - RAC
QOMY	The Queen's Own Mercian Yeomanry - RAC
QOY	The Queen's Own Yeomanry
DLOY	The Duke of Lancaster's Own Yeomanry - RAC
52 LOWLAND	52nd Lowland Volunteers - Scottish Division
51 HIGHLAND	51st Highland Volunteers - Scottish Division
YORKS	The Yorkshire Volunteers - King's Division
4 (V) R IRISH	The 4th(Volunteer)Battalion Royal Irish Rangers (27 (Inniskilling) 83rd and 87th (The North Irish Militia))
WESSEX	Wessex Regiment - Prince of Wales's Division
MERCIAN	Mercian Volunteers - Prince of Wales's Division
LI (V)	Light Infantry Volunteers - Light Division
UDR	The Ulster Defence Regiment

PRECEDENCE OF CORPS, ETC.

1. The Life Guards and The Blues and Royals
2. Royal Horse Artillery (a)
3. Royal Armoured Corps
4. Royal Regiment of Artillery (Royal Horse Artillery excepted)
5. Corps of Royal Engineers
6. Royal Corps of Signals
7. Regiments of Foot Guards
8. Regiments of Infantry (b)
9. Special Air Service Regiment
10. Army Air Corps
11. Royal Army Chaplains Department
12. Royal Corps of Transport
13. Royal Army Medical Corps
14. Royal Army Ordnance Corps
15. Corps of Royal Electrical and Mechanical Engineers
16. Corps of Royal Military Police
17. Royal Army Pay Corps
18. Royal Army Veterinary Corps
19. Small Arms School Corps
20. Military Provost Staff Corps
21. Royal Army Educational Corps
22. Royal Army Dental Corps
23. Royal Pioneer Corps
24. Intelligence Corps
25. Army Physical Training Corps
26. Army Catering Corps
27. Army Legal Corps
28. General Service Corps
29. Queen Alexandra's Royal Army Nursing Corps
30. Womens Royal Army Corps (d)
31. Royal Monmouthshire Royal Engineers (Militia) (Territorial Army)
32. The Honourable Artillery Company (Territorial Army)
33. Territorial Army(other than 31 and 32 above (c)
34. Ulster Defence Regiment

(a) But on parade, with their guns, to take the right and march at the head of the Household Cavalry.

(b) Divisions of Infantry have precedence as shown in the Corps Warrant. The precedence of the individual infantry regiments remains as it was before the grouping of Infantry Regiments was introduced.

(c) In order of arms as for the Regular Army.

(d) Women's Royal Army Corps personnel on the establishment of mixed units when parading with the male element of the unit will take precedence immediately after the male element.

PRECEDENCE OF INFANTRY REGIMENTS

The Royal Scots (The Royal Regiment)
The Queen's Regiment
The King's Own Royal Border Regiment
The Royal Regiment of Fusiliers
The King's Regiment
The Royal Anglian Regiment
The Devonshire and Dorset Regiment
The Light Infantry
The Prince of Wales's Own Regiment of Yorkshire
The Green Howards (Alexandra Princess of Wales's Own Yorkshire Regiment)
The Royal Highland Fusiliers (Princess Margaret's Own Glasgow and Ayrshire Regiment)
The Cheshire Regiment
The Royal Welch Fusiliers
The Royal Regiment of Wales (24th/41st Foot)
The King's Own Scottish Borderers
The Cameronians (Scottish Rifles)
The Royal Irish Rangers (27th (Inniskilling) 83rd and 87th)
The Gloucestershire Regiment
The Worcestershire and Sherwood Foresters Regiment (29th/45th Foot)
The Queen's Lancashire Regiment
The Duke of Wellington's Regiment (West Riding)
The Royal Hampshire Regiment
The Staffordshire Regiment (The Prince of Wales's)
The Black Watch (Royal Highland Regiment)
The Duke of Edinburgh's Royal Regiment (Berkshire and Wiltshire)
The York and Lancaster Regiment
Queen's Own Highlanders (Seaforth and Camerons)
The Gordon Highlanders
The Argyll and Sutherland Highlanders (Princess Louise's)
The Parachute Regiment
The Brigade of Gurkhas
The Royal Green Jackets

SECTION I

THE QUEEN

COLONEL IN CHIEF:— LG (060252), RHG/D (010469), SCOTS DG (020771), 16/5 L (060252), RTR (020653), RE (060252), GREN GDS (060252), COLDM GDS (060252), SG (060252), IG (060252), WG (060252), RWF (020653), QLR (250370), A and SH (060252), RGJ (010166), RAOC (020653), RMP (110677), QOMY (081073), DLOY (020653)

CAPTAIN GENERAL:— RA (060252), HAC (060252), CCF (020653)

Commonwealth Forces

COLONEL IN CHIEF:— Canadian Forces Military Engineers Branch, The King's Own Calgary Regiment, (RCAC), Royal 22e Regiment, Governor General's Foot Guards, The Canadian Grenadier Guards Le Regiment de la Chaudiere, 2nd Bn Royal New Brunswick Regiment (North Shore), The 48th Highlanders of Canada, The Argyll and Sutherland Highlanders of Canada (Princess Louise's), The Calgary Highlanders, Royal Australian Engineers, Royal Australian Infantry Corps, Royal Australian Army Ordnance Corps, Royal Australian Army Nursing Corps, The Corps of Royal New Zealand Engineers, Royal New Zealand Infantry Regiment, Royal New Zealand Army Ordnance Corps, Royal Malta Artillery, Malawi Rifles

CAPTAIN GENERAL:— Royal Regiment Canadian Artillery, Royal Regiment of Australian Artillery, Royal Regiment of New Zealand Artillery, Royal New Zealand Armoured Corps

MEMBERS OF THE ROYAL FAMILY

Her Majesty Queen Elizabeth, The Queen Mother

COLONEL IN CHIEF:— QDG (010159), QOH (031158), 9/12 L (110960), KINGS (010958), R ANGLIAN (010964), LI (100768), BW (020653), RAMC (020653)

COMMANDANT IN CHIEF:— WRAC (020653)

HONORARY COLONEL:— RY (180767), LOND SCOT (020653), University of London OTC (050858)

Commonwealth Forces

COLONEL IN CHIEF:— The Black Watch (Royal Highland Regiment) of Canada, The Toronto Scottish Regiment, Canadian Forces Medical Services, Royal Australian Army Medical Corps, Royal New Zealand Army Medical Corps

Field Marshal His Royal Highness The Prince PHILIP Duke of EDINBURGH KG KT OM GBE QSO

COLONEL IN CHIEF:— QRIH (241058), DERR (080659), QO HLDRS (070271), REME (010769), INT CORPS (110677), ACF (020653)

CAPTAIN GENERAL:— RM (020653)

COLONEL:— GREN GDS (010375)

HONORARY COLONEL:— Edinburgh and Heriot Watt Universities OTC (020653)

Commonwealth Forces

FIELD MARSHAL:— Australian Military Forces, New Zealand Army

COLONEL IN CHIEF:— The Royal Canadian Regiment, The Royal Hamilton Light Infantry (Wentworth Regiment) The Cameron Highlanders of Ottawa, The Queen's Own Cameron Highlanders of Canada, The Seaforth Highlanders of Canada, The Royal Canadian Army Cadets, The Royal Australian Electrical and Mechanical Engineers, The Australian Cadet Corps, Corps of Royal New Zealand Electrical and Mechanical Engineers

HONORARY COLONEL:— The Trinidad and Tobago Regiment

His Royal Highness The Prince of Wales KG KT GCB AK QSO ADC

COLONEL IN CHIEF:— 5 INNIS DG (090485), CHESHIRE (110677), RRW (010769), GORDONS (110677),PARA (110677), 2 GR (110677)

COLONEL:— WG (010375)

Commonwealth Forces

COLONEL IN CHIEF:— The Royal Canadian Dragoons, Lord Strathcona's Horse (Royal Canadians), Royal Regiment of Canada, Royal Winnipeg Rifles, Royal Australian Armoured Corps, The Royal Pacific Islands Regiment

Her Royal Highness The Princess of Wales

COLONEL IN CHIEF:— R HAMPS (030685)

Commonwealth Forces

COLONEL IN CHIEF:— The Princess of Wales' own Regiment (of Canada)

Her Royal Highness The Princess Anne, Mrs Mark Phillips GCVO

COLONEL IN CHIEF:— 14/20 H (010769), R SIGNALS (110677), RS (300683), WFR (280270)

Commonwealth Forces

COLONEL IN CHIEF:— 8th Canadian Hussars (Princess Louise's), Canadian Forces Communications and Electronics Branch, The Grey and Simcoe Foresters, (RCAC), The Regina Rifle Regiment, Royal Australian Corps of Signals, Royal New Zealand Corps of Signals, Royal New Zealand Nursing Corps

Her Royal Highness The Princess Margaret, Countess of Snowdon CI GCVO

COLONEL IN CHIEF:— 15/19 H (031158), RHF (200159), QARANC (280954)

DEPUTY COLONEL IN CHIEF:— R ANGLIAN (010964)

Commonwealth Forces

COLONEL IN CHIEF:— The Highland Fusiliers of Canada, The Princess Louise Fusiliers, Woman's Royal Australian Army Corps, The Bermuda Regiment Army Corps

Her Royal Highness Princess Alice, Duchess of Gloucester GCB CI GCVO GBE

COLONEL IN CHIEF:— RH (281069), KOSB (110537), RCT (080275)

DEPUTY COLONEL IN CHIEF:— R ANGLIAN (010964)

Commonwealth Forces

COLONEL IN CHIEF:— Royal Australian Corps of Transport, Royal New Zealand Corps of Transport

His Royal Highness The Duke of Gloucester GCVO

COLONEL IN CHIEF:— GLOSTERS (210375), RPC (110677)

HONORARY COLONEL:— R MON RE(M) (110677)

Her Royal Highness, The Duchess of Gloucester

COLONEL IN CHIEF:— RAEC (110677)

Commonwealth Forces

COLONEL IN CHIEF:— Royal Australian Army Educational Corps, Royal New Zealand Army Educational Corps

Major General His Royal Highness The Duke of Kent KG GCMG GCVO ADC

COLONEL IN CHIEF:— RRF (010769), D and D (110677)

COLONEL:— SG (090974)

Commonwealth Forces

COLONEL IN CHIEF:— The Lorne Scots (Peel, Dufferin and Hamilton Regiment)

Honorary Major General Her Royal Highness The Duchess of Kent GCVO

COLONEL IN CHIEF:— 4/7 DG (110677), PWO (070585), ACC (010769)

CONTROLLER COMMANDANT:— WRAC (280267)

HONORARY COLONEL:— YORKS (070568)

Her Royal Highness Princess Alexandra, the Hon Mrs Angus Ogilvy GCVO

COLONEL IN CHIEF:– 17/21 L (010769), KINGS OWN BORDER (110677)

DEPUTY COLONEL IN CHIEF:– LI (100768)

DEPUTY HONORARY COLONEL:– RY (010475)

Commonwealth Forces

COLONEL IN CHIEF:– The Queen's Own Rifles of Canada, The Canadian Scottish Regiment (Princess Mary's)

PERSONAL AIDES DE CAMP TO THE QUEEN

HRH The Prince of Wales *KG KT GCB AK QSO*
Maj Gen *HRH The Duke of* KENT *KG GCMG GCVO*
Capt M A P Phillips *CVO* ret

AIDES DE CAMP GENERAL TO THE QUEEN

Gen *Sir* Thomas Morony *KCB OBE*
Gen *Sir* Roland Guy *KCB CBE DSO*
Gen *Sir* Nigel Bagnall *GCB CVO MC*▪
Gen *Sir* Edward Burgess *KCB OBE*

AIDES DE CAMP TO THE QUEEN

Col B T John *CBE TD* TA
Brig H G Meechie *CBE* WRAC
Col W H F Stevens *OBE* TA
Brig A R Douglas-Nugent
Col W E Falloon *CBE TD* TA
Col P E Williams *TD* TA
Brig T G Leighs *CBE ED* (Territorial Forces) New Zealand Military Forces (Additional)
Brig K M Gordon *OBE* New Zealand Military Forces (Additional)
Col E C York *TD* TA
Col P J C Robinson *TD DL* TA
Col K D Brown *OBE TD DL* TA
Brig J A Turner
Brig P D Orchard-Lisle *TD* TA
Brig J B Wilks *CBE*
Brig P A Dally *CBE*
Brig C J Lee *CBE*
Col M J Dudding TA
Brig J R Burrows
Brig J E Killick
Brig C F Jebens *OBE*
Brig A D Myrtle *CBE*
Col D S Casstles *TD DL* TA
Brig T R M Pulverman
Col J G Evans *CBE TD* TA
Col J C V Hunt *OBE TD DL* TA
Brig M J Evans
Brig B K Warner
Brig I Mackay *MBE MC*
Col A H Hawksworth *TD DL* TA
Brig A MacLauchlan
Col A A F Terry *TD JP* TA
Brig A C Vivian *CBE*
Brig A K Dixon
Col J N Egan *TD* TA
Brig B V H Fullerton *CBE*

EQUERRIES TO THE QUEEN

Crown Equerry

Lt Col *Sir* John Miller *KCVO DSO MC* ret pay

Equerries

Lt Col (SL) B A Stewart-Wilson *LVO* ret pay *(Deputy Master of the Household)*
A/Maj H C L Lindsay 9/12 L

Temporary Equerry

Capt S D Holborow COLDM GDS

Extra Equerries

Lt Col R Myddelton *LVO* ret pay
Maj *Sir* Edward Ford *KCB KCVO*
Lt Col *The Lord* Charteris of Amisfield *GCB GCVO OBE QSO*
Lt Col *Sir* Eric Penn *GCVO OBE MC* ret pay
Lt Col *Sir* John Johnston *KCVO MC* ret pay *(Comptroller, Lord Chamberlain's Office)*
Brig *Sir* Geoffrey Hardy-Roberts *KCVO CB CBE DL*
Maj *Sir* Rennie Maudslay *GCVO KCB MBE*
Lt Col G A A-R West ret pay

HONORARY CHAPLAINS TO THE QUEEN

The Ven Archdeacon W F Johnston *CB* Chaplain General
Rev J Harkness *OBE* Deputy Chaplain General [C of S]
Rev W B Pugh Chaplain to the Forces 1st Class
Rev T H Robinson Chaplain to the Forces 1st Class

HONORARY PHYSICIANS TO THE QUEEN

Brig K A Hunter *OBE* Royal Canadian Army Medical Corps
Maj Gen J A G R Dupuis *CD* Surgeon General Canadian Forces
Brig Gen C J Knight *CD* Commandant National Defence Medical Centre, Canada
Brig D E Worsley
Maj Gen A J Shaw *CBE*
Brig N W J England
Maj Gen D M Roberts
Brig P H Swinhoe *OBE*
Col H S Platt *TD* TA
Col L Johnman TA

HONORARY SURGEONS TO THE QUEEN

Col D D Beard *RFD ED* Royal Aust Army Medical Corps
Brig D W Bray
Maj Gen B Livesey
Lt Gen *Sir* Cameron Moffat *KBE*
Brig D L Macphie
Col T R Austin TA
Col J P Alexander *TD* TA

HONORARY DENTAL SURGEONS TO THE QUEEN

Col L A Richardson *CD* Canadian Forces Dental Branch
Brig Gen J J N Wright *CD* Canadian Forces Dental Branch
Col J M Donely *CD* Canadian Forces Dental Branch
Col R Docherty
Lt Col R W Beckman Royal New Zealand Dental Corps
Col G D Stafford *TD*
Brig E Coulthard

HONORARY VETERINARY SURGEON TO THE QUEEN

Brig R J Clifford

HONORARY NURSING SISTERS TO THE QUEEN

Col H F Ott *CD* Director Nursing Services, Canadian Forces
Brig M B T Hennessy *MBE RRC* QARANC
Lt Col T M Kennedy Royal New Zealand Nursing Corps

HER MAJESTY'S BODY GUARD OF THE HON CORPS OF GENTLEMEN AT ARMS

(ESTABLISHED IN THE YEAR 1509)

Uniform - Scarlet *Facings* - Blue Velvet

Agents— Lloyds Bank PLC, Cox's & King's Branch

Captain

Lord Denham *PC* 070579

Lieutenant

Col R J V Crichton *CVO MC* ret pay (*late* COLDM GDS) 211081

Standard Bearer

Lt Col C E J Eagles (*late* RM) 180486

Clerk of the Cheque and Adjutant

VC Maj D Jamieson (*late* R NORFOLK) 211081

Harbinger

Col P Pardoe ret pay (*late* RGJ) 180486

Gentlemen-at-Arms

Lt Col N H R Speke *MC* (*late* 12 L) 230367
Lt Col D A St G Laurie *OBE MC* ret pay (*late* 9 L) 260368
Maj *Sir* Richard Rasch *Bt* (*late* GREN GDS) 230768
Lt Col P Hodgson (*late* 15/19 H) 261168
Lt Col R Steele *MBE* ret pay (*late* GREN GDS) 030669
Lt Col W S P Lithgow ret pay (*late* 10 H) 080570
Maj J D Dillon *DSC* (*late* RM) 191071
Hon Col A G Way *MC* ret pay (*late* GREN GDS) 070372
Maj *The Lord* Suffield *MC* (*late* COLDM GDS) 200473
Maj T E St Aubyn ret pay (*late* 2 GJ) 070573
Brig A N Breitmeyer ret pay (*late* GREN GDS) 080876
Lt Col *Sir* James Scott *Bt* ret pay (*late* LG) 080377
Maj *Sir* Torquhil Matheson of Matheson *Bt* ret pay (*late* COLDM GDS) 160977
Capt *The Lord* Monteagle of Brandon (*late* IG) 010478
Hon Maj F J Matheson ret pay (*late* COLDM GDS) 040279
Maj J A J Nunn ret pay (*late* 10 H) 040579
Maj *Sir* Philip Duncombe *Bt* (*late* GREN GDS) 110579
Maj I Ramsden *MBE* (*late* WG) 200779
Hon Col T A Hall *OBE* ret pay (*late* 11 H) 290780
Col *Sir* Piers Bengough *KCVO OBE* ret pay (*late* RH) 240181
Maj M J Drummond-Brady (*late* QUEENS) 150981
Maj A R F Arkwright ret pay (*late* 9/12 L) 211081
Lt Col R Mayfield *DSO* ret pay (*late* SG) 021181
Maj G M B Colenso-Jones ret pay (*late* RWF) 260582
Col *The Hon* R N Crossley *TD* (*late* 9 L) 260582
Col T Wilson (*late* RM) 090184
Col D V Fanshawe *OBE* ret pay (*late* GREN GDS) 180486

THE TOWER OF LONDON

Constable
Field Marshal *Sir* Roland Gibbs *GCB CBE DSO MC* (*late* PARA) 010885
(*Vice Lord Lieutenant Wiltshire*)

Lieutenant
Lt Gen *Sir* Peter Hudson *KCB CBE* ret pay 010386

Resident Governor and Keeper of the Jewel House
Maj Gen A P W MacLellan *CB MBE* ret pay (*late* COLDM GDS) 180784

Medical Officer
Surgeon/Capt A McEwan *OBE* RN ret pay 031179

Deputy Governor (Admin) and Ordnance Officer
Lt Col (OEO) J H Wynn RAOC 280286

Deputy Governor (Security)
Brig K J Mears *CBE* ret pay (*late* INT CORPS) 271279

THE QUEEN'S BODY GUARD OF THE YEOMEN OF THE GUARD

(INSTITUTED 1485)

Uniform - Scarlet *Facings* - Blue Velvet

Agents— Lloyds Bank PLC, Cox's & King's Branch

Captain
The Earl of Swinton 031182

Lieutenant
Col A B Pemberton *MBE* ret pay (*late* COLDM GDS) 051085

Clerk of the Cheque and Adjutant
Maj B M H Shand *MC DL* ret pay (*late* 12 L) 051085

Ensign
Col G W Tufnell ret pay (*late* GREN GDS) 051085

Exons
Lt Col R S Longsdon ret pay (*late* 17/21 L) 051085
Maj C R Marriott (*late* RB) 291185

WINDSOR CASTLE

Constable and Governor

Marshal of the RAF *Sir* John Grandy *GCB KBE DSO* 120878

MILITARY KNIGHTS OF WINDSOR

(INSTITUTED 1348)

Badges - (i) A Shield charged with Cross of St George (ii) The Star of the Order of the Garter

Uniform - Scarlet *Facings* - Blue

Governor

Maj Gen *Sir* Peter Gillett *KCVO CB OBE* ret pay (*late* RA)

Royal Foundation

Hon Lt Col R W Dobbin *OBE* ret pay (*late* RA)
Maj (QM) H Smith *MBE* ret pay (*late* SG)
Hon Lt Col C A Harvey ret pay (*late* HLI)
Hon Lt Col A R Clark *MC* ret pay (*late* R LEICESTERS)
Hon Maj A E Wollaston (*late* RE)
Brig A L Atkinson *OBE* ret pay (*late* R SIGNALS)
Hon Brig J F Lindner *OBE MC* ret pay (*late* RA)
Brig A C Tyler *CBE MC* ret pay (*late* WELCH)
Maj W L Thompson *MBE DCM* ret pay (*late* LG)
Maj (QM) J C Cowley *DCM* ret pay (*late* COLDM GDS)
Maj L W Dickerson ret pay (*late* KINGS)

8

THE QUEEN'S BODY GUARD FOR SCOTLAND ROYAL COMPANY OF ARCHERS

ORGANISED IN THE YEAR 1676 (RECONSTITUTED 1703)

Uniform - Green *Facings* - Black with Red Velvet

Captain-General

Col *The Earl of* Stair *KCVO MBE* ret pay (*late* SG) 121273

Captains

Maj *The Lord* Home *KT PC* 030474
The Duke of Buccleuch and Queensbury *KT VRD* 210476
Lt Col *Sir* John Gilmour *Bt DSO TD* 160481
Col *The Lord* Clydesmuir *KT CB MBE TD* 240485

Lieutenants

Maj *The Lord* Maclean of Duart & Morvern *KT GCVO KBE PC* 140477
Maj *Sir* Hew Hamilton-Dalrymple *Bt KCVO* 160481
Maj *The Earl of* Wemyss and March *KT* 220482
The Earl of Airlie *KT GCVO* 240485

Ensigns

Lt Gen *Sir* William Turner *KBE CB DSO* ret pay (*late* KOSB) 140477
Capt I M Tennant 160481
Maj *The Earl of* Dalhousie *KT GCVO GBE MC* 220482
Maj Gen *The Earl* Cathcart *CB DSO MC* ret pay (*late* SG) 240485

Brigadiers

Capt N E F Dalrymple-Hamilton *CVO MBE DSC* RN ret pay 210470
The Marquess of Lothian *KCVO* 140472
Commodore *Sir* John Clerk of Penicuik *Bt CBE VRD* 240473
The Earl of Elgin and Kincardine *KT* 030474
Col G R Simpson *DSO LVO TD* 030474
Maj D H Butter *MC* 020475
The Earl of Minto *OBE DL* 210476
Maj Gen *Sir* John Swinton *KCVO OBE* ret pay (*late* SG) 140477
Gen *Sir* Michael Gow *GCB* 160481
The Hon Lord Elliott *MC* 220482
Maj *The Hon* L H C Maclean 180484
The Rt Hon G Younger *TD MP* 240485
Capt G Burnet *LVO* 240485

Secretary

Col H F O Bewsher *OBE* ret pay (*late* RS) 220482

Adjutant

Maj *Sir* Hew Hamilton-Dalrymple *Bt KCVO* 210464

Surgeon

Dr M D L Finlay 240485

Chaplain

The Very Rev Ronald Selby-Wright *CVO TD DD* 071273

FOREIGN SOVEREIGNS
AND
MEMBERS OF FOREIGN ROYAL FAMILIES

who are Colonels in Chief or Honorary Colonels of Regiments, or hold rank in the Army

Her Royal Highness PRINCESS JULIANA OF THE NETHERLANDS
Allied Colonel in Chief QUEENS (311266)

His Majesty Olav V KING OF NORWAY *KG KT GCB GCVO*
Colonel in Chief GREEN HOWARDS (190858), Honorary Colonel 100 (Yeomanry) Field Regt RA (V) (010561)

Her Majesty QUEEN MARGRETHE II OF DENMARK
Allied Colonel in Chief QUEENS (270672)

His Majesty Birendra Bir Bikram Shah Dev KING OF NEPAL
Honorary Field Marshal (181180)

His Majesty Sir MUDA HASSANAL BOLKIAH MU'IZZADDIN WADDAULA SULTAN AND YANG DI-PERTUAN NEGARA BRUNEI DARUSSALAM *GCMG*
Honorary General (230284)

Colonel *His Highness* PRINCE GEORG OF DENMARK *KCVO*
Honorary Colonel 5 QUEENS (290475)

His Royal Higness Prince Mohamed Bolkiah of Brunei *CVO*
Honorary Lieutenant IG

His Royal Highness THE DUKE OF LUXEMBOURG *KG*
Colonel IG (210884)

10

DISBANDED REGIMENTS

GURKHA MILITARY POLICE

(*Disbanded* 1965)

The Royal Cypher between two kukris in saltire the blades upwards and inwards, all within a wreath of laurel thereunder a scroll inscribed "Gurkha Military Police" all in silver

ROYAL MILITARY ACADEMY BAND CORPS

(*Disbanded* 1985)

The Royal Cypher within a circlet bearing the words ROYAL MILITARY ACADEMY SANDHURST surmounted by a Crown. Below the circlet a scroll bearing the words — SERVE TO LEAD

SECTION II

12

DEFENCE COUNCIL

The Right Honourable GEORGE YOUNGER ***TD DL MP***
Secretary of State for Defence ***(Chairman of the Defence Council)***

The Right Honourable JOHN STANLEY ***MP***
Minister of State for the Armed Forces

THE LORD TREFGARNE
Minister of State for Defence Procurement

ROGER FREEMAN ***MP***
Minister of State for Defence Support

JOHN LEE ***MP***
Parliamentary Under-Secretary of State for Defence Procurement

Admiral of the Fleet Sir JOHN FIELDHOUSE ***GCB GBE***
Chief of the Defence Staff

Sir CLIVE WHITMORE ***KCB CVO***
Permanent Under-Secretary of State

Admiral Sir WILLIAM STAVELEY ***GCB ADC***
Chief of the Naval Staff and First Sea Lord

General Sir NIGEL BAGNALL ***GCB CVO MC■ ADC Gen***
Chief of the General Staff

Air Chief Marshal Sir DAVID CRAIG ***GCB OBE ADC***
Chief of the Air Staff

Air Chief Marshal Sir PATRICK HINE ***KCB***
Vice Chief of the Defence Staff

P K LEVENE
Chief of Defence Procurement

Professor R O C NORMAN ***FRS***
Chief Scientific Adviser

Sir DAVID PERRY ***KCB***
Chief of Defence Equipment Collaboration

J N H BLELLOCH ***CB***
Second Permanent Under Secretary of State

ARMY BOARD OF THE DEFENCE COUNCIL

The Right Honourable GEORGE YOUNGER *TD DL MP*
Secretary of State for Defence
(Chairman of the Defence Council and Chairman of the Army Board of the Defence Council)

The Right Honourable JOHN STANLEY *MP*
Minister of State for the Armed Forces

The Lord **TREFGARNE**
Minister of State for Defence Procurement

ROGER FREEMAN *MP*
Minister of State for Defence Support

JOHN LEE *MP*
Parliamentary Under-Secretary of State for Defence Procurement

---

General Sir NIGEL BAGNALL *GCB CVO MC ADC Gen*
Chief of the General Staff

J N H BLELLOCH *CB*
Second Permanent Under-Secretaty of State *(Secretary of the Army Board)*

General Sir ROLAND GUY *KCB CBE DSO ADC Gen*
Adjutant General

General Sir RICHARD TRANT *KCB*
Quartermaster General

Lieutenant General Sir RICHARD VINCENT *KCB DSO*
Master General of the Ordnance

Sir COLIN FIELDING *CB*
Controller R and D Establishments Research and Nuclear

ARMY BOARD SECRETARIAT

J M Legge

EXECUTIVE COMMITTEE OF THE ARMY BOARD

Chairman........................Chief of the General Staff
Members........................The Second Permanent Under Secretary of State
The Adjutant General
The Quartermaster General
The Master General of the Ordnance
The Assistant Chief of the General Staff

15

MINISTRY OF DEFENCE

SECRETARY OF STATE FOR DEFENCE

SECRETARY OF STATE FOR DEFENCE .... *The Right Honourable* GEORGE YOUNGER *TD DL MP*

Private Secretary .... R C Mottram

MINISTER OF STATE FOR THE ARMED FORCES .. *The Right Honourable* JOHN STANLEY *MP*

MINISTER OF STATE FOR DEFENCE PROCUREMENT

The Lord TREFGARNE

CHIEF OF THE DEFENCE STAFF .... Admiral of the Fleet *Sir* JOHN FIELDHOUSE *GCB GBE*

Principal Staff Officer .... Brig A S J Blacker *OBE*

PERMANENT UNDER-SECRETARY OF STATE .... *Sir* CLIVE WHITMORE *KCB CVO*

CHIEF OF NAVAL STAFF AND FIRST SEA LORD ... Admiral *Sir* WILLIAM STAVELEY *GCB ADC*

CHIEF OF THE GENERAL STAFF .... General *Sir* NIGEL BAGNALL *GCB CVO MC ADC Gen*

CHIEF OF THE AIR STAFF .... Air Chief Marshal *Sir* DAVID CRAIG *GCB OBE ADC*

VICE CHIEF OF THE DEFENCE STAFF .... Air Chief Marshal *Sir* Patrick Hine *KCB*

CHIEFS OF STAFF COMMITTEE

Secretary .... Gp Capt J S Allison *CBE*

DEFENCE SERVICES SECRETARY .... Air Vice Marshal R C F Peirse *CB*

DEFENCE STAFF

Defence Policy Staff

Deputy Under Secretary of State (Policy) .... D A Nicholls *CMG*

Assistant Chief of Defence Staff (Policy/Nuclear) .... Rear Admiral J C K Slater

Directors .... Brig *The Honourable* T P J Boyd-Carpenter *MBE*
D Fewtrell
Air Cdre P J Harding *CBE AFC*

Assistant Under Secretary of State (Defence Staff) ... N H Nicholls *CBE*

Directors .... B R Hawtin

Defence Programmes and Personnel Staff

Deputy Chief of the Defence Staff (Programmes & Personnel)
Lt Gen *Sir* John Chapple *KCB CBE*

Assistant Chief of the Defence Staff (Programmes) .. Air Vice Marshal R H Palin *CBE*

Directors .... Cdre J Todd *CBE*
Cdre P C Abbott
Brig R H Swinburn
Air Cdre A L Roberts *CBE AFC*

Director (Personnel) .... Brig R L Peck

Defence Medical Services Directorate

Surgeon General .... Maj Gen *Sir* Cameron Moffat *KBE QHS*

Deputy Surgeons General .... Air Marshal J G Donald *KBE QHP*
Surg Rear Admiral G F Milton Thompson *QHP*

Assistant Surgeons General .... Brig R S Blewett *OBE*
Brig B L Francis
Surg Cdre R E Snow *LVO OBE QHP*
Brig P H Swinhoe *OBE QHP*
Air Cdre C E Simpson *QHS*
Air Cdre M A Pallister

Defence Commitments Staff

Deputy Chief of the Defence Staff (Commitments) ... Vice Admiral *Sir* John Woodward *KCB*

Assistant Chief of the Defence Staff (NATO/UK) ...... Maj Gen G D Johnson *OBE MC*

Directors .... Cdre P M Goddard
Gp Capt J S B Price *CBE*
Col C J M Harrisson *OBE*
Lt Col S J Pack RM

Assistant Chief of Defence Staff (Overseas) .... Air Vice Marshal B Higgs *CBE*

Directors .... Air Commodore B T Sills
Brig I O J Sprackling *OBE*
Captain F A Collins RN
Col C D M Ritchie *OBE*
Gp Capt P L Gray

Assistant Chief of the Defence Staff (Logistics) .... Rear Admiral A J Richmond

Directors .... Gp Capt N T Carter *CBE*
Col E M Parry-Davies
Col F M Webb

Ministry of Defence — continued

Defence Systems Staff

Deputy Chief of the Defence Staff (Systems) ....Air Marshal *Sir* Donald Hall *KCB CBE AFC*
Assistant Chief of Defence Staff (Concepts).............Maj Gen J C Reilly *DSO*
Directors............Air Cdre C J Thompson *CBE AFC*
Brig R V Ockenden *OBE*
Assistant Chief of Defence Staff OR (Sea)............Rear Admiral J B Kerr
Director............Cdre J F Coward
Assistant Chief of Defence Staff OR (Land)............Maj Gen J J Stibbon *OBE*
Directors............Brig J W F Rucker
Brig J E Killick *ADC*
Brig J O C Alexander *OBE*
Assistant Chief of Defence Staff OR (Air)............Air Vice Marshal M K Adams *CB AFC*
Directors............Air Commodore W J Wratten *CBE AFC*
Air Commodore G C Williams *AFC*■
Assistant Chief of the Defence Staff (CIS)............Maj Gen G R Oehlers
DCCCIS (FITS)............Air Cdre D G J Breadner
DCIS (NATO)............C Thomas

Defence Intelligence Staff

Chief of Defence Intelligence............Lt Gen *Sir* Derek Boorman *KCB*
Assistant Chief of Defence Staff (Intelligence)............Rear Admiral T M Bevan *CB*
Director Management and Support Intelligence............Air Vice Marshal D Allison

Defence Public Relations Staff

Chief of Public Relations............J K Ledlie *OBE*

PERMANENT UNDER SECRETARY OF STATE

SECOND PERMANENT UNDER SECRETARY OF STATE

Second Permanent Under Secretary of State ....J N H BLELLOCH *CB*

OFFICE OF MANAGEMENT AND BUDGET

Deputy Under Secretary of State (Resources and Programmes)
K C MacDonald *CB*
Deputy Under Secretary of State (Finance) ....J G Ashcroft
Deputy Under Secretary of State (Personnel and Logistics)
B E Robson *CB*
Deputy Under Secretary of State (Civilian Management)
R M Hastie-Smith *CB*
Head of Resources and Programmes (Army) ....M J Legge
Director of Army Management and Audit...................D Dreher
Head of Army Management Services ....N S Bolton

DEFENCE SCIENTIFIC STAFF

Chief Scientific Adviser..*Prof* R O C Norman *FRS*
Deputy Chief Scientific Adviser ....N H Hughes
Assistant Chief Scientific Adviser (Project and Research)
Assistant Chief Scientific Adviser (Nuclear)...............*Dr* R G Ridley
Assistant Chief Scientific Adviser (Capabilities) ....J D Culshaw

PROCUREMENT EXECUTIVE

Chief of Defence Procurement ....P K Levene

DEFENCE EQUIPMENT COLLABORATION

Chief of Defence Equipment Collaboration ....*Sir* David Perry

DEFENCE ARMS CONTROL UNIT

Head ....J F Howe

ARMY DEPARTMENT

CHIEF OF THE GENERAL STAFF

CHIEF OF THE GENERAL STAFF .... GEN *SIR* NIGEL BAGNALL *GCB CVO MC▪ ADC Gen* 280785
Assistant Chief of the General Staff .... Maj Gen J R A MacMillan *CBE* 231184

DIRECTORATE OF MILITARY OPERATIONS
Director .... Brig L F H Busk

DIRECTORATE OF COMMAND CONTROL COMMUNICATIONS AND INFORMATION SYSTEMS (ARMY)
Director .... Brig A C D Lloyd

DIRECTORATE OF MILITARY SURVEY
Director .... Maj Gen C N Thompson 230384
Deputy .... Brig H C Woodrow 120384

DIRECTOR GENERAL TERRITORIAL ARMY AND ORGANISATION
Maj Gen C E W Jones *CBE* 140285

DIRECTORATE OF ARMY STAFF DUTIES
Director .... Brig R M Llewellyn *OBE* 130284

DIRECTORATE OF ARMY RESERVES AND CADETS
Director .... Brig M A Aris *CBE* 221184

ENGINEER IN CHIEF (ARMY)
Engineer in Chief .... Maj Gen C J Rougier *CB* 021285
Deputy .... Brig C W Woodburn 310184

SIGNAL OFFICER IN CHIEF (ARMY)
Signal Officer in Chief .... Maj Gen P D Alexander *MBE* 161285
Deputy .... Brig F R Maynard 071085

GENERAL STAFF SECRETARIAT
Head .... M L Scicluna

ARMY HISTORICAL BRANCH
Head .... *Miss* A I Ward

MILITARY SECRETARY

MILITARY SECRETARY .... LT GEN *SIR* DAVID MOSTYN *KCB CBE* 211283

Deputy Military Secretaries .... Brig D M Naylor *MBE* 270885
Brig P W Graham *CBE* 221085
Col R H Robinson *OBE* 311084

No 1 Selection Board (Appointments and Promotion to Major General)

President .... The Chief of the General Staff (or, in his absence the Adjutant General)
Members .... The Adjutant General
The Quartermaster General
The Master General of Ordnance
The Commander in Chief, British Army of the Rhine
The Commander in Chief, United Kingdom Land Forces
Secretary .... The Military Secretary
Assistant Secretary .... The Deputy Military Secretary (A)

No 2 Selection Board (Appointments and Promotion to Brigadier and Colonel)

President .... The Commandant Staff College (or in his absence, a member of the Board to be nominated by the Military Secretary)
Members .... Four officers drawn from:
The Director General Territorial Army & Organisation
The Director General of Manning & Recruiting
The Director General of Logistic Policy (Army)
The Vice Master General of the Ordnance
The Chief of Staff, British Army of the Rhine
The Chief of Staff, United Kingdom Land Forces
The Commandant, Royal Military Academy Sandhurst
The Commandant, Royal Military College of Science
Secretary .... The Deputy Military Secretary (A)
Assistant Secretary .... The Colonel MS2
The Board may co-opt additional members in the rank of Major General to assist them in their duties

No 3 Selection Board (Weapons Appointments)

President .... The Director General of Army Manning and Recruiting (or in his absence, the Assistant Chief of the Defence Staff Operational Requirements (Land Systems) or the Commandant, Royal Military College of Science)
Members .... Four officers drawn from:
The Vice Master General of the Ordnance
The Assistant Chief of the Defence Staff Operational Requirements (Land Systems)
The Commandant Royal Military College of Science
The Director General of Fighting Vehicles and Engineer Equipment
The Director General of Weapons (Army)
The Director, Royal Armament Research and Development Establishment
The Assistant Under Secretary of State (Civilian Management) (Specialists)
Secretary .... The Deputy Military Secretary (A)
Assistant Secretary .... The Staff Officer 1 MS3

Ministry of Defence — continued

No 4 Selection Board (Appointments and Promotions to Lieutenant Colonel)

President...The Director General of Army Manning & Recruiting (or in his absence the senior member of the Board)

Members..Four officers drawn from:
The Director General Territorial Army & Organisation
The Director Army Training
The Director General of Fighting Vehicles and Engineer Equipment
The Director General of Weapons (Army)
The Director Royal Armoured Corps
The Director Royal Artillery
The Engineer in Chief (Army)
The Signal Officer in Chief (Army)
The Director of Infantry
The Director of Army Air Corps
The Director General of Transport and Movements
The Director General of Ordnance Services
The Director General of Electrical and Mechanical Engineering
The Paymaster-in-Chief (Army)
The Director of Army Education
The Commandant, Royal Military College of Science
The GOC London District
The GOC Eastern District
The GOC South West District
The GOC North West District
The GOC Western District
The GOC Wales
The GOC North East District

In addition, the Director Special Air Services attends when Special Air Service command appointments are considered. The Provost Marshall (Army), the Director of Army Pioneers & Labour, the Director of the Intelligence Corps, the Director of the Army Catering Corps, the Director of the Women's Royal Army Corps and the Director of Veterinary and Remount Services, attend when officers of their respective Corps are being considered for promotion. The Colonels of the MOD(AD) personnel branches may be called upon to attend meetings of the Board when appointments of their Arms of the Service are under discussion.

The Military Secretary attends meetings of the Board when possible

Secretary...The Deputy Military Secretary (B)

Assistant Secretary............................The Staff Officer 1 MS4

No 5 Selection Board (Promotion to Major)

President..The Director of Manning Policy (Army)

Members..The Deputy Military Secretary (B)
The Colonel M6(A)
Two Brigadiers or Colonels to be nominated by the Military Secretary

Secretary...The Staff Officer 1 MS5

In Attendance ....The Colonel of the MOD (Army) personnel branch of the Arm or Corps being considered

ADJUTANT GENERAL

ADJUTANT GENERAL................GEN *SIR* ROLAND GUY *KCB CBE DSO ADC GEN*............310384

DIRECTOR GENERAL ARMY MANNING AND RECRUITING
A/Maj Gen A B Crowfoot *CBE*............080386

Director of Manning (Army)................Brig N H Thompson............200186

Director of Army Recruiting................Brig I S Baxter *CBE*............070685

Director of Army Personnel Research Establishment
E D T Strong............010781

Director of Army Sport Control Board................Brig P D F Thursby *OBE* ret pay............240973

DIRECTOR GENERAL OF PERSONAL SERVICES (ARMY)
Maj Gen J D G Pank............190485

Director of Army Service Conditions................Brig C G Mattingley *CBE*............030685

DIRECTOR OF ARMY TRAINING................Maj Gen K Spacie *OBE*............171284

Inspector of Physical and Adventurous Training....Brig R J Baddeley............240486

DIRECTOR OF SECURITY (ARMY)................Maj Gen H E M L Garrett *CBE* ret pay............100778

CHAPLAINCY SERVICES

Chaplain General................*The Ven Archdeacon* W F Johnston *CB QHC*............010780

Deputy Chaplain General................*Rev* J Harkness *OBE QHC* [C of S]............010185

Principal Roman Catholic Chaplain (Army)................*Rt Rev Mgr* J N Williams............180585

PROVOST MARSHALL (ARMY)................Brig B Thomas *CBE*............030683

PAYMASTER IN CHIEF................Maj Gen B M Bowen............030386

Inspector Pay Services................Brig B V H Fullerton *CBE ADC*............020985

DIRECTOR OF ARMY VETERINARY AND REMOUNT SERVICES
Brig R J Clifford *QHVS*............010583

DIRECTOR OF ARMY EDUCATION................Maj Gen D E Ryan............020484

DIRECTOR OF ARMY LEGAL SERVICES................Maj Gen J F Bowman *CB*............240284

DIRECTOR OF WOMENS ROYAL ARMY CORPS....Brig H G Meechie *CBE Hon ADC*............070382

ASSISTANT UNDER SECRETARY OF STATE (ADJUTANT GENERAL)
M J Culham............150882

Head AG Secretariat 1................A J H Adams............070185

Head AG Secretariat 2................P Archer............121081

Director of Army Management Audit................D Dreher............060884

QUARTERMASTER GENERAL

QUARTERMASTER GENERAL
GEN *SIR* RICHARD TRANT *KCB* 050983

DIRECTOR GENERAL OF LOGISTIC POLICY (ARMY)
Maj Gen P A Inge 170286

Director of Logistic Operations (Army)
Brig J A Hulme 121285

Director of Support Planning (Army)
Brig G G Blakey 020185

Director of Engineer Services
Brig D H A Swinburn 240284

Director of Army Pioneers and Labour
Brig H J Hickman *OBE* 180385

Director of Defence Postal and Courier Services
Brig D L Streatfield 110886

ASSISTANT UNDER SECRETARY (QUARTERMASTER)
J T Baugh

Head of QMG Secretariat
P Fraser

DIRECTOR OF ARMY QUARTERING
Brig M A Gardner 010386

DIRECTOR GENERAL OF TRANSPORT AND MOVEMENTS
A/Maj Gen D B H Colley *CBE* 010386

Deputy Director General of Transport and Movements
Brig C J Carey 110185

Director of Movements (Army)
Brig J K Pitt *OBE* 061285

DIRECTOR GENERAL OF ORDNANCE SERVICES
Maj Gen G B Berragan 020985

Deputy Director General of Ordnance Services
Brig A J Paviour 121285

Director of Clothing and Textiles
Brig C W Beckett 190385

Director of Supply Operations (Army)
Brig J A Jackson *MBE GM* 071085

Director of Land Services Ammunition
Brig M C Owen 250285

Director of Supply Computer Services
Brig D A Man 230985

Director of Supply Management (Army)
Brig J A Turner *ADC* 170383

DIRECTOR GENERAL OF ELECTRICAL AND MECHANICAL ENGINEERING
Maj Gen J Boyne *MBE* 291085

Director of Electrical and Mechanical Engineering (Organisation and Training)
Brig G M Hutchinson 170585

Director of Equipment Engineering 1
A/Brig S T Webber 020186

Director of Equipment Engineering 2
Brig R H Chown 200583

Director of Production Engineering
Brig R S Higson 240884

Director of Electrical and Mechanical Engineering (Management Services)
Brig P Winchcombe 270186

DIRECTOR OF ARMY CATERING CORPS
Brig M J Paterson 040485

PROCUREMENT EXECUTIVE

MASTER GENERAL OF THE ORDNANCE

MASTER GENERAL OF THE ORDNANCE ....LT GEN *SIR* RICHARD VINCENT *KCB DSO* 010983
Vice Master General of the Ordnance ....Maj Gen M T Skinner *CB* 170884
Assistant Under Secretary of State (Ordnance)
M D Tidy
Master General of the Ordnance Secretariat
Head ....D C M Duffus
Principal Directorate of Contracts (Ordnance)
Principal Director ....R G Woodman
Directorate of Contracts Military Weapons
Director...C M Clarkson
Directorate of Contracts Military Electronics
Director...J Walker
Directorate of Contracts Fighting Vehicles and Engineer Equipment
Director...D Cadman
Directorate General of Fighting Vehicles and Engineer Equipment
Director General ....A/Maj Gen S R A Stopford *MBE* 150585
Equipment Secretariat (Fighting Vehicles and Engineer Equipment) (Army)
Head ....D F Ingrey
Directorate of Projects (Fighting Vehicles and Engineer Equipment) 1
Director...Brig R C J Dick...300184
Directorate of Projects (Fighting Vehicles and Engineer Equipment) 2
Director...D M Campbell
Directorate of Projects (Fighting Vehicles and Engineer Equipment) 3
Director...B Trevelyan
Directorate General of Weapons (Army)
Director General ....Maj Gen R J Crossley *CBE* 280484
Equipment Secretariat Weapons (Army)
Head ....M M J Gammon
Directorate of Ammunition Procurement (Army)
Director...K Bannock
Directorate of Heavy Weapons Projects
Director...C H Oxlee
Directorate of Light Weapons Projects
Director...Brig A E K Karslake 030383
Directorate General Guided Weapons and Electronics
Director General ....P G Smith
Equipment Secretariat (Military Guided Weapons and Electronics)
Head ....R T Fairbairn
Directorate of Military Guided Weapons Projects
Director...P Woodger
Directorate of Surveillance and Instruments Projects
Director...L N Large
Directorate of Military Command Control and Communications Projects
Director...Brig M R Topple...070685
Director General of Defence Quality Assurance
Director General ....D Brighton
Directors of Quality Assurance
Director Project Support.................................Brig K A Timbers
Director Industry ....D F Whitwam
Director Technical Support ....J Scrivener
Director Policy...Cdre J P Loughman RN
Director Administration ....D R E Hopkins
Director Project Support Development...........P Baigent
Director of Standardization ....G A Price
Directorate of Proof and Experimental Establishments
Director...Brig P Marsh *MBE* 200186
Central Packaging Unit
Assistant Director ....*Dr* P M B Slate

OFFICE OF THE JUDGE ADVOCATE GENERAL OF THE FORCES

(Lord Chancellor's Establishment)

(Joint Service for the Army and Royal Air Force)

22, Kingsway, London, WC2B 6LE (*Tel No:* 01-430-5335)

JUDGE ADVOCATE GENERAL ....J STUART-SMITH *CB*
Vice Judge Advocate General..............................G Ll Chapman
Asst Judge Advocates General (London Office and Overseas)
C G Gould
G E Empson *(DJAG (British Forces in Germany))*
G R Canner
E G Moelwyn-Hughes
A P Pitts
S B Spence
Deputy Judge Advocates (London Office and Overseas)
A Labor
D M Berkson
M A Hunter
Registrar ....*Miss* S M Norman-Butler

DEFENCE AND MILITARY ADVISERS TO BRITISH HIGH COMMISSIONS WITHIN THE COMMONWEALTH

CANADA

OTTAWA

Defence and Military Adviser........................A/Brig W M R Addison 160186

AUSTRALIA

CANBERRA

Defence Adviser........................Cdre R M Lawson 141285
Military Adviser........................Col G D Farrell *MBE*........................140385
Assistant Defence Adviser........................Maj C S K Anderson LG 310186

(also New Zealand and Defence and Military Adviser Papua New Guinea)

NEW ZEALAND

WELLINGTON

Defence Adviser........................Capt R D Ferguson RN........................020684
Military Adviser........................Col G D Farrell *MBE*........................140385

(also Australia and Defence Adviser Papua New Guinea)
(Resident Canberra)

INDIA

NEW DELHI

Defence and Military Adviser........................Brig J R Cornell *CBE*........................290183

SRI LANKA

COLOMBO

Defence Adviser........................Lt Col R Holworthy LI........................190185

(also Defence Attache Maldive Islands)

GHANA

ACCRA

Defence Adviser........................Lt Col I P Howard-Harwood RA 160583

(also Sierra Leone and Defence Attache Ivory Coast and Togo)

MALAYSIA

KUALA LUMPUR

Defence Adviser........................Col D Glazebrook *OBE*........................170585

NIGERIA

LAGOS

Defence Adviser........................Col P B Evans 291184

KENYA

NAIROBI

Defence, Naval and Military Adviser..........Col R G Southerst 070484

CYPRUS

NICOSIA

Defence, Naval, Military and Air Adviser....Col F M K Tuck 230186

SINGAPORE

Defence Adviser........................Col M T O Lloyd *OBE*........................260184
Asst Defence Adviser........................Lt Cdr S J Buck *MBE* RN........................070685

Defence and Military Advisers to British High Commissions — continued

CARIBBEAN

Defence Adviser ....Col M R Tarver *OBE*..040186

(also Barbados, Dominica I, Grenada, Guyana, St Lucia, St Vincent, Trinidad & Tobago, Antigua & Barbuda & St Christopher & Nevis and Defence Attache Surinam and the Dependencies Anguilla, British Virgin Islands, Cayman Islands, Montserrat & the Turks & Caicos Islands)

(Resident Kingston)

BAHAMAS

NASSAU

Defence Adviser ....Capt C M J Carson RN..010186

(also Naval Adviser Barbados, Dominica I, Grenada, St Lucia, St Vincent and Trinidad & Tobago and Naval Attache Surinam)

ZIMBABWE

HARARE

Defence Adviser ....Col M C Bowden..220985

(also Defence Attache Mozambique)

BANGLADESH

DHAKA

Defence Adviser ....Col A D Bennett 120583

(also Defence Attache Burma)

MILITARY ATTACHES TO EMBASSIES IN FOREIGN COUNTRIES

ABIDJAN

Defence Attache..........Lt Col I P Howard-Harwood RA..........160583
(also Togo and Defence Adviser Sierra Leone and Ghana)
(Resident Accra)

ABU DHABI (UAE)

Defence, Naval, Military and Air Attache...Lt Col A D Pratt RA..........170684

ALGIERS

Defence, Naval, Military and Air Attache...Gp Capt W F Mullen RAF..........211284
Assistant Defence Attache..........A/Lt Col *The Hon* S J T Coleridge GREN GDS..........150485

AMMAN

Defence, Naval and Military Attache..........Col D C Whitten..........301184

ANKARA

Defence and Military Attache..........L/Brig C W G Bullocke *OBE*..........260883

ATHENS

Defence and Military Attache..........L/Brig J H Milburn *OBE*..........031083

BAGDHAD

Defence and Military Attache..........Col R G Eccles..........040883

BANGKOK

Defence and Military Attache..........A/Col M G Allen 10GR..........111085

BELGRADE

Defence and Military Attache..........Col E J Everett-Heath..........310385

BERNE

Defence, Naval and Military Attache..........Lt Col T H G Duke GORDONS..........080285

BOGOTA

Defence, Naval, Military and Air Attache...Lt Col R F Stewart RCT..........171183
(also Panama and Honduras)

BONN

Defence and Military Attache..........Brig T D G Quayle..........221083
Asst Military Attache (Tech)..........Lt Col G C Gray RTR..........101284

BRASILIA

Defence and Military Attache..........Col J B R Peecock..........201083

BRUSSELS

Defence and Military Attache..........Col P M Beaumont *MBE*..........111285
(also Defence Attache Luxembourg)

BUCHAREST

Defence, Naval and Military Attache..........Lt Col G M Longdon *OBE* PWO..........111284

BUDAPEST

Defence and Military Attache..........Lt Col A Cowie RE..........031183

Military Attachés — continued

CAIRO

Defence and Military Attache	Col R Osborne	090983

CARACAS

Defence, Naval, Military and Air Attache *(also Defence Attache Dominican Republic)*	Capt J B Lean RN	080285

COPENHAGEN

Defence, Naval, Military and Air Attache	Cdr T Goetz RN	010286
Asst Defence Attache (Tech)	Maj J N Price RA	090285

DAMASCUS

Defence,Naval, Military and Air Attache *(also Defence,Naval and Military Attache Lebanon)*	Col D H S L Maitland-Titterton	031085
Asst Defence Attache *(also Lebanon)* *(Resident Beirut)*	L/Lt Col M H Argue *MBE MC* PARA	070684

DUBLIN

Defence Attache	Brig J D Osborne ret pay	150484

THE HAGUE

Defence and Naval Attache	Capt B J Clarke RN	261183
Military and Air Attache	Lt Col M J Woodcock *OBE* RA	010581

HELSINKI

Defence, Naval Military and Air Attache	Lt Col W J Collings *MBE* RA	170884

ISLAMABAD

Defence and Military Attache	Brig M J Doyle *MBE*	170185

JAKARTA

Defence, Naval, Military and Air Attache	Col K A Mullins	080385
Asst Defence Attache	Maj C R Miller RA	211083

KATHMANDU

Defence and Military Attache	Lt Col C A Lees 10 GR	010285

KHARTOUM

Defence and Military Attache	Col C H Diamond	300483

LIMA

Defence, Naval, Military and Air Attache *(also Defence Attache Bolivia)*	Capt G A Hogg RN	190385

LISBON

Defence, Naval and Air Attache	Cdr D F Brown *LVO* RN	160885
Military Attache	Lt Col D K W Farrant LI	060585

MADRID

Defence and Military Attache	L/Brig J K Chater	190185
Asst Military Attache	Maj M H M C Perrett 17/21L	010283

MALE

Defence Attache *(also Defence Adviser Sri Lanka)* *(Resident Colombo)*	Lt Col R Holworthy LI	190185

MEXICO CITY

Defence, Naval and Air Attache .... Capt M R Nutt RN 090483
(also Defence Attache Cuba, El Salvador, Nicaragua & Honduras)
Military Attache .... Lt Col M P Brooke 16/5L 120286
(also El Salvador, Honduras & Nicaragua)

MONTEVIDEO

Defence, Naval, Military and Air Attache ... Col R D Garnett *MBE* 170585
(also Defence, Naval, Military and Air Attache Asuncion)

MOSCOW

Defence and Air Attache .... Air Cdre B L Robinson RAF 141283
Asst Military Attache (Tech) .... Maj D J S Hepburn RS 160185

MUSCAT

Defence and Military Attache .... Col B M Lees *LVO OBE* 170784

OSLO

Defence and Air Attache .... Wg Cdr J S Cresswell RAF 300983
Military Attache .... Lt Col B L Carter RM 260683

PARIS

Defence and Military Attache .... Brig A C Vivian *CBE ADC* 280983
Asst Military Attache (Tech) .... Lt Col B F Cox RE 200985

PEKING

Defence Military and Air Attache .... Col W H Clements 171085

PRAGUE

Defence and Military Attache .... Col R G Lee *OBE* 290783

QUITO

Defence, Naval, Military and Air Attache ... Gp Capt A Salter RAF 141185

RABAT

Defence, Naval, Military and Air Attache ... Lt Col G Latham QOH 251085
(also Defence Attache Tunisia)

RANGOON

Defence Attache .... Col A D Bennett 120583
(also Defence Adviser Bangladesh)
(Resident Dhaka)

RIYADH

Defence and Military Attache .... Col J R A Daniel 290284
(also Defence and Military Attache Sana'a)

ROME

Defence and Military Attache .... L/Brig M J Hague 051085

SANTIAGO

Defence, Naval, Military and Air Attache ... Capt M S Ashley RN 180284

SEOUL

Defence and Military Attache .... L/Brig T W Hackworth *OBE* 290685

SOFIA

Defence, Naval, Military and Air Attache ... L/Col P S H Lefever RA 290985

Military Attachés — continued

STOCKHOLM

Defence and Air Attache	Gp Capt J D Leary RAF	110585
Military Attache	Lt Col R W L Wright *MBE* RA	091185

TEL AVIV

Military Attache	Col R McCrum *MVO*	031085

TOKYO

Defence and Military Attache	Col N G S Gray	280985

VIENNA

Defence Attache	Lt Col M E Ledger RA	150286

WARSAW

Defence and Air Attache	Gp Capt M R Jackson RAF	090285
Naval and Military Attache	Lt Col P de S Barrow QUEENS	190984
Asst Military Attache (Tech)	Maj R A Hyde-Bales RE	221184

WASHINGTON

Defence Attache	Air Vice Marshal R Dick RAF	231184
Military Attache	Brig T K Thompson *MBE*	120485
Assistant Military Attache	Col R J W Ffrench Blake	011085

DEFENCE EQUIPMENT STAFF

Director of Munitions and Attache (Defence Equipment)

ARMY COMMANDS (UNITED KINGDOM)

UNITED KINGDOM LAND FORCES

COMMANDER IN CHIEF .... Gen *Sir* James Glover *KCB MBE* 010685

COMMANDER UK FIELD ARMY .... Lt Gen *Sir* John Akehurst *KCB CBE* 160484

COMMANDER TRAINING AND ARMS DIRECTORS
Lt Gen *Sir* Charles Huxtable *KCB CBE* 031083

COMMANDERS IN CHIEF COMMITTEES

Director of Plans/Joint Warfare .... Brig G C Safford 030584

STAFF

Chief of Staff .... Maj Gen A K F Walker 180385
Secretary UKLF .... M A Barnes 020185
Assistant Chief of Staff G2/G3 .... Brig A Makepeace-Warne *MBE* 161285
Assistant Chief of Staff G3 (Training) .... Brig J R Templer *OBE* 030184
Assistant Chief of Staff G1/G4 .... Brig D Shaw *CBE* 090185
TA Adviser .... Brig P D Orchard-Lisle *TD ADC* 300385

ADVISERS TO THE STAFF

Armour
Commander RAC Centre .... Brig R S Webster 121284

Artillery
Commander Artillery (South) .... Brig R S Mountford *OBE* 121184

Engineers
Commander Engineer Support .... Brig J B Wilks *CBE ADC* 070984

Communications
Commander .... Brig J R Burrows *ADC* 070984

Infantry
Director of Infantry .... Maj Gen *Sir* David Thorne *KBE* 170286

Aviation
Commander .... Brig C F Jebens *OBE ADC* 200382

UNITED KINGDOM LAND FORCES — continued

SERVICES

Chaplains

Chaplain General..*The Ven Archdeacon* W F Johnston *CB QHC*..............................010780
Senior Chaplain (RC)..................................*Rt Rev Mgr* J Moran *CBE*..150381

Medical

Principal Medical Officer..............................Maj Gen A J Shaw *CBE QHP*...031284
Deputy Director (Dental)..............................Col W P Fletcher...060884
Deputy Director (Nursing)............................Col C Morrison *ARRC* QARANC...040285

Provost

Provost Marshal...Col N C Allen *OBE* RMP...051084

Finance

Inspector of Pay Services.............................Col J Nicholson...020985

Veterinary

Director AVRS...Brig R J Clifford *QHVS*..010583

Education

Commander..Brig J J N Manson...200184

Pioneer

Commander 23 Group RPC.........................Col T N Buck RPC..221283

Catering

Commander..Col M Procter ACC...220385

Legal

Commander Legal Group UK.......................Brig M T Fugard ALC..221283

WRAC

Commander..Col S P Nield WRAC...110684

COMMANDER TRAINING AND ARMS DIRECTORS

COMMANDER...Lt Gen *Sir* Charles Huxtable *KCB CBE*..031083

Directorate of Intelligence

Director...A/Brig M P Ford...090386

Directorate Royal Armoured Corps

Director...Maj Gen S C Cooper..200784

Directorate Royal Artillery

Director...Maj Gen C G Cornock *MBE*...170484

Engineer in Chief (Army)

Engineer in Chief (A)..................................Maj Gen C J Rougier *CB*...021285

Signal Officer in Chief (Army)

Signal Officer in Chief (A)..........................Maj Gen P D Alexander *MBE*..161285

Directorate of Infantry

Director...Maj Gen *Sir* David Thorne *KBE*..170286

Directorate Army Air Corps

Director...Maj Gen J D W Goodman..071183

LONDON DISTRICT

Horse Guards (*Tel No:* 01-930 4466)

The City of London, the London Metropolitan Police Area, Windsor, The Barracks, Caterham, The Guards' Depot, Pirbright Camp, Brookwood.

Headquarters

GENERAL OFFICER COMMANDING LONDON DISTRICT AND MAJOR GENERAL COMMANDING THE HOUSEHOLD DIVISION .... Maj Gen C J Airy *CBE* 220286

Deputy Commander and Chief of Staff .... Brig D H Blundell-Hollinshead-Blundell 080385

Recruiting and Liaison

Commander Recruiting & Liaison Staff .... Lt Col R S Corkran GREN GDS 210483
Schools Liaison Officer .... Col J A Brake ret pay 220883
University Liaison Officer .... Brig R M Cockman ret pay 171284

ACIOs

Central London Recruiting Depot .... Maj W Baillie ret pay .... 3 Duncannon Street
Wembley .... Maj D A T Metherell *BEM* ret pay .... 594 High Road
Surbiton .... Maj R W Sider ret pay .... 62 Claremont Road
Forest Gate .... Maj R D Tozer ret pay .... 48 Woodgrange Road

EASTERN DISTRICT

Colchester (*Tel No: Colchester* 575121)

The Counties of Bedfordshire, Cambridgeshire, Derbyshire, Suffolk and Hertfordshire, Leicestershire, Lincolnshire, Norfolk, Northamptonshire, Nottinghamshire, Essex (excluding the Metropolitan Police Area)

Headquarters

GENERAL OFFICER COMMANDING .... Maj Gen C A Ramsay *OBE* 061184

Recruiting and Liaison

Commander Recruiting & Liaison Staff .... Lt Col C P Davies KINGS 281085
University Liaison Officer (East Anglia) .... Brig R M Cockman ret pay 140185
University Liaison Officer (East Midlands) .... Col A J Smith *OBE* ret pay 140185
Schools Liaison Officer (Colchester) .... Brig J Whitehead *MBE* ret pay 130880
Schools Liaison Officer (Grantham) .... Col P Todd ret pay 280880

ACIOs

Norwich .... Maj W Jones ret pay .... 2 Magdalen Street
Cambridge .... Lt Col B W W Barrett ret pay .... 24 Mill Road
Southend on Sea .... Lt Col A S R Alfred *MBE* ret pay .... 110 East Street, Prittlewell
Leicester .... Lt Col A S Barr ret pay .... 84 Charles Street
Lincoln .... Lt Col B A Allum ret pay .... 273 High Street
Nottingham .... Lt Col M A Willson-Lloyd ret pay .... 70 Victoria Centre, Milton Street

WOMEN'S SERVICES

St Albans .... Capt L G Kingham ret .... 2b Chequer Street
Nottingham .... Capt D Crawley QARANC ret .... 70 Victoria Centre, Milton Street

SOUTH EAST DISTRICT

Aldershot (*Tel No: Aldershot* 24431)

The Counties of Berkshire (excluding Windsor), Buckinghamshire, Hampshire (excluding Middle Wallop), Isle of Wight, Kent, Oxfordshire, Surrey (excluding the Metropolitan Police Area and Pirbright), and Sussex East and West

Headquarters

GENERAL OFFICER COMMANDING ....Lt Gen *Sir* Michael Gray *KCB OBE* 211285
Deputy Commander and Chief of Staff......Brig R B MacGregor-Oakford *OBE MC* 310383

Recruiting and Liaison

Commander Recruiting & Liaison Staff ....Lt Col C J Dawnay WG 130985
Schools Liaison Officer................Col P R S Smith ret pay

ACIOs

Canterbury................Lt Col J N Shephard ret pay................2 Roper Road
Brighton................Lt Col R D L Smart ret pay ....83 Queens Road
Reading ....Maj W F C Robertson ret pay ....19/20 The Butts
Southampton ....Maj F Bardsley ret pay................123 High Street, Below Bar

WOMEN'S SERVICES

Horsham ....Maj P J Nye WRAC ret................61 London Road
Reading ....Capt J M Catt ret................19/20 The Butts

SOUTH WEST DISTRICT

Bulford Camp, Salisbury, Wiltshire, SP4 9NY (*Tel No: Bulford Camp* 3371)

The Counties of Avon, Cornwall, Devonshire, Dorset, Gloucestershire, Somerset, Wiltshire. The area of Tidworth, Middle Wallop and Weyhill in Hampshire, The Scilly Isles, and the Channel Islands.

Headquarters

GENERAL OFFICER COMMANDING ....Maj Gen B M Lane *CB OBE* 060184
Deputy Commander................Brig M J Evans *ADC*................130484

Recruiting and Liaison

Commander Recruiting & Liaison Staff ....Lt Col P J Houghton WG................270785
Schools Liaison Officer................Col R E Waight *OBE* ret pay 090484

ACIOs

Bristol................Lt Col C E Potts *OBE* ret pay................35 Colston Avenue
Bournemouth ....Lt Col G A Groombridge ret pay ....244 Holdenhurst Road
Exeter................Lt Col B Couzens ret pay................Fountain House, Black Boy Roundabout, Western Way

WOMEN'S SERVICES

Bristol................Maj K M Howie WRAC ret ....35 Colston Avenue
Exeter................Capt E P Lewis WRAC ret................Fountain House, Black Boy Roundabout, Western Way

HEADQUARTERS 1 INFANTRY BRIGADE

Jellalabad Barracks, Tidworth, Hants, SP9 7AB

COMMANDER................Brig J F W Wilsey *CBE*................090484

HEADQUARTERS 43 INFANTRY BRIGADE

Wyvern Barracks, Exeter

COMMANDER................Brig N M Still *CBE* 090484

NORTH WEST DISTRICT

Fulwood Barracks, Fulwood, Preston, Lancs, PR2 4AA (*Tel No: Preston* 716543)

The Counties of Cheshire, Cumbria, Greater Manchester, Isle of Man, Lancashire and Merseyside.

Headquarters

GENERAL OFFICER COMMANDING ....Maj Gen C T Shortis *CBE*................240386

Recruiting and Liaison

Commander Recruiting & Liaison Staff ....Lt Col A S G Drew RGJ 130685
University Liaison Officer ....Col A J Smith *OBE* ret pay................010585
Schools Liaison Officer..............Col W P Weighill ret pay 030184

ACIOs

Carlisle..............Maj H Y Keir ret pay ....14 Abbey Street
Chester..............Lt Col B M Ayres *MBE* ....64 Watergate Street
Liverpool..............Lt Col B A Gait *DSO DCM* ret pay ....Graeme House, Derby Square
Manchester..............Lt Col C G Edwards ret pay ....Barnet House, 53 Fountain Street
Maj H Nicholson ret pay
Capt D A Townsend ret pay
Preston..............Lt Col J M Hardy ret pay................49 Fishergate

WOMEN'S SERVICES

Liverpool..............Capt P A Prince ret ....Graeme House, Derby Square

WESTERN DISTRICT

Shrewsbury (*Tel No: Shrewsbury* 52234)

The Counties of Hereford & Worcester, Shropshire, Staffordshire, Warwickshire and West Midlands.

Headquarters

GENERAL OFFICER COMMANDING ....Brig R W Ward *MBE* 300686

Recruiting and Liaison

Commander Recruiting & Liaison Staff ....Lt Col P Harman 14/20 H 170884
Schools Liaison Officer..............Brig A S Stepto *MBE* ret pay

ACIOs

Birmingham (includes Wolverhampton)..............Col R Ching ret pay ....46 The Shopping Centre, New Street
Capt J Shaw ret pay................43a Queen Street, Wolverhampton
Coventry ....Maj R L Wildgoose ret pay................Broaddale House, Upper Precinct
Shrewsbury ....Maj (QM) C W G Clark ret pay................46a Mardol Street
Stoke-on-Trent ....Maj E J O'Neill ret pay................36/38 Old Hall Street, Hanley

WOMEN'S SERVICES

Birmingham..............Capt D Luckyn-Malone ret...........46 The Shopping Centre, New Street

HEADQUARTERS WALES

Brecon (*Tel No: Brecon* 3111)

The Principality of Wales

Headquarters

GENERAL OFFICER COMMANDING ....Maj Gen P E de la C de la Billiere *CBE DSO MC*▪........................150985

Recruiting and Liaison

Commander Recruiting & Liaison Staff ....Lt Col J C M Garnett RRW 190485
Schools Liaison Officer..Brig K J Davey *CBE MC* ret pay..041185

ACIOs

Cardiff..Lt Col M Davies ret pay...109 St Mary Street
Swansea ....Maj (QM) R L Crabtree ret pay ....17 Castle Street
Wrexham..Maj K C Walker ret pay...10 Church Street

WOMEN'S SERVICES

Brecon ....Capt B M Young QARANC ret..The Barracks
Cardiff..Capt P J Reas ret ....109 St Mary Street

HEADQUARTERS 160 (WELSH) INFANTRY BRIGADE

COMMANDER...Brig C J Lee *CBE ADC* 250884

HEADQUARTERS NORTH EAST DISTRICT AND HEADQUARTERS 2nd INFANTRY DIVISION

Imphal Barracks, Fulford Road, York, YO1 4AU (*Tel No: York* 59811)

The Counties of Cleveland, Durham, Tyne and Wear, Northumberland, North Yorkshire, West Yorkshire, South Yorkshire and Humberside.

Headquarters

GENERAL OFFICER COMMANDING/COMMANDER
Maj Gen C R L Guthrie *LVO OBE* 180186
Deputy Commander..Brig J M Jones..161183

Recruiting and Liaison

Commander Recruiting & Liaison Staff ....Lt Col P D Ashton-Wickett RA 080285
Schools Liaison Officer (Yorkshire and Humberside)
Brig D W Shuttleworth *OBE* ret pay..020484
Schools Liaison Officer (Northumbria)...............Col E H Tremlett ret pay 130982
University Liaison Officer (North East)..............Col B J Smith ret pay...211283

ACIOs

Hull ....Maj G S Berrett ret pay ....4 Albion Street
Bradford...Maj P J Furse ret pay...33 Westgate
Leeds..Lt Col D Hall ret pay ....36 Wellington Street
Capt S D Macey WRAC ret pay
Middlesborough ....Maj J C Riordan *MBE* ret pay ....67 Borough Road
Capt W J G Morris ret pay
Newcastle-upon-Tyne ....Lt Col D Roberts ret pay...7 Ridley Place
Sheffield ....Maj K D Roberts *MBE* ret pay ....Castle Market Building, Waingate

WOMEN'S SERVICES

Newcastle-upon-Tyne ....Maj E A Angus *TD* WRAC ret...7 Ridley Place

HEADQUARTERS SCOTLAND

Edinburgh, EH1 2YX (*Tel No:* 031-336 1761)

Scotland, Orkney and Shetland Defences and the Fair Isles.

Headquarters

GENERAL OFFICER COMMANDING ....Lt Gen *Sir* Norman Arthur *KCB (Governor Edinburgh Castle)*....310585

Recruiting and Liaison

Commander Recruiting & Liaison Staff ....Lt Col J S D Robertson A and SH 310583
Schools Liaison Officer..........Col R T T Gurdon ret pay

ACIOs

Aberdeen ....Maj A Heffren ret pay ....377 Union Street
Dundee..........Maj D G Handley ret pay..........29/31 Bank Street
Inverness ....Maj R G D'A Anderson ret pay..........3 Bridge Street
Edinburgh..........Maj E F Gordon ret pay ....29 Rutland Square
Glasgow ....Lt Col D A Maclean ret pay ....Charlotte House, 78 Queen Street
Maj J F Lindsay ret pay

WOMEN'S SERVICES

Edinburgh..........Maj B Terry *BEM* QARANC ret pay..........29 Rutland Square
Glasgow ....Capt P M Stevenson WRAC ret ....Charlotte House, 78 Queen Street

HEADQUARTERS 52 LOWLAND BRIGADE

Edinburgh, EH1 2YT (*Tel No:* 031-336 1761)

South of a line from Fife Ness in the East to the Mull of Kintyre in the West, including the following regions—Strathclyde, Lothian, Dumfries and Galloway, and Borders.

COMMANDER..........Brig M Thomson *MBE*..........031185

HEADQUARTERS 51 HIGHLAND BRIGADE

Perth (*Tel No:* 0738 21281)

North of a line from Fife Ness in the East to the Mull of Kintyre in the West, including the following regions—Highland, Orkney and Shetland, Grampian, Tayside, Fife, Central and Strathclyde.

COMMANDER..........Brig F A L Alstead *CBE* 080185

HEADQUARTERS NORTHERN IRELAND

British Forces Post Office 825 (*Tel No: Lisburn* 5111)

Headquarters

GENERAL OFFICER COMMANDING ....Lt Gen *Sir* Robert Pascoe *KCB MBE*..230585

Recruiting and Liaison

Commander Recruiting & Liaison Staff ....Lt Col L H Brown *MBE* RCT..190586
Schools Liaison Officer..Maj D W F Twigg ret pay..010282

ACIOs

Belfast...Maj H N Benson ret..Palace Barracks, BFPO 806
Omagh ....Maj R H Martin ret ....St Lucia Barracks, BFPO 804

WOMEN'S SERVICES

Londonderry...Capt M D Boyce WRAC ret.............TA Centre, Artillery Road, Coleraine

CHANNEL ISLANDS

GUERNSEY AND ITS DEPENDENCIES

LT GOVERNOR & COMMANDER IN CHIEF.....Lt Gen *Sir* Alexander Boswell *KCB CBE*.......................................071085

JERSEY

LT GOVERNOR & COMMANDER IN CHIEF.....Admiral *Sir* William Pillar *GBE KCB* 090185

ARMY COMMANDS (OVERSEAS)

BRITISH ARMY OF THE RHINE

Headquarters

COMMANDER IN CHIEF	Gen *Sir* Martin Farndale *KCB*	010785
CHIEF OF STAFF	Maj Gen E H A Beckett *MBE*	171285
DEPUTY CHIEF OF STAFF OPERATIONS	Brig N G P Ansell *OBE*	211284
DEPUTY CHIEF OF STAFF INTELLIGENCE	Brig A K Crawford	170186
GENERAL STAFF DIVISION G1		
Assistant Chief of Staff	Brig J F J Johnston *CBE*	170186
ADVISERS TO THE STAFF		
Brigadier Royal Armoured Corps	Brig D A Williams	021285
Major General Royal Artillery	Maj Gen J H Learmont *CBE*	230285
Commander Engineer	Brig T S Sneyd	060484
Commander Communications	Maj Gen A Yeoman	160484
Brigadier Infantry	Brig W K L Prosser *CBE MC*	030184
Commander Aviation	Brig D E Canterbury	231084
SERVICES		
Senior Chaplain	*Rev* T H Robinson *QHC* Chaplain to the Forces 1st Class	291085
Commander Transport & Movement	Brig M H Turner	070285
Commander Medical	Maj Gen R S Blewett *OBE*	301185
Deputy Medical (Nursing)	Col J M Field *ARRC* QARANC	180385
Commander Supply	Brig P W E Istead *OBE GM*	210186
Commander Maintenance	Brig A MacLauchlan *ADC*	121084
Provost Marshal	Col G A Taylor RMP	110486
Commander Finance	Brig P K Conibear	240885
Commander Veterinary Services	Col S C Moffat	221085
Commander Education	Brig J S Lee *MBE*	011183
Commander Labour Resource	Col D R Higginbotham RPC	010385
Commander Catering	Col J B Bloxham ACC	240585
Brigadier Legal	Brig D A Boyle ALC	270184
Commander WRAC	Col N R Robertson *MBE* WRAC	030884
Commander Postal & Courier Services	Col L G Calcutt	110783
Senior Claims Officer	J W Dady	
CIVIL SECRETARIAT		
Civil Secretary	D Hanson	
DEPUTY JUDGE ADVOCATE GENERAL	G E Empson	
SENIOR DEFENCE AUDITOR	A Benney	

HONG KONG

GOVERNOR AND COMMANDER IN CHIEF	*Sir* Edward Youde *GCMG MBE*	200582

HEADQUARTERS BRITISH FORCES

COMMANDER BRITISH FORCES	Maj Gen T A Boam *CBE*	010685
DEPUTY COMMANDER BRITISH FORCES AND CHIEF OF STAFF	Brig I A Christie *CBE MC*	030286
CIVIL SECRETARIAT		
Civil Secretary	J Morgan	041083
SENIOR DEFENCE AUDITOR	R W Wood	020985

BRITISH FORCES CYPRUS

Headquarters

COMMANDER.........Air Vice Marshal K W Hayr *CB CBE AFC*.........241085
COMMAND SECRETARY.........A Narborough-Hall.........150884

LAND FORCES CYPRUS

Headquarters

COMMANDER.........Brig A D Myrtle *CBE ADC*.........300186
Commander Episkopi Garrison.........Col *The Hon* N C L Vivian.........011184
Commander Dhekelia Garrison.........Col D J Corner *OBE*.........150186

GIBRALTAR

GOVERNOR AND COMMANDER IN CHIEF.....Air Chief Marshal *Sir* Peter Terry *GCB AFC*.........191185

Fortress Headquarters

Officer Commanding Troops, Deputy Fortress Commander and Brigadier i/c Administration
Brig R T P Hume.........050984

THE SULTANATE OF BRUNEI

SULTAN AND COMMANDER IN CHIEF.........*His Majesty* The Sultan of Brunei *Sir* Muda Hassanal Bolkiah Muizzadin Waddaula *DK DPKG DPKT PSBNB PSNB PSLJ SPMB PANB GCMG DK(KELANTAN) DK(JOHORE)*

BRUNEI ARMED FORCES

COLONEL IN CHIEF.........*His Highness* Paduka Seri Begawan Sultan *Sir* Muda Omar Ali Saifuddin *DK PSPNB PSNB PSLJ KCMG DMN DK(KELANTAN) DK(JOHORE) DK(SELANGOR)*

FALKLAND ISLANDS AND THEIR DEPENDENCIES

GOVERNOR.........G W Jewkes.........110785
COMMANDER BRITISH FORCES

ST HELENA

GOVERNOR AND COMMANDER IN CHIEF.....J D Massingham.........100381

SEYCHELLES

GOVERNOR AND COMMANDER IN CHIEF.....*Sir* Colin Allan *KCMG OBE*.........181173

ARMY COMMANDS OF COMMONWEALTH COUNTRIES

(*The details in this list are based on information supplied by the Governments of the countries*)

CANADA

GOVERNOR GENERAL AND COMMANDER IN CHIEF
Her Exellency The Right Hon Jeanne Sauvé *CMM*
Secretary .... *Mr* Leopold Amyot
DEPUTY SECRETARY PLANS & PROGRAMS. *Mr* J Sevigny

DEPARTMENT OF NATIONAL DEFENCE

MINISTER OF NATIONAL DEFENCE.......... *The Honourable* Erik Nielsen
ASSOCIATE MINISTER OF NATIONAL DEFENCE
The Honourable Harvie Andre

DEFENCE COUNCIL

CHAIRMAN

MINISTER OF NATIONAL DEFENCE .... *The Honourable* Erik Nielsen

MEMBERS

Parliamentary Secretary to the Minister of National Defence
Robert L Wenman
Deputy Minister of National Defence .... D B Dewar
Chief of the Defence Staff .... Gen G C E Thériault *CMM CD BA AFSC*
Vice Chief of the Defence Staff .... Lt Gen J E Vance *CMM CD RMC BA* ndc

COMMAND AND STAFF APPOINTMENTS

Chief of Defence Staff .... Gen G C E Thériault *CMM CD BA AFSC*
Vice Chief of Defence Staff .... Lt Gen J E Vance *CMM CD RMC BA* ndc
Deputy Chief Defence Staff .... Vice Admiral N D Brodeur *CMM CD* ndc
Assistant Deputy Minister (Personnel) .... Lt Gen P D Manson *CMM CD RMC BSc* ndc
Chief Maritime Doctrine and Operations .... Rear Admiral C M Thomas *CD BEN MBA* ndc
Chief Land Doctrine and Operations .... Maj Gen G H Lessard *MB CD* ndc
Chief Air Doctrine and Operations .... Maj Gen L A Ashley *CMM CD BSc*
Surgeon General .... Maj Gen R W Fassold *CD MD DPH BSc*
Chief Intelligence & Security .... Maj Gen C W Hewson *CD RMC BAS* ndc
Associate Assistant Deputy Minister (Policy)
Maj Gen F J Norman *CD RMC BA* ndc
Associate Assistant Deputy Minister (Materiel)
Maj Gen G MacFarlane *CMM CD BA MSc* ndc
Judge Advocate General .... Brig Gen F Karwandy *CD LLB*

MARITIME COMMAND

COMMANDER .... Vice Admiral J C Wood *CMM CD* rcds

MOBILE COMMAND

COMMANDER .... Lt Gen C H Belzile *CMM CD BA*

AIR COMMAND

COMMANDER .... Lt Gen D M McNaughton *CMM CD*

MARITIME COMMAND (PACIFIC)

COMMANDER .... Rear Admiral R D Yanow *CD BAM* ndc

FIGHTER GROUP

COMMANDER..Maj Gen R W Morton *CD RMC BSc* ndc

CANADIAN FORCES EUROPE

COMMANDER..Maj Gen D R Wightman *CMM CD RMC BEN*

Canadian Defence Liaison Staff Washington

COMMANDER..Maj Gen G R Cheriton *CD* rcds

TRAINING SYSTEMS

COMMANDER..Brig Gen A C Brown *CMM CD RMC BASC* ndc

COMMUNICATIONS COMMAND

COMMANDER..Brig Gen J G Leech *CD RMC BSc* ndc

AIR TRANSPORT GROUP

COMMANDER..Brig Gen K O Simonson *CD*

HEADQUARTERS NORTHERN REGION

COMMANDER..Brig Gen M T Dodd *CD* ndc

Canadian Defence Liaison Staff London

1, Grosvenor Square, London, W1X OAB (*Tel:* 01-629-9492)

COMMANDER..Brig Gen C B Snider *MC CD* ndc

AUSTRALIA

GOVERNOR GENERAL AND COMMANDER IN CHIEF
His Exellency Sir Ninian Martin Stephen *AK GCMG GCVO KBE*
Official Secretary............D I Smith *CVO*
Comptroller and Military Secretary............Lt Col A G Warner *BSc* psc
MINISTER FOR DEFENCE............*The Hon* Kim C Beazley *MP*
CHIEF OF THE DEFENCE FORCE............Gen *Sir* Phillip Bennett *AC KBE DSO* rcds jssc psc ph............130484
CHIEF OF THE GENERAL STAFF............Lt Gen P C Gration *AO OBE BA BCE(Hons) BEC* awc(US) jssc psc............130484

PRINCIPAL STAFF OFFICERS

DEPUTY CHIEF OF THE GENERAL STAFF............Maj Gen P J Day *BCE* rcds jssc psc............010285
CHIEF OF PERSONNEL............Maj Gen G J Fitzgerald jssc psc............090184
CHIEF OF ARMY MATERIEL............Brig D M M Francis *OBE BCE* ndc(CAN) jssc psc............010585
CHIEF OF OPERATIONS............Maj Gen A Clunies-Ross *MBE BA* jssc psc psc(US)............111285
CHIEF OF LOGISTICS............Maj Gen J N Stein *AM BA Dipciv E* awc(US) psc............010285
MILITARY SECRETARY............Brig I G A Macinnes *BA* jssc psc............041285
JUDGE ADVOCATE GENERAL............Maj Gen *Hon* R F Mohr *ED*............260782

FIELD FORCE COMMAND

GENERAL OFFICER COMMANDING............Maj Gen L G O'Donnell *AO* rcds jssc psc tt............010285

TRAINING COMMAND

GENERAL OFFICER COMMANDING............Maj Gen K H Kirkland *CBE* psc psc(RI)............240284

LOGISTIC COMMAND

GENERAL OFFICER COMMANDING............Maj Gen D C J Deighton *AO MBE* jssc psc t............250185

1 DIVISION

COMMANDER............Maj Gen P M Jeffery *AM MC* rcds jssc psc............231285

MILITARY DISTRICTS (MD)

1 MD

COMMANDER............Brig N J Mcguire jssc psc t............030284

2 MD

COMMANDER............Brig J S Baker *AM BCE* jssc psc............290485

3 MD

COMMANDER............Brig B Wade psc............010285

4 MD

COMMANDER............Brig T H F Walker psc psc(US)............200184

5 MD

COMMANDER............Brig J H Townley *AM* jssc psc G(y)............141284

6 MD

COMMANDER............Col R P Beesley *AM* jssc psc............171284

7 MD

COMMANDER............Col B M Kemp *AM* jssc psc............270284

Office of the Military Attaché and Australian Army Staff (Washington)

Head Australian Defence Staff............Maj Gen H J Coates *MBE BA(Hons)* rcds jssc psc............270184
Australian Army Representative............Brig F K Cole *AM* jssc(US) psc............290385

Australian Defence Staff – United Kingdom

Australia House, London, WC2B 4LA (*Tel:* 01-836-2435)

Head Australian Defence Staff............Rear Admiral K Vonthethoff *AO* RAN ndc(I)............200284
Army Adviser............Col G D Burgess *MBE* jssc psc............200184

NEW ZEALAND

GOVERNOR GENERAL AND COMMANDER IN CHIEF

His Excellency The Most Reverend Sir Paul Reeves *GCMG GCVO Hon DCL(Oxon)*

Comptroller of the Household .... Gp Capt N E Richardson RNZAF ret

DEFENCE COUNCIL

CHAIRMAN AND MINISTER OF DEFENCE ..... *The Hon* Francis Duncan O'Flynn *QC LLM*

Deputy Chairman and Chief of Defence Staff
Air Marshal *Sir* David Jamieson *KBE CB* rcds jssc psc cfs

Deputy Chairman and Secretary of Defence
D B G McLean *MSc MA*

Chief of Naval Staff .... Rear Admiral L J Tempero rcds jssc
Chief of the General Staff .... Maj Gen J A Mace *CB OBE* Gen's List rcds jssc psc(UK)
Chief of the Air Staff .... Air Vice Marshal D M Crooks *CB OBE* rcds psc cfs*

DEFENCE STAFF

Deputy Chief of Defence Staff .... Brig K M Gordon *OBE ADC* Brig's List rcds psc(UK)
Asst Chief of Defence Staff (Policy) .... Air Cdre B J O'Connor *OBE AFC ADC* rcds jssc psc cfs
Asst Chief of Defence Staff (Personnel) .... Air Cdre J J Gordon *OBE* jssc psc
Asst Chief of Defence Staff (Support) .... Commodore K J Lewis *OBE* jssc psc
Commander NZ Force South East Asia ...... Brig G A Hitchings *MBE* Brig's List rcds psc(US)

THE ARMY GENERAL STAFF

Chief of the General Staff .... Maj Gen J A Mace *CB OBE* Gen's List rcds jssc psc(UK)
Deputy Chief of the General Staff .... Brig D S McIver *OBE* Brig's List rcds jssc psc

LAND FORCE COMMAND

Commander .... Brig R J Andrews *OBE* Brig's List cndc jssc psc(AS)
Commander 1st Task Force .... Col T A Aldridge Col's List jssc psc(A)
Commander 3rd Task Force .... Col A L Birks *MBE* Col's List jssc psc(AS)

SUPPORT COMMAND

Commander .... Brig E J Torrance *OBE* Brig's List jssc psc(AS)
Commander Army Training Group .... Col G D Birch *MBE* Col's List jssc psc(UK)
Commander Force Maintenance Group ..... Lt Col H E Wedde RNZE psc(AS)
Commander Base Area Wellington .... Lt Col C E McIver RNZCT psc(AS)

New Zealand Defence Liaison Staff London

New Zealand House, London, SW1Y 4TQ (*Tel:* 01-930-8422)

Head .... Air Cdre P Neville *OBE AFC* psc

THE REPUBLIC OF INDIA

PRESIDENT OF THE REPUBLIC OF INDIA	*Shri* Zail Singh	250782
Military Secretary	Air Vice Marshal R S Naidu *VM*	010783

ARMY HEADQUARTERS

CHIEF OF THE ARMY STAFF	Gen K Sundarji *PVSM*	010286
Vice Chief of the Army Staff	Lt Gen K K Hazari *PVSM AVSM*	0286
Deputy Chief of the Army Staff	Lt Gen C N Somanna *PVSM*	
Adjutant General	Lt Gen S Mazumdar	1185
Deputy Adjutant General	Maj Gen Karam Singh *PVSM*	030384
Quartermaster General	Lt Gen Rajinder Singh *PVSM*	0384
Deputy Quartermaster General	Maj Gen P K Joglekar	201084
Master General of the Ordnance	Lt Gen Anand Sarup *MVC*	1185
Deputy Master General of the Ordnance	Maj Gen V K Madhok	1284
Military Secretary	Lt Gen A K Chatterjee *VSM*	
Engineer in Chief	Lt Gen R K Dhawan	

HEADQUARTERS EASTERN COMMAND

GENERAL OFFICER COMMANDING IN CHIEF
Lt Gen J K Puri 010286

HEADQUARTERS SOUTHERN COMMAND

GENERAL OFFICER COMMANDING IN CHIEF
Lt Gen R S Dayal *PVSM MVC*

HEADQUARTERS WESTERN COMMAND

GENERAL OFFICER COMMANDING IN CHIEF
Lt Gen H Kaul *PVSM AVSM*

HEADQUARTERS CENTRAL COMMAND

GENERAL OFFICER COMMANDING IN CHIEF
Lt Gen B K B Mehta

HEADQUARTERS NORTHERN COMMAND

GENERAL OFFICER COMMANDING IN CHIEF
Lt Gen A K Handoo

Office of the Indian High Commissioner in London

India House, Aldwych, London, WC2B 4NA (*Tel:* 01-836 8484)

Military Adviser	Brig Satish Nambiar *V&C* psc.	1283

SRI LANKA

PRESIDENT	*His Excellency* J R Jayawardene	040278
PRIME MINISTER	*Hon* R Premadasa	070978
COMMANDER OF THE ARMY	Maj Gen G D G N Seneviratne *VSV* ndc	
Chief of Staff	Brig M Madawela *VSV*	
Military Secretary	Brig G D Fernando *VSV*	

STAFF ARMY HEADQUARTERS

Commandant Volunteer Force	Brig E G Thevanayagam *VSV*
Director of Operations and Training	Brig J G Balthazar
Director of Personnel Administration	Brig H G Silva *VSV* psc
Director of Budget and Financial Management	Col G V Elapata
Director of Logistics	Brig C A M N Silva *VSV* USAWC
Director of Army Medical Services	Col H I K Fernando
Director of Engineer Services	Col J R S de Silva

SUBORDINATE FORMATION COMMANDERS

Commander Support Forces	Brig C H Fernando psc
Commander Logistics Command	Col W A D Fernando
Commander Southern Command	Col L D C E Waidyaratne psc
Commander Central Command	Lt Col M T W Ponnamperuma SLLI
Commander North Central Command	Col K L de S Jayawardena
Commander Northern Command	Col C J Abeyratne
Commander South Eastern Command	Col D Wijeyesinghe

Office of the Sri Lanka High Commision in the United Kingdom

13, Hyde Park Gardens, London, W2 2LU (*Tel:* 01-262-1841)

THE REPUBLIC OF GHANA

CHAIRMAN OF PNDC AND COMMANDER IN CHIEF	*His Excellency* Flt Lt J J Rawlings	311281
Force Commander	Maj Gen A Quainoo psc jdc	250883
Military Secretary	Col R B Commey psc jdc	031085
Director Military Operations	Lt Col J H Smith psc jdc	291185
Director Personnel Administration	Col I Kpeto psc jdc	031085
Director Logistics	Capt (GN) D C Damah	291185
Director General Staff	Col F Ayittey psc jdc	031085
Commanders:		
Army	Maj Gen A Quainoo psc jdc	311281
Commander Northern Command	Col Guomil psc jdc	091085
Commander Southern Command	Col D L K Klutsey	230382

Office of the Ghana High Commission in the United Kingdom

13, Belgrave Square, London, SW1X 8PR (*Tel:* 01-235-4142)

Defence Adviser	Lt Col S K Obeng	100484

MALAYSIA

SUPREME COMMANDER....Duli Yang Maha Mulia Seri Paduka Baginda Yang Dipertuan Agong

MEMBERS OF THE ARMED FORCES COUNCIL

MINISTER OF DEFENCE....YB Datuk Abdullah bin Haji Ahmad Badawi *DMPN DJN KMN*

Chief of Defence Forces....Gen Tan Sri Dato' Mohamed Ghazali bin Haji Che Mat *PGAT PSM SPMJ SPTS ADK PGB*
Secretary General For Defence....Tan Sri Dato' Mohd Yusof bin Abdul Rahman *PSM DPMJ JMN KMN*
Chief of Army....Gen Dato' Sri Mohamed Hashim bin Mohd Ali *DPMS DSDK SPTS JMN SMS ABS FBIM*
Chief of Navy....Vice Admiral Dato' Abdul Wahab bin Haji Nawi *DPMJ DSSA JMN SMJ KMN*
Chief of Air Force....Lt Gen (Air) Dato' Mohamed bin Ngah Said *PGAT DPTS JMN SMP ABS PGP PTU*
Chief of Personnel Staff....Maj Gen Dato' Nik Mahmood Fakharuddin Kamil bin Tan Sri Nik Ahmad Kamil *DPSK SMJ JMN DSN*
Chief of Logistics Services....Maj Gen Abdul Rahman bin Haji Khamis *KMN PGB FBIM*

OTHER APPOINTMENTS

JOINT DEFENCE STAFF DIVISION

Chief of Staff (Operation)....Maj Gen Dato' Abdul Rahman bin Abdul Hamid *DPTS PAT PMP KMN*

DEPARTMENT OF ARMY

Deputy Chief of Army....Lt Gen Dato' Yacoob bin Mat Zain *DPTS DPSK JMN ADK PJK*
Chief of Staff....Brig Gen Dato Haji Mohd Isa bin Che Kak *DSDK JSD SMP KMN*
Army Corp Commander....Lt Gen Datuk Haji Mohamed Daud bin Abu Bakar *DPSK JMN PSK KPK*
GOC I DIV....Maj Gen Datuk Haji Ahmad bin Haji Abdul Kadir *DPMJ JMN SMJ ABS PIS PJK KPK*
GOC II DIV....Maj Gen Dato' Jaafar bin Hj Mohamed *DPSK PAT JMN SAP PSK BSK*
GOC III DIV....Maj Gen Dato' Harun bin Mohd Taib *DPMJ DPMT JMN PMK SMT KMN PIS PJK*
GOC IV DIV....Maj Gen Dato' Osman bin Mohd Zain *PSAT DPTS JMN SMP ADK ABS*
GOC XI DIV....Maj Gen Dato' Abdul As bin Ismail *DSDK PAT JMN PJK*

Office of the Malaysian High Commission in the United Kingdom
45/46 Belgrave Square, London, SW1X 8QT (*Tel:* 01-235 8033)

Defence Adviser....Col Yacoob bin Haji Salleh *KMN PJK*
Assistant Defence Adviser (Army)....Maj Abdul Rahman bin Dato Baginda *BCK*
Assistant Defence Adviser (Navy)....Lt Cdr Azizul Rahman *RMN*
Assistant Defence Adviser (Air)....Maj (Air) Othman bin Abd Majid

THE FEDERAL REPUBLIC OF NIGERIA

PRESIDENT AND COMMANDER IN CHIEF.....Maj Gen I B Babangida *CFR FSS* mni
Chief of Army Staff.....Maj Gen Sani Abacho *FSS* mni
Chief of Naval Staff.....Rear Admiral A A Aikhomu *FSS* psc mni
Chief of Air Staff.....Air Vice Marshal I M Alfa *FSS* psc Usawc
Commandant Nigerian Defence Academy.....Maj Gen P C Tarfa *FSS* psc mni
Commandant Command & Staff College.....Brig P U Omu *FSS* psc rcds

Office of the Nigerian High Commission in the United Kingdom

Nigeria House, 9, Northumberland Avenue London, WC2N 5BX (*Tel:* 01-839 1244)

Defence Adviser.....Col D A Dyeris *FSS* psc mni

THE REPUBLIC OF CYPRUS

PRESIDENT.....*His Excellency* Mr Spyros Kyprianou

Office of the Cyprus High Commission in the United Kingdom

93, Park Street, London, W1Y 4ET (*Tel:* 01-499 8272)

THE REPUBLIC OF SIERRA LEONE

PRESIDENT AND COMMANDER IN CHIEF.....*His Excellency Dr* Siaka P Stevens *GCRSL GCMG DCL*
Vice President.....S I Koroma *CRSL MP*
Second Vice President.....F M Minah *ORSL MP*

Republic of Sierra Leone Military Forces

COMMANDER.....Maj Gen J S Momoh *OR OBE MP*
Deputy Commander.....Brig S H King *OR*
Chief of Staff.....Brig M S Tarawallie *MR*jssc

Office of the Sierra Leone High Commission in the United Kingdom

33, Portland Place, London W1N 3AG (*Tel:* 01-636-6483)

THE UNITED REPUBLIC OF TANZANIA

PRESIDENT OF THE UNITED REPUBLIC AND COMMANDER IN CHIEF OF THE ARMED FORCES
Achaj Ali Hassan Mwinyi

Tanzania Peoples Defence Forces

COMMANDER AND CHIEF OF DEFENCE FORCES
Gen D B Musuguri

Office of the Tanzanian High Commission in the United Kingdom

43, Hertford Street, London W1Y 7TF (*Tel:* 01-499-8951)

JAMAICA

GOVERNOR GENERAL.....*His Excellency The Most Hon Sir* Florizel Glasspole *ON GCMG GCVO CD*
DEFENCE BOARD
PRIME MINISTER.....*The Rt Hon* Edward Seaga *PC MP*
MINISTER OF NATIONAL SECURITY.....*Hon* Winston Spaulding *MP*
Permanent Secretary Ministry of National Security
Mrs Clair Kean
Chief of Staff.....Maj Gen R J Neish *CD AFC ADC JP*
Defence Adviser.....Col A C dev Stern *OD*

Office of the Jamaican High Commission in the United Kingdom

50, St James's Street, London, SW1A 1JS (*Tel:* 01-499-8600)

REPUBLIC OF TRINIDAD AND TOBAGO

PRESIDENT .... *His Excellency Sir* Ellis Clarke *GCMG TC LLB*
Minister of National Security .... *The Hon* O Padmore
Chief of Defence Staff .... Commodore M Williams

Trinidad and Tobago Regiment

Commanding Officer .... Col J L Theodore
Commanding Officer Coast Guard .... Commander J E Williams

Office of the Trinidad and Tobago High Commission in the United Kingdom

42, Belgrave Square, London, SW1X 8NT (*Tel:* 01-245-9351)

REPUBLIC OF UGANDA

PRESIDENT AND COMMANDER IN CHIEF OF THE ARMED FORCES
Vacant
Minister of Defence .... Vacant

Uganda Armed Forces

Commander .... Vacant
Uganda Armed Forces Liaison Officer .... Vacant

KENYA

PRESIDENT AND COMMANDER IN CHIEF OF THE ARMED FORCES
His Excellency the Hon Daniel Toroitich arap Moi *CGH* MP

Office of the President (Department of Defence) Minister

Chief of the General Staff .... Gen J K Mulinge *MGH MBS* idc(UK)
Deputy Chief of the General Staff .... Lt Gen J M Sawe rcds(UK) psc(UK)

Kenya Army

Army Commander .... Lt Gen J M Sawe rcds(UK) psc(UK)

Office of the Kenya High Commission in the United Kingdom

45, Portland Place, London, W1N 4AS (*Tel:* 01-636-2371/5)

Kenya Defence Adviser .... Col B M Kurutu psc(UK)

MALAWI

PRESIDENT .... *His Excellency the Life President Ngwazi Dr* H Kamuzu Banda
MD LRCP LRCS LRFP & S PhB Hon LLD

Headquarters Malawi Army

Commander .... Gen M M Khanga *MSM* psc

Office of the Malawi High Commission in the United Kingdom

33, Grosvenor St, London, W1X 0DE (*Tel:* 01-491-4172)

REPUBLIC OF MALTA

PRESIDENT .... *Miss* Agatha Barbera
Prime Minister .... *The Hon Dr* Carmelo Mifsud Bonnici *BA LLD MP*

The Armed Forces of Malta

Commander Task Force .... Col J Cachia
Commander (AFM) .... Col J Spiteri

Office of the Malta High Commission in the United Kingdom

16, Kensington Square, London, SW8 5HH (*Tel:* 01-938-1712/6)

ZAMBIA

PRESIDENT & COMMANDER IN CHIEF..........*His Excellency Dr* K D Kaunda

Zambia National Defence Force

Minister..Gen M Masheke
Commander Army..Lt Gen C Tembo
Commander Air Force...Maj Gen H Lungu
Commander National Service.............................Brig Gen T Fara

Office of the Zambia High Commission in the United Kingdom

2, Palace Gate, Kensington, London, W8 5NG (*Tel:* 01-589-6655)

THE GAMBIA

PRESIDENT ....*His Excellency Sir* Dawda K Jawara
VICE PRESIDENT...*Hon* Bakari B Dabo

Office of the Gambia High Commission in the United Kingdom

57, Kensington Court, London, W8 5DG (*Tel:* 01-937-6316/7/8)

SINGAPORE

PRESIDENT ....*Mr* Wee Kim Wee
Minister of Defence..*Mr* Goh Chok Tong

Office of the Singapore High Commission in the United Kingdom

2, Wilton Crescent, London, SW1 8RW (*Tel:* 01-235-8315/6/7/8)

GUYANA

PRESIDENT ....*His Excellency* Hugh Desmond Hoyte *SC*
PRIME MINISTER...*Mr* Hamilton Green

Office of the Guyana High Commission in the United Kingdom

3, Palace Court, Bayswater Road, London W2 4LP (*Tel:* 01-229-7684/8)

THE REPUBLIC OF BOTSWANA

PRESIDENT ....*Dr* Quett Masire *LLD PH JP MP*

Office of the Botswana High Commission in the United Kingdom

6, Stratford Place, London, W1N 9AE (*Tel:* 01-499-0031)

THE KINGDOM OF LESOTHO

HEAD OF STATE...*His Majesty King* Moshoeshoe II
CHAIRMAN OF MILITARY COUNCIL..............Maj Gen T Lekhanya

Office of the Lesotho High Commission in the United Kingdom

10, Collingham Road, London, SW5 0NR (*Tel:* 01-373-8581/2)

BARBADOS

GOVERNOR GENERAL..*His Excellency Sir* Hugh Springer *GCMG GCVO KA CBE*
PRIME MINISTER & MINISTER OF FINANCE.*The Rt Hon* J M G M Adams *QC MP*

Office of the Barbados High Commission in the United Kingdom

6, Upper Belgrave Street, London, SW1X 8AZ (*Tel:* 01-235-8686/7/8/9)

MAURITIUS

GOVERNOR GENERAL ....*Sir* Vefrasamy Ringadoo *QC*

PRIME MINISTER..*Hon* Anerood Jugnauth *MA*

Office of the Mauritius High Commission in the United Kingdom

32/33, Elvaston Place, London, SW7 (*Tel:* 01-581-0294)

THE KINGDOM OF SWAZILAND

HEAD OF STATE..*Her Majesty Queen Regent* Ntombi

PRIME MINISTER...*Prince* Bhekimpi Alpheus Dlamini
COMMANDING OFFICER ....Brig F Dube

Office of the Swaziland High Commission in the United Kingdom

58, Pont Street, London, SW1X 0AE (*Tel:* 01-581-4976/8)

FIJI

GOVERNOR GENERAL AND COMMANDER IN CHIEF
Ratu *Sir* Penaia Ganilau *GCMG KCVO KBE DSO ED* 120283

Royal Fiji Military Forces

COMMANDER...Col Ratu Epeli Nailatikau *MVO OBE* jssc psc 220682
Chief of Staff...Lt Col J N Sanday *OBE* jssc psc 220682

Office of the Fiji High Commission in the United Kingdom

34, Hyde Park Gate, London, SW7 5BN (*Tel:* 01-584-3661)

THE PEOPLES REPUBLIC OF BANGLADESH

PRESIDENT, COMMANDER IN CHIEF AND CHIEF OF ARMY STAFF
Lt Gen H M Ershad ndc psc

Office of the Bangladesh High Commission in the United Kingdom

28, Queens Gate, London, SW7 5JA (*Tel:* 01-584-0081)

BAHAMAS

GOVERNOR GENERAL ....*His Excellency Sir* Gerald Cash *GCMG GCVO OBE JP*
PRIME MINISTER AND MINISTER FOR DEFENCE
The Rt Hon Sir Lynden Pindling *KCMG PC MP*

Royal Bahamas Defence Force

COMMANDER...Commodore L Smith

Office of the Bahamas High Commission in the United Kingdom

39, Pall Mall, London, SW1Y 5JG (*Tel:* 01-930-6967)

GRENADA

GOVERNOR GENERAL ....*His Excellency Sir* Paul Scoon *GCMG GCVO OBE*

Office of the Grenada High Commission in the United Kingdom

1, Collingham Gardens, Earls Court, London, SW5 0HW (*Tel:* 01-373-7808/9)

ZIMBABWE

PRESIDENT AND COMMANDER IN CHIEF.....*His Excellency the Rev* Canaan Banana *GCZM*
PRIME MINISTER AND MINISTER OF DEFENCE
The Hon R G Mugabe

COMMANDER DEFENCE FORCES
COMMANDER ZIMBABWE NATIONAL ARMY
Lt Gen R Nhongo

COMMANDER AIR FORCE OF ZIMBABWE.....Air Marshal J Tungamirayi

Office of the Zimbabwe High Commission in the United Kingdom

Zimbabwe House, 429, Strand, London WC2R 0SA (*Tel:* 01-836-7755)

BELIZE

GOVERNOR GENERAL ....*Dr* Minita Elmira Gordon *DCMG DCVO*

ESTABLISHMENTS

I. CENTRAL DEFENCE & JOINT SERVICE

ROYAL COLLEGE OF DEFENCE STUDIES

Seaford House, Belgrave Square, SW1X 8NS (*Tel No:* 01-235-1091)

Commandant......Admiral *Sir* David Hallifax *KCB KBE*......070186

Directing Staff

Senior Naval Member......Rear Admiral P N Marsden......020985
Senior Army Member......Maj Gen B C Gordon Lennox *CB MBE*......070186
Senior Air Force Member......Air Vice Marshal J F H Tetley *CVO*......280286
Senior Civilian Member......L J Middleton *CMG*......161084

JOINT SERVICE DEFENCE COLLEGE

Greenwich, London SE10 9NN (*Tel No:* 01-858-2154)

Commandant......Air Vice Marshal B H Newton *OBE*......010485

DEFENCE OPERATIONAL ANALYSIS ESTABLISHMENT (ARMY ELEMENT)

Parvis Road, West Byfleet, Surrey (*Tel No:* 093-23-41199)

Director......S H Hood......110385

JOINT AIR RECONNAISSANCE INTELLIGENCE CENTRE (UK)

RAF Brampton, Huntingdon (*Tel No:* 0480-52151)

Commanding Officer......Gp Capt G J Oxlee *OBE* RAF......190785

JOINT SCHOOL OF PHOTOGRAPHIC INTERPRETATION

RAF Wyton, Huntingdon, Cambs (*Tel No:* 0480-52451)

Officer Commanding......Sqn Ldr J S Barry *MBE* RAF......200884

II. ARMY DEPARTMENT

(i) SPONSORED BY THE DEPARTMENT OF THE UNDER-SECRETARY OF STATE FOR DEFENCE FOR THE ARMY

ARMY MEDAL OFFICE

Government Buildings, Droitwich, Worcestershire (*Tel No:* 0905-772323 *Ext:* 40)

Officer i/c .... Maj A J Parsons ret pay 160985

(ii) SPONSORED BY THE DEPARTMENT OF THE CHIEF OF THE GENERAL STAFF

INTELLIGENCE CENTRE

Templer Barracks, Ashford, Kent (*Tel No:* 0233-25251)

Headquarters Director of Intelligence Corps

Director Intelligence Corps & Commandant Intelligence Centre
A/Brig M P Ford 070386

Headquarters Intelligence Corps Depot & Centre

Officer Commanding Depot & Centre Lt Col C B T Grace INT CORPS 141083

School of Service Intelligence

Commandant .... Col M D Durman 011284

HEADQUARTERS DIRECTOR OF THE ROYAL ARMOURED CORPS

Bovington Camp, Wareham, Dorset (*Tel No: Bindon Abbey* 462 721 (STD 0929) *Ext:* 550)

Director .... Maj Gen S C Cooper 200784

ROYAL ARMOURED CORPS CENTRE

PO Box 1, Bovington Camp, Wareham, Dorset (*Tel No: Bindon Abbey* 462 721 (STD 0929))

Allied School— The Armoured School (Australia)

Headquarters

Commander .... Brig R S Webster 121284

Driving and Maintenance School

Commanding Officer & Chief Instructor

Lt Col O E V Holder RH 050485

Signal School

Commanding Officer & Chief Instructor

Lt Col C W Collier R SIGNALS 010485

Gunnery School

Commander .... Col R J Martin 141184

Armour School

Commanding Officer & Chief Instructor

Col A T Lindsay 080285

Armoured Trials & Development Unit

Commanding Officer .... Lt Col P R Barry 17/21 L 061184

RAC Centre Regiment

Commanding Officer .... Lt Col D S Balmain 15/19 H 111185

Junior Leaders Regiment

Commanding Officer .... Lt Col J L Longman RTR 131185

HEADQUARTERS DIRECTOR ROYAL ARTILLERY

Royal Artillery Barracks, Woolwich, London, SE18 4BH (*Tel No:* 01-856-5533)

Director .... Maj Gen C G Cornock *MBE* 170484

REGIMENTAL HEADQUARTERS RA AND HEADQUARTERS WOOLWICH GARRISON

Government House, New Road, Woolwich, SE18 6XR
(*Tel No:* 01-856-5533)

Headquarters

Commander/Regtl Brig .... Brig J H Howarth 041085

17 Training Regiment Royal Artillery & Depot

Royal Artillery Barracks, Woolwich, London, SE18 4BB (*Tel No:* 01-856-5533)

Commanding Officer .... Lt Col R J R Symonds RA 130285

Central Volunteer Headquarters, Royal Artillery

Royal Artillery Barracks, Woolwich, London, SE18 4BB (*Tel No:* 01-856-5533

Commanding Officer .... Lt Col (SL) W Stanford RA 111181

THE ROYAL SCHOOL OF ARTILLERY

Larkhill, Salisbury, Wilts, SP4 8QT (*Tel No:* 09803-3371)

Headquarters

Commandant .... Brig W E Winder 030185

14 Field Regt RA

Commanding Officer .... Lt Col I R G Stewart RA 151284

REME Wing

Commanding Officer .... Col R I C MacPherson 100984

HEADQUARTERS ENGINEER-IN-CHIEF (ARMY)

MOD, Old War Office Building, Whitehall, London, SW1 (*Tel No:* 01-218-5981)

Engineer-in-Chief (Army)...................Maj Gen C J Rougier *CB*..........021285
Deputy Engineer-in-Chief (Army)......Brig C W Woodburn..........310184
Director Engineer Services..................Brig D H A Swinburn..........240284

11 ENGINEER GROUP

Headquarters

Minley Manor, Blackwater, Camberley, Surrey (*Tel No:* 0252-876622 *Hawley Mil* 388)

Commander..........Brig G W Field *OBE*..........091285

1 Training Regiment, Royal Engineers

Gibraltar Barracks, Blackwater, Camberley, Surrey (*Tel No:* 0252-876622 *Hawley Mil* 248)

Commanding Officer..........Lt Col D J Martin RE..........101284

3 Training Regiment, Royal Engineers

Gibraltar Barracks, Blackwater, Camberley, Surrey (*Tel No:* 0252-876622 *Hawley Mil* 270)

Commanding Officer..........Lt Col A J Reed-Screen *OBE* RE..........150285

Central Volunteer Headquarters RE

Minley Manor, Blackwater, Camberley, Surrey (*Tel No:* 0252-876622 *Hawley Mil* 378)

Commander..........Brig G W Field *OBE*..........091285

Junior Leaders Regiment, Royal Engineers

Old Park Barracks, Dover (*Tel No:* 0304-820333 *Old Park Mil* 26)

Commanding Officer..........Lt Col J M Wyatt RE..........010486

ROYAL SCHOOL OF MILITARY ENGINEERING

Brompton Barracks, Chatham, Kent, ME4 4UG (*Tel No:* 0634-44555)

Headquarters

Commandant..........Brig D A Grove *OBE*..........021285

The Depot Regiment, RE

Commanding Officer..........Lt Col D R Humphrey RE..........170386

12 RSME Regiment

Chattenden Barracks, Hoo, Nr Rochester, Kent, ME3 8NQ (*Tel No:* 0634-44555)

Commanding Officer..........Lt Col P J Williams RE..........130186

Royal Engineer Diving Establishment

Marchwood, Southampton, SO4 4ZQ

Commanding Officer..........Lt Col R F Mundy RE..........260983

DEFENCE EXPLOSIVE ORDNANCE DISPOSAL SCHOOL

Lodge Hill Camp, Chattenden, Rochester, Kent, ME3 8NZ (*Tel No:* 0634-44555 *Exts:* 670/532/527/668)

Officer Commanding..........Maj J A Craib *QGM* RE..........010786

42 SURVEY ENGINEER GROUP

Hermitage, Newbury, Berks, RG16 9TP (*Tel No: Hermitage* 200371)

Group Headquarters

Commander..........Col R Wood..........010285

ARMY APPRENTICES COLLEGE

Beachley Camp, Chepstow, Gwent, NP6 7YG (*Tel No:* 029-12-2305/7)

Commandant..........A/Col A E Houlton RE..........270186

TRAINING GROUP ROYAL SIGNALS AND CATTERICK GARRISON

Catterick Garrison, North Yorkshire (*Tel No: Richmond* (0748) 832521)

Headquarters

Commander.........Brig R F Maynard *MBE*.........011085

Training Advisory & Control Team

Officer Commanding.........Lt Col K Ryding R SIGNALS.........280984

Army Apprentices College

Harrogate, North Yorkshire (*Tel No:* 0423-503024)

Commandant.........Col S R Carr-Smith.........030984

8th Signal Regiment

Commanding Officer.........Col B J Austin.........161283

11th Signal Regiment

Commanding Officer.........Lt Col E M Powell R SIGNALS.........230885

DEFENCE AUTOMATIC DATA PROCESSING TRAINING CENTRE

Blandford Garrison, Blandford Forum, Dorset DT11 8SP (*Tel No:* 0258-52581)

Commandant.........Capt J G Davies RN.........010886

SCHOOL OF SIGNALS

Blandford Camp, Blandford Forum, Dorset DT11 8RH (*Tel No:* 0258 52581)

Headquarters

Commander.........Brig J H Almonds.........071284

School Regiment

Officer Commanding.........Lt Col A C Stutchbury R SIGNALS.........280286

HEADQUARTERS DIRECTOR OF INFANTRY

Warminster, Wilts (*Tel No:* 0985-241000)

Director..........Maj Gen *Sir* David Thorne *KBE*..........170286

THE SCHOOL OF INFANTRY

Warminster, Wilts (*Tel No:* 0985-214000)

Headquarters

Commandant, Commandant SASC....Brig A J G Pollard..........171284

Warminster Support Unit

Commanding Officer..........Lt Col H V Bates R IRISH..........051184

Tactics Wing

Commandant..........Col H W R Pike *DSO MBE*.......... 280185

Small Arms Wing

Commandant and Depot Commandant SASC
Col R I L Ker.......... 010385

Signal Wing

Commandant..........A/Lt Col P C Pearson R SIGNALS..........030286

Support Weapons Wing

Netheravon, Wilts (*Tel No:* 098-07-306)

Commandant and Chief Instructor.....Col J G B Rigby *OBE*..........051084

NCO's Tactical Wing

Brecon (*Tel No:* 0874-3111)

Commandant..........Lt Col G F Smythe *OBE* RGJ..........140384

INFANTRY TRIALS AND DEVELOPMENT UNIT

Warminster, Wilts (*Tel No:* 0985-214000)

Commandant..........A/Lt Col R M Estcourt LI..........031284

JUNIOR INFANTRY BATTALION

Scottish and Kings Divisions

Ouston, Newcastle-upon-Tyne (*Tel No:* 06616 501)

Commanding Officer..........Lt Col J A Charteris *MC* RS..........010383

JUNIOR INFANTRY BATTALION

Shorncliffe, Kent (*Tel No:* 0303 39541)

Commanding Officer..........Lt Col D A B Williams RGJ..........150284

HEADQUARTERS DIRECTOR ARMY AIR CORPS

Middle Wallop, Nr Stockbridge, Hants, SO20 8DY (*Tel No:* 0264 62121)

Director ....Maj Gen J D W Goodman 071183

ARMY AIR CORPS CENTRE

Headquarters

Commandant Army Air Corps Centre .Col R J Abbott *MBE* 200585

Flying Wing

Officer Commanding & Chief Flying Instructor
Lt Col F J M Esson AAC 240183

Aircraft Engineering Training Wing

Commanding Officer ....Lt Col C R L Stevens REME 100984

Tactics Wing

Officer Commanding ....Lt Col E C Tait AAC..........041085

Depot Regiment AAC

Commanding Officer ....Lt Col G B McMeekin AAC 120584

(iii) SPONSORED BY THE DEPARTMENT OF THE ADJUTANT GENERAL

STAFF COLLEGE

Camberley, Surrey (*Tel No:* 0276 63344)

Commandant....................Maj Gen C J Waters *CBE*....................160186
Deputy Commandant....................Brig P R Davies....................060186

ROYAL MILITARY COLLEGE OF SCIENCE SHRIVENHAM

Swindon, Wilts, SN6 8LA (*Tel No:* 0793 782551)

Commandant....................Maj Gen J A M Evans....................090985
Principal & Dean....................*Prof* F R Hartley
Senior Military Director of Studies & Deputy Commandant
Brig C Tyler....................060885

ROYAL MILITARY ACADEMY SANDHURST

Camberley, Surrey (*Tel No:* 0276 63344)

Commandant....................Maj Gen R C Keightley....................151183
Assistant Commandant....................Brig P F B Hargrave *CBE*....................100186
Director of Studies....................*Dr* D E Lever

DEFENCE NUCLEAR BIOLOGICAL & CHEMICAL CENTRE

Winterbourne Gunner, Wilts, SP4 0ES (*Tel No:* 0980 611381)

Commandant....................Col D G McCord *MBE*....................250683

HEADQUARTERS INSPECTOR OF PHYSICAL & ADVENTUROUS TRAINING (ARMY) AND ARMY PHYSICAL TRAINING CORPS

First Avenue House, High Holborn, London WC1V 6HE (*Tel No:* 01-430 5649)

Inspector of Physical & Adventurous Training (Army) and Commandant APTC
Brig R J Baddeley....................240486

ARMY SCHOOL OF PHYSICAL TRAINING

Aldershot, Hants (*Tel No:* 0252 24431)

Commandant....................Lt Col R M G Brooks RE....................100185

JOINT SERVICE MOUNTAIN TRAINING CENTRE (WALES)

Morfa Camp, Tywyn, Gwynedd, LL36 9BH (*Tel No:* 0654-710 371)

Commandant....................Maj A J Muston RAOC....................120283

MANNING AND RECORD OFFICES

Household Cavalry, RAC

Queen's Park, Chester, CH4 7AW (*Tel No:* 0244 24666)

Officer in Charge..................................Col C H Bond *OBE*..................................081084

RA, HAC

Imphal Barracks, York, YO1 4HD (*Tel No:* 0904 59811)

Officer in Charge..................................Col D E A Tucker..................................041284

RE

Kentigern House, 65, Brown Street, Glasgow, G2 8EX (*Tel No:* 041-248-7890)

Officer in Charge..................................Col R M R Luxton..................................300486

R SIGNALS

Kentigern House, 65, Brown Street, Glasgow, G2 8EX (*Tel No:* 041-248-7890)

Officer in Charge..................................A/Col D M O Miller R SIGNALS..................................070386

Guards Division, Scottish Division, Kings Division, Prince of Wales's Division, GSC

Imphal Barracks, York, YO1 4HD (*Tel No:* 0904 59811)

Officer in Charge..................................Col A M Hinings *OBE*..................................291084

Queens Division, Light Division, PARA, SASC

Higher Barracks, Exeter EX4 4ND (*Tel No:* 0392 76581 *Ext* 218)

Officer in Charge..................................Col M V Hayward *OBE*..................................200784

The Brigade of Gurkhas

The Brigade of Gurkhas, Gun Club Barracks, Hong Kong

Officer in Charge..................................Maj A J J Watt 10 GR..................................180386

RCT

Kentigern House, 65, Brown Street, Glasgow, G2 8EX (*Tel No:* 041-248-7890)

Officer in Charge..................................Col D W Cooper..................................300686

RAMC, RADC, QARANC, WRAC

Queen's Park, Chester, CH4 7AW (*Tel No:* 0244 24666)

Officer in Charge..................................Col C O'Neill..................................140984

RAOC

Saffron Road, Wigston, Leicester, LE8 2US (*Tel No:* 0533 785361)

Officer in Charge..................................A/Col G F V Cowell *OBE* RAOC..................................100386

REME

Saffron Road, Wigston, Leicester, LE8 2US (*Tel No:* 0533 785361)

Officer in Charge..................................Col N McC Smithson..................................270186

AAC, RMP, RAPC, RAVC, MPSC, RAEC, RPC, INT CORPS, APTC, ACC, OTC

Higher Barracks, Exeter EX4 4ND (*Tel No:* 0392 76581 *Ext* 244)

Officer in Charge..................................Col C E Lane..................................010785

LSL, Officer Cadets RMA Central Army Index, Electoral Registration, ID Documents

Higher Barracks, Exeter EX4 4ND (*Tel No:* 0392 76581 *Ext* 239)

Officer in Charge..................................Lt Col (SL) D H McMurtrie LI..................................191182

All Officers' Records

MS(AODO), London Road, Stanmore, Middx, HA7 4PZ (*Tel No:* 01-958 6377 *Ext* 3139)

Officer in Charge..................................Col R D Upton *OBE* ret pay..................................201082

ROYAL MILITARY SCHOOL OF MUSIC

Kneller Hall, Twickenham, Middx, TW2 7DU (*Tel No:* 01-898 5533/4/5)

Commandant & Inspector of Army Bands..........Col C A Ewing *OBE*..........280685
Director of Music & Assistant Inspector of Army Bands
A/Lt Col D R Beat *LVO* SG..........061282

THE REGULAR COMMISSIONS BOARD

Leighton House, Westbury, Wilts (*Tel No:* 037-382 2181)

President..........Maj Gen R Benbow *CB*..........201285
Vice Presidents..........Brig D A G Edelsten..........170683
Brig A R Douglas-Nugent *ADC*..........061184
Brig T G Williams *OBE*..........150385

WELBECK COLLEGE

Worksop, Notts (*Tel No:* 0909 476326/7)

Principal..........Lt Col G H Silvey RAEC..........010985
Housemasters..........D F Pring
J P Broadbent

ARMY SCHOOL OF RECRUITING

St Georges Barracks, Rectory Road, Sutton Coldfield, W Midlands, B75 7PH (*Tel No:* 021-378 1282)

Commandant..........Lt Col E Ashley PARA..........270884

ARMY PERSONNEL SELECTION GROUP

Empress State Building, Lillie Road, London SW6 1TR (*Tel No:* 01-385 1244 *Ext* 3616)

Commander..........Col J R Collins *OBE*..........030685

ARMY PERSONNEL SELECTION CENTRE

St Georges Barracks, Rectory Road, Sutton Coldfield, W Midlands, B75 7PH (*Tel No:* 021-378 1282)

Officer Commanding..........Lt Col W J Briggs RA..........160585

ARMY PERSONNEL SELECTION CENTRE (SCOTTISH WING)

Inchdrewer House, Edinburgh, EH13 0LA (*Tel No:* 031-441 5111 *Ext* 252)

Officer in Charge/SPSO..........Maj L H Jamieson RE..........010682

ARMY SPORT CONTROL BOARD

Ministry of Defence, Clayton Barracks, Aldershot, Hants (*Tel No: Aldershot Mil* 2569/2570)

President..........Gen *Sir* Roland Guy *KCB CBE DSO*
Chairman..........A/Maj Gen A B Crowfoot *CBE*
Director & Treasurer and Inspector of Army Recreation Grounds
Brig P D F Thursby *OBE* ret pay

ROYAL ARMY MEDICAL CORPS TRAINING GROUP

Keogh Barracks, Ash Vale, Aldershot, Hants (*Tel No:* 0252 24431)

Headquarters

Commander Medical UKLF & Commander........Maj Gen A J Shaw *CBE QHP*........031284

RAMC Training Centre

Commandant........Col G Banks........100984

Headquarters Army Medical Services Territorial Army

Officer in Charge........Brig D E Worsley *QHP*........170286

THE DAVID BRUCE LABORATORIES

East Everleigh, Marlborough, Wilts (*Tel No:* 026-485 212)

Officer Commanding........Maj N S Cumberland RAMC........020186

ARMY BLOOD SUPPLY DEPOT

Ordnance Road, Aldershot, Hants (*Tel No:* 0252 24431 *Ext* 3389)

Commanding Officer........Col D C Robson........310585

ROYAL ARMY MEDICAL COLLEGE AND REGIMENTAL HEADQUARTERS ROYAL ARMY MEDICAL CORPS

Millbank, London, SW1 (*Tel No:* 01-834 9060)

Commandant & Postgraduate Dean........Maj Gen B Livesey *QHS*........030184
Director of Army Surgery and Consulting Surgeon to the Army
A/Maj Gen P K Coakley........100186
Director of Army Medicine and Consulting Physician to the Army
Maj Gen D M Roberts *QHP*........080284
Director of Army Pathology and Consulting Pathologist to the Army
Brig N W J England *QHP*........110581
Director of Army Psychiatry and Consulting Psychiatrist to the Army
Brig P Abraham........300384
Director of Army General Practice
Brig A O Billinghurst........190685
Professor of Military Surgery........Col I R Haywood RAMC........251185
Professor of Military Medicine........Brig C J Garrett........160985
Professor of Pathology........Lt Col R C Menzies RAMC........290785
Professor of Psychiatry........Maj J S McPherson RAMC........161285
Professor of Army Preventative Medicine........Col C J Lewthwaite........101284
Senior Lecturer in Military Surgery........Lt Col R P Craig RAMC
Senior Lecturer in Military Medicine
Reader in Pathology
Consultant Adviser in Dental Surgery........A/Brig M J Newell........300384
Honorary Research Assistant to Wound Ballistics and Missile Injury Databank
L D Payne........270979

Consultants Emeritus to the Army

Rt Hon Lord Richardson *MVO (late Consultant Physician to the Army)*
Mr Myles Formby *CBE TD (late Consultant ENT Surgeon to the Army)*
Lord Porritt *GCMG GCVO CBE (late Consultant Surgeon to the Army)*
Sir Terence Ward *Kt CBE (late Consultant Dental Surgeon to the Army)*
Prof T Cecil Gray *(late Consultant Anaesthetist to the Army)*
Sir Ian Fraser *DSO OBE (late Consultant Surgeon to the Army)*
Lord Smith of Marlow *KBE (late Consultant Surgeon to the Army)*
Mr T L T Lewis *CBE (late Consultant Obstetrician to the Army)*
Dr Walter Somerville *CBE (late Consultant Cardiologist to the Army)*

Honorary Consultants to the Army at Home

Anaesthetic & Resuscitation	*Sir* James Robson *CBE*
Applied Physiology & Physiology	*Prof* J V G A Durnin
Aviation Medicine	*Dr* G Bennett
Blood Transfusion	*Dr* W Wagstaff
Cardiology	*Dr* M M Webb-Peploe
Cardiothoracic Surgery	*Mr* B T Williams
	Mr M V Braimbridge
Child & Adolescent Psychiatry	*Dr* A D Cox
Colon & Rectal Surgery	*Mr* P R Hawley
Community Medicine	*Prof Sir* John Reid *KCMG CB TD*
Dental Surgery	*Prof* R Duckworth
	Dr D Henderson
Dermatology	*Dr* M M Black
Diseases of the Chest	*Dr* E E Keal
Endocrinology	*Dr* M N Maisey
Entomology	*Prof* W W MacDonald
Forensic Medicine	*Prof* J M Cameron
Gastro-Enterology	*Dr* B Creamer
General Practice	*Dr* J Fry *OBE*
	Prof V M W Drury
Genito-Urinary Medicine	*Dr* R N T Thin
Haematology	*Prof* P T Flute *TD*
Histopathology	*Prof* J R Tighe
Malariology	*Prof* C M H Gilles
Microbiology	*Prof* F W O'Grady *CBE TD*
Neonatology	*Dr* N McIntosh
Neurology	*Dr* K J Zilkha
Neuro-Surgery	*Mr* R M Gibson *ERD TD*
Nuclear Medicine	*Dr* M N Maisey
Nutrition	Maj Gen J P Crowdy *CB* ret pay
Obstetrics & Gynaecology	*Dr* E D Morris
Occupational Medicine	*Prof* R I McCallum
Ophthalmology	*Mr* A H Chignell
Orthodontics	*Mr* H S Orton
Orthopaedic Surgery	*Mr* D R Sweetman
Oto-Rhino-Laryngology	*Mr* R A Williams
Paediatrics	*Dr* D B Grant
Paediatric Orthopaedic Surgery	*Mr* J A Fixsen
Paediatric Surgery	*Prof* L Spitz
Pharmacology	*Prof* J B E Baker
Physicians	*Dr* C L Joiner
	Dr N F Jones
Plastic Surgery	*Mr* A Wallace
Psychiatry	*Prof* J P Watson
Radiology	*Dr* J W Laws *CBE*
Radiotherapeutics	*Dr* R H Phillips
Restorative Dentistry	*Dr* B G N Smith
Rheumatology & Rehabilitation	*Dr* D A H Yates
Speech Therapy	*Dr* J M Cooper
Surgery	*Prof* H Ellis
	Mr G Westbury
	Prof I McColl
Tropical Diseases	*Dr* A D M Bryceson
Urology	*Mr* J P Williams
Vascular Surgery	*Prof* N L Browse
Vaccination & Immunisation	*Dr* J W G Smith

Honorary Consultants to the Army in Scotland

Ophthalmology .... *Prof* C I Philips
Orthopaedic Surgery .... *Prof* D L Hambien
Physician .... *Dr* J D Matthews
Surgery .... *Mr* J W W Thomson

Honorary Consulting Staff Northern Ireland

Medicine .... *Dr* J A Weaver
Surgery .... *Mr* A McCalister

Honorary Consulting Staff The Queen Elizabeth Military Hospital Woolwich

Dental Surgery .... *Mr* R Haskell
Dermatology .... *Dr* W A D Griffiths
Neuro-Surgery .... *Mr* C E Polkey
Ophthalmology .... *Mr* J S Shilling
Orthodontics .... *Mr* J Metcalf
Orthopaedic Surgery .... *Mr* R Q Crellin
Oto-Rhino-Laryngology .... *Mr* J N G Evans
Plastic Surgery .... *Mr* T D Cochrane
Radiology .... *Dr* H M Saxton
Radiotherapeutics .... *Dr* R H Phillips

Honorary Consulting Staff The Duchess of Kent's Military Hospital Catterick

Dermatology .... *Dr* T C Hindson
Oto-Rhino-Laryngology .... *Mr* R G Williams *TD*

Honorary Consulting Staff Cambridge Military Hospital

Anaesthetics .... *Dr* T B Boulton
Dental Surgery .... *Mr* D Wilson
Neuro-Surgery .... *Mr* J S Garfield
Oto-Rhino-Laryngology .... *Mr* D Wright
Paediatric Cardiology .... *Prof* M J Tynan
Plastic Surgery .... *Mr* J V Jeffs
Radiotherapy & Nuclear Medicine .... *Dr* W F White

Honorary Consulting Staff British Army of the Rhine

Medicine .... *Prof Dr Med* H Losse
Dr T O F Wagner

Honorary Consulting Staff Military Hospital Hong Kong

Anaesthetics & Resuscitation .... *Prof* J A Thornton
Medicine .... *Prof* J A Vallence-Owen
Orthopaedic Surgery .... *Dr* J C Y Leong
Oto-Rhino-Laryngology .... *Dr* G Wing Sien Choa
Paediatrics .... *Dr* Alice Chau
Paediatric Surgery .... *Dr* P C K Yue
Pathology .... *Prof* J Lee
Psychiatry .... *Dr* W Green
Surgery .... *Prof* G B Ong *OBE*

HEADQUARTERS PROVOST MARSHAL (ARMY)

Empress State Building, Lillie Road, London, SW6 1TR (*Tel No:* 01-385 1244)

Provost Marshal (Army) and Inspector of Military Establishments
Brig B Thomas *CBE*RMP.......030683

ROYAL MILITARY POLICE TRAINING CENTRE

Roussillon Barracks, Chichester, West Sussex (*Tel No:* 0243 786311)

Headquarters

Commandant.......Lt Col J P Curtin RMP.......040285

MILITARY CORRECTIVE TRAINING CENTRE

Colchester (*Tel No:* 0206 575121)

Commandant.......Lt Col A P H Parsons SG.......200284

RAPC TRAINING CENTRE

Worthy Down, Winchester, Hants SO21 2RG (*Tel No:* 0962 880880)

Commandant.......Col A A S Adams.......311284

RAPC COMPUTER CENTRE

Worthy Down, Winchester, Hants SO21 2RG (*Tel No:* 0962 880880)

Chief Paymaster ADP.......Brig P S Bray.......260785

ARMY PAY OFFICE (Officers' Accounts)

Rogers House, Rosehill Road, Ashton-under-Lyne, Lancs OL6 8HU (*Tel No:* 061-330 4541)

Chief Paymaster.......Col G M Gadd.......311083

COMMAND PAY OFFICE UKLF

Gould House, Worthy Down, Winchester, Hants SO21 2RG (*Tel No:* 0962 880880)

Commanding Officer.......Col G E Cauchi.......100484

ARMY PENSIONS OFFICE

Wellesley House, 103-109 Waterloo Street, Glasgow, G2 7BN (*Tel No:* 041-248 7890)

Senior Executive Officer.......J Fallon

COMMAND PAY OFFICES (Overseas)

British Army of the Rhine
British Forces Post Office 40

Commanding Officer.......Col B C Bingle.......300784

Hong Kong
British Forces Post Office 1

Commanding Officer.......Lt Col E Lowndes RAPC.......170286

Land Forces Cyprus
British Forces Post Office 53

Commanding Officer.......Lt Col B A Lloyd RAPC.......070585

REGIMENTAL PAY OFFICES

RE, R SIGNALS, RCT

Kentigern House, 65 Brown Street, Glasgow, G2 8EX (*Tel No:* 041-248 7890)

Regimental Paymaster.........................Col J A Davis 010986

RAOC, REME

Glen Parva Barracks, Saffron Road, Wigston, Leicester, LE8 2US (*Tel No:* 0537 785361)

Regimental Paymaster.........................Col S M B O'Meara 100386

Household Cavalry, RAC, Medical Services, WRAC, Secondments

Queen's Park, Chester, CH4 7AW (*Tel No:* 0244 24666)

Regimental Paymaster.........................Col A J A Rea *MBE*..........260885

RA, The Guards Division, The Scottish Division, The Kings Division, The Price of Wales's Division, GSC

Imphal Barracks, York, YO1 4HD (*Tel No:* 0904 59811)

Regimental Paymaster.........................Col D Bunney..........280885

The Queens Division, The Light Division, PARA, AAC, RMP, RAPC, RAVC, SASC, MPSC, RAEC, RPC, INT CORPS, APTC, ACC, RMAS Officer Cadets, OTC, Long Service List

Jellalabad Barracks, Taunton, Somerset, TA1 3NS (*Tel No:* 0823 3434)

Regimental Paymaster.........................Col A B Crossley..........050784

HEADQUARTERS DIRECTOR OF ARMY VETERINARY & REMOUNT SERVICES

Government Office Building, Droitwich, Worcs, WR9 8AU (*Tel No:* 0905 772323)

Director......Brig R J Clifford *QHVS*......010583

ROYAL ARMY VETERINARY CORPS TRAINING CENTRE

Melton Mowbray, Leics, LE13 0SL (*Tel No:* 0664 63281)

Commandant......Col G R Durrant *MBE*......301085

ROYAL ARMY VETERINARY CORPS LABORATORY AND STORES

Gallwey Road, Aldershot, Hants, GU11 2DQ (*Tel No:* 0252 24431 *Ext* 2262)

Officer Commanding......Maj A H Roache RAVC......030985

RAEC CENTRE

Wilton Park, Beaconsfield (*Tel No:* 04946 6121)

Commandant......Brig D E Thwaites......080584

Army School of Education

Commanding Officer......Lt Col W H P J Fitzsimons RAEC......160184

Defence School of Languages

Commanding Officer......Lt Col J M MacFarlane RAEC......191283

Army School of Training Support

Commanding Officer......Col D H Oxley......270186

No 1 RESETTLEMENT CENTRE

Hipswell Lodge, Catterick Garrison, North Yorkshire (*Tel No: Catterick Garrison* 2521)

Commandant......Lt Col R C Drewe RAEC......170984

No 2 RESETTLEMENT CENTRE

Galway Road, Aldershot, Hants (*Tel No:* 0252 24431)

Commandant......Lt Col K Millsop RAEC......280185

HEADQUARTERS & CENTRAL GROUP ROYAL ARMY DENTAL CORPS

Evelyn Woods Road, Aldershot, Hants (*Tel No:* 0252 24431)

Commandant and Inspector of Training
Col D R Jack......121284

QUEEN ALEXANDRA'S ROYAL ARMY NURSING CORPS TRAINING CENTRE

The Royal Pavilion, Farnborough Road, Aldershot, Hants (*Tel No:* 0252 24431)

Commandant......Col V J Smith *RRC* QARANC......190983

WOMEN'S ROYAL ARMY CORPS CENTRE

Queen Elizabeth Park, Guildford, Surrey, GU2 6QH (*Tel No:* 0252 24431)

Commandant......Col A J Smith WRAC......200884

CADET TRAINING CENTRE

Frimley Park, Frimley Road, Camberley, Surrey, GU16 5HD (*Tel No:* 0276 65155)

Commandant......Col J H Bryant......310785

(iv) SPONSORED BY THE DEPARTMENT OF THE QUARTERMASTER GENERAL

DIRECTORATE OF DEFENCE POSTAL AND COURIER SERVICES

British Forces Post Office 777 (*Tel No:* 01-930 4466)

Director .... Col D L Streatfield 110886

POSTAL AND COURIER DEPOT RE

Inglis Barracks, Mill Hill, London, NW7 1PX (*Tel No:* 01-346 2611)

Headquarters

Commandant .... Lt Col P Wescott RE 110886

Central Volunteer Headquarters RE PCS

Commander .... Lt Col P Wescott RE 110886

DIRECTORATE GENERAL OF TRANSPORT AND MOVEMENTS

Logistic Executive (Army), Portway, Monxton Road, Andover, Hants, SP11 8HT (*Tel No:* 0264 82111)

Director General .... A/Maj Gen D B H Colley *CBE* 010386
Deputy Director General of Transport and Movements
Brig C J Carey 110185
Director of Movements (Army) .... Brig J K Pitt *OBE* 061285
Director of Transport Operations .... Brig C M Boyd 170186

ARMY SCHOOL OF MECHANICAL TRANSPORT

Normandy Barracks, Leconfield, Beverly, North Humberside, HU17 7LX (*Tel No:* 0401 50386)

Headquarters

Commandant .... Brig P J Marzetti 010485

School Regiment

Officer Commanding .... Lt Col J Tarvit RCT 151084

THE TRAINING GROUP ROYAL CORPS OF TRANSPORT

Buller Barracks, Aldershot, Hants, GU11 2BX (*Tel No:* 0252 24431)

Headquarters

Commander .... Brig P I Palmer *OBE* 110684

School of Transportation

Commandant .... A/Col I J Hellberg *OBE* RCT 211085

Depot and Training Regiment RCT

Officer Commanding .... Lt Col M B Carver RCT 180486

Junior Leaders Regiment RCT/RAOC

Azimgur Barracks, Colerne, nr Chippenham, Wilts, SN14 8QY (*Tel No:* 0225 743240)

Officer Commanding .... Lt Col B J Burgess RCT 220585

HQ RCT TA and Depot RCT TA

Prince William of Gloucester Barracks, Grantham, Lincs (*Tel No:* 0476 67413)

Commander .... Brig M Winn 021185
Colonel of Volunteers RCT .... Col J A Butler *MC TD* 270785

HEADQUARTERS DIRECTOR GENERAL OF ORDNANCE SERVICES

Logistic Executive (Army), Portway, Monxton Road, Andover, Hants, SP11 8HT (*Tel No:* 0264 82111)

Director General..................................Maj Gen G B Berragan..................................020985
Deputy Director General.......................Brig A J Paviour..................................221185

ROYAL ARMY ORDNANCE CORPS TRAINING CENTRE

Blackdown Barracks, Deepcut, Camberley (*Tel No:* 04867 4511)

Headquarters

Commander..................................Brig C E Van Orton..................................230985

School of Ordnance

Commandant..................................Col J F G Cook..................................231085

Training Battalion and Depot RAOC

Commanding Officer..........................Lt Col B J Dickson RAOC..................................130484

Employment Training School RAOC

Commandant..................................Lt Col B F Williamson RAOC..................................141284

Headquarters RAOC Territorial Army

Basil Hill Barracks, Spring Lane, Corsham, Wilts, SN13 9NR (*Tel No:* 0255 810342)

Commander..................................Brig P Forshaw *CBE*..................................280984

DIRECTOR OF SUPPLY OPERATIONS (ARMY)

Logistic Executive (Army), Portway, Monxton Road, Andover, Hants, SP11 8HT (*Tel No:* 0264 82111)

Director..................................Brig J A Jackson *MBE GM*..................................071085

DIRECTORATE OF LAND SERVICE AMMUNITION

Vauxhall Barracks, Didcot, Oxfordshire (*Tel No:* 023-581 5191)

Director..................................Brig M C Owen..................................250285

DIRECTORATE OF SUPPLY COMPUTER SERVICES

St David's Barracks, Graven Hill, Bicester, Oxfordshire (*Tel No:* 08692 3311)

Director..................................Brig D A Man..................................230985

DIRECTORATE OF SUPPLY MANAGEMENT

Logistic Executive (Army), Portway, Monxton Road, Andover, Hants, SP11 8HT (*Tel No:* 0264 82111)

Director..................................Brig J A Turner *ADC*..................................170383

DIRECTORATE OF CLOTHING AND TEXTILES

Logistic Executive (Army), Portway, Monxton Road, Andover, Hants, SP11 8HT (*Tel No:* 0264 82111)

Director..................................Brig C W Beckett..................................190385

INSPECTOR OF REGIMENTAL COLOURS

Heralds' College, Queen Victoria Street, London, EC4

Inspector..................................*Sir* Colin Cole *KCVO TD*

CENTRAL ORDNANCE DEPOTS RAOC

Bicester (*Tel No:* 086 92 3311)

Commandant..........Brig P W Symes *CBE*..........070186

Donnington (*Tel No:* 095-260 3144)

Commandant..........Brig D S Parker..........260985

CENTRAL AMMUNITION DEPOTS RAOC

Longtown (*Tel No:* 022-879 383/493)

Commandant..........Col M L Mathams *OBE*..........040385

Kineton (*Tel No:* 0926-640 331)

Commandant..........Col W J Manuel..........100685

ARMY SCHOOL OF AMMUNITION

Kineton (*Tel No:* 0926-640 331)

Officer Commanding..........Lt Col S G de Wolf RAOC..........011185

PETROLEUM CENTRE RAOC

West Moors, Wimborne, Dorset (*Tel No:* 0202 872271)

Commandant/Chief Instructor..........Lt Col M A Marshall RAOC..........030284

CENTRAL VEHICLE DEPOT

Ashchurch, Tewksbury, Gloucestershire (*Tel No:* 0684 293165)

Commandant..........Col R B Bowden..........270683

ARMOURED VEHICLE SUB DEPOT

Ludgershall (*Tel No:* 09804 3221)

Officer Commanding..........Maj P Carter RAOC..........060985

VEHICLE SUB DEPOT

Hilton (*Tel No:* 0283 732361)

Officer in Charge..........W L Clay..........180679

HEADQUARTERS ARMY FIRE SERVICE

Delhi Barracks, Tidworth, Hants (*Tel No:* 09804 6221 *Ext* 2234)

Chief Fire Service Officer..........G F H Mitchell *QFSM*

HEADQUARTERS DIRECTOR GENERAL OF ELECTRICAL AND MECHANICAL ENGINEERING

Logistic Executive (Army), Portway, Monxton Road, Andover, Hants, SP11 8HT (*Tel No:* 0264 82111)

Director General..........Maj Gen J Boyne *MBE*..........291085
Directors..........Brig R H Chown..........200583
Brig R S Higson..........240884
Brig G M Hutchinson..........170585
A/Brig S T Webber..........020186
Brig P Winchcombe..........270186

LOGISTIC EXECUTIVE (ARMY) REME CONTROLLED UNITS

Aircraft Branch REME
Middle Wallop, Stockbridge, Hants, SO20 8DY (*Tel No:* 0264 62121)

Officer Commanding..........Col B D Porter..........150884

Army Scaling Authority
Ha Ha Road, Woolwich, London, SE18 4QA (*Tel No:* 01-856 5533)

Officer Commanding..........Col B S Turner..........171284

Contract Repair Branch REME
Portway, Monxton Road, Andover, Hants, SP11 8HT (*Tel No:* 0264 82111)

Officer in Charge..........D A Harrison..........230784

HQ REME Central Vehicle Depot RAOC UK
Ashchurch, Tewkesbury, Glos GL20 8LZ (*Tel No:* 0684 293165)

Commander Maintenance..........Lt Col (SL) P R Hemsley REME..........231184

Maritime Branch REME
St Georges Barracks, Gosport, Hants PO12 1AB (*Tel No:* 0705 587111)

Officer in Charge..........A S Blight..........090968

REME Methods Engineering Unit UK
Old Dalby, Leics, LE14 3NQ (*Tel No:* 0664 822351)

Officer in Charge..........B C Jones..........011282

REME Data Centre
Repository Road, Woolwich, London, SE18 4QA (*Tel No:* 01-856 5533)

Officer Commanding..........Col T L Elkins..........030884

REME Publications Centre
Repository Road, Woolwich, London, SE18 4QA (*Tel No:* 01-856 5533)

Officer Commanding..........Lt Col N A E Clothier REME..........110185

Stores Inspection Branch REME
Portway, Monxton Road, Andover, Hants, SP11 8HT (*Tel No:* 0264 82111)

Officer Commanding..........Lt Col (EMAE) B D Stacey REME..........140486

Electronics Branch REME
Leigh Sintern Road, Malvern, Worcs, WR14 1LL (*Tel No:* 06845 2781)

Officer Commanding..........Col W K Palmer..........091184

Vehicles and Weapons Branch REME
Chobham Lane, Chertsey, Surrey, KT16 0EE (*Tel No:* 0990 23366)

Officer Commanding..........Col D R Axson..........300184

Workshop Technology Branch REME
Ha Ha Road, Woolwich, London, SE18 4QA (*Tel No:* 01-856 5533)

Officer Commanding..........Lt Col F Booth REME..........070486

18 Base Workshop REME
Bovington Camp, Wareham, Dorset, BH20 6JA (*Tel No:* 0929 462721)

Commanding Officer..........A/Col E W Mabbett REME..........200985

32 Base Workshop REME
Bicester, Oxon, OX6 0LD (*Tel No:* 0869 253311)

Commanding Officer..........Lt Col R M Ayscough REME..........230885

34 Base Workshop REME
Donnington, Telford, Salop TF2 8QE (*Tel No:* 095260 3144)

Commanding Officer............................A/Col S V Durn REME..070984

35 Base Workshop REME
Old Dalby, Melton Mowbray, Leics LE14 3NQ (*Tel No:* 066482 2351)

Commanding Officer............................Col R A Holdsworth..051084

33 Central Workshop REME
Lincoln Road, Newark, Notts,NG24 2EA (*Tel No:* 0636 703421)

Commanding Officer............................Lt Col C P T Brown REME..080584

38 Central Workshop REME
Chilwell, Beeston, Notts, NG9 5HB (*Tel No:* 0602 254811)

Commanding Officer............................Col B D Gotts..230983

91 Vehicle Depot Workshop REME
Hilton, Derby, DE6 5FS (*Tel No:* 028373 2361)

Officer in Charge............................F Woods..121184

93 Vehicle Depot Workshop REME
Ashchurch, Tewkesbury, Glos GL20 8LZ (*Tel No:* 0684 293165)

Officer Commanding............................Capt P Dolphin REME..100186

96 Vehicle Depot Workshop REME
Ludgershall, Andover, Hants SP11 9RP (*Tel No:* 09803 3371)

Officer Commanding............................Maj (EMAE) A G Chalmers REME..130784

ROYAL ELECTRICAL AND MECHANICAL ENGINEERS TRAINING CENTRE

Arborfield, Reading, Berks (*Tel No:* 0734-760421)

Headquarters

Commandant............................Brig J G Till..210984

REME Officers School

Commandant............................Col C J B Nitsch..081284

School of Electronic Engineering

Hazebrouck Barracks, Arborfield, Reading, Berks

Commandant............................A/Col J F Le Quesne REME..151185

Princess Marina College

Arborfield, Reading, Berks

Commandant............................A/Col A A Soar REME..200985

Training Battalion Depot REME

Rowcroft Barracks, Arborfield, Reading, Berks

Officer Commanding............................Lt Col R W P Mullin REME..051084

SCHOOL OF ELECTRICAL AND MECHANICAL ENGINEERING

Prince Philip Barracks, Bordon, Hants, GU35 0JE (*Tel No:* 04203 3611)

Commandant............................A/Brig G J Quirke..210286

Headquarters REME Territorial Army
Louisberg Barracks, Bordon, Hants, GU35 0NE (*Tel No:* 04203 3611)

Commander............................Brig G R Stubbington..280685

HEADQUARTERS DIRECTOR OF ARMY PIONEERS AND LABOUR

Simpson Barracks, Wootton, Northampton (*Tel No:* 0604 62742 *Ext* 61)

Director & Inspector RPC ....Brig H J Hickman *OBE* 180385

ROYAL PIONEER CORPS CENTRE

Simpson Barracks, Wootton, Northampton (*Tel No:* 0604 62742/3)

Headquarters

Commandant ....Lt Col M C Le Masurier RPC 080984

Central Volunteer Headquarters RPC

Commander ....Lt Col M C Le Masurier RPC 080984

HEADQUARTERS DIRECTOR ARMY CATERING CORPS

St Omer Barracks, Aldershot, Hants, GU11 2BN (*Tel No:* 0252 24431)

Director ....Brig M J Paterson ACC 040485

ARMY CATERING CORPS TRAINING CENTRE

St Omer Barracks, Aldershot, Hants, GU11 2BN (*Tel No:* 0252 24431)

Headquarters

Commandant ....Brig R N Maddy ACC 140685

Headquarters Army School of Catering

Commanding Officer & Chief Instructor
Lt Col G Wilkinson ACC 030585

Headquarters Army Apprentices College (ACC)

Commanding Officer ....Lt Col M J Dickinson ACC 010385

Headquarters Training Battalion and Depot ACC

Commanding Officer ....Lt Col E J MacDonald ACC 241083

Central Volunteer Headquarters ACC

Commander ....Lt Col P A Drewett *OBE* ACC 220785

(v) SPONSORED BY THE DEPARTMENT OF THE CHIEF SCIENTIST (ARMY)

ARMY PERSONNEL RESEARCH ESTABLISHMENT

c/o RAE Farnborough, Hampshire (*Tel No:* 0252 24461)

Director..........E D T Strong

(vi) SPONSORED BY THE DEPARTMENT OF THE MASTER GENERAL OF THE ORDNANCE

ORDNANCE BOARD

Empress State Building, Lillie Road, London, SW6 1TR (*Tel No:* 01-385 1244)

President..........A/Maj Gen E G Willmott *OBE*..........110486
Vice Presidents..........Cdre P Reeves..........300484
Chairman..........Air Cdre B R L Easton..........110486

Military Laser Safety Committee:

Chairman..........Air Cdre B R L Easton..........110486

Explosives, Storage and Transport Committee

Chairman..........Cdre P Reeves..........290785

Defence Explosives Safety Authority

Chairman..........Cdre P Reeves..........010186

(vii) SPONSORED BY THE DEPARTMENT OF THE DEPUTY UNDER-SECRETARY OF STATE (PERSONNEL & LOGISTICS)

ROYAL ARMY CHAPLAINS' DEPARTMENT CENTRE

Bagshot Park, Surrey (*Tel No:* 0276 71717)

Warden..........*Rev* P B Denton RAChD *Chaplain to the Forces 2nd Class*..........140186

III. PROCUREMENT EXECUTIVE, MINISTRY OF DEFENCE

SPONSORED BY THE CERN (PE)

ROYAL AIRCRAFT ESTABLISHMENT

Farnborough, Hampshire (*Tel No:* 0252 24461)

Director ....*Dr* G G Pope *CB*

AEROPLANE & ARMAMENT EXPERIMENTAL ESTABLISHMENT

Boscombe Down, Salisbury, SP4 0JF (*Tel No:* 0980 23331)

Commandant...Air Cdre G C Williams *AFC* RAF 100983

ROYAL SIGNALS & RADAR ESTABLISHMENT

St Andrews Road, Malvern, Worcs, WR14 3PS (*Tel No:* 06845 2733)

Director ....*Dr* A C Baynham
Deputy Directors...................................S J Robinson
Dr A J Fox

ROYAL ARMAMENT RESEARCH AND DEVELOPMENT ESTABLISHMENT

Fort Halstead, Sevenoaks,Kent, TN14 7BP (*Tel No:* 0959 32222)

Director ....*Dr* T P McLean
Deputy Directors...................................L G H Cockett
Dr R H Warren
Brig (W) and Senior Military Officer..Brig P M Blagden *CBE* 211284

Chobham Lane, Chertsey, Surrey KT16 0EE (*Tel No:* 0202 484431)

Deputy Director (Vehicles) and Head of RARDE (Chertsey)
C R Evans

Barrack Road, Christcurch, Dorset, BH23 2BB (*Tel No:* 0202 484431)

Head of RARDE (Christchurch) and Head of Engineer Equipment Group
Dr P S Bulson *CBE*..010674

Girdsting Wood, Dundrennan, Kircudbrightshire (*Tel No:* 05575 271)

Commanding Officer...........................Lt Col R T Cliff 13/18 H 050282

Powdermill Lane, Waltham Abbey, Essex EN9 1BP (*Tel No:* 0992 713030)

Head of RARDE (Waltham Abbey) ....*Dr* A J Owen

CHEMICAL DEFENCE ESTABLISHMENT

Porton, nr Salisbury, Wilts, SP4 0JQ (*Tel No:* 0980 610211)

Director ....*Dr* G S Pearson 180684

ATOMIC WEAPONS RESEARCH ESTABLISHMENT

Aldermaston, nr Reading, Berks, RG7 JPR (*Tel No:* 07356 4111 *ext* 7731)

Director ....P G E F Jones *CB*

SPONSORED BY THE DEPARTMENT OF THE MASTER GENERAL OF THE ORDNANCE

PROOF AND EXPERIMENTAL ESTABLISHMENTS

New Ranges, Shoeburyness,Essex, SS3 9SR (*Tel No:* 03708 2271)

Superintendent......A/Col D H C Creswell RA......140186

Inchterf, Milton of Campsie, Glasgow, G65 8AQ (*Tel No:* 041-776 2313-5)

Superintendent......Lt Col R Tarsnane REME......210984

Eskmeals, Millon, Cumbria, LA19 5YR (*Tel No:* 06577 631)

Superintendent......Lt Col P J Wiseman RA......250783

Pendine, Carmarthen, Dyfed, SA33 4UA (*Tel No:* 09945 243)

Superintendent......Lt Col E G Archer RAOC......011183

Cold Meece, Stone, Staffs, ST15 0QR (*Tel No:* 0785 760060)

Superintendent......Lt Col M A Toomey R IRISH......130185

Environmental Test Centre, Foulness, Southend-on-Sea,Essex, SS3 9XJ (*Tel No:* 09020 217272)

Superintendent......R J Chum......250285

IV. MISCELLANEOUS

THE NAVY ARMY AND AIR FORCE INSTITUTES

(A Company Limited by guarantee)

Registered office: Imperial Court, Kennington Lane, London, SE11 5QX (*Tel No:* 01-735 1200)

PATRON ....THE QUEEN

Council

Service Members appointed by the Admiralty Board
Vice Admiral *Sir* Anthony Tippet *KCB*
Rear Admiral B T Brown *CBE*
Service Members appointed by the Army Board
Gen *Sir* Richard Trant *KCB (Vice President)*
Maj Gen J D G Pank
Service Members appointed by the Air Force Board
Air Marshal *Sir* Michael Armitage *KCB CBE (President)*
Air Vice Marshal K A Campbell RAF
Other Members appointed jointly by the Admiralty Board, Army Board and Air Force Board
Sir James Spooner *Chairman, Board of Management)*
B E Robson *CB*

Board of Management

Civilian Directors nominated jointly by the Admiralty Board, Army Board and Air Force Board
Sir James Spooner (*Chairman*)
M D Field

Service Directors
Nominated by the Admiralty Board....Capt M J Appleton RN
Nominated by the Army Board ....Col C W Denton
Nominated by the Air Force Board.....Gp Capt P G Hearn *AFC* RAF
Civilian Directors nominated by the Board of Management
Sir Adrian Swire
J C Bartholemew *TD DL*
C J M Hardie *CBE*
Air Chief Marshal *Sir* David Evans *GCB CBE*
C S Cullimore *CBE*
B E Whitaker *CBE (Managing Director)*
J Morgan *OBE (Assistant Managing Director)*
N Webb-Bourne *(Supplies Director)*
R W Day *(Trading Director)*

THE SERVICES SOUND AND VISION CORPORATION

Chalfont Grove, Narcot Lane, Chalfont St Peter, Gerrards Cross, Bucks, SL9 8TN
(*Tel No:* 02407 4461)

Council

Appointed by the Army Board ....Adjutant General
Appointed by the Air Force Board......Air Member for Personnel
Appointed by the Admiralty Board.....Chief of Naval Personnel & Second Sea Lord
Appointed by the PUS.........................J N H Blelloch *CB*
Chairman of the Board of Management

Board of Management

Chairman ....Gp Capt *Sir* Gordon Pirie *CBE DL* RAF (ret)
Managing Director...............................J F Grist
Members ....Maj Gen J D G Pank
Rear Admiral B T Brown *CBE*
Air Vice Marshal K A Campbell RAF
Sir James Redmond
P Livingstone
B Tesler *CBE*
R A Webster
D E Hatch
J V Cowen
Deputy Managing Director & Secretary
Air Vice Marshal D G Bailey *CB CBE* RAF (retd)

THE ARMY BENEVOLENT FUND

41, Queen's Gate, South Kensington, London, SW7 5HR

PATRON ....THE QUEEN
President...Gen *Sir* John Mogg *GCB CBE DSO*▪ ret pay
Vice Lord Lieutenant Oxfordshire
Chairman Executive Committee ....Gen *Sir* Robert Ford *GCB CBE* ret pay
Controller..Maj Gen P J Bush *OBE* ret pay

(*Tel Nos:—Controller* 01-584 5232 *Appeals Secretary* 01-584 5233 *Grants Secretary* 01-584 5235)

THE NATIONAL ARMY MUSEUM

Royal Hospital Road, Chelsea, London,SW3 4HT (*Tel No:* 01-730 0717)

Council ....Minister of State for Defence Support
Gen *Sir* Jack Harman *GCB OBE MC* ret pay
The Adjutant General
The Assistant Under Secretary of State (Army)
Sir Arthur Drew *KCB JP*
Sir David Steel *DSO MC TD*
Sir Basil Hall *KCB MC TD*
R Mahaffey
Lt Gen *Sir* John Chapple *KCB KBE*
Dr Piers Mackesy
B E Robson *CB*

Director ....W Reid

THE DUKE OF YORK'S ROYAL MILITARY SCHOOL

Dover, Kent, CT15 5EQ (*Tel No: Dover* 203012)

Journal:–"The Yorkist"

President.......Maj Gen *HRH The Duke of* Kent *KG GCMG GCVO ADC*

Commissioners

Chairman.......The Paymaster General
The Assistant Under Secretary of State (Army)
The Judge Advocate General
The Chaplain General
Director General Army Manning & Recruiting
Director of Army Training
The Director of Army Quartering
The Director of Army Education
The GOC South East District

Specially Appointed.......Gen *Sir* Charles Harington *GCB CBE DSO MC* ret pay
Maj Gen *Sir* John Bates *KBE CB MC* ret pay
Gen *Sir* Antony Read *GCB CBE DSO MC* ret pay
Gen *Sir* Peter Hunt *GCB DSO OBE DL* ret pay

Headmaster Commanding Officer.......Col A F P Petrie.......010882

QUEEN VICTORIA SCHOOL FOR THE SONS OF SCOTTISH SAILORS SOLDIERS AND AIRMEN

Dunblane, Perthshire FK15 OJY (*Tel No:* 0786 822288)

Journal:–"The Victorian"

Patron.......Field Marshal *HRH The Prince* Philip *Duke of* Edinburgh *KG KT OM GBE QSO*

Commissioners

President.......The Secretary of State for Scotland
Vice President.......The GOC HQ Scotland
Ex Officio.......The Lord Justice Clerk
The Adjutant General

Nominated by the Scottish Education Department
J A Scott *LVO (Secretary to the Scottish Education Department)*

Nominated by the Secretary of State for Scotland
Maj Gen F C C Graham *CB DSO* ret pay
R G Duthie *CBE*
A Wallace
Lt Gen *Sir* David Young *KBE CB DFC* ret pay
J L Morrison

Nominated by the General Officer Commanding HQ Scotland
D B McMurray
Vice Admiral *Sir* Thomas Baird *KCB*
Col G R Simpson *DSO LVO TD DL*
M J Culham *AUS(A) (AD) Ministry of Defence*
Air Marshal *Sir* Peter Bairsto *KBE CB AFC*
C D Pighills
Maj Gen R Lyon *CB OBE* ret pay

Nominated by the Ministry of Defence Navy Department
Rear Admiral D A Dunbar-Nasmith *CB DSC* ret pay

Nominated by the Ministry of Defence Air Department
Air Marshal *Sir* Richard Wakeford *KCB LVO OBE AFC*

Commandant & Secretary to the Commissioners
Brig O R Tweedy ret pay.......080185

Headmaster.......J D Hankinson.......070480

ROYAL HOSPITAL CHELSEA

Commissioners

Ex-officio	The Paymaster General	
	The Minister of State for the Armed Forces	
	The Minister of State for Defence Support	
	The Governor of The Royal Hospital Chelsea	
	The Surgeon General and Director of Army Medical Services	
	The Director General Territorial Army & Organisation	
	The Director General of Personal Services (Army)	
	The Director General of Logistic Policy	
	The Assistant Under Secretary of State (Adjutant General)	
	The Lieutenant Governor and Secretary of the Royal Hospital Chelsea	
Specially Appointed	Maj Gen P Blunt *CB MBE GM* ret pay	150880
	Gen *Sir* Patrick Howard-Dobson *GCB* ret pay	250982
	D V Palmer	250982
	Sir Ewen Broadbent *KCB CMG*	111082
	The Rt Rev M A Mann	050784
	Maj Gen F J Plaskett *CB MBE* ret pay	160985
Governor	Gen *Sir* Robert Ford *GCB CBE* ret pay	010881
Lieutenant Governor and Secretary	Maj Gen A L Watson *CB* ret pay	140184
Assistant Secretary	D R J Stephen *CB*	220782
Adjutant	Col G A Allen *OBE* ret pay	010782
Physician and Surgeon	Maj Gen H S Moore *MBE* ret pay	010384
Chaplain	*Rev* A D Bartlett. ret pay	270781
Deputy Surgeon	*Dr* P B Biddell *MC*■	020182
Assistant Surgeon	Maj Gen A T Cook ret pay	010386
Quartermaster	Lt Col (Staff QM) N Welch *OBE* COLDM GDS	201079
Chief Clerk	R V Murray	090485
Captains of Invalids	Maj D H Donnelly ret pay	010466
	Maj B T S Clarke ret pay	210576
	Lt Col J J Kelly *OBE* ret pay	011179
	Lt Col T G Glendenning ret pay	070483
	Col E S Newport *TD* ret pay	260384
	Lt Col D J Daly ret pay	060186

Consultants in Medicine & Surgery

Medicine	Maj Gen D M Roberts
Surgery	Maj Gen W J Pryn *OBE QHS*

Honorary Consultants

Cardiology	*Dr* M M Webb-Peploe
Dermatology	*Dr* R C D Staughton
Dietician	*Miss* R Evans
Medicine	*Dr* N F Jones
Neurology	*Dr* K J Zilkha
Ophthalmology	*Mr* J L K Bankes
Orthopaedic Surgery	*Mr* D R Sweetnam
Psychiatry	*Dr* O S Frank
Radiology	*Dr* B Strickland
Surgery	*Prof* H Ellis
Thoracic Medicine	*Dr* J V Collins
Urology	*Mr* J P Williams

O St J & BRCS SERVICE HOSPITALS WELFARE & VAD DEPARTMENT

4 Grosvenor Crescent, London SW1X 7EQ (*Tel No:* 01-235 5454 *Ext* 298)

Chairman .... *Dame* Anne Bryans *DBE*
Director .... *Miss* S Goldthorpe

THE MOST VENERABLE ORDER OF ST JOHN OF JERUSALEM

St Johns Gate, Clerkenwell, London, EC1M 4DA (*Tel No:* 01-253 6644)

Sovereign Head .... THE QUEEN

Grand Prior .... *HRH THE DUKE OF* GLOUCESTER *GCVO*

Lord Prior .... Maj Gen *The Earl* Cathcart *CB DSO MC* ret pay
Chancellor .... *The Earl* St Aldwyn *GBE TD PC JP DL*
Secretary General .... Lt Gen *Sir* Peter Hudson *KCB CBE DL* ret pay

The St John Ambulance Association & Brigade

1 Grosvenor Crescent, London, SW1X 7EF (*Tel No:* 01-235 5231)

Grand President .... *HRH THE PRINCESS* MARGARET *COUNTESS OF* SNOWDON

Commandant-in-Chief (Nursing) .... *HM* QUEEN ELIZABETH THE QUEEN MOTHER

Commandant-in-Chief (Ambulance & Nursing Cadets)
HRH THE PRINCESS ANNE, *MRS* MARK PHILLIPS

Deputy Commandant-in-Chief (Nursing)
HRH PRINCESS ALICE, *DUCHESS OF* GLOUCESTER

Commandant-in-Chief for Wales *HRH THE DUCHESS OF* GLOUCESTER

Chief Commander .... Maj Gen P R Leuchars *CBE* ret pay

The St John Ophthalmic Hospital

PO Box 19960, Jerusalem (*Tel No:* 282325)

Hospitaller .... *Sir* Stephen Miller *KCVO*

THE ST ANDREW'S AMBULANCE ASSOCIATION

Milton Street Glasgow, G4 (*Tel No:* 041-332 4031)

Patron .... *HM* QUEEN ELIZABETH THE QUEEN MOTHER

President .... Lt Cdr *The Duke of* Buccleuch and Queensbury *KT VRD*
(HM Lieutenant Selkirk) (Captain Queen's Body Guard for Scotland)
Chairman of Council .... *Dr* H R F Macdonald *OBE*
Director General & Secretary .... J W R Cunningham

THE BRITISH RED CROSS SOCIETY

9 Grosvenor Crescent, London, SW1X 7EJ (*Tel No:* 01-235 5454)

Patron and President .... THE QUEEN

Deputy President .... *HM* QUEEN ELIZABETH THE QUEEN MOTHER

Vice Presidents .... *HRH Princess* Alexandra *The Hon Mrs* Angus Ogilvy *GCVO*
The Countess Mountbatten of Burma *CD JP DL*

Patron of Red Cross Youth .... *HRH The Princess of* Wales

Chairman of Council .... *The Countess of* Limerick

Vice Chairman of The Council .... *The Lady* Palmer

The Council .... Mrs P H Samuelson *DL*
Sir Leonard Figg *KCMG*
P J Grant

Director General .... J C Burke-Gaffney

WOMEN'S ORGANISATION

WOMEN'S TRANSPORT SERVICE (FANY)

Duke of York's Headquarters, Chelsea, London SW3 4RX (*Tel No:* 01-730 2058)

Commandant in Chief.........................*HRH THE PRINCESS* ANNE, *MRS* MARK PHILLIPS

Honorary Colonel................................Maj Gen C E Page *CB MBE* ret pay
Chairman of the Advisory Council......Col N A C Croft *DSO OBE* ret pay
Corps Commander...............................*Mrs* S Y Parkinson *OBE*
H Q Administrator...............................*Mrs* H D Irwin-Clark

COUNCIL OF VOLUNTARY WELFARE WORK

(For HM Forces)

Duke of York's Headquarters, Chelsea, London SW3 4RX (*Tel No:* 01-730 3161)

Chairman...*Sir* Arthur Drew *KCB*

General Secretary................................Brig D R Green *CBE MC* ret pay
Representatives of...............................The Navy Department
The Army Department
The Air Force Department
The Young Men's Christian Association
The Young Women's Christian Association
The Salvation Army
The Church Army
The Methodist Church Force's Centres
TOC H
The Church of England Soldiers' Sailors' and Airmen's Clubs
Mission to Military Garrisons
Royal Sailors' Rests
Sandes Soldiers'and Airmen's Homes
SASRA/Miss Daniell's Homes

Associated...The Catholic Women's League
Women's Royal Voluntary Service

COMMONWEALTH WAR GRAVES COMMISSION

2 Marlow Road, Maidenhead, Berkshire, SL6 7DX (*Tel No: Maidenhead* 34221)

President..Maj Gen *HRH The Duke of* Kent *KG GCMG GCVO ADC*

Members..The Secretary of State for Defence (Chairman)
Air Chief Marshal *Sir* John Barraclough *KCB CBE DFC AFC*
The Minister for Housing & Construction
High Commissioner for Canada
High Commissioner for the Commonwealth of Australia
High Commissioner for New Zealand
Ambassador of the Republic of South Africa
High Commissioner for the Republic of India
Sir Edward Gardner *QC MP*
The Rt Hon Lord Wallace of Coslany
Sir Edward Goschen *Bt DSO*
Admiral *Sir* David Williams *GCB DL*
Gen *Sir* Robert Ford *GCB CBE* ret pay
Sir David Muirhead *KCMG CVO*
Sir Donald Maitland *GCMG OBE*
Prof The Baroness McFarlane of Llanduff

Director General....................................*Sir* Arthur Hockaday *KCB CMG (Secretary to the Commission)*
Deputy Director General......................P R Matthew *CBE (Assistant Secretary to the Commission)*
Director of External Relations.............P H M Swan
Director of Information and Secretariat
S G Campbell *MC*
Assistant Director General (Operations)
W J Symons *OBE (Assistant Secretary to the Commission)*
Assistant Director General (Administration)
J Saynor *(Assistant Secretary to the Commission)*
Establishment Officer..........................H Westland
Chief Finance Officer...........................M S Johnson
Organisation & Audit Officer..............D R Parker
Legal Adviser & Solicitor....................G C Reddie
Director of Works.................................N B Osborn
Director of Horticulture.......................J B Paton *OBE*
Private Secretary to Director General
Mrs P E Gibson

Established under Royal Charter in 1917, whereby the Member Governments co-operate directly in the maintenance of war graves and memorials.

V. COMMONWEALTH COUNTRIES

These details are based on the information supplied by the several countries

CANADA

NATIONAL DEFENCE COLLEGE
(Kingston, Ontario)

Commandant..Maj Gen R J Evraire *CD RMC BSc*

CANADIAN FORCES COLLEGE
(Toronto, Ontario)

Commandant..Brig Gen P J Taggart *OMM CD RMC BA*

CANADIAN LAND FORCES COMMAND & STAFF COLLEGE
(Kingston, Ontario)

Commandant..Brig Gen R I Stewart *CD BA*

ROYAL MILITARY COLLEGE
(Kingston, Ontario)

Commandant..Brig Gen W Niemy *CD RMC BEng BAS*

COLLEGE MILITAIRE ROYALE
(St Jean, Quebec)

Commandant..Brig Gen J J R Parent *OMM CD RMC BSc*

ROYAL ROADS MILITARY COLLEGE
(Victoria, BC)

Commandant..Col A I Goode *CD RMC BA*

COMBAT TRAINING SCHOOL
(Gagetown, NB)

Commandant..Brig Gen G S Kells *CD RMC BA* ndc

AUSTRALIA

ROYAL MILITARY COLLEGE
(Duntroon, ACT)

Commandant..Maj Gen B H Hockney *BSc* rcds psc te..090184

COMMAND AND STAFF COLLEGE
(Queenscliff, Victoria)

Commandant..Brig J C Grey jssc psc..200186

LAND WARFARE CENTRE
(Canungra, Quuensland)

Commandant..Col P M Arnison *BEc* jssc psc..111284

THE REPUBLIC OF INDIA

DEFENCE SERVICES STAFF COLLEGE
(Wellington, Nilgiri Hills, South India)

Commandant..Lt Gen F N Bilimoria

NATIONAL DEFENCE ACADEMY
(Kharakwasla)

Commandant..Lt Gen Sami Khan

INDIAN MILITARY ACADEMY
(Dehra Dun)

Commandant..Lt Gen S S Brar

COLLEGE OF COMBAT
(Mhow)

Commandant..Lt Gen R M Vohra *MVC*

INFANTRY SCHOOL
(Mhow)

Commandant..Lt Gen Ranbir Singh

ARMY TRANSPORT SUPPORT SCHOOL
(Agra)

Commandant..Col N Tata

ARMY SCHOOL OF PHYSICAL TRAINING
(Pune)

Commandant..Col G S Sandhu *VSM*

ARMY SCHOOL OF MECHANICAL TRANSPORT
(Bangalore)

Commandant

ARMOURED CORPS CENTRE AND SCHOOL
(Ahmednagar)

Commandant..Lt Gen J S Klev *AVSM*

SCHOOL OF ARTILLERY
(Devlali)

Commandant..Lt Gen Satnam Singh

COLLEGE OF MILITARY ENGINEERING
(Pune)

Commandant..Lt Gen L M Mishra

MILITARY COLLEGE OF TELECOM ENGINEERING
(Mhow)

Commandant..Lt Gen S L Mehrotra

ARMY SERVICE CORPS SCHOOL
(Bareilly)

Commandant...Lt Gen Daljit Singh

MILITARY COLLEGE OF ELECTRONICS & MECHANICAL ENGINEERING
(Trimulgheery)

Commandant...Lt Gen Tripath Singh

ELECTRICAL & MECHANICAL ENGINEERING SCHOOL
(Baroda)

Commandant...Maj Gen B P Roy

ARMY ORNANCE CORPS SCHOOL
(Jabalpur)

Commandant...Lt Gen M L Yadav

INTELLIGENCE TRAINING SCHOOL AND DEPOT
(Pune)

Commandant...Maj Gen P D Sherlekar

AEC TRAINING COLLEGE AND CENTRE
(Pachmarhi)

Commandant...Brig R C Baijal

CMP CENTRE AND SCHOOL
(Bangalore)

Commandant...Brig K D Issar *AVSM*

SECTION III

GRADATION LIST

OFFICERS OF THE ARMY ON THE ACTIVE LIST

FIELD MARSHALS

His Royal Highness The Prince PHILIP *Duke of* EDINBURGH *KG KT OM GBE QSO* Field Marshal Australian Military Forces and New Zealand Army, Capt Gen RM, Col in Chief QRIH, DERR, QO HLDRS, REME, INT CORPS, ACF, The Royal Canadian Regiment, The Royal Hamilton Light Infantry, The Cameron Highlanders of Ottawa, The Queen's own Cameron Highlanders of Canada, The Seaforth Highlanders of Canada, The Royal Canadian Army Cadets, The Royal Australian Electrical and Mechanical Engineers, The Australian Cadet Corps and Corps of Royal New Zealand Electrical and Mechanical Engineers, Col GREN GDS psc(n) (Hon Col OTC and The Trinidad and Tobago Regiment) 150153
HARDING of Petherton *The Lord GCB CBE DSO▪▪ MC* psc 210753
HULL *Sir* Richard *KG GCB DSO MA LLD* idc psc 080265
CASSELS *Sir* James *GCB KBE DSO* idc psc 290268
CARVER *The Lord GCB CBE DSO▪ MC* idc jssc psc 180773
GIBBS *Sir* Roland *GCB CBE DSO MC* idc jssc psc (*Vice Lord Lieutenant Wiltshire*) (*Constable Tower of London*) 130779
BRAMALL *Sir* Edwin *GCB OBE MC* Col 2 GR idc psc (*HM Lord Lieutenant Greater London*) 010882
STANIER *Sir* John *GCB MBE* idc jssc psc 100785

GENERALS

Bagnall *Sir* Nigel *GCB CVO MC▪ ADC Gen* (*late* 4/7 DG) Col Comdt RAC Col Comdt APTC df jssc psc 010982
Morony *Sir* Thomas *KCB OBE ADC Gen* (*late* RA) Col Comdt RA Col Comdt RHA Master Gunner St James's Park psc† psc 011082
Lawson *Sir* Richard *KCB DSO OBE* (*late* RTR) rcds odc(US) psc 151182
Guy *Sir* Roland *KCB CBE DSO ADC Gen* (*late* RGJ) Col Comdt RGJ Col Comdt SASC rcds psc 010983
Burgess *Sir* Edward *KCB OBE ADC Gen* (*late* RA) Col Comdt RA jssc psc 150983
Trant *Sir* Richard *KCB* (*late* RA) Col Comdt RA Col Comdt RAOC Col Comdt HAC jssc psc 290983
Glover *Sir* James *KCB MBE* (*late* RGJ) Col Comdt RGJ, RMP, RAEC rcds jssc psc 290685
Farndale *Sir* Martin *KCB* (*late* RA) Col Comdt RA Col Comdt AAC Hon Col 3 YORKS(V) psc 260785
Howlett *Sir* Geoffrey *KBE MC* (*late* PARA) Col Comdt PARA Col Comdt ACC rcds jssc psc(a) 100286

LIEUTENANT GENERALS

Mostyn *Sir* David *KCB CBE* (*late* RGJ) Col Comdt LIGHT DIV Col Comdt ALC rcds psc 310383
Akehurst *Sir* John *KCB CBE* (*late* R ANGLIAN) Dep Col R ANGLIAN rcds psc 010883
Vincent *Sir* Richard *KCB DSO* (*late* RA) Col Comdt RA Col Comdt REME Hon Col 100 FD REGT RA(V) rcds psc† psc ptsc G(a) 010983
Huxtable *Sir* Charles *KCB CBE* (*late* DWR) Col Comdt KINGS DIV Col DWR jssc psc 031083
Boorman *Sir* Derek *KCB* (*late* STAFFORDS) Col STAFFORDS Col 6 GR rcds jssc psc 010185
Chapple *Sir* John *KCB CBE MA* (*late* 2 GR) df jssc psc 020185
Arthur *Sir* Norman *KCB* (*late* SCOTS DG) Col SCOTS DG Col Comdt MPSC Governor Edinburgh Castle rcds jssc psc 030185
Kenny *Sir* Brian *KCB CBE* (*late* QRIH) Col QRIH Col Comdt RAVC rcds psc pl 040185
Pascoe *Sir* Robert *KCB MBE* (*late* RGJ) rcds psc050185
Moffat *Sir* Cameron *KBE QHS MB ChB FRCS DTM&H* (*late* RAMC) 280185
Gray *Sir* Michael *KCB OBE FBIM* (*late* PARA) Dep Col Comdt PARA Hon Col 10 PARA(V) rcds psc 211285

MAJOR GENERALS

Watts J P B C *CB CBE MC* (*late* R IRISH) odc(US) psc (L/Lt Gen 181284) 010479
Reynolds M F *CB* (*late* QUEENS) Col Comdt QUEENS DIV rcds psc 010480
Lane B M *CB OBE* (*late* LI) Col LI rcds psc 010181
Reilly J C *DSO* (*late* RRF) Col RRF psc 010481
Thorne *Sir* David *KBE* (*late* R ANGLIAN) Dep Col R ANGLIAN rcds jssc psc psc(a) 010481
Walker A K F (*late* RTR) Col Comdt RTR psc 010681
Boam T A *CBE* (*late* SG) rcds psc osc(NIG) 180681
Boyne J *MBE BSc(Eng) CEng FIMechE FBIM* (*late* REME) rcds jssc psc 180681
Keightley R C (*late* 5 INNIS DG) Col 5 INNIS DG rcds ndc psc 180681
Macmillan J R A *CBE MA* (*late* GORDONS) Col GORDONS rcds psc 180681
Palmer C P R *CBE* (*late* A and SH) Col A and SH rcds psc 180681
Watkins G H *CB OBE* (*late* RA) psc 180681
Rougier C J *CB MA* (*late* RE) rcds jssc psc 151081
Steele M C M *MBE* (*late* RA) ocds(CAN) psc 151081
Davies P M *OBE* (*late* RS) rcds ndc psc 180282
Palmer T B *CB CEng FIMechE MBIM* (*late* REME) Col Comdt REME jssc ptsc 180282
Benbow R *CB* (*late* R SIGNALS) Col Comdt R SIGNALS Col QG SIGS rcds odc(US) psc 170682
Bowman J F *CB MA* ALC 170682
Goodman J D W (*late* RA) rcds jssc psc ph 170682
Gordon Lennox B C *CB MBE* (*late* GREN GDS) rcds jssc psc psc(a) 170682
Oehlers G R *CEng FIEE MIERE* (*late* R SIGNALS) sq TE 170682
Shortis C T *CBE* (*late* D and D) Col Comdt PRINCE OF WALES DIV Col D and D rcds psc 170682
Stibbon J J *OBE BSc(Eng)* (*late* RE) Col Comdt RAPC Col Comdt RPC rcds psc sq 170682
Waters C J *CBE* (*late* GLOSTERS) Col GLOSTERS rcds psc† 170682
Braggins D H *CB FCIT FBIM* (*late* RCT) Col Comdt RCT jssc psc 211082
Miller D E *CB CBE MC* (*late* KINGS OWN BORDER) ndc jssc psc 211082
Cornock C G *MBE FBIM* (*late* RA) rcds odc(US) psc 240283
Crossley R J *CBE FBIM* (*late* RA) psc† ptsc G pl 240283
Pank J D G (*late* LI) psc 240283
Ryan D E *LLB* (*late* RAEC) psc 240283
Spacie K *OBE* (*late* PARA) rcds ndc psc 240283
Thompson C N *BA FRICS FBIM* (*late* RE) SVY(pg) SVY 240283
*Kent *HRH The Duke of KG GCMG GCVO ADC* (*late* SCOTS DG) Col in Chief RRF & D and D Col SG psc 110683
Airy C J *CBE* (*late* SG) rcds ndc psc 200683
de la Billiere P E de la C *CBE DSO MC*▪ (*late* LI) rcds psc 200683
Inge P A (*late* GREEN HOWARDS) Col GREEN HOWARDS jssc psc 200683
McGuinness B P *CB* (*late* RA) rcds psc 200683
Ramsbotham D J *CBE MA* (*late* RGJ) rcds psc 200683
Skinner M T *CB FBIM* (*late* RA) psc ptsc 200683
Cooper S C (*late* LG) rcds psc 201083
Yeoman A (*late* R SIGNALS) psc 201083
Livesey B *QHS MB ChB FRCS DLO* (*late* RAMC) 110384
Roberts D M *QHP MD BS FRCPEd* (*late* RAMC) 300384
Guthrie C R L *LVO OBE* (*late* WG) Col Comdt INT CORPS psc 220684
Hobbs M F *CBE* (*late* GREN GDS) psc 220684
Jeapes A S *OBE MC* (*late* D and D) ndc psc osc(BLD) 220684
Johnson G D *OBE MC* (*late* RGJ) Col 10 GR rcds ndc psc 220684
Jones C E W *CBE* (*late* RGJ) rcds psc 220684
Learmont J H *CBE FBIM* (*late* RA) rcds psc 220684
Mullens A R G *OBE* (*late* 4/7 DG) psc 220684
Ramsay C A *OBE* (*late* SCOTS DG) psc 220684
Alexander P D *MBE* (*late* R SIGNALS) rcds ndc psc 251084
Beckett E H A *MBE* (*late* PWO) ndc psc sq 251084
Berragan G B *FBIM* (*late* RAOC) ndc psc 251084
Brooking P G *MBE* (*late* 5 INNIS DG) rcds psc 251084
Evans J A M *MA FBIM* (*late* RE) rcds psc† 251084
Stopford S R A *MBE* (*late* SCOTS DG) ptsc tt 251084
Shaw A J *CBE QHP MB BChir FFCM MRCS LRCP DObstRCOG DTM&H* (*late* RAMC) ndc psc 031284
Blewett R S *OBE MB BS MFCM DObstRCOG DTM&H* (*late* RAMC) psc 030386

*Supernumary

HOUSEHOLD CAVALRY

THE LIFE GUARDS

April 1922

The 1st Life Guards and

The 2nd Life Guards amalgamated to form:

The Life Guards (1st and 2nd)

June 1928

Redesignated The Life Guards

The Royal Arms

Dettingen, Peninsula, Waterloo, Tel-el-Kebir, Egypt 1882, Relief of Kimberley, Paardeberg, South Africa 1899-1900

The Great War— **Mons, Le Cateau,** Retreat from Mons, **Marne 1914, Aisne 1914, Messines 1914,** Armentieres 1914, **Ypres 1914, 15, 17,** Langemarck 1914, Gheluvelt, Nonne Bosschen, St Julien, Frezenberg, **Somme 1916, 18,** Albert 1916, **Arras 1917, 18,** Scarpe 1917, 18, Broodseinde, Poelcappelle, Passchendaele, Bapaume 1918, **Hindenburg Line,** Epehy, St Quentin Canal, Beaurevoir, Cambrai 1918, Selle, **France and Flanders 1914-18**

The Second World War— Mont Pincon, **Souleuvre,** Noireau Crossing, Amiens 1944, **Brussels,** Neerpelt, Nederrijn, Nijmegen, Lingen, Bentheim, **North-West Europe 1944-45,** Baghdad 1941, **Iraq 1941, Palmyra, Syria 1941, El Alamein, North Africa 1942-43,** Arezzo, Advance to Florence, Gothic Line, **Italy 1944**

Regimental Marches

Quick March..(i) Milanollo (ii) Men of Harlech
Slow March..(i) The Life Guards Slow March (ii) Men of Harlech

Agents..Lloyds Bank PLC Cox's & King's Branch

Regimental Headquarters....................Horse Guards, Whitehall, London, SW1A 2AX
(*Tel No:* 01-930-4466 *Ext:* 2213)

Allied Regiment of the Pakistan Army

The President's Bodyguard

Colonel in Chief..................................THE QUEEN

Colonel ....Maj Gen *Lord* Michael Fitzalan Howard *GCVO CB CBE MC DL* ret pay..........211179

Officer Commanding Household Cavalry
Col J B Emson *CBE* 160186

Colonels

Gooch A B S H psc sq	300683
Emson J B *CBE* ndc sq	300684

Lieutenant Colonels

D'Oyly C J osc(FR) sq	300683
Earl T J sq	300683
Harcourt-Smith C S psc ph	300683
Goodhew V A L *MBE* psc	300684

Majors

Gilbart-Denham S V sq	311274
Simpson Gee C J sq tt	311274
Morrisey Paine R J psc	311275
Anderson C S K I	300980
Bayley J R sq	300980
Ellery J W M sq	300980
D'Ambrumenil N J	300981
De Ritter A P psc	300982
Adderley *The Hon* N J aic	300983
Falkner P S W F psc	300983
Vetch S D G	300983
Hunter P R L psc(n)†	300984
Sampson R C B	300984
Forbes-Cockell I S	300985

Captains

Hayward S F	080981
Scott H S J	281281
Doughty W S G	060982
Waterhouse D C	240783
Sunnucks J L *BA*	200384
Hopkins J C *BA*	010884
Graham C H N	081084
Stibbe G G E *BA*	091284
Stewart J W *BA*	010285
Dyson H D aic	050285
Perry-Warnes J H	050285
Boldero J D	040286

Lieutenants

Van Der Lande M C *BA*	110483
Mitford-Slade C N *BSc*	090484
Spowers A R W *BA*	090484

2nd Lieutenants

††Mahony D J G	020983
††Smyth-Osbourne E A	051083

Quartermasters

Lumb L A	*Capt*	010480
Leighton J	*Capt*	010484

Directors of Music

McColl J G *ARCM* psm	310377
Maj	310385

Special Regular Officers

Captains

Hewitt J L	081084

Short Service Officers

Captains

Kelly A	101182
Watson A J	050285
Watson *The Hon* M R M	050285
McKie B J	220785

Lieutenants

Cherrington A M	280282
Knowles J D	300482
Fraser C T de M	131282
Slater C R	010283
Faulkner T J K (*L/Capt* 151084)	110483
Cape J R	090484
Oswald W A M	070884
Ley C I	111284

Household Cavalry — continued

Assheton T	060885
Clark A McK	060885
Griffin R R D	070486
Sunley E J	070486

2nd Lieutenants

Dalgliesh J D A	040884
Garrett N D	040884
Marks S J	040884
Harris P L	081284
Connolly E S	130485
Ogden A C	141285
Thorneycroft T E	141285

Medical Officers

Surgeon Majors

Stewart D *MB BS*	120383

THE BLUES AND ROYALS
(ROYAL HORSE GUARDS AND 1st DRAGOONS)

On 29 March 1969

Royal Horse Guards (The Blues) and

The Royal Dragoons (1st Dragoons) amalgamated to form:

The Blues and Royals (Royal Horse Guards and 1st Dragoons)

The Royal Arms

Tangier 1662-80, Dettingen, Warburg, Beaumont, Willems, Fuentes D'onor, Peninsula, Waterloo, Balaklava, Sevastopol, Egypt, Tel-el-Kebir, Relief of Kimberley, Paardeberg, Relief of Ladysmith, South Africa 1899-1902

The Great War– Mons, **Le Cateau,** Retreat from Mons, **Marne 1914,** Aisne 1914, **Messines 1914,** Armentieres 1914, **Ypres 1914, 15-17,** Langemarck 1914, **Gheluvelt,** Nonne Bosschen, St Julien, **Frezenberg, Loos, Arras 1917,** Scarpe 1917, **Somme 1918,** St Quentin, Avre, Broodseinde, Poelcappelle, Passchendaele, **Amiens, Hindenburg Line,** Beaurevoir, **Cambrai 1918, Sambre, Pursuit to Mons, France and Flanders 1914-18**

The Second World War– Mont Pincon, **Souleuvre,** Noireau Crossing, Amiens 1944, **Brussels,** Neerpelt, **Nederrijn,** Veghel, Nijmegen, **Rhine,** Lingen, Bentheim, **North-West Europe 1944-45,** Baghdad 1941, **Iraq 1941, Palmyra, Syria 1941,** Msus, Gazala, **Knightsbridge,** Defence of Alamein Line, **El Alamein,** El Agheila, **Advance on Tripoli, North Africa 1941-43, Sicily 1943,** Arezzo, Advance to Florence, Gothic Line, **Italy 1943-44**

Falkland Islands 1982

Regimental Marches

Quick March..Regimental Quick March of the Blues and Royals
Grand March from Aida and The Royals

Slow March..Slow March of the Blues and Royals

Agents..Lloyds Bank PLC Cox's & King's Branch

Regimental Headquarters....................Horse Guards, Whitehall, London, SW1A 2AX
(*Tel No:* 01-930-4466 *Ext:* 2213)

Alliances

Canadian Armed Forces......................The Royal Canadian Dragoons
The Governor General's Horse Guards

Colonel in Chief..............................THE QUEEN

Colonel..Gen *Sir* Desmond Fitzpatrick *GCB DSO MBE MC* ret pay 171279

Officer Commanding Household Cavalry
Col J B Emson *CBE* 160186

Colonels

Boyd D S A psc† ptsc tt 300681
Hamilton-Russell J G *MBE* psc 300682
Keightley P T osc(GE) 300685

Lieutenant Colonels

Morris T C (SL) *LVO* sq 300676
Hugh Smith H O *LVO BA* psc 300677
Aylen J A psc† osc(ZIM) 300679
Parker-Bowles A H *OBE* sq 300680
Scott J J F (SL) 300680
Smith-Bingham J D ndc sq 300681
Davies H W *MA* psc aic 300685
Sulivan T J *BSc(Eng)* psc(a) 300685

Majors

Tweedie G H *MA* sq 300677
Weston I M D L sq ph 300677
Rogers P B psc jsdc 311278
Hardy D T L sq 300980
Olivier J S sq tt 300980
Birdwood G T R 300981
Reed-Felstead D M ph 300981
Massey H P D psc 300983
Holcroft H St J *BA* psc 300984

Captains

Lukas F G S *BSc* 010279
Hadden-Paton N 301279
Shaw J 301279
Rollo W R *MA* 040380
Bucknall C C (*A/Maj* 110985) 090980
Browne W T (*A/Maj* 270286) 291280
White-Spunner B W B *MA* 010881
Miller-Bakewell A J aic 080981
Tabor P J *BA* aic 010282
Wood A A (*L/Maj* 010286) 170982
Lendrum R C D 081083
Bernard J A S *BA* 021084
Coreth M R 090685

Lieutenants

Stratton-Christensen M J J E *BA* 120482
Cowen S H 080883
Onslow R J 121283
McCullough G M D 070884
Jacobs S D 090485

Cornets

Wingfield Digby J H 081284
Jowitt W R B 100885
†Clee C B B *BSc(Hons)* 060985
†Lane-Fox G C N 060985
††Bagnell W E H 240985
††Garnett C H E 240985

Medical Officers

Surgeon Colonels

Page J P A *MA MB BChir DTM&H* 010286

Surgeon Majors

Staunton M A *MB BS MRCS LRCP* 080982

Quartermasters

Giles R R 310774
Lt Col 180184
Peck J *Capt* 010480
Patterson M A *Capt* 010484

Household Cavalry — continued

Livingstone J A *Capt* 310784

Directors of Music

Keeling B T *LRAM ARCM* 270970
Maj 010479
Watts S A *LRAM* *Capt* 011182

Special Regular Officers

Majors

Lane B W 300980
Barclay T P E *MFH* 300984
Kersting A W 300984

Short Service Officers

Captains

Sellars J W 160383
Hanmer E H 090685

Lieutenants

Sibley S
(*A/Capt* 310885) 010182
Johnsen J W *BA*
(*A/Capt* 060386) 120482
McGregor D
(*A/Capt* 060785) 011082
Clayton J W 251282
Mountain E B S
(*A/Capt* 031185) 080883
Swayne J S P
(*A/Capt* 040485) 121283
Tanburn J C 060885
Owen C S 141085
Ward-Thomas C R F 101285
Broughton J H A 070486

Cornets

Reid J D D 081284
Woyka G V de la F 081284
Cragoe G L 130485
†Holland Q C A *BSc(Hons)* 060985
Scott A C 141285

ROYAL ARMOURED CORPS

In front of two concentric circles broken and barbed at the top, a gauntlet, clenched, charged with a billet. Inscribed with the letters "R.A.C." the whole ensigned with The Crown

Alliances

Canadian Armed Forces......................Armoured Branch
Australian Military Forces....................The Royal Australian Armoured Corps
Colonel Commandant..........................Gen *Sir* Nigel Bagnall *GCB CVO MC*▪ *ADC Gen*..010885

The origins of amalgamated Regiments now included in The Royal Armoured Corps are as follows:–

1st THE QUEEN'S DRAGOON GUARDS

On 1 January 1959
1st King's Dragoon Guards and
The Queen's Bays (2nd Dragoon Guards) amalgamated to form:
1st The Queen's Dragoon Guards

THE ROYAL SCOTS DRAGOON GUARDS (CARABINIERS AND GREYS)

On 11 April 1922
3rd Dragoon Guards (Prince of Wales's) and
The Carabiniers (6th Dragoon Guards) amalgamated to form:
3rd/6th Dragoon Guards
On 31 December 1928 the Regiment was redesignated
3rd Carabiniers (Prince of Wales's Dragoon Guards)
On 2 July 1971
3rd Carabiniers (Prince of Wales's Dragoon Guards) and
The Royal Scots Greys (2nd Dragoons) amalgamated to form:
The Royal Scots Dragoon Guards (Carabiniers and Greys)

4th/7th ROYAL DRAGOON GUARDS

On 11 April 1922
4th Royal Irish Dragoon Guards and
7th Dragoon Guards (Princess Royal's) amalgamated to form:
4th/7th Dragoon Guards
On 31 October 1936 the Regiment was redesignated
4th/7th Royal Dragoon Guards

5th ROYAL INNISKILLING DRAGOON GUARDS

On 11 April 1922
5th Dragoon Guards (Princess Charlotte of Wales's) and
The Inniskillings (6th Dragoons) amalgamated to form:
5th/6th Dragoons
On 31 May 1927 the Regiment was redesignated
5th Inniskilling Dragoon Guards
On 30 June 1935 the Regiment was redesignated
5th Royal Inniskilling Dragoon Guards

THE QUEEN'S OWN HUSSARS

On 3 November 1958
3rd The King's Own Hussars and
7th Queen's Own Hussars amalgamated to form:
The Queen's Own Hussars

THE QUEEN'S ROYAL IRISH HUSSARS

On 24 October 1958
4th Queen's Own Hussars and
8th King's Royal Irish Hussars amalgamated to form:
The Queen's Royal Irish Hussars

9th/12th ROYAL LANCERS (PRINCE OF WALES'S)

On 11 September 1960
9th Queen's Royal Lancers and
12th Royal Lancers (Prince of Wales's) amalgamated to form:
9th/12th Royal Lancers (Prince of Wales's)

THE ROYAL HUSSARS (PRINCE OF WALES'S OWN)

On 25 October 1969
10th Royal Hussars (Prince of Wales's Own) and
11th Hussars (Prince Albert's Own) amalgamated to form:
The Royal Hussars (Prince of Wales's Own)

13th/18th ROYAL HUSSARS (QUEEN MARY'S OWN)

On 11 April 1922
13th Hussars and
18th Royal Hussars (Queen Mary's Own) amalgamated to form:
13th/18th Hussars
On 31 December 1935 the Regiment was redesignated
13th/18th Royal Hussars (Queen Mary's Own)

14th/20th KING'S HUSSARS

On 11 April 1922
14th King's Hussars and
20th Hussars amalgamated to form:
14th/20th Hussars
On 31 December 1936 the Regiment was redesignated
14th/20th King's Hussars

15th/19th THE KING'S ROYAL HUSSARS

On 11 April 1922

15th The King's Hussars and

19th Royal Hussars (Queen Alexandra's Own) amalgamated to form:

15th/19th Hussars

On 31 October 1932 the Regiment was redesignated

15th The King's Royal Hussars

On 31 December 1933 the Regiment was redesignated

15th/19th The King's Royal Hussars

16th/5th THE QUEEN'S ROYAL LANCERS

On 11 April 1922

16th The Queen's Lancers and

5th Royal Irish Lancers amalgamated to form:

16th/5th Lancers

On 16 June 1954 the Regiment was redesignated

16th/5th The Queen's Royal Lancers

17th/21st LANCERS

On 11 April 1922

17th Lancers (Duke of Cambridge's Own) and

21st Lancers (Empress of India's) amalgamated to form:

17th/21st Lancers

ROYAL TANK REGIMENT

On 28 July 1917

The Tank Corps was formed from the Heavy Branch of the Machine Gun Corps

On 18 October 1923

The Corps was redesignated Royal Tank Corps

On 4 April 1939

The Corps was redesignated The Royal Tank Regiment

1st THE QUEEN'S DRAGOON GUARDS

The Cypher of Queen Caroline within the Garter

'Pro Rege et Patria'

Blenheim, Ramillies, Oudenarde, Malplaquet, Dettingen, Warburg, Beaumont, Willems, Waterloo, Sevastopol, Lucknow, Taku Forts, Pekin 1860, South Africa 1879, South Africa 1901-02

The Great War— **Mons, Le Cateau,** Retreat from Mons, **Marne 1914,** Aisne 1914, **Messines 1914,** Armentieres 1914, **Ypres 1914, 15,** Frezenberg, Bellewaarde, **Somme 1916, 18,** Flers-Courcelette, **Morval,** Arras 1917, **Scarpe 1917, Cambrai 1917, 18,** St Quentin, Bapaume 1918, Rosieres, **Amiens,** Albert 1918, Hindenburg Line, St Quentin Canal, Beaurevoir, **Pursuit to Mons, France and Flanders 1914-18**

Afghanistan 1919

The Second World War— **Somme 1940,** Withdrawal to Seine, North-West Europe 1940, **Beda Fomm, Defence of Tobruk,** Tobruk 1941, Tobruk Sortie, Relief of Tobruk, Msus, **Gazala,** Bir El Aslagh, Bir Hacheim, Cauldron, Knightsbridge, Via Balbia, Mersa Matruh, **Defence of Alamein Line,** Alam El Halfa, **El Alamein, El Agheila, Advance on Tripoli, Tebaga Gap,** Point 201 (Roman Wall), **El Hamma,** Akarit, El Kourzia, Djebel Kournine, **Tunis,** Creteville Pass, **North Africa 1941-43,** Capture of Naples, Scafati Bridge, **Monte Camino,** Garagliano Crossing, Capture of Perugia, Arezzo, **Gothic Line, Coriano,** Carpineta, **Lamone Crossing,** Defence of Lamone Bridgehead, **Rimini Line,** Ceriano Ridge, Cesena,**Argenta Gap, Italy 1943-45,** Athens, Greece 1944-45

Regimental Marches

Quick March ....Regimental March of 1st The Queen's Dragoon Guards
(Radetsky March and Rusty Buckles)
Slow March ....(i) 1st Dragoon Guards Slow March (ii) 2nd Dragoon Guards Slow March

Agents ....Lloyds Bank PLC Cox's & King's Branch

Home Headquarters ....Maindy Barracks, Whitchurch Rd, Cardiff, CF4 3YE
(*Tel No:* 0222-27611 *Ext:* 213)

Alliances

Canadian Armed Forces ....The Governor General's Horse Guards
Australian Military Forces.................1st/15th Royal New South Wales Lancers
Pakistan Army....................................11th Cavalry (Frontier Force)
Sri Lanka Army...................................1st Reconnaissance Regiment

Colonel in Chief ....*HM* QUEEN ELIZABETH THE QUEEN MOTHER

Colonel...Maj Gen D H G Rice *CVO CBE* ret pay..011180

Brigadiers

Ward R W *MBE* ocds(CAN) ndc psc(n) tt 300679

Colonels

de Candole J A V *MC MBIM* sq 300680
Pocock J I *MBE* psc(a) osc(NIG) 300681
Bond C H *OBE* odc(US) sq 300685
Ferguson J G G de P *OBE* psc ph 300685

Lieutenant Colonels

Peacocke C G *BSc* psc† osc(NIG) (*A/Col* 011185) 300680
Critien A D R psc jsdc 300684
O'Brien E J K sq 300684
Treasure D J C odc(GE) osc(GE) sq 300684
Boissard M G *BA* psc jsdc 300685

Majors

Flanagan J I 311273
Holmes T J D sq ph 311278
Russell D A sq aic 311278
Gates R A sq aic 300679
Stewart S M P *MBE* psc 300980
Langlands C J G sq 300981
Mackenzie-Beevor C D psc (*A/Lt Col* 211285) 300981
Crosbie Dawson W G psc 300983
Holdsworth P B 300983
Eliot M R M psc† 300984
Macdonald H L A psc 300985
Ward S A B aic 300985

Captains

Joyce M T A (*L/Maj* 140581) 181276
Hookey C A *BSc(Eng)* (*A/Maj* 100186) 100979
Coleman J A *MA* 101081
Dennis R J P *BSc(Econ)* aic (*L/Maj* 040386) 201081
Browell Q J *BA* 010283
Andrews P J 050285

Lieutenants

Daniell W H *BA* 120482
Renwick A I (*A/Capt* 311085) 131282
Baldwin G T (*A/Capt* 161285) 080883
Lonsdale D J 121283
Roxburgh A M 121283
Deacon G H J *BA FRGS* 090484

2nd Lieutenants

Benham-Crosswell P J 130485
Gray J N J 130485

Quartermasters

Wilson F *MBE MBIM* 070177
Maj 070185
Dakin K J *MBE* 010479
Maj 040286
Boas R McG 010480
Maj 011285
Bell B W *Capt* 010483

Special Regular Officers

Majors

Harris M W 300985

Captains

Hole W M 290276

Short Service Officers

Captains

Healey J A 011181
Corfield A D 011083
Dakin V T 111084

Lieutenants

Clay A J (*A/Capt* 011285) 100682
Gwillim R J 250782
Janion S P *BA* 110483
Norris D W H *LLB* 110483
Robson P N *BA* 190483
Benda J C A *BA* 080883
Blaksley R E 090484
Goldsbrough R W *BA* 090484
Wright R J S *MSc* 090484
Ashley-Miller M 070884
Owen D T 060885

Parry R J	060885	*2nd Lieutenants*		Pittman A J	081284
Bridge A W M	070486			Woods R G S	130485
Wilson T R	070486	Bull M S H	040884	Woodward T P	141285
		Heywood T C	040884		

THE ROYAL SCOTS DRAGOON GUARDS (CARABINIERS AND GREYS)

The Thistle within the circle and motto of the Order of the Thistle

In the first corner, White Horse of Hanover within a Scroll. In the second corner The plume of The Prince of Wales within a wreath of Roses, Thistles and Shamrocks upon a yellow ground. In the third corner, SCOTS DG in gold within a wreath of Roses, Thistles and Shamrocks upon a yellow ground. The Red Dragon of Wales Within a Scroll.

Blenheim, Ramillies, Oudenarde, Malplaquet, Dettingen, Warburg, Beaumont, Willems, Waterloo, Talavera, Albuhera, Vittoria, Peninsula, Balaklava, Sevastopol, Delhi 1857, Abyssinia, Afghanistan 1879-80, Relief of Kimberley, Paardeberg, South Africa 1899-1902

The Great War— Mons, Le Cateau, **Retreat from Mons, Marne 1914, Aisne 1914, Messines 1914,** Armentieres 1914 **Ypres 1914, 15,** Nonne Bosschen, Gheluvelt, Neuve Chapelle, St Julien, Frezenberg, Bellewaarde, Loos, **Arras 1917,** Scarpe 1917, **Cambrai 1917, 18,** Lys, Hazebrouck, **Somme 1918,** St Quentin, Avre, **Amiens,** Albert 1918, Bapaume 1918, **Hindenburg Line, Canal du Nord,** St Quentin Canal, Beaurevoir, Selle, Sambre, **Pursuit to Mons,** France and Flanders 1914-18

The Second World War— Caen, *Hill 112, Falaise,* Venlo Pocket, **Hochwald, Aller,** Bremen, North-West Europe 1944-45, **Merjayun,** Syria 1941, **Alam el Halfa, El Alamein,** El Agheila, **Nofilia,** Advance on Tripoli, North Africa 1942-43, **Salerno,** Battipaglia, Volturno Crossing, Italy 1943, **Imphal,** Tamu road, **Nunshigum, Bishenpur, Kanglatongbi, Kennedy Peak,** Shwebo, **Sagaing, Mandalay, Ava, Irrawaddy,** Yenangyaung 1945, Burma 1944-45

Honorary distinction

A Napoleonic Eagle superimposed upon two carbines in Saltire upon a Plinth inscribed Waterloo

Regimental Marches

Military Band
Quick March......"3 DGs"
Slow March......The Garb of Old Gaul

Pipes and Drums
Quick March......Hielan' Laddie
Slow March......My Home

Agents......Holts Branch, Royal Bank of Scotland PLC, Lawrie House, Farnborough, Hants

Home Headquarters......The Castle, Edinburgh, EH1 2YX (*Tel No:* 031-336-1761 *Ext:* 4228)

Alliances

Canadian Armed Forces......The Windsor Regiment (RCAC)
Australian Military Forces......12th/16th Hunter River Lancers
New Zealand Army......1st and 2nd Squadrons, New Zealand and Scottish (RNZAC)

Colonel in Chief ......THE QUEEN

Colonel ......Lt Gen *Sir* Norman Arthur *KCB* 060584

Colonels

Notley C R S psc† tt 300683

Lieutenant Colonels

Coombs M E C psc† ph 300681
Fishbourne P C E psc 300681
Ross J M A ndc psc† 300682
Hall J M F C psc 300683
Jameson M S sq 300684
Bartholomew P G E sq tt 300685

Majors

Knight W H A sq tt 300670
Stanley M J sq 300674
Webb C I P *MA* sq tt 300675
Pyman C McA psc 311276
Hancock G A S psc aic ph 311277
Veillard-Thomas M L sq 311277
Trevelyan A C psc ph 311278
Horne R R sq ph 300679
Scrivener J R sq aic 300980
Callander J H 300981
Sharples J F B sq 300981
Auchinleck M H 300982
Mockridge M J aic 300982
Seymour N D A psc 300982
McSwiney B A 300983
Allen S R B psc 300984
Donnithorne-Tait M A D *BA(Hons) MA* psc(n)† 300985
Ramsden R A B 300985

Captains

Stormonth Darling A J *BA* (*A/Maj* 281085) 010280
Farquharson D H 090980
Stagg C R M *BA* 281281
Deverell J D 270782
Tayler A H aic 060982
Cuming A N *BA* 120183
Biron J C 070283
Hall-Wilson T F S 110683
Tippett M R 081083
Vickers R P H *BA* 010284
Elston H J (*A/Maj* 040884) 060284
Oyler R G T aic 060284
Hearn S N R 100684
Bullen M P A 081084
Phillips A M 081084
Oliver N D 090685
Allfrey H D 040286

Lieutenants

Campbell J D (*A/Capt* 100885) 081281
Oliver S D (*A/Capt* 110885) 110483
Wheeler G F 080883
Butler B R E 070884

2nd Lieutenants

††Melville C K B 230984
††Blayney A O 240985
††Young J J M M 240985

Quartermasters

Roberts D 010478
Maj 300583
Graham M *Capt* 010481
Tyson J V *Capt* 041083
Crease A J *BEM* *Capt* 010485

Special Regular Officers

Captains

Dunkley N C W 110683
Thorburn D H S 050285

Short Service Officers

Captains

McGhie J W S 210881
Ravnkilde P M *MA* 150883
Orr N S 210684

Lieutenants

McMahon T 180482
Fullard D M *BEM* 010183
Kelton J S G *BA* 110483
Martyr S G P *BSc* 110483
Cushnir J H M *BA* 090484
Gather R E *LLB* 070884
Malcolmson J C 090485
Blackman H H 060885
Melville J L 101285
Lambert C F 070486
Rittson-Thomas R O 070486

2nd Lieutenants

Bracher G P 040884
Maclachlan R C 040884
Marsh J P F 130485
†Edwards B P *MA(Hons)* 060985
Maclean J H S *MRAC* 141285

Short Service Volunteer Officers

Lieutenants

Rankin J W H 010684

4th/7th ROYAL DRAGOON GUARDS

The Star of the Order of St Patrick

In the third corner The Harp and Crown. In the fourth corner The Coronet of Her late Majesty the Empress and Queen Frederick of Germany and Prussia as Princess Royal of Great Britain and Ireland

Blenheim, Ramillies, Oudenarde, Malplaquet, Dettingen, Warburg, Peninsula, South Africa 1846-47, Balaklava, Sevastopol, Tel-el-Kebir, Egypt 1882, South Africa 1900-02

The Great War— Mons, Le Cateau, Retreat from Mons, **Marne 1914, Aisne 1914, La Bassee 1914,** Messines 1914, Armentieres 1914, **Ypres** 1914, 15, Givenchy 1914, St Julien, Frezenberg, Bellewaarde, **Somme 1916,** 18, Bazentin, Flers-Courcelette, Arras 1917, Scarpe 1917, Cambrai 1917, 18, St Quentin, Rosieres, Avre, Lys, Hazebrouck, **Amiens,** Albert 1918, **Hindenburg Line,** St Quentin Canal, Beaurevoir, **Pursuit to Mons,** France and Flanders 1914-18

The Second World War— **Dyle, Dunkirk 1940, Normandy Landing, Odon, Mont Pincon,** Seine 1944, **Nederrijn, Geilenkirchen,** Roer, **Rhineland, Cleve Rhine,** Bremen, North-West Europe 1940, 44-45

Regimental Marches

Quick March..........St Patrick's Day
Slow Marches..........(i) 4th Dragoon Guards Slow March (ii) 7th Dragoon Guards Slow March

Agents..........Holts Branch, Royal Bank of Scotland PLC, Lawrie House, Farnborough, Hants

Home Headquarters..........3 Tower Street, York, YO1 1SB (*Tel No:* 0904-59811 *Ext:* 2310)

Alliances

Canadian Armed Forces..........The Fort Garry Horse
Australian Military Forces..........4th/19th Prince of Wales's Light Horse
New Zealand Army..........Queen Alexandra's (Waikato/Wellington East Coast) Squadron RNZAC
Pakistan Army..........15 Lancers

Colonel-in-Chief..........Hon Maj Gen *HRH The Duchess of* Kent *GCVO*

Colonel..........Gen *Sir* Robert Ford *GCB CBE* ret pay..........311283

Brigadiers

Baddeley R J psc 300684

Colonels

Le Blanc-Smith W A *MBE* ndc sq 300683
Wright C T J psc osc(SUD) 300683
Evans G R A psc† osc(NIG) 300685

Lieutenant Colonels

Webber R G (SL) odc(US) sq 300672
Faith P W psc tt 300678
Gilruth P A M sq (*A/Col* 191285) 300678
Corbin D A J *BSc(Eng)* psc† 300683
Daukes C D psc 300684
Leigh M R O psc 300684
Price C K psc 300684
Jenkins S J M psc 300685
Turner C P G psc 300685

Majors

Lerwill M G psc ph 311276
Harding-Newman R E sq tt 311277
Lawton K J A psc† aic ph 300678
Eavis J R R 311279
Illingworth R H 300981
McDonald-Joyce D aic 300981
Talbot R I psc 300981
Morris R J *BA* psc 300982
Snowball P J R *MA* psc 300982
Barstow C W 300983
Cardozo G C *MBE* psc 300983
Ford S R P aic 300983
Thwaites C J G psc 300983

Captains

Nicole T M *MA* 010879
Sutton R C aic 291280
Leach R C *BA* 280282
Sandbach C P L 080582
Mackain-Bremner J N D aic 060982
Cary R A P 070283
Clifford R C L aic 060284
Firth R L M 060284
Elliott *The Hon BA* 010884
Pain M A R 071085
Smailes M I T *BSc* 071085

Lieutenants

Millen N C T *LHCIMA* (*A/Capt* 250684) 120482
Fielder C H (*A/Capt* 030286) 110483
Tindall C L (*A/Capt* 041185) 110483
Morrison H M (*A/Capt* 270685) 080883
Archibald J L 090484

2nd Lieutenants

††Cardozo B D N *BA(Hons)* 071082
Cray J N A 100885

Quartermasters

Stanley J R W *Capt* 010479
Zambelli K A *Capt* 010482
Macdonald I *Capt* 020285

Short Service Officers

Lieutenants

Reeves M A *MISM MIMS FInstBTM AFBA* 280681
Brodermann M E D *BA* 120482
Willson D C 210283
Nabavi B S *BSc(Econ)* 080883
Hamilton N G C 081283
Goodall C P 121283
Neish A W 070884
Theakston E D 090485
Hunter D J 101285

2nd Lieutenants

Taylor M R 081284
Valletta E F P 081284
Brown A N R 130485
Packshaw J J 100885
†Taylor-Smith D J B *BSc* 060985
Cocks H J G 141285
Hopkinson Woolley C B 141285

5th ROYAL INNISKILLING DRAGOON GUARDS

The Castle of Inniskilling with the St George's colours above the monogram "V.D.G."

In the second corner "V. PCW. DG" on a blue ground, and in the third corner the Castle of Inniskilling also on a blue ground

Blenheim, Ramillies, Oudenarde, Malplaquet, Dettingen, Warburg, Beaumont, Willems, Salamanca, Vittoria, Toulouse, Peninsula, Waterloo, Balaklava, Sevastopol, Defence of Ladysmith, South Africa 1899-1902

The Great War— **Mons, Le Cateau,** Retreat from Mons, **Marne 1914,** Aisne 1914, La Bassee 1914, Messines 1914, Armentieres 1914, Ypres 1914, 15, Frezenberg, Bellewaarde, **Somme 1916,** 18, Flers-Courcelette, Morval, Arras 1917, Scarpe 1917, **Cambrai 1917,** 18, St Quentin, Rosieres, Avre, Lys, Hazebrouck, **Amiens,** Albert 1918, **Hindenburg Line,** St Quentin Canal, Beaurevoir, **Pursuit to Mons,** France and Flanders 1914-18

The Second World War— **Withdrawal to Escaut, St Omer-La Bassee, Dunkirk 1940, Mont Pincon,** St Piere La Vielle Lisieux, Risle Crossing, **Lower Maas,** Roer, Ibbenburen, North-West Europe 1940, 44-45

The Hook 1952, Korea 1951-52

Regimental Marches

Quick March..........Fare Ye Well Inniskilling
Slow March..........The Soldiers Chorus

Agents..........Lloyds Bank PLC Cox's & King's Branch
Home Headquarters..........The Castle, Chester, CH1 2DN (*Tel No:* 0244-24666 *Ext:* 52)

Alliances

Canadian Armed Forces..........The British Columbia Dragoons
Australian Military Forces..........3rd/9th South Australian Mounted Rifles

Colonel in Chief..........*HRH The Prince of* Wales *KG KT GCB AK QSO ADC*

Colonel..........Maj Gen R C Keightley..........210386

Brigadiers

Ansell N G P *OBE MA* rcds psc 300681
Evans W A *MA* psc(a) 300683
Courage W J *MBE* sq ph 300685

Lieutenant Colonels

Rich E J sq tt 300681
Cordingley P A J psc† 300682
Ingall I C T *MA* psc† 300682
Kinsella-Bevan R D *MA* psc 300682

Majors

Gabbey H C G psc† 300679
Anderson B R *EQ* sq (*A/Lt Col* 140286) 311279
Blott J W R psc 300980
Day C J R psc 300981
Gammond G S psc(GE) aic 300983
Montgomery D W *BA* psc 300983
Bone D R L psc 300985
Dover M J psc 300985
Torrens-Spence E J *BSc* 300985

Captains

Wathen J P G (*A/Maj* 031183) 100580
Wilson C G 090980
Duckworth L 291280
Potter G R A 291280
Anderson M G *BA LLB* 190381
Roskelly C M De W 080981
Faulkner M W B (*A/Maj* 050984) 281281
Spencer R J *BSc* aic 310782
Lamb N *BA* 290882
Moseley S H 060982
Samler C H *BA* 041182
Shaw C De V 070283
Rawlings C D A 110683
Coldrey C G 060284
Gorst J E *BA* 010885
Orr D W E *BA* 010885

Lieutenants

Eaton R J C aic 081281
Cumming R P (*A/Capt* 091283) 120482
Haslam G F C *BA* 120482
Garton-Jones W N *BSc* 110483
Walker P W *MA* 110483

2nd Lieutenants

††Baxter J W L 020983
††Rich P J P 230984
††Whittaker I D G 240985

Quartermasters

Latham A J A *MBE* 010478
Maj 120484
Cooney E A *Capt* 010480
McGarry M D 010481
Maj 010286
McCleery N *Capt* 010485

Special Regular Officers

Captains

Butler M T D 071085

Short Service Officers

Captains

Etherington J 010983
Folliss T S A *BA* 130284
Freeman N C C *BA* 030484

Lieutenants

Hough M J *BA* 120482
Lambert N T (*A/Capt* 110685) 090882
Jennings-Bramly G G 020283
Scott Barber J R *BA* 110483
Tottenham C H L *BA* 110483
Rooney B J *BA* 090484
Moody C A 190484
Findlay O F O 070884
Monier-Williams M J 070884
Johnson B G B 090485
Mills S C 150585
Brooks Ward J W 060885
Shelford M G McN 060885
Constantine D L 101285
Craig-Harvey C A 101285
Bedford J A 070486

2nd Lieutenants

†Boulton R J C *BA(Hons)* 060985
Bell H N J 141285

THE QUEEN'S OWN HUSSARS

Q.O. above the White Horse of Hanover, within the Garter

'Nec Aspera Terrent'

Dettingen, Warburg, Beaumont, Willems, Salamanca, Vittoria, Orthes, Toulouse, Peninsula, Waterloo, Cabool 1842, Moodkee, Ferozeshah, Sobraon, Chillianwallah, Goojerat, Punjab, Lucknow, South Africa 1901-02, South Africa 1902

The Great War— Mons, Le Cateau, **Retreat from Mons, Marne 1914,** Aisne 1914, Messines 1914, Armentieres 1914, **Ypres 1914, 15,** Gheluvelt, St Julien, Bellewaarde, Arras 1917, Scarpe 1917, **Cambrai 1917, 18, Somme 1918,** St Quentin, Lys, Hazebrouck, **Amiens,** Bapaume 1918, Hindenburg Line, Canal du Nord, Selle, Sambre, **France and Flanders 1914-18, Khan Baghdadi, Sharqat, Mesopotamia 1917-18**

The Second World War— **Egyptian Frontier 1940,** Sidi Barrani, **Buq Buq, Beda Fomm,** Sidi Suleiman, **Sidi Rezegh 1941, El Alamein, North Africa 1940-42, Citta Della Pieve,** Pegu, Paungde, Citta di Castello, **Ancona,** Rimini Line, **Italy 1944-45,** Italy 1944, **Crete, Burma 1942**

Regimental Marches

Quick March..Light Cavalry
Slow Marches..(i) The 3rd Hussars Slow March (ii) The Garb of Old Gaul

Agents..Lloyds Bank PLC Cox's & King's Branch

Home Headquarters..............................28 Jury Street, Warwick (*Tel No:* 0926 492035)

Alliances

Canadian Armed Forces........................The Sherbrooke Hussars
Australian Military Forces....................3rd/9th South Australian Mounted Rifles
New Zealand Army...............................Queen Alexandra's (Waikato/Wellington East Coast) Squadron RNZAC

Colonel in Chief...................................*HM* QUEEN ELIZABETH THE QUEEN MOTHER

Colonel..Lt Gen *Sir* Robin Carnegie *KCB OBE* ret pay..050681

Brigadiers

Rucker J W F rcds psc	300680

Colonels

Greenwood R D H H psc	300682
Sandars H M ndc psc† tt	300684

Lieutenant Colonels

Williamson E F (SL) psc† tt	300676
Phipps J J J odc(US) sq	300681
Younger D J psc	300681
Jenkins D J M *BA* psc†	300683

Majors

Thomas T J	030864
Risby D C sq (*L/Lt Col* 100576)	300667
Bulkeley J E R sq	300678
Butler M R sq	300679
Mumford G M sq tt	300679
Fox R S psc	300980
Watson J M C *BSc(Eng)* psc†	300980
Gordon-Finlayson J C aic	300982
Apps N G psc	300983
Carter C W M *BSc(Eng) DipRMCS*	300983
Phillips H V C aic	300983
Potter S M J *BA* psc	300983
Bromley Gardner M R psc	300984
Watts T E A	300984
Rodwell S C *BA* psc†	300985
Simson K B L	300985

Captains

Myatt T V (*A/Maj* 160186)	100979
Jackson S *BSc* aic	010881
Tolfree P W K	080981
Ledger A W	080582
Metcalfe R J D	080582
Vernon C H	060982
Smith N G	070283
Barrow M P	110683
James R C D	050285
Ambler M C	071085
Bromley Gardner C A J *BSc*	071085
Lewis T P	071085

Lieutenants

Bishop C R M (*A/Capt* 010385)	081281

2nd Lieutenants

††Seagrim J C	230984
††Felsing A R	081085

Quartermasters

Elcock E		120377
	Maj	010983
Strong C C	*Capt*	010482
Mellor B D	*Capt*	120783

Special Regular Officers

Majors

Beattie J A *MBE*	300984
Owen C G aic	300985

Short Service Officers

Captains

Waters M G *MISM*	010281
Budd J L	130984

Lieutenants

Orr P N *BA* (*A/Capt* 071185)	120482
Boole N D (*A/Capt* 101285)	131282
Taylor R C	010183
Shattock M J *BA*	040483
Popp E S M *BSc*	090484
Medlicott-Goodwin G G	111284
Thomas N J	090485
Everett S P	101285
Labouchere D H	101285
Berger M M	070486
Rogerson J F	070486

2nd Lieutenants

Durand-Deslongrais A R C	081284
Touche E M	081284
Easby T R	130485
†Colahan J D	060985

THE QUEEN'S ROYAL IRISH HUSSARS

The Irish Harp surmounted by the Royal Crest
'Mente et Manu' 'Pristinae Virtutis Memores'

Dettingen, Leswarree, Hindoostan, Talavera, Albuhera, Salamanca, Vittoria, Toulouse, Peninsula, Ghuznee 1839, Affghanistan 1839, Alma, Balaklava, Inkerman, Sevastopol, Central India, Afghanistan 1879-80, South Africa 1900-02

The Great War— **Mons, Le Cateau,** Retreat from Mons, **Marne 1914, Aisne 1914,** Messines 1914, Armentieres 1914, **Ypres 1914, 15,** Langemarck 1914, Gheluvelt, **Givenchy 1914, St Julien,** Bellewaarde, **Somme 1916, 18,** Bazentin, Flers-Courcelette, Arras 1917, Scarpe 1917, **Cambrai 1917, 18,** St Quentin, **Bapaume 1918, Rosieres, Amiens, Albert 1918,** Hindenburg Line, Canal du Nord, St Quentin Canal, **Beaurevoir, Pursuit to Mons, France and Flanders** 1914-18

The Second World War— **Villers Bocage,** Mont Pincon, Dives Crossing, Nederrijn, Best, **Lower Maas, Roer, Rhine, North-West Europe 1944-45,** Egyptian Frontier 1940, Sidi Barrani, **Buq, Buq, Sidi, Rezegh 1941,** Relief of Tobruk, **Gazala,** Bir el Igela, Mersa Matruh, Defence of Alamein Line, **Ruweisat, Alam el Halfa, El Alamein, North Africa 1940-42, Coriano,** San Clemente, **Senio Pocket, Rimini Line,** Conventello-Comacchio, Senio, Saterno Crossing, **Argenta Gap,** Italy 1944-45, Proasteion, Corinth Canal, Greece 1941,

Seoul, Hill 327, **Imjin,** Kowang-San, **Korea 1950-51**

Regimental Marches

Quick March............St Patrick's Day, Berkeley's Dragoons and A Galloping 8th Hussar
(The Regimental Quick March of The Queens Royal Irish Hussars)
Slow March............(i) Loretto — Slow March of the 4th Hussars
(ii) March of the Scottish Archers — Slow March of The 8th Hussars

Agents............Lloyds Bank PLC Cox's & King's Branch
Home Headquarters............Regents Park Barracks, Albany Street, London, NW1
(*Tel No:* 01-387-3471 *Ext:* 17/19)

Alliances

Canadian Armed Forces............The Royal Canadian Hussars (Montreal)
8th Canadian Hussars (Princess Louise's)
Australian Military Forces............2nd/14th Queensland Mounted Infantry
8th/13th Victorian Mounted Rifles
3rd Battalion The Royal Australian Regiment

Colonel in Chief............Field Marshal *HRH The Prince* Philip *Duke of* Edinburgh, *KG KT OM GBE QSO*
Colonel............Lt Gen *Sir* Brian Kenny *KCB CBE*............010785

Brigadiers

Rhoderick-Jones R J rcds psc† ph 300682
Barron R E psc† 300684
Webster R S ndc psc 300684

Colonels

Anson T P ndc sq 300683
Martin R J sq 300684

Lieutenant Colonels

Daniell S R ndc sq ph 300682
Hibbert P C odc(FR) osc(FR) sq 300685

Majors

Acworth H J sq tt 060266
Cormack D G sq 300667
White M D sq tt 300669
Hoare R H G *MBE* sq 311275
Earle J J sq ph 300676
Miller A G G *MA* sq aic 300676
Lowther *Sir* Charles *Bt* psc 311278
Hartigan P W C *MBIM* sq 300679
Varvill S P psc 311279
Crichton R F A *MA* sq aic 300980
Denaro A G psc† 300980
Rooke H J P D sq 300980
Moody J M W 300982
Franklin S P C 300984
Pilleau M D *BSc* aic 300984
Thornely R M 300984
Beer N Q W *BA* psc† 300985
Bellamy A N *BA* psc 300985
Comyn C L psc 300985
Larsen-Burnett C 300985

Captains

Coldrey M J 060982
Hurst J M 060982
Hill N L 070283
O'Reilly M S M 081083
Mellows W A N ph 060284
Blackmore A C T 081084
Pierson H T K 081084
Thompson J H 081084
Chitty M O M *BSc* 010285
Currie R W aic 050285
Maddison V J T *BA* 090285
Kenney M J S *BA* 050386

Lieutenants

Cuthbert A C *BA* 110483

Cornets

††Paley R G T *BA(Hons)* 030982
††Stables H M D 020983

Quartermasters

McLucas W J *MBE* 301175
Maj 090982
Flynn J *Capt* 010480
Goulding D E *Capt* 010484
Innes-Lumsden D J *Capt* 010484

Special Regular Officers

Lieutenants

Acheson V R 090485

Short Service Officers

Captains

Montgomery H E J *BA* 030985
Swann D J L *BA* 071085
Timmons P J 140486

Lieutenants

Wallace D W *MInstAM MISM* 280282
Hogg A (*L/Capt* 010385) 010982
Nunn P D 241282
Noone R A (*A/Capt* 030585) 110483
Perkins J N T *BA* 110483
Alms J J *BTech* 080883
Macready N W K 080883
Hutton R C 090484
Shewell A M E *BSc* 090484
Barrow C A K 070884
Ormerod J C 070884
Martin E J D 101285

Cornets

Beckett T A 040884
Paine A F W 040884
Troughton J B M 040884
Acheson A D F 081284
Bowdler M R 141285

9th/12th ROYAL LANCERS (PRINCE OF WALES'S)

The Plume of the Prince of Wales upon two lances crossed in saltire, within the Garter

The Cypher of Queen Elizabeth The Queen Mother. The Cypher of Queen Adelaide reversed and interlaced. Sphinx superscribed "Egypt"

Salamanca, Peninsula, Waterloo, Punniar, Sobraon, Chillianwallah, Goojerat, Punjaub, South Africa 1851-53, Sevastopol, Delhi 1857, Central India, Lucknow, Charasiah, Kabul 1879, Kandahar 1880, Afghanistan 1878-80, Modder River, Relief of Kimberley, Paardeberg, South Africa 1899-1902

The Great War— **Mons,** Le Cateau, **Retreat from Mons, Marne 1914, Aisne 1914,** La Bassee 1914, **Messines 1914,** Armentieres 1914, **Ypres 1914, 15,** Neuve Chapelle, Gravenstafel, St Julien, Frezenberg, Bellewaarde, **Somme 1916, 18,** Pozieres, Flers-Courcelette, **Arras 1917,** Scarpe 1917, **Cambrai 1917, 18,** St Quentin, **Rosieres,** Avre, Lys, Hazebrouck, Amiens, Albert 1918, Hindenburg Line, St Quentin Canal, Beaurevoir, **Sambre, Pursuit to Mons,** France and Flanders 1914-18

The Second World War— **Dyle,** Defence of Arras, Arras Counter Attack, **Dunkirk 1940, Somme 1940,** Withdrawal to Seine, **North-West Europe 1940, Chor es Sufan,** Saunnu, **Gazala,** Bir el Aslagh, Sidi Rezegh 1942, Defence of Alamein Line, **Ruweisat,** Ruweisat Ridge, Alam el Halfa, **El Alamein,** Advance on Tripoli, Tebaga Gap, **El Hamma,** Akarit, El Kourzia, Djebel Kournine, **Tunis,** Creteville Pass, **North Africa 1941-43,** Citerna, Gothic Line, Coriano, Capture of Forli, Lamone Crossing, Pideura, **Defence of Lamone Bridgehead,** Conventello-Comacchio, **Argenta Gap, Bologna,** Sillaro Crossing, Idice Bridgehead, **Italy 1944-45**

Regimental Marches

Quick March..God Bless The Prince of Wales
Slow Marches......................................(i) Men of Harlech — Slow March of 9th Lancers
(ii) Coburg — Slow March of 12th Lancers

Agents..Lloyds Bank PLC Cox's & King's Branch

Home Headquarters..............................Glen Parva Barracks, South Wigston, Leicester (*Tel No:* 0533-785425)

Alliances

Canadian Armed Forces.......................The Prince Edward Island Regiment
Pakistan Army.......................................12th Cavalry

Colonel in Chief....................................*HM* QUEEN ELIZABETH THE QUEEN MOTHER

Colonel..Col M ff Woodhead *OBE* ret pay..010186

Colonels

Maitland-Titterton D H S L jssc sq	300678
Pye H W K odc(US) psc	300682
Nash L J R psc ph	300685

Lieutenant Colonels

Lewis *The Hon* P H sq ph	300679
Readhead R M psc† ph	300682
Hutchins J sq	300685
Searby R V psc	300685

Majors

Twickel A R F N Z *MIL*	311275
Lort-Phillips P G F sq ph	300678
Price A R *MBIM AIL* sq tt	300678
Wright W H sq	300679
Strudley D *MBE MBIM* psc†	300980
Burgess R I S psc	300981
Dickens H T psc	300981
Thring E P W	300981
Morpeth *Viscount BA* psc	300982
Short J H T *BSc* psc†	300983
Bennett R G psc	300984
Crofton *The Hon* G P G aic	300984
Lindsay H C L	300985

Captains

Rutledge M J *MA*	050979
Hopkinson C P (*L/Maj* 011081)	080581
Abraham A M *BA*	290681
Everard N C *BA*	081081
Routledge J P S	060982
Mackaness J R St D (*L/Maj* 140581)	070283
Jones A J *MSc* mvt	290383
Robertson H G	081083
Monckton *The Hon* A L C *MA*	250385
Woodbridge I R	071085

Lieutenants

Reed A L (*A/Capt* 130685)	080883
Stafford N M T (*A/Capt* 200385)	080883

2nd Lieutenants

††Marriott J R	240985

Staff Quartermasters

Paton H S	110570
Maj	010479

Quartermasters

Warlow D J	010478
Maj	230683
Jones G K *Capt*	010484

Special Regular Officers

Majors

Goldsmith T R	300984
Grant W	300984

Captains

Wathen N C J	200484

Short Service Officers

Captains

Lumsden N H	090685

Lieutenants

Underhill M (*A/Capt* 300885)	010182
Martin J M *BSc* (*A/Capt* 160985)	120482
Charrington R A *BA*	110483
Simpson J A *BEM*	290583
Bennett D M *BA*	090484
Cooke C E A	090484
Rigby C R *BA*	090484
Zeidler R A *BA*	090484
Cooke A G A	090485
Wilson A G T	090485
Bailey N J W	060885
Hercock T R	060885
Crewdson C W N	070486

2nd Lieutenants

Pooley J D	081284
Tyszkiewicz J Z	081284
Douglas-Miller R P	100885
Pedrick J G	100885
Diamond J H B	141285

THE ROYAL HUSSARS (PRINCE OF WALES'S OWN)

The Plume of the Prince of Wales within the Garter. The Rising Sun. The Red Dragon. The White Horse of Hanover. The Crest and Motto of HRH the late Prince Albert The Sphinx, superscribed Egypt

Warburg, Beaumont, Willems, Salamanca, Peninsula, Waterloo, Bhurtpore, Alma, Balaklava, Inkerman, Sevastopol, Ali Masjid, Afghanistan 1878-79, Egypt 1884, Relief of Kimberley, Paardeburg, South Africa 1899-1902

The Great War— Mons, **Le Cateau, Retreat from Mons, Marne 1914, Aisne 1914, Messines 1914,** Armentieres 1914, Ypres 1914, 15, Langemark 1914, Gheluvelt, Nonne Bosschen, **Frezenberg,** Bellewaarde, **Loos, Somme 1916, 18,** Flers-Courcelette, **Arras 1917, 18,** Scarpe 1917, **Cambrai 1917, 18,** St Quentin, Rosieres, Avre, **Amiens,** Albert 1918, **Drocourt-Queant,** Hindenburg Line, St Quentin Canal, Beaurevoir, **Cambrai 1918, Selle, Pursuit to Mons, France and Flanders 1914-18**

The Second World War— **Somme 1940, Villers Bocage,** Bourguebus Ridge, Mont Pincon, Jurques, Dives Crossing La Vie Crossing, Lisieux, Le Touques Crossing, Risle Crossing, **Roer, Rhine,** Ibbenburen, Aller, **North-West Europe 1940, 44-45, Egyptian Frontier 1940,** Withdrawal to Matruh, Bir Enba, **Sidi Barrani,** Buq Buq, Bardia 1941, Capture of Tobruk, **Beda Fomm,** Halfaya 1941, Sidi Suleiman, Tobruk 1941, Gubi I, II, Gabr Saleh, **Sidi Rezegh 1941,** Taieb el Essem, Relief of Tobruk, **Saunnu,** Msus, **Gazala,** Bir el Aslagh, Defence of Alamein Line, Alam el Halfa, **El Alamein,** Advance on Tripoli, **El Hamma,** Enfidaville, El Kourzia, Djebel Kournine, **Tunis,** North Africa 1940-43, Capture of Naples, Volturno Crossing, **Coriano, Santarcangelo,** Cosina Canal Crossing, Senio Pocket, Cesena, **Valli di Comacchio, Argenta Gap, Italy 1943-45**

Regimental Marches

Quick March..The Merry Month of May
Slow March..Coburg

Agents..Lloyds Bank PLC Cox's & King's Branch
Home Headquarters..Lower Barracks, Winchester, Hants (*Tel No:* 0962-63751)

Alliances

Canadian Armed Forces..1st Hussars
Australian Military Forces..10th Light Horse
Pakistan Army..The Guides Cavalry

Colonel in Chief..*HRH Princess* Alice *Duchess of* Gloucester *GCB CI GCVO GBE*

Colonel..Lt Col *Sir* Piers Bengough *KCVO OBE* ret pay..010184

Brigadiers

Friedberger J P W *CBE* psc† 300681
Hayman-Joyce R J *OBE BA* psc† tt 300683

Lieutenant Colonels

Mesquita P D (SL) *OBE* 300679
Malet G J W ndc psc 300680
Edwards D C *MA* psc† ph 300681
Morrison E C W *OBE* odc(US) sq 300681
Kaye P C C psc† tt 300682
Turner J R psc† ph 300683
Holder O E V sq 300684
Thompson *Sir* Christopher *Bt* psc† 300685
Thoyts J H psc jsdc 300685

Majors

Seely V R psc 300674
Perry R L sq ph 311274
Beresford P J C sq tt 300676
Roe D E sq 300676
Tuck N J sq 300677
Fearnehough R ph 311277
Wilkinson R A sq 300678
East R H sq 311278
Scholfield P V tt 300679
Powell A J W psc (*A/Lt Col* 021285) 311279
Boon R C H sq 300980
Watt C R G 300980
Howard O C psc 300981
Rogers J J *BA* psc 300981
MacDonald W R *BA* psc aic 300982
Kaye J R D psc 300983
Kitson C H M *BSc(Eng)* 300983
Burrell C H A 300984
Flach P R C *MBE* aic 300985

Captains

Bowring R A W *BSc(Eng)* 090379
Darell C H D *BA* aic (*A/Maj* 151185) 010880
Howard J A F *BA* 010281
Hezlet C T R 270182
Duckworth R 110683
Grant-Thorold N 081083
Lawson P J 040286
McGregor A C A aic 020386

Lieutenants

Allen T C (*A/Capt* 010684) 081281
Danvers C H D (*A/Capt* 010684) 120482
Moir J D S *BA* 150582
Adams B J (*A/Capt* 010685) 110483
Merton S R B (*A/Capt* 030985) 080883
Allfrey C J 090485

2nd Lieutenants

††Bridge S T W 230984

Quartermasters

Gillott F P 010677
Lt Col 280186
Boulter S C W *Capt* 010483
Keats M W *Capt* 200785

Special Regular Officers

Captains

Cray R V 050183
de Normann J R C 040286

Short Service Officers

Captains

Swinden C E L 210181

Lieutenants

Lowsley-Williams G D S (*A/Capt* 180185) 090882
Goy C H L (*A/Capt* 070486) 190982
de Normann A L *BA* 110483
Offer H J M *BA* 110483
Yates C J K (*A/Capt* 010685) 080883
Bueno De Mesquita N P (*A/Capt* 030785) 121283
Sutcliffe J M B 101285

2nd Lieutenants

Godfrey-Faussett C B 040884
Winter J H P 040884
Daly D C 130485
Trotter J W D 100885
Bathurst A E S 141285
Hamilton P A 141285
Hannay R J 141285

13th/18th ROYAL HUSSARS (QUEEN MARY'S OWN)

The Cypher Q.M.O. interlaced

"Viret in Aeternum" "Pro Rege, Pro Lege, pro Patria conamur"

Albuhera, Vittoria, Orthes, Toulouse, Peninsula, Waterloo, Alma, Balaklava, Inkerman, Sevastopol, Defence of Ladysmith, Relief of Ladysmith, South Africa 1899-1902

The Great War— **Mons,** Le Cateau, Retreat from Mons, **Marne 1914, Aisne 1914,** La Bassee 1914, **Messines 1914,** Armentieres 1914, **Ypres 1914, 15,** Gravenstafel, St Julien, Frezenberg, Bellewaarde, **Somme 1916, 18,** Flers-Courcelette, Arras 1917, Scarpe 1917, **Cambrai 1917, 18,** St Quentin, Rosieres, **Amiens,** Albert 1918, **Hindenburg Line,** Pursuit to Mons, **France and Flanders 1914-18, Kut al Amara 1917, Baghdad, Sharqat, Mesopotamia 1916-18**

The Second World War— Dyle, Withdrawal to Escaut, **Ypres-Comines Canal, Normandy Landing,** Bretteville, **Caen,** Bourguebus Ridge, **Mont Pincon,** St Pierre la Vielle, **Geilenkirchen, Roer, Rhineland,** Waal Flats, **Goch,** Rhine, Bremen, **North-West Europe 1940, 44-45**

Regimental Marches

Quick March..Balaklava
Slow Marches..(i) 13th Hussars Slow March
(ii) 18th Hussars Slow March

Agents..Lloyds Bank PLC Cox's & King's Branch
Home Headquarters..3 Tower Street, York, YO1 1SB
(*Tel No:* 0904-59811 *Ext:* 2310)

Alliances

Canadian Armed Forces..The Royal Canadian Hussars (Montreal)
Indian Army..Skinner's Horse (1st Duke of York's Own Cavalry)
Pakistan Army..6 Lancers
Malaysian Armed Forces..2nd Royal Reconnaissance Regiment

Colonel..Maj Gen H S R Watson *CBE* ret pay..110579

Brigadiers

Edelsten D A G ndc psc 300682

Colonels

Delamain C J G *MA* ptsc aic 300679
Ffrench Blake R J W psc 300685
Stephen G McL *OBE* ndc psc 300685

Lieutenant Colonels

Blakiston J A C psc† 300681
Cliff R T (SL) sq tt 300681
Cordy-Simpson R A *OBE* psc 300681
Yorke E L psc 300684

Majors

Beaver P C sq 300671
Delius D J *MBE* sq 300673
Robinson C A G B sq tt (*A/Lt Col* 260985) 300674
Hope-Johnstone P W sq 311276
Collis A J N sq ph 311277
Sievwright D A H osc(SP) sq 300679
Gibson P A J sq 311279
Le Hardy C A sq 300980
Selfe J A M A *BA* psc(n)† 300980
Southward N S psc 300980
Mallinson A L *BA* psc 300981
Nutting R C B psc† aic 300982
Peto W G psc† aic 300982
Griffith-Jones M D *DipRMCS* psc† aic gw 300983
Coker A D *BSc(Econ)* psc 300984
Quicke R N B 300984
Stewart A R E De C psc 300984
Brook M B 300985
Colacicchi M P 300985
Nall E W J 300985

Captains

Baker Baker W G 080981
Shryane N A *BA* 290981
Fishwick S N 271281
Burgess S D *BA* aic 120382
Ledger S W 080582
Mackenzie A H 081083
Roberts P T 081083
Blunt C J R 040286

Lieutenants

Amos D R 120482
Levey S R 120482
Ibbotson A D C 101285

2nd Lieutenants

Jones C G 130485

Quartermasters

Lang R 010478
Maj 010885
Winter J T *Capt* 010480
Smith G A *Capt* 010484

Special Regular Officers

Captains

Keane R M 100684

Short Service Officers

Captains

Baxendale H 180485
Prince-Smith J W 040286

Lieutenants

Cunningham M A 211181
Locker G E 140782
Ogden J W *BA* 110483
Pakenham-Walsh R M *BA* 110483
Scott-Masson P A G 110483
Peel R *BSc* 070884
Payne C J (*A/Capt* 170286) 111284
Ellwood O C B 060885
Burles T R 101285
Martin T J 070486

2nd Lieutenants

Good C P 081284
Newton C J H 081284
Whitaker C J S 081284
Nicholson T M 100885
Saker I R M 100885
†Collin T C D E 060985
†Steven A T *BSc* 060985
Curtis W G 141285
Mayo C E A 141285

14th/20th KING'S HUSSARS

The Prussian Eagle

Vimiera, Douro, Talavara, Fuentes D'Onor, Salamanca, Vittoria, Pyrenees, Orthes, Peninsula, Chillianwallah, Goojerat, Punjaub, Persia, Central India, Suakin 1885, Relief of Ladysmith, South Africa 1900-02

The Great War— **Mons, Retreat from Mons, Marne 1914, Aisne 1914, Messines 1914, Ypres 1914, 15,** Neuve Chapelle, St Julien, Bellewaarde, Arras 1917, Scarpe 1917, **Cambrai 1917, 18, Somme 1918,** St Quentin, Lys, Hazebrouck, **Amiens,** Albert 1918, Bapaume 1918, Hindenburg Line, St Quentin Canal, Beaurevoir, **Sambre,** France and Flanders 1914-18, **Tigris 1916, Kut al Amara 1917, Baghdad, Mesopotamia 1915-18, Persia 1918**

The Second World War— **Bologna, Medicina, Italy 1945**

Regimental Marches

Quick March..Royal Sussex
Slow March..The Eagle

Agents..Lloyds Bank PLC Cox's & King's Branch
Home Headquarters..Fulwood Barracks, Fulwood, Preston, PR2 4AA
(*Tel No: Preston Military Ext:* 310)

Alliances

Australian Military Forces..2nd/14th Queensland Mounted Infantry
8th/13th Victorian Mounted Rifles
New Zealand Army..Queen Alexandra's Squadron, RNZAC
Zambia Army..Zambia Armoured Car Regiment

Affiliated Regiment

6th Queen Elizabeth's Own Gurkha Rifles

Colonel in Chief..*HRH The Princess* Anne *Mrs* Mark Phillips *GCVO*

Colonel..Maj Gen *Sir* Michael Palmer *KCVO* ret pay..150281

Brigadiers

Williams T G *CBE* psc 300682

Lieutenant Colonels

Goodhart M H (SL) odc(US) sq tt 300674
de Beaujeu D L *OBE* ndc odc(BE) sq 300679
Harman P odc(US) sq 300680
Clifton-Bligh J R *BA* psc† tt 300681
Smales J R psc 300681
Cullinan M A sq 300682
Coombes J D sq 300683
Bowles W G C *MBE* sq aic 300684

Majors

Hodson K M sq tt 300674
Rawlins J P sq 300675
Edge W R T sq tt 300677
Dean C R K sq 300678
Scott T P psc ph 311278
Moger J M D 300980
Vickery M J H psc† aic 300980
Eliott-Lockhart P N psc 300981
Fairman H N psc 300982
Grey *The Hon* J F A psc 300982
Woodd D J B psc 300982
Fellowes R J L psc aic 300984
Singer A R E psc ph 300984
Suchanek S W G *BSc* psc† 300984
Tennent C M I psc 300984
Lang S E L 300985
Tilney G H R 300985

Captains

Garbutt P D W aic (*A/Maj* 140185) 301279
Tayler T C *BA CGIA* 100580
Shirreff A R D *BA(Hons) MA* 010880
Ashbrooke A F B *BA MA(Hons)* 040281
Clarke C V *BA* 090581
Hammick M P S L *BSc* aic 010882
Polley N G T *BA* 280982
Wade M W E 010283
Bradshaw A J *BSc* ph 030583
Herrtage J C P 300983
Dodworth M P *BA* 010284
Murray N M 081084
Wicks H A O 081084
Bankes C W N *LLB* 090385
Wells B S *BA* 100685

Lieutenants

Milverton N J 120482
O'Neil Donnellon P P 120482
Palmer J R M (*A/Capt* 020186) 120482
Reynolds C J *BA* 120482
Gossage A A 111284
Carter J W D 060885
Ross A C G 070486

2nd Lieutenants

††Jenkins M B D 240985

Quartermasters

Howard J P *Capt* 010481
Burgess M H *Capt* 010483
Draper B J M *Capt* 010484

Special Regular Officers

Captains

Ogden A 020486

2nd Lieutenants

Joynson H R D 081284

Short Service Officers

Captains

Sutcliffe R W H *BA* 290882
Nutsford P J *BMus* 101085
Beardsall J H 040286

Lieutenants

Jackson N D F *BSc* 120482
Schofield J 211282
Wagstaff A G 240283
Stuart-Mills A B *BA* 110483
Metherell J R *BSc* 070884
Gordon J B MacK 060885
Williams M A C 060885
Allan J A 101285
Winterton R N 101285
Baxter S R W 070486

2nd Lieutenants

Ross E T 130485
Searight S R C 130485
Skinner M G 130485
Goldie J K 100885
†Milne M K *BA(Hons)* 060985
†Morgan D H *BSc* 060985
Orr J N N 141285

15th/19th THE KING'S ROYAL HUSSARS

The Crest of England within the Garter. The Elephant superscribed Assaye

"Merebimur"

Emsdorf, Mysore, Villers-en-Cauchies, Willems, Seringapatam, Egmont-op-Zee, Sahagun, Vittoria, Niagara, Peninsula, Waterloo, Afghanistan 1870-80, Tel-el-Kebir, Egypt 1882-84, Nile 1884-85, Abu Klea, Defence of Ladysmith, South Africa 1899-1902

The Great War— Mons, **La Cateau, Retreat from Mons, Marne 1914, Aisne 1914, Armentieres 1914, Ypres 1914, 15,** Langemarck 1914, Gheluvelt, Nonne Bosschen, Frezenberg, **Bellewaarde, Somme 1916, 18,** Flers-Courcelette, **Cambrai** 1917, 18, St Quentin, **Rosieres, Amiens,** Albert 1918, Bapaume 1918, Hindenburg Line, St Quentin Canal, Beaurevoir, **Pursuit to Mons, France and Flanders 1914-18**

The Second World War— **Withdrawal to Escaut, Seine 1944,** Hechtel, **Nederrijn,** Venraji, **Rhineland, Hochwald, Rhine, Ibbenburen, Aller, North-West Europe 1940, 44-45**

Regimental Marches

Quick March..........The Bold King's Hussars
Slow Marches..........(i) Elliots Light Horse — 15th Hussars Slow March
(i) Denmark — 19th Hussars Slow March

Agents..........Lloyds Bank PLC Cox's & King's Branch

Home Headquarters..........Fenham Barracks, Newcastle-upon-Tyne, NE2 4NP (*Tel No:* 0632-29855)

Alliances

Canadian Armed Forces..........The South Alberta Light Horse
Australian Military Forces..........1st/15th Royal New South Wales Lancers
Pakistan Army..........19 Lancers

Colonel in Chief..........*HRH The Princess* Margaret *Countess of* Snowdon *CI GCVO*

Colonel..........Brig J R D Sharpe *CBE* ret pay..........010183

Brigadiers

McCarthy R H G odc(US) psc 300684

Colonels

Barneby M P psc† tt 300683
Wells C A G *BA* psc 300684

Lieutenant Colonels

Knox J S psc (*A/Col* 211285) 300679
Gordon R P D sq 300680
Hervey P V ndc psc 300680
Witheridge A G *MA* odc(FR) osc(FR) sq I 300682
Villiers T C psc 300683
Balmain D S psc jsdc 300684

Majors

Teale M E sq 120267
Hanbury R F sq tt 300672
Gregg T D psc 311279
Brook-Fox V J sq 300980
Gillman J C W *BSc(Eng)* psc† 300981
Portman M B sq 300981
Forsyth C M psc aic 300982
Harris M R 300982
Prestwich C T S 300983
Sample M W ph 300983
Woosnam R B psc† 300983
Ahern D M 300984
Braithwaite C H *BA* psc 300984

Captains

Mayall S V *BA* (*A/Maj* 080685) 010281
Straker M A 090581
Rigby S J *BA* 010282
Cusack D J aic 060982
Checketts T J 070283
Hunter A J De C 070283
Rutherford-Jones D J 060284
Edwards S R 100684
Tabor A J *BA* 040984
Browell M H aic 050285
Good M R 040286

Lieutenants

De Lotbiniere G A J (*A/Capt* 020985) 120482
Pearson M A (*A/Capt* 260385) 120482
Polley R D S 120482
Riddell S F *BA* 120482
Harris M D 090882
Riall T R P 090882
Darling P J A 080883

2nd Lieutenants

Jansen J 040884
†Chitty R O M *BScEng(Civil)* 060985

Quartermasters

Walls J F 010478 *Maj* 011184
Bulman A *Capt* 010480
Christian J *Capt* 190983

Special Regular Officers

Majors

Bennett T 300674
Mackie A R 300984

Captains

Godfrey J L 150981

Short Service Officers

Captains

Kennedy P W 020383

Lieutenants

Turnbull H A (*A/Capt* 070385) 171181
Dunn H C H *BA* 020382
Maclean R G S *BA* 230183
Leaf G E J *BA* 110483
Fisher J D M *BA* 090484
Akroyd S G 070884
Naylor J D H 111284
Sheldon J J K 101285

2nd Lieutenants

Straker S C 130485
Hutton K C 100885
†Lloyd J S *BA(Hons)* 060985
†Whitehouse A A J I *BSc(Hons) BSc(Eng)* 060985
Fitzmaurice R J L 141285
Frost E J S 141285

16th/5th THE QUEEN'S ROYAL LANCERS

The Royal Cypher

Aut cursu, aut cominus armis

Blenheim, Ramilles, Oudenarde, Malplaquet, Beaumont, Willems, Talavera, Fuentes D'Onor, Salamanca, Vittoria, Nive, Peninsula, Waterloo, Bhurtpore, Ghuznee 1839, Affghanistan 1839, Maharajpore, Aliwal, Sobraon, Suakin 1885, Defence of Ladysmith, Relief of Kimberley, Paardeberg, South Africa 1899-1902

The Great War— **Mons, Le Cateau, Retreat from Mons, Marne, 1914, Aisne 1914, Messines 1914,** Armentieres 1914, **Ypres 1914, 15,** Gheluvelt, St Julien, **Bellewaarde, Arras 1917,** Scarpe 1917, **Cambrai 1917, Somme 1918, St Quentin,** Amiens, Hindenburg Line, Canal du Nord, **Pursuit to Mons,** France and Flanders 1914-18

The Second World War— Kasserine, **Fondouk,** Kairouan, **Bordj, Djebel Kournine, Tunis,** Gromballa, Bou Ficha, **North Africa 1942-43, Cassino II, Liri Valley,** Monte Piccolo, Capture of Perugia, Arezzo, **Advance to Florence, Argenta Gap,** Traghetto, **Italy 1944-45**

Regimental Marches

Quick March.......Scarlet And Green
Slow March.......The Queen Charlotte

Agents.......Lloyds Bank PLC Cox's & King's Branch

Home Headquarters.......Kitchener House, Lammascote Road, Stafford (*Tel No:* 0785-45840)

Alliances

Australian Military Forces.......12th/16th Hunter River Lancers

Colonel in Chief.......THE QUEEN

Colonel.......Brig J L Pownall *OBE* ret pay.......311085

Colonels

Vivian *The Hon* N C L sq 300682
Radford C J *MC* psc 300685

Lieutenant Colonels

Wright J A *MBE* ndc sq 300680
Brooke M P sq 300681
Hedley A A *OBE* psc tt (*A/Col* 311085) 300681
O'Callaghan D M psc† 300683

Majors

Lyall Grant A H *MA* psc† aic 311272
Speers C N P sq aic 311276
Baker R D sq 300677
Illingworth M A *MA MSc* psc† dis tt 300677
Squire J E psc aic jsdc 311277
Faulkner R E S sq jsdc 300678
Durie A J D sq 300679
Radford M F C sq 311279
Coombs J T H sq aic ph 300980
Scott P E sq 300980
Waterhouse W R sq 300980
Musgrave N P C *BA* aic 300981
Campbell P Macl aic 300982
Clarke M E aic 300982
Crosse H J aic 300983
Boddy A F 300984
Carter J E M psc† 300985

Captains

Finlayson A I 080379
Grant C F S ph 100580
Cade T J *BSc* (*A/Maj* 051185) 080981
Vivian-Neal P F R (*A/Maj* 220485) 080981
Phillips A G K (*A/Maj* 170386) 281281
Ridley N M A *MA* 200583
Lunt N J *BA* 050384
Skinner D G O 100684
Snell J O 100684
Gill M J 071085
Rickcord R G 071085
Eadie D J 040286

2nd Lieutenants

Gibb I J 130485
Vaughan-Edwards S A 141285

Quartermasters

Corrigan J *MBE* 280271
Lt Col 221183
Taylor S A 061179
Maj 010980
Ghillyer T W K 010481
Maj 111185
Verrall M J *LRAM* *Capt* 230883
Causer R A *MM* *Capt* 251083

Special Regular Officers

Majors

Connolly P G 300984

Short Service Officers

Captains

Gill B P *MA* 050583
Norbury J P M *BA* 071085
Cook W 171285

Lieutenants

Holman J M 081181
Dutton A J *MBE* 141181
Campbell A H E *BA* (*A/Capt* 010985) 120482
Cheetham A N M *BA* 120782
Oulton N R R *BA* 090882
O'Brien T W P 110483
Chatfeild-Roberts J H *BA(Hons)* 070884
Whitcomb E F P *BSc* 070884
Bullen P J S 090485
Vintcent T N 090485
Moore C M S 060885
Wills N H C 060885
Hansard C C T 101285
Payne R G 101285

2nd Lieutenants

Mobley A J 040884
Bulloch J D C 130485
Noel R G H 130485
Morley C 100885
Nixon-Eckersall R B 100885
Simpson J G M 100885
†Harvey F D *BSc* 060985
Fisher W J 141285

17th/21st LANCERS

Death's Head *'Or Glory'*

Alma, Balaklava, Inkerman, Sevastopol, Central India, South Africa 1879, Khartoum, South Africa 1900-02

The Great War— **Festubert 1914, Somme 1916, 18, Morval, Cambrai 1917, 18, St Quentin, Avre,** Lys, **Hazebrouck, Amiens,** Hindenburg Line, St Quentin Canal, Beaurevoir, **Pursuit to Mons, France and Flanders 1914-18, NW Frontier India 1915, 16**

The Second World War— **Tebourba Gap,** Bou Arada, **Kasserine,** Thala, **Fondouk El Kourzia, Tunis,** Hammam Lif, **North Africa 1942-43, Cassino II,** Monte Piccolo, **Capture of Perugia,** Advance to Florence, **Argenta Gap,** Fossa Cembalina, **Italy 1944-45**

Regimental Marches

Quick March..The White Lancer
Slow March...Rienzi

Agents..Lloyds Bank PLC Cox's & King's Branch
Home Headquarters..............................Prince William of Gloucester Barracks, Grantham, Lincs
(*Tel No:* 0476-67413 *Ext:* 252)

Alliance

Canadian Armed Forces.......................Lord Strathcona's Horse (Royal Canadians)

Colonel in Chief..................................*HRH Princess* Alexandra *the Hon Mrs* Angus Ogilvy *GCVO*

Colonel..Brig J W Turner ret pay........................300683

Brigadiers

Douglas-Nugent A R *ADC* psc 300678
Swinburn R H rcds psc† 300682
Still N M *CBE BA* psc 300684

Colonels

Lindsay A T *MA* ndc psc† aic 300685

Lieutenant Colonels

Hamilton-Russell B G psc tt 300680
Purbrick R I S *MBE* sq jsdc ph 300684
Barry P R *BSc* psc(n)† 300685
Woolley J D V sq 300685

Majors

Timmis M F sq 311267
Gradidge A F sq ph tt 300673
Churton C H psc† 311273
Perrett M H M C sq aic ph 311276
Templer J M *MBE* psc† 311277
Hurrell W J sq (*A/Lt Col* 220885) 311278
Pearson R A F I 300679
Barkas A D T ph 300980
Cumming A A J R psc 300981
Goldsmith R J D aic 300982
Kingscote M J F 300982
Marriott S M 300982
Simpson D B psc 300982
Buxton C J psc 300983
Gordon R D S *MA* psc† 300983
Halford C H B 300983
McKenzie Johnston R A *MA* psc† 300983

Captains

Robinson C E 080981
Fulton H R G 080582
Obolensky *Prince* Nicholas *BA* 060982
Leasor S N M *BA* 050983
Wertheim R N *BA* 130983
Marriott P C 081083
Hunter J R G 060284
Springman P W E *BA* 060284
Dewell C A B 050285

Lieutenants

Wieloch W R (*A/Capt* 130983) 081281
Akerman J H S (*A/Capt* 140983) 120482
Harding-Rolls M A C (*A/Capt* 300985) 131282
Pinney G R *BSc* 110483
Newitt C N (*A/Capt* 300386) 080883
English W P O 121283
Fattorini C S 070884
Everard J R 090485
Wallington J C G 101285

2nd Lieutenants

Watson R G J 141285

Quartermasters

Prosser A D *MBE* 160975 *Maj* 160983
Neil G T *Capt* 010481
Westbrook V T *Capt* 010482
Woodbridge A *Capt* 240583

Short Service Officers

Captains

Hodges J R 031085

Lieutenants

Bateman A L 100382
Hutchings S W 100382
Backhouse R 140782
Bostock W V *BSc* 090882
Garforth-Bles T J (*A/Capt* 190684) 131282
Fountain J G 080883
Mulloy W A M 080883
Horlock M J P 121283
Milne R J *BA* 090484
Daly P M R *BA(Hons)* 070884
Henderson N B 090485
Barker G St J 060885
Hankinson P D P 070486

2nd Lieutenants

Shields A C G 081284
Wilson J C E 081284
†Cockram D D L *BA(Hons)* 060985
†Hughes A G 060985
Daly J P K 141285
Franklyn-Jones C W 141285
Henson T J 141285

ROYAL TANK REGIMENT

A tank encircled by a wreath of laurel and surmounted by The Crown

"Fear naught"

The Great War— **Somme 1916, 18, Arras 1917, 18, Messines 1917, Ypres 1917, Cambrai 1917,** St Quentin 1918, **Villers Bretonneux, Amiens, Bapaume 1918, Hindenburg Line,** Epehy, Selle, **France and Flanders 1916-18,** Gaza

The Second World War— Arras counter attack, Calais 1940, St Omer-La Bassee, Somme 1940, Odon, Caen, Bourguebus Ridge, Mont Pincon, Falaise, Nederrijn, Scheldt, Venlo Pocket, Rhineland, **Rhine,** Bremen, **North-West Europe 1940, 44-45, Abyssinia 1940,** Sidi Barrani, Beda Fomm, Sidi Suleiman, **Tobruk 1941,** Sidi Rezegh 1941, Belhamed, Gazala, Cauldron, Knightsbridge, Defence of Alamein Line, Alam el Halfa, **El Alamein,** Mareth, Akarit, Fondouk, El Kourzia, Medjez Plain, Tunis, **North Africa 1940-43,** Primosole Bridge, Gerbini, Adrano, **Sicily 1943,** Sangro, Salerno, Volturno Crossing, Garigliano Crossing, Anzio, Advance to Florence, Gothic Line, Coriano, Lamone Crossing, Rimini Line, Argenta Gap, **Italy 1943-45, Greece 1941, Burma 1942**

Korea 1951-53

Regimental Marches

Quick March..........Regimental March of The Royal Tank Regiment— My Boy Willie
Slow March..........Royal Tank Regiment Slow March

Agents..........Holts Branch, Royal Bank of Scotland PLC, Lawrie House, Farnborough, Hants

Regimental Headquarters..........1 Elverton Street, Horseferry Road, London, SW1P 2QJ (*Tel No:* 01-828-0330)

Alliances

Canadian Armed Forces..........12e Régiment Blindé du Canada
Australian Military Forces..........1st Armoured Regiment RAAC
New Zealand Army..........Royal New Zealand Armoured Corps
Indian Army..........2nd Lancers
Pakistan Army..........13 Lancers

Colonel in Chief..........THE QUEEN

Colonels Commandant..........Maj Gen R M Jerram *CB MBE* ret pay..........010682
*Maj Gen A K F Walker..........121283
Maj Gen L A W New *CB CBE* ret pay..........010186

Brigadiers

Bastick J D *MBE MBIM* jssc psc 300680
Blacker A S J *OBE BA* psc† 300682
Evans M J *ADC* psc 300683
Cocking N H psc 300684
Dick R C J psc† 300685
Lewis D L *OBE* rcds ndc psc 300685
Ockenden R V *CBE* nadc psc 300685
Williams D A psc† 300685

Colonels

Glazebrook D *OBE* psc 300678
Ivy D R *AAAI FBIM FIIM* psc† ptsc gw 300679
Osborne R psc 300683
Pepper E J ndc psc 300683
Bentley P D psc osc(SUD) 300684
Sanders P J psc tt 300684

Lieutenant Colonels

Lewis S D B (SL) ndc psc osc(BLD) 300672
Wallerstein A B (SL) psc 300673
Gregson P F (SL) *MBE* ndc psc 300675
Warren H A (SL) psc tt 300675
Darlington J (SL) *MBIM* ptsc tt 300676
Hammond P ndc psc 300676
Clitherow N A H (SL) psc 300678
Phillips H B J *MBE* psc 300678
Tweed M G ndc psc ph 300678
Walcot T (SL) sq (*L/Col* 250485) 300678
Bale W S psc 300679
Kan M *BSc(Eng)* psc† (*A/Col* 041085) 300679
Rash J D *MBE BSc* psc† (*A/Col* 090985) 300679
Gray G C psc† tt 300680
Jones A R psc ph 300680
Seymour M *MBE* psc 300680
Duncan B A C *MBE* psc 300681
Scott P G ndc psc 300681
Taylor J H B psc† tt 300681
Terry T W *MBE* psc† 300681
Duncan H D C *MBE* odc(US) psc 300682
Hammerbeck C J A *MBIM* psc 300682
McAfee R W M psc ph 300682
McCombe B S psc 300682
Nelson P A psc† tt 300682
Woodward J ndc sq tt 300682
Graves J R W psc 300683
Keun M I *BA* odc(US) psc 300683
Oliver R G psc† tt 300683
Longman J L sq jsdc 300684
Napper M J *BSc* psc† 300684
Williams J J sq 300684
Cantley W D *MBE* psc 300685
Dealtry P G sq tt 300685
Sullivan R sq 300685

Majors

Smith L G G ph pl 090565
Grimwade J G psc pl (*L/Lt Col* 110285) 131066
Osborne R W L *BSc* sq gw 120267
O'Flaherty M A tt 300669
Robertson N C H ph tt 300669
Moriarty M N S sq 311269
Golding F W V sq gw tt 300671
Robins G F E sq 311271
Goodwin M R sq tt 311274
Holmes J P B psc 311274
Robinson J F E psc 311274
Scragg C A 311274
King H R psc 300675
Prendergast J H V sq tt 300675
Hodgson I F B P osc(ID) 311275
Taylor Firth J N sq 311275
Tomlinson G R sq 311275
Preston G E sq aic 300676
Williams J D psc aic 300676
Warner N S sq 311276
Russell W H psc 311278
Mileham P J R sq 300679
Smedley J E B *BA* sq 300679
Goodson M J H psc jsdc 311279
Lloyd-Edwards D psc 311279
McBean C J *BA* psc† 311279
Pugh C M E sq 311279
Gould E J psc 300980
Gudgin M J sq 300980
Harrison R L N *BA* sq tt 300980
Morgan R V O ph 300980
Patey C G psc 300980

*Representative Colonel Commandant for 1986

Royal Armoured Corps — continued

Brummitt R W *MBE* psc (*A/Lt Col* 060186)	300981
Coles G R sq ph	300981
Dening-Smitherman P C H	300981
Freeman F M psc aic	300981
Hall T E psc	300981
Hill R A L sq	300981
Owen J M psc	300981
Stevens I P G psc aic	300981
Wallington A E sq	300981
Coombe N S psc	300982
Gadsby A C I psc†	300982
Maunsell E R osc(MAL)	300982
Ridgway A P psc ph	300982
Speller M N E *MBE BSc* psc(n)†	300982
Wheeler G F psc†	300982
Withington J C psc	300982
Ambidge M W aic	300983
Bangham P H	300983
Carroll A G R psc	300983
Hine R N	300983
Stephenson M G V psc	300983
Vane Percy C R psc	300983
Vaux R P C aic	300983
Crisford T J N aic	300984
Elliot-Square A H *BA MSc* psc† aic gw	300984
Gilchrist P psc† aic	300984
Kendell R N	300984
Leakey A D *MA* psc	300984
Masters M D psc	300984
McFarland R A	300984
Trape J A R *LLB*	300984
Tozer S A	300985
Viccars D I psc	300985
White S J B *MBE BA* psc	300985

Captains

Coombe T B J *BSc* (*A/Maj* 241282)	010278
Roach A T psc† aic	080379
Strong B	090379
Godfrey R G A *BSc* aic	050979
Lewis N A E aic (*A/Maj* 230985)	100979
Best A J C	301279
Beardsworth J P B *BSc*	180280
Clements M J (*A/Maj* 081185)	100580
Ellison H C H *BSc* (*A/Maj* 060186)	170780
Gloyens M J	090980
Pugh M J	090980
Stephenson A V aic	090980
Lemon J R	291280
Logan S R	291280
Aylwin-Foster N R F *BA* (*A/Maj* 050486)	010281
Vesey-Holt G M *BA*	010281
Loggie P M *BEng* aic	120281
Rodley I J *BSc*	120281
Dixon R G *LLB*	290381
Mason N B aic	140681
Murray H *BA*	190881
Davis R W J *MA*	080981
Ellis A M	080981
Roberts M C G	080981
Outhwaite M R C *BSc*	271081
May S J	281281
Harrison S J D *BA*	180382
Jasper S A *BA*	180382
Eccles D C *BA*	270582
Bodian N E	070283
Caraffi S	070283
Garnett J W *BSc(Eng)*	070283
Crawford S W *BA CGIA*	280383
Jammes R F	110683
Millington R D F aic (*L/Maj* 160781)	110683
Fyfe A W	120983
Brookshaw R C (*L/Maj* 170981)	081083
Chapman A D H	060284
Shapland M P	060284
Pelling C M *BSc BSc(Econ)*	090684
Chesterfield R T aic	081084
Collins R M	081084
Prior S J *BA*	081084
Deverell C M *BA*	010285
Gould R C G *BA*	010285
Lines A J *BA*	010285
Miller P *BA*	010285
Houston C J	050285
Powe J J	050285
Tustin S R	050285
Simpson A W J *BA*	250785
Clitherow P K H aic	071085
Douglass J W G	071085
Lightfoot A D	071085
Nobbs N F	071085
Polin J C	071085
Allison P J	040286
Van Grutten M W	040286

Lieutenants

Gent S M (*A/Capt* 060186)	081281
Charlesworth J R	120482
Colley J B D *BA*	120482
Green B J W (*A/Capt* 190486)	120482
McGregor R A ph	120482
Shapcott W J *BA* (*A/Capt* 050386)	120482
Macnaughton A N	090882
Hennah R D *BSc(Eng)*	131282
Laurence W J (*A/Capt* 120485)	131282
Spicer P G	131282
Ecclestone R L *BA*	110483
Foster T C *BA*	110483
Jacomb P S (*A/Capt* 210685)	110483
Judd G A (*A/Capt* 291085)	110483
Edwards P D *BA*	080883
Allen S A W	121283
Hanson J R	121283
Couzens D M A *BSc*	090484
Birks N T	060885
Brown G F	070486

2nd Lieutenants

††Grayson E R	101084
††Gash A S	121084
Mitchell C A	070785
†Hutchings M T E *BA(Hons)*	060985
†Kidd P J *BA(Hons)*	060985
Van Berckel C E	141285

Staff Quartermasters

Clarke C F		070277
	Lt Col	020285

Quartermasters

Hayward-Cripps B H *OBE*		090774
	Lt Col	221283
Broughton T E *BEM*		180875
	Maj	050679
Evans M D *MBE*		201176
	Lt Col	010285
Wheatley A B *MBE*		140877
	Maj	020481
Horne T		010478
	Maj	010582
Walton R		010480
	Maj	280186
Corbin P S		170780
	Maj	201284
Riordan G V I		010481
	Maj	281284
Broadhurst B S *MBE*		010482
	Maj	290186
Rutterford B D	*Capt*	010482
Aquilina R J	*Capt*	010483
Burgin J	*Capt*	010483
Dennison H	*Capt*	010483
Henzie A	*Capt*	220583
Briggs C J psm		010484
	Maj	030385
Lyman J	*Capt*	110685

Directors of Music

Tomlinson R G *BA LGSM FTCL ARCM* psm	*Capt*	210279
Marshall D J *LTCL ARCM BBCM* psm	*Capt*	150885

Special Regular Officers

Majors

Lawson I D aic	300984

Captains

Buxton D A	011277
Whyte P M aic	281281
Lyon S R *BSc* aic	060882
Pheby M A	050285
Dixon A S	040286
Palmer D L	050286

Lieutenants

Wilson C B	060885

Short Service Officers

Captains

Waddell A J	170481
Nicholls D	230882
Howard V M	120183
Thornton J P *BA*	150283
Wallis J A *BA*	280583
Ream P N *BA*	130284
Whatling C H J	110384
Gibbs J R M *BA*	050285
Butterworth P J *BA*	030385
Nolan T	060585
Lupton C R	020885
Dell S J *BA*	180186
Cobb J P L *MA(Hons)*	020386
Ternent E	010486

Lieutenants

Pratt B J	200182
Cornish P N *MA(Hons) MSc*	120482
Robson A G *BA*	120482
Wright B E	120582
Lyall P A	180782
Craven-Griffiths R C *MA(Hons)*	090882
Watt E J	120183
Johnson J C	010483

Carr W P *BSc*	110483
Farthing J G D *BA*	110483
Longson M F *BEd*	110483
Macfarlane N *BA*	110483
Mason K J St J *BSc*	110483
Wilson S B *BA*	110483
Fitzwater A L *BA*	080883
Watts A C I ph	121283
Heyman R M St J *BA*	090484
Pine J N *BA*	090484
Rilot S J *BA*	090484
Tucker P C *BSc*	090484
Cooper D O	060885
Corbin P A	060885
Willis I H	060885
Cleverly C J	070486
Corbin S M	070486
King S D T	070486
Patterson J R	070486

2nd Lieutenants

Bullivant D R	040884
Harrison C F	040884
Shackleton R C E	040884
Spence N J G	081284
Baylis R A	100885
Hall S J	100885
†Hook J H *BA*	060985
†Keil A D *BA*	060985
†Laird R J K *BSc(Hons)*	060985
†Smith R H M *BSc*	060985
Bidwell A C	141285
Bristow S E	141285
Brown R A	141285
Lucy R J	141285
Macdonald R I	141285
Master R	141285
Prosser N R	141285
Rhys-Thomas M D	141285
Roberts J D C	141285
Smith P R	141285
†Macleod A	060186

ROYAL REGIMENT OF ARTILLERY

A Gun between two Scrolls, that above inscribed UBIQUE, that beneath inscribed QUO FAS ET GLORIA DUCUNT; the whole ensigned with The Crown all Gold

Regimental Marches

Quick March..The RA Quick March
Slow March..Royal Artillery Slow March

Agents..Lloyds Bank PLC Cox's & King's Branch

Regimental Headquarters....................Government House, New Road, Woolwich, London, SE18 6XR
(*Tel No:* 01-856-5533 *Ext:* 504)

Alliances

Canadian Armed Forces.......................The Royal Regiment of Canadian Artillery
Australian Military Forces....................The Royal Regiment of Australian Artillery
New Zealand Army..............................The Royal Regiment of New Zealand Artillery
Indian Army..Regiment of Artillery
Pakistan Army.......................................Artillery of Pakistan
Sri Lanka Army.....................................The Sri Lanka Artillery
Malaysian Armed Forces......................Malaysian Artillery
Singapore Armed Forces......................The Singapore Volunteer Artillery
Fiji...The Fiji Artillery

Captain-General..................................THE QUEEN

Master Gunner, St James's Park.........Gen *Sir* Thomas Morony *KCB OBE ADC Gen* 010583

Colonels Commandant.........................Maj Gen R Lyon *CB OBE* ret pay 230476
Gen *Sir* Thomas Morony *KCB OBE ADC Gen* 010978
Maj Gen T S C Streatfield *CB MBE* ret pay..240680
Maj Gen A G E Stewart-Cox *DFC* ret pay 070880
Maj Gen L H Plummer *CBE* ret pay..040881
Lt Gen *Sir* Edward Burgess *KCB OBE ADC Gen* 010582
Gen *Sir* Richard Trant *KCB* 250582
Gen *Sir* Martin Farndale *KCB* 210882
Maj Gen M J Tomlinson *CB OBE* ret pay...010982
Maj Gen R Staveley ret pay..210982
Lt Gen *Sir* Richard Vincent *KCB DSO*..160183
*Maj Gen W D Mangham *CB* ret pay...010583
Maj Gen J A Stephenson *CB OBE* ret pay 150584

Hon Colonels Commandant................Col G E Gilchrist *TD* 291182
Brig P D Orchard-Lisle *TD ADC DL* 010186

Brigadiers

Perkins M J *CBE ADC* rcds psc 300675
Killick J E *ADC* rcds psc psc(n) 300678
Jones D M psc G(gw) 300680
Quayle T D G *BA* psc† 300680
Templer J R *OBE* rcds psc 300680
Bonnet P R F *MBE BSc(Eng)* psc† 300681
Duchesne P R *OBE* psc(n)† psc 300681
Jones J M psc 300681
Howarth J H ndc psc 300682
Mountford R S *OBE* psc 300682
Safford G C psc 300682
Pennicott B T *MBIM* ndc psc† 300683
Ransby G P R *FBIM* psc osc(NIG) 300683
Wilkes M J *OBE* psc† 300683
Winder W E psc 300683
Arnold G G odc(US) psc(n) 300684
Marsh P *MBE BSc(Eng)* odc(US) psc† G 300684
O'Connor M R S psc 300684
Warner B K *ADC* psc 300684
Harley A G H *OBE* psc 300685
Pughe N M psc(a)† psc 300685
Tennant M T psc† osc(NIG) 300685
Thompson T K *MBE MA* nadc psc† 300685
Timbers K A *MBIM* psc† G 300685
Townsend I G psc† G 300685

Colonels

Brumham P H psc 300674
Cross J P *OBE* jssc psc 300677
Denton C W odc(US) psc G 300678
Fleetwood G M *CBE* psc 300679
Jackson P R S *OBE* nadc psc 300679
Gray-Newton D G 300680
Harding B C M *CBE MC* psc (*L/Brig* 190386) 300680
Hughes J E M *OBE* ndc psc osc(SUD) 300680
Morland A D *MBE* ndc psc 300680
Weston A R N *BSc* psc† 300680
Elliot R G *OBE* psc G 300681
Hudson M J H *MBIM MInstAM* df psc ph 300681
Morgan W M *FBIM* psc 300681
Murray M A C jssc psc (*L/Brig* 250784) 300681
Painter P J F psc G(a) 300681
Robinson J R *MBE MBIM* ndc psc† G 300681
Bennett J S *OBE MBIM* sq G 300682
Colley H E P *OBE* ndc psc sq 300682
de Fonblanque H B psc 300682
Fowler A K ndc nadc sq 300682
Jack I G psc† psc(a) 300682
Jones P *MBE LLB* psc 300682
Sexstone P A *MBIM* psc† G 300682
Smith A K psc 300682
Tucker D E A *BSc* psc† osc(SUD) G(a) 300682
Wilkinson C A odc(GE) psc osc(GE) 300682
Back R W psc 300683
Bennett A D psc 300683
Bittles W J *OBE* odc(GE) psc osc(GE) 300683
Clark A J McD *FBIM* psc 300683
Corner D J *OBE* sq 300683
Gordon J C M psc† 300683
Gray N G S odc(FR) psc osc(FR) 300683
Hunter-Choat A *OBE* psc 300683
Peecock J B R psc 300683
Shellard M F L *MBIM* ndc psc G(gw) (*A/Brig* 011185) 300683
Stone A C P psc† (*A/Brig* 100486) 300683
Williams D S psc† 300683
Arnell N R *MA* psc† 300684

*Representative Colonel Commandant for 1986

Crawshaw J S *FBIM* odc(US) sq 300684
Daniell P J ndc psc† 300684
Eastwood T J S ndc psc 300684
Hall R W S psc† 300684
Holt G A psc 300684
Landrey P R F psc† G 300684
McQuoid R F P psc 300684
Mews H H ndc psc 300684
Bowden M C ndc psc 300685
Bremridge T J psc 300685
Cattaway A R *MA* psc† 300685
Coward A G psc(a) 300685
Evans I D ndc psc G 300685
Ewing C A *OBE LLB* odc(US) psc 300685
Fowler I B R psc† 300685
Gordon A F psc† 300685
Hollands G S psc† 300685
Holroyd Smith M J *OBE* ndc sq 300685
McCarthy C D *OBE MBIM* odc(AUST) sq 300685
Shields D N *MBE* sq 300685
Walsh R E W psc† G 300685
Willcocks M A *BSc* psc† 300685

Lieutenant Colonels

Truell G D S (SL) *MBE* psc 300667
Message T S (SL) psc 300671
Dunstone J G (SL) *MBE* psc 300673
Hole A P M (SL) *OBE* ndc psc 300673
Wilby K G (SL) psc† 300673
Barden J P (SL) *MBE* sq 300674
Bordass T D (SL) psc 300674
Darmody M J (SL) psc 300674
Redford R J (SL) sq G(s) 300674
Attard Manche G A (SL) psc (*L/Col* 290184) 300675
Dickins W A (SL) *LLB(Hons)* psc osc(NIG) 300675
Green P J (SL) *BA MBIM* sq G 300675
Horwood P A (SL) psc 300675
Hudson R M A (SL) *CDipAF* ptsc 300675
Michie J D V (SL) psc osc(NIG) 300675
Molesworth A J L *MBE* ndc psc (*A/Col* 070286) 300675
Robertson P (SL) osc(GE) 300675
Earlam D P (SL) ndc psc 300676
Elliot D R A (SL) psc 300676
Kearon M B (SL) *MBE* sq 300676
O'Hara B C (SL) sowc sq 300676
Payne A J (SL) sq G 300676
Smith K T G (SL) psc osc(NIG) 300676
Webber J C (SL) psc† 300676
Ayers R C (SL) *OBE* G(y) 300677
Briggs W J psc osc(NIG) 300677
Hornby R N D sq 300677
Letchworth R C psc osc(GH) 300677
Woodcock M J *OBE* odc(US) psc osc(NIG) 300677
Barker P W *OBE* sq G 300678
Barnard T A (SL) sq G(a) 300678
Bolton R psc G 300678
Brown R G W *BA* psc† ph 300678
Cornick A E psc 300678
Gray S D (SL) *MBE* psc† G 300678
Mesch J M *MBIM* ndc psc† 300678
Parsons T G (SL) *MRAeS* ptsc aws ph pl 300678
Payne C W (SL) G(a) 300678
Reavill D R (SL) psc 300678
Richards P J M (SL) *MITO* sq G 300678
Beckingsale J M *MBE MC* sq 300679
Bolton-Clark J ndc sq 300679
Bremridge M F *MC* sq 300679
Jago J M (SL) *OBE* sq 300679
Leighton R H ndc psc† G (*A/Col* 190386) 300679
McNaught L W psc† sq G 300679
Orr G S (SL) G 300679
Salisbury P A (SL) *MBIM* sq G(a) 300679
Sampson R K (SL) *OBE* sq ph 300679
Thomson J M F psc 300679
Whyte A MacG ndc psc 300679
Wiseman P J *MA* psc† 300679
Alford J N *BSc(Eng)* psc† 300680
Ashton-Wickett P D ndc psc 300680
Bird N J *MBIM* G 300680
Bolwell M (SL) sq G(s) 300680
Burson C R psc† psc G 300680
Craven R C F sq G 300680
Edmunds M C *OBE* psc osc(NIG) 300680
Faith C S *OBE* psc 300680
Freeth D psc osc(ZIM) 300680
Gay D S psc 300680
Lambe S D odc(US) psc† ph 300680
Lawrence G P psc 300680
Lefever P S H ndc sq (*L/Col* 190985) 300680
Morris G A psc† G 300680
Pearson R T (SL) psc 300680
Pinion A J *BA* psc† osc(SUD) 300680
Pratt A D sq 300680
Prior P A R *OBE* ndc sq G (*A/Col* 020185) 300680
Tarr R P S ndc sq 300680
Wilkes L A psc† 300680
Wilmshurst A *MBIM* sq G(y) 300680
Anderson M G R *MBE* psc† 300681
Andrew J R D *OBE* psc 300681
Barnard D M (SL) G(ss) 300681
Brown K B *BSc MBIM* psc† 300681
Burton E F G *OBE MA* psc(n)† (*A/Col* 100186) 300681
Chamberlain R C sq G 300681
Colson J D sq 300681
Cook C P ndc psc 300681
Copeland C J B psc osc(NIG) 300681
Creswell D H C psc† G(y) (*A/Col* 301285) 300681
Crimp R F *MIMC MMS* 300681
Cross M D sq 300681
Forward I K psc† 300681
Kincaid J W M *MA* ndc psc† 300681
Ledger M E sq 300681
Miller G H (SL) *MBIM* sq G(a) 300681
O'Connor N P S *MA* odc(US) psc† 300681
Vasey R E S ndc psc 300681
Vere R M *MBE* psc ph 300681
Walpole A C *MBE* sq 300681
Walton J E F sq 300681
Williams C N C psc† 300681
Bagshawe-Mattei J A (SL) *MBIM* psc† 300682
Beachus J W osc(GE) 300682
Burkey R W psc 300682
Cater J ndc sq 300682
Claypoole N J odc(US) sq 300682
Collings W J *MBE* sq 300682
Davies F N J *MBIM* sq 300682
Dawson C B *MBE BSc* ndc sq 300682
Douglas-Withers M G *BSc(Eng)* psc† 300682
Estcourt E J *MBIM* sq G 300682
Johnston J I *MBE* ndc sq 300682
Lowe D M P *MBE* psc 300682
Middlemas R G psc 300682
Middleton J D odc(US) sq ph 300682
Mitcheson K A *MA* psc 300682
Nicholson M J *MBE* psc 300682
Richards N W F *MA* psc(n)† 300682
Stevens A J *BSc* psc† 300682
Stevens W B *MBE MC* psc 300682
Brown M C *MBIM* sq G(a) 300683
Dean J G W psc† 300683
Dumas J J psc osc(NIG) 300683
Hoggarth T P B psc G(a) 300683
Howard-Harwood I P *MBIM* sq 300683
Nicholson B G G *OBE* ndc sq 300683
Richards M J N psc 300683
Smith V T M psc† ph 300683
Smith G F W *MBE* psc 300683
Stott H *MBIM* sq G 300683
Strong W E psc† G 300683
Wagstaffe P J psc† ph 300683
Walker R C *BSc* psc† 300683
Webb R J M C G 300683
Welby-Everard H E *MBE* psc 300683
Wilkinson I A psc 300683
Bell P R psc 300684
Durie I G C *MA* psc† jsdc 300684
Eager C J sq G jsdc 300684
Fletcher-Wood C *OBE BA* odc(AUST) psc 300684
Granville-Chapman T J *MA* psc† 300684
Kidner R H *MBIM* sq 300684
Kirby P B *BA* odc(US) psc† 300684
Lambe R M *MBE* sq jsdc 300684
Lewin J H *MBE* psc 300684
Miles D W psc† 300684
Milne J psc ph s 300684
Patrick J M *MBE* psc† jsdc 300684
Starmer-Smith J N G *OBE* psc 300684
Stewart I R G sq jsdc 300684
Strathern F A psc† 300684
Symonds R J R psc† 300684
Walmsley D R psc† 300684
Wright R W L *MBE* psc† ph 300684
Bearfoot E J psc† 300685
Blythe G E J *BSc* psc(n)† 300685
Bray D R *MBIM* 300685
Broke G R S *LVO* psc ph 300685
Gordon-Smith B M psc† 300685
Gwyn R T odc(US) psc† 300685
Hodges M G sq 300685
Holden C A psc† 300685
Holl R D sq 300685
Isaac D psc 300685
Kerr G psc† jsdc 300685
King-Harman A W psc† 300685
Kingaby A W G 300685
Launders N H *MSc MBIM* sq G(a) gw 300685
Longfield J C *MBE* sq ph 300685
Miller R A psc 300685
Moorby A L psc 300685
Nisbet C J *LLB* psc 300685
Preston B D S sq ph 300685
Rutter-Jerome M S psc† jsdc 300685
Scarisbrick A A psc 300685

Royal Regiment of Artillery — continued

Street N J psc(n)† 300685

Majors

D'Ambrumenil A Y ptsc 221261
Corrigan J B G(a) 140762
Butler R P H G(a) 030864
Cooke D L psc(a) 080265
Jordan J P G pl 080265
Reay D C ptsc gw 080265
Spencer P A H 080265
Williamson D F *MBE* sq 080265
Greig R M W *MMS* G(a) 010865
Whitcomb S A 010865
Savage J C 251065
Maidwell N W J ptsc G(a) 091165
Soffe T sq 060266
Thatcher G D B G 140366
Littlejohns B D 250466
Powell S B *MBIM* sq 270566
De Vivenot F X 310766
Whitmore S B *MBE* ptsc gw 310766
Macfarlane I P 051266
Fenech A D J G(a) 120267
Singer J C W G(y) 120267
Picton I R *MBE* G(a) 300667
Porter R J M psc† aic G 300667
Peile J H H psc 311267
Statham P R *MBIM* psc† G 311267
Brooks A J P *BSc* sq G(y) gw 300668
de Salis R J *BA* sq G(y) 300668
Eden J A *MBE* G(y) 300668
Hickie J *MBE* 300668
Hills W G sq G 300668
Lucas P J G 300668
Stewart I A *MCIT* sq G 300668
Bond L C *MBIM* sq ph pl 311268
Cookson E P T G(y) 311268
Haughton C J W 311268
Booth J A G tt 300669
Irven C N L *DipRMCS* sq G(a) gw 300669
Freeman J Le B 311269
Peel J A *MC* G(a) 110570
Aylward J C ph 300670
Dann K G F sq G(a) 300670
Flowers J E sq G 300670
Gillingham H J H sq G(a) 300670
Leaning J M C *FBIM MInstAM* psc 300670
Parry E L G(y) 300670
Price J N psc† 300670
Price J R sq 300670
Prior T M G 300670
Blunt J M C sq G 300671
Goatley G F *BSc* psc† gw 300671
Hebbert C M sq 300671
Munson T St J sq G(y) 300671
Nolan T *MBE* sq 300671
Sanders G sq tt 300671
Boulter H C sq 311271
Bush W P A psc (*A/Lt Col* 221185) 311271
Thomson R D S G 311271
Wilson A J psc† (*A/Lt Col* 310186) 311271
Girdlestone M O sq G 300672
Naesmyth of Posso R W 300672
Reed V B 300672
Sawrey-Cookson J H C 300672
Gard R M G 311272
Ransome Williams H B sq aic G (*A/Lt Col* 181085) 311272
Craigie A J *OBE* sq G(a) s (*A/Lt Col* 240284) 300673
Gaite A F E *MBE* sq 300673
Naughton P M J *BSc* sq 300673
Allison R W psc† 311273
Fleming J N sq G ph (*A/Lt Col* 060186) 311273
Hyland M T P M sq 311273
Sjoberg R sq G 311273
Jackson D A G(a) 300674
Lyons T M odc(FR) sq G 300674
Cameron R N sq 311274
d'Apice P A J sq G (*A/Lt Col* 150186) 311274
Stuart Nash C *BA* psc† 311274
Swann J C psc 311274
Whitworth D B D sq G(y) gw 311274
Young R B H sq 311274
Easterbrook W J sq G 300675
McLeod D N K sq ph 300675
Millard R J G 300675
Rowlandson M W M *BSc* psc† G 300675
Bowe A D G 311275
Boys R A *MBIM* psc† G(y) 311275
Brayshaw C R *MBE* psc† G 311275
Bryan K R sq G(a) 311275
Irven P C D sq 311275
McNee A S psc† G(y) 311275
Middleton G C sq 311275
Miskelly J B psc 311275
Mount A R Le-B P *BSc* sq 311275
Pitt J R M psc G 311275
Potts D H sq G 311275
Arney R W G(y) 300676
Brightman C J sq 300676
Carter E C D *MBE BSc* psc† (*A/Lt Col* 210186) 300676
Harvey A S sq 300676
Thatcher W R psc† 300676
Tucker P sq 300676
Watson M G psc† G 300676
Wright M C S sq 300676
Adams J sq aic G 311276
Clayton R S *BSc FBIM* psc(n)† 311276
George N sq 311276
Johnston W M *MBIM* sq 311276
McKeown R D psc† 311276
Meggy J sq ph (*A/Lt Col* 010486) 311276
Moffatt R H I *DipRMCS* sq G(a) gw 311276
Morley M H G 311276
Orr A J P sq 311276
Stewart R J M sq 311276
Bogie C F A sq 300677
Carter A E S *BA* sq 300677
Hardy M H *MBE* sq 300677
Hazlerigg A P J psc 300677
Hooton J C *BSc(Eng)* psc† 300677
Inness C H P G 300677
Miller C R osc(ID) sq 300677
Sulman P J G(a) 300677
Abela H C *MBIM* psc(IT) sq (*L/Lt Col* 081084) 311277
Barnes K J G 311277
Blessington P M T psc† G 311277
Clement F A B psc 311277
Hope P E A psc† ph 311277
Kersley Baker D R sq (*A/Lt Col* 060386) 311277
Allardice S S M A sq ph 300678
Buss N J sq G 300678
D'Alton A A M 300678
Eliot J H psc† 300678
Evans N F *BA MSc* dis sq G 300678
Grieve R V E ph 300678
Lloyd J H L *BA* psc G 300678
Lloyd-Jones P A aic 300678
Middleton R ph 300678
Pelly G M H sq aic 300678
Phillips J M *BA MBIM MInstAM* psc 300678
Shepherd M M 300678
Acland *Sir* Guy *Bt* psc 311278
Berry D R I psc 311278
Burt-Andrews R C psc ph 311278
Fielding R E sq 311278
Foster A F *MA* sq aic 311278
Gaillard M C de L sq 311278
Gillson R A *MSc* gw 311278
Harrington J E *CGIA* psc† 311278
Harris S P psc 311278
Hinton J P R sq 311278
Langford D E aic G 311278
McComas P M *BSc* sq 311278
Stoddart C sq 311278
Wheelwright B D *BA* psc† jsdc 311278
Anderson M H sq 300679
Baker A W G 300679
Carr S J S 300679
Crump P G 300679
Fowler T A M *MBIM MITD* sq gw G(gw) 300679
Gibbon F J *BA* psc jsdc 300679
Graham M J *BSc(Eng) MSc* sq gw 300679
Hall D J M sq aic G 300679
Lake A L *MSc MBCS* dis G(y) 300679
Macaulay N P H ph(cfs) ph(i) ph pl 300679
March F M H sq 300679
Muirhead A P 300679
Nash E J *MBIM MInstAM* psc 300679
Read P W C G 300679
Shahinian P A *BSc* psc† 300679
Tulloch J S M sq 300679
Webb R W G(gw) 300679
Rees V H G 131179
Afford N A sq 311279
Arthur D R 311279
Bleakley J A *BA* sq 311279
Clubley D G *BSc* psc† 311279
Creswell A J psc† G 311279
Deuchar A D psc† 311279
Dodgson G sq 311279
Fairman B J *MBE* sq 311279
Fallon M H G 311279
Glover J J psc 311279
Harrison R P sq 311279
Hatton R R G(a) 311279
Johnson A P *CGIA* psc† 311279
Kelly R V *BSc(Eng)* psc† (*A/Lt Col* 170286) 311279
Lang N G W *BA* sq 311279
Newell P J psc 311279
Rooke J L K sq 311279
Stevens S P B sq G(gw) 311279
Stevenson K A P psc† 311279
Thornton J L M *BSc* sq adp 311279
Williams R K G 311279
Workman D J *BA CGIA* psc† 311279
Wray C B ph 311279
Akhurst G R *MBE* G 300980
Aldous D P G 300980
Beaves H W 300980
Bennett J A 300980
Bennett R G M *BA* 300980
Bonney C P 300980
Burden R M G 300980
Carr N H G 300980
Carter M N *MBE* sq 300980
Cheesman N C G 300980
Christopherson R J G(y) 300980
Cooper M B 300980
Cottam P V *MA* psc 300980
Cowlishaw R G *MBIM* ph 300980
Currie A P N *BA* psc† 300980
Dore M I V *BSc* 300980

Dumas T R G 300980
Fitzgerald-Smith J de W *BSc* gw 300980
Gibbins J B G(a) 300980
Goodfellow M R sq 300980
Hamilton S F G 300980
Hobden D J ph 300980
Hodkinson G A sq G 300980
Hopkin S P M G(gw) 300980
Howard-Vyse J C psc(n) 300980
Hunt P H psc 300980
Lambe B C psc 300980
Lawson P 300980
Manton A R 300980
McIntosh L M sq 300980
McLaren D E G 300980
Morgan M J sq 300980
Neame N sq 300980
Parks C E 300980
Preece M D G *BSc(Eng) MSc* dis G 300980
Price K A *CGIA* psc† 300980
Rice A J 300980
Richards J *BSc(Eng) MSc* dis sq 300980
Rose P I G 300980
Scott-Hayward M D A 300980
Shaw-Brown R D *BA* psc 300980
Stewart I B 300980
Stokes T O G sq 300980
Stormonth R J G 300980
Thomas D M G 300980
Warburton J B W G(gw) 300980
Wilkinson J H G(gw) 300980
Wilson J D *BA* psc 300980
Winfield B C *BSc(Eng)* psc† 300980
Bloxwich J S psc 300981
Burgess D B 300981
Clayton R R H *MBE* 300981
Cole T D P 300981
Corbet Burcher M A *BA* psc(a) 300981
Deakin J A C *MSc* sq 300981
du Pre G M G 300981
Ewence M W sq G 300981
Gillett G M V *BSc(Eng)* psc† 300981
Happe E G psc† 300981
Hurst P J H G 300981
Kerr G L psc 300981
Marwood P H *BSc* psc† 300981
McKitrick R A S S G(y) 300981
Morris M D A ph 300981
Moulton D G G 300981
Myers P S C 300981
Oakley J H G 300981
Powrie I G C psc 300981
Quarrelle N G psc 300981
Radcliffe D E psc 300981
Raworth M R psc 300981
Self R A H G(gw) 300981
Sims D R M G(y) ph 300981
Smith A C psc† 300981
Smythe M psc† 300981
Stones W R G(y) 300981
Styles R L psc† 300981
West P R psc 300981
White R J *MSc* sq gw 300981
Wilkinson P R *MBE* psc† 300981
Wilton T J *MBE BSc* 300981
Bazzard J A C 300982
Brown D L gw 300982
Burdick M W 300982
Charlton-Weedy M A psc† 300982
Coats C M B psc† 300982
Cowdery N M 300982
Evans W G O G adp 300982
Felton M G G(y) 300982
Gray A J *BA* psc† 300982
Hunt P M G 300982
Hunter J A G psc(CAN) 300982
Kenyon C F R psc 300982
Kirke C M St G *MA CGIA* psc† 300982
Lang J D 300982
Lucas M A 300982
Lunn C D psc 300982
Marfleet A S G 300982
Molyneaux P C C psc(a)† 300982
Preedy R E *BSc* psc† 300982
Prentice K H N *BSc* psc† 300982
Ritchie D S psc† 300982
Shaw A M J 300982
Smith P H J psc(a)† 300982
Tar L C G 300982
Thomas S O psc† 300982
Tucker M C *BSc* psc† 300982
Villalard P C psc 300982
Wallace N psc† 300982
Williams P R psc(IT) 300982
Allen G D *QGM* psc(GE) 300983
Allinson C T *BSc* G(y) 300983
Ashton T C psc 300983
Bailey J B A *MBE BA* psc 300983
Barry P G psc† 300983
Brown J P M psc 300983
Cook W O psc† 300983
Dutton J R W psc† 300983
Fairley J A 300983
Forster M J D *BA* psc 300983
Fowler C P W 300983
Graham D *BSc(Eng) MSc* mvt 300983
Hawkins R W G 300983
Marsh K J 300983
McKechnie A M D 300983
Radice R J 300983
Ross J McL *BAcc* 300983
Sleap M K *MA* G(gw) 300983
Stiven N S psc(PAK)† 300983
Street M J G 300983
Townend W A H *BA* psc 300983
Viggers F R psc 300983
Williams P B psc† 300983
Arnold K D psc 300984
Bleasdale J D 300984
Blease D H A psc(AUS)† 300984
Bruce A T 300984
Campbell I D S psc 300984
Clarke T P psc† 300984
Cooke N D psc 300984
Ellis Jones E O G(gw) 300984
Faith A J psc 300984
Gillespie A E psc 300984
Hamilton R A *CGIA* psc(IND)† 300984
Johnson C D 300984
Johnson M 300984
Kazocins J *BA* psc 300984
Keattch D T psc 300984
Keeling J J psc(n)† 300984
Kelly K W 300984
King S H S *MSc* aic gw 300984
Knyvett A D *BA* psc† 300984
McCracken W A *MC* 300984
Pope M D M psc† 300984
Raley R M E 300984
Raley I D *BA* 300984
Ratcliffe N G D 300984
Reed S C *BA* psc 300984
Reynolds P W 300984
Richards D J *BA* psc 300984
Romberg C R *BA* psc 300984
Sanderson K S psc 300984
Vacher M J psc† 300984
Westlake-Toms J S G(a) 300984
Wills M J G(gw) 300984
Adderley J R 300985
Amberton D A S G 300985
Badham-Thornhill M L G 300985
Clark R C D G 300985
Cowgill D B *BSc* 300985
Dickey R C psc 300985
Dowdeswell I M *MSc* G 300985
Dutton R K G 300985
Frank A R psc† 300985
Gibbon J H psc† 300985
Gledhill S M *BA* psc 300985
Harding E J S 300985
Hawkes D M 300985
Hutchinson S C J psc† 300985
Inkster A D K *BA* 300985
James T D R *BSocSc(Hons)* psc 300985
Lewthwaite D W *BSc(Eng)* psc† 300985
Lynch P M *BSc ARCS* psc† 300985
Lyon D G psc† 300985
Manson M P *MA* psc† 300985
McIntosh C R G *BSc* 300985
McManners J H *MA FRGS* psc 300985
Moore C L 300985
Ritchie A S *BA* psc 300985
Russell G W G 300985
Simison J C *BCom* psc† 300985
Smith R J S *QGM* psc† 300985
Snowdon A J *MA* psc† 300985
Sparkes S *BA* 300985
Tippett G J 300985
Vere Nicoll I A 300985
Wilson C C *CGIA* 300985

Captains

d'Apice J N C 220476
Dawson J N 181276
Riddick M J *FRGS* 300777
Tedman C C 300777
Bone G D F *BSc(Eng)* psc† (*A/Maj* 240186) 010877
Taylor T H P *BA* 220778
Grant G A B 160179
Smith P J *BSc* 150279
Sinclair T J B *BA* psc† (*A/Maj* 201285) 080379
Haynes R J H 090379
Wadsworth G R 090379
Weldon M H De W psc† 090379
Mercer N H *BA* 100379
Austin C G *BSc* 050979
Farrow M J W 100979
Jammes R R (*A/Maj* 190685) 100979
Nicholls C J *BSc* 100979
Prior W G *CGIA* 100979
Pritchard D J 100979
Rouse R L G 100979
Wilson L R ph 100979
Young S A J 100979
Begbie R M 301279
Gower J R M 301279
Jackson N B 301279
Kelly P F 301279
Moor G 301279
Nicol W D 301279
Geary P J *BA* 120180
Down C J *BSc* 010280
Brown C C *LLB* 260480
Buchanan J C 100580
Foster N J 100580
Lane C F *BSc(Eng)* G 100580
Piper P G ph 100580
Sanderson S C psc (*A/Maj* 090186) 100580
Smart M J *BA* 100580
Pedder A V *BSc* 190580
Eggar R N M *BA* G 010880
Ash R F *BSc* 080880

Royal Regiment of Artillery – continued

Mehers S I *BA*
(*A/Maj* 291084) 040980
Angus P J *BSc(Eng)* 090980
Applegate R A D *BA(Hons)* 090980
Cameron A G H 090980
Fairclough C A 090980
Gibbins D A 090980
Griffith P M 090980
Ramsay P G 090980
Sweet T J 090980
Yiend S J *BA(Hons) MA*
(*A/Maj* 020186) 021080
Atwell P V *BSc(Eng)* 291280
Marment J H
(*A/Maj* 090784) 291280
Holtby D 070181
Lungmuss R P *BSc* 020481
Johnston A M A *BSc* 090481
Cook S K
(*A/Maj* 130585) 090581
Howes R G *BSc* 090581
Lemon M J A S J 090581
Baxter J R J *BA* 290681
Collett J A *BSc*
(*A/Maj* 140286) 010881
Lane C W S *BSc MA* 010881
Martin J T *BSc*
(*A/Maj* 070186) 010881
Sinclair I R *BA* 010881
Logan K S *BSc* ae 130881
Briggs J S *BSc* 180881
Bedford N A 080981
Berendt P R 080981
Horridge A G C *BSc* 080981
Lloyd S J A 080981
Nelson C J W *BSc* G(gw) 080981
Sishton P A *BSc*
(*A/Maj* 060186) 080981
Skillman D J
(*A/Maj* 230186) 080981
Smith P E ph 080981
Tate J R 080981
Watson J N E *BA*
(*A/Maj* 281085) 080981
Waddell G W C *BA* 100981
Howells D W *BSc* 201081
Reece M J 101181
Hile N F W *BSc* 121281
Upton S N *BSc* 251281
Brinton P J 281281
Brown-Hovelt A J A 281281
Cooke D J A 281281
Davies D A 281281
Drage B K 281281
Shaw W E 281281
Smith M S 281281
Stanley P K 281281
Turner S N 281281
Walters B D *BSc(Eng)* 281281
Pointet D A J *BA* 120182
Lonsdale I D *BA* 190182
Pountain M N *BA* 010282
Pugh G M *BA* 010282
Richards D P *BCom* 010282
Danby P J *BSc* 090282
Glover P A *BA* 300382
Mullarkey T A P *BA* 270482
Lyne-Pirkis C J A *BA* 080582
Stadward J N J 080582
Perriman S R *BA* 090782
Foster A J *BSc* 220782
Soar P C H *BSc(Hons)* 010882
Moore W H *BA* 240882
Burke P A *BSc* 290882
Dixon M S *BSc* 290882
Barnard A P *BA* 060982
Bate S C 060982
Bennett M J 060982
Budd A D H 060982
Dyer T J *BSc* 060982
Elbourne M R *BA(Hons)* 060982
Frend S W C 060982
Kilgour G 060982
Lee J T *BSc* 060982
Moss N J W *BSc* ph 060982
Potts D R *BA* 060982
Shaw D A H 060982
Sykes R M M 060982
Van Poeteren J S M G 060982
Williams M G 060982
Hill M A *BA* 280982
Hilton J C *BSc* 280982
McGilvray R J 141182
Mercer A G B 261182
Tomlinson P H *BA* 081282
Barrington-Brown C *MA* G 091282
Seed C J *BA* 221282
Purdy R W H *MA* 010283
Tough S G *BA* 010283
Boyes R M L 070283
Clissitt N A 070283
Miller K H 070283
Tadier C W 070283
Vye M A 070283
Wheeler-Mallows K J 070283
Fox P A *BA* G 110283
Philpott N B *BSc*
(*A/Maj* 161285) 150283
Young G A *MA* psc
(*A/Maj* 201285) 150283
Lane P R L *BSc* 050383
Nash T G(gw) 300483
Borland J G 110683
Lincoln-Jones C 110683
Potter J P F 110683
White A J *BSc(Eng)* 110683
Spender H S T 190683
Waring M E 210683
Adams D C B *BSc* 150883
Park R J J *BA* 050983
Russell P A *BSc* 050983
Guest T J *BSc* 130983
Brake T J *BD* 031083
Wikeley J P *BA* 051083
Astbury A 081083
Best N C *BSc* 081083
Bower J D 081083
Challes D N 081083
Houghton M A 081083
Newbury D G 081083
Plummer C J *BSc* 081083
Potter J A H 081083
Pye A N *BSc(Eng)* 081083
Riddlestone S W 081083
Royall T G 081083
Sharp T A ph 081083
Tucker P W *BSc* 081083
Barrons R L *BA MA(Cantab&Oxon)*
171183
Grew A L *BA* 010284
Lawford H R *BA* 010284
Duncan P A 060284
Knightley C A G 060284
Leeming C F 060284
Liddicoat M R H 060284
Riall R A H G 060284
Barnard T S *BA* 050384
Stock C B W *BSc* 200384
Thomas D H *BA* 180484
McFadden S J R 290484
Beeson R A 100684
Clark C R 100684
Lawson D A L 100684
Royal M J 100684
Smith K M 100684
Wardall R C 100684
Rowe D H A *BA* 200684
Godfrey S R 120884
Ross M C *BA* 220984
Crosby R I ph 081084
Forsyth W D S 081084
Gregory A R *BA* 081084
Griffiths I D G 081084
Groom A J *BSc* 081084
Hargreaves W 081084
Jolly R I 081084
Marshall P D J *BSc* 081084
Morris T H 081084
Sharp J G(gw) 081084
Stone R Q J 081084
James S G *BSc(Eng)* 241084
Minshall M 221184
Holdom G J L *BSc MHCIMA*
010285
Milligan M A L *BA* 010285
Bayless I J 050285
Burch N J 050285
Cox S J 050285
Crowe C P A 050285
Davies S P 050285
Francis D R K *BA* 050285
Fraser I R G G(a) 050285
Harvey K M 050285
Mears A J 050285
Musgrove C J *BSc* 050285
Williamson K P *BSc* 050285
Wilson T G 010385
Vincent M A F *BSc* 030385
Gwizdala J P A *BA* 020485
Walsh C N P *BSc* 050685
Archer B B 090685
Bennion M J 090685
Kidwell T G 090685
MacDonald I R 090685
Templeton G K 180685
Cannon T J B *BSc* 010885
Howard M R J *BA* 010885
McKechnie J E 180885
Brundle C 071085
Butt G L 071085
Caiger J G 071085
Down G M 071085
Heath P B 071085
Jackson R S 071085
Jones D B *BScTech* 071085
Kay C d'O MacM 071085
Marjot T *BSc* 071085
Murphy J M 071085
Quaile M H K 071085
Robson R W 071085
Waddell A O M 071085
Winchester R A 071085
Camp T J *MM* 060186
Bates P N 040286
Carter M G J 040286
Cogan P J 040286
Crawshay R C *BSc* 040286
Grant T J M 210286
Cook T K A *BSocSc* 050386

Lieutenants

Berragan G W
(*A/Capt* 041185) 081281
Lacey M G 081281
Taylor K M 081281
Purdy A J *BSc(Eng)* 010282
Wakefield R J *BSc* 020382
Abraham K D *MA*
(*A/Capt* 130186) 120482
Drage J W *BSc* 120482
Eeles N H *BSc* 120482
Kingdon W J F *BA* 120482
Polden A J
(*A/Capt* 060186) 120482
Price T J E
(*A/Capt* 070685) 120482
Stone J P F 120482
Beazley N D J 090882
Calascione J P B 090882

Calderwood C 090882
Lang C P 090882
Pullman A C (*A/Capt* 070685) 090882
Taverner A I (*A/Capt* 010385) 090882
Cameron A H M 131282
Redmond M G 131282
Brooks K M T 110483
Bryson R N *BA* 110483
Caldwell R B 110483
Halliday S E *BSc* 110483
Lipscombe N J (*A/Capt* 130885) 110483
Mackenzie P J 110483
Mileham P C E *BA* 110483
Mohan S T 110483
O'Gorman S J *BA* 110483
Payne B W *BSc* 110483
Southworth J *BSc* 110483
Stratton J B W *BSc* 110483
Telford A R T 110483
Wolsey S P 110483
Wright P H D *BA* (*A/Capt* 060186) 110483
Field A J 080883
Le Gresley E M 080883
Mason S E 080883
Rodgers S P *BSc* 080883
Waller A J *BA* 080883
Caton L I 131083
Weighill R P M (*A/Capt* 060186) 121283
Bermingham D J *LLB* 090484
Cauchi J P *BA* 090484
Cullen D M 090484
Hamer-Philip A J *BA* 090484
Higham C D *BSc* 090484
Masters G A R 090484
Moss J J *BA* 090484
Warren R P 090484
Baker R *BA* 070884
Edwards T C 070884
Jones A M 070884
Lowles D J 070884
Muntz S G A (*A/Capt* 071085) 070884
Tacon P J *BA* 070884
Bradley C D 111284
Heathcote C J 111284
Ingham C R 111284
Leyden L E 111284
Coker T M 090485
Grace W A 090485
Harrington D R 090485
Harrison I G 090485
Timbers S R 060885
Weston C P A 060885
Bolton R B 101285
Hudson D J 101285
O'Brien M T 101285
Shakespeare P H 101285
Berryman M 070486
Harden T P 070486
Hickie P L 070486
Kernohan D A 070486
Steele J D 070486

2nd Lieutenants

††Cameron N W *BSc(Hons)* 030982
††Campbell R W G *BA(Hons)* 030982
††Coulcher N B *BA(Hons)* 030982
††Nugee R E *BA(Hons)* 030982
††Thompson P R C *BA(Hons)* 030982
††Lockhart A W J *LLB(Hons)* 061082
††Ambrose G A *BA(Hons)* 020983
††Jones D C H 020983
††Page S F J 020983
Chambers C J 040884
Tilley P H 040884
††Lee R M 230984
††Pughe R N I 230984
††Stremes J T 230984
††Carr R A 081084
Hammond D 081284
Hibbert N S 081284
Ingram P H 081284
Bryant J D 130485
Butcher C S 130485
Connell W J G 130485
Cooper B P R 130485
Robins D J 130485
Belcourt P L 100885
Hodgson I B 100885
Marshall N 100885
Walker D J W 100885
†Abberton J M *BSc(Hons)* 060985
†Badman S J G *BSc(Hons)* 060985
†Farndale R M *BA(Hons)* 060985
†Fox D P *BA(Hons)* 060985
†Hambleton R J M *BSc(Hons)* 060985
†Luck D W *BA* 060985
†O'Brien R *BA(Hons)* 060985
†Ruddock-West W G 060985
††Bailie I A 240985
††Woodward-Carlton D 240985
††Young A A M 240985
††Weir R A M 031085
Barber J G M 141285
Gamble M J 141285
Humphrey S L 141285
Robinson S J 141285
Scorey N S 141285
Vosper-Brown G 141285

Staff Quartermasters

Bender D J 030671, *Lt Col* 311280
Smith D 170574, *Lt Col* 171285

Quartermasters

Clarke M J 121272, *Lt Col* 020285
Taylor R C *MBE* 121272, *Lt Col* 220682
Cannon J A *MBE* 230373, *Lt Col* 010784
Beale R J L 240674, *Lt Col* 130386
Logie A 170774, *Lt Col* 150486
Charge G J *MBIM MASMC* 190774, *Maj* 070881
Simpson T 220774, *Lt Col* 180885
Hood A R 010175, *Maj* 140582
Owens F 210775, *Maj* 210683
Allan J 011075, *Maj* 011083
Macdonald W J *MBIM* 290376, *Maj* 070881
Baker R G 240576, *Maj* 101078
Solly K R 240576, *Maj* 040879
Lewis P *MBE* 250976, *Maj* 250984
Winchester N W *MBIM MASMC* 151076, *Maj* 161078
Gray J D 221176, *Maj* 060882
Moore K C 210177, *Maj* 210185
Johnston A F 160577, *Maj* 010479
Steele J *MBE* 190577, *Maj* 190585
Head M S 230577, *Lt Col* 210885
Green J R 220977, *Maj* 220985
Scott P H 140278, *Maj* 040879
Langford M 290378, *Maj* 290386
Collins G H 190379, *Maj* 010479
Moore M R 190379, *Maj* 020885
Munro D R B *MBE* 190379, *Maj* 010479
Cullingford A W 110679, *Maj* 050883
Boothroyd R *Capt* 210679
Fryatt G A *Capt* 210679
Chaytors A E *MISM* *Capt* 171279
Simpson S J *Capt* 230180
Blackmore M R *BEM MISM MASMC* *Capt* 100380
Clarkson A H *Maj* 100380
Feeney E J O'R 090680, *Maj* 020885
Wood H *MBE* *Capt* 090680
Fixter L J J *Capt* 300680
Thomas D E *Capt* 031180
Hollingsworth J A *MBIM* *Maj* 140181
McSherry T E *MBE* *Capt* 120281
Spedding J R 160281, *Maj* 020885
Smith L *MBE* *Capt* 030681
Jenkins L O *Capt* 010781
Ennis L J *Capt* 210781
Edwards B W *Capt* 161081
Newell R W *MBE* *Capt* 231081
Dare L *Capt* 251181
McCudden R A *Capt* 041281
Covell R A *Capt* 010482
Prewer A L R *Maj* 010482
Dalrymple D J *Capt* 030882
Hamilton J D *Capt* 050882
Jeffries P G *MBE* *Maj* 060882
Waterland G *Capt* 291182
Young M J C *Capt* 291182
Casey D E *Capt* 010483
Gent D C *Capt* 010483
Harmes R F *Capt* 010483
Mallinder A *MBE* *Capt* 010483
Mannings K M *MBE* *Capt* 010483
McLachlan I H *Capt* 010483
Miles J F *Capt* 010483
Kirchel W A *Capt* 010683
Thomas R *MBE* *Capt* 080683
Friedman B *Capt* 070983
Armitage B 120983, *Maj* 020885
Abrahart F J *Capt* 010484
Hughes T R J *MBE* 010484, *Maj* 020885
Johns K I *Capt* 010484
Timlin D *Capt* 010484
Fields C L *Capt* 010684
Hampson M J *Capt* 110684
Roynon A *Maj* 030884
Redding B M W *Capt* 060884

Royal Regiment of Artillery — continued

Falzon J F *BEM* *Capt* 031184
Carr S *Capt* 010485
Daly J J *Capt* 010485
McPherson I *Capt* 010485
Taylor J A B *Capt* 010485
Toyer R F *Capt* 010485
Verdon P J *MInstAM*
Capt 010485
Whitham M A *Capt* 010485
Grant D R *Capt* 260785
Hoey H D *Capt* 260785
Pritchard R *Capt* 011185

Technical Instructors in Gunnery

Cook R 140573
Lt Col 170284
Nicolls J C 220774
Maj 220782
Pringle D H J 250774
Maj 010379
Brisby G B 251174
Lt Col 200784
Rawson D G 281175
Maj 281183
McLaughlin E 010476
Maj 080880
Hennessey K 020876
Maj 020884
Lodge D J N 030177
Maj 030185
Coleman R C 100177
Maj 030884
Holden K A 120478
Maj 120486
Double M M *Capt* 310778
Fuller A 310778
Maj 050883
Smith H 310778
Maj 080880
Tandy B W *Capt* 310778
Clegg C G *Capt* 090179
Russell J W *Capt* 211179
Collis B W *Capt* 050580
Jackson A L *Capt* 060580
Guille R J *MBE* *Capt* 211080
Claridge D A *Capt* 290781
Johnson E *Capt* 290781
Reid R J *Capt* 290781
Ruddleston F I *Capt* 290781
Wilson J F *Capt* 290781
Weir J M *Capt* 150881
Comben M *Capt* 040382
Coombs M J *Capt* 010482
Cooper A G 010482
Maj 030884
Aylmer M R *Capt* 010483
Powell J *Capt* 010483
Robertson H B *Capt* 010483
Brownhill N H *Capt* 080683
Macallister N J *Capt* 010484
Price G C *Capt* 010484
Cobley B W *Capt* 260984
Murphy W P *Capt* 010485
Porter A J *Capt* 010485
Thorington F D *MISM AMITD*
Capt 010485
Webb L A *Capt* 010485
Wetherell B L *Capt* 010485

Technical Instructors in Gunnery (AD)

Pinder G A 260572
Maj 251277
Bowker P R 300974
Lt Col 220685
Concannon B P *MBE* 011075
Maj 011083

Butler D 310377
Maj 310385
Deane P C 090178
Maj 090186
Feek A J 211179
Maj 090186
Dyer G F *Capt* 060581
Parfitt J W *Capt* 020482
McMillan B P A *Capt* 010483
Eaton I S R *Capt* 010484
Boulton P *Capt* 010485

Directors of Music

Patch S W *LRAM ARCM* psm
280970
Lt Col 040782
Renton F A *ARCM* psm
Capt 080578
Garrity C R C *LTCL* psm
Capt 010582

Special Regular Officers

Majors

Bryson E R 311277
Munden J F G 311278
Middleton J D G 311279
Morley T C G 300980
Wilkinson R J G(gw) 300980
Bridges E A 300981
Mallett A R *MBIM* 300981
Delaney R W 300983
Harnden M B 300983
Faull M R 300984
Hoyle S C 300984
Thompson A A 300984
Cuthbertson I R 300985
Dunn B C 300985
Leach M J 300985
Robertson D McN *MInstAM MISM*
300985
Tindall M G 300985
Turner T D R *BSc* G(a) 300985
Wilson C M N 300985

Captains

McKenna R G
(*A/Maj* 250386) 140972
Wild S R 131178
Nicol J *BSc* 150279
Jenkins R A 090379
Lamb P A 301279
Dillon-Lee M J 090980
Makeig-Jones R J ph 090581
Robinson C N 110382
Bounsall R H *BSc(Eng)* 080582
Baldwin F W K *BSc* 130582
Surgenor P J 300782
Leigh E L
(*A/Maj* 101284) 200882
Ross C A M 060982
Drummond H R 170982
Hothersall P
(*A/Maj* 221283) 170982
Blenkinsopp P G 080483
Swinton K G 060583
Wardrop A D 110683
Allmond D A 081083
Seabrook K S 121283
Joslyn M A 020184
Hermon R J S 060284
Stovell R J *BSc(Eng) AIB* 060284
Smith C S G 220684
Abbott J C 081084
Holland C G 081084
Taylor D C 141184

Greenwood D J 050285
McIntosh J K 050285
Silverlock D R 020685
Baynham S A 210685
Gould C H 071085
Powrie R D G 071085
Smith N A 071085
Gordon M C R 040286

Lieutenants

Relph M D
(*A/Capt* 130685) 150382
Bray J C J 120482
Sparks G P
(*A/Capt* 020186) 120482
Wellesley A E ph 120482
Greenhalgh M R ph 090882
Lukes A W 120383
Neate M C 210683
Miller T L 070884
Neale A D 240984
Taxis C L 120185
Calder-Smith J D 090485
Lingard S D 060885
Carmichael S R 171085
Brealey B 101285

2nd Lieutenants

Davies S H L 040884
Hobbs R J D 040884
Shapland G D 141285
Stokes T 141285
Yates T R 141285

Short Service Officers

Captains

Bailey M V *MInstAM* 150880
McHugh A J *BSc DIS* 290981
Tunney P J
(*A/Maj* 031284) 200382
Welsh D A 300782
Slinger N J B *BA* 280982
Morris A D *LLB* 120283
Hacon A N *BA* 050383
Rollinson A 060583
Bond J R 290783
Littler J 290783
Healey M R *BA MBIM* 250883
Eames P L 080184
Booth J 020484
Penfold N 130584
Tierney K A S 050884
Roper D G
(*A/Maj* 290885) 160984
Bailey J 130185
Robinson W K M *MA* 020485
Forteath J M *QGM* 080685
Shepherd A J *BA* 030985
Robertson H 070985
Cawley N R L 071085
Jones R L *BA* 071085
Griffiths P A P 241185
Mahan D 241185
Tucker W M *BSc* 131285
Barker C A H *BA* 220186
Campbell P M *BSc* 040286
Hinton G P P G *BSc* 040286
Jacobs C M *BA* 040286
Tinsley I *BA* 040286
Walton M R 040286
Isaacs M L *BA* 100286
Bowater I G 150286
Clarke W G 150286
Tarling C J 150286
Utteridge P W 150286

McMeekin J 130486

Lieutenants

Banham M P (*A/Capt* 110985) 040881
Walkin R P (*A/Capt* 290584) 161181
Collins P R (*A/Capt* 040684) 011281
Newman G R 041281
Chaldecott R J 081281
Fleetwood T M A 081281
Potter C M (*A/Capt* 121085) 081281
Ravenhill G W (*A/Capt* 110784) 110182
Naylor D E *MBE* (*A/Capt* 240884) 240282
Fox R J (*A/Capt* 210984) 210382
Banner G T E *BSc* 120482
Everett T P *BSc(Econ)* 120482
Gordon N V *BA* 120482
Haly R S O'G *BA* 120482
Muir G J (*A/Capt* 170286) 120482
Reed D M H *BSc* (*A/Capt* 010186) 120482
Smith C S H 120482
Webster I *BSc(Econ)* 120482
Williams D G *BSc(SocSc)* 120482
Nation M L (*A/Capt* 240186) 190482
Tilson D P (*A/Capt* 020185) 190482
Green J A (*A/Capt* 061284) 040682
Renshaw A M (*A/Capt* 041284) 040682
Dawes I M G (*A/Capt* 051285) 060682
Ashmore N D *BA* 090882
Coups J M 090882
Fowle S R 090882
Hardisty P J *BA* 090882
Jefferson N T *BSc* 090882
Smith M D *BA* 090882
Willatt J M G *BA* 090882
Worsley P S P (*A/Capt* 181084) 090882
Young P A (*A/Capt* 150585) 050982
Crew E (*A/Capt* 050386) 071182
Lines G D 071182
Martin D (*A/Capt* 011085) 071182
Tarling P A (*A/Capt* 130585) 071182
Tasker W J (*A/Capt* 270585) 071182
McCreadie D S 131182
Beard N J W (*A/Capt* 300386) 131282
Ingle J F 131282
Martin T M ph (*A/Capt* 031285) 131282
Thornton-Smith W J 131282
Boddy R A (*A/Capt* 080785) 020183
Churchley C J (*A/Capt* 111185) 020183
Cockburn T O 020183
Hallam C J (*A/Capt* 080785) 020183
Hills N J 020183
Skerry G M (*A/Capt* 090785) 020183
Wilson A D (*A/Capt* 210985) 020183
Le Blanc D A J 180183
Gray S J 210283
Ferguson D I 210383
Merritt D C *MBIM FIMS FIDE* (*A/Capt* 201185) 240383
Walsh G M (*A/Capt* 300985) 240383
Winch B (*A/Capt* 300985) 240383
Alderson A *BSc* 110483
Bennett P R *BA* 110483
Boddy J W O *BSc* 110483
Clegg S P 110483
Evans D R *BSc* 110483
Herbert J J *BA* 110483
Rafferty A C *BSc* 110483
Robinson S C *MA* 110483
Sprott M G *BSc(Econ)* 110483
Sullivan R A D *BA* 110483
Syrett N S *BA* 110483
Thorne P *BSc* 110483
Turner M *BA* 110483
Winchcombe J P *BA* 110483
May S J 300483
Auckland-Lewis J C *BA* 080883
Edwards T J H 080883
Iffland D M 080883
Napier G R *BA* 080883
Rudd I R J *BSc(Econ)* 080883
Stuart A R *BA* 080883
Battershill B (*A/Capt* 130386) 040983
Brown G R 040983
Cave R 040983
Day A R 040983
Stothard C A (*A/Capt* 050386) 040983
Ward P N (*A/Capt* 100386) 040983
Wheeler R D 291083
Shanks A E C 261183
Valenzia M D 121283
Ginder J C 120184
Anderson-Brown D J *BSc* 090484
Campbell J C *BSc* 090484
Copland I D *BA* 090484
Dare R A 090484
Gillece C D *BEng* 090484
Green G T D *BA* 090484
Hartgill D C *BSc* 090484
Makin N S *BSc* 090484
Mason C J 090484
McCardle J A *BSc* 090484
Paine M C *BSc* 090484
Reed P E *BA* 090484
Robinson P D 090484
Sayer C P *BSc* 090484
Smith A M 090484
Swinhoe-Standen R A P *BSc* 090484
Tyson E J *BA* 090484
Whetstone R A S *BA* 090484
Wood T M *BA* 090484
Beaumont S J 070884
Coyle N S *BSc* 070884
Freeman C S D *BA* 070884
Gibson T R S 070884
Hurlock J 070884
Kerr H R *BSc* 070884
Markham J *BSocSc* 070884
Moore P A J 070884
Pocock M C 070884
Smart T R *BA* 070884
Ronaldson D A A 030984
Wordsworth T N J 071084
Fitzgerald N O 111284
Holley D B 111284
Ross J T T 111284
Sims J C 111284
Holmes D W 090485
Jennings B D T 090485
Blair R I 070785
Ellett S 060885
Grace E C 060885
†Compton J R E *BSc(Hons)* 060985
Ball A E 101285
Neve N J F 070486
Roberts P M L 070486

2nd Lieutenants

Bell I R 040884
Collins S M C 040884
Crane J S H 040884
Jenkins B W 040884
Morris R W 040884
Mystkowski G M F 040884
Poulter P A 040884
Welsh A C 040884
Woolfe T M 040884
Brown M E 081284
Metcalfe R S 081284
Roberts M 081284
Wells G M 081284
Campbell A M 130485
Eve R R T 130485
Ganner R B 130485
Hutchinson A S L 130485
Wright T S 130485
Adams O J 100885
Clamp P J 100885
Harvey K K 100885
Inglesant R J 100885
Jarvis A G 100885
Kerry-Williams C P 100885
Mackay D J 100885
Ryan D F 100885
†Austin S P *BSc(Hons)* 060985
†Fox M A *BA(Hons)* 060985
†Nel A G G *BSc(Hons)* 060985
†Pallis T M *BSc(Hons)* 060985
†Servaes M J P *BA(Hons)* 060985
†Shellard R J S *BA(Hons)* 060985
†Staveley R *BA(Hons)* 060985
†Steel R J *BSc* 060985
†Watkins P R *BA BA(Hons) MSc* 060985
†West S R *BSc* 060985
†Wombwell D A *BSc* 060985
†Baker-Monteys S P *BA* 060186
†Bartlett A T *BSc* 060186
†Grey R N A *BA(Hons)* 060186
†Nightingale R J *BA* 060186
†Sibbald J *BSc* 060186
†Wastie C P J *BSc* 060186

CORPS OF ROYAL ENGINEERS

The Royal Arms and Supporters — *"Ubique"* and *"Quo Fas et Gloria ducunt"*

Regimental March

Quick March..Wings

Agents..Lloyds Bank PLC Cox's & King's Branch

Corps Headquarters.............................Brompton Barracks, Chatham, Kent,(*Tel No: Medway* 0634-44555)

Alliances

The Canadian Armed Forces ....Military Engineering Branch
Australian Military Forces....................The Corps of Royal Australian Engineers
New Zealand Army...............................The Corps of Royal New Zealand Engineers
Indian Army..Indian Engineers
Pakistan Army ....Pakistan Engineers
Sri Lanka Army ....The Sri Lanka Engineers
Malaysian Armed Forces......................Malaysian Engineer Corps
Zambian Army.......................................Zambia Corps of Engineers
Fiji ....The Corps of Fiji Engineers

Affiliated Regiment

The Queen's Gurkha Engineers

Colonel in Chief...................................THE QUEEN

Chief Royal Engineer...........................Gen *Sir* Hugh Beach *GBE KCB MC* ret pay
(*Vice Lord Lieutenant Greater London* 211282

Colonels Commandant.........................Gen *Sir* Hugh Beach *GBE KCB MC* ret pay
(*Vice Lord Lieutenant Greater London* 211277
Gen *Sir* George Cooper *GCB KCB MC* ret pay 200880
Maj Gen C P Campbell *CBE* ret pay..........................181081
Maj Gen E W Barton *CB MBE* ret pay 020782
Maj Gen C B Pollard ret pay 020782
Maj Gen H E M L Garrett *CBE* ret pay 141182
Maj Gen C J Popham *CB* ret pay 211282
Maj Gen G B Sinclair *CB CBE* ret pay 250383
*Maj Gen J P Groom *CB CBE* ret pay..........................020783
Maj Gen W N J Withall *CB* ret pay 150484
Maj Gen M Matthews *CB* ret pay..........................121185
Maj Gen C R Grey *CBE* ret pay..........................010486

Brigadiers

Woodburn C W *MA* jssc psc† psc ptsc 300677
Beckett C W *BSc(Eng)* psc† tt 300679
Lloyd A C D *MA* nadc psc† 300679
Swinburn D H A *MA* rcds jssc psc 300679
Bevan F G *BA MINucE* rcds psc† 300680
Willmott E G *OBE MA* rcds psc† (*A/Maj Gen* 120486) 300680
Busk L F H *BSc(Eng)* rcds psc† 300681
Fawcus G B *MA* psc† (*A/Maj Gen* 280486) 300681
Peck R L *BSc(Eng)* rcds psc† 300681
Thompson N H *BSc(Eng) CEng FICE* rcds psc† psc C 300682
Wilks J B *CBE ADC* jssc psc 300682
Barr J A J P psc† 300683
Carlier A N *OBE BSc(Eng)* psc(n)† 300683
Pulverman T R M *ADC BSc(Eng) FIPlantE MBIM* ndc odc(US) psc 300684
Sneyd T S ndc psc 300684
Sugden F G *OBE* rcds psc 300684
White N M *BSc(Eng)* odc(AUST) psc 300684
Woodrow H C *BSc(Eng) ARICS* SVY(pg) SVY 300684
Blagden P M *CBE BSc(Eng)* ndc psc† 300685
Brownson D *CBE* ndc psc† 300685
Edwards J H *BSc* psc ptsc 300685
Fagan P F *MBE MSc FRICS FBIM* SVY(pg) SVY 300685
Field G W *OBE* psc† 300685
Grove D A *OBE BSc* psc† 300685
Symons J S psc 300685

Colonels

Morrison P E *MBE* psc 300677
Drake J N S *BSc(Eng) CEng MICE MIE(AUST)* C 300679
Whitehorn A psc 300679
Addison W M R *BSc MLitt* df psc† (*A/Brig* 160186) 300680
Fraser S E G *OBE ARICS* SVY(gy) SVY 300680
Tuck F M K *MA* psc† psc ptsc 300680
Black A E N *OBE FBIM* psc† osc(GH) 300681
Chater J K *BSc(Eng)* psc† 300681
Clowes E R *BA* SVY 300681
Kitching J E *MBIM* psc† 300681
Whitten D C *BSc(Eng)* psc† pl(cfs) ph pl 300681
Barker E H *CBE MA* psc† 300682
Blashford-Snell J N *MBE* psc† 300682
Bown B O *MBE MICE* C 300682
Dennison W T *OBE* ndc sq 300682
Stephens M J F *BA CEng MICE* psc C 300682
Williams D W *OBE BSc(Econ) CEng MICE* psc† psc ptsc 300682
Daly B P *BSc(Eng) MICE* sq C 300683
Dobbie W I C *BSc(Eng)* psc† psc(a) 300683
Hewish G A *MBE* psc† osc(NIG) 300683
Luxton R M R ndc sq 300683
Speight J *OBE* ndc nadc psc† 300683
Williams J W *BSc* sq SVY 300683
Campbell G B L *BSc(Eng)* ocds(US) psc(n)† psc 300684
Codd J F *BSc(Eng)* SVY(gy) SVY 300684
Corsellis D H G *BSc(Eng)* ndc psc† 300684
Garnett R D *MBE* psc† 300684
Grainger F G E *BA FBIM* ndc psc(a)† ph 300684
Hill P M *OBE BSc(Eng) CEng MICE* ndc sq C 300684
Hyde G psc† 300684
Johnson D A *MA MICE FBIM* C 300684
Matthews A E H *FRICS* SVY(pg) SVY 300684
Sheppard P J *OBE BSc(Eng)* psc† 300684

*Representative Colonel Commandant for 1986

Stancombe R M *BSc(Eng) MICE MBIM* ndc sq C 300684
Stott M W *MA* psc† 300684
Elder J P *MAppSci* SVY SVY(cg) 300685
Grant S C *MA* psc† 300685
Oliver R A *OBE* psc† 300685
Owens G R psc 300685
Payne M J *MA* psc† 300685
Sanderson B J *OBE* sq 300685
Thompson J J J *MBE* odc(US) psc 300685
Wood R *MA MSc FRICS* SVY(pg) SVY 300685

Lieutenant Colonels

Rawlins A G (SL) *OBE MBIM* ptsc 300672
Marks W W (SL) *BA* odc(AUST) sq 300673
Pritchett C B (SL) *MA* psc† ptsc 300673
Wilson J P M (SL) *MBIM* sq tt 300673
Charles N H (SL) SVY(pr) SVY 300674
French J (SL) ptsc 300674
Eagle R W M (SL) *MBE MICE* C 300675
Licence B E (SL) *MBIM* EM 300675
Nias J R (SL) *FRGS MIPlantE* sq pl 300675
Graham I G (SL) sq 300676
Kennedy L J (SL) *MBE BSc(Eng) MICE* C 300676
Adams M J E (SL) *MBE MA MIMechE MIEE* EM 300677
Bailey G D *MIPlantE MIHT* psc osc(NIG) 300677
Crawshaw W M *OBE* psc† (*A/Col* 011085) 300677
Hayes J P R (SL) psc 300677
Stokes J T (SL) *CEng MICE MBIM* C 300677
Watson M R (SL) *BSc(Eng)* psc† 300677
Weston G V J (SL) psc† 300677
Aylmore R H *MA* ndc sq 300678
Barker J L *MA MICE* sq C 300678
Burnet J W (SL) *BA MINucE MBIM* psc† 300678
de Planta de Wildenberg C M G (SL) *LVO MBIM AIL* odc(FR) osc(FR) sq 300678
Fisher F T *BEng MSc CEng MICE MIPlantE* ndc psc (*A/Col* 120984) 300678
Hill G M (SL) sq 300678
Simpson J P W psc† 300678
Worthington P J *BSc(Eng)* ndc psc† 300678
Croft J A N SVY(pr) SVY 300679
Gilbert S R psc† (*A/Col* 081185) 300679
Ievers P R *BA* ndc psc† aic (*A/Col* 020985) 300679
McKeown J H *MPhil* psc psc(a) 300679
Nolan M A *BSc* SVY 300679
Vialou Clark H E *BSc(Eng) MICE* C 300679
Cooper M R *BA* psc† 300680
Eggleston W C *BSc(Eng)* psc† 300680
Gaffney M psc† (*A/Col* 011185) 300680
Hook K A *MA* psc† 300680
Houlton A E psc (*A/Col* 270186) 300680
Howgate A ndc psc† ph 300680
Jardine S (SL) sq TN 300680
Jarvis C J F *BSc(Eng)* psc 300680
Jolley A D *MBE BSc(Eng)* odc(US) psc† 300680
Kerr H H *OBE BSc(Eng)* sq (*A/Col* 210386) 300680
Lucken J M *BSc(Eng)* psc† (*A/Col* 251085) 300680
Milsom R J *OBE* ndc sq 300680
Mounde M B *MBE* psc 300680
Nowers J E *BSc(Econ)* psc† aic (*A/Col* 030286) 300680
Osborn R G (SL) *BSc(Eng) CEng MICE* C (*L/Col* 240186) 300680
Shackell W E *MA* psc(n)† osc(NIG) 300680
Verschoyle D *BA MICE* psc C 300680
Wareham C D *FBIM* psc(a) 300680
Webb M C S (SL) *BSc(Eng) MICE MIHT* C 300680
Adamson D M *MA DipHM CEng MICE MIEE* psc(a) C 300681
Berchem I R *BSc(Eng)* psc 300681
Cooper J A ndc osc(NIG) sq 300681
Cowie A *BSc(Eng)* psc† 300681
Day M W H *MA MICE* ndc psc C 300681
Fawcus R K *BSc(Eng)* psc† 300681
Galloway C C *BSc(Eng)* odc(US) psc† 300681
Gibson R J *MA MSc ARICS FBIM* SVY(pg) SVY 300681
Griffith P D *BSc(Eng)* psc† 300681
Lacey J N H psc 300681
Lipscomb M H *MA* psc† 300681
Pigott A D *OBE MA* psc 300681
Ray J W sq 300681
Read J A C SVY 300681
Rycroft D G F (SL) *MIPM MBIM* sq 300681
Sandiford A J *BSc(Eng)* psc 300681
Williams R J B sq 300681
Bambury P J psc† 300682
Bickford J M *BSc(Eng) CEng MICE* sq C 300682
Bradbury R A *BSc(Eng)* psc C 300682
Clements D F psc 300682
Cook P W odc(US) psc† 300682
Cox B F *BSc(Eng) MICE* psc C I 300682
Daniell F A F ndc sq 300682
Hume R J psc† 300682
Kruger D F sq 300682
Meston R J C *BSc CEng MICE* C 300682
Reive R I *OBE* ndc sq tt 300682
Shellswell M A *MA* SVY SVY(cg) 300682
Smales R N C *BSc(Eng)* psc† aic 300682
Streeten J D R *MA* psc psc(a) EM 300682
Taylor J C M *MBE BA* sq 300682
Wright T R psc ph 300682
Barber J G ndc psc 300683
Bates C P R *BSc(Eng)* psc† 300683
Chesshyre W J *MA* ndc psc 300683
Hawkins J N *BA CEng MICE* sq C 300683
Hill P M R *MA* psc C 300683
Hoon A J *BSc(Eng) FBIM MIOP* SVY 300683
Johnson J F *BSc(Eng) MICE* psc C 300683
Mackie P J *MBE BSc(Eng)* psc† 300683
Mundy R F *MIPlantE MIHVE* sq 300683
Reed-Screen A J *OBE BSc* psc† 300683
Stuart J N B *BSc(Eng)* psc† 300683
Thorp J A *MBE MA* psc† 300683
Williams P J *BSc(Eng)* psc† osc(NIG) aic 300683
Wilson M P B G SVY(pg) SVY 300683
Brooks R M G *BSc(Eng)* psc† 300684
Davies C M *MBE BEng* psc 300684
Drewienkiewicz K J *MA* psc 300684
Elliott C L *MBE BSc(Eng)* psc 300684
Farmbrough J S *BSc(Eng) MICE* psc C ph 300684
Harris M J *BSc(Eng)* psc† 300684
Harrison J R *MBE BSc* psc(n)† 300684
Hawken R B *BSc* psc† 300684
Holman A G R sq 300684
Hughes W J R *MA* psc 300684
Kirkpatrick T R *BSc(Eng)* sq C 300684
Lane-Jones S *BSc BSc(Eng)* psc† 300684
Martin D J psc 300684
Mercer I S psc† 300684
Norris B W *MA* psc 300684
O'Donoghue K *BSc* psc 300684
Page P B *MBE* psc† 300684
Preiss W J *MA MSc FRAS ARICS* SVY(gy) SVY 300684
Reid D I *MA MICE* psc C 300684
Robertson T J W *BSc(Eng)* psc(n)† jsdc 300684
Rogers J W G psc† 300684
Spaight W H T *BSc(Eng) MICE MIHT FBIM* sq C 300684
Tomlinson N W A *BSc(Eng) MICE* C 300684
Wildman P R *BSc(Eng)* psc SVY 300684
Wright A J *BA* psc(a)† 300684
Baker J G *MBE BSc(Eng)* psc† 300685
Bearder L A *MA CEng MIMechE* sq EM 300685
Bennett J B *BSc CEng MICE FIPlantE* sq C 300685
Bradbury C C *BA MICE* C 300685
Charlton C W psc† 300685
Davidson W M *BSc(Eng) MICE* sq C 300685
Evans M A *BSc* psc† 300685
Foster M W *BSc MICE* C 300685
Harvey M *MA MSc* SVY(pg) SVY 300685
Hills R A *BSc(Eng)* psc† jsdc 300685
Hornby P C *BSc(Eng) MIMechE* EM 300685
Humphrey D R *MBIM MInstAM* psc jsdc 300685
Isbell B R *BSc(Eng) MSc* psc 300685
Ludlam T J *BSc(Eng)* sq jsdc 300685
McGill I D T *BSc(Eng) CEng MICE* psc C 300685
Nash C G A *MBIM MIOP* SVY 300685
Reid R J D sq 300685
Robertson J G H psc† 300685
Sweeting J W F *LLB* psc 300685

Corps of Royal Engineers — continued

Walpole J A F *BSc(Eng)* psc† 300685
Weld S C E osc(ID) sq 300685
Whittington R H *MBE* psc 300685

Majors

Gallard P A sq 161262
Jackson A sq 090264
Batterham D M R *ARICS MBIM* SVY 110865
Heath M H S 120267
Thomson M H R sq 200467
Getley J C sq 311267
Cameron B 300668
Plommer G L psc† tt 300668
Cronchey G R SVY 311268
Allen J M *MBE BSc(Eng) CEng MIMechE FIPlantE* psc EM 300669
Thompson M F *BA* psc 311270
Ellis R A SVY(pg) SVY 300671
Read R A 300671
Rogers S psc† ph 300671
Jamieson L H P 311271
Lawson B R *MBIM MIIM* sq 311271
Reedman P sq 311271
Bailey R A SVY(pr) SVY 300672
Green G E F sq 311272
Bonney D F L *MBE TEng(CEI) MIPlantE* sq 300673
Pass F G *BSc(Eng) CEng MIMechE* EM (*L/Lt Col* 100681) 300673
Willatts D C *BSc(Eng) MICE* C 300673
Paterson-Fox R J A sq 311273
Wilson M S 311273
Brown A P sq 300674
Robinson G P G *FRGS MBIM* SVY 300674
Scarlett P F *BSc(Eng)* psc† 300674
Boyd-Heron A D sq 311274
Jennings-Bramly J A *MA CEng MICE* sq C 311274
Prendergast N H D *BSc(Eng)* psc† (*A/Lt Col* 020486) 311274
Griffin P W A *BSc(Eng) MICE* C 300675
Meheux C C P 300675
Brain M A *BSc(Eng) CEng MICE* sq C 311275
Clements G A sq 311275
Edwards G G *BSc(Eng) MICE* C 311275
Golby F C sq 311275
Stanbridge M J SVY 311275
Terry P C sq ph 311275
Druitt P G C P sq (*A/Lt Col* 160985) 300676
Neale M A SVY(pg) SVY 300676
Newman R A sq 300676
Robertson J C *BSc(Eng) CEng MICE* sq C 300676
Wyatt J G H *BSc(Eng) MICE* sq C 300676
Cooke R J H psc† 311276
Fossey M G *BA* psc† 311276
Smitherman R H *BScEng(Civil) MICE* C (*A/Lt Col* 070286) 311276
Chapman J W A sq 300677
Cowan H A *BSc CEng MICE MIPlantE* C ENG 300677
Forbes J G *BSc(Eng)* SVY(pg) SVY 300677
Heier P sq 300677
MacArthur R I M sq 300677
Marett P J 300677
Montgomery M G R *BSc(Eng) CEng MIMechE* sq EM 300677
Nash R H J sq 300677
Yerbury J T *BA MICE* sq C 300677
Holtby D J sq aic 311277
Marsh J P *BSc(Eng) CEng MICE* psc C (*A/Lt Col* 240885) 311277
McLennan J R sq P 311277
Reeve A J aic P 311277
Saunders D G *BSc(Eng) MSc CEng MICE* dis C 311277
Sinclair K R sq 311277
Skinner A W *MA* psc† 311277
Tew E D C 311277
Boyd E A *MBE* P 300678
Bridges M G le G *BSc(Eng)* EM (*A/Lt Col* 260386) 300678
Craib J A *QGM* sq SVY 300678
Ferguson I R sq 300678
Hulton F G *BSc MA MICE* C 300678
Hunt R M R *BSc(Eng)* psc† 300678
Kingston A M *BSc(Eng) CEng MICE* sq C 300678
Parkes G C SVY 300678
Stack D J R *BSc(Eng)* psc 300678
Adams P S *MBE BSc(Eng)* psc† (*A/Lt Col* 090885) 311278
Bullock W F *BSc* sq C 311278
Lester R M S *BSc(Eng) MSc* dis sq 311278
Semple B M *BA* psc 311278
Birch B J 300679
Bradwell T R *BSc(Eng)* sq 300679
Bray P M *BSc* C (*A/Lt Col* 170186) 300679
Davis D A S *BSc BSc(Eng) CEng MICE* C 300679
Johnson I H *BSc MICE* C 300679
Jude R A *BSc CEng MICE* C 300679
Lucas G S 300679
Ris J A *BSc(Eng)* psc† 300679
Sandy R J *BSc(Eng)* sq 300679
Stephenson D P *BSc(Eng) CEng MICE* psc C (*A/Lt Col* 270386) 300679
Warren M W M *BA* psc 300679
Whittington I F G *BSc(Eng) MBIM MIOP* SVY 300679
Brett A T *BSc(Eng)* psc† 311279
Douglas A F M *MA* psc† 311279
Hutchinson A R E *BSc(Eng)* psc† jsdc 311279
Hyde-Bales R A psc 311279
Moorhouse J C H psc† 311279
Plant I M sq 311279
Reed P R sq 311279
Setchell D G sq 311279
Sloan C E E *BEng CEng MIEE MBIM* psc† (*A/Lt Col* 200985) 311279
Wilson A A *BSc(Eng) MIHT* psc(n)† 311279
Wyatt J R *MBE* sq 311279
Wyatt J M sq (*A/Lt Col* 301085) 311279
Campbell M S *BSc MICE* C 300980
Chilton G P *BSc(Eng)* sq 300980
Cooper M D *BSc(Eng) CEng MIMechE FIPlantE* EM 300980
Dudin R A *BSc(Eng) MICE* psc† C 300980
Farmer A C *BSc* psc† 300980
Farrington G C *MA MCIBSE* EM 300980
Gill D M *MBE BSc(Eng)* psc† (*A/Lt Col* 251085) 300980
Hart R C psc 300980
Haskell C W *BSc* psc† aic 300980
Hayward-Broomfield P W psc 300980
Hoey H M *BSc(Eng)* C 300980
Iwanek V G sq 300980
Johnston R M *MAppSci* SVY SVY(cg) 300980
Kennedy-Smith G M *MSc* dis SVY 300980
Little R J *BSc(Eng)* sq 300980
Macdonald R *MBE BSc(Eng)* sq (*A/Lt Col* 150286) 300980
Mackenzie A M *MBE* sq 300980
McLean A A J *BSc(Eng) CEng MIMechE MBIM* EM 300980
Mitchell D C psc† 300980
Morgan R C *MVO BSc(Eng) MICE* sq C 300980
Mulliner N F *BSc(Eng)* psc† 300980
Owen R J F 300980
Quin J W *DipEd* 300980
Reynolds M D *BSc(Eng) CEng MICE FIPlantE* C 300980
Russell-Jones P J *BSc(Eng)* psc† (*A/Lt Col* 210386) 300980
Snape J E *FRICS* sq 300980
Story P C T P ph 300980
Stow A J *MA CEng MICE* C 300980
Thackwell W T R *BSc(Eng)* C 300980
Tuggey A S *BSc(Eng)* osc(MAL) 300980
Waddington J aic 300980
Ward G E 300980
Wiggins M F *BSc(Eng)* psc† 300980
Williams R H *BSc(Eng) MICE* C 300980
Wills M R 300980
Alexander R J R *MIPlantE* P 300981
Anderson J D C *BSc(Eng)* psc(n)† 300981
Brooke M H H sq 300981
Burton B V SVY 300981
Campbell J M *ARICS FBIM* SVY 300981
Collins J F *BSc(Eng)* psc† SVY 300981
Dennis R B sq 300981
Dickinson R L F *BSc(Eng)* sq 300981
Enzer P J *BSc(Eng)* psc† 300981
Eskell S 300981
Field J S psc 300981
Hesketh S W *BSc* sq 300981
Hoddinott T G *BSc* psc† 300981
Kershaw G C *BSc(Eng) MICE* C 300981
Lewin R A *BSc(Eng) MBIM MIOP* SVY(pr) SVY 300981
Lilleyman P *BSc(Eng)* psc† aic 300981
Macdonald G *MBE CGIA* psc† 300981
Mackenzie J F *BSc(Eng) MIE(AUST)* C 300981
Mildinhall C A ph 300981
Mosedale M J Q *BTech CEng MICE* C 300981
Newns R A psc† 300981
Paterson M G *BSc(Eng)* psc† 300981
Pickles C S *BSc(Eng) CEng MICE* C 300981
Pilkington A J *MA MSc* SVY(pg) SVY 300981
Rayner J M *BSc(Eng)* EM 300981
Searle P R *BSc(Eng) MSc* SVY(pg) SVY 300981

Shearer D L *BSc CEng MICE* C 300981
Steele A H *BSc(Eng)* C 300981
Summers D R *BSc(Eng)* sq 300981
Taylor P M *BSc(Eng)* psc 300981
Waitson A R sq 300981
Watt R *BSc* EM 300981
Watts B A *BSc MIMechE* psc EM 300981
White G M 300981
Armstrong P M *BSc(Eng)* C 300982
Bend R M *BEng* EM 300982
Blad T J *MA* psc† 300982
Clarke S K E 300982
Clarke R H *BSc(Eng)* EM 300982
Cooper P C *BSc* 300982
Cozens W B *BSc(Eng) MICE* C 300982
Crosskey R M *BSc(Eng) MICE* C 300982
Dixon R W *BSc(Eng)* EM 300982
Edwards I D *BSc MICE* C 300982
Flower L T aic 300982
Foulkes T H E *BSc(Eng)* psc† 300982
Lavies P R W *MA MICE* C 300982
McAslan A R R *BSc(Eng)* psc† 300982
McCabe M C *BSc(Eng)* psc† 300982
Moore-Bick J D *MA* psc(GE) 300982
Munro N *MA* C 300982
Norbury M S psc 300982
Pawson J R *MBE BSc(Eng)* 300982
Peebles C McF *BSc(Eng)* psc† 300982
Pridham R *BSc* psc† 300982
Sheridan P A J *BSc(Eng)* psc† 300982
Sinclair R D *BSc* 300982
Stalker A J L *BSc(Eng) MICE* C 300982
Turpin K P M *BSc(Eng)* C 300982
Walker A P *BSc(Eng)* psc† SVY 300982
Walker D A *BSc(Eng)* psc† 300982
Wardrop A R T *MSc* dis SVY 300982
Wilson A R M *BSc MICE* C 300982
Beazley M G psc 300983
Bouwens C P 300983
Breach M C *MA MSc ARICS* SVY 300983
Canipel P G 300983
Champion J E *BSc* EM 300983
Cima K H psc(a)† 300983
Court S C *MSc* dis 300983
Craig A S *BSc(Eng)* psc 300983
Daniell I M *BSc* psc 300983
Douglass S J 300983
Faucherand S G *BSc(Eng)* psc† 300983
Fickling N T *BSc(Eng) MSc* SVY(pg) SVY 300983
Griffiths R J psc 300983
Guthkelch C N psc 300983
Hamilton I K *BSc* 300983
Heminsley W J *BSc(Eng)* 300983
Kirby D M J 300983
Murphy S P *BSc(Eng) CEng MICE* C 300983
Pinel J A psc 300983
Ross I A M *MAppSci* SVY SVY(cg) 300983
Savage W R *BSc(Eng)* SVY 300983
Smale J F 300983
Tait I M *BSc(Eng)* C 300983
Talbot G M S *MA* psc† 300983
Tolley R E *MCIOB* 300983
Webb D M *MBE* 300983
Wheeley J F psc 300983
Willis S 300983
Zimmermann C E *BSc(Eng) MICE* C 300983
Bailey W A *BSc(Eng)* psc 300984
Beaton D J *BSc(Eng)* psc† 300984
Boydell A P P 300984
Bratt A D *BA* 300984
Campbell M R *BSc(Eng)* psc 300984
Chadwick C B *BSc* 300984
Claber K J *MA* C 300984
Clark W J H *BSc(Eng)* psc 300984
Crawford C W *MBE* 300984
Croft M H G *BSc* 300984
Dawson G W *BSc(Eng)* psc† 300984
Eagan S M R 300984
Forrestal N R 300984
Gore W C 300984
Greaves C N *BSc(Eng)* psc† 300984
Harris A P 300984
Herber-Davies A J P 300984
Hoskinson J P *BSc(Eng)* psc† 300984
Jones A J 300984
Kay A *BSc* EM 300984
Lewis S R psc 300984
Marsh P C *BSc(Eng) CEng MICE* C 300984
O'Sullivan J P J psc 300984
Park D A M *BSc(Eng) FGS CEng MICE* C 300984
Roberts I L *BSc(Eng)* EM 300984
Roland-Price A *BSc(Eng)* psc 300984
Rose G A 300984
Standbridge N B 300984
Sutherland N A *BSc(Eng)* psc 300984
Sykes S W *BArch BSc* SVY 300984
Walmisley J C *BSc(Eng)* C 300984
Wright D SVY 300984
Wright A M *BSc(Eng)* 300984
Beaumont J D *BEng* psc 300985
Birchall G G 300985
Bowen D C 300985
Burnside A P *BSc* C 300985
Carruth A P *BTech* psc EM 300985
Chapman L W 300985
Chisholm D J *BSc(Eng)* 300985
Clarke P W I 300985
Cooke B J *MA CGIA* 300985
Crompton J F *BSc(Eng)* psc 300985
Cross A P *BSc(Eng)* SVY 300985
Farley S L *BSc(Eng)* SVY 300985
Goulton N S *BSc(Eng)* P 300985
Gritten M R *BA* psc† 300985
Hall D J *BSc(Eng)* SVY 300985
Innes D R ff *BSc(Eng)* psc 300985
Jarrett-Kerr C C N *BSc(Eng)* psc 300985
Killick R W *BSc(Eng)* psc† 300985
McNamara G M 300985
Munnoch G R C *BSc(Eng)* psc† 300985
Pearce S J *BSc(Eng) CEng MICE* C 300985
Peebles A A *BSc BSc(Eng)* 300985
Pope A C *BSc(Eng)* psc† 300985
Richards R D *MA* psc 300985
Thomas A D L *BSc* psc† 300985
Watts G C 300985
Whitley A E psc 300985
Winfield R M P 300985

Captains

Mercer-Wilson P R aic 310776
Williams D J *BSc(Eng)* 300777
Smith G *BA* 061077
Brown A *BSc* (*A/Maj* 290485) 090978
Painter N J *BEng* C 291078
Anderson S M *BSc* SVY 290179
Montgomery K H *BSc* 010279
Braithwaite R I'A *BSc* psc† (*A/Maj* 201285) 050379
Duffus J B *BSc* SVY 050379
Blundell P H *BSc(Eng)* 080379
Fawkner-Corbett W D *MA* 080379
Watson P 080379
Attwater D H E *MA* SVY 090379
Larkin N H *BSc* 250679
Cobbold R N *BSc(Eng)* C 020879
Harrison R M C *BSc(Eng)* 110879
Poole P A H *BSc* (*A/Maj* 040285) 190879
Douglas A H *BSc(Eng)* psc(n) (*A/Maj* 100186) 100979
Lomas S *BSc(Eng)* 100979
Mantell A C *BA* 100979
Molony A N S 100979
Woollven R C J *BSc(Eng)* psc† (*A/Maj* 201285) 100979
Perkins D M *BSc* 101179
Hicks A P (*A/Maj* 030386) 131279
Allen M K (*A/Maj* 161285) 301279
Bill D R *BSc(Eng)* (*A/Maj* 310584) 301279
Kemp F C (*A/Maj* 030183) 301279
Sheldon R P *BSc(Eng)* 301279
Hughes M A C *BSc(Eng)* 010280
Rigby R N *BSc* SVY 130280
Taylor D W *BSc(Eng)* 120380
Price G J F *BSc* 030480
Rowe P G F *BSc(Eng)* (*A/Maj* 020784) 100580
Spence F S *BSc(Eng)* SVY 100580
Cox S R *BSc* ph 060680
Shuler R (*A/Maj* 041185) 180780
Bateson D S *MA* (*A/Maj* 150984) 010880
Macleod A W H H *BSc(Eng)* 010880
Sexton C M *MA* 010880
Edwards N J *MA* (*A/Maj* 100485) 180880
Stevens D C *BSc* 260880
Jenkinson R J *BSc* 060980
Bayliss A H *MA* 090980
Bennett B W P *BA* (*A/Maj* 100286) 090980
Davies S J 090980
Fresson N O (*A/Maj* 230385) 090980
Johnson P D *BSc(Eng)* 090980
Kerr A B 090980
Mans M F N (*A/Maj* 220485) 090980
Oak-Rhind N V R *BSc(Eng)* 090980
Taylor G *MA* 090980
Wall P A *BA* 090980
Wilcox D I *BSc(Eng)* 090980
Willett R L *BSc(Eng)* 090980
Holland N M *BSc* 141080
Gunns J M *BSc* 301180
Foxley D *BA* 291280
Grossmith G B *BSc(Eng)* 291280
Prain J F *MA ARICS* SVY 291280
Swanson R C *BSc(Eng)* 291280
Luscombe P D *BSc TEng* 010181
Stewart R C *BSc* 290381
Davies P M *BSc* 020481
Durance J R *BSc(Eng)* psc 090581

Corps of Royal Engineers — continued

Name	Date
Smith P J *BSc(Eng)* SVY	090581
Fairclough N M *BA(Hons)*	140581
Shergold S *BSc(Eng)*	010881
Olley J B *BSc*	140881
Gibson R D *BSc*	030981
McAlpine M G *BSc*	030981
Strong J A R *MA*	030981
Dinwiddie P G *BSc(Eng)* SVY	080981
Fenn N H W	080981
Heron J M *BSc(Eng)*	080981
Hyslop C S ph	080981
Kemp N C *BSc(Eng)*	080981
Lane G S *MA*	080981
Lodge P *BSc(Eng)*	080981
Melvin R A M S *BA*	080981
Ogden I A *BSc(Eng)*	080981
Vernon M R (*A/Maj* 101285)	080981
Gilbert P J *BSc*	290981
Perkins S P *BSc*	290981
Francis P J *BSc*	071081
Duggleby T R *BSc*	151081
Sherry S F	201281
Burns D R *BSc(Eng)*	281281
Dunford M A *BSc(Eng)*	281281
Gilson M W *BSc(Eng)* SVY	281281
Henly S J R	281281
Iron R M *BA*	281281
Mumford M J	281281
Taylor D J A	281281
Ward S P *BSc(Eng)*	281281
Wilson A D	281281
Kinghan J S *BSc*	291281
Phillips G D *BA*	010282
Chambers P B *BSc(Eng)*	110282
Wakefield T J *BSc* (*A/Maj* 140685)	290382
Naile S L *BSc(Eng)* (*A/Maj* 060186)	080582
Thorn J W R *BSc(Eng)*	080582
Wallace-Tarry P A	080582
Macklin A D *MA*	160682
Carter M P *BSc*	270682
Wright I D *BEd*	090882
Edington A J S *BSc*	290882
Caws I M *BSc(Eng)*	060982
Day J J D *BA*	060982
Day K V B	060982
Dennis A P	060982
Dorman C G *BSc(Eng)* SVY	060982
Hendicott R C *MA*	060982
Hignett J J	060982
Kershaw-Naylor J P *BSc(Eng)*	060982
Kirk R S *BSc(Eng)*	060982
Kirkland R L	060982
Livingstone C R	060982
Randall T M *BSc(Eng)*	060982
Rollo N H *BSc(Eng)*	060982
Stewart C J P ph	060982
Pyatt S J *BSc*	280982
Wootton J D *BA*	101182
Whittaker D C *BEng*	010283
Wright R J *BSc*	010283
Francis R C *BSc(Eng)*	070283
Hall M C S *BSc(Eng)*	070283
Harking A D *BSc(Eng)*	070283
Harvey C J *BSc(Eng)*	070283
Mullin J G *MA*	070283
Oldham B S	070283
Souter A M *BSc(Eng)*	070283
Ward C J	070283
Wright I R A *BEng*	050383
Bowen P C *BSc*	090383
Hainge C M *BSc(Eng)*	110683
Lewis D	110683
White J R *BSc(Eng)*	110683
Young M W *BA*	070783
Hawksfield C M *BSc*	150883
McManners P J *BSc*	150883
Andrews M B *BSc(Econ)*	050983
Hodder S P *BSc*	050983
Wood C R *BSc*	050983
Cooper J D W *BA*	060983
Burrows M R H *BSc*	180983
Durrant P W *MA*	260983
King S R C *BSc*	021083
Bailey C W *BSc(Eng)*	081083
Blanks I J *BSc(Eng)*	081083
Cobley I S	081083
Friling S M aic	081083
Grimshaw T P	081083
Morris W M G *BSc(Eng)*	081083
Parrish M W *BA*	081083
Richardson A B *BA*	081083
Smethurst J R *BA*	081083
Stewart R J N	081083
Tims M A *BSc(Eng)*	081083
Wood J F	081083
Lemay J J J	101083
Cox M J *BSc*	211083
Ince C D S *BSc*	291083
Montagu N E *BA*	171183
Thomas M F *BA*	301183
Hopwood J W *BA*	010284
Ball A R *BSc(Eng)*	060284
Chick J A	060284
Dodds G C W *BSc(Eng)*	060284
Goodier G C *BEng*	060284
Greathead T J	060284
Holman C N	060284
Jones D G *BA*	060284
Rosenvinge I	060284
Tenison S G *BSc(Eng)*	060284
Thompson A D	060284
Gibbs G K	280284
Mozley R J D *BSc*	040384
Alderman G J *BSc*	200384
Block S J *BSc*	200384
Shaw P J *BSc(Eng)*	010584
Whitchurch M W	070584
Payne M A	100684
Clark N R *BSc*	010884
Furness J S *BSc*	010884
Wilmshurst-Smith G E *BSc*	010984
Daniel P M *BSc(Eng)*	081084
Efford J C *BA(Hons)*	081084
Fennell J H C *BSc(Eng)*	081084
Foden M W *BSc(Eng)*	081084
Freeland S C	081084
Jackson D G	081084
James I D *BSc(Eng)*	081084
Miller J P *BSc*	081084
Mills A M *BSc*	081084
Mitchell J W *BSc(Eng)*	081084
Nield G A *BSc*	081084
Richardson M G H *BSc(Eng)*	081084
Webb A J	081084
Wilks C L *BA*	101184
McConaghy A J W	291284
Evans S J *BSc*	010285
Beaumont C M *BSc*	050285
Clews M *BSc(Eng)*	050285
Hughes D G *BEng*	050285
Naylor P M	050285
Pennington J C *BSc(Eng)*	050285
Riches P J *BSc*	050285
Sanderson I A *BSc(Eng)*	050285
Simpson J B M	050285
Tonkins R M *BSc BSc*	050285
Williams R J *BSc(Eng)*	050285
Price N J *BCom*	190285
Owen S P *BSc*	030385
Ruddy J M *BA*	030385
Deverill J E *BSc*	080385
Jones A K *BSc(Eng)*	010485
Ward E J *BSc(Eng)*	090685
Neville M R *BSc*	010885
Piper R A *BSc*	030985
James I S *BSc*	051085
Belk M A *BSc*	071085
Cockerill C M *BSc*	071085
Fenn M A *BSc(Eng)*	071085
Hannington G J	071085
Hitchcock I G	071085
Le Grys B J	071085
Lightfoot P L *BSc*	071085
Marsh R J *BSc*	071085
Pope C M *BSc(Eng)*	071085
Roberts T J P	071085
Sole S J *BSc*	071085
Walne J N *BSc*	210186
Pelton J F *BSc(Eng)*	220186
Freeman M A *BSc*	260186
Greaves J J	040286
Inglis N *BSc*	040286
Pateman-Jones A J *BA*	040286
Platts A C *BSc(Hons)*	040286
Sheppard A C	040286
Gibson S D *BSc BCom*	020386
Welch P *BSc*	020386

Lieutenants

Name	Date
Sonnex P S	081281
Bilson C P	120482
Coutts G M L *BSc*	120482
Ferris T H *BA*	120482
MacGinnis G R W *BA* (*A/Capt* 190286)	120482
Ridley S M *BSc(Eng)* (*A/Capt* 181185)	120482
Skeat C N R *BSc(Eng)*	120482
Thomas I M *BSc(Eng)* (*A/Capt* 130186)	120482
Wilman C J *BSc(Eng)* (*A/Capt* 130186)	120482
Knights C M (*A/Capt* 140685)	120682
Baxter G H L *BA*	240682
Gidney M A J (*A/Capt* 210186)	090882
Lewis J D (*A/Capt* 141085)	090882
Scopes A I M *BSc(Eng)*	090882
Smith N C R G *BSc(Eng)*	090882
Temple S A (*A/Capt* 010484)	090882
Tucker S J	090882
Perrey A D	131282
Stringer M	131282
Cliffe A M	110483
Cubbin M A	110483
Davis R R *BSc*	110483
Gimson S G S *BSc(Eng)*	110483
Gooding A C P *BSc*	110483
Honey W D C	110483
Honey A P *BEng*	110483
Kedar J D *BSc(Eng)*	110483
Leonard M D P *BSc(Eng)*	110483
Moody N C *BSc*	110483
Parker H J (*A/Capt* 300484)	110483
Phillipson A	110483
Potts J N *BSc*	110483
Simonds J D *BSc*	110483
Smith J P	110483
Stapleton M	110483
Wastie L F *BSc*	110483
Watson M S *BSc*	110483
Wright S A	110483
Dickinson A S	070683
Brand G K	080883
Foxley A	080883
King C	080883
Langston C R P	080883
Wolstenholme R P *BSc*	080883

Lowth R G *BA(HonsCantab)* 150983
Buckingham G E L *BA BAI* 021283
Spreckley J G 121283
Butler G T 271283
Bowyer D G *BA* 090484
Cameron A St J E *BSc* 090484
Cottee T R 090484
Isaac T W D 090484
Lane J L A *BSc* 090484
Levett-Scrivener M J *BSc* 090484
Pallas J *BSc* 090484
Roberts J A 090484
Shallcross J R 090484
Stevens A T *BSc ALCM* 090484
Strawbridge D L 090484
Stuart J B *BSc* 090484
Vaughan T D 090484
Williams R E *BSc(Eng)* 090484
Wettern L P *BA* 040584
Cripwell R J 070884
Morgan J P 070884
Morris D *BSc* 070884
Hudson D C 111284
Scholes P 111284
Slater R P 111284
Aitken M G 090485
Banwell M J 090485
Culley D P 090485
Fairweather J G 090485
Skehel M S A 090485
Conn N M M 060885
Passmore J E 060885
Quinn L T 060885
Rich A H 060885
Jones-Mathias M D 101285
Prichard J L 101285
Tickell C L 101285
Hargreaves D S 070486
Marot G L 070486
Marsh A D 070486
Poynter N G 070486
Urch T R 070486
Wilman J G 070486
Winkworth S A 070486

2nd Lieutenants

††Oliver M K *BA(Hons)* 040981
††Whitworth B C T *LLB* 030982
Brookes A D 060883
††Birkett A A R *BSc(Hons)* 020983
††Burnet R J de J *BA(Hons)* 020983
††Perry C G 020983
††Sutherland N 020983
Richardson P 040884
Williams D G C 040884
††Cavanagh N J 230984
††Glasgow A C 230984
††Hyslop N J 230984
††Rider R J 230984
††Stephens R A C 230984
††Vince A E 230984
††Wardle M A 230984
††Mercer R J 011084
Harper M J 081284
Hemmings B R E 081284
Dainty A W 130485
Denison D R 130485
Hilton A C 130485
Lang W R S 130485
Nightingale C S W 130485
Stanton L J 130485
Bigger D L D 100885
Machin A J 100885
Wildish T C L 100885
†Grealy V M *BSc* 060985
†Grundy P K C *BSc(Hons)* 060985
†Howard J A D *BSc(Hons)* 060985
†Killip J Q *BSc BSc(Hons)* 060985
†Newsome J M *BSc* 060985
†Swan R I A *BSc(Eng)* 060985
††Brambell D J 240985
††Collier J C 240985
††Peet R J 240985
††Reed C G S J 240985
†Boyd S P W 031085
Dash R G 141285
Dean J J 141285
Speer S S 141285
Walker J M I 141285
†Jackson M C F *BEng* 060186
†Parke A G *BSc* 060186

Staff Quartermasters

Hicks A J 010570
Lt Col 051184
Morgan J *MBIM MISM MASMC* 230674
Lt Col 310183
Carradus E J 220974
Lt Col 020383
Anthony I R E 081176
Lt Col 080685
Shaw D *MInstAM* 160979
Maj 311275

Quartermasters

Wilson L F T *MBIM* 020773
Lt Col 050883
Hawkins T D *MBE* 121173
Lt Col 020582
Church P M 200475
Lt Col 150885
Green W M *MBIM* 270575
Lt Col 311284
Wilkins N C *MBE MBIM MISM* 241175
Lt Col 130284
Austin R 011275
Maj 010479
Hurst R D 160276
Maj 140581
Pye R F *MBE* 130476
Lt Col 121185
Craig J E 030576
Lt Col 070685
Ingram R F 190676
Maj 010882
Chantler D H 160876
Maj 010479
Urquhart D A *TEng(CEI) MIWHTE* 010976
Maj 070684
Kimpton G H 151276
Maj 200979
Murison W 140177
Maj 120980
Scoble P W 300377
Lt Col 121185
Eades A 010877
Maj 160982
Leach T B 290977
Maj 030283
Moore S J 300977
Maj 120680
Hall A J 011077
Maj 240584
Woodward B W 121077
Maj 191084
Holloway D M *MBE* 011277
Maj 020982
Festorazzi R A *MInstAM* 170178
Maj 040183
Donald G *MBE* 140278
Maj 171083
Walker R L 090678
Maj 220483
Morris R V 010778
Maj 200184
Wilks B N *MISM* 040778
Maj 240179
Dee J 010878
Maj 181283
Bain P J 020878
Maj 130784
Geoghegan J 020878
Maj 121285
Folwell D B 070878
Maj 260784
Overd R J 110978
Maj 120583
Webb C J 061078
Maj 150983
Ismay R J L *MISM AIIRSM* 311078
Maj 270984
Mason J J 081278
Maj 240383
Titmuss G 140279
Maj 260985
Gallagher B B 160279
Maj 030283
Rawlings J W C 010479
Maj 270984
Purcell A W 020579
Maj 270984
MacKinnon D H 310579
Maj 260985
Scott W H 260779
Maj 270984
McConnell A S H 310779
Maj 230585
Overd A J 300879
Maj 150983
Crofton E I 030979
Maj 180883
Skidmore A F 011179
Maj 230585
Whitton M G W 171179
Maj 230585
Teesdale G W 051279
Maj 310185
Humphreys N D 191279
Maj 310185
Kinnear A G R 311279
Maj 150885
Lampard R J 311279
Maj 230186
Mansley K C *Capt* 311279
Dunn W 290280
Maj 050985
Jolly K R 210380
Maj 030186
Flower D H *Capt* 010480
Cox B W *Capt* 280480
Winter R *Capt* 110580
Pallott M R C *AMITD* *Capt* 180880
Haggie B *Capt* 010980
Dunkley I *Capt* 011080
Davies A J *MBE* *Capt* 010181
Suart B *Capt* 010281
Bunting A J *Capt* 020481
Benson J H C *Capt* 010681
Grant A M W *Capt* 110681
Clark J S *BEM* *Capt* 200781
Hazard K J *MBE* *Capt* 010981
Reynolds J A *Capt* 010981
Gilham J E *Capt* 261081
Harrison W S *Capt* 021181
Clifton T D *Capt* 311281
Burns J *Capt* 010182
Dick W J *Capt* 010182
Smee M J *Capt* 010182
Clarke J A *Capt* 070282
Squires J H *Capt* 010482

Corps of Royal Engineers — continued

Stubbs J P V *Capt* 010482
Troy P T *Capt* 010482
Hayward A *MInstAM* *Capt* 010582
Barton H R *AIIM MISM* *Capt* 280582
Nicholson J W *Capt* 080682
Rogers P E *Capt* 290682
Jackson K *Capt* 151182
Crozier R S *Capt* 010383
Kinnear I *Capt* 020383
Treasure J H G *Capt* 010483
Wood L E *Capt* 010683
Fulton R W *Capt* 030683
Winder N F *Capt* 200683
Rees H W *Capt* 120983
Leonard R A *MISM* *Capt* 011183
Baldwin B R *Capt* 011283
Pickles S *Capt* 111283
Hunt T *Capt* 241283
Baron G W *Capt* 080184
Roberts A M *Capt* 290184
Olford J D *Capt* 210584
Banks E C *Capt* 170784
Bridgett F N G *Capt* 170784
Chapplow P *Capt* 170784
Cockburn N *Capt* 170784
Day M W *Capt* 170784
Gibson W D J *Capt* 170784
Inge L S I *Capt* 170784
Orr H *Capt* 170784
Saywell R M *Capt* 170784
Sparham J C *Capt* 170784
Ullah D V *Capt* 170784
Aldridge J D *Capt* 010885
Arthur A *Capt* 010885
Benefield J W *Capt* 010885
Bourne E C *MISM* *Capt* 010885
Cottrell P J *Capt* 010885
Edwards R J *Capt* 010885
Foster B K *TEng(CEI) FHTTA FSCET* *Capt* 010885
Harding D H *Capt* 010885
Henderson K R *Capt* 010885
Jones T B *Capt* 010885
Kightley E J *MISM* *Capt* 010885
Ludlow F D *Capt* 010885
Miller B L *Capt* 010885
Patrick I K *Capt* 010885
Regan P *Capt* 010885
Simpson R G *Capt* 010885
Stafford B H *BEM* *Capt* 010885
Stewart W *Capt* 010885
Toogood M A G *Capt* 010885

Survey Executive Officers

Gerhard B F *FIOP MIOP* SVY(pr) 270474 *Maj* 070679
Webster P H 061077 *Maj* 170981
Frost J B *AMInstMP MIOP* *Capt* 070680
Shaw J A C *Capt* 070683

Garrison Engineers (Construction)

Nesbitt A *MBIM MRSH* 010269 *Lt Col* 261081
Jessop D P 110573 *Lt Col* 300582
Riley W E *BEM* 151283 *Lt Col* 271082
Sparks D A 310874 *Maj* 010479
Tucker D F T 010575 *Maj* 200979

Jarratt H R 300675 *Lt Col* 080784
Gaunt J 100476 *Maj* 120281
Caulfield H A 280776 *Maj* 060981
Brynolf C *FICW* 110677 *Maj* 110882
Collett S R *MBE* 011177 *Maj* 081084
Whennell C G L 070278 *Maj* 130582
Winstanley C W 080478 *Maj* 010782
Wells J B 010578 *Maj* 120484
Earnshaw M B 280778 *Maj* 310185
Sheppard F G 310878 *Maj* 151184
Morgan H M *MBE* *Capt* 311078
Geany J P *MBE* *Capt* 020579
Taylor M A *Capt* 311079
Winship D *MBE* *Capt* 070480
McGahan J *Capt* 141181
Haxton F E *Capt* 050182
Gardner A J *TEng(CEI) MIWHTE MIAT* *Capt* 050582
Stokes S P *MCIOB* *Capt* 300582
Nightingale J G P *Capt* 020982
Cross R J *Capt* 301082
Dyer B S *Capt* 011282
Cook J V *Capt* 170183
Wade J E *Capt* 090583
Foote I R *MICW FPWI* *Capt* 010683
Butcher R N *Capt* 201184
Bassett D R *MCIOB* *Capt* 010885
Burman F E *Capt* 010885
Gall D G *MHTTA MISM* *Capt* 010885
Robinson R L D *Capt* 010885

Garrison Engineers (Electrical)

Wilsher R F *MIPlantE MITE MBIM* 010375 *Lt Col* 021184
Kerr W D A *MITE* 010976 *Maj* 130582
Wright J E 090577 *Maj* 170485
Mackenzie R B 221177 *Maj* 021285
Ferguson N A *TEng(CEI) MITE* *Capt* 310578
Hobbs G W *MBE* 010678 *Maj* 230585
Hodson M J T *TEng(CEI) MITE* *Capt* 041078
Murrell C M V *Capt* 060479
Jarvis E A N *Capt* 020582
Carpenter C *Capt* 230483
Gibb J E *TEng(CEI) MIElecIE* *Capt* 200284
Holmes D *Capt* 010885

Garrison Engineers (Mechanical)

Tims D W *MIPlantE* 151073 *Lt Col* 230285
Blow K M 050974 *Maj* 060280
Penn C J *TEng(CEI) MIPlantE* 170275 *Maj* 061279
Howard E G *TEng(CEI) MIPlantE MASEE* 150975 *Maj* 150983

Shand M J *TEng(CEI) MIPlantE* 140477 *Maj* 181084
Dure J B *BEM MIPlantE MIMGTechE* 071077 *Maj* 021285
Jenkinson R A 060478 *Maj* 260985
Gleeson T D 040878 *Maj* 151184
Harris K T *TEng(CEI) MIPlantE* *Capt* 010179
Murrant I L W *TEng(CEI) MIPlantE MASEE* *Capt* 220179
Nicholls R A *MBE* *Capt* 220179
Hartley S R *Capt* 010779
Small G *Capt* 050879
Cowe G M *Capt* 100480
Green P J *Capt* 010481
Ebdon W S H *Capt* 160981
Williams P D *TEng(CEI) MIPlantE* *Capt* 180482
Hardaway M J *Capt* 020582
Hemstock B G *TEng(CEI) MIPlantE MIHOSPE* *Capt* 250882
Buchanan R F *Capt* 280283
Bennett R *Capt* 271083
Williams D H *Capt* 170784
Oldridge L G A *Capt* 010885

Directors of Music

Pryce D E *MBE* 171172 *Maj* 171180
Evans P R *LTCL FVCM A(Mus)LCM* psm *Capt* 150579

Special Regular Officers

Majors

Shaw M T C *BSc BSc(Eng) CEng MIEE* EM 280976
Ward J W *BEM* 300679
Cobb W B 300980
Harcourt N H *DLC(Eng)* SVY 300980
Mawhinney T H M P 300980
Biscombe P J W 300984
Johnstone A J *ARICS* 300984
Taylor R G *BSc(Eng)* EM 300984
Vickers A J M *BSc* SVY 300984
Ford W A 300985
Keeley A *BSc* CG SVY SVY(cg) 300985

Captains

Dyer M L (*A/Maj* 221084) 170366
Grant J D C *MBIM* (*A/Maj* 040385) 220168
Hough P J Q ato 310776
Iwanek R M 060877
Parkinson R D *BSc* C 010478
Hill R D 020379
Fitzgerald J F H *BSc* SVY 231080
Walker S R *BEng* SVY 030981
Lauder M A 080981
Henry R J 240981
Crook P E 281281
Kingswell R S 210182
Braybrook R C F 080582
Wood P F *MIOP* 190582
Morgan H P 060982
Hall R G R 070283
Maddock P *BSc* 140683
Kimber D P 070983
Berridge H R I 081083

Whitty G J (*A/Maj* 010885)	081083
Jones G B O R *BSc*	171183
Nicklin R M P SVY	171183
Wilson E J (*A/Maj* 250285)	181283
Smith P	060284
Whiting W D *BSc(Eng)*	130284
Jones A	100684
O'Boyle M W F *BSc(Eng)*	100684
Charlesworth J	230984
Brand T S	081084
Donaldson R A *BSc*	081084
Castle J W	141284
Miller A M O	050285
Morrison R L	050285
Hirst P	090385
Perry M	250985
Henderson R J	040286

Lieutenants

Evans B R (*A/Capt* 210584)	131181
Taylor A P	120482
Townsley J M H (*A/Capt* 201085)	200782
Law M C (*A/Capt* 131184)	090882
Redshaw M A (*A/Capt* 010785)	090882
Robertson A J F (*A/Capt* 080485)	131282
Boag C J	030583
Bado F (*A/Capt* 041085)	050783
Murphy I L	040883
Annal H R	180685
Stevenson M	070486

2nd Lieutenants

Welsh J G	040884
Fawcett S A M	081284

Short Service Officers

Captains

Mitchell P R (*A/Maj* 020682)	140178
Wiltshire C C (*A/Maj* 260983)	230579
Berrington R *LIOB* (*A/Maj* 020885)	020580
Grainger B A (*A/Maj* 140285)	150580
Sage J W *BSc*	290981
Wiseman V A	081081
Elsby K J	190582
Law I G	190582
Robinson N E	210782
Guthrie R C *BSc*	110982
McGregor A R *BScTech*	050383
Deuchar B F C	270483
Neill D J	110583
Vosper R J *MISM*	110583
Craigie A	150683
Wills D G	310783
Brown A D ph	081083
Kerrigan K A *BSc(Eng)* ph	050384
Rose C J *BSc*	050384
Shaw L	090584
Shaw B	090584
Wareham A C *BSc*	040984
Wilson K S *BSc*	130984
McIlroy J D *BSc*	081084
Nichols R M *BA*	030385
Othen A *BSc*	020485
Rose M D	150485
Berry J	060585
Coyle D E	150585
Mitchell K V H	150585
Francis D C *BSc*	140785
Keary M E *MIPlantE MISM*	090885
McCartney W N *MISM*	260985
Hibbert N K *BSc*	071085
Mansell J B *BSc*	071085
Moffat A I *BSc FRGS PGCE*	071085
Ormesher I F *BSc*	071085
Robson J C *BSc*	071085
Kerridge D H *MISM*	141185
Putter E K *BSc*	190286
Rivers D J H *BSc*	020386
Harber K D *BSc*	030386
Wilson B C	120386

Lieutenants

Palmer R J (*A/Capt* 100884)	110581
Stuart N *BSc*	030981
Butler D (*A/Capt* 220285)	131181
Pattenden G G P (*A/Capt* 281085)	131181
Smith B F (*A/Capt* 080585)	131181
Maillardet P E (*A/Capt* 140485)	060182
Castree C J (*A/Capt* 120685)	160182
Plenderleith R (*A/Capt* 300485)	300182
Stanford R C	030282
Coltman C (*A/Capt* 240685)	240282
Mitchell H J	230382
Wye T W (*A/Capt* 210685)	230382
Worrall R G *BSc AMIMechE*	280382
Ainslie R L *BSc* (*A/Capt* 060186)	120482
Armitage D S *BSc*	120482
Cannons S R *BSc*	120482
Cuthbertson J G *BSc*	120482
Deuchars C M *BSc*	120482
Jefferson P A S *BA*	120482
Malin K *BSc*	120482
Inman F (*A/Capt* 190485)	260482
Caples P (*A/Capt* 070885)	070582
Treanor T L V *BA*	010782
Armstrong T D (*A/Capt* 300985)	200782
Batty J F (*A/Capt* 300985)	200782
Dykes R L (*A/Capt* 130885)	200782
Kerr D A	200782
Purvis D D F (*A/Capt* 300985)	200782
Saunderson J P (*A/Capt* 300985)	200782
Senior R (*A/Capt* 200185)	200782
Sheldrick B V (*A/Capt* 010985)	200782
Abbott R J *BSc*	090882
Newby-Robson M E	090882
Rainey R K (*A/Capt* 180285)	180882
Holt A J L *BSc*	020982
Sales R W (*A/Capt* 251185)	110982
Dowsett J D (*A/Capt* 150385)	150982
Bingham G (*A/Capt* 070585)	210982
Evans C J *MISM MSST* (*A/Capt* 300985)	011082
Phillips J H *DSC* (*A/Capt* 070585)	031182
Boyne D J (*A/Capt* 120585)	121182
Compton F S (*A/Capt* 120585)	121182
Hylands J (*A/Capt* 300985)	121182
Jones V B (*A/Capt* 010785)	121182
Lobb M (*A/Capt* 300985)	121182
Matten D R (*A/Capt* 300985)	121182
Parmley N (*A/Capt* 200585)	121182
Reader K *BEM LIOB AICW* (*A/Capt* 120585)	121182
Riley K B	121182
Stimpson R F (*A/Capt* 300985)	121182
Ness S J (*A/Capt* 300985)	231182
Hopkins N St J ph	131282
Robinson A M (*A/Capt* 060585)	131282
Tyndall R F C (*A/Capt* 300985)	220183
Crawford A J (*A/Capt* 230885)	230283
Dyson C (*A/Capt* 050985)	050383
Barker J A	220383
Gordon A A *MSST* (*A/Capt* 300985)	220383
Gray F O (*A/Capt* 300985)	220383
Hinchliffe R G (*A/Capt* 300985)	220383
Hoyland J A (*A/Capt* 300985)	220383
Humphreys P J	220383
McKeague D M (*A/Capt* 300985)	220383
Peters R A (*A/Capt* 300985)	220383
Goddard C S (*A/Capt* 071085)	040483
Anderson D R *BSc*	110483
Botting A *BSc(Econ)*	110483
Butler G R *BSc*	110483
Cole A R H *BSc*	110483
Cook P D *BSc*	110483
Cox M G *BSc*	110483
Finley S P *BSc*	110483
Fisher H W P *BSc(Econ)*	110483
Green F J *BSc*	110483
Innes S C (*A/Capt* 011185)	110483
Jones P R O	110483
Marjot C *BSc* (*A/Capt* 080186)	110483
Somers R M *BSc*	110483
Sutton N C *BSc*	110483
Symons R *BSc(Eng)*	110483
Tetley C M H *BSc*	110483
Welch J A H *BA(Hons)*	110483
White J M R *BSc*	110483
Cawson R W *MISM* (*A/Capt* 251085)	250483
Canning P F	010583
Rollason A (*A/Capt* 251185)	250583
Cantellow K (*A/Capt* 061285)	060683

Corps of Royal Engineers — continued

Neary D P
(*A/Capt* 260186) 100783
Hughes J V M 260783
Opie M J
(*A/Capt* 260186) 260783
Palmer A R *MICW*
(*A/Capt* 260186) 260783
Rutter D J
(*A/Capt* 260186) 260783
Aldwinckle P W *BSc* 080883
Dow R I L *BSc* 080883
Franks M McG *BSc* 080883
Fuller P J *BSc* 080883
Hardern C O *BSc* 080883
Heard C D *BA* 080883
Prowse C J *BSc* 080883
Ruxton S J *BSc* 080883
Sinclair T B R *BA* 080883
Vandennieuwenhuysen S M *BSc* 080883
Watkinson J P 080883
Burley S A
(*A/Capt* 100386) 121283
Kirk K M 121283
Vinnicombe I K 121283
Alexander D A *BA* 090484
Batt M E P *BSc* 090484
Bedford R T S 090484
Bowden J A *BA* 090484
Curtis T J M *BA* 090484
Dower M J *BSc* 090484
Frankland A J 090484
Guise-Brown C P 090484
Howe N S *LLB* 090484
Jones D M *BSc* 090484
Macdonald H S 090484
Phillips A W *BA* 090484
Sallitt W T B *BSc* 090484
Shallcross A D M 090484
Smith N H *BSc* 090484
Stewart A V G *BSc* 090484
Swanson M A *BA* 090484
Tilley M N *BSc(Hons)* 090484
Winfield R J *BSc* 090484
Caulfield D A 070884
Clarke R D S *BSc* 070884
Cowie C D *BSc* 070884
Gayler A 070884
Henshaw G P *BSc* 070884
Keeley R 070884
Methley D J *BSc* 070884
Sawford A T 070884
Swann D J *BSc* 070884
Taplin I A *BSc* 070884
Wastie J F *BSc* 070884
Wierzbicki S J P
(*A/Capt* 130585) 070884
Richardson M P 111284
Shanahan J W 111284
Evans G St J 060885
Smith L C 060885
Collin M P de E 101285
Page N A 070486
Phillips S J 070486

2nd Lieutenants

Bush S J *BEng* 080881
Moore A M 230584
Garner C G 040884
Welsh R A W 040884
Cowan S C 081284
Jaquiery P J 081284
Langford P J 081284
Lewis R G 081284
Banfield M G 130485
Daubney M E 130485
Dwyer A S 130485
Hayes A M 130485
McDougall I A 130485
Redwood I D 130485
Ridsdill-Smith M I 130485
Roberts V B 130485
Moreton D A 100885
†Cook G R N *BSc* 060985
†Cook B C *BSc(Hons)* 060985
†Cooke S *BSc* 060985
†Denton T J C *BSc(Hons)* 060985
†Erskine J H *BSc(Hons)* 060985
†Faulkner M C *BSc(Hons)* 060985
†Gladen A P *BSc(Hons)* 060985
†Noble F R *BSc* 060985
†Noyle N J *BSc* 060985
†Porter K C *BScTech* 060985
†Rose A S *BSc* 060985
†Smith S J E *BSc* 060985
†Thompson G J H *BSc(Hons)* 060985
†Thurlow R D *BSc* 060985
†Turk J T *BSc* 060985
†Unwin M S *BSc* 060985
†Verdon T J *BSc* 060985
†Wakeman A J *BSc* 060985
Baveystock N G 141285
Bell B St J 141285
Pope N 141285
Stewart S A 141285
†Armstrong J K *BSc* 060186
†D'Anger P J *BSc(Eng)* 060186
†Derben S J *BSc* 060186
†Donnelly N *BSc* 060186
†Griffin M J *BSc* 060186
†King M A *BSc* 060186
†Knox T H 060186
†Oliver M S *BSc(Hons)* 060186
†Semple R J *BSc* 060186
†Skidmore J P *BA(Hons)* 060186
†Tomlinson R K *BSc* 060186
†Wallace D I *BSc* 060186

Short Service Volunteer Officers

Lieutenants

Sinclair D J 290485

2nd Lieutenants

Stanton I P 290785

POSTAL AND COURIER SECTION

Brigadiers

James R N R P *FAAI FBIM FInstAM* 300683

Colonels

Calcutt L G 300680
Streatfield D L *FBIM* 300680
Kelly R J N 300683

Lieutenant Colonels

Lea F H 300679
Wescott P 300679
Platt J R *AAAI* 300680
Browne M A 300681
Swanson D 300682
Butt W F *AAAI* 300683

Majors

Winfield I *MBIM MIIM* 311275
McCandlish B A 311276
Miles B V 300678
Stanley H P 311279
Brown T McG *CGIA* psc† 300980
Cash B J *AAAI MBIM* 300980
Linden B 300980
Grimes P J 300984
McIntosh S B *BA(Hons)* psc† 300984
Morris P D 300984

Captains

Meacher G J (*A/Maj* 090985) 070982
Kent D J (*A/Maj* 090484) 241182
Faulkner M E 060284
Wand N J 060284
Hillyer C G *TEng(CEI) ASERT* (*A/Maj* 171284) 220284
Finnigan C J 110784
Fenwick S C 090685
Small R S 040286

Lieutenants

Whittaker T P 021081
Bingham K K (*A/Capt* 011185) 230183
Knight P A 110584

Postal Executive Officers

Twigg W E 160577
Maj 260985
Damant W N *Capt* 220383
O'Rourke P J *Capt* 300484

Special Regular Officers

Majors

Siddall I M 300679
Lyons E J 300981
Linney P B 300982
Eeles W 300983
Cussons P B 300984
MacFarlane S M 300984

Captains

Prewer E R lcc 251075
Austin K V *TEng(CEI) FSERT* 120780
Ruggiero C (*A/Maj* 141085) 230381
Wilson A B 190582
Hughes H A *BA* 280383
Redfern P L 110583

Lieutenants

Strickland A J 090985

Short Service Officers

Captains

Burlinson A (*A/Maj* 100286) 010881
Barr S 230185
Buckley M A *BEM* 230185
Learmont M 040286

Lieutenants

Donovan J R (*A/Capt* 300985) 010982

2nd Lieutenants

Hardiman S M 280285

ROYAL CORPS OF SIGNALS

The figure of Mercury holding a Caduceus in the left hand the right hand aloft poised with the left foot on a globe all silver, above the globe a Scroll inscribed *'Certa Cito'* and below on each side six laurel leaves all gold, the whole ensigned with The Crown in gold.

Regimental Marches

Quick March..........The Royal Signals March — Begone Dull Care
Slow March..........HRH The Princess Anne

Agents..........Lloyds Bank PLC Cox's & King's Branch

Corps Headquarters..........56 Regency Street, London, SW1P 4AD
(*Tel No: Millbank Military* 240)

Alliances

The Canadian Armed Forces..........Communications and Electronics Branch
Australian Military Forces..........The Royal Australian Corps of Signals
New Zealand Army..........Royal New Zealand Corps of Signals
Indian Army..........Corps of Signals
Pakistan Army..........Signal Corps
Sri Lanka Army..........The Signal Corps
Malaysian Armed Forces..........Malaysian Signal Corps
Zambia Army..........Zambia Corps of Signals

Affiliated Regiment

Queen's Gurkha Signals

Colonel in Chief..........*HRH The Princess* Anne *Mrs* Mark Phillips *GCVO*

Master of Signals..........Maj Gen J M W Badcock *CB MBE DL* ret pay..........271182

Colonels Commandant..........Maj Gen A A G Anderson *CB* ret pay..........180680
Maj Gen E J Hellier *CBE* ret pay..........010281
Maj Gen J M W Badcock *CB MBE DL* ret pay..........271182
*Maj Gen A C Birtwistle *CB CBE* ret pay..........110683
Maj Gen J H Hild *MBE*..........100684
Maj Gen R Benbow *CB*..........181185

Brigadiers

Alexander J O C *OBE* rcds psc† 300680
Burrows J R *ADC BA* jssc psc 300681
Last C N *OBE* ndc psc† 300681
Sprackling I O J *OBE BSc(Eng)* rcds psc† 300681
Dally P A *CBE ADC* sq TE 300682
Davies P R rcds psc† 300682
Shapter I R D psc† osc(NIG) 300682
Cook R F L *MSc CEng FIEE CPhysMInstP* psc† 300683
Maynard F R psc 300683
Olds K H sq 300683
Russell J A P nadc jssc psc 300683
Westlake J *MBIM* psc osc(NIG) 300683
Almonds J H *BSc CEng MIEE MIERE FBIM* psc† TE 300684
Wheawell T H *BSc(Eng)* psc† 300684
Cowan S *OBE BA* psc† 300685
Marples M *OBE* ndc psc 300685
Maynard R F *MBE BSc(Eng)* psc† 300685
Topple M R psc† 300685

Colonels

Hackworth T W *OBE BSc(Eng) MSc CEng FIEE MBCS* ndc sq TE (*L/Brig* 290685) 300679
Tanner R J *CEng MIEE* sq TE 300679
Verdon G C *OBE FBIM* psc 300681
Whitehead D C psc† 300681
Hales M J *CEng FIERE MBIM* sq TE 300682
Moss N *MIEE FBIM* psc† TE (*A/Brig* 210286) 300682
Barnett G *MBE MBIM MISM* sq TE 300683
Colman M F H ndc sq 300683
Goldney P *MBIM* ndc psc† ph pl 300683
Gordon S G McK psc† 300683
Mackinlay H G *LVO* sq 300683
Austin B J psc 300684
Carr-Smith S R psc† 300684
Garton C T psc 300684
Pickard M J ndc psc 300684
Robins W J P *OBE BEng CEng MIEE* psc† 300684
Rowland P J *FBIM* psc 300684
Ayrton M M psc† 300685
Bell R *BA* odc(US) psc† 300685
Bromley J D *OBE* psc 300685
Brown C A sq 300685
Burke K P *BSc(Eng) CEng MIEE* psc† TE 300685
Fielding J V *CEng MIEE* ndc psc† osc(NIG) TE 300685
Mulley E ndc psc† 300685
Walter N A *CEng MIEE MIERE* sq TE 300685
Webb P sq 300685

Lieutenant Colonels

Rigby T (SL) sq 300671
Hills R F (SL) ndc ptsc 300674
Pedley F H (SL) psc 300674
Swindells J W (SL) sq 300674
Weiner M R C (SL) *MBIM* ptsc 300674
Rogers H S De N (SL) sq 300675
Cross C H D *BA* odc(IT) sq ph (*A/Col* 081185) 300676
Hill A J (SL) sq 300676
Wilson H S (SL) psc 300676
Burridge D M A (SL) sq 300677
Jennings M L W psc (*A/Col* 150186) 300677
Jolly D J sq 300677
Spooner P A (SL) sq 300677
Birch G D psc† 300678
Powell C K (SL) sq TE 300678
Spence M C psc (*L/Col* 311285) 300678
Bonaker H M A ndc sq TE 300679
Burke B J (SL) psc† 300679
Crouch I J psc† TE 300679
Graham I *MBIM* psc† 300679
Kennedy W C A *MA AMIEE* psc† sq adp (*A/Col* 120485) 300679
Miller D M O ndc psc (*A/Col* 070386) 300679
Nealon J H T (SL) psc† 300679
Vandyck N A *MBIM* psc† 300679
Belton B L psc† TE 300680
Billingham J G (SL) sq ph pl 300680
Blessington C D A *MBIM* odc(US) psc 300680
Boyle A H *MA* psc† TE (*A/Col* 131285) 300680
Burton D T *MBE* ndc sq 300680
Carter A F *MBE* sq TE 300680
de Bretton-Gordon A P sq 300680

*Representative Colonel Commandant for 1986

Hunt D *OBE CEng MIEE* odc(GE) psc(a)† osc(GE) TE (*A/Col* 200985) 300680
Kavanagh B F sq ph 300680
Lance M J odc(US) psc† 300680
O'Connor B T (SL) sq TEM 300680
Roper W *CEng MIEE* psc† TE (*A/Col* 240585) 300680
Saville R sq 300680
Thompson R D K *OBE BSc(Eng)* psc† TE (*A/Col* 140286) 300680
Chaddock P E A *BA AMIEE* psc† TE (*A/Col* 310186) 300681
Cook D W psc† 300681
Cullen J J psc† 300681
Dudley D G psc† TE 300681
Eastburn A F psc† 300681
Hamilton I J sq 300681
Hervey A J *BSc(Eng) MPhil AIL* odc(FR) osc(FR) sq TE 300681
Louden M S psc 300681
Martin A R *MA* psc† psc 300681
Penny E W sq TE 300681
Siderfin R A C psc 300681
Turner K G *MBE* psc† 300681
Walker M P *MBIM* ndc sq 300681
Waugh T I M *MBE* psc† 300681
Bailey A R psc† 300682
Baly R F psc† 300682
Brown P J R sq 300682
Glydon C H *CEng MIEE* sq TE adp 300682
Hunt A W de V ndc sq 300682
Kerr I E *BA CEng MIEE* psc(a)† TE 300682
Pickup E sq 300682
Ryding K sq 300682
Stutchbury A C sq 300682
Taylor M G *MBE* psc 300682
Webster P B *BSc(Eng) CEng MIEE MIERE MBIM* psc† TE 300682
Wood N F *MA AMIEE* psc† osc(NIG) 300682
Backhouse W H psc† 300683
Budd J F sq 300683
Galloway M J C *OBE* psc 300683
Howard G W *CEng MIERE* psc† TE 300683
Lee S M A psc† 300683
Milford J C sq TE adp 300683
Muir N C sq 300683
Neeve J E psc† osc(NIG) 300683
Payne M A *BSc(Eng)* psc† 300683
Powell E M sq 300683
Shaw M P S *BSc(Eng) CEng MIEE* psc† 300683
Smith R B *CEng MIEE* sq TE 300683
Storr J F *MA* psc(n)† TE 300683
Strong D sq 300683
Walden D J *MBE* psc(a) 300683
Wright R A *BSc(Eng)* psc† TE 300683
Yolland R M psc† 300683
Barrett G J *BSc CEng MIEE* psc† jsdc TE 300684
Bowen M J *BSc* sq jsdc 300684
Carson M K psc† 300684
Clare W R psc TE 300684
Cox J D psc† 300684
Culley H A *MBIM* psc† 300684
Jackman A J R *CEng MIEE* psc(a)† TE 300684
Lowe J H *BSc(Eng) CEng MIEE* psc† TE 300684
Mann G J *BSc(Eng) CEng MIEE* psc† 300684
Munnery J P *BSc(Eng) CEng MIEE* psc† 300684
Overton D G McH *AMIEE* psc† TE 300684
Pritchard P J *BSc(Eng)* psc† 300684
Ridlington M J *BA(Hons) FBIM* psc 300684
Roberts M W H *MBE BSc(Eng) CEng MIEE MBCS MBIM* psc† 300684
Shiner R P *CEng MIEE* sq TE 300684
Steane A L W G sq 300684
Stephenson M R *BSc(Eng) CEng MIEE* psc† 300684
Stokoe J D *MBE* psc† jsdc 300684
Thorne M A psc† 300684
Truluck A E G psc† 300684
Turner I psc† 300684
Walters C J psc† 300684
Butler W K *BSc(Eng)* psc† TEM 300685
Collier C W psc† 300685
Collyer D F M sq 300685
Coltman S A *MBIM* psc 300685
Davies M S *MBE BSc(Eng) CEng MIEE* sq TE 300685
Elford R H G *MBE* psc† 300685
Farrimond R A *BSc(Eng)* psc† 300685
Gardiner D G W sq 300685
Grenville-Jones H *BSc(Eng)* psc† aic TE 300685
Griffin J H *BSc(Eng)* odc(AUST) jsdc 300685
Holmes R J *MBE* psc† 300685
Lowe D J sq TEM 300685
Macklin M J *CEng MIEE* psc† TE 300685
Patterson M D *MBIM* sq 300685
Roberts J H *BA* psc† 300685
Sambell E H sq TEM 300685
Stark R W *BSc(Eng) CEng MIEE MIERE MBIM* sq TE 300685
Whitemore P *BSc CEng MIERE* psc† TEM 300685
Willsher R F sq 300685
Young J C psc(n)† 300685

Majors

Grice T E 090264
Welch A J 030864
Anthonisz D F B *MBIM MInstAM* 151164
Bolt E T 300165
Barrett M C *OBE* (*L/Lt Col* 180281) 080265
Wilson K A C ph pl 010865
Lycett-Gregson D 031265
Hunt E W 060266
Fender J 310766
Garway-Templeman P D 310766
Watson B A 310766
Cunningham W G *MBIM* 240966
Copeland D L *MBE* 120267
Roberts J R ph 120267
Bird M O N 300667
Fletcher F R sq 300667
Carrel E F *MBIM MMS* 300668
Lavender D P J *MBIM* sq TEM 300668
Treseder P A 311268
Hincks J M *MBIM MIIM* psc 300669
Rayner C J 300669
Reynolds R A F *MBIM* 300669
Wilson-Brown M S sq 311269
Mansfield R S 300670
Stubbs D W 300670
Gryspeerdt J L E sq TE 311270
Thomas W P B 311270
Cheal A S 300671
Griffiths W A C *BA(Hons)* 300671
Hoghton R A H 300672
Ingram R B sq 300672
Ovenden J R S 300672
Price W A ph pl 300672
Grist G J H sq 311272
May J H sq TEM 311272
Barrett J *MBE* 300673
Finney G M *AMIEE* sq TE (*A/Lt Col* 300985) 300673
Funnell G R psc† 300673
Higton J F sq TE 300673
Edgar J McD sq 300674
Fraser L G *BScEng(Elec)* sq 311274
Brewis P R *MBIM* sq pl TE TEM (*A/Lt Col* 220885) 300675
Cartwright M J sq 300675
Etheridge R C 300675
Hood R C sq 300675
Law S *MBE* sq 300675
Allen G A ndc sq (*A/Lt Col* 070186) 311275
Lewis O M sq 311275
Browne A F sq 300676
Drew R E S sq 300676
Falla S G 300676
Gravestock R P *MBIM* sq 300676
Podevin D C sq 300676
Robinson B *BA* sq 300676
Windmill R L *CEng MIEE* sq TE 300676
Moncur T F *BSc CEng MIEE MBIM AIL* sq TEM (*A/Lt Col* 100286) 311276
Vigurs Q sq 311276
Briggs A J *BSc* sq TEM 300677
Dickinson P J K sq 300677
Harrison R P sq 300677
Melhuish C D sq 300677
Rumford R J G M sq 300677
Sweetman J M *BSc(Eng) CEng MIEE MIERE* sq TE 300677
Tilson L R J sq (*A/Lt Col* 061285) 300677
Alden M J M sq TE 311277
Case D J 311277
Dick-Peter P R sq 311277
McLean D J sq 311277
Meakin G *MA* psc† 311277
Pearson P C sq (*A/Lt Col* 140286) 311277
Rice M A *BSc(Eng) CEng MIEE* dis sq TEM 311277
Saunders A J *BSc(Eng) CEng MIEE* sq TEM 311277
Treeby C R sq 311277
Exon H J P *BSc* sq TEM 300678
Grierson J A sq 300678
Hallett P A 300678
Ingram J D M sq 300678
Kemp C D McK sq TEM 300678
Lidster W G *BEM* 300678
Martin M L sq 300678
Reed V J sq 300678
Stokes R G 300678
Stuart J F *BSc* sq TEM 300678
Symmons A H sq TE TEM 300678
Urquhart C R *BSc(Eng) MIEE CDipAF* sq TEM 300678
Arthur C *BA AMIEE* sq TE 311278
Dobson D W sq 311278
Doody J S *MBIM MIIM* sq TEM (*A/Lt Col* 011185) 311278
Gale A R *MBE* sq (*A/Lt Col* 080186) 311278
Gardner R A J psc(a)† 311278
Greig C B sq TE TEM 311278

Royal Corps of Signals – continued

Hughes D P *BSc(Eng) CEng* sq 311278
Jessett D J *BSc CEng MIERE* sq TEM (*A/Lt Col* 141185) 311278
Kimber A T B sq 311278
McLuckie D S psc 311278
Shuker I C psc† 311278
Siddall S M *BSc(Eng)* psc† 311278
Abbott R D *MA* sq 300679
Danby K G *MA* sq 300679
French L G sq 300679
Hayes J P sq TEM 300679
Higson B C P *BSc(Eng)* TEM 300679
Mountford T P 300679
Thwaites R C A *BSc(Eng) CEng MIEE* sq 300679
Todd P W *BEM* 300679
Tydeman J D *BSc(Eng)* sq adp 300679
Carmichael G A sq 311279
Ebdon R J *BSc(Eng)* psc† TEM 311279
Fairley N C sq 311279
Garrod F J sq TE TEM 311279
Goodman G H odc(NL) sq 311279
Innocent P T psc† 311279
Kington P J J *BSc(Eng)* sq TEM 311279
Paul S S *BSc(Eng)* psc† (*A/Lt Col* 061285) 311279
Rutherford R F sq 311279
Wallace A M *BSc(Eng)* psc 311279
Wilkinson M C *MA* psc TEM 311279
Adams H M *MBE* sq 300980
Amberton J R S sq 300980
Anderson M J *MBIM* 300980
Brown R J *MASEE MISM* 300980
Chambers J C *BSc(Eng)* psc(a)† 300980
Chubb B *BSc(Eng)* psc† TEM 300980
Clarke W M *BSc(Eng)* TEM 300980
Conlon C P 300980
Donaldson G N sq 300980
Drake R G 300980
Elliot G R psc† 300980
Fish T G B sq 300980
Freeman R N B *BSc* sq TE TEM 300980
Graham R D M *BSc(Eng)* TEM 300980
Ham H H *BSc* psc† 300980
Harper C R *BA* psc† 300980
Hughes B J *BSc(Eng) CEng MIEE* sq TEM 300980
Lovatt A M *BSc* psc† TEM 300980
Maddren G P sq TEM 300980
Nind C V psc aic 300980
Reid M S psc† 300980
Richardson D C 300980
Sanders R J 300980
Schuler A J *BSc(Eng)* psc† (*A/Lt Col* 140386) 300980
Simpson J C B *BSc(Eng)* TEM 300980
Skaife R J *BSc(Eng)* psc 300980
Smith J T *BA* TE TEM 300980
Spencer C I *BSc(Eng)* sq TEM 300980
Strivens V G sq 300980
Strong I M G 300980
Sugdon A 300980
Symonds R D 300980
Thomas G J *AMBCS* sq ph adp 300980
Wallis M S *BSc(Eng)* sq TEM 300980
Williams P 300980
Bannister D R 300981
Binham R F *MBE BSc(Eng)* TEM 300981
Blake J psc† 300981
Bowles P J 300981
Clark A J 300981
Collins M J P sq TE TEM 300981
Donaghy C P sq 300981
Evans R J *BSc BSc(Econ)* psc† 300981
Galpin S D TE TEM 300981
Gibb A H ph 300981
Heck J D *BEng AMIEE* TEM 300981
Hill R G L 300981
Howshall D P *BSc(Eng)* TEM 300981
Hoyle R H *BA* 300981
Hryhoruk P J 300981
Hussey R M J *CGIA* psc† 300981
Jones D B 300981
Kirby J E F psc 300981
Merrick A W *MBE* psc 300981
Noble I A 300981
Palmer D F *BSc(Eng)* sq TEM 300981
Richards P 300981
Sinton M J *BSc(Eng)* sq 300981
Wannell R A 300981
West R J R psc† 300981
Whiddett A G 300981
Axton R F A *BSc(Eng) MBIM* TE TEM adp 300982
Bingham I D *BSc(Eng)* TEM 300982
Brewin W E ph 300982
Burnage J F 300982
Bushell T 300982
Cook J R B psc† 300982
Elson D J 300982
Emslie M J M 300982
Griffiths A J 300982
Helm A 300982
Hope N K P *MBE BSc(Eng)* psc† 300982
Hughes S G *BSc(Eng) MIEE* psc† 300982
Hutt A J 300982
Jefferis M J adp 300982
Lloyd-Jones R J 300982
McKinlay M J 300982
Sheehan M A J *MA* psc 300982
Stabler J W *BSc MPhil* 300982
Wraith J A *MBE* 300982
Allan J N 300983
Burton C J psc† 300983
Crowley W P *BSc(Eng) AMIEE* psc† 300983
Cuthbert R C T TEM 300983
Elford A H G 300983
Grant I R 300983
Grey P J *MA* TEM 300983
Hancock H A R psc† 300983
Hewitt R S *BA* 300983
Hudson J P *BA* psc 300983
Jones A M psc† ph 300983
Kidner S J *BSc* psc† 300983
Maloney P L sq 300983
Parfitt P *BSc* TEM 300983
Poppleton A J *BEng* psc† psc(n) 300983
Raper A J *MA* psc† 300983
Richardson T E M psc† 300983
Shaw J M *MBE* psc 300983
Shepherd J A TE TEM 300983
Stretch M K 300983
Wood A B *BSc(Eng)* TE TEM 300983
Wright C L G *BSc(Eng) CEng MIEE* TEM 300983
Barton-Ancliffe B J TEM 300984
Davies J L psc† 300984
Duncan A 300984
Durham C J adp 300984
Ewbank J K 300984
Fisher M S *BSc(Eng)* 300984
Fisher N F *BSc(Eng)* 300984
Gorford P K 300984
Greig I N 300984
Grey A J *BSc(Eng)* psc† 300984
Hadfield K J psc 300984
Henderson J S A *BSc* psc† 300984
Hoole R T *CGIA* 300984
Johnston M N *BSc* 300984
Johnstone A J 300984
Jones P S TEM 300984
Lawson D J 300984
Lynam D A *MBE BSc(Eng)* psc† 300984
Macfarlane J A *BSc* psc† aic 300984
Manders T R *BSc* TE TEM 300984
Mardo R H psc† 300984
McColville C C psc† 300984
McConnell D *BSc* TEM 300984
Parsons K K W 300984
Ross H A 300984
Rouse P A R 300984
Scott-Morton B J psc† 300984
Shipley G M S psc† 300984
Smedley V T 300984
Turnbull R J 300984
Wills D J *BSc* psc(n)† 300984
Baxter R psc† 300985
Brannigan R V J 300985
Bryning T J P *BSc(Eng)* TE TEM 300985
Crombie R M 300985
Gareze J J C *BSc(Eng)* TE TEM 300985
Holmes R R *BSc(Eng) MSc* psc† dis 300985
Jackson B M M 300985
Jackson N C 300985
Le Gallais C L *BSc(Eng)* 300985
Martin-Rhind D M 300985
Moreland J P TEM 300985
Neale P B *MA* 300985
Robertshaw P 300985
Thompson N J *BSc* 300985

Captains

Conran D W M adp 191275
Holden P S 191275
Stanners M R S 181276
White A P R 140478
Anderson M ph 040878
Brown I R C 040878
Evans A T *BSc(Eng) MSc* psc† dis TEM (*A/Maj* 201285) 080379
Beach A D *BSc(Eng)* TEM 090379
Costello P J 090379
Cox C M *BSc(Eng)* TEM 090379
Grieves M N *BSc* psc† (*A/Maj* 201285) 090379
Griffiths I W *BSc(Eng)* (*A/Maj* 100186) 090379
Ellis R J J *BSc* 110879
Batho R W 100979
Harrison A W H *BSc(Eng)* TEM 100979
Proctor D G 100979
Robertson I O (*A/Maj* 090284) 100979
Hewitt B *BSc* 031079
Bowering A J 301279
Cary G J *BSc(Eng)* TE TEM 301279
Corbet G D 301279

Robertson D J TEM
(*A/Maj* 090784) 301279
Byrne L K *BSc* 130280
Fielder I R *BSc* TEM
(*A/Maj* 200286) 130280
Plumb L J *BSc* 040380
Kite A J R 050980
Blum R W 090980
Day P R *BSc(Eng) FRGS*
(*A/Maj* 041185) 090980
Forster A D 090980
Kinnaird R J 090980
Little M A *BSc* TEM 090980
Moore N T *BA* 090980
Rimell T P 090980
Rollins J W *BSocSc*
(*A/Maj* 300985) 090980
Stockdale M R G *BSc(Eng)* TEM
090980
Turpin S J *BSc* 090980
Whittaker C J *BSc(Eng)* 090980
Willis J M 090980
Canham T W 291280
Colborn H N S 291280
Dyer M J M
(*A/Maj* 291185) 291280
McGrath J R M 291280
Thurston R M *BSc(Eng)* 291280
Davis R B *BSc(Eng) AKC* 030281
Johnstone A H *BA* 030381
Pritchard K 090581
Weston R T 090581
Wilson K G *BSc(Eng)* TEM
(*A/Maj* 040685) 090581
Smith S J 170581
Russ A W *BSc* 120881
Ellis P N *MA* 030981
Ewing D S *BSc(Eng)* 080981
Fletcher J L 080981
Jones S W *BSc(Eng)* 080981
Roberts A P R 080981
Steed R J 080981
Thomas J E *MBE* 080981
Walker P G 080981
Ward A J *BSc(Eng)* TEM 080981
Ridley-Jones A K *BSc FGS* 290981
Andrews S I *BSc(Eng)* TEM
(*A/Maj* 010785) 281281
Butler M *BSc(Eng)* 281281
Corbin N J 281281
Foxley I *BSc* 281281
Gigg T J *BSc* TEM
(*A/Maj* 010785) 281281
Goodfellow K W *BSc(Eng)* 281281
Harrison A J H *BSc(Eng)* TEM
281281
Young S J S *BSc* 281281
Taylor K *BSc* TEM 260382
Moseley P J *MA* 030482
Good R J *BSc(Eng)* TEM 080582
Steele D MacD *BSc* 080582
McDowall D 090682
Barfoot R D *BA* 060982
Barrett K P *BSc(Eng)* 060982
Evans R O N *BSc(Eng)* 060982
Gale J M 060982
Harris S J *BSc(Eng)* 060982
Heath S J 060982
Inshaw T G *BSc(Eng)* 060982
Leach G R *BSc(Eng)*
(*A/Maj* 161285) 060982
McIntyre J TEM 060982
Oldfield P J 060982
Pearce A L 060982
Rowlinson D E *BSc(Eng)* 060982
Williamson R J 130982
Coulthard J P MacD 070283
Field A *BSc* 070283
Hogan J E 210383
Tuson A J *BSc* 050983

Durward K J *BSc* 031083
Hargreaves D A *MA* 031083
Peacocke T J *BSc* 031083
Smith G *BA* 031083
Cousins R F M *BSc(Eng)* 081083
Eaton P H *BA* 081083
Gilyeat M C 081083
Lunn S O *BA* 081083
Mackenzie I W *BSc(Eng)* 081083
Owen C *BSc(Eng)* 081083
Pratley P A *BSc(Eng) AMIEE*
081083
Swainson N A *BSc(Eng)* 081083
Telford P M 081083
Whyman G J 081083
Burtenshaw C N *BSc(Eng)* 060284
Complin M R 060284
Ewell A A 060284
King P *BSc* 060284
Larkam D W 060284
Lithgow M *BSc(Eng)* 060284
Rough M A *BSc BSc(Eng)* 060284
Whitby D J *BSc(Eng)* 060284
Nicholson-Taylor P T *BSc* 070284
Johns S C 150284
Cost M 230284
Kendall A E *BSc* 050384
Turner C H *BA* 110384
Thomas R G 010484
Yeoell N J *BSc* 030484
Vardy D J *BSc* 110484
Seraph I W R 100684
Terrington J A 100684
Dryburgh J 230784
Hunt S P *BSc* 010884
Mills D M 160984
Coram B A *BSc* 240984
Fisher K P *BSc(Eng)* 260984
Austen N H D 081084
Condie I A J *BSc* 081084
Crawford D A *BA* 081084
Green S C 081084
King C R *BSc(Eng)* 081084
Nicholson R G 081084
Pincott M E *BSc(Eng)* 081084
Rafferty G J T *BSc* 081084
Taylor P C J *BSc(Eng)* 081084
Wood N R N *BSc* 081084
Crane A P *BSc* 010285
Avison B P *BSc(Eng)* 050285
Coupland W P 050285
Herniman S A 050285
James G A *BSc* 050285
Johnson J S H *BSc* 050285
Leyland G R 050285
McNeill G J 050285
Morphet A N 050285
Tiffin D A *BSc BSc(Eng) AMIEE*
050285
Tucker M F *BSc* 050285
Harrison N P 040685
Clark J W 090685
Edwards M W 090685
Grogan P J 090685
Flint E M *BA* 010885
Peck J G 010885
Keen N *BA* 030985
Campbell W M 071085
Grant F N *BSc* 071085
Leigh S A *BSc* 071085
Meyer D P 071085
Powell D W *BA* 071085
Richardson S J *BSc(Eng)* 071085
Rowley J *BSc(Eng)* 071085
Strawbridge R F *BSc* 071085
Sullivan D A 071085
Westerman I D *BSc* 071085
Dent M J 011185
Burden D J H *BSc(Eng) ACGI*
091185

Thatcher V J *BSc* 201285
Harwell A A S *MA* 231285
Rock A J 230186
Brand A G *BSc(Hons)* 040286
Bucklow I K *BSc(Eng)* 040286
Holman M S *BSc(Eng)* 040286
Jones D A H 040286
Kennedy N D pl 040286
Macaulay D G *BSc(Eng)* 040286
Miller C W S 040286
Moloney P J D 040286
Towers P R *BA(Cantab)* 040286
Couch N D 140286

Lieutenants

Bradley H T
(*A/Capt* 030985) 081281
Gillespie P 081281
Johnson A M 081281
May S J 081281
Wilson J P *BSc(Eng)* 081281
Ford P R 210282
Body J E *BSc(Eng)* 020382
Brown P A *BSc(Eng)* 120482
Clapp R N *BSc(Eng)* 120482
Connor F J *BSc(Eng)* 120482
Higgs A B *BA* 120482
Lowe S P R *BSc(Eng)* 120482
Lugg J S *BSc* 120482
McComb A W T 120482
Owen C R *BSc(Eng)* 120482
James A W 250482
Perry M J 060882
Callaghan S J 090882
Davies N R 090882
Dexter S C 090882
McAllister D E A 090882
McGrory C D 090882
Pender-Johns T W *BSc* 090882
Renfrey S R 090882
Smith G M *BSc* 090882
Sparshatt R G C 090882
Wadey T C *BA* 090882
Watts T J P 090882
Wise M P 090882
Wood A J *BScTech* 090882
Goff A A 131282
Hodges S D
(*A/Capt* 020985) 131282
Bunce J R C *BSc* 110483
Castle-Smith M S 110483
Eaton M A 110483
Herstell S J 110483
Osment P A *BA* 110483
Perks J P B
(*A/Capt* 010185) 110483
Pope N A W *BA* 110483
Pratt D M *BSc* 110483
Roberts F P 110483
Sharp R A 110483
Borrill N J 080883
Mason G R *BSc* 080883
Richards C C 080883
Thompson N F 080883
Whitehead K 080883
Holliday P J 121283
Hudson A P 121283
Shaw M G 121283
Turner J 121283
Alexander M D W 090484
Ardagh-Walter S J *BSc* 090484
Baines M 090484
Dakin J W 090484
Felton S E *BSc* 090484
Glibbery P W 090484
Harris J E 090484
Morley-Kirk J H R *BA* 090484
Mullan A H 090484
Wilson R P 090484

Royal Corps of Signals – continued

Workman S R 090484
Bertram J C R 070884
Butlin R M *BSc* 070884
Campbell-Black A H 070884
Campbell-Black L B 070884
Clark C M 070884
Metcalfe N P 070884
Norton G R *BSc* 070884
Odling G H A 070884
Pople P V 070884
Somerville D W 070884
Trimble A K 070884
Quinlan R J 111284
Broad A D R 090485
Cary R N 090485
Davis M 090485
Halstead D G 090485
Hudson D B 090485
Ross A G 090485
Vickery S J 090485
Macrostie S K 060885
Thackray C J 060885
Charnock J S 070486
Stevens N S 070486
Williams J C 070486

2nd Lieutenants

††Flint H M *BA(Oxon)* 030982
††Trevor R L 020983
Warne D B 070484
Appleton R S 040884
Compston J A 040884
Cooper T C 040884
Hill A G 040884
Horn G P 040884
Peel P D 040884
Swindells J E 040884
Walker M A 040884
††Grant G R 230984
†Stringer A J 230984
Evans K L 081284
Fensom M J 081284
Adams J S 130485
Bizley D J M 130485
Brammer J S 130485
Burgin A D 130485
Coldrey N C 130485
Dewar N I R 130485
Egan J A 130485
Graham P A 130485
Hanson M G 130485
Healey R J 130485
Holden N G 130485
Hunter I N 130485
Jenkins H A 130485
Tod J R 130485
Walker N A 130485
Williamson S M 130485
Freeman R J 100885
Hinsley C J 100885
Hix D P 100885
Hodges J M 100885
Maclennan F G S 100885
Munday A K 100885
Owen G L 100885
††Ayers J E 240985
††Picknell A D J 240985
Duncan A J 141285
Jones T M 141285

Staff Quartermasters

Knight R F *MBE* 301174
Lt Col 071084

Quartermasters

Wilson M E 171172
Lt Col 160283
Orr F M *OBE* 080373
Lt Col 061281
Cowe A J 011273
Maj 010479
Cleaver B 311273
Lt Col 290883
Thomas D G 010774
Maj 010479
Simpson A J 120775
Lt Col 010584
Rose J A *AInstTA MBIM MISM* 071175
Lt Col 230984
Acott R 301276
Maj 010479
Ient J E 270377
Maj 010479
Peake R A *BEM* 010477
Maj 020879
Cran T E B *MInstAM MASMC* 010677
Lt Col 100985
Noble P A 270877
Maj 061180
Keany T 271177
Maj 030682
Breese R C 090178
Maj 010479
Richardson C H 060378
Maj 151179
Izzo J H 140878
Maj 081083
Meekings H A C *MISM* 161078
Maj 090481
Vasper R 011178
Maj 060183
Haydon J M 290179
Maj 061180
Brodie R C 260379
Maj 010885
Hope G W E 050779
Maj 050784
Rogers F D 030979
Maj 010782
Stephens C E 011079
Maj 041182
Styles B J 280180
Maj 030283
Markie C 010380
Maj 020284
Webster E T A 101180
Maj 201185
Wallace W G 221280
Maj 040785
Abbott A E *MBE MISM* 050181
Maj 070684
Danells R L 050181
Maj 041084
Davies A *MBIM* 050181
Maj 050484
Richardson J H 060481
Maj 020884
Prees J V 130781
Maj 041182
Davies-Stewart K C A 211281
Maj 010885
French C K R 211281
Maj 070684
Jennings M *Capt* 170582
Jarrett T *Capt* 180982
Smart M C K *MBE* *Capt* 061282
Worrall F E *Capt* 040483
Nicoll J R *Capt* 090583
Hudson B M *Capt* 040783
Akehurst J G P *Capt* 110783
Pearce R *MInstAM MISM* 031083
Maj 070285
Hargreaves S *Capt* 090184
Morgan A G *Capt* 090184
Robinson M N *Capt* 090184
Laverick F *BEM MInstAM MISM* 200284
Maj 090186
Gainford T R *MISM* *Capt* 270484
Vale R G *Capt* 270484
Buckley R I *Capt* 140185
Young B *Capt* 250185
Homewood C E *Capt* 060285
McLaren R W *Capt* 060285
Jeffery L A *MInstAM MISM*
Maj 250385
Platts G *MISM* *Capt* 280385
Lockwood C W *Capt* 300385
Turner J N *Capt* 010585
Zimmer V T P *Capt* 010585
Fortune R *BEM* *Capt* 010785
Lamerton D A *MISM*
Capt 060985
Collins R M D *Capt* 010186
Longhurst D G *Capt* 190286
Evans S *Capt* 210486

Technical Officers in Telecommunications

Jenkins R E 080267
Maj 240975
Soward P F 110967
Lt Col 300484
Devanney P 010168
Lt Col 010282
Boulter R C 310368
Lt Col 051083
Johnson P *TEng(CEI) FSERT* 110469
Maj 190279
Murray A J *BA* 050569
Maj 010479
Kimber B A 300669
Maj 010479
Lund R 300669
Maj 010479
Lidstone I R *BA CEng MIERE* 291269
Maj 010479
Armitage C N *MBE* 280570
Maj 010479
Smith F A *TEng(CEI) MASEE FSERT AIIM* 010870
Maj 010479
Cherry M D *CEng MIERE* 170870
Maj 010479
Short E M *TEng(CEI) FSERT* 170371
Lt Col 190284
Butler M *MBE* 020871
Lt Col 291082
Stoddart T McK *MBE TEng(CEI) MASEE MITE* 270372
Lt Col 040186
Graham W F *MBE* 010972
Maj 050281
Holland E 061172
Maj 061180
Goodman R *BEM* 011272
Lt Col 310583
Steeples J P *TEng(CEI) FSERT* 090773
Maj 090781
Prime D 031273
Maj 060582
O'Connor D 161273
Maj 070182
Webb C G 100374
Maj 060881
Langford M 010474
Maj 010482

Bridgeman J V		080474
	Maj	060582
Brown D *MBE*		010974
	Maj	050682
Phillips J A		011175
	Maj	050583
Everett T J		270476
	Maj	060183
Knox J D *TEng(CEI) FSERT*		150576
	Maj	260184
Dyer A F *MBE TEng(CEI) MASEE*		010876
	Maj	291084
Hammonds J M		100377
	Maj	040785
Limb R M		160377
	Maj	040785
Freeston D J		260677
	Maj	050484
Tricker R L *TEng(CEI) MASEE FSERT MBIM MIExE*		121277
	Maj	030584
McKay R A *MBE*		010478
	Maj	031085
McMullen A B		030778
	Maj	070385
Porritt A J	*Capt*	030778
Maltby B W		310778
	Maj	050784
Cochrane W G S *TEng(CEI) FSERT MISM*	*Capt*	061178
Kay T	*Capt*	050279
Meachin B A *TEng(CEI)*		230479
	Maj	030185
Lynn A	*Capt*	060879
Scriven R C	*Capt*	060879
Gould A B		030979
	Maj	020585
Wherry R J	*Capt*	190580
Forbes I	*Capt*	050181
Harries D J *TEng(CEI)*	*Capt*	050181
Kent W P *MBE*	*Capt*	050181
McRae K R	*Capt*	050181
Yule G *BEM*	*Capt*	010581
Sullivan G J	*Capt*	050581
Kelbie R B	*Capt*	060781
Campbell M G H	*Capt*	040182
Hope I D *TEng(CEI) FSERT*	*Capt*	010382
Macdonald J	*Capt*	010382
Turner A G *BEM*	*Capt*	010382
Lawson W	*Capt*	050782
Pettifer B P	*Capt*	030183
Smith J M *MBE*	*Capt*	070383
Brittenden A G A	*Capt*	030583
Rotherham D G	*Capt*	040783
Smurthwaite P C	*Capt*	040783
Davis P H *BA*	*Capt*	031083
Gallagher B J *TEng(CEI) FSERT*	*Capt*	031083
Patton N	*Capt*	090184
Jasiok J R *BA TEng(CEI) MASEE FSERT*	*Capt*	020484
Spearpoint G S	*Capt*	010584
Connor H E	*Capt*	020784
Offord R C *MBE*	*Capt*	100984
Payne C W *TEng(CEI) FSERT MIElecIE*	*Capt*	140185
White J	*Capt*	040385
Hall A J *MBE*	*Capt*	060485
Farrow S D	*Capt*	010785
Howes R N	*Capt*	060885
Shawyer P D *MIEE*	*Capt*	030985
Tanner L	*Capt*	300985
James R A	*Capt*	021285
Woodhouse D M	*Capt*	171285

Traffic Officers

Davies A J D		010168
	Maj	160276
Elliott J J *MBE*		170568
	Lt Col	290584
Howie A M P *BEM*		291270
	Lt Col	121081
French K M		220972
	Lt Col	311284
Coxon W		240173
	Maj	100480
Ankers J W		180973
	Maj	080580
Abbiss B		260474
	Maj	060380
Leitch A *MBIM MISM*		070475
	Maj	060483
Beasley J P		070676
	Maj	021080
Cudlip A W *MITD*		140976
	Maj	030383
Ferguson J M *MISM*		140277
	Maj	020683
Gurr R H *MBIM MISM*		310377
	Maj	050484
Price R D		130677
	Maj	130685
Dodman R A		010178
	Maj	031183
Lightfoot C N		220578
	Maj	020284
Lile G	*Capt*	021078
Noon J T		041278
	Maj	060183
Morrison J		160179
	Maj	030185
Powell G		050279
	Maj	061083
Ross J M	*Capt*	020479
Daniel P J	*Capt*	020779
Yates L	*Capt*	020779
Tunmore D J *QGM*	*Capt*	221079
Waumsley L T		300780
	Maj	300780
Cheesman W J	*Capt*	050181
Meehan J R	*Capt*	050181
Whydell A J *MISM*	*Capt*	050181
Nichols J T *QGM*	*Capt*	050581
McLoughlin F C	*Capt*	060781
Eastland C M	*Capt*	211281
Harkins A O	*Capt*	040182
Baker R A		010282
	Maj	311085
Mansfield R W	*Capt*	010382
Lovell J E *MISM*	*Capt*	220382
Jones E C	*Capt*	040582
Vannan J O S	*Capt*	030183
McLoughlin P J	*Capt*	070383
Rayment J D	*Capt*	210383
Locke W A *MBE*	*Capt*	040483
Heyes D R	*Capt*	040783
Nicol M	*Capt*	040783
Isherwood J	*Capt*	020484
Chisholm R C W	*Capt*	010584
Sleightholm I	*Capt*	010584
Castle P M	*Capt*	020784
Doherty J G T *MBE*	*Capt*	011084
Letori G A	*Capt*	011084
McAneny B	*Capt*	050285
Donnelly W J	*Capt*	300485
Weston D G	*Capt*	300485
Birchall C H	*Capt*	010785
Gilchrist D I	*Capt*	170985
Papworth R C	*Capt*	300985
Rix L	*Capt*	221085
Clay R F	*Capt*	181185
Rattray W M	*Capt*	021285
Naylor N J H	*Capt*	171285
McLoughlin T J	*Capt*	110286

Traffic Officers (Radio)

Storey L G H *BEM*		010975
	Maj	020683
Cooper A B		031077
	Maj	031085
Wills D G *MBE*	*Capt*	030583
Smith D D	*Capt*	260484
Honor C T	*Capt*	010385
Westwell P *MISM*	*Capt*	040385
Good R J	*Capt*	170685

Directors of Music

Turner G *MBE BA LGSM FTCL ARCM ALCM* psm		040274
	Maj	220981

Special Regular Officers

Majors

Selby J R *MBIM MIIM* TEM	300677
Halliburton D G	300679
MacCulloch P H	300679
Fiskel W J L	300981
Pawlow D S	300981
Cory N J	300982
Adamson R *MISM*	300984
Boyle J	300984
Byrne J P	300984
Ladds N E	300984
McGann P T	300984
Campbell F B	300985
Clark W J *MBE*	300985

Captains

Bardell H J (*A/Maj* 100186)	100979
Clague R A ph (*A/Maj* 090985)	090980
Crane S A	291280
Harrison B	080181
Lockie S	270681
Cole P D (*A/Maj* 280386)	020781
Harris J A *MISM* (*A/Maj* 170885)	040881
McVeigh A D J (*A/Maj* 210685)	100981
Wise D L	061281
Brownlee I P	210382
Briant R C A	061082
McMahon J P	061082
Trevis G J	261282
Filby P J *BSc(Eng)*	070283
Lawrence C R	070283
Perkin T A	300383
Mills R G	050583
Kearns P	060783
Clark G	051083
Kirkman J M	051083
Courtney R J *MBE*	040184
Wilkin P G F	060284
Boyle A M	010384
Banham E J W	040584
Etherton R P	040584
Keenan A E	140684
Gallie A D	041084
Hewett A D *MInstAM*	041084
Lumley G M	041084
Robinson P D	041084
Hocking E S *BSc*	050285
Russell A	070385

Royal Corps of Signals – continued

Allen J A	030585
Boag A W (*A/Maj* 090985)	030585
Mason C S	030585
Riley F T J A	020785
Wakerley C	080186
Long S J	060286
Coupar M A	200286
Hannagan R	050386
Miles W V	050386
Stevenson M A	260386

Lieutenants

Marshall S G	011181
Neillings B P (*A/Capt* 290684)	011181
Newman J M M	020182
Sheldon R J (*A/Capt* 110285)	020182
Pengelley T J (*A/Capt* 180285)	050882
Hails R (*A/Capt* 100385)	040982
Olive M S (*A/Capt* 110385)	040982
Radford M J *MBE* (*A/Capt* 220785)	021082
Stubbings C G (*A/Capt* 040985)	021082
Turnbull S J (*A/Capt* 071185)	191082
Adam J (*A/Capt* 160985)	301082
Hornby J W (*A/Capt* 260985)	181282
Bonnett J (*A/Capt* 011185)	010183
Clarke P (*A/Capt* 150785)	010183
Peel B R (*A/Capt* 050386)	010183
Cheetham C (*A/Capt* 120885)	060283
Jackson S N *BEM*	100283
Walker D J	030383
Bancroft F A (*A/Capt* 310386)	300383
Fogg M D (*A/Capt* 141085)	300383
Smith B	300383
Ledwards M V (*A/Capt* 010186)	100683
Hearn G	210883
Hamilton R A	030983
Hornsby D (*L/Capt* 100386)	030983
Richardson J E	010484
McDonnell J A	111284
Hume I	090485
Anderson G D	060885
Cooper J W	060885
Finneran M A	060885
Griffiths N J	101285
Longley N P	100186
Kenyon D F H	070486
McCourt L D	070486

2nd Lieutenants

Nott M	040884
Purser S J	081284
Dobson R M	100885
Cotterell R C *MCSP*	141285
Elliott G W S	141285
O'Connor P C	141285

Short Service Officers

Captains

Bresloff R S *MISM*	060177
Heath A R (*A/Maj* 040484)	061077
Park G *MInstAM MISM*	050979
Guest T *MISM AMIMS*	020481
Lee F R *MBE MInstAM*	100981
Wood D G *MBE MISM* (*A/Maj* 020985)	100981
Poole D J T *MBE*	030382
Springer M G *BEM MISM*	060582
Bates R (*A/Maj* 190486)	070782
Hill A B	070782
Frost J W L *ASTA*	020383
Kellett E J P	010384
Butterworth E	050484
Bateson N J *BSc*	041084
Thwaites P	271084
Lancaster J S A	050285
Haughie G G	070385
Marman J *BSc*	150385
Gibson N D *BSc*	071085
Hall J E *BSc*	071085
Keegan C B *BSc*	071085
Wallis S P	071085
Cameron-Mowat I *MA(Hons)*	040286
Lewis-Taylor G M *BSc*	040286
Knobel P B	110386
Millard C E *BA*	150387

Lieutenants

Hodgkiss P A *BSc*	040881
Harris R	011181
Windsor Brown S P	081281
Cain P (*A/Capt* 150984)	040382
Gill N W *BSc*	120482
Madsen A J *BSc*	120482
Wilson A J	270482
Allman A J *BSc*	090882
Stephenson P *BA*	090882
Thornber K P	090882
Lockwood R W (*A/Capt* 050386)	301082
Lund H	010183
Budworth E L (*A/Capt* 241085)	300383
Hunt G W T	300383
Croft S *BSc*	110483
Davis E A *LLB(Hons)*	110483
Giles R P *BA*	110483
Griffiths M *BSc*	110483
Grimson M A *BSc*	110483
King J P *BA*	110483
Mather R G *BSc*	110483
Raleigh D S *BSc*	110483
Dunn M B *BSc*	080883
Hancock M D J	080883
Hearn A P	080883
Spencer D P *BSc*	080883
Wallace J R *BEM*	030983
Llewellyn M P *FRGS*	090484
Phillips R C *BSc*	090484
Bristow A P	070884
Sharman S R *BA DipLA*	070884
Godbolt N D	100984
Lewis C M R	111284
Wareham H M	090485
Bradshaw I J	060885
Favager I G	060885
Salvoni R C P	060885
Henschel G H	200985
Bailey P A	101285
Hogarth N E	101285
Metcalfe A	101285
Wood D G R	101285
Davies P J	070486
Parry-Jones R E W	070486

2nd Lieutenants

†Standen I G *BA*	
†Watt P J *MA*	
Field J S	040884
Howie R A	040884
Billingham M G	081284
Caleb N R N	081284
Llewellyn D C	081284
Bewsher R G G	130485
Birleson I P	130485
Bowers K W	100885
Evans P R M	100885
Fletcher A J	100885
Fraser J H	100885
Whimpenny D I	100885
†Paterson A *BSc(Hons)*	060985
†Pool R C A *BA*	060985
†Ramshaw M *BSc*	060985
†Woodham M J *BSc*	060985
Coleman M S	141285
Deans G	141285
†Lawrence I G *BSc(Hons)*	060186
†Smith J A F *BSc*	060186
†Vlasto J *BA*	060186

Short Service Volunteer Officers

Lieutenants

Wenlock P D *BSc*	010385
Kelly R J	250685

THE GUARDS DIVISION

GRENADIER GUARDS

The Queen's Colours:—

1st Battalion—Gules (crimson): In the centre The Crown; in base a Grenade fired proper.

2nd Battalion—Gules (crimson): In the centre the Royal Cypher reversed and interlaced or, ensigned with The Crown: in base a Grenade fired proper; in the dexter canton the Union.

3rd Battalion— As for the 2nd Battalion, with, for difference, issuing from the Union in bend a pile wavy or. (Suspended Animation)

The Regimental Colours:—

The Union: In the centre a company badge ensigned with The Crown; in base a Grenade fired proper. The 30 company badges are borne in rotation, 3 at a time, one on the Regimental Colour of each of the Battalions.

The Battle Honours shown in heavy type below are borne upon the Queen's and Regimental Colours:—

Tangier 1680, Namur 1695, Gibraltar 1704-5, Blenheim, Ramillies, Oudenarde, Malplaquet, Dettingen, Lincelles, Egmont-op-Zee, Corunna, Barrosa, Nive, Penisula, Waterloo, Alma, Inkerman, Sevastopol, Tel-el-Kebir, Egypt 1882, Suakin 1885, Khartoum, Modder River, South Africa 1889-1902

The Great War—Mons, Retreat from Mons, **Marne 1914, Aisne 1914, Ypres 1914-17,** Langemarck 1914, Gheluvelt, Nonne Bosschen, Neuve Chapelle, Aubers, Festubert 1915, **Loos, Somme 1916, 18,** Ginchy, Flers-Courcelette, Morval, Pilckem, Menin Road, Poelcappelle, Passchendaele, **Cambrai 1917, 18,** St Quentin, Bapaume 1918, **Arras 1918,** Lys, **Hazebrouck,** Albert 1918, Scarpe 1918, **Hindenburg Line,** Havrincourt, Canal du Nord, Selle, Sambre, **France and Flanders 1914-18**

The Second World War— Dyle, **Dunkirk 1940,** North Africa 1942-43, **Mareth, Medjez Plain, Salerno,** Volturno Crossing, **Monte Camino, Anzio,** Cagny, **Mont Pincon,** Gothic Line, **Nijmegen,** Battaglia, Reichswald, **Rhine,** Italy 1943-45, North-West Europe 1940, 44-45

Regimental Marches

Quick March..(i) The British Grenadiers (ii) The Grenadiers March
Slow March..(i) March from Scipio (ii) The Duke of York

Agents..Lloyds Bank PLC Cox's & King's Branch

Regimental Headquarters....................Wellington Barracks, Birdcage Walk, London, SW1E 6HQ (*Tel no:* 01-930-4466)

Alliances

Canadian Armed Forces.......................The Canadian Grenadier Guards
Australian Military Forces....................1st Battalion The Royal Australian Regiment

Colonel in Chief..................................THE QUEEN

Colonel..................................Field Marshal *HRH The Prince* Philip *Duke of* Edinburgh *KG KT OM GBE QSO*

Officer Commanding the Regt and Regt District
Col A T W Duncan *LVO OBE*..........................251182

Brigadiers

Baskervyle-Glegg J *MBE* rcds psc 300684
Blundell-Hollinshead-Blundell D H psc osc(SUD) 300685
Denison-Smith A A *MBE* psc 300685

Colonels

Duncan A T W *LVO OBE* ndc psc 300682

Lieutenant Colonels

Corkran R S *BA* ndc psc 300676
Lindsay O J M *MBIM FRHistS* ndc psc 300680
Hanning H S *MA* psc† 300681
Heroys A ndc psc 300681
O'Connell J V E F ndc psc 300682
Webb-Carter E J psc 300684
Woodrow A J C *MC QGM* sq jsdc 300684
Craster J M *MA* psc 300685
Holcroft P R *BA* psc 300685
Hudson E T *MBE* sq 300685

Majors

Tedder T J sq (*A/Lt Col* 030286) 300674
Coleridge *The Hon* S J T odc(FR) osc(FR) sq ph (*A/Lt Col* 080485) 311274
Seymour C J E sq 300675
Mather A C McC *MBE* sq 311276
Baillie H A sq 311277
Lort-Phillips T T R sq ph 311277
March Phillipps de Lisle H L R sq 311279
Lindsay C S S sq 300980
Drage M G A psc 300981
Scott-Clarke J S psc(n)† 300981
Houstoun E H *MBE* sq 300982
Lesinski G F psc 300982
Wiggin C R J psc 300982
Wigram *The Hon* A F C 300982
Wynn-Pope R C M 300982
Budge D L aic 300983
Cartwright R G psc(n)† 300983
Bruce *Sir* Hervey *Bt* psc 300984
de Burgh Milne D C L *BA* psc(IT) 300984
Bagnall A R K 300985
Bolton C T G 300985
Cecil *The Lord* Valentine psc 300985
Hargreaves J P *BSc* psc† 300985
Lloyd J S *BA* psc 300985

Captains

Drummond A H 080379
Done T E M *MA* (*A/Maj* 040783) 010280
Aubrey-Fletcher R E H (*A/Maj* 090981) 100580
Bolitho E T *MA* 300680
Sewell D N W (*A/Maj* 011085) 090980
Hutchison A D *MA* (*A/Maj* 120384) 091180
Sanford N P 090581
Bartrum O P *BA BSc* 240382
Ford A C 081083
Mitchell L C C *BSc* 131183
Baker G V A 060284
Davies N J R 081084
Koch de Gooreynd P F L 081084
Breitmeyer T H 090685
Gottlieb G C R *BA* 010885

The Guards Division — continued

Hobbs E F 040286

Lieutenants

Fraser A J (*A/Capt* 170685) 090882
Maddan D J H *BSc* 090882
Gordon Lennox E C (*A/Capt* 011283) 131282
Bennett C A G 110483
Bibby G K (*A/Capt* 170485) 110483
Chipperfield O R P *BA* 110483
Whitaker G D H 110483
Norton G P R *BA* 270583
Levine J L J 080883
Mills R H G 121283
Hutchings M C J 090484
Krasinski P Z M 090484
Smith H V L 070884
Gatehouse J P W 111284
Gordon Lennox A C 070486

2nd Lieutenants

††Russell-Parsons D J C 020983
†Hogarth G N P *BA* 060985
†Reeve T W *BA(Hons)* 060985

Quartermasters

Whitehead G R *RVM MBIM* 010474
Lt Col 200685
Clarke W R *MBE* 020675
Maj 040981
Collins N *MBE* 151078
Maj 241082
Webster D J *Capt* 010480
Rossi D R *MBE* *Capt* 010483

Directors of Music

Kimberley D R *MBE* psm 250770
Lt Col 271184

Special Regular Officers

Lieutenants

Wauchope F A (*A/Capt* 010185) 040782

Short Service Officers

Captains

Horn D D 210882
Nolan T S 011282
Joyce M J 010885
Holland M B 010386

Lieutenants

Halford S R 010282
Dunkerley P T 070282
Kitchen C E 170183
Rolfe T A 100283
Goodman J P W (*A/Capt* 040385) 110483
Maitland J W *BA* 110483
Everist H M 060783
Allen C C (*A/Capt* 141085) 121283
Bolitho A R (*A/Capt* 231185) 070884

2nd Lieutenants

Brassey E
Winstanley R D 040884
Swire P H M 130485
Rocke G J 141285
†Adams R G 060186
†Openshaw R A *BSc* 060186

Short Service Volunteer Officers

2nd Lieutenants

Jalland T W 230885

COLDSTREAM GUARDS

'Nulli Secundus'

The Queen's Colours:–

1st Battalion—Gules(crimson): In the centre the Star of the Order of the Garter proper, ensigned with The Crown; in base a Sphinx argent between two branches of laurel and tied with a riband vert; above a scroll or, the word 'Egypt' in black letters.

2nd Battalion—Gules(crimson): In the centre a star of eight points argent, within the Garter proper, ensigned with The Crown; in base the Sphinx superscribed 'Egypt' as for 1st Battalion; in the dexter canton the Union.

3rd Battalion— As for the 1st Battalion, and, for difference, in the dexter canton, the Union, and issuing therefrom in bend a pile wavy or. (Suspended Animation)

The Regimental Colours:–

The Union: In the centre a company badge ensigned with The Crown; in base the Sphinx superscribed 'Egypt'. The 24 company badges are borne in rotation, 3 at a time,one on the Regimental Colour of each of the 3 Battalions.

The Battle Honours shown in heavy type below are borne upon the Queen's and Regimental Colours:–

Tangier 1680, Namur 1695, Gibraltar 1704-5, Oudenarde, Malplaquet, Dettingen, Lincelles, Talavera, Barrosa, Fuentes d'Onor, Salamanca, Nive, Peninsula, Waterloo, Alma, Inkerman, Sevastopol, Tel-el-Kebir, Egypt 1882, Suakin 1885, Modder River, South Africa 1899-1902

The Great War– Mons **Retreat from Mons, Marne 1914, Aisne 1914, Ypres 1914, 17,** Langemarck 1914, Gheluvelt, Nonne Bosschen, Givenchy 1914, Neuve Chapelle, Aubers, Festubert 1915, **Loos,** Mount Sorrel, **Somme 1916, 18,** Flers-Courcelette, Morval, Pilckem, Menin Road, Poelcappelle, Passchendaele, **Cambrai 1917, 18,** St Quentin, Bapaume 1918, **Arras 1918,** Lys, **Hazebrouck,** Albert 1918, Scarpe 1918, Drocourt-Queant, **Hindenburg Line,** Havrincourt, Canal du Nord, Selle, Sambre, France and Flanders 1914-18

The Second World War– Dyle, Defence of Escaut, **Dunkirk 1940,** Cagny, **Mont Pincon,** Quarry Hill, Estry, Heppen Nederrijn, Venraij, Meijel, Roer, **Rhineland,** Reichswald, Cleve, Goch, Moyalnd, Hochwald, Rhine, Lingen, Uelzen, **North-West Europe 1940, 44-45,** Egyptian Frontier 1940, **Sidi Barrani,** Halfaya 1941, **Tobruk 1941, 1942,** Msus, Knightsbridge, Defence of Alamein Line, Medenine, Mareth, Longstop Hill 1942, Sbiba, Steamroller Farm, **Tunis,** Hammam Lif, North Africa 1940-43, **Salerno,** Battipaglia, Cappezano, Volturno Crossing, Monte Camino, Calabritto, Garigliano Crossing, **Monte Ornito,** Monte Piccolo, Capture of Perugia, Arezzo, Advance to Florence, Monte Domini, Catarelto Ridge, Argenta Gap, **Italy 1943-45**

Regimental Marches

Quick March..Regimental March of the Coldstream Guards 'Milanollo'
Slow March..'Figaro'

Agents..Lloyds Bank PLC Cox's & King's Branch

Regimental Headquarters....................Wellington Barracks, Birdcage Walk, London SW1E 6HQ (*Tel No:* 01-930-4466)

Alliances

Canadian Armed Forces.......................Governor General's Foot Guards
Australian Military Forces....................2nd/4th Battalion The Royal Australian Regiment

Colonel in Chief..................................THE QUEEN

Colonel..Maj Gen *Sir* George Burns *KCVO CB DSO OBE MC* ret pay........................080566

Officer Commanding the Regt and Regt District
Col H M C Havergal *OBE*..060484

Brigadiers

Rous *The Hon* W E *OBE* psc 300682
Rose H M *OBE QGM BA* psc 300683

Colonels

Adair P R *LVO* psc 300679
Salusbury-Trelawny J W *OBE* odc(US) psc† 300680
Maxse M W F *LVO* psc 300681
Havergal H M C *OBE* sq 300683

Lieutenant Colonels

Barttelot *Sir* Brian *Bt OBE* psc 300681
Heywood R J *MBE* psc 300681
Wardle R J S psc 300682
Frisby M R *OBE MA* psc 300683
Innes J R sq 300684
Armitstead E B L psc 300685
Zvegintzov I D *MBE BA* psc jsdc 300685

Majors

Sweeting R N F sq 300674
Thornewill D N sq ph 311275
Alderson R E R sq 300677
Crisp J R G psc ph 300678
Emson N E *MC BA* psc 311278
Breakwell O R St J *MBE* sq ph 300679
Crofton E M sq 300679
Cazenove R de L 300980
Evans A H B *MSc* sq gw 300980
Somervell M H sq 300980
Bradford C R W osc(MAL) 300981
Fraser S B sq 300981
Lomer C R L psc 300981
McNeil I H psc 300981
Mills P H 300981
Alabaster S M 300982
Biggs A R psc 300983
Turner-Bridger J M 300983
Raymer A J M 300984
Robathan A R G *MA* psc 300984
Williams P G *MBE MA AIL* psc 300984

Captains

Boscawen H G R *BA* 050379
Johnston F R G 080379
Parsons N J W *LLB* 260379
Matheson A F *BA* (*A/Maj* 140385) 010879
Hicks P E D *JP* (*A/Maj* 200484) 100979
Hibbert-Hingston M A T psc (*A/Maj* 201285) 100580
Style W B 100580
Toler D H psc (*A/Maj* 201285) 100580

The Guards Division — continued

Vandeleur D D S A *BSc*
(*A/Maj* 181185) 090481
Smart B B 090581
Holborow S D
(*Eq to the Queen (Temp)*)
080981
Law *The Hon* R E H
(*A/Maj* 281085) 080981
Hingston P J ph 281281
Clowes R C G *BSc* 290882
Barrett H C 070283
Cubitt W G *BSc* 190883
Johnston A J B 081083
Parker H R L *MA* 010284
McLean G W 060284
Wake-Walker M J 100684
Windsor-Clive O J 100684
Bourne-May J J S 081084
Bucknall J J C 081084

Lieutenants

Allhusen R F
(*A/Capt* 151185) 081281
Vernon J M
(*A/Capt* 200186) 090882
Blyth A D N 080883
Mansbridge S D W 080883
Blackett J W B 070486

2nd Lieutenants

††Moore J R B *BA(Hons)* 030982
††Tubbs R I C 020983
Giles J E J N 040884
Henty C J C 040884
††Pettifer C E 230984
Bucknall H C 100885
††Whitworth B W 240985

Staff Quartermasters

Welch N *OBE* 060572
Lt Col 150682

Quartermasters

Holbrook W J *MBE* 301173
Lt Col 010984
Storey T N 190678
Maj 010584
Smith A V *MBE* 010479
Maj 010984
Elliott D I 010480
Maj 170486
Louch C J *Capt* 010481
Savelle J G *Capt* 010481
Rigby J T M *Capt* 010482

Directors of Music

Swift R G *LRAM LTCL ARCM* psm
Capt 110281

Special Regular Officers

Captains

Woods P R
(*A/Maj* 220483) 081177
Cox C J G 110683
Bradborn A H 160783

Short Service Officers

Captains

Blackmore W K 010183
Nicholls E T
(*L/Maj* 040186) 150683
Mather B 110184
Yorke D R 120184
Watson R 050384
Candlin C 010484
Pratt J C 121285
Drax R G 100386
Robinson J 120386

Lieutenants

Gane A C M *BA* 110483
Pearson-Gee W O C 121283
Margesson *The Hon* R F D *BA*
090484
Perry C E 070884
Lowe E C H 111284
Gittings J G B 090485
Gaze J P C 101285
Hanbury J A C 101285
Morgan-Grenville G S 101285

2nd Lieutenants

Batt F R 040884
Tower W J 040884
Vestey G M W 040884
Merriman C R 081284
Osborn-Smith B R 130485
Sims-Hilditch J E 130485
Waud T H D 100885
†Vandeleur A W *BA* 060985
Chilton M K 141285
Rodney D J 141285
†Tatham W P H *BA* 060186

SCOTS GUARDS

The Queen's Colours:–

1st Battalion–Gules (crimson): In the centre Royal Arms of Scotland, ensigned with The Crown Motto *'En Ferus Hostis'*; in base the Sphinx superscribed "Egypt"

2nd Battalion–Gules (crimson): In the centre the Thistle and the Red and White Roses conjoined, issuant from the same stalk all proper, ensigned with The Crown. Motto *'Unita Fortior'*; in base the Sphinx superscribed 'Egypt'; in the dexter canton the Union

The Regimental Colours:–

The Union: In the centre a company badge ensigned with The Crown; in base the Sphinx superscribed 'Egypt' The 24 company badges are borne in rotation, 2 at a time, one on the Regimental Colour of each of the two Battalions The Battle Honours shown in heavy type below are borne upon the Queen's and Regimental Colours:–

Namur 1695, Dettigen, Lincelles, Talavera, Barrosa, Fuentes d'Onor, Salamanca, Nive, Peninsula, Waterloo, Alma, Inkerman, Sevastopol, Tel-el-Kebir, Egypt 1882, Suakin 1885, Modder River, South Africa 1889-1902

The Great War– **Retreat from Mons, Marne 1914, Aisne 1914, Ypres 1914, 17,** Langemarck 1914, Gheluvelt Nonne Bosschen, Givenchy 1914, Neuve Chapelle, Aubers, **Festubert 1915, Loos, Somme 1916, 18,** Flers-Courcelette, Morval, Pilckem, Poelcappelle, Passchendaele, **Cambrai 1917, 18,** St Quentin, Albert 1918, Bapaume 1918, Arras 1918, Drocourt-Queant, **Hindenburg Line,** Havrincourt, Canal du Nord, Selle, Sambre, **France and Flanders 1914-18**

The Second World War– Stien, Norway 1940, Halfaya 1941, Sidi Suleiman, Tobruk 1941, **Gazala,** Knightsbridge, Defence of Alamein Line, **Medenine,** Tadjera Khir, Medjez Plain, Grich el Oued, **Djebel Bou Aoukax 1943, I, North Africa 1941-3,** Salerno, Battipaglia, Volturno Crossing, Rocchetta e Croce, **Monte Camino, Anzio,** Campoleone, Carroceto, Trasimene Line, Advance to Florence, Monte San Michele, Catarelto Ridge, Argenta Gap, **Italy 1943-45,** Mont Pincon, **Quarry Hills,** Estry, Venlo Pocket, **Rhineland,** Reichswald, Cleve, Moyland, Hochwald, Rhine, Lingen, Uelzen, **North West Europe 1944-45.**

Tumbledown Mountain, **Falkland Islands 1982**

Regimental Marches

Pipes and Drums
Quick March..........Hielan' Laddie
Slow March..........The Garb of Old Gaul

Regimental Band
Quick March..........Hielan' Laddie
Slow March..........The Garb of Old Gaul

Agents..........Lloyds Bank PLC Cox's & King's Branch

Regimental Headquarters..........Wellington Barracks, Birdcage Walk, London, SW1E 6HQ (*Tel No:* 01-930-4466)

Alliance

Australian Military Forces..........3rd Battalion The Royal Australian Regiment

Colonel in Chief..........THE QUEEN

Colonel..........Maj Gen *HRH The Duke of* Kent *KG GCMG GCVO ADC*..........090974

Officer Commanding the Regt and Regt District
Col J M Clavering *OBE MC*..........120485

Brigadiers

Naylor D M *MBE* rcds psc 300681
Boyd-Carpenter *The Hon* T P J *MBE* df psc 300682
Scott M I E *DSO* psc 300684

Colonels

Dunsmure J A *OBE* psc 300682
Clavering J M *OBE MC* sq 300684
McLaughlan I W *OBE* psc 300684
Buchanan-Dunlop R D *OBE* odc(US) psc 300685
Carnegie-Brown M M odc(US) psc osc(NIG) 300685
Nurton J M A *OBE MC MA* psc† 300685
Ross A G *OBE* psc 300685

Lieutenant Colonels

Seddon-Brown J L psc 300680
Whiteley M G L ndc psc 300680
Leask A de C L *OBE* psc† 300681
Mackay-Dick I C *MBE* psc 300682
Ross W H M sq 300682
Parsons A P H psc 300684
Smart M C B *MBE* nadc psc 300684
Gordon A I C psc† psc(PAK)† 300685
Kiszely J P *MC* psc 300685

Majors

Nicol of Ardmarnoch D N D psc (*L/Lt Col* 010782) 300671
Cox J J D 311275
Warren J F sq 311277
Cameron N E A G sq aic 300678
Forbes of Rothiemay Younger A D K 300678
Lawrie J W S sq 300678
Joscelyne A M H psc aic 311278
Dalzel-Job I E *BSc(Eng)* sq 300980
Lancaster J A S *MBE* psc 300980
Cargill J J *MA* psc 300981
Crichton-Stuart J N A 300981
Erskine Crum D V psc 300981
Holmes J T *MC* psc 300981
Napier J A 300981
Woods E A 300981
Bethell *The Hon* R N *MBE* psc 300982
Greenfield J A H *MA* psc 300982
Potter R N 300982
Whyte R E 110483
Gascoigne P E C 300983
Price S A C psc(AUS) 300984
Spicer T S psc 300984
Fitzalan Howard T M *BA* psc 300985

Captains

The Guards Division – continued

Crowe J E M	
(*A/Maj* 110584)	301279
Ingleby-Mackenzie R A *BA*	100580
Turner M N D *BSc*	290882
Foster A W	060982
Stewart J C	110683
Cottrell E A C *BA*	010284
Joynson M W *BA*	240384
Kelway-Bamber E G	050285
Morrison A F	050285
Farrelly P J L	090685
Varney M L B	090685
Armstrong R W F *MA*	010885
Campbell-Lamerton M P *BA*	071085
Dobson D S C C	040286
Mitchell A M *BA(Hons)*	040286

Lieutenants

MacGregor of MacGregor M G C	
(*A/Capt* 140685)	081281
Alves N J H	
(*A/Capt* 140685)	200882
Thornhill S	
(*A/Capt* 010584)	131282
Stuart J D	080883
de Haldevang J H	070884
Vail P D	
(*A/Capt* 140585)	070884
Nickerson G H F	070486

2nd Lieutenants

Bell A B P	040884
Swinton W H C	100885
†McLeod R J *BA*	060985

Quartermasters

Lawrie E *MBE*		010175
	Maj	141185
Cooper G I *MBE*		300677
	Maj	020884
Brown C		281077
	Maj	140780
Bunton J M *MBE*	*Capt*	220679
Beck I	*Capt*	010481
Paterson R	*Capt*	010483
Wilkie R J	*Capt*	010483

Directors of Music

Beat D R *LVO ARCM* psm		280874 •
	Maj	100178
Carson D *MBE*		200275
	Maj	200283

Special Regular Officers

Captains

Moncrieff C S S	081083

Short Service Officers

Captains

Moody F J *MBE*	080982
Blount C J *BA*	130284
Carnegie S J	020484
Veitch B	060685
Hayward J R *BSc*	040286
Mathewson A D *BA*	040286

Lieutenants

Macpherson A C S *BA*	
(*A/Capt* 170185)	030182
Mackenzie R J C *MBE*	150482
Macfarlane J Mc C *BEM*	
(*A/Capt* 310186)	011082
Ingram L M	131182
Kelly J R	211282
Varney G N B *BA*	150583
Bence-Trower M G *BA*	080883
Dalrymple *The Viscount*	121283
Page C S T	
(*A/Capt* 160585)	121283
Drummond J E M *BA*	070884
Edmonstone A E C	070884
Knollys P N M	111284
Campbell-Lamerton I A	090485
Ingham-Clark F T	090485
Stisted C D	101285
Hutton J K	070486
Wilson D C A	070486

2nd Lieutenants

Barrah I M	100885
Marr M A D C	100885
Prior J D	100885
†Hill P C W *BA*	060985
Falkland *The Master of*	141285
Thompson D H	141285

IRISH GUARDS

The Queen's Colours:—

1st Battalion—Gules(crimson): In the centre the Royal Cypher or, within the Collar of the Order of St Patrick with badge appendant proper, ensigned with The Crown

2nd Battalion—Gules(crimson): In the centre the Star of the Order of St Patrick ensigned with The Crown; in the dexter canton the Union (Suspended Animation)

The Regimental Colours:—

The Union, in the centre a company badge ensigned with The Crown. The 22 company badges are borne in rotation
The Battle Honours shown in heavy type below are borne upon the Queen's and Regimental Colours:—

The Great War— Mons, **Retreat from Mons, Marne 1914, Aisne 1914, Ypres, 1914,17,** Langemarck 1914, Gheluvelt, Nonne Bosschen, **Festubert 1915, Loos, Somme, 1916, 18,** Flers-Courcelette, Morval, Pilckem, Poelcappelle, Passchendaele, **Cambrai 1917, 18,** St Quentin, Lys, **Hazebrouck,** Albert 1918,Bapaume 1918, Arras 1918, Scarpe 1918, Drocourt-Queant, **Hindenburg Line,** Canal du Nord, Selle, Sambre, France and Flanders 1914-18

The Second World War— Pothus, **Norway 1940, Boulogne 1940,** Cagny, **Mont Pincon, Neerpelt, Nijmegen,** Aam, **Rhineland,** Hochwald, Rhine, Bentheim, **North-West Europe 1944-45,** Medjez Plain, **Djebel Bou Aoukaz 1943, North Africa 1943, Anzio,** Aprilia, Carroceto, Italy 1943-44

Regimental Marches

Pipes and Drums
Quick March..........St Patrick's Day
Slow March..........Let Erin Remember

Regimental Band
Quick March..........St Patrick's Day
Slow March..........Let Erin Remember

Agents..........Lloyds Bank PLC Cox's & King's Branch

Regimental Headquarters..........Wellington Barracks, Birdcage Walk, London, SW1E 6HQ (*Tel No:* 01-930-4466)

Alliance

Australian Military Forces..........2nd/4th Battalion The Royal Australian Regiment

Colonel in Chief..........THE QUEEN

Colonel..........*HRH The Grand Duke of* Luxembourg *KG*..........210884

Officer Commanding the Regt and Regt District
Col W W Mahon..........310785

Brigadiers

Hume R T P jssc psc	300683
Corbett R J S *MBIM* odc(US) psc	300684
Webb-Carter D B W *OBE MC* odc(US) psc	300684

Colonels

Baker J H psc	300682
Mahon W W psc psc(n)	300685

Lieutenant Colonels

O'Dwyer S G ndc psc†	300681
Wilson H R G *LLB* psc	300685

Majors

Blosse Lynch H C sq	170667
Bullock-Webster R J S sq	311277
Keigwin R T *MBIM* psc†	300678
Lloyd S J H psc	311279
O'Gorman J B sq	300980
O'Reilly P B	300980
Warrender M J V *BA* psc	300981
Holt B W F *BSc* psc	300982
Kennard J D psc	300982
Purdon T C R B *MBE* psc	300982
Langton C R *AIL* psc	300983
Sheridan A J D *BA* psc(n)†	300983
Coe J H R	300984
De Stacpoole D H O	300984
MacMullen T W J *BA*	300984
Shakerley P G D *BA*	300984
Foster D C G	300985
Grimshaw R H *LVO MBE* psc(CAN)	300985
Purcell H M *MA* psc	300985

Captains

Roberts S J L *MA*	030480
Pollock J H O'H (*A/Maj* 250485)	090980
Hornung B P	070283
Frewen R E J	081083
Windham A G R *LVO FRGS*	060284
Donegan S P	100684
Morrissey M P	050285

Lieutenants

Lowther-Pinkerton A J M *MVO* (*A/Capt* 011183)	081281
Stopford J R H (*A/Capt* 180784)	090882
Hall N J (*A/Capt* 140385)	110483
Harris J C J *LLB(Hons)*	090484
Knaggs C P H	090484
Moriarty G M	090484
Shaw R C O	070884

2nd Lieutenants

††Carleton-Smith M A P *BA(Hons)*	030982
Boyle R A R	040884
Carter H L S	040884
††Macewan A C B	240985

Quartermasters

Cowap R *MBE*		010574
	Lt Col	240585
Groves H F		140875
	Maj	240682
Matthews W E *AMASMC*		120878
	Maj	121282
Young T H	*Capt*	010482

Directors of Music

Lane M G *ARCM* psm		310377
	Maj	251179

Short Service Officers

Captains

Pidgeon G J	121080
Connor T	010683
Wilkinson D	091184
McLean V F P	090685
Clegg J	130685
Mackean S C R	170885

The Guards Division — continued

Millar S D B 071085

Lieutenants

Butterworth C M
(*A/Capt* 240685) 240282
Beeley A P M *BA* 120482
Bonham-Carter T D *BA* 120482
Grotrian J B
(*A/Capt* 180784) 120482
Matthews G C *BA* 120482
Middlemiss M *BA* 090882
Howard-Allen H 090484
Roberts C B L L 111284
Greer F J M 101285

2nd Lieutenants

Gibbs P J 040884
Bassett G A C 081284
Blakey W D 081284
Pratt J C R 081284
Colborne-Malpas T W 130485
Sharp R J T 130485
Shapland H C M 100885
Young R J P 100885

WELSH GUARDS

The Queen's Colours:–

1st Battalion—Gules(crimson). In the centre a Dragon passant or,underneath a scroll with motto 'Cymru Am Byth', the whole ensigned with The Crown

2nd Battalion—Gules(crimson). In the centre a leek or within the Garter, ensigned with The Crown, in the dexter canton the Union (Suspended Animation)

The Regimental Colours:–

The Union. In the centre a company badge ensigned with The Crown
The 15 company badges are borne in rotation
The Battle Honours shown in heavy type below are borne upon the Queen's and Regimental Colours:–

The Great War– **Loos,** Somme 1916, 18, **Ginchy, Flers-Courcelette, Morval,** Ypres 1917, **Pilckem, Poelcappelle,** Passchedaele, **Cambrai 1917, 18, Bapaume 1918,** Arras 1918, Albert 1918, Drocourt-Queant, Hindenburg Line, Havincourt, **Canal du Nord,** Selle, **Sambre** France and Flanders 1915-18

The Second World War– **Defence of Arras, Boulogne 1940,** St Omer-La Bassee, Bourguebus Ridge, Cagny, **Mont Pincon, Brussels, Hechtel,** Nederrijn, Rhineland, Lingen, North-West Europe 1940, 44-45, **Fondouk,** Djebel el Rhorab, Tunis, **Hammam Lif,** North Africa 1943, **Monte Ornito,** Liri Valley, **Monte Piccolo,** Capture of Perigua, Arezzo, Advance to Florence, Gothic Line, **Battaglia,** Italy 1944-45

Falkland Islands 1982

Regimental Marches

Quick March..........Rising of the Lark
Slow March..........Men of Harlech

Agents..........Lloyds Bank PLC Cox's & King's Branch

Regimental Headquarters..........Wellington Barracks, Birdcage Walk, London, SW1E 6HQ (*Tel no:* 01-930 4446 *Ext:* 3291)

Alliance

Australian Military Forces..........5th/7th Battalion The Royal Australian Regiment

Colonel in Chief..........THE QUEEN

Colonel..........*HRH The Prince of* Wales *KG KT GCB AK QSO ADC*

Officer Commanding the Regt and Regt District
Col D R P Lewis..........011182

Brigadiers

Rickett J F *OBE* psc	300683
Lee M R *OBE* psc osc(US)	300684
Williams P R G psc	300685

Colonels

Gaussen S C C psc	300680
Lewis D R P sq	300685
Powell R F psc	300685

Lieutenant Colonels

Macdonald Milner D C (SL) psc	300675
Houghton P J sq	300680
Wood L D ndc psc(a)†	300680
Dawnay C J odc(US) psc	300681
Drewry C F *BA* psc	300684
Stephens C F B sq	300684
Glyn-Owen D T I *FRGS* sq	300685

Majors

Fordham S sq	300676
Goodridge J L *MA* psc(n)†	311276
Barnes M P R sq aic gw ph	300677
Griffiths-Eyton J D sq	300677
Wall A D I *MBE* sq	300677
Belcher D P psc† (*A/Lt Col* 060186)	311277
Sayle G N R *MBE MA* psc jsdc (*A/Lt Col* 190486)	300678
Senior M R sq	300679
Bremner C M psc	311279
David R E H *MBE*	311279
Watt C R *MA* psc	300982
Henderson J A psc	300983
Bonas T C S *BA* psc	300984
Richards A C psc	300985
Wight A J G *MC BA* psc	300985

Captains

Syms M L *LLB* (*A/Maj* 100585)	010280
Gwatkin P F S (*A/Maj* 050784)	260580
Sayers J D G	090980
Stephenson S D	281281
Malcolm A J E	060982
Traherne R L	060982
de Zulueta P G (*A/Maj* 161185)	070283
Ballard A W	081083
Owen-Edmunds P *BA*	010284
Dymoke P H M	060284
Scott-Bowden J R *BSc(Eng)*	060284
Sale R P A	071085
Syms W J	071085

Lieutenants

Black C N (*A/Capt* 010186)	110483
Macdonald Milner T C *BA*	110483
Scriven M G A *BA*	110483
Richardson O C de R	080883
Cockcroft R H B	111284
Warburton-Lee J H B	090485
Hearn N C	070486

2nd Lieutenants

††Gaffney R D T *BA(Hons)*	030982
††Bathurst B J	020983

Quartermasters

Morgan B D *MBE*		200776
	Maj	180783
White G		071077
	Maj	071085
Pridham E L *MBE*	*Capt*	010482
Davies A J *MBE*	*Capt*	010485

Directors of Music

Hannam P *BEM* psm	*Capt*	020779

Special Regular Officers

Majors

Evans G L	300985

Captains

Lewis B C M	050285

Short Service Officers

Captains

Davies D M	270783
Bowen A O	211185

The Guards Division — continued

Lieutenants

Evans D R	201182
Morgan A S (*A/Capt* 180285)	131282
Daniel J W H *BA*	110483
Parry R J	120583
Bodington R H W St G (*A/Capt* 161285)	080883
Farquharson J E H (*A/Capt* 071085)	080883
Isaac J D G	070884
Pritchard-Barrett J R	070884
Talbot Rice R H	090485
Dyer S J G	070486
Treadgold S J N	070486

2nd Lieutenants

Rudd M J B	040884
Ford J M H	130485
Presland M W	100885
†Ratcliffe R K *LLB*	060985
Lyle R C C	141285
Rees D J M	141285

THE SCOTTISH DIVISION

Comprising ....The Royal Scots (The Royal Regiment) (1 Regular Battalion)
The Royal Highland Fusiliers (Princess Margaret's Own Glasgow and Ayrshire Regiment) (1 Regular Battalion)
The King's Own Scottish Borderers (1 Regular Battalion)
The Cameronians (Scottish Rifles)
The Black Watch (Royal Highland Regiment) (1 Regular Battalion)
Queen's Own Highlanders (Seaforth and Camerons) (1 Regular Battalion)
The Gordon Highlanders (1 Regular Battalion)
The Argyll and Sutherland Highlanders (Princess Louise's) (1 Regular Battalion)
52nd Lowland Volunteers (2 Battalions)
51st Highland Volunteers (3 Battalions)

Divisional Headquarters ....The Castle, Edinburgh, EH1 2YT (*Tel no:* 031-336-1761 *Ext:* 4-274)

Colonel Commandant ....Lt Gen *Sir* Alexander Boswell *KCB CBE* ret pay 120782

Divisional Brigadier ....Brig E D Cameron *OBE* 090184

The origins of amalgamated Regiments now included in the Scottish Division are as follows:—

THE ROYAL HIGHLAND FUSILIERS (PRINCESS MARGARET'S OWN GLASGOW AND AYRSHIRE REGIMENT)

On 20 January 1959

The Royal Scots Fusiliers (21) and
The Highland Light Infantry (City of Glasgow Regiment) (71 and 74) amalgamated to form:
The Royal Highland Fusiliers (Princess Maragaret's Own Glasgow and Ayrshire Regiment)

QUEEN'S OWN HIGHLANDERS (SEAFORTH AND CAMERONS)

On 7 February 1961 the

Seaforth Highlanders (Ross-shire Buffs, The Duke of Albany's) (72 and 78) and
The Queen's Own Cameron Highlanders (79) amalgamated to form:
Queen's Own Highlanders (Seaforth and Camerons)

THE ROYAL SCOTS (THE ROYAL REGIMENT) (1)

The Royal Cypher within the Collar of the Order of the Thistle with the Badge appendant
In each of the four corners the Thistle within the Circle and motto of the Order, ensigned with The Crown. The Sphinx, superscribed Egypt

Tangier 1680, Namur 1695, Blenheim, Ramillies, Oudenarde, Malplaquet, Louisburg, Havannah, Egmont-op-Zee, St Lucia 1803, Corunna, Busaco, Salamanca, Vittoria, St Sebastian, Nive, Peninsula, Niagara, Waterloo, Nagpore, Maheidpoor, Ava, Alma, Inkerman, Sevastopol, Taku Forts, Pekin 1860, South Africa 1899-1902

The Great War– Mons, **Le Cateau,** Retreat from Mons, **Marne 1914,18,** Aisne 1914, La Bassee 1914, Neuve Chapelle, **Ypres 1915,17,18,** Gravenstafel, St Julien, Frezenburg, Bellewaarde, Aubers, Festubert 1915, **Loos, Somme 1916,18,** Albert 1916,18, Bazentin, Pozieres, Flers-Courcelette, Le Transloy, Ancre Heights, Ancre 1916, 18, **Arras 1917,18,** Scarpe 1917,18, Arleux, Pilckem, Langemarck 1917, Menin Road, Polygon Wood, Poelcappelle, Passchendaele, Cambrai 1917, St Quentin, Rosieres, **Lys,** Estaires, Messines 1918, Hazebrouck, Bailleul, Kemmel, Bethune, Soissonnais-Ourcq, Tardenois, Amiens, Bapaume 1918, Drocourt-Queant, Hindenburg Line, Canal du Nord, St Quentin Canal, Beaurevoir, Courtrai, Selle, Sambre, France and Flanders 1914-18, **Struma,** Macedonia 1915-18, Helles, Landing at Helles, Krithia, Suvla, Scimitar Hill, **Gallipoli 1915-16,** Rumani, Egypt 1915-16, Gaza, El Mughar, Nebi Samwil, Jaffa, **Palestine 1917-18,** Archangel 1918-19

The Second World War– Dyle, **Defence of Escaut,** St Omer-La Bassee, **Odon,** Cheux, Defence of Rauray, Caen, Esquay, Mont Pincon, **Aart,** Nederrijn, Best, Scheldt, **Flushing,** Meijel, Venlo Pocket, Roer, Rhineland, Reichswald, Cleve, Goch, **Rhine,** Uelzen, Bremen, Artlenberg, **North-West Europe 1940, 44-45, Gothic Line,** Marradi, Monte Gamberaldi, **Italy 1944-45,** South East Asia 1941, Donbaik, **Kohima,** Relief of Kohima, Aradura, Shwebo, Mandalay, **Burma 1943-45**

Regimental Marches

Pipes and Drums
Quick March..........Dumbarton's Drums
Slow March..........The Garb of Old Gaul

Regimental Band
Quick March..........Dumbarton's Drums
Slow March..........The Garb of Old Gaul

Agents..........Lloyds Bank PLC Cox's & King's Branch

Regimental Headquarters..........The Castle, Edinburgh EH1 2YT(*Tel No*: 031-336 1761 *Ext:* 4265)

Alliances

Canadian Armed Forces..........The Canadian Scottish Regiment (Princess Mary's)
The Royal Newfoundland Regiment

Affiliated Regiment

10th Princess Mary's Own Gurkha Rifles

Colonel in Chief..........*HRH The Princess* Anne *Mrs* Mark Phillips *GVCO*

Colonel..........Lt Gen *Sir* Robert Richardson *KCB CVO CBE* ret pay..........310880

Colonels

Lucas J N D ndc psc 300682
Ashmore M B H *OBE* psc† ph 300684
Gibb F F ndc psc 300684

Lieutenant Colonels

Addison A R G (SL) *MBE* psc 300678
Cardwell Moore P J *MBE* psc 300680
Cowan A E F *OBE* psc 300680
Ritchie C D M *OBE* ndc psc (*A/Col* 070985) 300680
Watson R S B odc(US) psc 300680
Paterson R H *OBE BA MBIM* psc 300682
Mitchinson C G F *MBE* psc 300683
Strudwick M J sq 300684
Charteris J A *MC* sq ph 300685
Gibson M F *MBE* sq 300685
Whittington P R M odc(US) psc 300685

Majors

McGinty W sq 311268
Barnetson S J M *QGM* sq 300676
Caverhill J C sq ph 300676
Hepburn D J S *MBIM* sq aic 300676
O'Neil Roe D G D psc 300676
Finlay J G *MBE* psc 311277
Mason R P sq 300678
MacIntyre P D psc (*A/Lt Col* 181185) 300679
Rhind J *JP* sq aic 300679
Maclean F R J sq 300980
Johnstone I A psc† psc(n) 300981
Blythe W J 300982
Dickson D S P 300983
Millar H A psc† 300983
Sylvester W P *BA* psc 300983
Cran M W H 300984
Drew-Wilkinson P A C 300984

Captains

Thomson B St C 080379
Gillies K R (*A/Maj* 270186) 100580
Rae G J aic 291280
Scott-Bowden R L *BSc(Eng)* 291280
de la Haye B G 090581
McDowall A R M ph 090581
Wells R D 080981
Stuart-Monteith D *BA* 090683
Simpson D G 110683
Gibson P M 081083
Richardson C B S *MA* 010284
Cargin D A R B 060284

Lieutenants

Soutar N G S (*A/Capt* 010585) 081281
Barr-Sim A M B (*A/Capt* 111185) 090882
Fulton D P J 080883
Stevenson J I S 080883
Whitney M R L 080883
Smith D R R 121283
Milne J R 090484
MacKichan I C A 070884

2nd Lieutenants

Gibb C I F 040884
Jack D T 081284
Lowder G E 100885
McLeod A R 100885
†Onslow M P D *BA(Hons)* 060985
††Stobie A M M 240985

Quartermasters

McDonald R L 010477
Maj 020281
McMeekin D C 010480
Maj 040785
Sands J *Capt* 010482
Waugh G C W *Capt* 010485

Directors of Music

Reeves C J *LTCL* psm
Capt 160985

Special Regular Officers

Majors

Blamire R G A 300981

Barclay-Steuart C J 300984

Captains

Taylor D G L 070283

Lieutenants

Fraser-Hopewell P D
(*A/Capt* 011082) 120183

Short Service Officers

Captains

Morecroft P W 011182
Buchanan T 010485

Standen-McDougal A J 040286
Telfer S F McK *MA* 040286

Lieutenants

Johnstone I C 190682
McMeechan D G 270982
McGrath W H 150283
Stewart J C
(*A/Capt* 180385) 070884
Burnett A D 060885
Durrant R J 070486
Wallace C P 070486

2nd Lieutenants

Gillespie-Payne J M L 081284
Richardson G S 100885

THE ROYAL HIGHLAND FUSILIERS (PRINCESS MARGARET'S OWN GLASGOW AND AYRSHIRE REGIMENT) (21, 71 and 74)

The monogram H.L.I. surmounted by The Crown upon a grenade, with the motto, Nemo Nos Impune Lacessit.

The Royal Cypher surmounted by the Crown. The Castle and Key superscribed "Gibraltar, 1780-83", and with the motto *"Montis Insignia Calpe"*. An Elephant superscribed Assaye

Blenheim, Ramillies, Oudenarde, Malplaquet, Dettingen, Belleisle, Carnatic, Hindoostan, Sholinghur, Mysore, Martinique 1794, Seringapatam, Cape of Good Hope 1806, Rolica, Vimiera, Corunna, Busaco, Fuentes D'Onor Almaraz, Ciudad Rodrigo, Badajoz, Salamanca, Vittoria, Pyrenees, Nivelle, Nive, Orthes, Toulouse, Peninsula, Bladensburg, Waterloo, South Africa 1851-53, Alma, Inkerman, Sevastopol, Central India, South Africa 1879, Tel-El-Kebir, Egypt 1882, Burma 1885-87, Tirah, Modder-River, Relief of Ladysmith, South Africa 1899-1902

The Great War— **Mons,** Le Cateau, Retreat from Mons, **Marne 1914, Aisne, 1914, La Bassee 1914, Ypres 1914, 15, 17, 18,** Langemarck 1914,17, Gheluvelt, Nonne Bosschen, Givenchy 1914, Neuve Chapelle, St Julien, Aubers, Festubert 1915, **Loos, Somme 1916,18,** Albert 1916,18, Bazentin, Delville Wood, Pozieres, Flers-Courcelette, Le Transloy, Ancre Heights, Ancre 1916, 18, **Arras 1917, 18,** Vimy 1917, Scarpe 1917,18, Arleux, Messines 1917,18, Pilckem, Menin Road, Polygon Wood, Passchendaele, Cambrai 1917,18, St Quentin, Bapaume 1918, Rosieres, **Lys** Estaires, Hazebrouck, Bailleul, Kemmel, Bethune, Scherpenberg, Amiens, Queant, **Hindenburg Line,** Havrincourt, Canal Du Nord, St Quentin Canal, Beaurevoir, Courtrai, Selle, Sambre, France and Flanders 1914-18, **Doiran 1917, 18,** Macedonia 1916-18, Helles, **Gallipoli 1915-16,** Rumani, Egypt 1916-17, Gaza, El Mughar, Nebi Samwil, Jerusalem, Jaffa, Tell' Asur, **Palestine 1917-18,** Tigris 1916, Kut Al Amara 1917, Sharqat, **Mesopotamia 1916-18**

Murman 1919, **Archangel 1919**

The Second World War— Defence of Arras, **Ypres-Comines Canal,** Somme 1940, Withdrawal to Seine, Withdrawal to Cherbourg, **Odon,** Fontenay Le Pesnil, Cheux, Defence of Rauray, Esquay, Mont Pincon, Quarry Hill, Estry, **Falaise,** Le Vie Crossing La Touques Crossing, Seine 1944, Aart, Nederrijn, Best, Le Havre, Antwerp-Turnhout Canal, **Scheldt,** South Beveland, **Walcheren Causeway,** Lower Maas, Meijel, Venlo Pocket, Roer, Ourthe, Rhineland, **Reichswald,** Cleve, Goch, Moyland Wood, Weeze, **Rhine,** Ibbenburen, Dreirwalde, Aller, Ulzen, **Bremen,** Artlenberg, **North West Europe 1940, 44-45,** Jebel Shiba, Barentu, **Keren,** Massawa, Abyssinia 1941, Gazala, **Cauldron,** Mersa Matruh, Fuka, North Africa 1940-42, **Landing in Sicily 1943,** Sangro, **Garigliano Crossing,** Minturno, Anzio, Advance to Tiber, Italy 1943, 44, 45, Madagascar, Adriatic, Middle East 1942, 44, Athens **Greece 1944-45, North Arakan,** Razabil, **Pinwe,** Shweli, Mandalay, Burma 1944-45

Regimental Marches

Pipes and Drums
Quick March..(i) Hielan Laddie (ii) Blue Bonnets are over the Border
Slow March..My Home

Regimental Band
Quick March..(i) British Grenadiers (ii) Whistle o'er the Lave o't
Slow March..(i)The Garb of Old Gaul (ii)March of the 21st Regiment

Agents..Holts Branch, Royal Bank of Scotland PLC, Lawrie House, Farnborough, Hants

Regimental Headquarters....................518 Sauchiehall Street, Glasgow, G2 3LW (*Tel No:* 041-332-5634)

Alliances

Canadian Armed Forces......................The Highland Fusiliers of Canada
New Zealand Army..............................1st Battalion The Royal New Zealand Infantry Regiment
Pakistan Army......................................11th Battalion The Baluch Regiment

Colonel in Chief..................................*HRH The Princess* Margaret *Countess of* Snowdon *CI GCVO*

Colonel..Maj Gen R L S Green ret pay..010179

Brigadiers

Mackay I *CBE MC ADC* psc 300677

Colonels

Campbell G B *OBE* psc 300683
Drummond J D psc 300685

Lieutenant Colonels

Craigie Halkett C D (SL) *MBE* sq 300673
Cartwright I G S *MBE* ndc sq 300679
Thorburn R E MacN *MBIM* ndc psc 300679
Armstrong R C *BSc PhD* psc† psc 300680
Channer R H De R *MBE* sq 300680
Cross R N R sq 300681
Reid I S *OBE* psc 300682
Shepherd I psc† 300684
Ramsay A I psc jsdc 300685

Majors

Rayner R F *BA* psc 311268
Dent L *MA* 311273
Channer P N De R psc 300675
Lorimer I B odc(FR) sq tt 300676
Lyde J W sq ph adp 300676
Dunbar C C K sq 300678
Fox R P sq aic 300678
Winter C S *LLB* osc(ID) sq I* (*A/Lt Col* 161285) 300678
Harvey A C H sq 300679
Hills D H psc 311279
Haldane P J psc(n)† 300981
Knox M R 300981
Scott D W *MBE* sq 300981
Dallas G McG 300982
Hope Thomson T J *BA* 300982
Dunlop B W J aic 300983
Kelly J L *BSc* psc† 300983
Roberts A J psc 300983
Souter E M 300983
Edwardes J S M psc(n)† 300984
Archibald N A *BD* 300985
Hislop G F psc 300985

Captains

Duncan H E 090379
Allison C G psc (*A/Maj* 161285) 100979
Common W A *MA* 010280
Loudon W E B 080981
Miln H M 080981
Potter J *BSc* 290882
Middleton A D 060982
Pickard I D R *BA* 280583
Bray J M 110683

Campbell N T	110683
Johnston A D *BSc*	130284
Cameron H C D *BA*	040384
Whitmore A C	100684
Clews M J	081084
Kirk D C	081084
Reid A L *BA*	030985

Lieutenants

Castle J M (*A/Capt* 300186)	081281
Garven J	081281
Cartwright P A S *BA*	120482
Wade J A *MA*	010882
Shepherd N R	090882
Hillis C W	080883
Whitelaw A C B	090484
Crumlish D	101285

2nd Lieutenants

††Channer N H DeR *BA(Hons)*	030982
††Fenton R D	240985
††Steel D G	081085

Quartermasters

Kenyon A D		010478
	Maj	140483
Shaw W *MBE*		010479
	Maj	150885
Hutton J M *BEM*	*Capt*	010485
Cameron H	*Capt*	010486

Special Regular Officers

Majors

Bryson A C	300985

Short Service Officers

Captains

Laird M	071277

Lieutenants

Mathews W	040782
Scott S R J	121283

2nd Lieutenants

Strachan J L	100885
†Campbell N B V *BA(Hons)*	060985
McKendrick E A	141285
McMenigall A S	141285

Short Service Volunteer Officers

2nd Lieutenants

Quinn T	011085

THE KING'S OWN SCOTTISH BORDERERS (25)

The Castle of Edinburgh. *'Nisi Dominus frustra'*

In the first and fourth corners the Royal Crest, with the motto *'In Veritate Religionis confido'*
In the second and third corners the White Horse with the motto *'Nec aspera terrent'*
The Sphinx, superscribed Egypt

Namur 1695, Minden, Egmont-op-Zee, Martinique 1809, Afghanistan 1878-80, Chitral, Tirah, Paardedberg, South Africa 1900-02

The Great War– **Mons,** Le Cateau, Retreat from Mons, Marne 1914, 18, **Aisne 1914,** La Bassee 1914, Messines 1914, **Ypres 1914, 15, 17, 18,** Nonne Bosschen, Hill 60, Gravenstafel, St Julien, Frezenberg, Bellewaarde, **Loos, Somme 1916, 18,** Albert 1916, 18, Bazentin, Delville, Wood, Pozieres, Guillemont, Flers-Courcelette, Morval, Le Transloy, Ancre Heights, **Arras 1917, 18,** Vimy 1917, Scarpe 1917, 18, Arleux, Pilckem, Langemarck 1917, Menin Road, Polygon Wood, Broodseinde, Poelcapelle, Passchendaele, Cambrai 1917, 18, St Quentin, Lys, Estaires, Hazebrouck, Kemmel, **Soissonnais-Ourcq,** Bapaume 1918, Drocourt-Queant, **Hindenburg Line,** Epehy, Canal du Nord, Courtrai, Selle, Sambre, France and Flanders 1914-18, Italy 1917-18, Helles, Landing at Helles, Krithia, Suvla, Scimitar Hill, **Gallipoli 1915-16,** Rumani, Egypt 1916, **Gaza, El Mughar, Nebi Samwil, Jaffa, Palestine 1917-18**

The Second World War– **Dunkirk 1940,** Cambes, **Odon,** Cheux, Defence or Rauray, **Caen,** Esquay, Troarn, Mont Pincon, Estry, Aart, Nederrijn, **Arnhem 1944,** Best, Scheldt, **Flushing,** Venraij, Meijel, Venlo Pocket, Roer, Rhineland, Reichswald, Cleve, Goch, **Rhine,** Ibbenburen, Lingen, Dreirwalde, Uelzen, **Bremen** Artlenberg, North-West Europe 1940, 44-45, North Arakan, Buthidaung, **Ngakyedauk Pass, Imphal,** Kanglatongbi, Ukhrul, Meiktila, **Irrawaddy, Kama, Burma 1943, 45**

Kowang-San, Maryang-San, **Korea 1951-52**

Regimental Marches

Pipes and Drums
Quick March..........Blue Bonnets are over the Border
Slow March..........The Borderers

Regimental Band
Quick March..........Blue Bonnets are over the Border
Slow March..........The Garb of Old Gaul

Agents..........Lloyds Bank PLC Cox's & King's Branch

Regimental Headquarters..........The Barracks, Berwick-on-Tweed, Northumberland, TD15 1DQ (*Tel No:* 0289-307426)

Alliances

Canadian Armed Forces..........1st Battalion The Royal New Brunswick Regiment (Carleton and York)
Australian Military Forces..........25th Battalion, The Royal Queensland Regiment
Malaysian Armed Forces..........5th Battalion The Royal Malay Regiment

Colonel in Chief..........*HRH Princess* Alice *Duchess of* Gloucester *GCB CI GCVO GBE*

Colonel..........Brig R W Riddle *OBE* ret pay..........240685

Brigadiers

Myrtle A D *CBE ADC* rcds psc 300676
Christie I A *CBE MC* rcds psc 300679
Mattingley C G *CBE* rcds ndc psc 300682
Stevenson P I B *CBE* jssc psc 300683
Alstead F A L *CBE FBIM* jssc psc(n) 300685
Thomson M *MBE* psc osc(ZIM) 300685
Toyne Sewell T P psc ph 300685

Lieutenant Colonels

Redwood *Sir* Peter *Bt* ndc psc (*A/Col* 250286) 300678
Reynolds M J (SL) ndc osc(ZIM) sq 300679
Crooke I W T *DSO* sq 300683
Lowis I J A sq 300683
Fairweather C B psc 300684
Hulf R A *BA* psc jsdc 300684
Hogg C G O sq 300685

Majors

Lindsay C 300668
Rundell G F W osc(ID) sq 300673
Young R A G sq 300673
Innes-Wilson D K M *MA* psc 300674
Eydes P W sq 311276
Scroggie E F R 300677
Taylor R H psc 311278
Minchin R W 300980
Legg R A E 300981
Middlemiss G A osc(MAL) 300981
Darnell C I *BA* psc† 300982
Dobbie C W G psc 300982
Kirkwood J A psc 300982
Walker J S M 300982
McLean R W K 300983
Middlemiss P W psc 300983

Captains

Rennie P J 130280
Andrew R F C 100580
Jackson A C ph 090980
McCurdy J A M 090581
Cooper J (*A/Maj* 180384) 080981
Stanton J R M *BA* 290981
Linaker M A C *BA* 121182
Gibbs I D H 070283
Combe R S 081083
Wood A J 300984
Loudon A J *BA* 081084
Moynan G M 050285
Barnes R A 090685
Macmillan-Scott A H C *BA* 100885
Horsburgh A G 040286

Lieutenants

Aitken P 120482
Gunn L A *BCom* 080682
Hubberstey N J 090882
Johnston B C (*A/Capt* 050285) 131282
Ballantyne A N (*A/Capt* 091184) 110483
Craig J M R 110483
Ramsay G A C *MA* 110483
McCutcheon P 090484

2nd Lieutenants

†Buchanan A J R 060985

Quartermasters

Arnott N R 010482
Maj 231184
Larsen J *Capt* 010484
Fraser R A *Capt* 010485

Wood G *MBE* 010485
Maj 011185

Special Regular Officers

Captains

Oliver J 160183
Orr I A 060284
Peck B A L 060284
Looms C J B 040286

Lieutenants

Mackay A D 121283
(*A/Capt* 141285)

Short Service Officers

Captains

Johnstone D C 020486
Hogg P D 270486

Lieutenants

Pullman J A 270182
Marshall S W *BA* 120482
Gagnier M J *BA* 110483
Macgillivray R A B 111284
Pope K A 210985

2nd Lieutenants

Aichroth M J P 081284
Burton C C 081284
Kerr J A 130485
†Falk M H P *BSc(Eng) ARSM* 060985

THE CAMERONIANS (SCOTTISH RIFLES) (26 and 90)

The Sphinx, superscribed Egypt   The Dragon superscribed China

Blenheim, Ramillies, Oudenarde, Malplaquet, Mandora, Corunna, Martinique 1809, Guadaloupe 1810, South Africa 1846-7, Sevastopol, Lucknow, Abyssinia, South Africa 1877-8-9, Relief of Ladysmith, South Africa 1899-1902

The Great War— **Mons,** Le Cateau, Retreat from Mons, **Marne 1914, 18, Aisne 1914, La Bassee 1914, Armentieres 1914, Neuve Chapelle,** Aubers, **Loos, Somme 1916, 18,** Albert 1916, Bazentin Pozieres, Flers-Courcelette, Le Transloy, Ancre Heights, Arras 1917,18, Scarpe 1917, 18, Arleux, **Ypres 1917, 18,** Pilckem, Langemarck 1917, Menin Road, Polygon Wood, Passchendaele, St Quentin, Rosieres, Avre, Lys, Hazebrouck, Bailleul, Kemmel, Scherpenberg, Soissonnais-Ourcq, Drocourt-Queant, **Hindenburg Line,** Ephey, Canal du Nord, St Quentin Canal, Cambrai 1918, Courtrai, Selle, Sambre, France and Flanders 1914-18, Doiran 1917, 18, **Macedonia 1915-18, Gallipoli 1915-16,** Rumani, Egypt 1916-17, Gaza, El Mughar, Nebi Samwil, Jaffa, **Palestine 1917-18**

The Second World War— Ypres-Comines Canal, **Odon,** Cheux, Caen, Mont Pincon, Estry, Nederrijn, Best, **Scheldt,** South Beveland, Walcheron Causeway, Asten, Roer, **Rhineland,** Reichswald, Moyland, Rhine, Dreirwalde, Bremen, Artenburg, **North-West Europe 1940,44-45,** Landing in Sicily, Simeto Bridgehead, **Sicily 1943,** Garigliano crossing, **Anzio,** Advance to Tiber, **Italy 1943-44,** Pegu 1942, Paungde, Yenagyaung 1942, **Chindits 1944, Burma 1942, 44**

Regimental Marches

Pipes and Drums
Quick Marches......................................(i) Kenmuir's on and awa' (ii) The Gathering of the Grahams

Regimental Band
Quick March..Within a Mile of Edinboro' Town

Agents..Lloyds Bank PLC Cox's & King's Branch

Regimental Headquarters....................More Hill, Off Muir Street, Hamilton, Lanarkshire, ML3 6BY

Alliances

New Zealand Army...............................The Otago and Southland Regiment
Ghana Military Forces..........................2nd Battalion Ghana Regiment of Infantry

Affiliated Regiment

7th Duke of Edinburgh's Own Gurkha Rifles

Representive Colonel..........................Brig D B Riddell-Webster *OBE* ret pay 111174

THE BLACK WATCH (ROYAL HIGHLAND REGIMENT) (42 and 73)

The Royal Cypher Within The Garter. the badge and motto of the Order of the Thistle
In each of the four corners the Royal Cypher ensigned with Crown
The Sphinx, superscribed Egypt

Guadaloupe 1759, Martinique 1762, Havannah, North America 1763-64, Mangalore, Mysore, Seringapatam, Corunna, Busaco, Fuentes d'Onor, Salamanca, Pyrenees, Nivelle, Nive, Orthes, Toulouse, Peninsula, Waterloo, South Africa 1846-7, 1851-2-3, Alma, Sevastopol, Lucknow, Ashantee 1873-4, Tel-el-Kebir, Egypt 1882, 1884, Kirbekan, Nile 1884-85, Paardeberg, South Africa 1899-1902

The Great War— Retreat from Mons, **Marne 1914,18,** Aisne 1914, La Basse **1914, Ypres 1914, 17, 18,** Langemarck 1914, Gheluvelt, Nonne Bosschen, Givenchy 1914, Neuve Chapelle, Aubers, Festubert 1915, **Loos, Somme 1916, 18,** Albert 1916, Bazentin, Delville Wood, Pozieres, Flers-Courcelette, Morval, Thiepval, Le Ancre Heights, Ancre 1916, **Arras 1917, 18,** Vimy 1917, Scarpe 1917, 18, Arleux, Pilckem, Menin Road, Polygon Wood, Poelcappelle, Passchendaele, Cambrai 1917, 18, St Quentin, Bapaume 1918, Rosieres, **Lys,** Estaires, Messines 1918, Hazebrouck, Kemmel, Bethune, Scherpenberg, Soissonnais-Ourcq, Tardenois, Drocourt-Queant, **Hindenburg Line,** Epehy, St Quentin Canal, Bearevoir, Courtrai, Selle, Sambre, France and Flanders 1914-18, **Doiran 1917,** Macedonia 1915-18, Egypt 1916, Gaza, Jerusalem, Tell'Asur, **Megiddo,** Sharon, Damascus, Palestine 1917-18, Tigris 1916, **Kut al Amara 1917,** Baghdad, Mesopotamia 1915-17

The Second World War— Defence of Arras, Ypres-Comines Canal, Dunkirk 1940, Somme 1940, St Valery-en-Caux, Saar, Breville, Odon, Fontenay le Pesnil, Defence of Rauray, Caen, Falaise, **Falaise Road,** La Vie Crossing, Le Havre, Lower Maas, Venlo Pocket, Ourthe, Rhineland, Reichswald, Goch, **Rhine,** North-West Europe 1940, 44-45, Barkasan, British Somaliland 1940, **Tobruk 1941,** Tobruk Sortie, **El Alamein,** Advance on Tripoli, Medenine, Zemlet el Lebene, Mareth, **Akarit,** Wadi Akarit East, Djebel Roumana, Medjez Plain, Si Mediene, **Tunis,** North Africa 1941-43, Landing in Sicily, Vizzini, Sferro, Gerbini, Adrano, Sferro Hills, **Sicily 1943, Cassino II,** Liri Valley, Advance to Florence, Monte Scalari, Casa Fortis, Rimini Line, Casa Fabbri Ridge, Savio Bridgehead, Italy 1944-45, Athens, Greece 1944-45, **Crete,** Heraklion, Middle East 1941, Chindits 1944, **Burma 1944**

The Hook 1952, Korea 1952-53

Regimental Marches

Pipes and Drums
Quick March..........Hielan' Laddie
Slow March..........(i) My Home (ii) Highland Cradle Song

Regimental Band
Quick March..........All The Blue Bonnets are over the Border
Slow March..........The Garb of Old Gaul

Agents..........Lloyds Bank PLC Cox's & King's Branch

Regimental Headquarters..........Balhousie Castle, Perth, PH1 5HR (*Tel No:* 0738-21281 *Ext:* 30)

Alliances

Canadian Armed Forces..........The Prince Edward Island Regiment
The Black Watch (Royal Highland Regiment) of Canada
The Lanark and Renfrew Scottish Regiment
Australian Military Forces..........The Royal Queensland Regiment
The Royal New South Wales Regiment
New Zealand Army..........1st and 2nd Squadron New Zealand Scottish, RNZAC

Colonel in Chief..........*HM* QUEEN ELIZABETH THE QUEEN MOTHER

Colonel..........Maj Gen A L Watson *CB* ret pay..........280981

Brigadiers

Cameron E D *OBE* ocds(IND) psc 300680
Barnett G C *OBE* psc 300683

Colonels

Ker R I L psc osc(ZIM) 300685

Lieutenant Colonels

Le Maitre G H (SL) *OBE* psc 300674
de Broe-Ferguson E N de B de B *MBE* sq 300682
Lindsay S J psc 300683
Halford-Macleod A P L sq 300685
Irwin A S H *MA* psc(PAK)† 300685

Majors

Rose H R *MA* psc(n)† 300679
Lindsay-Stewart M C sq 300980
Wilson D R psc† 300981
Lithgow N C D psc 300982
Macleod T J aic 300982
Thornycroft D C *MA* psc(PAK) aic 300982
Gilchrist R A L psc 300983
Nunneley R A H *MBE* 300984
Ogilvy-Wedderburn *Sir* Andrew 300985
Watson A A L *MA CGIA* psc† 300985

Captains

Riddell R M 301279
Monteith J D 090980
Coles T A 291280
Bradford R J K *BSc(For)* 300982
Loudon A W B *BA* 150283
Erskine J M K 081083
McKinnell R W 060284
Riddell-Webster M L *BSc* 030985
Carmichael T J O 071085

Lieutenants

Forrest R A (*A/Capt* 011285) 120482
Macdonald A A S (*A/Capt* 011285) 120482
Maitland-Makgill-Crichton C W 131282
Carmichael W B G 121283
Tweedy C J 090484
Baillie-Hamilton A N B 090485

2nd Lieutenants

††Cowan J M 020983
††Sutton P R B 230984

Quartermasters

Beattie F L *MBE* 010480
Maj 090186
McNally J W *Capt* 010481
Phillips H K *Capt* 010483

The Scottish Division – continued

Special Regular Officers

Majors

Ritchie R C B *MBE*	300981
Macduff-Duncan S C	300985

Captains

Allen H J B	040286

Short Service Officers

Captains

Proctor R J W B	020486

Lieutenants

Todd P J S *MA*	120482
Craig K R *BA*	280782
Bruce M A *BSc*	110483
Nisbet I L *BA*	110483
Dinsmore R G	111284
Welch J M	070486

2nd Lieutenants

Bell S R	081284
O'Donnell F P D	130485
†Denholm D W M *MA*	060985
†Howatson J A C *BA(Hons)*	060985
†Perriam A H *MA(Hons)*	060985

QUEEN'S OWN HIGHLANDERS (SEAFORTH AND CAMERONS) (72, 78 and 79)

A stag's head caboshed, between the attires the Thistle ensigned with the Crown
The Cypher of Queen Victoria within the Garter. The Cypher of the Duke of York. The Sphinx, superscribed Egypt
The Elephant, superscribed Assaye. The Cypher of the Duke of Edinburgh
"Cuidich 'n Righ"

Carnatic, Hindoostan, Mysore, Egmont-op-Zee, Cape of Good Hope 1806, Maida, Corunna, Busaco, Fuentes d'Onor, Java, Salamanca, Pyrenees, Nivelle, Nive, Toulouse, Peninsula, Waterloo, South Africa 1835, Alma, Sevastopol, Koosh-ab, Persia, Lucknow, Central India, Peiwar Kotal, Charasiah, Kabul 1879, Kandahar 1880, Afghanistan 1878-80, Tel-el-Kebir, Egypt 1882, Nile 1884-85, Chitral, Atbara, Khartoum, Paardeberg, South Africa 1899-1902

The Great War— Le Cateau, Retreat from Mons, **Marne 1914, 18, Aisne 1914,** La Bassee 1914, Armentieres 1914, **Ypres 1914, 15, 17, 18,** Langemarck 1914, Gheluvelt, Nonne Bosschen, Festubert 1914, 15, Givenchy 1914, **Neuve Chapelle,** Hill 60, Gravenstafel, St Julien, Frezenberg, Bellewaarde, Aubers, **Loos, Somme 1916, 18,** Albert 1916, Bazentin, **Delville Wood,** Pozieres, Flers-Courcelette, Morval, Le Transloy, Ancre Heights, Ancre 1916, **Arras 1917, 18, Vimy 1917,** Scarpe 1917, 18 Arleux, Pilckem, Menin Road, Polygon Wood, Broodseinde, Poelcappelle, Passchendaele, **Cambria 1917, 18,** St Quentin, Bapaume 1918, Lys, Estaires, Messines 1918, Hazebrouck, Bailleul, Kemmel, Bethune, Soissonais-Ourcq, Tardenois, Drocourt-Queant, Hindenburg Line, Epehy, St Quentin Canal, Courtrai, Selle, **Valenciennes, Sambre,** France and Flanders 1914-18, Struma, **Macedonia 1915-18,** Megiddo, Sharon, **Palestine 1918,** Tigris 1916, Kut al Amara 1917, **Baghdad,** Mesopotamia 1915-18

The Second World War— Defence of Escaut, **St Omer-La Bassee,** Ypres-Comines Canal, Somme 1940, Withdrawal to Seine, **St Valery-en-Caux,** Odon, Cheux, **Caen,** Troarn, Mont Pincon, Quarry Hill, Falaise, Falaise Road, Dives Crossing, La Vie Crossing, Lisieux, Nederrijn, Best, Le Havre, Lower Maas, Meijel, Venlo Pocket, Ourthe, **Rhineland, Reichswald,** Goch, Moyland, **Rhine,** Uelzen, Artlenberg, North-West Europe 1940, 44-45, Agordat, **Keren,** Abyssinia 1941, **Sidi Barrani,** Tobruk 1941, 42, Gubi ii, Carmusa, Gazala, **El Alamein,** Advance on Tripoli, Mareth, Wadi Zigzaou, **Akarit,** Djebel Roumana, North Africa 1940-43, Landing in Sicily, Augusta, Francofonte, Adrano, Sferro Hills, **Sicily 1943,** Garigliano Crossing, **Anzio,** Cassino i, Poggio del Grillo, **Gothic Line,** Tavoleto, Coriano, Pian di Castello, Monte Reggiano, Rimini Line, San Marino, Italy 1943-44, **Madagascar,** Middle East 1942, **Imphal,** Shenam Pass, Litan, **Kohima,** Relief of Kohima, Naga Village, Aradura, Tengnoupal, Shwebo, **Mandalay,** Ava, Irrawaddy, Mt Popa, **Burma 1942-45**

Regimental Marches

Pipes and Drums
Quick March..........Pibroch O'Donuil Dubh
Slow March..........The Garb of Old Gaul

Regimental Band
Quick March..........Regimental March of Queen's Own Highlanders (Seaforth and Camerons) (Arrangement of Scotland for Ever and Cameron Men)
Slow March..........The Garb of Old Gaul

Agents..........Holts Branch, Royal Bank of Scotland PLC, Lawrie House, Farnborough, Hants

Regimental Headquarters..........Cameron Barracks, Inverness, Scotland (*Tel No:* Inverness(0463) 224380)

Alliances

Canadian Armed Forces..........The Cameron Highlanders of Ottawa
The Queen's Own Cameron Highlanders of Canada
The Seaforth Highlanders of Canada
Australian Military Forces..........The Royal South Australia Regiment
The Royal Western Australia Regiment
New Zealand Army..........7th Battalion (Wellington(City of Wellington's Own) and Hawkes Bay),Royal New Zealand Infantry Regiment
4th Battalion (Otago and Southland) Royal New Zealand Infantry Regiment

Affiliated Regiment

7th Duke of Edinburgh's Own Gurkha Rifles

Colonel in Chief..........Field Marshal *HRH The Prince* Philip *Duke of* Edinburgh *KG KT OM GBE QSO*

Colonel..........Maj Gen J C O R Hopkinson *CB* ret pay..........070283

Brigadiers

Mackenzie J J G *OBE* psc 300684

Colonels

Miers D A N C psc 300677
Tait J B *BSc* ptsc aic 300679
Langlands J C psc† 300680
Nason I G ndc psc osc(NIG) 300683
White M H psc 300683
Ridley N J *OBE* psc† 300685

Lieutenant Colonels

Murray G B (SL) *MBIM* psc osc(NIG) 300677
Cameron J P *OBE* sq 300678
Gordon Duff R *MBE BA* psc 300679
Latham G odc(US) psc 300679
Hunt R C V sq 300684

Majors

Crowe C M C *MBE* sq 230465
Nason J H 310766
Wilson M D McP sq 120267
McLaren R M sq 311267
Holt P H E L sq (*L/Col* 260185) 300668
MacCallum J A *MBE* sq 300669
Cassels R J K sq 300675
Young H G sq 311277
Watson D N *MBE* psc† 311278
Gilmour C E sq aic 311279
Grant Peterkin A P *BA* psc 311279
Macnair W P C *BA* psc 311279
Murray I J 300980
Grant C S *CGIA* psc† 300981

The Scottish Division – continued

Washington N J C *MA* psc 300981
Monro S H R H psc 300982
Campbell *The Hon* A J C *BA* psc 300984
Taylor C D psc 300984
Graham J A N 300985
Hall R P *LLB* psc 300985
Lamb G C M psc 300985
Monro H B H E psc 300985

Captains

Maitland-Makgill-Crichton D E (*A/Maj* 130985) 050878
Torp-Petersen K 090980
Miller R D J 080981
Wimberley M C 080981
Cole R 280981
Rattray R C *BSc(EstMan)* 290981
Darnley R A *BA* 060982
Macnair H P A 110683
Watson P D M *BSc* 050983
Philip Q M C *BA* 031083
Braithwaite-Exley M 081083
Luton G O *BSc(Econ)* 081083
Maclennan D R *BA* 130384
Morpeth C R D *BSc(SocSc)* *MA* 010285
Campbell J F R 050285
Gibson A J G 090685
Macrae M R S 071085

Lieutenants

Lewis T G D 131282
Anderson M A D'A 080883
Murray M R *BSc* 070884
Braybrooke R N 060885
Hay D W 070486

2nd Lieutenants

†Nevill C G S J *BSc* 060985
††Tait G J N 240985

Quartermasters

Cosgrove J 010476
Maj 120181
Millar C P D 010477
Maj 100183
Smith N G 010477
Maj 010479
Macdonald M A *Capt* 010483
Macleod M *Capt* 010485

Special Regular Officers

Majors

Grime P L S 300985

Short Service Officers

Captains

Anderson G S *MBE* 070779
Allan J M 020781
Shepherd D W 310783
Compson G M 200184

Lieutenants

Towns R J 140583
Macdonald A A H 080883
MacNally H D (*A/Capt* 130885) 080883
Duncan A S J 090484
McEwen A F 060885
Forbes A W A 070486
Turnbull N P 070486

2nd Lieutenants

†Sloan A G C *BA* 060985

THE GORDON HIGHLANDERS (75 and 92)

The Crest of the Marquess of Huntly within a wreath of Ivy, with the motto Bydand
The Royal Tiger, superscribed India. The Sphinx, superscribed Egypt

Mysore, Seringapatam, Egmont-op-Zee, Mandora, Corunna, Fuentes d'Onor, Almaraz, Vittoria, Pyrenees, Nive, Orthes, Peninsula, Waterloo, South Africa 1835, Delhi 1857, Lucknow, Charasiah, Kabul 1879, Kandahar 1880, Afghanistan 1878-80, Tel-el-Kebir, Egypt 1882, 1884, Nile 1884-85, Chitral, Tirah, Defence of Ladysmith, Paardeberg, South Africa 1899-1902

The Great War– **Mons, Le Cateau,** Retreat from Mons, **Marne, 1914, 18,** Aisne 1914, La Bassee 1914, Messines 1914, Armentieres 1914, **Ypres 1914, 15, 17,** Langemarck 1914, Gheluvelt, Nonne Bosschen, Neuve Chapelle, Frezenberg, Bellewaarde, Aubers, Festubert 1915, Hooge 1915, **Loos, Somme 1916, 18, Albert 1916, 18,** Bazentin, Delville Wood, Pozieres, Guillemont, Flers-Courcelette, Le Transloy, **Ancre 1916, Arras 1917, 18,** Vimy 1917, Scarpe 1917, 18, Arleux, Bullecourt, Pilckem, Menin Road, Polygon Wood, Broodseinde, Poelcappelle, Passchendaele, **Cambrai 1917, 18,** St Quentin, Bapaume 1918, Rosieres, Lys, Estaires, Hazebrouck, Bethune, Soissonnais-Ourcq, Tardenois, Hindenburg Line, Canal du Nord, Selle, Sambre, France and Flanders 1914-18, Piave, **Vittorio Veneto,** Italy 1917-18

The Second World War– Withdrawal to Escaut, Ypres-Comines Canal, Dunkirk 1940, Somme 1940, St Valery-en-Caux, **Odon,** La Vie Crossing, Lower Maas, Venlo Pocket, Rhineland, **Reichswald,** Cleve, **Goch, Rhine, North-West Europe 1940, 44-45, El Alamein,** Advance on Tripoli, **Mareth,** Medjez Plain, **North Africa 1942-43,** Landing in Sicily, **Sferro,** Sicily 1943, **Anzio,** Rome, Italy 1944-45

Regimental Marches

Drums and Pipes
Quick March....................Cock o' the North
Slow March....................St Andrews Cross

Regimental Band
Quick March....................Cock o' the North
Slow March....................The Garb of Old Gaul

Agents....................Holts Branch, Royal Bank of Scotland PLC, Lawrie House, Farnborough, Hants

Regimental Headquarters....................Viewfield Road, Aberdeen, Scotland (*Tel No:* 0224-318174)

Alliances

Canadian Armed Forces....................48th Highlanders of Canada
The Toronto Scottish Regiment
Australian Military Forces....................5th/6th Battalion The Royal Victoria Regiment

Colonel-in-Chief....................*HRH The Prince of* Wales *KG KT GCB AK QSO ADC*
Colonel....................Maj Gen J R A MacMillan *CBE*....................010778

Brigadiers

Graham P W *CBE* ocds(CAN) psc 300682

Lieutenant Colonels

Van der Noot C H *MBE* psc(a) (*A/Col* 240186) 300678
Duke T H G psc† I 300680
Fawcus R S *MBE* sq ph 300680
Peebles G H *OBE* rcds psc (*A/Col* 310186) 300680
Napier D M psc† 300682
Kennedy A I G odc(US) psc† 300683
Cumming A M osc(MAL) sq 300685
Stenhouse J M W psc 300685

Majors

Oxley N F M sq 311270
Ord R D odc(US) psc ph 311276
Price C E psc 311279
Nicol B D 300980
Durcan A J M *LLB MA* psc 300981
Broadfoot D N 300983
Chant-Sempill *The Hon* I D W 300983
Connon D L 300984
McDonald S C aic 300984
Kerr C N *BEd* 300985

Captains

Sloan C P C *LLB* 031079
Sutton N J 301279
Maitland-Makgill-Crichton A J 100580
Chalmers E D J 291280
Irvine-Fortescue G A 291280
Ogilvy N MacI 300481
Legge K G 080981
Stewart D N F *BSc* 290981
Robertson W A S *BSc* 050983
Gibson M R M 060284
Philip F M 050285
Hobbs P V *BA* 270485
Barron D C N 040286
Dodson M P 040286
Harnden R L 040286
Smith N P 040286
Wade R P A *BSc* 080286

Lieutenants

Potts K M (*A/Capt* 130885) 070884
Millar C J 060885
Wells M R 070486

2nd Lieutenants

††Wanstall I R *BA* 030982
Ogilvie J R A 081284
West S R 130485
††Macmillan G J 240985

Quartermasters

Greenhowe R *MBE* 010479
Maj 151283
Sharp J *Capt* 010481
Easson J C *Capt* 010482
Ritchie B M *Capt* 010485
McGill W M *BEM* *Capt* 010486

Special Regular Officers

Captains

Stewart A N 301279

Short Service Officers

Captains

Mackie M M 010683
Donald N *BEM* 161285

Lieutenants

Everett C J 131282
Buchanan-Smith J C *BSc* 070884
Cruickshank P M 070486

2nd Lieutenants

Stichbury J D 081284
Shepherd R W 130485
Godley J P 100885

THE ARGYLL AND SUTHERLAND HIGHLANDERS (PRINCESS LOUISE'S) (91 and 93)

The Princess Louise's Cypher and Coronet. A boar's head, with the motto *Ne obliviscaris,* within a wreath of myrtle, and a cat, with the motto *"San Peur"*, within a wreath of broom, over all the label as represented in the Arms of the Princess Louise and surmounted with Her Royal Highness's Coronet.

Cape of Good Hope 1806, Rolica, Vimiera, Corunna, Pyrenees, Nivelle, Nive, Orthes, Toulouse, Peninsula, South Africa 1846-7, 1851-2-3, Alma, Balaklava, Sevastopol, Lucknow, South Africa 1879, Modder River, Paardeberg, South Africa 1899-1902

The Great War— **Mons, Le Cateau,** Retreat from Mons, **Marne 1914, 18,** Aisne 1914, La Bassee 1914,Messines 1914, 18, Armentieres 1914, **Ypres 1915, 17, 18,** Gravenstafel, St Julien, Frezenberg, Bellewaarde, Festubert 1915, **Loos, Somme 1916, 18,** Albert 1916, 18, Bazentin, Delville Wood, Pozieres, Flers-Courcelette, Morval, Le Transloy, Ancre Heights, Ancre 1916, **Arras 1917, 18,** Scarpe 1917, 18, Arleux, Pilckem, Menin Road, Polygon Wood, Broodseinde, Poelcappelle, Passchendaele, **Cambrai 1917, 18,** St Quentin, Bapaume 1918, Rosieres, Estaires, Hazebrouck, Bailleul, Kemmel, Bethune, Soissonnais-Ourcq, Tardenois, Amiens, Hindenburg Line, Epehy, Canal du Nord, St Quentin Canal, Beaurevoir, Courtrai, Selle, Sambre, France and Flanders 1914-18, Italy 1917- 18, Struma, **Doiran 1917, 18,** Macedonia 1915-18, Gallipoli 1915-16, Rumani, Egypt 1916, **Gaza,** El Mughar, Nebi Samwil, Jaffa, Palestine 1917-18

The Second World War— Somme 1940, Odon, Tourmauville Bridge, Caen, Esquay, Mont Pincon, Quarry Hill, Estry, Falaise, Dives Crossing, Aart, Lower Maas, Meijel, Venlo Pocket, Ourthe, Rhineland, Reichswald, **Rhine,** Uelzen, Artlenberg, North-West Europe 1940, 44-45, Abyssinia 1941, **Sidi Barrani, El Alamein,** Medenine, **Akarit,** Diebel Azzag 1942, Kef Ouiba Pass, Mine de Sedjenane, Medjez Plain, **Longstop Hill 1943,** North Africa 1940-43 Landing in Sicily, Gerbini, Adrano, Centuripe, Sicily 1943, Termoli, Sangro, Cassino 11, Liri Valley, Aquino, Monte Casalino, Monte Spaduro, Monte Grande, Senio, Santerno Crossing, Argenta Gap, **Italy 1943-45, Crete,** Heraklion, Middle East 1941, North Malaya, **Grik Road,** Central Malaya, Ipoh, Slim River, Singapore Island, **Malaya 1941-42**

Pakchon, Korea 1950-51

Regimental Marches

Pipes and Drums
Quick Marches.....................................(i) Campbells are Coming (ii) Hielan' Laddie
Slow March..Loch Duich

Regimental Band
Quick March...The Thin Red Line
Slow March...The Garb of Old Gaul

Agents...Lloyds Bank PLC Cox's & King's Branch

Regimental Headquarters....................The Castle, Stirling, Scotland (*Tel No:* 0786-2881 *Ext:* 274)

Alliances

Canadian Armed Forces.......................The Argyll and Sutherland Highlanders of Canada (Princess Louise's)
The Calgary Highlanders
Australian Military Forces....................The Royal New South Wales Regiment
Pakistan Army.......................................The Punjab Frontier Force

Colonel in Chief..................................THE QUEEN

Colonel...Maj Gen C P R Palmer *CBE*...011182

Colonels

Purves-Hume I C psc 300683
Thomson D P *MC* psc 300685

Lieutenant Colonels

Scott Elliot A W (SL) sq 300674
Clark H L ndc psc osc(GH) 300680
Neilson G A ndc psc 300681
Robertson J S D sq 300682

Majors

Buchanan C F R 300669
Ross J A sq 300671
Park-Weir I C sq 300673
Graham E A M psc 311276
Clark H D sq 300678
Ross D G psc 311278
Steele D K P *MBE* sq 300679
McVittie M R psc
(*A/Lt Col* 060186) 311279
Campbell-Baldwin J D C aic 300980
Blackett A W psc 300981
Miller A K M *BA* psc 300983
Douglas G A psc 300984
Campbell C A 300985
Macgregor-Smith D N psc 300985

Captains

Campbell A P W *BD* 040980
Evans C J A 090980
Salisbury N J N
(*A/Maj* 270284) 291280
Graham A J N *BA* 210481
Keate D H P
(*A/Maj* 010585) 281281
Powrie R A D 060982
Boswell A L S 070283
Wade R N H A de V 060284
Henderson C B *LLB* 010285
Macnaughton A M *LLB* 050285
Scott N W 050285
Stafford I W H 050285
Troup J A 090685
McAlister I R 071085

Lieutenants

Boswell C L S
(*A/Capt* 150584) 090882
Matthews V J G 110483
Pritchard A W
(*A/Capt* 210985) 110483
Fergusson P 090484

2nd Lieutenants

Storey N J 130485
Scott J A 141285

Quartermasters

Lloyd W S *MBIM MInstAM* 010475
Maj 010479
Lauder J McM 010478
Maj 090881
Grant A McL *Capt* 010485

Short Service Officers

Captains

Allison J G 180184
MacGillivray M R 010784

Lieutenants

Beevor J M *LLB*	120482
Russell B W O *BSc*	120482
Russell J A O *BSc* (*A/Capt* 050885)	120482
Bain J V G	061182
Mailer-Howat G M B *BA*	110483
Balfour D M	080883
McGhie A J	121283
Mackenzie T P	070486

2nd Lieutenants

Gray J D	040884
McKie W H	040884
Wilson G C	040884
†Paterson T J *BSc*	060985

THE QUEENS DIVISION

Comprising ....The Queen's Regiment (3 Regular Battalions, 3 Volunteer Battalions)
The Royal Regiment of Fusiliers (3 Regular Battalions, 2 Volunteer Battalions)
The Royal Anglian Regiment (3 Regular Battalions, 3 Volunteer Battalions)

Divisional Headquarters ....Bassingbourn Barracks, Royston, Hertfordshire, SG8 5LX
(*Tel no:* 0763-42271 *Ext:* 322)

Colonel Commandant ....Maj Gen M F Reynolds *CB* 010784

Divisional Brigadier ....Brig C M J Barnes *OBE* 200985

The origins of amalgamated Regiments now included in The Queen's Division are as follows:—

THE QUEEN'S REGIMENT

On 14 October 1959

The Queen's Royal Regiment (West Surrey)(2) and
The East Surrey Regiment (31 and 70) amalgamated to form:
The Queen's Royal Surrey Regiment

On 1 March 1961

The Buffs (Royal East Kent Regiment)(3) and
The Queen's Own Royal West Kent Regiment (50 and 97) amalgamated to form:
The Queen's Own Buffs, The Royal Kent Regiment

On 31 December 1966

The Queen's Royal Surrey Regiment
The Queen's Own Buffs, The Royal Kent Regiment
The Royal Sussex Regiment (35 and 107) and
The Middlesex Regiment (Duke of Cambridge's Own)(57 and 77) amalgamated to form:
The Queen's Regiment

THE ROYAL REGIMENT OF FUSILIERS

On 23 April 1968

The Royal Northumberland Fusiliers (5)
The Royal Warwickshire Fusiliers (6)
The Royal Fusiliers (City of London Regiment) (7) and
The Lancashire Fusiliers (20) amalgamated to form:
The Royal Regiment of Fusiliers

THE ROYAL ANGLIAN REGIMENT

On 2 June 1958

The Bedfordshire and Hertfordshire Regiment (16) and

The Essex Regiment (44 and 56) amalgamated to form:

The 3rd East Anglian Regiment (16th/44th Foot)

On 29 August 1959

The Royal Norfolk Regiment (9) and

The Suffolk Regiment (12) amalgamated to form:

The 1st East Anglian Regiment (Royal Norfolk and Suffolk)

On 1 June 1960

The Royal Lincolnshire Regiment (10) and

The Northamptonshire Regiment (48 and 58) amalgamated to form:

The 2nd East Anglian Regiment (Duchess of Gloucester's Own Royal Lincolnshire and Northamptonshire)

On 1 September 1964

1st East Anglian Regiment (Royal Norfolk and Suffolk)

2nd East Anglian Regiment (Duchess of Gloucester's Own Royal Lincolnshire and Northamptonshire)

3rd East Anglian Regiment (16th/44th Foot) and

The Royal Leicestershire Regiment (17) amalgamated to form:

The Royal Anglian Regiment

THE QUEEN'S REGIMENT (2, 3, 31, 35, 50, 57, 70, 77, 97, 107)

A Dragon upon a mount within the Garter. Above the Dragon and superimposed on the Garter the Plume of the Prince of Wales

A Paschal Lamb upon an eight pointed Star ensigned with The Crown. A White Horse rampant above a scroll inscribed Invicta. The Star of the Order of the Garter over the Roussillon Plume. The Plume of the Prince of Wales above the Coronet and Cypher of the Duke of Cambridge. A Naval Crown superscribed 1st June 1794. The Sphinx superscribed Egypt. The Cypher of Queen Catherine

Unconquered I Serve

Tangier 1662-80, Namur 1695, Gibraltar 1704-5, Blenheim, Ramillies, Oudenarde, **Malplaquet, Dettingen, Louisburg, Guadaloupe 1759, Quebec 1759,** Belleisle, **Martinque 1762,** Havannah, **St Lucia 1778,** Mysore, Martinque 1794, **Seringapatam, Maida, Vimiera, Corunna, Douro, Talavera,** Guadaloupe 1810, **Albuhera, Almaraz,** Ciudad Rodrigo, **Badajoz, Salamanca, Vittoria,** Pyrennes, Nivelle, Nive, Orthes, Toulouse, Peninsula, Ghuznee 1839, Khelat, **Affghanistan 1839,** Cabool 1842, **Punniar, Moodkee,** Ferozeshah, Aliwal, **Sobraon,** South Africa 1851-3, Alma, **Inkerman, Sevastopol, Lucknow, Taku Forts,** Pekin 1860, **New Zealand,** Afghanistan 1878-79, **South Africa 1879,** Egypt 1882, Abu Klea, **Nile 1884-85,** Suakin 1885, **Burma 1885-87, Chitral,** Tirah, **Relief of Ladysmith, Relief of Kimberley,** Paardeberg, **South Africa 1899-1902**

The Great War— **Mons,** Le Cateau, Retreat from Mons, **Marne 1914, 18, Aisne 1914,** La Bassee 1914, Messines 1914, 17, 18, Armentieres 1914, **Ypres 1914, 15, 17, 18,** Langemarck 1914, 17, Gheluvelt, Nonne Bosschen, Givenchy 1914, Neuve Chapelle, **Hill 60,** Gravenstafel, St Julien, Frezenberg, Bellewaarde, Aubers, **Festubert 1915,** Hooge 1915, Loos, **Somme 1916, 18, Albert 1916, 18,** Bazentin, Delville Wood, Pozieres, Guillemont, Ginchy, Flers-Courcelette, Morval, Thiepval, Le Transloy, Ancre Heights, Ancre 1916, 18, Bapaume 1917, 18, Arras 1917, 18, **Vimy 1917,** Scarpe 1917, 18, Arleux, Oppy, Bullecourt, Pilckem, Menin Road, Polygon Wood, Broodseinde, Poelcappelle, Passchendaele, **Cambrai 1917, 18,** St Quentin, Rosieres, Avre, Villers Bretonneux, Lys, Estaires, Hazebrouck, Bailleul, Kemmel, Scherpenberg, Soissonnais-Ourcq, Amiens, Drocourt-Queant, **Hindenburg Line,** Epehy, Canal du Nord, St Quentin Canal, Beaurevoir, Courtrai, Selle, Valenciennes, Sambre, France and Flanders 1914-18, Piave, Vittorio Veneto, **Italy 1917-18,** Struma, Doiran 1917, 18, **Macedonia 1915-18,** Suvla, Landing at Suvla, Scimitar Hill, **Gallipoli 1915,** Rumani, Egypt 1915-17 **Gaza,** El Mughar, Nebi Samwil, **Jerusalem,** Jericho, Jordan, Tell' Asur, Megiddo, Sharon, **Palestine 1917-18,** Aden, Defence of **Kut Al Amara,** Tigris 1916, Kut al Amara 1917, Baghdad, Khan Baghdadi, Sharqat, **Mesopotamia 1915-18, NW Frontier India 1915, 1916-17,** Murman 1918-19, Dukhovskaya, Siberia 1918-19

Afghanistan 1919

The Second World War— Dyle, Defence of Escaut, Amiens 1940, St Omer-La Bassee, Foret de Nieppe Ypres-Comines Canal, **Dunkirk 1940,** Withdrawal to Seine, **Normandy Landing,** Cambes, Breville, Villers Bocage, Odon, Caen, Orne, Hill 112, Bourguebus Ridge, Troarn, Mont Pincon, Falaise, Seine 1944, Nederrijn, Le Havre, Lower Maas, Venraij, Meijel, Geilenkirchen, Venlo Pocket, Roer, Rhineland, Reichswald, Goch, Rhine, Lingen, Brinkum, Bremen, **North-West Europe 1940, 44-45,** Karora-Marsa Taclai, Cubcub, Mescelit Pass, Keren, Mt. Englahat Massawa, **Abyssinia 1941,** Syria 1941, Sidi Barrani, Sidi Suleiman, Tobruk 41, Tobruk Sortie, **Omars,** Alem Hamza, Benghazi, **Alam el Halfa,** Deir El Munassib, **El Alamein,** El Agheila, Advance on Tripoli, Medenine, Mareth, Tebaga Gap, El Hamma, Akarit, Djebel el Meida, Djebel Roumana, Djebel Abiod, Tebourba, Djebel Azzag 1942, 43, Robaa Valley, Fort McGregor, Oued Zarga, Djebel Bech Chekaoui, Djebel Ang, Heidous, Djebel Djaffa Pass, Medjez Plain, **Longstop Hill 1943,** Si Abdallah, Tunis, Montarnaud, **North Africa 1940-43,** Francofonte, Sferro, Adrano, Sferro Hills, Centuripe, Monte Rivoglia, **Sicily 1943,** Termoli, Trigno, San Salvo, **Sangro,** Romagnoli, Impossible Bridge, Villa Grande, **Salerno,** Monte Stella, Scafati Bridge, Volturno Crossing, Monte Camino, Garigliano Crossing, Damiano, **Anzio,** Carroceto, **Cassino,** Monastery Hill, Castle Hill, Liri Valley, Aquino, Piedimonte Hill, Rome, Trasimene Line, Arezzo, Advance to Florence, Monte Scalari, Gothic Line, Coriano, Pian di Castello, Gemmano Ridge, Monte Reggiano, Capture of Forli, Cassa Fortis, Senio Pocket, Senio Floodbank, Rimini Line, Casa Fabbri Ridge, Savio Bridgehead, Monte Pianoereno, Monte Spaduro, Monte Grande, Senio, Menate, Filo, Argenta Gap, **Italy 1943-45,** Greece 1944-45, Leros, Middle East 1943, **Malta 1940-42,** Kampar, **Malaya 1941-42, Hong Kong,** South East Asia 1941, North Arakin, Razabil, Mayu Tunnels, Kohima, **Defence of Kohima,** Pinwe, Shweli, Myitson, Taungtha, Yenangyaung 1945, Sittang 1945, Chindits 1944, **Burma 1943-45**

Naktong Bridgehead, Chongju, Chongchon II, Chaum-Ni, Kapyong-chon, Kapyong, **Korea 1950-51**

Regimental Marches

Quick March..The Soldiers of the Queen
Slow March..The Caledonian

Agents..Lloyds Bank PLC Cox's & King's Branch
Regimental Headquarters....................Howe Barracks, Canterbury, Kent (*Tel No:* 0227-457411)

Alliances

Canadian Armed Forces	The Queen's York Rangers (1st American Regiment) (RCAC)
	The South Alberta Light Horse (RCAC)
	The Queen's Own Rifles of Canada
	The Hastings and Prince Edward Regiment
	1st Battalion The Royal New Brunswick Regiment (Carleton and York)
	The Essex and Kent Scottish
Australian Military Forces	The Royal New South Wales Regiment
	The Royal Western Australia Regiment
	The University of New South Wales Regiment
New Zealand Army	2nd Battalion (Canterbury, Nelson, Marlborough and West Coast)
	The Royal New Zealand Infantry Regiment
	5th Battalion (Wellington, West Coast and Taranaki)
	The Royal New Zealand Infantry Regiment
Pakistan Army	12th, 14th, 15th and 17th Battalions The Punjab Regiment
Colonial Forces	The Royal Hong Kong Regiment (The Volunteers)

Allied Colonels in Chief ...... *Her Royal Highness* Princess Juliana of the Netherlands

Her Majesty Queen Margrethe II of Denmark

Colonel ...... Brig H C Millman *OBE* ret pay 010184

Deputy Colonels ...... Col J C Holman *OBE* 010184
Col R W Acworth 020486
A/Col M R I Constantine QUEENS 020486

Brigadiers

Doyle M J *MBE FBIM* jssc psc 300684

Colonels

Hayward M V *OBE* jssc psc(n) 300677
Tarver C L *MBE* jssc psc 300678
Lea R *DSO MBE* sq 300679
Anderson S T W *OBE MC* psc 300682
Trotman T L ndc psc 300682
Tarver H N *BSc* ndc psc† 300683
Acworth R W psc 300684
Holman J C *OBE* psc 300684
Champion C G psc(a) 300685
Dickins D J C *MBE* psc 300685
Hiscock P *BSc(Eng)* psc† 300685

Lieutenant Colonels

Chappell R H (SL) *OBE* psc 300671
Newall M R M (SL) *OBE* psc 300673
Courtenay P H (SL) *BA* odc(US) psc pl 300675
Bulloch G *MBE* ndc psc 300677
Barrow P de S ndc psc 300678
Boucher S M ndc psc 300678
Bateman G B *OBE* ndc psc 300679
Graham R H *MBE MA MPhil* ndc psc 300680
Legg M D (SL) *MA* psc 300680
Panton P V *OBE* ndc psc ph 300680
Ward A C *OBE* psc 300680
Baillie I G psc(n)† 300681
Constantine M R I *OBE* psc (*A/Col* 220386) 300681
Arnold R M psc 300682
Beveridge D A *MBE BA* psc 300682
Hubert P J *OBE* sq 300682
Ling A F S *MBE* psc 300682
Shephard D H A sq 300683
Hunter N S *BSc MBIM MRSC* psc† 300684
Ball M J sq 300685
Bishop P sq 300685
Cook P C psc jsdc 300685
Joint C M psc 300685
Low R M M psc 300685
Willis M C *BA* psc† jsdc 300685

Majors

Girling M E sq 080265
Neve R W *MC* psc 080265
Lloyd I M E sq 120267
Crumley W G A sq 300667
Williams R T P *MMS* 271167
Langhorne J 300668
Reid J D W sq (*L/Lt Col* 010579) 300668
Clarke P D J odc(GE) psc osc(GE) 300669
Christian E L psc 311269
Mallalieu P sq 311269
Gybbon-Monypenny P J psc 311272
Carlston B A *MBE* sq (*A/Lt Col* 240286) 311273
Bartlett R A 300674
Critchley P P psc 300674
Gwilliam P A sq 300674
Murphy R P sq 300674
Mellotte R T W sq 311274
Dawson A C psc 300675
Grove C M M *BSc* sq adp 300675
Thorpe S C sq 300675
Montgomery M B psc 311275
Brown G C sq 311276
Jonklaas J D *MIL* psc(IT) sq 311276
Gancz R psc† aic 311277
Harris N P psc 311277
Dowse S M sq 300678
Jones I R aic 300678
Yorke H A P sq 300678
Christmas R A M *BA* psc 300679
Gouda D C F odc(BE) sq 300679
Charter C G F psc 311279
McGhie R M psc (*A/Lt Col* 110386) 311279
Acworth J C sq 300980
Cann N C G 300980
Hitchcock P R sq 300980
Howe P R P psc 300980
Jelf A M F sq 300980
McGill P M H psc 300980
McLelland P D psc 300980
Pearce P L *BA* psc 300980
Salmon J A B *LLB* psc(a) 300980
Barratt A W *BSc* psc(n)† 300981
Harcus J M sq 300981
Huskisson J F 300981
Jackson R M *BA* psc† 300981
Mieville A C *BSc(Eng)* psc† 300981
Mills J P S sq 300981
Russell N F 300981
Swanson P R P *MBE* 300981
Ewart J 300982
Lawson M P 300982
Myles J N C 300982
Stirling J B psc 300982
Beattie A A A psc(IND) 300983
Carter D S 300983
Partridge J R *MA* 300983
Quinn M S 300983
Cooper M J psc 300984
Pratten J N 300984
Roberts A J psc 300984
Russell A W psc 300984
Russell J D K *BA* psc 300984
Wake D J psc 300984
Grant N J 300985
Harber W R *BA* 300985
Knight-Hughes W 300985
Whithouse R F psc† 300985

Captains

Knight R J *BSc* 100979
Riley J P *BA* 090980
Wilby R W (*A/Maj* 090985) 090980
Edwards L R 080981
Hurley T J 080981
Keyes N P L *MA* 290981
Goulden A M 281281
Rayner M P (*A/Maj* 310885) 281281
Watson D V 281281
Maltman J C *BA* (*A/Maj* 161285) 090282
Eagan H W R 080582
Barr J 060982
Mans L S P 060982
Newman P J *BSc* 060982
Hames K S 241282
Castle J P 070283
Graham J S 110683
Walker R 110683
Ashton J V *BSc* 150883
Gamlin J C F 081083
Hurman M J 220184
Newell C A 060284
Kilpatrick S P B *BA* 240584

The Queens Division – continued

Cross G W	100684
Noble J P	100684
Sharples N	081084
Deakin S F *BSc(Econ)*	240185
Raynes I D	090685
Bourne G F	071085
Corden P R *BA*	071085
Duggan S T D *BA*	071085
Newman M A D	071085
Phipps D J	071085
Greenfield D J	040286

Lieutenants

Brown M J *BA*	120482
Crowley P T (*A/Capt* 090785)	120482
Strutt D G	120482
Dixon J	090882
Garrett S C	131282
Farrell J J *BA*	110483
Cameron J E	080883
Haywood Smith M J	080883
Scott M G *BSc*	080883
Ramsey A R	121283
Powell J R J	090484
Williams M J *BSc*	090484
Wright J P S *BA*	090484
McLeod C G A	060885
O'Connor J R	060885
Wilson S S	090885

2nd Lieutenants

Bascombe A J	040884
Johns S J	130485
Harknett R I	100885
†Hind J E *LLB*	060985
†Maer M P *BSc*	060985

Quartermasters

Benson R J		010476
	Maj	010479
Ayling M J		010478
	Maj	270584
Fisher T S	*Capt*	010480
Marshall W D	*Capt*	010480
Aylward M J *MBE*	*Capt*	010482
Barnacle I	*Capt*	010485
Ebbens V D	*Capt*	010485

Directors of Music

Wall D F psm	*Capt*	130884

Special Regular Officers

Majors

O'Gorman A P *MInstAM*	300980
Rogerson J C	300981
Maloney M D *BEM*	300985

Captains

Bromfield C T	080182
Lambert C G	050583
Wood G J	040286

Lieutenants

Martin D A	060885
Bulpitt J R	021185

2nd Lieutenants

Fotheringham G I	100885

Short Service Officers

Captains

Hill A	280884
Beeson H M	170285
Anthony P J *QGM*	010385
Crosbie-Wood R P	050985
Burke J F	020286

Lieutenants

Frost J A *BEM*	090182
Garton C W *BEM*	300182
Versloot N J *BA*	120482
Munday W R (*A/Capt* 010186)	040982
Rowney M R	240483
Burrows J R *BA*	080883
Rowland J M *BA*	080883
Reynolds P B M	030184
Gubbin K W *BSc*	090484
Brown A V	060885
Goddard D J K	060885
Davis I P	101285
Holmes A St J	101285
Perry J C	101285

2nd Lieutenants

Bolton A R	040884
Jones A G	040884
Beat P D	081284
Owen R J	081284
Haynes B A W	130485
Goble N M J	100885
†Ingledow M F *BA(Hons)*	060985
Laidlaw A N	141285
†Halliday J S *BA*	060186

Short Service Volunteer Officers

2nd Lieutenants

Blackburn K F	020186

THE ROYAL REGIMENT OF FUSILIERS (5, 6, 7 and 20)

St George and the Dragon within the Garter

The United Red and White Rose slipped ensigned with the Royal Crest. An Antelope, gorged with a ducal coronet with rope reflexed over back. The White Horse of Hanover. The Red Rose of Lancaster
The Sphinx superscribed Egypt

Namur 1695, Dettingen, Minden, Wilhelmstahl, St Lucia 1778, Martinique 1794, 1809, Egmont-op-Zee, Maida, Rolica, Vimiera, Corunna, Talavera, Busaco, Ciudad Rodrigo, Badajoz, Albuhera, Salamanca, Vittoria, Pyrenees, Nivelle, Othes, Toulouse, Peninsula, Niagara, South Africa 1846-47, 1851, 2, 3, Alma, Inkerman, Sevastopol, Lucknow, Kandahar 1880, Afghanistan 1878-80, Atbara, Khartoum, Modder River, Relief of Ladysmith, South Africa 1899-1902

The Great War— **Mons,** Le Cateau, Retreat from Mons, **Marne 1914, 18, Aisne 1914, 18,** La Bassee 1914, Messines 1914, 17, 18, Armentieres 1914, **Ypres 1914, 15, 17, 18,** Langemarck 1914, 17, Gheluvelt, Nonne Bosschen, Neuve Chapelle, Gravenstafel, **St Julien,** Frezenburg, Bellewaarde, Hooge 1915, Aubers, Festubert 1915, Loos, **Somme 1916, 18,** Albert 1916, 18, Bazentin, Delville Wood, Pozieres, Guillemont, Ginchy, Flers-Courcelette, Morval, Thiepval, Le Transloy, Ancre Heights, Ancre 1916, 18, **Arras 1917, 18,** Vimy 1917, Scarpe 1917, 18, Arleux, Bullecourt, Oppy, Pilckem, Menin Road, Polygon Wood, Broodseinde, Poelcappelle, **Passchendaele, Cambrai 1917, 18,** St Quentin, Bapaume 1918, Rosieres, Avre, Villers Bretonneux, **Lys,** Estaires, Hazebrouck, Bailleul, Kemmel, Bethune, Scherpenberg, Amiens, Drocourt-Queant, **Hindenburg Line,** Havrincourt, Epehy, Canal du Nord, St Quentin Canal, Beaurevoir, Courtrai, Selle, Valenciennes, Sambre, France and Flanders 1914-18, **Piave,** Vittorio Veneto, Italy 1917-18, **Struma,** Doiran 1917, **Macedonia 1915-18,** Helles, **Landing at Helles,** Krithia, **Suvla, Sari Bair,** Landing at Suvla, Scimitar Hill, **Gallipoli 1915-16,** Rumani, **Egypt 1915-17,** Megiddo, Nablus, Palestine 1918, Tigris 1916, Kut al Amara 1917, **Baghdad,** Mesopotamia 1916-18, Baku, Persia 1918, Troitsa, Archangel 1919, Kilimanjaro, Behobeho, Nyangao, East Africa 1915-17

The Second World War— **Defence of Escaut,** Arras counter attack, St Omer-La Bassee, Wormhoudt, Ypres-Comines Canal, **Dunkirk 1940, Normandy Landing,** Odon, **Caen,** Bourguebus Ridge, Cagny, Mont Pincon, Falaise, Nederrijn, Venraji, **Rhineland,** Lingen, Brinkum, **Bremen, North-West Europe 1940, 44-45,** Agordat, **Keren,** Syria 1941, Sidi Barrani, **Defence of Tobruk,** Tobruk 1941, Belhamed, Cauldron, Ruweisat Ridge, El Alamein, Advance on Tripoli, Medenine, Djebel Tebaga, **Medjez el Bab,** Oued Zarga, Peter's Corner, **North Africa 1940-43,** Adrano, Sicily 1943, Termoli, Trigno, **Sangro, Mozzagrogna,** Caldari, **Salerno,** St Lucia, Battipaglia, Teano, Volturno Crossing, Monte Camino, Garigliano Crossing, Damiano, **Anzio, Cassino II,** Ripa Ridge, Trasimene Line, Gabbiano, Advance to Florence, Monte Scalari, **Gothic Line,** Coriano, Croce, Monte Ceco, Casa Fortis, Monte Spaduro, Savio Bridge head, Vali di Comacchio, Senio, Argenta Gap, Italy 1943-45, Athens, Greece 1944-45, **Malta 1941-42,** Singapore Island, Rathedaung, Htizwe, **Kohima,** Naga Village, Chindits 1944, **Burma 1943-45**

Seoul, **Imjin,** Kowang-San, **Korea 1950-53**

Regimental Marches

Quick March..The British Grenadiers
Slow March..Rule Britannia, De Normandie
(i) St George (Northumberland)
(ii) Macbean's Slow March (Warwickshire)
(iii) De Normandie (London)
(iv) Slow March of the former Lancashire Fusiliers

Agents..Lloyds Bank PLC Cox's & King's Branch
Regimental Headquarters....................HM Tower of London, Tower Hill, London, EC3N 4AB
(*Tel No:* 01-709-0765)

Alliances

Canadian Armed Forces........................The Elgin Regiment
The Royal Canadian Regiment
The Lorne Scots (Peel, Dufferin and Halton Regiment)
Les Fusiliers du St Laurent
The Royal Westminster Regiment
Australian Military Forces....................5th/6th Battalion The Royal Victoria Regiment
New Zealand Army..............................6th Battalion (Hauraki) Royal New Zealand Infantry Regiment

Colonel in Chief..............................Maj Gen *HRH The Duke of* Kent *KG GCMG GCVO ADC*
Colonel..............................Maj Gen J C Reilly *DSO*..............................020486
Deputy Colonels
London..............................Maj Gen B C Webster *CB CBE* ret pay..............................150576
Northumberland..............................Col R E Blenkinsop *OBE* ret pay..............................011178
Lancashire..............................Col I R Cartwright *CBE* ret pay..............................300482

Colonels

Aldridge B *OBE* sq 300681
Sincock P J *MBE* psc 300681
Daniel J R A ndc psc 300683
Tarver M R *OBE* psc 300683
Houlton D *MBE* psc 300684
Rigby J G B *OBE* odc(US) psc 300684

Lieutenant Colonels

Kelly M J (SL) *OBE MBIM MISM FInstSM* sq 300675
Robinson N G D *MBE* psc (*A/Col* 060985) 300679
Aldous J G psc 300680
Curtis A G H *BA MA(Cantab&Oxon)* psc† 300680
Hayley M A odc(US) psc(a) 300680
Youll G M *OBE* ndc psc 300680
Shervington P F *MBE* odc(US) psc 300682
Berry C M L sq 300683
Biggart D A K *MBE* ndc sq 300683
Coutts-Britton T A sq 300683
Wellwood C N B psc 300683
Bibbey P G *MBE* psc(a) 300684
Willans W J sq jsdc 300684
Brook R P D odc(US) sq 300685
Buckton R G *MA* sq 300685
Greenhouse R M *MBE* sq 300685
Hunt J C F sq 300685
Rice A J M sq 300685

The Queens Division – continued

Majors

Name	Date
Thompson D M *MInstAM MIMS* sq	300667
Brown N C sq	311268
Connelly S V psc	300669
Ross-Thomas M psc†	311270
Conner G R psc	300671
Stemp G L sq	311271
St Maur Sheil J W M	300672
Valentine C H C psc	300672
Tomes I M *MC* psc(a)	311272
Hughes A J H *MBE* psc	300673
Jackson C F psc	300674
Helps T P G sq	300675
Carter G B M *MBE* sq	311275
Burton H D S sq	300676
Riddick D W G sq	300676
Peters I J sq	311276
Whiteman K R psc	311276
Cook K M *MBE* sq	300678
Edwards M C K sq	300678
Spackman D I A psc	300678
Gunnell J C psc (*A/Lt Col* 270186)	311278
Ingham J sq	311278
Edgar M J B	110479
Colbeck S J T sq	300679
Molyneux-Carter K B sq	300679
Shaw J R sq	300679
Waterworth D L sq	300679
Cleveland S C H psc	311279
Hawkins T E A *MBE* sq	311279
McDonald W *BEM* psc	311279
Merritt T V sq	311279
Wilde R M psc†	311279
Brunt N J P sq	300980
Henderson G W psc†	300980
Horsey A P M sq	300980
James D psc	300980
Mills R G	300980
Seed D psc	300980
Bradbury H J M	300981
Church J W psc	300981
Fisher P B psc	300981
Wooldridge J R	300981
Illing C A B	300982
Petrie A G *MA DipEd* psc	300982
Sneesby J D ph	300982
Andrews J C aic	300983
de Hochepied Larpent A L D *BSc* psc	300983
Porter J K R *BA* psc	300983
Winn C D L	300983
Bowes-Crick C P	300984
Kirkham S G *MC* psc(CAN)	300984
Sanderson S H P psc(a)†	300984
Wolfenden R C	300984
Bain A G *BA*	300985
Beswick N W *MA* psc†	300985
Bottomley D R	300985
Greenwood A G psc	300985
Jequier J R *LRAM ARCM*	300985
Minter T J *BA* psc	300985

Captains

Name	Date
Kiddie K W *BA* psc (*A/Maj* 161285)	050478
Jordan T W V *BSc* aic	011278
Smith P J *BA* psc (*A/Maj* 201285)	100979
O'Brien T C	301279
Gorski B M *BSc*	020180
Bull R W *BA*	090980
Cole A P A	090980
Robertson B D *MA*	291180
Cass G P (*A/Maj* 161184)	291280
Gutteridge C L	291280
Sturtivant P A	291280
Cross P T	080981
Whistler A J	080981
Brazier I A	281281
Turpin R J	281281
Vyvyan-Robinson P J	281281
Smallwood D *BSc*	270282
Wilson C G *BA*	010882
Farrell R A *BSc*	060982
Liles I R	060982
Lupson D J	060982
Brown A R *BSc*	290383
Murray-Playfair J L *BA*	170783
Stack P A *BA*	031083
Burrows P G *BSc*	191283
Welch A L	060284
Weston S W J *BA*	200384
Harris A R G	100684
Marriott A G	100684
Warren A C	100684
Longley P M *BA*	040984
Dawson S A	021084
Bright J R	081084
Harward R B	091184
Leadsom S S	090685
Oliver G G	130985
Hiskett M W *MSc*	071085
Haugh K	211085
Macey P J	040286

Lieutenants

Name	Date
Aldridge W N *BA*	120482
Denny J W *BA(Hons)* (*A/Capt* 010286)	120482
Coates E G	090882
John T *BSc*	090882
Long C I	090882
Redpath D (*A/Capt* 050385)	090882
Harris P M D	131282
Wisbey G R	131282
Dowling S *BA*	110483
O'Connell T S *BA*	110483
Reay J M *BA*	110483
Teal N M	110483
Thompson I M *BA*	110483
Whitehouse J G *BA*	110483
Cook D J	080883
Lucas P H	121283
Beverley A *BA*	090484
Clover J P	090484
Cotton S J	090484
Whitwam J C E *BA*	070884
Winckle D J	111284
Claridge C R	090485
Marr S R D (*A/Capt* 010386)	060885
Moncur G D	060885
Sincock J S	060885
Harnby G R	020386

2nd Lieutenants

Name	Date
††Bailey J H	020983
Travers M P M	040884
††Briselden A G	230984
††Whiteside P A J	230984
Evans H S	100885
†Chapman A P *MA(Hons)*	060985

Quartermasters

Name	Rank	Date
Bateman P R		010473
	Maj	010479
Dalby K		010475
	Lt Col	290984
Ramsey F R *MBE*		010478
	Maj	020585
Bath B E	*Capt*	010481
Laight K J		010482
	Maj	020184
Prescott D W	*Capt*	070185
Anderson J C J	*Capt*	010485
Ingham L *BEM*	*Capt*	010485
Jones A T	*Capt*	010485
Rodgers V H *BEM*	*Capt*	010485

Special Regular Officers

Captains

Name	Date
Hayman J D	010483
Nelson E A (*A/Maj* 251185)	040184

Lieutenants

Name	Date
Niven W G	030485

Short Service Officers

Captains

Name	Date
Rowland W	260683
Wright B M	290184
Bliss R A *BSc*	040984
Cloake J N *BA*	290585
Foster J J L	260785
Wischhusen M W	220885
Diggins S L C *BA*	071185
Wall M J	020186
Mulkern T P	020286
Whitfield N *DCM*	010386

Lieutenants

Name	Date
Brooks N I	051281
Owen C *BEM*	040782
Baron J C *BA*	090882
Davis J R	081282
Hollywood J *BEM*	080183
Sexton A W	270283
Curtis A J	160383
Kendrick S W M *BSc*	110483
Paterson D J *BSc*	110483
White C D *LLB*	080883
Cartwright A I	090484
McGowan A P I *BA*	090484
Silcocks M G *BA*	090484
Eastwood C C *BA*	070884
Kippen I R *BA*	070884
Garratt J P J	090485
Bell J L	040286
Elletson H	070486
Merriman P W	070486
Smith N P	070486

2nd Lieutenants

Name	Date
King A C	130485
Shirley M J L	130485
†Renny A C	060985
†Strachan D J *BA*	060985
†Collicutt R J *BA*	060186
†Yiannopoullos D N M *BA*	060186

Short Service Volunteer Officers

2nd Lieutenants

Name	Date
Potts C W	200186

THE ROYAL ANGLIAN REGIMENT
(9, 10, 12, 16, 17, 44, 48, 56, 58)

The Castle and Key of Gibraltar upon an eight pointed Star

The figure of Britannia. The Sphinx superscribed Egypt. The Castle and Key superscribed Gibraltar, 1779-83 and with the motto *Montis Insignia Calpe* underneath. The Royal Tiger superscribed Hindoostan. An Eagle within the Garter

Namur 1695, Blenheim, Ramillies, Oudenarde, Malplaquet, Dettingen, Louisberg, Minden, Quebec 1759, Belleisle, **Martinique 1762, 1794** Moro, **Havannah,** India, **Seringapatam,** Surinam, Maida, Rolica, Vimiera, **Peninsula, Corunna,** Douro, **Talavera,** Busaca, **Albuhera, Badajoz, Salamanca, Vittoria,** Pyrenees, St Sebastian, Nivelle, Nive, Orthes, Toulouse, **Bladensburg, Waterloo, Ava,** Affghanistan 1839, **Ghuznee 1839, Khelat, Cabool 1842, 79, Moodkee, Ferozeshah, Sobraon, New Zealand,** Mooltan, **Goojerat, Punjaub, South Africa 1851-53,** Alma, **Inkerman, Sevastopol, Lucknow, Taku Forts,** South Africa 1879, **Afghanistan 1878-80,** Ali Masjid, **Nile 1884-85,** Chitral, **Tirah, Atbara, Khartoum, South Africa 1899-1902,** Modder River, Relief of Kimberley, **Paardeburg, Defence of Ladysmith.**

The Great War– **Mons, Le Cateau,** Retreat from Mons, **Marne 1914, Aisne 1914, 18,** La Bassee 1914, Messines 1914, 17, 18, Armentieres 1914, Givenchy 1914, **Ypres 1914, 15, 17, 18,** Langemarck 1914, 17, Gheluvelt, Nonne Bosschen, Festubert 1914, 15, **Neuve Chapelle,** Hill 60, Gravenstafel, St Julien, Frezenberg, Bellewaarde, Aubers, Hooge 1915, **Loos, Somme 1916, 18,** Albert 1916, 18, Bazentin, Delville Wood, Pozieres, Guillemont, Flers Courcelette, Morval, Thiepval, Le Transloy, Ancre Heights, Ancre 1916, 18, Bapaume 1917, 18, **Arras 1917, 18,** Vimy 1917, Scarpe 1917, 18, Arleux, Oppy, Pilckem, Menin Road, Polygon Wood, Broodseinde, Poelcappelle, Passchendaele, **Cambrai 1917, 18,** St Quentin, Rosieres, Avre, Villers Bretonneux, Lys, Estaires, Hazebrouck, Bailleul, Kemmel, Bethune, Scherpenberg, Amiens, Drocourt-Queant, Hindenburg Line, Havrincourt, Epehy, Canal du Nord, St Quentin Canal, Beaurevoir, Courtrai, Selle, Valenciennes, Sambre, **France and Flanders 1914-18,** Italy 1917-18, Helles, Landing at Helles, Struma, Doiran 1918, **Macedonia 1915-18,** Krithia, Suvla, Landing at Suvla, Scimitar Hill, **Gallipoli 1915-16,** Rumani, Egypt 1915-17, **Gaza,** El Mughar, Nebi Samwil, Jerusalem, Jaffa, Tell' Asur, Megiddo, Sharon, Damascus, **Palestine 1917-18,** Tigris 1916, **Shaiba,** Kut al Amara 1915, 17, Ctesiphon, Defence of Kut al Amara, Baghdad, **Mesopotamia 1914-18.**

The Second World War– Vist, Norway 1940, Defence of Escaut, **St Omar-la Bassee,** Defence of Arras, Ypres-Comines Canal, **Dunkirk 1940,** St Valery-en-Caux, **Normandy Landing,** Cambes, Tilly sur Seulles, Fontenay le Pesnil, Odon, Defence of Rauray, Caen, Orne, Bourguebus Ridge, Troarn, Le Perier Ridge, **Brieux Bridgehead,** Falaise, Nederrijn, Le Havre, Antwerp-Turnhout Canal, Scheldt, **Venraij,** Venlo Pocket, Zetten, Rhineland, Hochwald, Lingen, Brinkum, Bremen, Arnhem 1945, **North-West Europe 1940, 44-45,** Abyssinia 1940, Falluja, Tobruk Sortie, Belhamed, Baghdad 1941, Iraq 1941, Palmyra, Jebel Mazar, Syria 1941, Sidi Barrani **Tobruk 1941,** Tobruk Sortie, Belhamed, Mersa Matruh, **Defence of Alamein Line** Deir El Shein, Ruweisat, Ruweisat Ridge, El Alamein, Matmata Hills, Akarit, Enfidaville, Djebel Garci, Djedeida, Djebel Djaffa, Montagne Farm, Sedjenane 1, Mine de Sedjenane, Oued Zarga, Djebel Tanngoucha, Argoub Sellah, Sidi Ahmed, Tunis, Ragoubet Souissi, **North Africa 1940-43,** Landing in Sicily, Adrano, Sicily 1943, Trigno, Sangro, **Villa Grande, Salerno,** Vietri Pass, Capture of Naples, Cava di Tirreni, Volturno Crossing, Calabritto, Garigliano Crossing, Monte Tuga, **Anzio, Cassino i-ii,** Castle Hill, Hangman's Hill, Monte Gaddione, Trasimene Line, **Gothic Line,** Monte Gridolfo, Gemmano Ridge, Lamone Crossing, Monte Colombo, San Marino, Monte La Pieve, Argenta Gap, **Italy 1943-45,** Athens, Greece 1944-45, **Crete,**Heraklion, Madagascar, Kampar, Johore, Muar, Batu Pahat, **Singapore Island, Malaya 1941-42,** Donbaik, Point 201 (Arakan), **Yu,** North Arakan, Buthidaung, **Ngakyedauk Pass, Imphal,** Tamu Road, Bishenpur, **Kohima,** Aradura, Monywa 1945, Mandalay, Myinmu Bridgehead, Irrawaddy, Ramree, **Chindits 1944, Burma 1943-45.**

Maryang-San, **Korea 1951-53.**

Regimental Marches

Quick March..Rule Britannia and Speed the Plough
Slow March...The Slow March of The Northamptonshire Regiment

Agents...Holts Branch, Royal Bank of Scotland PLC, Lawrie House, Farnborough, Hants

Regimental Headquarters.....................The Keep, Gibraltar Barracks, Bury St Edmunds, Suffolk, IP33 3RN (*Tel No:* 0284-2394)

Alliances

Canadian Armed Forces........................Sherbrooke Hussars
The Lincoln and Welland Regiment
The Essex and Kent Scottish
The Lake Superior Scottish Regiment
Australian Military Forces....................The Royal Tasmania Regiment
New Zealand Army................................3rd Battalion (Auckland(Countess of Ranfurly's Own) and Northland) Royal New Zealand Infantry Regiment
Pakistan Army.......................................5th Battalion The Frontier Force Regiment
Malaysian Armed Forces.......................1st Battalion The Royal Malay Regiment
Barbados...The Barbados Regiment
Colonial Forces.....................................The Bermuda Regiment
The Gibraltar Regiment

The Queens Division — continued

Colonel in Chief......*HM* QUEEN ELIZABETH THE QUEEN MOTHER

Deputy Colonels in Chief......*HRH The Princess* Margaret *Countess of* Snowdon *CI GCVO*

HRH Princess Alice *Duchess of* Gloucester *GCB CL GCVO GBE*

Colonel......Gen *Sir* Timothy Creasey *KCB OBE* ret pay......061182

Deputy Colonels......Lt Gen *Sir* John Akehurst *KCB CBE*......010181
Maj Gen *Sir* David Thorne *KBE*......050881
Maj Gen J A Ward-Booth *OBE* ret pay......050282

Brigadiers

Aris M A *CBE* psc 300682
Pollard A J G *CBE* ndc psc
(*A/Maj Gen* 191185) 300682
Thorne M E *CBE* odc(US) psc 300683
Stone P P D *CBE* psc(a) 300684
Barnes C M J *OBE* ndc psc 300685
Dodd W T *OBE* psc 300685

Colonels

Green S A *OBE* psc 300680
Pike W R W psc 300680
Robinson R H *OBE* sq 300682
Hart J R *MBE* odc(US) psc 300684

Lieutenant Colonels

Dean T D (SL) *OBE* ndc psc 300672
Mosse R J MacG (SL) *BA* ptsc 300677
Swallow F A H *OBE* ndc psc I 311277
Drummond R J M *OBE* psc 300678
Baily D R *MBE* psc 300679
Woodrow K psc I 300679
Howe R *OBE* psc
(*A/Col* 280386) 300680
Veitch A R A psc† 300680
Calder A J K *OBE* ndc psc
(*A/Col* 160186) 300681
Houchin J S *MBE* psc† 300681
Lambert H W *OBE* psc 300681
Taylor T T *MBE BA* ndc psc 300681
Thomas T B *OBE* psc 300681
Thompson A E *MBE MC* psc 300681
Browne D J W *MBE BA* psc† 300682
Long P B D *OBE* psc 300682
Walker M J D *OBE* psc† 300682
Groves C psc 300683
Goldschmidt M K psc jsdc 300684
Romilly M E *BSc* ndc psc† 300684
Sutherell J C B *MBE BA* psc 300684
Veitch T D A psc 300684
Greenham R G psc 300685
Rawlins P P *MBE BA* psc† 300685

Majors

Lumby C W T psc 300669
King P W 300671
Ross P K R 311271
Halcrow H M P sq 300672
Jefferson I W sq 300672
Child P J S *BSc* psc† 311273
Reeve W H sq 300674
Styles C A sq 300674
Davenport B H M sq 300675
Hawkins W J *MBE* sq 300675
Menage M J *MBE* sq 300675
Williamson P H *MBE MA* psc(n)† aic 300675
Wright D J psc 300675
Hipkin G W M 311275
Brett G I G psc† ph
(*A/Lt Col* 130985) 311276
Taylor A C psc
(*L/Lt Col* 140486) 311276
Boocock M J sq 311277
Cornish B R sq 311277
Haes R E psc 300679
Heal W F A sq 300679
Pepper R H sq 300679
Underwood S R H 300679
Chambers M D psc 311279
Dixon P R C psc† 311279
Behagg A *MBE MA* psc† 300980
Domeisen A P psc 300980
Duff A N sq 300980
Lacey J D psc 300980
Longland T *MBE* psc 300980
Slater A D psc† 300980
Barnes P psc 300981
Ferrary P M L osc(SP) aic 300981
Otter T P G psc† 300981
Walsh J M P 300981
Willdridge M D *BA* sq 300981
Deed A P *MSc* psc(IND) 300982
Field P W psc 300982
Gould R C 300982
Mooring W R psc 300982
Stallard C G psc 300982
Thompson R M psc 300982
Tomlin G F 300982
Chisnall R M psc 300983
Power T M T 300983
Prescott J B C 300983
Ryan K M *BA* 300983
Willdridge P H 300983
Badger S P B 300984
Duthoit G D 300984
Groom C J B 300984
Hodgson K psc 300984
McColl J C psc 300984
Phipps D S B *BA* psc 300984
Baylis D J W *BA* psc(IND)† 300985
Holme P M 300985

Captains

Richardson N J *LLB* psc
(*A/Maj* 161285) 010279
Hall I R M 090379
Borthwick J A B
(*A/Maj* 280885) 100979
Brunt R M *MA* 010280
Page C T *BA* 010280
Blyth S P M 100580
Beard M J 090980
Godkin M P aic 090980
Pearce C J
(*A/Maj* 010884) 090980
Antolik F R *FRGS* 291280
Bacon S J 090581
Clements D J *BSc*
(*A/Maj* 181185) 110581
Harrold R E 080981
Lucas R H C 080582
Macdonald J F 080782
Hare R J 060982
Webster C R 060982
Lamb S W 070283
Edmondson-Jones R J 081083
Froud F M 081083
Tansley K P *BA* 081083
Branch S H 100684
Cope R G A 100684
Marriner S J 100684
Bowns S H *BA* 041084
Dean J F 081084
Burrell N G *BA* 030285
Kemp R J 050285
Townley T D G *BA* 050285
Goodin R C J 071085
Wild A J C *BA* 071085
Wenham M H 040286

Lieutenants

Pollard J C D G
(*A/Capt* 011085) 081281
Willmott W A
(*A/Capt* 201284) 081281
Porter S L
(*A/Capt* 011082) 290182
Gaskin P H *BA* 120482
Venn D F *BA* 120482
Jones P D
(*A/Capt* 010286) 131282
Ward A G W
(*A/Capt* 071185) 131282
Ladley R J 080883
Marsh A R J 010584
Miles A M L 130784
Etherington S D 090485
Fell A M D 090485
Thorne E E C 090485
Westmacott S J 060685
Howard W J 101285

2nd Lieutenants

††Kemp C P 020983
††O'Driscoll D P 020983
††Crawshaw N C 061083
†Crawley L J C *BSc(Hons)* 230984
††Foster B A 031084
†Till D J *BA* 060985
††Cooper N P 240985
††Halsall D R 240985
††Nottingham N F C 240985

Staff Quartermasters

Kinson M J 010475
Lt Col 070985

Quartermasters

James A I 010476
Maj 010479
Bullock H S 010478
Maj 210483
Edwards D R 010478
Maj 010184
Greenfield D H *MBE* 010478
Maj 100784
Fletcher J D 010478
Maj 010885

Perry F J *MBE*		010478
	Maj	170984
Spalding D W		010481
	Maj	260985
Rourke J S J	*Capt*	010482
Kett C J C	*Capt*	010483
McDonnell B	*Capt*	010484
Ross J G G	*Capt*	010485

Special Regular Officers

Majors

Seccombe W P	300984

Captains

Pryce D N	130883
Morling P J	090685
Brunt S B	040286

Lieutenants

Napier D C (*A/Capt* 010484)	120482
Boast S J	131282
Knox R A	110483

Short Service Officers

Captains

Jackson R J (*A/Maj* 011084)	200177
Denny P W	020482
Taylor D	140782
Burford W	080785
Keogh L B	031085
Duffield A R *BSc*	071085
Spinks N *BA*	071085

Lieutenants

Fisk J (*A/Capt* 010386)	020182
Powell A (*A/Capt* 070486)	010382
Coe D C (*A/Capt* 101184)	100582
Eke R E	070782
Whitehead D	290982
Clements R J (*A/Capt* 040186)	131282
Hill C R	190283
Taylor G N	020383
Skingsley M G D *BA*	080883
Tilbrook T M *BSc*	080883
Lynch D D	121283
De Planta De Wildenberg F M G *BA*	090484
Hallam P W	090484
Andrews S T H *BSc*	070884
Willis D J	070884
Smith T J	051285

2nd Lieutenants

Blakeney-Edwards J M	040884
Jolly P A	040884
Taylor S P	081284
Vass R T	081284
Weightman T	081284
Wellfair A L	081284
Wormald S P	081284
Barnes C J	130485
Dean P C T	130485
Reid G P	130485
†Beven R G J *BA(Hons)*	060985
†Cattermole G D *BA(Hons)*	060985
†Dyer A S *BSc*	060985
†Wylie A M *BSc(Hons)*	060985
Dicker M B	141285
Gosling A	141285
Knight R D	141285
†Jackson A T D *BA*	060186
†Latham A P *BA*	060186

Short Service Volunteer Officers

Lieutenants

Wadman A J	060884
Vincent D G	310785

THE KINGS DIVISION

Comprising ....The King's Own Royal Border Regiment (1 Regular Battalion, 1 Volunteer Battalion)
The King's Regiment (1 Regular Battalion, 1 Volunteer Battalion)
The Prince of Wales's Own Regiment of Yorkshire (1 Regular Battalion)
The Green Howards (Alexandra, Princess of Wales's Own Yorkshire Regiment) (1 Regular Battalion)
The Royal Irish Rangers (27th (Inniskilling), 83rd and 87th) (2 Regular Battalions, 2 Volunteer Battalions)
The Queen's Lancashire Regiment (1 Regular Battalion, 1 Volunteer Battalion)
The Duke of Wellington's Regiment (West Riding) (1 Regular Battalion)
The York and Lancaster Regiment
1st Battalion Yorkshire Volunteers
2nd Battalion Yorkshire Volunteers
3rd Battalion Yorkshire Volunteers

Divisional Headquarters ....Imphal Barracks, York, YO1 4HD (*Tel No:* 0904-59811 *Ext:* 2268)
Colonel Commandant ....Lt Gen *Sir* Charles Huxtable *KCB CBE*..010783
Divisional Brigadier ....Brig M H Sharpe..020885

The origins of amalgamated Regiments now included in The King's Division are as follows:—

THE KINGS OWN ROYAL BORDER REGIMENT

On 1 October 1959
The King's Own Royal Regiment (Lancaster) (4) and
The Border Regiment (34 and 55) amalgamated to form:
The King's Own Royal Border Regiment

THE KINGS REGIMENT

On 1 September 1958
The King's Regiment (Liverpool) (8) and
The Manchester Regiment (63 and 96) amalgamated to form:
The King's Regiment (Manchester and Liverpool) (8, 63 and 96)
On 13 December 1968 the Regiment was redesignated
The King's Regiment

THE PRINCE OF WALES'S OWN REGIMENT OF YORKSHIRE

On 25 April 1958
The West Yorkshire Regiment (The Prince of Wales's Own) (14) and
The East Yorkshire Regiment (Duke of York's Own) (15) amalgamated to form:
The Prince of Wales's Own Regiment of Yorkshire

THE ROYAL IRISH RANGERS
(27th (INNISKILLING) 83rd and 87th)

On 1 July 1968

The Royal Inniskilling Fusiliers (27 and 108)

The Royal Ulster Rifles (83 and 86) and

The Royal Irish Fusiliers (Princess Victoria's) (87 and 89) amalgamated to form:

The Royal Irish Rangers (27th (Inniskilling) 83rd and 87th)

THE QUEEN'S LANCASHIRE REGIMENT

On 1 July 1958

The East Lancashire Regiment (30 and 59) and

The South Lancashire Regiment (The Prince of Wales's Volunteers) (40 and 82) amalgamated to form:

The Lancashire Regiment (Prince of Wales's Volunteers)

On 25 March 1970

The Lancashire Regiment (Prince of Wales's Volunteers) (30, 40, 59 and 82) and

The Loyal Regiment (North Lancashire) (47 and 81) amalgamated to form:

The Queen's Lancashire Regiment

THE KING'S OWN ROYAL BORDER REGIMENT (4, 34 and 55)

The Royal Cypher within the garter all within a wreath of laurel. The Lion of England in each corner, Dragon Superscribed China

Namur 1695 Gibraltar 1704-5, Guadaloupe 1759, Havannah, St Lucia 1778, Corunna, Albuhera, Arroyo Dos Molinos, Badajoz, Salamanca, Vittoria, St Sebastian, Pyrenees, Nivelle, Nive, Orthes, Peninsula, Bladensburg, Waterloo, Alma, Inkerman, Sevastopol, Lucknow, Abyssinia, South Africa 1879, Relief of Ladysmith, South Africa 1899-1902

The Great War— Le Cateau, Retreat from Mons, **Marne 1914,** Aisne 1914, Armentieres 1914, **Ypres 1914, 15, 17, 18, Langemarck 1914, 17,** Gheluvelt, Neuve Chapelle, Gravenstafel, St Julien, Frezenberg, Bellewaarde, Aubers, Festubert 1915, Loos, **Somme 1916, 18,** Albert 1916, 18, Bazentin, Delville Wood, Pozieres, Guillemont, Ginchy, Flers-Courcelette, Morval, Thiepval, Le Transloy, Ancre Heights, Ancre 1916, **Arras 1917, 18,** Scarpe 1917, 18, Arleux, Bullecourt, **Messines 1917, 18,** Pilckem, Menin Road, Polygon Wood, Broodseinde, Poelcappelle, Passchendaele, **Cambrai, 1917, 18,** St Quentin, Rosieres, **Lys,** Estaires, Hazebrouck, Bailleul, Kemmel, Bethune, Scherpenberg, Aisne 1918, Amiens, Bapaume 1918, Drocourt-Queant, Hindenburg Line, Epehy, Canal du Nord, St Quentin Canal, Beaurevoir, Courtrai, Selle, Valenciennes, Sambre, **France and Flanders 1914-18,** Piave, **Vittorio Veneto,** Italy 1917-18, Struma, Doiran 1917, 18, **Macedonia 1915-18,** Helles, Landing at Helles, Krithia, Suvla, Sari Bair, Landing at Suvla, Scimitar Hill, **Gallipoli 1915-16,** Egypt 1916, Tigris 1916, Kut al Amara 1917, Baghdad, **Mesopotamia 1916-18,** NW Frontier India 1916-17

Afghanistan 1919

The Second World War— Defence of Escaut, St Omer-La Bassee, **Dunkirk 1940,** Somme 1940, **Arnhem 1944, North-West Europe 1940, 44, Defence of Habbaniya,** Falluja, Iraq 1941, **Merjayun,** Jebel Mazar, Syria 1941, **Tobruk 1941, Tobruk Sortie, North Africa 1940-42, Landing in Sicily, Montone,** Citta di Castello, San Martino Sogliano, **Lamone Bridghead,** Italy 1944-45, **Malta 1941-42, Imphal,** Sakawng, Tamu Road, Shenam Pass, Kohima, Ukhrul, Mandalay, **Myinmu Bridgehead, Meiktila,** Rangoon Road, Pyawbwe, Sittang 1945, **Chindits 1944, Burma 1943-45**

Regimental Marches

Quick March..........Arrangement of 'John Peel' and 'Corn Rigs are Bonnie'
Slow March..........Trelawny

Agents..........Lloyds Bank PLC Cox's & King's Branch

Regimental Headquarters..........The Castle, Carlisle, Cumbria, CA3 8UR (*Tel No:* 0228-21275)

Alliances

Canadian Armed Forces..........The King's Own Calgary Regiment
Australian Military Forces..........The Royal Queensland Regiment
Pakistan Army..........15th Battalion The Frontier Force Regiment

Colonel in Chief..........*HRH Princess* Alexandra *The Hon Mrs* Angus Ogilvy *GCVO*

Colonel..........Maj Gen D E Miller *CB CBE MC*..........050281

Brigadiers

Hodges R J *OBE* rcds psc	300681
Pett R A *MBE* psc	300685

Colonels

de Cordova J G *OBE* psc osc(GH)	300679
Milburn J H *OBE* psc osc(US)	300680
Elrington P L ptsc tt	300681
Wolverson R C *OBE MA* psc†	300685

Lieutenant Colonels

Smith R J *MBE* sq	300681
Day C R psc	300682
Pheysey D H sq	300682
Davidson A F *MBE* psc	300685

Majors

Farrell J A sq	300671
Underwood J B L psc	300672
Pattinson S J H sq	311276
Clarke D C	311277
Warren C sq	311277
Kirkpatrick D sq	311278
James P sq	311279
Strickland S W L psc	300980
Welsh J R K	300980
Macdonald A J L psc†	300981
Flanagan S J A *MC* psc	300982
Jarvis-Bicknell T C *MBE* psc	300982
Longhurst A R	300982
Flynn D N J psc(IT)	300983
Lynam J M psc	300983
Allardice D H psc†	300984

Captains

Mawdsley S D *MA* I* (*L/Maj* 190984)	050379
Bruce R D	100979
Hanna T J	090980
Hudson P J	080981
Gray C H W	281281
Barrett T R	080582
Urquhart M N S	060284
Perkin M S	081084
Schumacher A (*A/Maj* 120286)	081084
Griffiths M T *BSc(Hons)*	050285
Hampson P T	040286
Keough T J	040286

Lieutenants

Eaden R J (*A/Capt* 210386)	110483
Willison J D *BA*	110483
Hewitt G M *BA*	070884
Sharpe J M A	060885
Halliday M L	070486

2nd Lieutenants

Norton M J	040884
††Harrison M J B	240985

Quartermasters

Smethurst A		010479
	Maj	070684
Hodgson P H		010480
	Maj	161185
Harrison V A	*Capt*	010482
McCartney J	*Capt*	010482

Special Regular Officers

Captains

Snowball A J (*A/Maj* 150386)	281281
Norris S J W	060982
Coleman S J	030384
Wright L	100684

Lieutenants

Jones H M R (*A/Capt* 010785)	090484

Short Service Officers

Captains

Durney E L	030683
Craig F	100284
Whiteford R G *BEM*	160186

Lieutenants

Martin K R (*A/Capt* 010885)	300182
Mavromatis N *LLB* (*A/Capt* 010186)	120482
Stewart B P B *BA* (*A/Capt* 161285)	090882
Parsonage D	020683
Woodburn S E	020683
Hopton R	090683
Dennis A *BSc*	090484
Watkins M J G *BA*	090484
Griffin H B *BA*	070884
Moss G P *BSocSc*	070884
Woolf D J	070884
Morgan G	090485

2nd Lieutenants

Baldwin B L	081284
†Peyton S S *BA(Hons)*	060985

Short Service Volunteer Officers

Captains

Fecitt H *AIPM MBIM MIIM*	180684

Lieutenants

Williams C D A	230585

THE KING'S REGIMENT (8, 63 and 96)

The White Horse of Hanover superimposed upon Fleur-de-Lys. The Royal Cypher surmounted by The Crown
The Sphinx superscribed Egypt

Blenheim, Ramillies, Oudenarde, Malplaquet, Dettingen, Guadaloupe 1759, Egmont-op-Zee, Peninsula, Martinique 1809, Guadaloupe 1810, Niagara, New Zealand, Alma, Inkerman, Sevastopol, Delhi 1857, Lucknow, Peiwar Kotal, Afghanistan 1878-80, Egypt 1882, Burma 1885-87, Defence of Ladysmith, South Africa 1899-1902

The Great War— **Mons,** Le Cateau, **Retreat from Mons, Marne 1914, Aisne 1914,** La Bassee 1914, Armentieres 1914, **Ypres 1914, 15, 17, 18,** Langemarck 1914, 17, Gheluvelt, Nonne Bosschen, **Givenchy 1914,** Neuve Chapelle, Gravenstafel, St Julien, Frenzenberg, Bellewarde, Aubers, **Festubert 1915, Loos, Somme 1916, 18,** Albert 1916, 18, Bazentin, Delville Wood, Guillemont, Ginchy, Flers-Courcelette, Morval, Thiepval, Le Transloy, Ancre Heights, Ancre 1916, 18, Bapaume 1917, 18, **Arras 1917-18, Scarpe 1917, 18,** Arleux, Bullecourt, Messines 1917, 18, Pilckem, Menin Road, Polygon Wood, Broodseinde, Poelcappelle, Passchendale, **Cambrai 1917, 18,** St Quentin, Rosieres, Avre, Lys, Estaires, Bailleul, Kemmel, Bethune, Amiens, Scherpenberg, Drocourt-Queant, **Hindenburgh Line,** Epehy Canal du Nord, St Quentin Canal, Beaurevoir, Courtrai, Selle, Sambre, France and Flanders 1914-18, **Piave,** Vittorio Veneto, Italy 1917-18, Doiran 1917, **Macedonia 1915-18,** Helles, Krithia, Suvla, Landing at Suvla, Scimitar Hill, **Gallipoli 1915,** Rumani, Egypt 1915-17, **Megiddo,** Sharon, Palestine 1918, Tigris 1916, Kut al Amara 1917, **Baghdad,** Mesopotamia 1916-18, NW Frontier India 1915,

Archangel 1918-19 **Afghanistan 1919**

The Second World War— **Dyle,** Withdrawal to Escaut, Defence of Escaut, **Defence of Arras,** St Omer-la-Bassee, Ypres-Comines Canal, **Normandy Landing, Caen,** Esquay, Falaise, Nederrijn, **Scheldt,** Walcharen Causeway, Flushing, **Lower Maas,** Venlo Pocket, **Roer,** Ourthe, Rhineland, **Reichswald,** Goch, Weeze, Rhine, Ibbenburen, Dreirwalde, Aller, Bremen, North-West Europe 1940, 44-45, **Cassino II, Trasimene Line, Tuori, Gothic Line,** Monte Gridolfo, Coriano, San Clemente, Gemmano Ridge, Montilgallo, **Capture of Forli,** Lamone Crossing, Defence of Lamone Bridghead, **Rimini Line,** Montescudo, Cesena, Italy 1944-45, **Malta 1940, Athens,** Greece 1944-45, Singapore Island, Malaya 1941-42, North Arakan, **Kohima,** Pinwe, Schwebo, Myinmu Bridgehead, Irrawaddy, **Chindits 1943, Chindits 1944,** Burma 1943-45

The Hook 1953, Korea 1952-53

Regimental Marches

Quick March..........The Kingsman
Slow March..........Lord Ferrars March

Agents..........Lloyds Bank PLC Cox's & King's Branch

Regimental Headquarters..........TA Centre, Townsend Avenue, Liverpool, L11 5AF (*Tel No:* 051-226-9905 *Ext:* 3)

*Regimental Headquarters (Increment)*TA Centre, Ardwick Green, Manchester, M12 6HD (*Tel No:* 061-273 6191)

Alliances

Canadian Armed Forces..........The Royal Regiment of Canada
Australian Military Forces..........The Royal South Australia Regiment
New Zealand Army..........4th Battalion Otago and Southland Royal Zealand Infantry Regiment
Pakistan Army..........1st Battalion (Scinde) The Frontier Force Regiment

Colonel in Chief..........*HM* QUEEN ELIZABETH THE QUEEN MOTHER

Colonel..........Col *Sir* Geoffrey Errington *Bt* ret pay..........280675

Colonels

Lee R G *OBE CEng MIERE FBIM* psc† ptsc	300679
Denning C V psc osc(GH)	300683
Simm A P psc	300685

Lieutenant Colonels

Davies C P ndc psc	300680
Hepworth N G R *OBE* psc (*A/Col* 081085)	300680
Herring J C G sq	300680
Carrington M R psc	300683
Woodhouse C P psc	300683
Gaskell J J sq	300684
Grant Haworth M A psc jsdc	300685
Lawrence-Brown D D J psc	300685

Majors

Cross J C P *MBE* sq	300668
Andrews J M	311268
Bruce I C sq	311271
Hepworth C F psc†	311275
Francis P H L sq ph	300677
Hislop R L sq	300678
Walsh A J psc	300679
Amlot M G C sq	300980
Horsford I T	300981
Walsh D V	300981
Oates M E	300982
Filler P St J	300983
McDonald G A psc	300983
Parish M C *BA* psc	300983
Hodges R E L psc	300984
Turley J F	300985
Wilkinson J P	300985

Captains

Roberts J P *BA*	030479
Hodges C O *BA*	100979
Owen C W *BSc*	211281
Leyland P J L	281281
Fletcher J H *BA*	280982
Hammond S A	081083
Phythian A D	060284
Wright S J A	081084
Jackson S A *BSc*	050285
Mitchell S J aic	050285

Lieutenants

Nicholls M	110483
Baxter S P (*A/Capt* 030386)	070884
Light T D	070884
Smith N D S	070884
Payne M D	111284
Hutchinson S D	060885
Docherty A J	070486

2nd Lieutenants

Deakin G C	130485

Quartermasters

Oakley P S	*Capt*	010481

Special Regular Officers

Majors

David J T	300980

Lieutenants

Ainslie H M (*A/Capt* 010286)	110483

Short Service Officers

Captains

Sharp C N R	110383
Storr J P *BSc(Eng)*	071085

Lieutenants

Lee H T	220882
Grimes P J	011082
Cain T D *BA*	110483
George E M *BA*	090484
Rafferty P S *BSc*	090484
Wainwright J G *BA*	090484
Lettin G D *BA*	070884
Goodall A J	250985
Barnett S N	101285
Payne J P H	101285
Simpson R M	101285
Griffin C M	070486

2nd Lieutenants

Pullan A M	100885
†Heaton T C G *BSc PGCE*	060985

THE PRINCE OF WALES'S OWN REGIMENT OF YORKSHIRE

(14 and 15)

The White Rose of York superimposed upon an eight-pointed star
The Prince of Wales's Plume. The White Horse of Hanover with motto *"Nec aspera terrent"*
The Royal Tiger superscribed India

Namur 1695, Blenheim, Ramillies, Oudenarde, Malplaquet, Louiseberg, Quebec 1759, Martinique 1762, Havannah, St Lucia 1778, Martinique 1794, 1809, Tournay, Corunna, Guadaloupe 1810, Java, Waterloo, Bhurtpore, Sevastopol, New Zealand, Afghanistan 1879-80, Relief of Ladysmith, South Africa 1899-1902

The Great War— **Aisne 1914, 18, Armentieres 1914, Neuve Chapelle, Ypres 1915, 17, 18,** Gravenstafel, St Julien, Frezenberg, Bellewaarde, Aubers, Hooge 1915, **Loos, Somme 1916, 18,** Albert 1916, 18, Bazentin, Delville Wood, Pozieres, Flers-Courcelette, Morval, Thiepval, Le Transloy, Ancre Heights, Ancre 1916, **Arras 1917, 18,** Scarpe 1917, 18, Arleux, Oppy, Bullecourt, Hill 70, Messines 1917, 18, Pilckem, Langemarck 1917, Menin Road, Polygon Wood, Broodseinde, Poelcappelle, Passchendaele, **Cambrai 1917, 18,** St Quentin, Bapaume 1918, Rosieres, **Villers Bretonneux, Lys,** Estaires, Hazebrouck, Bailleul, Kemmel, Scherpenberg, Marne 1918, **Tardenois,** Amiens, Drocourt-Queant, Hindenburg Line, Havrincourt, Epehy, Canal du Nord, St Quentin Canal, **Selle,** Valenciennes, Sambre, France and Flanders, 1914-18, **Piave,** Vittorio Veneto, Italy 1917-18, Struma, **Doiran 1917,** Macedonia 1915-18, **Suvla,** Landing at Suvla, Scimitar Hill, **Gallipoli 1915,** Egypt 1915-16

The Second World War— Withdrawal to Escaut, Defence of Escaut, Defence of Arras, French Frontier 1940, Ypres-Comines Canal, **Dunkirk 1940, Normandy Landing,** Tilly sur Seulles, **Odon,** Caen, Bourguebus Ridge, Troarn, Mont Pincon, St Pierre la Vielle, Gheel, Nederrijn, Aam, Venraij, Rhineland, **Schaddenhof,** Brinkum, Bremen, **North-West Europe 1940, 44-45,** Jebel Dafeis, **Keren,** Ad Teclesan, Abyssinia 1940-41, **Gazala,** Cauldron, Mersa Matruh, **Defence of Alamein Line, El Alamein, Mareth,** Wadi Zigzaou, Akarit, North Africa 1940-43, Primosole Bridge, **Sicily 1943, Pegu 1942, Yenangyaung 1942,** North Arakan, **Maungdaw, Defence of Sinzweya, Imphal, Bishenpur,** Kanglatongbi, Meiktila, Capture of Meiktila, Defence of **Meiktila,** Rangdon Road, Pyawbwe, **Sittang 1945, Burma 1942-45**

Honorary Distinction:

The Leeds Rifles— A Badge of the Royal Tank Regiment, with year-dates 1942-45 and two scrolls: North Africa, Italy

Regimental Marches

Quick March..(i) Ca Ira (ii) The Yorkshire Lass (The March of The Prince of Wales's Own Regiment of Yorkshire).
Slow March...(i) God Bless The Prince of Wales (Slow March of the West Yorks Regiment)
(ii) March of the XV Regiment (Slow March of The East Yorks Regiment)

Agents..Lloyds Bank PLC Cox's & King's Branch

Regimental Headquarters.....................3 Tower Street, York, YO1 1SB (*Tel No:* 0904-59811 *Ext:* 2310)

Alliances

Canadian Armed Forces.......................Les Voltigeurs de Quebec
1st Battalion The Royal New Brunswick Regiment (Carleton and York)
The Royal Montreal Regiment
Falkland Islands...................................The Falkland Islands Defence Force

Colonel in Chief...................................Hon Maj Gen *HRH The Duchess of* Kent *GCVO* 070585

Colonel ....Maj Gen H M Tillotson *CB CBE* ret pay 220679

Brigadiers

Crowfoot A B *CBE* ocds(US) psc (*A/Maj Gen* 080386) 300680
Sharpe M H ndc psc 300685

Lieutenant Colonels

Filor F J W psc osc(NIG) 300676
Longdon G M *OBE* psc osc(GH) 300678
Woolley P E *OBE* psc ph (*A/Col* 190685) 300681
Forsyth R H J psc 300683

Majors

Wood P R 060266
Desmond J H *MBIM* sq 311272
Hincks A D sq (*A/Lt Col* 280286) 300673
Scott Lewis I R sq 300673
Orum M G *MBE* 311273
Vines T C E sq 311273
Wilkins E B psc 300674
Holroyd H D osc(MAL) sq 300675
Robbin K F *MBE MBIM* sq aic 311275
Woolsey R G 311276
Green D A H sq (*A/Lt Col* 240386) 300677
Phelan A J psc ph 311277
Robinson H A sq 311277
Peacock K A psc (*A/Lt Col* 210386) 311278
Lyburn D B St J sq 311279
Ashby S sq 300980
Pinder D N sq 300980
Porter N S 300980
Potter A C L psc† 300980
Knopp J F 300981
Watson M J 300981
Allbeury N Le B psc 300982
Blanch A C G 300982
Duncan A D A psc† 300984
Evans N R H *BA* psc† 300984
Le Brun C G psc 300984
Hunt G H *MA* psc† 300985
Waistell N J 300985

Captains

Barley D A *BA* 260980
Watson R J 291280
Caley S R 090581
Biggins K W *BA* 120881
Jones P D 080981
Thurlow M R C 060982
Dransfield M J A *BA* 270583
Binns G J 110683
Tracy E P 100684
Howard K 081084
Kent-Payne V R 081084
Parker N R M 050285

Lieutenants

Padgett S 120482
Schofield C J 120482
Middleton K 080883
Stanton K F 080883

Sawtell R F		111284
Welsh A		090485

2nd Lieutenants

††Germain P S	230984
††Reevell S J	240985

Quartermasters

Barham M J	*Capt*	010480
Blyth P		010480
	Maj	191285
Miles K W		010480
	Maj	151184
Bostock A	*Capt*	010481
Darley T R	*Capt*	010483
Matthews D A	*Capt*	010483
Senior T H	*Capt*	010483
Hutchinson P	*Capt*	010484

Special Regular Officers

Captains

Hunter R *BA* I	080982
Harrison T J S	110683
Hill D A	251084
Dockerty C J *BA*	010885

Lieutenants

Jackson G L (*A/Capt* 010285)	120482

Short Service Officers

Captains

Stevenson A J *BA*	120483
Kennedy S A	180486

Jolly D	250486

Lieutenants

Shoebridge C H *BA*	090882
Moffat D	031082
Sullivan M L (*A/Capt* 020885)	011182
Hancock D S *BA*	110483
Patterson J *BA*	110483
Maude A J	070486

2nd Lieutenants

Bradley H	081284
Broadbent A G	081284
Lavan D M	081284
Francis N D	130485
†Jackson A T *BA(Hons)*	060985
†Whittall A J *BA*	060985
Beckett M A	141285
Wagstaff T E	141285

THE GREEN HOWARDS (ALEXANDRA, PRINCESS OF WALES'S OWN YORKSHIRE REGIMENT) (19)

The Cypher of HRH Alexandra, Princess of Wales, in gold (thereon Alexandra), interlaced with the Dannebrog enscribed with the date 1875, the Roman numerals XIX below and the whole surmounted by the Coronet of the Princess

Malplaquet, Belle Isle, Alma, Inkerman, Sevastopol, Tirah, Relief of Kimberley, Paardeberg, South Africa 1899-1902

The Great War— **Ypres 1914, 15, 17,** Langemarck 1914, 17, Gheluvelt, Neuve Chappelle, St Julien, Frezenberg, Bellewaarde, Aubers, Festubert 1915, **Loos, Somme 1916, 18,** Albert 1916, Bazentin, Poziers, Flers-Courcelette, Morval, Thiepval, Le Transloy, Ancre Heights, Ancre 1916, **Arras 1917, 18,** Scarpe 1917, 18, **Messines 1917, 18,** Pilckem, Menin Road, Polygon Wood, Broodseinde, Poelcappelle, Passchendaele, Cambrai 1917, 18, St Quentin, Hindenburg Line, Canal du Nord, Beaurevoir, Selle, **Valenciennes, Sambre, France and Flanders 1914-18,** Piave, **Vittorio Veneto,** Italy 1917-18, **Suvla,** Landing at Suvla, Scimitar Hill, Gallipoli 1915, Egypt 1916, Archangel 1918

Afghanistan 1919

The Second World War— Otta, **Norway 1940,** Defence of Arras, Dunkirk 1940, **Normandy Landing,** Tilly sur Seulles, St Pierre La Vielle, Gheel, Nederrijn, **North-West Europe 1940,44-45 Gazala,** Defence of Alamein Line, **El Alamein, Mareth, Akarit,** North Africa 1942-43, Landing in Sicily, Lentini, **Sicily 1943, Minturno, Anzio,** Italy 1943-44, Arakan Beaches, Burma 1945

Regimental Marches

Quick March...Bonnie English Rose
Slow March..Maria Theresa

Agents...Holts Branch, Royal Bank of Scotland PLC, Lawrie House, Farnborough, Hants

Regimental Headquarters....................Trinity Church Square, The Market Place, Richmond, North Yorkshire (*Tel No:* 0748-2133)

Alliances

Canadian Armed Forces......................The Rocky Mountain Rangers
The Queen's York Rangers (1st American Regiment)

Colonel in Chief..................................*His Majesty* Olav V *King of* Norway *KG KT GCB GCVO*

Colonel...Maj Gen P A Inge..........190782

Colonels

Johnson B G psc(a)	300685

Lieutenant Colonels

Byrne J C H S (SL) *OBE* osc(SUD) sq	300678
Marchant Smith C J *BSc* psc†	300679
Norman W G (SL) *MBE MBIM MIPR*	300679
Ibbetson W B sq	300681
Rockett R T (SL) *MBIM* psc	300681
Smeeton C B K *OBE* psc	300681
Adlington S G psc	300684
Powell J S W *BA* psc†	300685

Majors

Brook L R B sq	300670
Banbury P A J sq	300676
Nicholson D J sq ph	311276
Pick M A H	300677
Bailey R I	300678
Bradley M E sq aic	300678
Johnston R M sq aic	311278
Robey G T psc	311279
Westlake J R *MBE MA* psc	300980
Cooper G M	300981
King J C L *MBE* psc	300981
Mantell R C *MBE* sq	300981
Dannatt F R *MC BA* psc	300982
Simmons N J	300984
Thom C E psc	300984
Farquhar A P *MBE BEng*	300985
Santa-Olalla D M *MC* psc	300985

Captains

Hall N St J *BA AKC* psc (*A/Maj* 201285)	301279
Wylde A J B *MA*	130880
Houghton J N R *BA*	090980
Rynn N J *BA*	090980
Longworth S J *BA*	050383
Green G N	060284
Panton J F	100684
Watt J N *BA*	010885
Laycock M J	071085
Rose D J *BA*	071085
Denison J N	040286

Lieutenants

Tovey M W (*A/Capt* 290584)	081281
Leighton P J (*A/Capt* 220485)	120482
Pugh J K (*A/Capt* 021285)	060882
Fenner C M (*A/Capt* 170186)	121283
O'Kelly D R E *BA*	090484

2nd Lieutenants

††Jackson A G *BA(Hons)*	030982
Willis J M G	040884
†Glover D S *BA(Hons)*	060985

Quartermasters

Hodgetts T G *MBE*		010477
	Maj	140484
Johnson M R		010480
	Maj	050486
Urwin I E	*Capt*	010484

Special Regular Officers

Captains

Scott C M G	060982
Biegel M P *BEd*	150883

Short Service Officers

Captains

Laws W A (*A/Maj* 170386)	010982
Moses T A *BEM MISM*	140384

Lieutenants

James J R *BA*	120482
Mowll B (*A/Capt* 220485)	280882
Martin R (*A/Capt* 061085)	060483
Buchanan I A *BA*	080883
Barker R C	081083
Bridgeman-Sutton F W O *BA*	090484
Hillkirk C J (*A/Capt* 030585)	090484

2nd Lieutenants

Milligan T B	040884
Brasher J J	081284
Hinde M G	081284
Crabtree T H M	100885
Webster A J	141285

THE ROYAL IRISH RANGERS (27th (INNISKILLING) 83rd and 87th)

An Irish Harp and Crown above a motto *Faugh a Ballagh* (Clear the way).

Martinique 1762, Havannah, St Lucia 1778, 1796, India, Cape of Good Hope 1806, Maida, Monte Video, Talavera, Bourbon,Busaco, Barrosa, Fuentes d'Onor, Java, Tarifa, Cuidad Rodrigo, Badajoz, Salamanca, Vittoria, Pyrenees, Nivelle, Niagara, Orthes, Toulouse, Peninsula, Waterloo, Ava, South Africa 1835, 1846-7, Sevastopol, Central India, Tel-el-Kebir, Egypt 1882, 1884, Relief of Ladysmith, South Africa 1899-1902

The Great War– **Mons, Le Cateau,** Retreat from Mons, **Marne 1914,** Aisne 1914, La Bassee 1914, **Messines 1914, 17, 18,** Armentieres 1914, **Ypres 1914, 15, 17, 18,** Nonne Bosschen, **Neuve Chapelle, Loos,** Frezenberg, Aubers, Festubert 1915, Gravenstafel, St Julien, Bellewaarde, **Somme 1916, 18, Albert 1916,** Bazentin, Pozieres, Guillemont, Ginchy, Le Transloy, Ancre, Ancre Heights, **Arras 1917,** Scarpe 1917, Pilckem, Langemarck 1917, Polygon Wood, Broodseinde, Poelcappelle, **Cambrai 1917, 18, St Quentin,** Rosieres, **Hindenburg Line,** Lys, Bailleul, Beaurevoir, Kemmel, Courtrai, Selle, Sambre, **France and Flanders 1914-18,** Kosturino, Struma, **Macedonia 1915-17,** Helles, Landing at Helles, Krithia, **Suvla,** Sari Bair, Landing at Suvla, Scimitar Hill, **Gallipoli 1915-16,** Egypt 1916, **Gaza, Jerusalem,** Tell 'Asur, Megiddo, Nablus, **Palestine 1917-18**

The Second World War– **Dyle,** Withdrawal to Escaut, Defence of Arras, **St Omer-La Bassee,** Ypres-Comines Canal, **Dunkirk 1940, Normandy Landing,** Cambes, **Caen,** Troarn, Venlo Pocket, **Rhine, Bremen,** North-West Europe 1940, 44-45, Two Tree Hill, **Bou Arada,** Stuka Farm, Oued Zarga, Djebel Bel Mahdi, Djebel Ang, **Djebel Tanngoucha, North Africa 1942-43,** Landing in Sicily, Solarino, Simeto Bridgehead, Adrano, **Centuripe,** Salso Crossing, Simeto Crossing,Malleto, Pursuit to Messina, **Sicily 1943,** Termoli, Trigno, San Salvo, **Sangro,** Fossacesia, **Garigliano Crossing,** Minturno, **Anzio, Cassino II,** Massa Tambourini, Liri Valley, Rome, Advance to Tiber, Trasimene Line, Monte Spaduro, Monte Grande, **Argenta Gap,** San Nicolo Canal, **Italy 1943-45,** Leros, Middle East 1942, **Malta 1940, Yenangyaung 1942,** Donbaik, **Burma 1942-43**

Seoul, **Imjin, Korea 1950-51**

Regimental Marches

Quick March..Regimental March of the Royal Irish Rangers 'Killaloe'
Slow March..Eileen Allanagh

Agents..Lloyds Bank PLC Cox's & King's Branch

Regimental Headquarters....................BFPO 808 (*Tel No:* Belfast 0232-232086)

Alliances

Canadian Armed Forces.......................The Princess Louise Fusiliers
2nd Battalion The Irish Regiment of Canada (Sudbury)
The Irish Fusiliers of Canada (Vancouver Regiment)
Australian Military Forces...................Adelaide University Regiment
New Zealand Army...............................2nd Battalion (Canterbury and Nelson, Marlborough and West Coast) Royal New Zealand Infantry Regiment
Pakistan Army.....................................1st Battalion The Punjab Regiment
9th Battalion (Wilde's) The Frontier Force Regiment

Colonel..Brig M N S McCord *CBE MC* ret pay........................270885

Deputy Colonels..............................Brig R C Rothery *OBE*........................010981
Col D G McCord *MBE*........................150583

Brigadiers

Wheeler R N *CBE MA* psc 300684
Rothery R C *OBE* ndc sq 300685

Colonels

Hiles W J ndc psc(a) (*L/Brig* 100984) 300678
McCord D G *MBE* jssc psc(a)† psc ptsc 300678
McCrum R *MVO MPhil* psc 300682
Heard R J B ndc psc† ph 300683
Clements W H *LLB* psc osc(NIG) 300684
Carson R J M *OBE MBIM* psc osc(NIG) 300685

Lieutenant Colonels

McFrederick J J (SL) odc(GE) psc osc(GE) 300674
Toomey M A (SL) *BSc* psc† 300675
Vining M E (SL) psc 300675
Illingworth T J R (SL) *OBE* sq 300676
Leonard J N (SL) psc 300676
Bates H V sq 300680
Larkin C W *OBE* psc 300681
Lefroy N J psc 300681
Moody A M T psc 300681
Cochrane J C *OBE MA* ndc psc 300682
Dunseath D P psc† 300682
Naughten A P M J *MA* ndc psc 300682
Brooke T C P psc 300683
O'Lone R D *BSc* psc† 300683
Phelan P A psc 300683
Burke W S D odc(US) psc 300684
Cargin J M V McI *LVO* psc 300684
O'Byrne N M psc gw 300684
Sankey J D *MSc* odc(US) psc 300685

Majors

Wood D R D sq 050565
Smith B R C *BA* ptsc 010865
French A J *MBIM* psc 120267
Magrane N P sq 300667
Tennant J M sq 311270
Emmett D C J sq 300672
Condon J P B *MBE* sq 300675
Robjohn M S sq 300675
Philip D N sq 311276
Brocksopp C G psc 300677
Holmes I J sq 300677
Thompson J H S *MBIM* sq 300677
Harrison R B A sq 311277
Robertson J sq 311277
Weekes N C F *MBIM* psc 311277
Jordan A P V psc 300678
George P I D sq 311278
Lowry M A *BA* psc† aic 311278
O'Sullivan M sq 311278
Linford C sq 300679
Turner J D J A sq 300679
Allen F J *MBE BSc(Econ)* sq 311279
Gray C R L psc 311279
McIlveen J D psc 311279
Rowe R G *BA* sq 311279
Chambers H P M *MBE MBIM* sq 300980
Dowey T O 300980
Hutchison C L R sq 300980
MacCarthy-Morrogh J T D 300980
Morgan P J sq 300980
Trousdell P C C psc 300980
Barry J F G 300981
Fletcher D 300981
Mitchell H D P sq 300981
Davidson B R N 300982
Glover E 300982
Linford J 300982

The Kings Division — continued

Potter A M F 300982
Grimshaw R E psc 300983
Rutherford A C *BSc MPS* 300983
Baxter P St J L *BA* psc† 300984
Sturgeon H psc 300984
Bergin D J A aic 300985
Little R C L psc† 300985
McCourt R L *BA* psc(IND) 300985

Captains

Bettesworth G P 210279
Morwood M B *MBE BSc* 080379
Brooks J C W 090980
Theobald M W L 090581
Kitson C J *LLB* 010881
Douglas J S 060982
McIlveen T I 060982
Devlin M D C 210583
Jones N H 081083
Russell R G 081083
Woolford A N *BSc* 241083
Howard G R G 060284
Murdoch A R 140384
Lane A D *BA* 030484
Spender G F A 100684
Fordham S A 081084
Hiles J E 081084
Simmons S G 081084
Gobourn A D C *BA* 010285
Harbinson T J 090685
Beswick J 071085
Collins T T C *BSocSc* 071085
Maxwell W *BSc* 071085
O'Hanlon M P J *BSc(Hons)* 071085

Lieutenants

Jones A D
(*A/Capt* 281085) 120482
Riley M T 040582
Leadsom J H 090882
McCord A C J *BA* 131282
McConnell T R 110483
Strangways R G 110483
Furphy T D 080883
Robinson R A 080883
Davis M M A 090484
Hartigan M P 111284
McCausland A M 060885

2nd Lieutenants

Freely E B 130485

Quartermasters

Cairns W *MBE* 010475
Maj 010483
Murphy J P *BEM BA* 010477
Maj 010479
Dowling F J 010478
Maj 030186
Synnott W *Capt* 010678
Murphy M B *Capt* 010479
Guidera P M 010481
Maj 270186
Ross A *Capt* 010484
Toney H A V *Capt* 010485

Special Regular Officers

Majors

Hyland C G S 300980
Freeman M H 300984

Captains

Meeke B A 090581
McSherry I R 290881
Edgeworth P A 100684
Kelly M J 240285

Lieutenants

Wilkinson T L
(*A/Capt* 010186) 120482

2nd Lieutenants

O'Sullivan J S S 100885

Short Service Officers

Captains

Baker J S C *BA* 050983
O'Rourke C H *BA* 011184
Walker R J *MBE* 010386

Lieutenants

Babington D J *BA* 120482
Connolly P J 141082
Cotter W J 010183
McFrederick M J *BA* 110483
McConnell J N 250583
Marvin R P *BSc* 090484
Bailie G A 070884
Russell A 070884
Corrigan D P 101285
Cullen A K 101285
Hill R J 070486
Roberts N R A 070486

2nd Lieutenants

McClean J C 040884
Piggins J D 040884
Hunter M C 081284
Hart A M 100885
Harvey A 141285
†Heyburn P *BA* 060186
†McGovern M A J *MA(Hons)*
060186

THE QUEEN'S LANCASHIRE REGIMENT (30, 40, 47, 59, 81 and 82)

The Red Rose of Lancaster

The Red Rose of Lancaster ensigned with the Plume of the Prince of Wales. The Red Rose ensigned with the Sphinx subscribed Egypt. A Sphinx superscribed Egypt ensigned with the Plume of the Prince of Wales

The Red Rose ensigned with the Royal Crest

A Sphinx Superscribed Egypt

Loyally I Serve

Gibraltar 1704-5, Louisburg, Quebec 1759, Bellisle, Martinique 1762, **Havannah,** St Lucia 1778, **Cape of Good Hope 1806, Maida, Monte Video,** Rolica, **Vimiera, Corunna, Talavera, Java, Tarifa, Badajoz, Salamanca, Vittoria, St Sebastian, Pyrenees, Nivelle, Nive, Orthes, Toulouse,** Peninsula, **Niagara, Waterloo, Ava, Bhurtpore, Candahar 1842, Ghuznee 1842, Cabool 1842, Maharajpore, Alma, Inkerman, Sevastopol, Lucknow, Canton, New Zealand, Ali Masjid, Ahmed Khel,** Afghanistan 1878-80, **Chitral, Defence of Kimberley, Relief of Ladysmith,** South Africa 1899-1902

The Great War– **Mons,** Le Cateau, **Retreat from Mons, Marne 1914,18, Aisne 1914, 18,** La Bassee 1914, **Messines 1914, 17, 18,** Armentieres 1914, **Ypres 1914, 15, 17, 18,** Langemarck 1914, 17, Gheluvelt, Nonne Bosschen, Givenchy 1914, **Neuve Chapelle,** St Julien, Frezenberg, Bellewaarde, Aubers, Festubert 1915, Loos, **Somme 1916, 18,** Albert 1916, 18, Bazentin, Pozieres, Guillemont, Ginchy, Flers-Courcelette, Morval, Le Transloy, Ancre Heights, Ancre 1916, 18, **Arras 1917, 18,** Vimy 1917, Scarpe 1917, 18, Arleux, Oppy, Pilckem, Menin Road, Polygon Wood, Broodseinde, Poelcappelle, Passchendaele, Cambrai 1917, 18, St Quentin, Bapaume 1918, Rosieres, Villers-Bretonneux, **Lys,** Estaires, Hazebrouck, Bailleul, Kemmel, Bethune, Scherpenberg, Soissonnais-Ourcq, Drocourt-Queant, **Hindenburg Line,** Epehy, Canal du Nord, St Quentin Canal, Courtrai, Selle, Valenciennes, Sambre, France and Flanders 1914-18, Kosturino, **Doiran 1917, 18,** Macedonia 1915-18, **Helles,** Krithia, **Suvla, Sari, Bair,** Gallipoli 1915, Rumani, Egypt 1915-17, **Gaza,** Nebi Samwil, Jerusalem, Jaffa, Tell'Asur, Palestine 1917-18, Tigris 1916, **Kut al Amara 1917, Baghdad,** Mesopotamia 1916-18, **Kilimanjaro,** East Africa 1914-16, **Baluchistan 1918**

Afghanistan 1919

The Second World War– Defence of Escaut, **Dunkirk 1940, Normandy Landing,** Odon, Caen, **Bourguebus Ridge,** Troarn, **Falaise,** Nederrijn, **Lower Maas,** Venraij, **Ourthe, Rhineland, Reichswald, Weeze,** Hochwald, Rhine, Ibbenburen, **Aller,** Bremen, North-West Europe 1940, 44-45, Banana Ridge, **Djebel KessKiss,** Medjez Plain, **Gueriat El Atach Ridge,** Gab Gab Gap, Djebel Bou Aoukaz 1943, North Africa 1943, **Anzio,** Rome, **Fiesole,** Gothic Line, Monte Gamberaldi, Monte Ceco, **Monte Grande,** Italy 1944-45, **Madagascar,** Middle East 1942, **Johore,** Batu Pahat, **Singapore Island,** Malaya 1941-42, **North Arakan,** Mayu Tunnels, **Kohima, Pinwe,** Meiktila, **Nyaungu Bridgehead,** Letse, Irrawaddy, Burma 1943-45

Regimental Marches

Quick March..L'Attaque - The Red Rose
Slow March..Long Live Elizabeth (from Selection No 2 Merrie England)

Agents..Lloyds Bank PLC Cox's & King's Branch
Regimental Headquarters....................Fulwood Barracks, Preston, PR2 4AA (*Tel No:* 0772-716543 *Ext:* 362)

Alliances

Canadian Armed Forces......................The Princess of Wales's Own Regiment
The West Nova Scotia Regiment
The Loyal Edmonton Regiment (4th Battalion Princess Patricia's Canadian Light Infantry)
Australian Military Forces..................The Royal Tasmania Regiment
New Zealand Army..............................7th Battalion (Wellington (City of Wellington's Own) and Hawkes Bay) Royal New Zealand Infanty Regiment
Pakistan Army......................................8th Battalion The Punjab Regiment
14th Battalion The Punjab Regiment
Malaysian Armed Forces......................2nd Battalion The Royal Malay Regiment

Colonel in Chief................................THE QUEEN

Colonel................................Maj Gen D Houston *CBE* ret pay................................310883

Brigadiers

Jebens C F *OBE ADC CBIM* ndc psc ph pl 300681

Colonels

Hinings A M *OBE* psc 300681

Lieutenant Colonels

Hurley I St P sq 300676
Rogers H F (SL) *MBE* ndc psc 300676
Thompson P S F *MBIM* ndc psc 300677
Busby M J (SL) sq 300678
Hemesley A E psc 300678
Diffin J psc 300682
Black D M psc 300683
Reid W T psc 300683
Scrase M W *MBE* psc 300683
Kearns C *MBE MA* psc 300684

Majors

Green M J sq 031265
Redman P B sq 170766
Ostrowski A J sq 300668
Mackenzie B S sq 300669
Fitzpatrick-Robertson L F E sq 311269
Green M E F *MBE* sq 311269
Brown C M *MBIM* 300673
Freeman D M sq 300675
Downham E J *MBE BA* psc (*L/Lt Col* 020486) 311276
Hogge S P sq 300677
Barton C J sq aic 311277
Lloyd J F sq 300678
Gething R J psc 311278
Claridge B E B sq 311279
Cummings D F J 300980
Aldis R C psc aic 300981
Birtwistle A F *MA* psc 300981
Dallow J R psc 300981
Sheldon J A *BA* psc(GE) 300981
Guest G E 300982
Bush N H 300983
Upton H C 300984
Beaumont G A 300985

The Kings Division — continued

Sheldon G P *BA* psc†	300985

Captains

Shearman M J *BSc* psc† (*A/Maj* 161285)	130280
Flood G H P *BA*	040980
Wright G R aic	281281
d'Apice M H R *BSc*	050282
Brearley A J *LLB*	130582
Meeson V J	060982
Courteney-Harris R J *BA*	150283
Cherry J T	060284
Davies S	221084

Lieutenants

Sanderson D J	090882
Ingham J C D	131282
Bostock S E *BA*	110483
Janes J R E *BSc*	110483
Mendonca J E	090484
Brown R D I	070884

Quartermasters

Maher A J *MBE*	*Capt*	010481
Fairhurst J A *MBE*	*Capt*	010483
Skilbeck W D	*Capt*	010483

Special Regular Officers

Majors

Poucher M S	300984

Captains

Howard C A	090379
Strong C *MISM*	080582
Brown K G	070283
Glover M J *BA*	210583
Hodge B M	040185

Short Service Officers

Captains

Anderson R A *BA(Hons)*	300483
James D C *MA*	160984
Hornby A R	180385
Cowgill J R *LLB*	071085

Lieutenants

Chester A J	010483
Dee G J	010883
Jefferies R A *BSocSc*	090484
Procter A *BSc*	070884
Loynds I A	090485

2nd Lieutenants

Howcroft D J B	040884
†Livingstone K *BA(Hons)*	060985
†Rix A C *BSc*	060985
†Wharton N J T *BSc(Hons)*	060985

THE DUKE OF WELLINGTON'S REGIMENT (WEST RIDING) (33 and 76)

The Duke of Wellington's Crest, with the motto Virtutis fortuna comes
An Elephant, with howdah and mahout, circumscribed Hindoostan, ensigned with The Crown

Dettingen, Mysore, Seringapatam, Ally Ghur, Delhi 1803, Leswarree, Deig, Corunna, Nive, Peninsula, Waterloo, Alma, Inkerman, Sevastopol, Abyssinia, Relief of Kimberley, Paardeberg, South Africa 1900-02

The Great War— **Mons,** Le Cateau, Retreat from Mons, **Marne 1914,18,** Aisne, 1914, La Bassee 1914, **Ypres 1914, 15, 17,** Nonne Bosschen, **Hill 60,** Gravenstafel, St Julien, Aubers, **Somme 1916,18,** Albert 1916, 18, Bazentin, Delville Wood, Pozieres, Flers-Courcelette, Morval, Thiepval, Le Transloy, Ancre Heights, **Arras 1917,18,** Scarpe 1917,18, Arleux, Bullecourt, Messines 1917,18, Langemarck 1917, Menin Road, Polygon Wood, Broodseinde, Poelcappelle, Passchendaele, **Cambrai 1917,18,** St Quentin, Ancre 1918, **Lys,** Estaires, Hazebrouck, Bailleul, Kemmel, Bethune, Scherpenberg, Tardenois, Amiens, Bapaume 1918, Drocourt-Queant, Hindenburg Line, Havrincourt, Epehy, Canal du Nord, Selle, Valenciennes, Sambre, France and Flanders 1914-18, **Piave,** Vittorio Veneto, Italy 1917-18, Suvla, **Landing at Suvla,** Scimitar Hill, Gallipoli 1915, Egypt 1916

Afghanistan 1919

The Second World War— **Dunkirk 1940, St Valery-en-Caux,** Tilly sur Seulles, Odon, **Fontenay Le Pesnil, North-West Europe 1940, 44-45,** Banana Ridge, Mediez Plain, Gueriat el Atach Ridge, Tunis, **Djebel Bou Aoukaz 1943,** North Africa 1943, **Anzio,** Campoleone, Rome, **Monte Ceco,** Italy 1943-45, **Sittang 1942,** Paungde, Kohima, **Chindits 1944, Burma 1942-44**

The Hook 1953, Korea 1952-53

Regimental March

Quick March..The Wellesley

Agents..Lloyds Bank PLC Cox's & King's Branch

Regimental Headquarters......................Wellesley Park, Halifax, Yorkshire, HX2 0BA (*Tel No:* 0422-61671)

Alliances

Canadian Armed Forces........................Les Voltigeurs de Quebec
Pakistan Army...10th Battalion The Baluch Regiment

Colonel in Chief....................................Col (Hon Brig) *The Duke of* Wellington *LVO OBE MC DL* ret pay 230174

Colonel..Lt Gen *Sir* Charles Huxtable *KCB CBE*..221082

Brigadiers

Mundell W R *OBE* psc 300682
Greenway J B K *CBE* psc(a) 300684

Colonels

Bray M R N *MPhil* ndc psc† 300681
Cumberlege J R P *FBIM* psc osc(NIG) 300682
Cumberlege C R ndc psc 300685

Lieutenant Colonels

Stevens R L *MBE MBIM* ndc psc 300676
Lupton T D (SL) ndc sq 300677
Charlesworth W F *OBE* ndc sq 300679
Nash S J (SL) sq 300680
Walker E J W psc 300681
Nicholson T J *MBIM* psc 300682
Redwood-Davies A R *MBE* psc 300684
Andrews P D D J psc 300685
Gardner P D psc 300685
Roberts A D *MBE* psc† 300685
Thorn J M psc 300685

Majors

Pugh D M sq 311269
Reid I P sq 300672
Puttock P J 300673
Bunbury C N St P *MBE* sq 300674
Fitzgerald C G sq 311274
Mellor P J sq 311275
Ward J R A *MBIM* psc 311279
Gilbert C J W psc 300980
Sherlock M S 300981
Harrap D L J *LLB* psc† aic 300982
Isles T J 300982
Pitchers A J *BEd* 300982
Grieve C F psc 300983
Meek A D 300983
Best K psc 300984
Drake A H S *MBE* 300984

Captains

Richardson D I 100979
Stone M J *BA* 021279
Kilburn G A 090980
Shuttleworth G D (*A/Maj* 010885) 090980
Morgan S J N *BA* (*A/Maj* 071085) 010881
Newton S C 281281
Harvey P J 110683
Dixon S H 081083
Drake M J B 081083
Harvey C A *BA* 150284
Borwell N G 100684
Wood J W 100684
Pugh R J M 090685
Brear A J *BA* 010885
Lehmann C S T *BSc* 071085

Lieutenants

Bruce D S (*A/Capt* 061285) 120482
Rumball P M 120482
Lewis P M 110483
Smith C R T 080883
Preston J C 070884
Chadwick R N 090485
Tinsley M 060885

2nd Lieutenants

Harvey D 130485
†Holroyd R C *BA* 060985

Quartermasters

Tighe R A *MBE* 010477
Maj 010479
Carter M 010478
Maj 121285
Robinson P *Capt* 010483
Wilkinson P *Capt* 010485

Special Regular Officers

Majors

Whittaker D 300985

Captains

Bailey P R S (*A/Maj* 040885) 040284

Lieutenants

Twelftree M A 021083

2nd Lieutenants

Adams A J 040884

The Kings Division — continued

Short Service Officers

Captains

Coll B 010783
Tuley M G *MA* 071085

Lieutenants

Hill J C *BA* 110483
Heron R
(*A/Capt* 011185) 150483
Bailey J C *BA* 080883
Lodge M A *BA* 080883
Downes A J *BSc* 090484
Kelly H A *BA* 090484
McNeilis A J 090485
Preston S D 070486

2nd Lieutenants

Neath S R 040884
†Brear T A *BA* 060985
†Best R G *BSc* 060186

THE YORK AND LANCASTER REGIMENT (65 and 84)

The Union Rose. The Royal Tiger, superscribed India

Guadaloupe 1759, Martinique 1794, India 1796-1819, Nive, Peninsula, Arabia, New Zealand, Lucknow, Tel-el-Kebir, Egypt 1882-1884, Relief of Ladysmith, South Africa 1899-1902

The Great War— Aisne 1914, Armentieres 1914, **Ypres 1915, 17, 18,** Gravenstafel, St Julien, Frezenberg, Bellewaarde, Hooge 1915, Loos, **Somme, 1916, 18,** Albert 1916, Pozieres, Flers-Courcelette, Morval, Thiepval, Le Transloy, Ancre Heights, Ancre 1916, Arras 1917, 18, Scarpe 1917, 18, Arleux, Oppy, **Messines 1917, 18,** Langemarck 1917, Menin Road, Polygon Wood, Broodseinde, Poelcappelle, **Passchendaele, Cambrai 1917, 18,** St Quentin, Bapaume 1918, **Lys,** Hazebrouck, Bailleul, Kemmel, Scherpenberg, Marne 1918, Tardenois, Drocourt-Queant, Hindenburg Line, Havrincourt, Epehy, Canal du Nord, **Selle,** Valenciennes, Sambre, France and Flanders 1914-18, Piave, Vittorio Veneto, Italy 1917-18, Struma, Doiran 1917, **Macedonia 1915-18,** Suvla, Landing at Suvla, Scimitar Hill, **Gallipoli 1915,** Egypt 1916

The Second World War— Norway 1940, Odon, **Fontenay Le Pesnil,** Caen, La Vie Crossing, La Touques Crossing, Foret de Bretonne, Le Havre, **Antwerp-Turnhout Canal,** Scheldt, Lower Maas, Arnhem 1945, North-West Europe 1940, 44-45, **Tobruk 1941,** Tobruk Sortie 1941, **Mine de Sedjenane,** Djebel Kournine, North Africa 1941, 43, Landing in Sicily, Simeto Bridgehead, Pursuit to Messina, **Sicily 1943, Salerno,** Vietri Pass, Capture of Naples, Cava di Terreni, Volturno Crossing, Monte Camino, Calabritto, Colle Cedro, Garigliano Crossing, **Minturno,** Monte Tuga, Anzio, Advance to Tiber, Gothic Line, Coriano, San Clemente, Gemmano Ridge, Carpineta, Lamone Crossing, Defence of Lamone Bridgehead, Rimini Line, San Marino, Italy 1943-45, Crete, Heraklion, Middle East 1941, **North Arakan,** Maungdaw, Rangoon Road, Toungoo, Arakan Beaches, **Chindits 1944,** Burma 1943-45

Regimental Marches

Quick March..........York and Lancaster
Slow March..........York and Lancaster

Agents..........Lloyds Bank PLC Cox's & King's Branch

Regimental Headquarters..........Endcliffe Hall, Endcliffe Vale Road, Sheffield, Yorks, S10 3EU

Alliances

Canadian Armed Forces..........Les Fusiliers Mont-Royal
New Zealand Army..........7th Battalion (Wellington (City of Wellington's Own) and Hawkes Bay) Royal New Zealand Infantry Regiment
Malaysian Armed Forces..........7th Battalion The Royal Malay Regiment

Representative Colonel..........Brig R Eccles *DSO* ret pay..........281079

THE PRINCE OF WALES'S DIVISION

Comprising ....The Devonshire and Dorset Regiment (1 Regular Battalion)
The Cheshire Regiment (1 Regular Battalion, 1 Volunteer Battalion)
The Royal Welch Fusiliers (1 Regular Battalion, 1 Volunteer Battalion)
The Royal Regiment of Wales (24th/41st Foot) (1 Regular Battalion, 2 Volunteer Battalions)
The Gloucestershire Regiment (1 Regular Battalion)
The Worcestershire and Sherwood Foresters Regiment (29th/45th Foot) (1 Regular Battalion, 1 Volunteer Battalion)
The Royal Hampshire Regiment (1 Regular Battalion)
The Staffordshire Regiment (The Prince of Wales's) (1 Regular Battalion)
The Duke of Edinburgh's Royal Regiment (Berkshire and Wiltshire) (1 Regular Battalion)
1st Battalion The Wessex Regiment (Rifle Volunteers)
2nd Battalion The Wessex Regiment (Volunteers)
1st Battalion Mercian Volunteers
2nd Battalion Mercian Volunteers

Divisional Headquarters ....Whittington Barracks, Lichfield, Staffs, WS14 9PY (*Tel No:* 0543-433333)

Colonel Commandant ....Maj Gen C T Shortis *CBE* 010983

Divisional Brigadier ....Brig W G R Turner *CBE*

The origins of amalgamated Regiments now included in The Prince of Wales's Division are as follows:—

THE DEVONSHIRE AND DORSET REGIMENT

On 17 May 1958

The Devonshire Regiment (11) and
The Dorset Regiment (39 and 54) amalgamated to form:
The Devonshire and Dorset Regiment

THE ROYAL REGIMENT OF WALES (24th/41st FOOT)

On 11 June 1969

The South Wales Borderers (24) and
The Welch Regiment (41 and 69) amalgamated to form:
The Royal Regiment of Wales (24th/41st Foot)

THE WORCESTERSHIRE AND SHERWOOD FORESTERS REGIMENT (29th/45th FOOT)

On 28 February 1970

The Worcestershire Regiment (29 and 36) and
The Sherwood Foresters (Nottinghamshire and Derbyshire Regiment) (45 and 95) amalgamated to form:
The Worcestershire and Sherwood Foresters Regiment (29th/45th Foot)

THE STAFFORDSHIRE REGIMENT (THE PRINCE OF WALES'S)

On 31 January 1959

The South Staffordshire Regiment (38 and 80) and
The North Staffordshire Regiment (The Prince of Wales's) (64 and 98) amalgamated to form:
The Staffordshire Regiment (The Prince of Wales's)

THE DUKE OF EDINBURGH'S ROYAL REGIMENT (BERKSHIRE AND WILTSHIRE)

On 9 June 1959

The Royal Berkshire Regiment (Princess Charlotte of Wales's) (49 and 66) and

The Wiltshire Regiment (Duke of Edinburgh's) (62 and 99) amalgamated to form:

The Duke of Edinburgh's Royal Regiment (Berkshire and Wiltshire)

THE DEVONSHIRE AND DORSET REGIMENT (11, 39 and 54)

The Sphinx superimposed upon the Castle of Exeter

The Castle and Key superscribed Gibraltar, 1779-83 and with the motto *Montis Insignia Calpe*

The Sphinx superscribed *Semper Fidelis Primus in Indis*

Dettingen, Plassey, Martinique 1794, Marabout, Albuhera, Salamanca, Vittoria, Pyrenees, Nivelle, Nive, Orthes, Toulouse, Peninsula, Ava, Maharajpore, Sevastopol, Afghanistan 1879-80, Tirah, Defence of Ladysmith, Relief of Ladysmith, South Africa 1899-1902

The Great War— **Mons,** Le Cateau, Retreat from Mons, **Marne 1914,** Aisne 1914, 18, **La Bassee 1914,** Armentieres 1914, Neuve Chapelle, Hill 60, **Ypres 1915, 17,** Gravenstafel, St Julien, Frezenberg, Bellewaarde, Aubers, **Loos, Somme 1916, 18,** Albert 1916, 18, Bazentin, Delville Wood, Guillemont, Flers-Courcelette, Morval, Thiepval, Ancre 1916, 18, Arras 1917, Vimy 1917, Scarpe 1917, Bullecourt, Messines 1917, Pilckem, Langemarck 1917, Polygon Wood, Broodseinde, Poelcappelle, Passchendaele, St Quentin, Rosieres, Villers Bretonneux Lys, Hazebrouck **Bois des Buttes,** Marne 1918, Tardenois, Amiens, Bapaume 1918, **Hindenburg Line,** Havrincourt, Epehy, Canal du Nord, St Quentin Canal, Beaurevoir, Cambrai 1918, **Sambre,** France and Flanders 1914-18, Piave, **Vittorio Veneto,** Italy 1917-18, **Doiran 1917, 18,** Macedonia 1915-18, **Suvla,** Landing at Suvla, Scimitar Hill, Gallipoli 1915, Egypt 1916-17, **Gaza,** El Mughar, Nebi Samwil, Jerusalem, Tell'Asur, Megiddo, Sharon, **Palestine 1917-18,** Basra, **Shaiba,** Kut al Amara 1915, 17, **Ctesiphon,** Defence of Kut al Amara, Tigris 1916, Baghdad, **Khan Baghdadi, Mesopotamia 1916-18**

The Second World War— **St Omer-La Bassee, Normandy Landing,** Port en Bessin, Villers Bocage, Tilly sur Suelles, **Caen,** Mont Pincon, St Pierre La Vielle, Nederrijn, **Arnhem 1944, Aam, Geilenkirchen,** Roer, Goch, **Rhine,** Ibbenburen, Twente Canal, **North-West Europe 1940, 44-45, Landing in Sicily,** Agira, **Regalbuto,** Sicily 1943, Landing at Porto San Venere, Italy 1943, **Malta 1940-42, Imphal,** Tamu Road, Shenam Pass, **Kohima,** Ukhrul,**Mandalay, Myinmu Bridgehead,** Kyaukse 1945, Mt Popa, **Burma 1943-45**

Regimental Marches

Quick March..Arrangement of 'Widecombe Fair', 'We've Lived and Loved Together' & 'The Maid of Glenconnel'

Agents..Holts Branch, Royal Bank of Scotland PLC, Lawrie House, Farnborough, Hants

Regimental Headquarters....................Wyvern Barracks, Exeter, Devon (*Tel No:* 0392 218178)

Alliances

Canadian Armed Forces.......................Les Fusiliers de Sherbrooke
Australian Military Forces....................The Royal New South Wales Regiment
Malaysian Armed Forces......................6th Battalion The Royal Malay Regiment

Colonel in Chief..................................Maj Gen *HRH The Duke of* Kent *KG GCMG GCVO ADC*

Colonel...Maj Gen C T Shortis *CBE*..301184

Brigadiers

Wilsey J F W *CBE* psc 300684

Colonels

Bullocke C W G *OBE* psc 300682
Hewitt J M *OBE* odc(US) psc 300684

Lieutenant Colonels

Laurie-Chiswell A G (SL) *MBE MBIM* psc 300675
King-Fretts P D nadc psc 300678
Dutton B H *OBE* psc† 300681
Thomas D G sq 300681
Field J J F *OBE MC* psc 300682
Pook R J *MBIM* psc† psc(n) 300684
Jefferies G *BA* sq 300685
Shaw D C N *MBE* psc 300685

Majors

Reid J J sq 300669
Cann F J psc 311269
Turrall R D odc(GE) sq 300670
Steptoe R P sq 311277
Cooper C E sq 300678
James H L sq aic 300678
Pape C L 300678
White J W psc 311279
Delves C N G *DSO* psc (*A/Lt Col* 050885) 300980
Collings A B S *MBE BSc(Econ)* sq 300981
Langdon S J sq 300981
Rogers C T psc aic 300981
Hambrook T W psc 300982
Thornburn A W *MBE* 300982
Richardson M F psc 300983
Young S D 300983
Biles C J psc 300984
Gaye J D psc 300984
King M P psc(CAN) 300984
Nicholls G S 300984
Steevenson D M M 300985

Captains

Startin A M 100979
Bredin A D O (*A/Maj* 220385) 090581
Trevis A J 090581
Randle W A J *BA* 070881
Hale T R 080981
Sharpe W M *BA* 010282
Saunders T J J 060982
Clayden T J C *BA* 050983
Wallace N R D *BA* 031083
Barnes R W *MBE* 081083
Harrison D J 100684
Underhill P F C 081084
Watson J F *MA* 071085
Reynolds M D *BA* 051285

Lieutenants

Toomey R H D (*A/Capt* 040585) 120482
Goodbody J E (*A/Capt* 040585) 131282
Mollison J K (*A/Capt* 100386) 131282
Warren R W 121283
Storrie A J S *BA* 090484

2nd Lieutenants

††Messervy P S *MA(Hons)* 040981
††Hunt J E M 240985

Staff Quartermasters

Roberts D R *BEM* 010476
Lt Col 021085

Quartermasters

Brown L D *MBE* 020578
Maj 201284
Walter W C 010480
Maj 080585
Burrlock L C *Capt* 010482
Mitchell J *BEM* *Capt* 010485

Directors of Music

Henderson M J *Capt* 060186

Special Regular Officers

Captains

Frankland J G T	090685
Blewett I P	071085
Beattie A M	040286

Lieutenants

Field D C E	101285

Short Service Officers

Captains

McFarlane A C S	050285

Lieutenants

Jellard H	140382
Backhouse N A N (*A/Capt* 231184)	090882
Henderson M J	081082
Kinney M W *BA*	110483
Shave G M	270783
Lawson A J	101285
Terrey K E	101285
House T W	070486
Norman-Walker A K J	070486

2nd Lieutenants

Jones M A	081284
Beattie C J	130485
Brock G S	140585
†Blencowe J C W *BA*	060985

The Prince of Wales's Division – continued

THE CHESHIRE REGIMENT (22)

An Acorn leaved and slipped.

Louisburg, Martinique 1762, Havannah, Meeanee, Hyderabad, Scinde, South Africa 1900-02

The Great War— **Mons,** Le Cateau, Re*reat from Mons, Marne 1914, 18, Aisne 1914, 18, La Bassee 1914, Armentieres 1914, **Ypres 1914, 15, 17, 18,** Nonne Bosschen, Hill 60, Gravenstafel, St Julien, Frezenberg, Bellewaarde, Loos, **Somme 1916, 18,** Albert 1916, 18, Bazentin, Delville Wood, Pozieres, Guillemont, Flers-Courcelette, Morval, Thiepval, Le Transloy, Ancre Heights, Ancre 1916, **Arras 1917, 18,** Vimy 1917, Scarpe 1917, 18, Oppy, **Messines 1917, 18,** Pilckem, Langemarck 1917, Menin Road, Polygon Wood, Broodseinde, Poelcapelle, Passchendaele, Cambrai 1917, 18, St Quentin, **Bapaume 1918,** Rosieres, Lys, Estaires, Hazebrouck, Bailleul, Kemmel, Scherpenberg, Soissonnais-Ourcq, Hindenburg Line, Canal du Nord, Courtrai, Selle, Valenciennes, Sambre, France and Flanders 1914-18, Italy 1917-18, Struma, **Doiran 1917, 18,** Macedonia 1915-18, **Suvla,** Sari Bair, Landing at Suvla, Scimitar Hill, Gallipoli 1915, Egypt 1915, 17, **Gaza,** El Mughar, Jerusalem, Jericho, Tell'Asur, Palestine 1917, 18, Tigris 1916, **Kut al Amara 1917,** Baghdad, Mesopotamia 1916, 18

The Second World War— Dyle, Withdrawal to Escaut, **St Omer-La Bassee,** Wormhoudt, Cassel, Dunkirk 1940, **Normandy Landing,** Mont Pincon, St Pierre La Vielle, Gheel, Nederrijn, Aam, Aller, North-West Europe 1940, 44,45, Sidi Barrani, **Capture of Tobruk,** Gazala, Mersa Matruh, Defence of Alamein Line, Deir el Shein, **El Alamein, Mareth,** Wadi Zeuss East, Wadi Sigzaou, Akarit, Wadi Akarit East, Enfidaville, North Africa 1940-43, Landing in Sicily, Primosole Bridge, Simeto Bridgehead, **Sicily 1943,** Sangro, **Salerno,** Santa Lucia, Battipaglia, Volturno Crossing, Monte Maro, Teano, Monte Camino, Garigliano Crossing, Minturno, Damiano, Anzio, **Rome, Gothic Line,** Coriano, Gemmano Ridge, Savignano, Senio Floodbank, Rimini Line, Ceriano Ridge, Vali di Comacchio, Italy 1943-45, **Malta 1941-42**

Regimental Marches

Quick March..........Wha wadna fecht for Charlie
Slow March..........The 22nd Regiment Slow March 1772

Agents..........Lloyds Bank PLC Cox's & King's Branch

Regimental Headquarters..........The Castle, Chester, CH1 2DN
(*Tel No:* Chester Castle Mil *Ext:* 40 and Civil 0244 27617)

Alliance

Candian Armed Forces..........2nd Battalion The Nova Scotia Highlanders (Cape Breton)

Colonel in Chief..........*HRH The Prince of* Wales *KG KT GCB AK QSO ADC*

Colonel..........Brig W K L Prosser *CBE MC*..........310385

Brigadiers

Prosser W K L *CBE MC* rcds psc 300680
Percival A J MacG *OBE* rcds psc(a) 300685

Colonels

Lane C E psc 300681

Lieutenant Colonels

Gauvain A de P psc 300680
Lockhart D psc 300682
Henderson P A psc 300683
Twiss A V psc 300684

Majors

Goddard F J *MBE* sq 120267
Hawtrey M G psc 311270
Moody P 311272
Russell P F *MBE* psc 300675
Watson D J 300676
Wilde P W psc 311276
Bock T J sq 300679
Bridge P R sq 300679
Jenner H D sq 300679
Beck E G 311279
Hazlewood M V *MISM* 311279
Hart M A *MBE QGM*▪ sq 300980
Hine N A *MBE* sq 300980
Skempton K psc 300981
Stewart R A *BSc* psc 300981
Huntriss M G psc 300982
Smith O D A psc 300982
Colebourn D J 300983
Sernberg A C W N 300983
Park T A *QGM* 300985

Captains

Rule D W N *BSc* (*A/Maj* 060985) 100979
Watters B S C 100979
Fuller M N 090581
Sernberg J R J *LLB* 010283
Cliff P G 081083
Jennings P F A *BA* 081083
Rule A W 081083
Thomas G M *BSc* 060284
Jenkins R P 050285

Lieutenants

Sharpe A R D (*A/Capt* 090385) 081281
Astle P A 120482
Blagbrough M D (*A/Capt* 090385) 120482
Thomas D A *BSc* (*A/Capt* 201285) 120482
Maund M (*A/Capt* 201285) 020782
Beech J J (*A/Capt* 201285) 090882
Sharpe J P D 080883
Thomas A D 090484
Donnelly J P S 070884
Ellis J M 111284
Hockedy M E 111284
Nias S R 060885

2nd Lieutenants

Waltier R D F 040884

Staff Quartermasters

Oakley G *MBE* 010475
Maj 230980

Quartermasters

Tarbuck H M *MBE* 010477
Maj 010882
Evans W J 010480
Maj 061084
Baddeley D S *Capt* 010483
Goodwin R S *Capt* 010485

Special Regular Officers

Majors

Brown P C 300983

Captains

Oak D M 160782

Lieutenants

Garlick R W 070884

Short Service Officers

Captains

Burke M S 281185

Lieutenants

Stuart-Smith P C *BA* (*A/Capt* 201285) 120482
Allmark A J 160582
Shaw R H M 211282
Robinson S P U 060885
Cook D H I 041285
Etherington J B 070486

2nd Lieutenants

Dale P S 040884
Roberts M J 081284
Lonergan K M 130485
†Ellis J R 060985

THE ROYAL WELCH FUSILIERS (23)

A Grenade flamed, proper; within, the crest of The Prince of Wales.

In the first and fourth corners the Rising Sun. In the second corner the Red Dragon. In the third corner the White Horse with motto, *Nec aspera terrent.* The Sphinx superscribed EGYPT

Namur 1695, Blenheim, Ramillies, Oudenarde, Malplaquet, Dettingen, Minden, Egypt, Corunna, Martinque 1809, Albuhera, Badajoz, Salamanca, Vittoria, Pyrennees, Nivelle, Orthes, Toulouse, Peninsula, Waterloo, Alma, Inkerman, Sevastopol, Lucknow, Ashantee 1873-4, Burma 1885-87, Relief of Ladysmith, South Africa 1899-1902, Pekin 1900

The Great War— Mons, Le Cateau, Retreat from Mons, **Marne 1914,** Aisne 1914, 18, La Bassee 1914, Messines 1914, 17, 18, Armentieres 1914, **Ypres 1914, 17, 18,** Langemarck 1914, 17, Gheluvelt, Givenchy 1914, Neuve Chapelle, Aubers, Festubert 1915, Loos, **Somme 1916, 18,** Albert 1916, 18, Bazentin, Deville Wood, Pozieres, Guilemont, Flers-Courcelette, Morval, Le Transloy, Ancre Heights, Ancre 1916, 18, Arras 1917, Scarpe 1917, Arleux, Bullecourt, Pilckem, Menin Road, Polygon Wood, Broodseinde, Poelcappelle, Passchendaele, Cambrai 1917, 18, St Quentin, Bapaume 1918, Lys, Bailleul, Kemmel, Scherpenberg, **Hindenburg Line,** Havrincourt, Epehy, St Quentin Canal, Beaurevoir, Selle, Valenciennes, Sambre, France and Flanders 1914, 18, Piave, **Vittorio Veneto,** Italy 1917, 18, **Doiran 1917, 18,** Macedonia 1915-18 Suvla, Sari Bair, Landing at Suvla, Scimitar Hill, **Gallipoli 1915-16,** Rumani **Egypt 1915, 17, Gaza,** El Mughar, Jerusalem, Tel'Asur, Megiddo, Nablus, Palestine 1917, 18, Tigris 1916, Kut al Amara 1917, **Baghdad,** Mesopotamia 1916, 18

The Second World War— Dyle, Defence of Escaut, **St Omer-La Bassee, Caen,** Esquay, Falaise, Nederrijn, **Lower Maas,** Venlo Pocket, Ourthe, Rhineland, **Reichswald,** Goch, **Weeze, Rhine,** Ibbenburen, Aller, NW Europe 1940, 44-45, **Madagascar,** Middle East 1942, **Donbaik, North Arakan, Kohima,** Mandalay, Ava, Burma 1943-45

Regimental Marches

Quick March..The British Grenadiers
Slow Marches..(i) The War Song of The Men of Glamorgan
(ii) Forth to the Battle

Agents..Lloyds Bank PLC Cox's & King's Branch

Regimental Headquarters....................Hightown Barracks, Wrexham, Clwyd, LL13 8RD (*Tel No* 0978 264521)

Alliances

Canadian Armed Forces.......................Royal 22e Regiment
Pakistan Army.......................................3rd Battalion The Frontier Force Regiment
Malaysian Armed Forces......................4th Battalion The Royal Malay Regiment

Colonel in Chief...................................THE QUEEN

Colonel..Brig A C Vivian *CBE ADC* 040384

Brigadiers

Vivian A C *CBE ADC* psc osc(GH) 300679
Llewellyn R M *OBE* psc 300681

Colonels

Reece P H *DSO* psc psc(CAN) ph 300684
Cadogan H M E *OBE* psc 300685

Lieutenant Colonels

Coate R J *MA* psc 300681
Humphreys-Evans J G sq 300682
Porter T L M *MBE FBIM* psc† 300682
Clarke R W psc 300683
Channing Williams N sq 300684
Williams J C W *MC* sq 300685

Majors

Hughes A S 251066
Bible T J sq 300669
Wodehouse A J sq 300670
Crocker P A sq 300674
Pearson P D sq 300676
Perkins A J sq 311277
Broad J S psc 311278
Knox P J psc 311279
Ross D J *MBE* psc 311279
Lewis M H L psc 300980
Plummer B P *BA* sq jsdc 300980
Davies G I psc 300981
Davies M L 300981
Lloyd R C 300982
Lloyd M A *MA MBIM* psc† psc(a)† 300982
Silverside T G W 300982
Rees P C K 300984
Ross R J V psc 300984
Boileau Goad J G I D 300985

Captains

Tritton I G psc (*A/Maj* 201285) 090379
Martin C P G 090980
Parsons J W G ph 090980
Morris J N *BSc* 010282
Walters H O *BSc(Econ)* 090583
Price-Edwards I 081083
Smith-Jones G C 081083
Kilvert-Jones T D *BA(Hons)* 010284
Raikes G E W T *BA* 050384
Hughes S M M 100684
Pedley N C *BA* 300684
Robson P A *BSc* 010884
Davies J P A 071085
Sim R P 071085

Lieutenants

Porter R J M 090882
Gillett S C 131282
Glynn-Williams S (*A/Capt* 020384) 110483
Taylor A W 110483
Wynne C A 110483
Brown C T B 080883
Knocker R K 101285
Johnson C N 070486
Westley R J 070486

2nd Lieutenants

††Slay J P 020983
††Garrow N J 230984

Staff Quartermasters

Down M J *MBE* 010474
Lt Col 090783

Quartermasters

Tomlinson G W 010478
Maj 070785
Bohana L W *Capt* 010479
Wiseman R J 010481
Maj 010481
Phillips A M *Capt* 010485

Special Regular Officers

Captains

Beaumont A J B *BSc* 290981

Short Service Officers

Captains

Lafrance A L H 100284

Lieutenants

Doak R A B	250782
Davies A C *BA*	090882
Ellingham A	220183
Ford M D *LLB*	110483
Nield D M *BSc(Econ)*	080883
Minter-Kemp R J E	101285

2nd Lieutenants

Lamb A M A	040884
Barham J E E	100885
†Gunn J C *BSc*	060985
†Wheeler G H *BSc*	060985
Muscat J J	141285

THE ROYAL REGIMENT OF WALES (24th/41st Foot)

The Queen's Colour—**A Silver wreath of immortelles** borne around the colour pike

A silver wreath of immortelles with the red dragon superimposed. The Royal Cypher. The Rose and Thistle on the same stalk within the Garter, and the Crown over. The Sphinx superscribed Egypt. A Naval Crown superscribed 12th April, 1782. *Gwell angau na Chywilydd*

Blenheim, Ramillies, Oudenarde, Malplaquet, Belleisle, Martinique 1762, St Vincent 1797, Cape of Good Hope 1806, India, Talavera, Bourbon, Busaco, Fuentes d'Onor, Java, Salamanca, Detroit, Queenstown, Miami, Vittoria, Pyrenees, Nivelle, Niagara, Orthes, Peninsula, Waterloo, Ava, Candahar 1842, Ghuznee 1842, Cabool 1842, Chillianwallah, Goojerat, Punjaub, Alma, Inkerman, Sevastopol, South Africa 1877-8-9, Burma 1885-87, Relief Of Kimberley, Paardeberg, South Africa 1899-1902

The Great War— **Mons,** Retreat from Mons, **Marne 1914, Aisne 1914, 18, Ypres 1914, 15, 17, 18,** Langemarck 1914, 17, **Gheluvelt,** Nonne Bosschen, Givenchy 1914, Gravenstafel, St Julien, Frezenberg, Bellewaarde, Aubers, **Loos, Somme 1916, 18,** Albert 1916, 18, Bazentin, Pozieres, Flers-Courcelette, Morval, Ancre Heights, Ancre 1916, 18, Arras 1917, 18, Scarpe 1917, Messines 1917, 18, **Pilckem,** Menin Road, Polygon Wood, Broodseinde, Poelcappelle, Passchendaele, **Cambrai 1917, 18,** St Quentin, Bapaume 1918, Lys, Estaires, Hazebrouck, Bailleul, Kemmel, Bethune, Scherpenberg, Drocourt-Queant, Hindenburg Line, Havrincourt, Epehy, St Quentin Canal, Beaurevoir, Courtrai, Selle, Valenciennes, Sambre, France and Flanders 1914-18, Struma, **Doiran 1917, 18, Macedonia 1915-18,** Helles, **Landing at Helles,** Krithia, Suvla, Sari Bair, Landing at Suvla, Scimitar Hill, **Gallipoli 1915-16,** Egypt 1915-17, **Gaza,** El Mughar, Jerusalem, Jericho, Tell'Asur, Megiddo, Nablus, Palestine 1917-18, Aden, Tigris 1916, Kut al Amara 1917, **Baghdad,** Mesopotamia 1916-18, **Tsingtao**

The Second World War— **Norway 1940, Normandy Landing, Sully,** Odon, **Caen,** Bourguebus Ridge, Mont Pincon, Souleuvre, Le Perier Ridge, **Falaise,** Risle Crossing, Antwerp, Nederrijn, **Le Havre,** Antwerp-Turnhout Canal, Scheldt, **Lower Maas,** Venlo Pocket, Zetten, Ourthe, Rhineland, **Reichswald,** Weeze, Hochwald, Rhine, Ibbenburen, Aller, Arnhem 1945, **North-West Europe 1944-45,** Benghazi, Gazala, **North Africa 1940-42,** Sicily 1943, Coriano, **Croce,** Rimini Line, Ceriano Ridge, Argenta Gap, **Italy 1943-45, Crete, Canea,** Withdrawal to Sphakia, Middle East 1941, North Arakan, **Mayu Tunnels, Pinwe, Kyaukmyaung Bridgehead,** Shweli, Myitson, Maymyo, Rangoon Road, **Sittang 1945, Burma 1944-45**

Korea 1951-52

Regimental Marches

Quick March..Men of Harlech
Slow March..Scipio

Agents..Holts Branch, Royal Bank of Scotland PLC, Lawrie House, Farnborough, Hants

Regimental Headquarters....................The Barracks, Cardiff, CF4 3YE (*Tel No:* 0222-27611 *Ext:* 207)

Alliances

Canadian Armed Forces.......................The Ontario Regiment RCAC
Australian Military Forces....................The Royal New South Wales Regiment

Colonel in Chief..................................*HRH The Prince of* Wales *KG KT GCB AK QSO ADC*

Colonel..................................Maj Gen L A H Napier *CB OBE MC DL* ret pay 311282

Brigadiers

Lee C J *CBE ADC FBIM* jssc psc 300682

Colonels

Diamond C H *FBIM* ndc sq 300683
Lloyd M T O *OBE* psc 300683
Lane J E J ndc psc 300685

Lieutenant Colonels

Burford R J odc(GE) psc† 300678
Bromham D C psc 300679
Brown T S (SL) *OBE* sq 300679
Stocker S R A *OBE* psc 300680
Roberts M G R *MBE* psc 300681
Roberts O M *OBE* psc 300681
Garnett J C M psc 300682
Grundy J M psc 300682
Bromhead D de G *LVO EQ FRGS* psc ph 300683
Harry M J H psc osc(NIG) 300684
Jones C B psc 300684
Watson W R M *MBE* psc 300684
Elliott C H psc 300685

Majors

Collins D E sq tt 300669
Matthews P J *MBE* sq 300669
Ayres J W sq 300670
Davies J G 311271
Nash A C 300672
Howes M M *MBE* 300674
de Lukacs-Lessner De Szeged A J sq 300676
McSheehy E P V sq 300676
Ashwood R J sq 300677
Gordon P D sq 300677
Martin A J sq 300677
Davies P G sq I 300678
Harry P D sq 300678
Phillips G J psc(a)† 300678
Davies A J sq 311279
Kerruish G P psc 300981
Wheadon T P 300981
Norrington-Davies P *LLB* psc 300982
Quinton Adams J 300982
Davies P psc† 300983
Goodall R C psc 300984
Wilks C W *BSc* 300985

Captains

Margesson H D 100580
Griffin M C C aic (*L/Maj* 130286) 090980
Cholerton I D *BSc(Econ)* 190581
Powell J M N *LLB* 120881
Poyntz C H N *BSc* 081281
Norrington-Davies P J (*A/Maj* 290785) 281281
Morgan R H *BA* 081083
Howells G *BA* 130284
Aitken R H T 100684
Bustin I D S 310186

Lieutenants

Gittins M I (*A/Capt* 031284) 081281
Kilmister J C St J (*A/Capt* 010185) 081281
Wilson J G G (*A/Capt* 190685) 110483
Lee S N *BA* 080883

2nd Lieutenants

††Hitchcock D J *BA(Hons)* 031082
††Carling W D C 240985

Staff Quartermasters

Amphlett G I *MVO MBE* 010473
Lt Col 230784

Edger R C *MBE MBIM MIPR* 010474
Maj 010479

Quartermasters

Vidler M J	*Capt*	010483
Husein J	*Capt*	010485

Special Regular Officers

Captains

Betteridge M J	081084
Harper I G	170985

Lieutenants

Powell J N	090882
Lewis S P P	070884

Short Service Officers

Captains

Terry M D	290182
Davies H	010782
Jones R J	160284
Coxell S G *BEd*	030484
James P C	010685
Gettins J R	011185

Lieutenants

Draycott K F	240382
Green M F T *BSc*	120482
McGregor R J A *BA*	120482
Morris D W *BEM*■	070782
O'Connor A	180882
Richards D J	131282
Withers R J *BA*	110483
Snook M R *BA*	090484
Beattie S J	111284
Baird Murray S K	170685

2nd Lieutenants

Barnett J C G	081284
Bromham A D C	081284
Price S J F	130485
Hammond G S	100885
Terry A J	100885
†Cutting E M *BA(Hons)*	060985
†Williams W H *BA(Hons)*	060985
†Rudd O F R *BA(Hons)*	060186

Short Service Volunteer Officers

Lieutenants

Hughes R P	300985

THE GLOUCESTERSHIRE REGIMENT (28 and 61)

Within a laurel wreath upon a pedestal inscribed Egypt, a sphinx

Ramillies, Louisburg, Guadaloupe 1759, Quebec 1759, Martinique 1762, Havannah, St Lucia 1778, Maida, Corunna, Talavera, Busaco, Barrosa, Albuhera, Salamanca, Vittoria, Pyrenees, Nivelle, Nive, Orthes, Toulouse, Peninsula, Waterloo, Chillianwallah, Goojerat, Punjaub, Alma, Inkerman, Sevastopol, Delhi 1857, Defence of Ladysmith, Relief of Kimberley, Paardeberg, South Africa 1899-1902

The Great War— **Mons,** Retreat from Mons, Marne 1914, Aisne 1914, 18, **Ypres 1914, 15, 17,** Langemarck 1914, 17, Gheluvelt, Nonne Bosschen, Givenchy 1914, Gravenstafel, St Julien, Frezenberg, Bellewaarde, Aubers, **Loos, Somme 1916, 18,** Albert 1916, 18, Bazentin, Delville Wood, Pozieres, Guillemont, Flers-Courcelette, Morval, Ancre Heights, Ancre 1916, Arras 1917, 18, Vimy 1917, Scarpe 1917, Messines 1917, 18, Pilckem, Menin Road, Polygon Wood, Broodseinde, Poelcappelle, Passchendaele, Cambrai 1917, 18, St Quentin, Bapaume 1918, Rosieres, Avre, **Lys,** Estaires, Hazebrouck, Bailleul, Kemmel, Bethune, Drocourt Queant, Hindenburg Line, Epehy, Canal du Nord, St Quentin Canal, Beaurevoir, **Selle,** Valenciennes, Sambre, France and Flanders 1914, 18, Piave, **Vittorio Veneto,** Italy 1917,18, Struma, **Doiran 1917,** Macedonia 1915, 18, Suvla, **Sari Bair,** Scimitar Hill, Gallipoli 1915, 16, Egypt 1916, Tigris 1916, Kut al Amara 1917, **Baghdad,** Mesopotamia 1916, 18, Persia 1918

The Second World War— **Defence of Escaut,** St Omer-La-Bassee, Wormhoudt, **Cassel,** Villers Bocage, **Mont Pincon, Falaise,** Risle Crossing, Le Havre, Zetten, **North-West Europe 1940, 44-45, Taukyan, Paungde,** Monywa 1942, North Arakan, Mayu Tunnels, **Pinwe,** Shweli, **Myitson, Burma 1942, 44-45**

Hill 327, **Imjin, Korea 1950-51**

Honorary Distinctions

(5th Battalion)

A Badge of the Reconnaissance Corps, with year dates 1944-45 and scroll: North-West Europe

Regimental Marches

Quick March............The Kinnegad Slashers
Slow March............'28th/61st'
Composed by G Plummer (late Bandmaster 1st Bn The Gloucester Regiment)

Agents............Lloyds Bank PLC Cox's & King's Branch

Regimental Headquarters............Custom House, 31 Commercial Rd, Gloucester, GL1 2HE
(*Tel No:* 0452-22682)

Alliances

Canadian Armed Forces............The Royal Canadian Regiment
Australian Military Forces............The Royal Western Australia Regiment
Kenya Army............3rd Battalion The Kenya Rifles

Colonel in Chief............*HRH The Duke of* Gloucester *GCVO*

Colonel............Maj Gen C J Waters *CBE*............311284

Brigadiers

Grist R D *OBE* psc† ph 300684

Colonels

Firth S D A *OBE* psc 300682
Rostron P R *MBE BA* psc 300684

Lieutenant Colonels

Giles R L *OBE* psc 300679
Dutton T B *OBE BSc(Eng)* psc† 300681
Newbould C J *MBE* psc 300682
Arengo-Jones A P A psc 300684

Majors

Thompson N C psc 300670
Ladds W R N sq 311270
Smith-Rewse M G sq 300673
James R P sq 311276
Dixon D R *MBE* psc jsdc 311279
Ongley T G sq 311279
Wakelin C S psc 311279
Webster J P O'F *MBE* psc(n)† 311279
Cable P J psc 300980
Durrant P J *MBE BA* psc 300981
Shaw J A 300981
Littlewood P R 300982
Gordon C J C psc 300984
Barratt M G A *LLB* 300985
Vine M S psc 300985

Captains

Oxlade S J aic (*A/Maj* 011285) 100979
Marks P J *BSc(Eng) MSc* mvt (*A/Maj* 130184) 301279
Nurick M E 090980
Jones A H 291280
Hony G H 080981
Motum M J R 080981
Masters N J 081083
Hall R L 060284
Lavender C M 060284
Noel-Smith M 081084
Venus A A 081084
Brown E D 040286

Lieutenants

Harris I V K (*A/Capt* 240484) 081281
Woodcock G E C (*A/Capt* 010186) 090882
Grist R M 110483
Bullock P C 080883
Sugden A M 121283
Franklin M 090484
Holt R P *BA* 090484

2nd Lieutenants

†Felton R F P *BSc* 060985
††Waters G C 240985

Quartermasters

Proom D K *MBE* 010476 *Maj* 020784
Lambie J P *Capt* 010482
England G P *Capt* 010483
Goss P *Capt* 010483

Directors of Music

Wearne R *ARCM* psm *Capt* 041185

Special Regular Officers

Captains

Hall P H 020481
Cokayne M T 070383
Clarke T A E 040286

Lieutenants

Keeling L R (*A/Capt* 040186) 011182
Kingsberry T L 070884

Short Service Officers

Captains

Evans W G	030584

Lieutenants

Parfitt S R	060783
Idziaszczyk M *BSc*	080883
Williams A P *BA*	080883
Cole-Mackintosh R C *BA*	090484
Welch N *BSc*	090484
Carter C W *BSc*	070884
Chynoweth M	090485

2nd Lieutenants

Lawrance C M	141285
†Hooper I *BSc(Econ)*	060186

Short Service Volunteer Officers

Lieutenants

Goulding N W S	200186
Dent J K	220186

THE WORCESTERSHIRE AND SHERWOOD FORESTERS REGIMENT (29th/45th FOOT) (29, 36, 45 and 95)

A Maltese Cross pommettee charged with the Garter in Gold encircling a Stag in Silver lodged on water proper thereunder a plinth inscribed FIRM in Gold the whole upon an elongated star of eights in Silver

Upon a pedestal inscribed Firm the Lion of the Royal Crest. A Maltese Cross charged in the centre with a Stag lodged on water within a wreath of oak. A Naval Crown superscribed **1st June 1794**

Ramillies, Belleisle, Mysore, Hindoostan, Louisburg, Rolica, Vimiera, Corunna, Talavera, Busaco, Fuentes D'Onor, Albuhera, Ciudad Rodrigo, Badajoz, Salamanca, Vittoria, Pyrenees, Nivelle, Nive, Orthes, Toulouse, Peninsula, Ava, Ferozeshah, Sobraon, South Africa 1846-7, Chillianwallah, Goojerat, Punjaub, Alma, Inkerman, Sevastopol, Central India, Abyssinia, Egypt 1882, Tirah, South Africa 1899-1902

The Great War— **Mons,** Le Cateau, Retreat from Mons, Marne 1914, **Aisne 1914, 18,** La Bassee 1914, Armentieres 1914, **Ypres 1914, 15, 17, 18,** Langemarck 1914, 17, **Gheluvelt** Nonne Bosschen, **Neuve Chapelle** Aubers, Festubert 1915, Hooge 1915, **Loos, Somme 1916, 18,** Albert 1916, 18, Bazentin, Delville Wood, Pozieres, Ginchy, Flers-Courcelette, Morval, Thiepval, Le Transloy, Ancre Heights, Ancre 1916, Arras 1917,18, Vimy 1917, Scarpe 1917, 18, Arleux, Messines 1917, 18, Pilckem, Langemarck 1917, Menin Road, Polygon Wood, Broodseinde, **Poelcappelle,** Passchendaele, **Cambrai 1917, 18,** St Quentin, Bapaume 1918, Rosieres, Villers Bretonneux, **Lys,** Estaires, Hazebrouck, Bailleul, Kemmel, Scherpenberg, Amiens, Drocourt-Queant, Hindenburg Line, Epehy, Canal du Nord, **St Quentin Canal,** Beaurevoir, Courtrai, Selle, Valenciennes, Sambre, **France and Flanders 1914-18,** Piave, Vittorio Veneto, **Italy 1917-18,** Doiran 1917,18, Macedonia 1915-18, Helles, Landing at Helles, Krithia, Suvla, Sari Bair, Landing at Suvla, Scimitar Hill, **Gallipoli 1915-16,** Egypt 1916, Tigris 1916, Kut al Amara 1917, **Baghdad,** Mesopotamia 1916-18, Baku, Persia 1918

The Second World War— **Norway 1940,** Defence of Escaut, St Omer-La Bassee, Ypres-Comines Canal, Wormhoudt, Dunkirk 1940, Odon, Bourguebus Ridge, Maltot, **Mont Pincon,** Jurques, La Variniere, Noirau Crossing, **Seine 1944,** Nederrijn, **Geilenkirchen,** Rhineland, **Goch,** Rhine, **North-West Europe 1940, 44-45,** Gogni, Barentu, **Keren,** Amba Alagi, Abyssinia 1940, 41, **Gazala,** Via Balbia, **El Alamein,** Djebel Guerba, Tamera, Medjez Plain, **Tunis,** North Africa 1941-43, **Salerno,** Volturno Crossing, Monte Camino, **Anzio, Campoleone,** Advance to Tiber, **Gothic Line, Coriano,** Cosina Canal Crossing, Monte Ceco, Italy 1943-45, **Singapore Island,** Malaya 1942, **Kohima,** Relief of Kohima, Naga Village, Mao Songsang, Shwebo, **Mandalay,** Irrawaddy, Mt Popa, **Burma 1944-45**

Regimental Marches

Quick March..Arrangement of 'Young May Moon' and 'Royal Windsor'
Slow March...'Duchess of Kent'

Agents...Lloyds Bank PLC Cox's & King's Branch

Regimental Headquarters....................Norton Barracks, Worcester (*Tel No:* 0905 354359)

Alliances

Canadian Armed Forces.......................The Grey and Simcoe Foresters
Pakistan Army ....13th Battalion The Punjab Regiment

Colonel in Chief...................................*HRH The Princess* Anne *Mrs* Mark Phillips *GCVO*

Colonel ....Brig P F B Hargrave *CBE*.................................010383

Brigadiers

Hargrave P F B *CBE* ndc jssc psc 300679

Colonels

Bryant J H psc 300682
Lowles H J *MBE* psc 300682
Jameson R W *OBE* psc 300683
Woolnough H A *OBE* ndc psc(n) 300683

Lieutenant Colonels

Wright A P *MBE* ndc psc† 300678
Jerram A L O *MBE* psc osc(SUD) 300679
Waters R J psc 300681
Silk R G psc 300682
Townsend J R M psc jsdc 300683
Weller J P *MBE* psc† 300684
Heron C A C psc 300685
Holmes P K *MBIM* sq 300685

Majors

Martin J M F 310766
Ireland E A sq 251166
Reeve D W sq 311270
Fox R H sq 311273
Varley J H *MBIM* psc 311275
Clarke I R S sq ph 300676
Evans C R sq 300676
Hackett J O M sq (*L/Lt Col* 080383) 300676
Henton M G A sq 311276
Thewles E F sq 311276
Tulloch M M sq 300677
Wood A R sq 300677
Ashworth S C H psc 300678
Prophet R S 311278
Hopkins A H psc 311279
Lees R J *MC* psc† 311279
Martin R L psc† aic 300980
Hackett J R M psc† 300981
Walsh M J J *MSc* psc† (*A/Lt Col* 141085) 300981
Howse C R psc 300982
Baldwyn D S 300983
Silk G A psc 300983
Jackson M L psc 300984
Macfarlane J H 300985

Captains

Bowen E H C 080379
Martin M W G 301279
Moreton A K *BA* (*A/Maj* 101085) 020280
Smith P E W 090980
Galvin K E *BSocSc* 210980
Norman S W 090581
Witcher J P 090581
Hackett R L M 080981
Mercer P J *BA* 080981
Fox P L D 060982
Cotterill J H 081084
Field A W 081084
Simpson M S McD 081084
Alun-Jones P H G *BA* 071085
Richards H A *BSc(Econ)* 071085

Lieutenants

Shaw M J (*A/Capt* 240386) 090882
Claydon M N 131282
Cserjen R L 121283
Holden M A 090484
Moss P W *BSocSc* 090484
Phillips E T 070884
Spencer B D 090485
Willoughby S E 090485

Welgold C M 060885

2nd Lieutenants

Thompson J M 040884
††Richards B L 230984
Wardner M R 130485
Williams S R 130485

Quartermasters

Harris J F 010477
Maj 301182
Allen T F 010478
Maj 011182
Gay A L *Capt* 010482
Elsam D J *Capt* 010483
Pitman G D *Capt* 010483
Ford R J *Capt* 010485

Special Regular Officers

Majors

Preston L 300985

Short Service Officers

Captains

Roderick P J W 010485
Townsend M K *DCM* 051285

Lieutenants

Tysall S W 271182
Cholerton A R *BA* 110483
Short C B H 080883
Walters G B A *BA DipLA* 070884
Claydon C J 060885
Cartwright J C 070486

2nd Lieutenants

Dickinson T J S 081284
Glover S C 130485
Glover T W 100885
Turner J R G 100885

THE ROYAL HAMPSHIRE REGIMENT (37 and 67)

A double red rose fimbriated gold. The Royal Tiger, superscribed India

Blenheim, Ramillies, Oudenarde, Malplaquet, Dettingen, Minden, Belleisle, Tournay, Barrosa, Peninsula, Taku Forts, Pekin 1860, Charasiah, Kabul 1879, Afghanistan 1879-80, Burma 1885-87, Paardeberg, South Africa 1900-02

The Great War— Le Cateau, **Retreat from Mons,** Marne 1914, 18, Aisne 1914, Armentieres 1914, **Ypres 1915, 17, 18,** St Julien, Frezenberg, Bellewaarde, **Somme 1916, 18,** Albert 1916, Guillemont, Ginchy, Flers-Courcelette, Thiepval, Le Transloy, Ancre Heights, Ancre 1916, **Arras 1917, 18,** Vimy 1917, Scarpe 1917, 18, Messines 1917, 18, Pilckem, Langemarck 1917, Menin Road, Polygon wood, Broodseinde, Poelcappelle, Passchendaele, **Cambrai 1917, 18,** St Quentin, Bapaume 1918, Rosieres, Lys, Estaires, Hazebrouck, Bailleul, Kemmel, Bethune, Tardenois, Drocourt-Queant, Hindenburg Line, Havrincourt, Canal du Nord, Courtrai, Selle, Valenciennes, Sambre, France and Flanders 1914-18, Italy 1917-18, Kosturino, Struma, **Doiran 1917, 18,** Macedonia 1915-18, Helles, **Landing at Helles,** Krithia, **Suvla,** Sari Bair, Landing at Suvla, Scimitar Hill, Gallipoli 1915-16, Egypt 1915-17, **Gaza,** El Mughar, Nebi Samwil, Jerusalem, Jaffa, Tell'Asur, Megiddo, Sharon, Palestine 1917-18, Aden, Shaiba, **Kut al Amara 1915, 17,** Tigris 1916, Baghdad, Sharqat, Mesopotamia 1915-18

Persia 1918-19, Archangel 1919, Siberia 1918-19

The Second World War— **Dunkirk 1940, Normandy Landing,** Tilly sur Seulles, **Caen,** Hill 112, Mont Pincon, Jurques, St Pierre La Vielle, Nederrijn, Roer, Rhineland, Goch, **Rhine,** North-West Europe 1940, 44-45, **Tebourba Gap,** Sidi Nsir, **Hunt's Gap,** Montagne Farm, Fondouk, Pichon, El Kourzia, Ber Rabai, North Africa 1940-43, Landing in Sicily, Regalbuto, Sicily 1943, Landing at Porto San Venere, **Salerno,** Salerno Hills, Battipaglia, Cava di Tirreni, Volturno Crossing, Garigliano Crossing, Damiano, Monte Ornito, Cerasola, **Cassino II,** Massa Vertecchi, Trasimene Line, Advance to Florence, Gothic Line, Monte Gridolfo, Montegaudio, Coriano, Montilgallo, Capture of Forli, Cosina Canal Crossing, Lamone Crossing, Pideura, Rimini Line, Montescudo, Frisoni, Italy 1943-45, Athens, Greece 1944-45, **Malta 1941-42,**

Regimental March

Quick March..The Hampshire

Agents..Lloyds Bank PLC Cox's & King's Branch

Regimental Headquarters....................Serle's House, Southgate Street, Winchester, Hants
(*Tel No:* 0962-63658)

Alliances

Canadian Armed Forces.......................49th (Sault St Marie) Field Artillery Regiment RCA(M)
New Zealand Army...............................5th Battalion (Wellington, West Coast and Taranaki) The Royal New Zealand Infantry Regiment

Colonel in Chief....................................*HRH The Princess of* Wales..

Colonel ....Gen *Sir* David Fraser *GCB OBE DL* ret pay 070981

Brigadiers

Long R G *OBE MC BA* psc	300685

Lieutenant Colonels

Southwood J G T *MBIM* psc	300677
Churcher E G psc	300681
Hanscomb R D *OBE* psc	300682
Neville D H psc	300682
Willing B J odc(US) psc†	300682
Freemantle A W *MBE* psc†	300683
Keatinge H D H psc	300684

Majors

Woodward N P H sq	300668
Ashenden R psc ph	311273
Withers A R *MBE* sq	311273
Glass T A L *BA MSc* psc	300678
Shepherd P J W osc(MAL) sq	300678
Dewar J G T psc	311278
Hannah D A C sq	311279
Davis P A psc	300980
Doodson H N sq	300980
Madigan B D	300980
Warren R H sq	300980
Hughes P W L	300981
Reeve-Tucker T M psc	300982
Alderman N S psc	300983
Baty B *BA*	300983
Edwards A J B psc	300985
Finklaire T S psc†	300985
Pryce A H psc† aic	300985

Captains

Russell R P *BA*	031079
Frere-Cook S A C *BSc(Eng)*	090980
Steevenson N T R	090980
Sim N A (*A/Maj* 040385)	090581
Martin G J *BA*	030981
Newton P R (*A/Maj* 200685)	080981
Stanley I M *BSc* aic	290981
Macdonald A R aic	080582
Hatton P J *BA*	170383
Jordan R J *BA*	110683
Jones P P	081083
Emery P W	060284
Passingham I *BA*	100684
Dennis R W	081084
Coburn M A *BSc*	010285
Bulleid C A	090685
Pearce M F	040286

Lieutenants

Dodd F C J (*A/Capt* 250485)	081281
Phipps J C D (*A/Capt* 240685)	131282
Laybourne J E (*A/Capt* 290785)	110483
Warren C F	080883
Spooner J A	070884
O'Sullivan P S	060885

2nd Lieutenants

Stephens K J	020584
Jones S R	130485

Quartermasters

Kimberley E C	*Capt*	010480

Special Regular Officers

Majors

Hawker P W	300984

Captains

Williams G N	081083

Lieutenants

Barnes A M (*A/Capt* 011085)	090882

Short Service Officers

Captains

Wolfe A L	130881
Le-Galloudec L B	090186

Lieutenants

Dabell A W *BSc*	090882
Burnett C D (*A/Capt* 130585)	250982
Gibson M W	081282
Parminter M D *BA*	110483
Macdowell C N *BSc*	080883
Prior A M	090484
Clements R M S	101285

2nd Lieutenants

Edmunds A J	081284
Eldridge J J	081284
Eustace R A	081284
Wright D A	130485
Sibeth P A	100885
Walch R T	100885
Hanscomb M R	141285

THE STAFFORDSHIRE REGIMENT (THE PRINCE OF WALES'S) (38, 64, 80 and 98)

The Prince of Wales's Plume within the Stafford Knot. The Sphinx, Superscribed Egypt
The Dragon, Superscribed China

Guadaloupe 1759, Martinique 1762, Martinique 1794, St Lucia 1803, Surinam, Monte Video, Rolica, Vimiera, Corunna, Busaco, Badajoz, Salamanca, Vittoria, St Sebastian, Nive, Peninsula, Ava, Moodkee, Ferozeshah, Sobraon, Punjaub, Pegu, Alma, Inkerman, Sevastopol, Reshire, Bushire, Koosh-Ab, Persia, Lucknow, Central India, South Africa 1878-79, Egypt 1882, Kirbekan, Nile 1884-85, Hafir, South Africa 1900-02

The Great War– **Mons,** Retreat from Mons, **Marne 1914, Aisne 1914, 18, Armentieres 1914, Ypres 1914, 17, 18, Langemarck 1914, 17, Gheluvelt, Nonne Bosschen, Neuve Chapelle, Aubers, Festubert 1915, Loos, Somme 1916, 18,** Albert 1916, 18, Bazentin, Delville Wood, Pozieres, Guillemont, Flers-Courcelette, Morval, Thiepval, Ancre Heights, Ancre 1916, Bapaume 1917, 18, **Arras 1917, 18,** Scarpe 1917,18, Arleux, Bullecourt, Hill 70, **Messines 1917, 18,** Pilckem, Menin Road ,Polygon Wood, Broodseinde, Poelcappelle, Passchendaele, **Cambrai 1917, 18,** St Quentin, Rosieres, Avre, Lys, Bailleul, Kemmel, Scherpenberg, Drocourt-Queant, Hindenburg Line, Havrincourt, Canal du Nord, **St Quentin Canal,** Beaurevoir, Courtrai, **Selle,** Valenciennes, Sambre, France and Flanders 1914-18, Piave, **Vittorio Veneto,** Italy 1917-18, **Suvla, Sari Bair,** Landing at Suvla, Scimitar Hill, Gallipoli 1915-16, Egypt 1916, Tigris 1916, **Kut al Amara 1917,** Baghdad, Mesopotamia 1916-18, Baku, Persia 1918, **NW Frontier, India 1915**

Afghanistan 1919

The Second World War– **Dyle,** Defence of Escaut, **Ypres-Comines Canal, Caen,** Orne, **Noyers,** Mont Pincon, **Brieux Bridgehead, Falaise, Arnhem 1944, North-West Europe 1940, 44,** Sidi Barrani, Djebel Kesskiss, **Medjez Plain,** Gueriat et Atach Ridge, Gab Gab Gap, **North Africa 1940, 43, Landing in Sicily, Sicily 1943, Anzio, Carroceto, Rome,** Advance to Tiber, Gothic Line, Marradi, Italy 1943-45, Chindits 1944, Burma 1943, 44

Regimental Marches

Quick March..........The Staffordshire Regiment (arrangement of "Come Lassies and Lads" and "The days we went a gipsying")
Slow March..........."God Bless The Prince of Wales"

Agents..........Lloyds Bank PLC Cox's & King's Branch
Regimental Headquarters..........Whittington Barracks, Lichfield, Staffs (*Tel No:* 0543-433333 *Ext:* 240)

Alliances

Canadian Armed Forces..........4e Battalion, Royal 22e Regiment (Chateauguay)
Australian Military Forces..........2nd Battalion The Royal Victoria Regiment
Leeward Islands..........The Antigua and Barbuda Defence Force
Pakistan Army..........7th Battalion The Baluch Regiment
Jamaica Defence Force..........The Jamaica Regiment

Colonel..........Lt Gen *Sir* Derek Boorman *KCB*..........141285

Brigadiers

Freer I L *OBE* psc 300685

Colonels

Hague M J psc (*L/Brig* 071085) 300681
Collins J R *OBE* psc(n) osc(NIG) 300685

Lieutenant Colonels

Umbers J M *MA* psc(a) 300677
Scott A J *MBE* psc† 300680
Willmore H G *OBE* sq 300682
Cottis T R *MBE* psc 300684

Majors

McLean R D W 310766
Hawke J A 051266
Davis M C J 300674
Armstrong J A 311277
Amery R T 300678
Smethurst C J sq aic 300678
Dawes N C E psc 300679
Green E psc† 311279
Brown N H C psc 300980
Catling G F psc 300980
Fennings-Mills R S psc 300980

Captains

Massey J B *BA* 311079
Moss F G *BSc* 090980
Tanner J K *BA* (*A/Maj* 010985) 010281
Knapper S J (*A/Maj* 250285) 080981
Parry-Jones D M 080981
Rochelle J M (*A/Maj* 011185) 080981
Rusby R M (*A/Maj* 011185) 080981
Eustace R J ph (*L/Maj* 140281) 281281
Rider C R F *BA* 110382
Butler G N A R *BSc(Econ)* 060982
Lockwood J Q 060982
Gatfield T S K 070283
Morley G W *BSc* 180783
Klein C A *BA* 271083
Cook J R *MC* 021283
Simpkins M J 081084
Chafer K I ph 050285
Holt D M 050285
Stamper W H *BA* 020386

Lieutenants

Hartington E 160383
Benson N J 110483
Chandler S P *BA* 090484
Sandiford T A *BA* 090484
Steed M 070884

Quartermasters

McKechnie G S *Capt* 010479
Ore M J *Capt* 010482

Special Regular Officers

Majors

Cobley P R 280185

Captains

Jones M P *BSc* 150283
Griffiths A C P 110683
Joynson C J 301084
Dyer C F 050285

Short Service Officers

Lieutenants

Nichols M A *BA* 120482
Ireland G F 140782
Ellison T J 301082
Mulingani P C 250483
Wootton R G *BA* 080883
Hughes C G S *BA* 090883
Spragg M E *BA* 090484
Mattey C R D 111284
Foster N S 101285
Frowen K D 101285

2nd Lieutenants

Holman A M L 141285

THE DUKE OF EDINBURGH'S ROYAL REGIMENT (BERKSHIRE AND WILTSHIRE) (49, 62, 66 and 99)

A Dragon superimposed upon a cross pattee. A Dragon, superscribed China

A Naval Crown, superscribed 2nd April, 1801

Louiseburg, St Lucia 1778, Egmont-op-Zee, Copenhagen, Douro, Talavera, Albuhera, Queenstown, Vittoria, Pyrenees, Nivelle, Nive, Orthes, Peninsula, New Zealand, Ferozeshah, Sobraon, Alma, Inkerman, Sevastopol, Pekin 1860, Kandahar 1880, Afghanistan 1879-80, Egypt 1882, Tofrek, Suakin 1885, South Africa 1879, 1899-1902

The Great War– Mons, Le Cateau, **Retreat from Mons,** Marne 1914, Aisne 1914, 18, La Bassee 1914, **Messines 1914, 17, 18,** Armentieres 1914, **Ypres 1914, 17,** Langemarck 1914, 17, Gheluvelt, Nonne Bosschen, **Neuve Chappelle,** Aubers, Festubert 1915, **Loos, Somme 1916, 18,** Albert 1916, 18, Bazentin, Delville Wood, Pozieres, Flers-Courcelette, Morval, Thiepval, Le Transloy, Ancre Heights, Ancre 1916, 18, **Arras 1917, 18,** Scarpe 1917, 18, Arleux, Pilckem, Menin Road, Polygon Wood, Broodseinde, Poelcappelle, Passchendaele, **Cambrai 1917, 18,** St Quentin, **Bapaume 1918,** Rosieres, Avre, Villers Bretonneux, Lys, Hazebrouck, Bailleul, Kemmel, Bethune, Scherpenberg, Amiens, Hindenberg Line, Havrincourt, Epehy, Canal du Nord, St Quentin Canal, Beaurevoir, **Selle,** Valenciennes, Sambre, France and Flanders 1914-18, Piave, **Vittorio Veneto,** Italy 1917-18, **Doiran 1917, 18, Macedonia 1915-18,** Suvla, Sari Bair, **Gallipoli 1915-16,** Gaza, Nebi Samwil, Jerusalem, Meggido, Sharon,

Palestine 1917-18, Tigris 1916, Kut al Amara 1917, **Baghdad,** Mesopotamia 1916-18

The Second World War– **Dyle,** Defence of Arras, St Omer-La Bassee, Ypres-Comines Canal, **Dunkirk 1940, Normandy Landing,** Odon, Caen, **Hill 112,** Bourgebus Ridge, **Maltot, Mont Pincon,** La Variniere, **Seine 1944,** Nederrijn, Roer, Rhineland, **Cleve,** Goch, Xanten, **Rhine,** Bremen, North-West Europe 1940, 44-45, Solarino, Simeto Bridgehead, Pursuit to Messina, **Sicily 1943,** Monte Camino, Calabritto, **Garigliano Crossing,** Minturno, **Damiano, Anzio,** Carroceto, **Rome,** Advance to Tiber, Italy 1943-45, Middle East 1942, Donbaik, **North Arakan,** Point 551, Mayu Tunnels, Ngakyedauk Pass, **Kohima,** Mao Songsang, Shwebo, Kyaukmyaung Bridgehead, **Mandalay,** Fort Dufferin, Rangoon Road, Toungoo, **Burma 1942-45**

Regimental Marches

Quick March..'Farmers Boy'
Slow March..Old Robin Gray

Agents..Lloyds Bank PLC Cox's & King's Branch

Regimental Headquarters....................The Wardrobe, 58 The Close, Salisbury, Wilts, SP1 2EX
(*Tel No: Salisbury* (0772) 336222 2683)

Alliances

Canadian Armed Forces......................The Lincoln and Welland Regiment
The Algonquin Regiment
The New Zealand Army ....7th Battalion (Wellington (City of Wellington's Own) and Hawke's Bay) Royal New Zealand Infantry Regiment
Pakistan Army ....13th Battalion The Frontier Force Regiment

Colonel in Chief..................................Field Marshal *HRH The Prince* Philip *Duke of* Edinburgh *KG KT OM GBE QSO*

Colonel..Maj Gen D T Crabtree *CB* ret pay..011182

Brigadiers

Turner W G R *CBE* ndc psc 300684

Colonels

Coxon G *CBE* odc(US) psc 300682
Redding J D psc 300682
Mackereth W A psc ph 300685

Lieutenant Colonels

Tremellen L C (SL) ndc psc 300672
Ridley V H (SL) *MBE QGM MBIM* psc 300676
Rose A J (SL) psc 300680
Kenway A C psc 300684

Majors

Ward J P sq 080265
Murray D C psc 131065
West N R sq 140775
Daly T M A psc† jsdc ph (*A/Lt Col* 221185) 311275
Parslow C J sq 300678
Cornwell M J sq 300980
Saunders S W J *BSc* psc (*A/Lt Col* 100186) 300980
Stone D J A psc 300980
Titley R K *BA* 300980
Westlake A E G *MBE BA* 300980
Briard A sq aic 300981
Paddison R B 300981
Lake A P B psc odc(BE) 300983
Silvester J L 300983
Coates A N 300984
Franklin B R F *BSc* 300984
Walker N J 300984

Captains

Davidson-Houston P E O'R-B *BSc(Eng)* 230878
Bowkett S E *BA* 040379
Cook S G (*A/Maj* 130286) 090581
Durant S A 281281
Wort J C *BSc* 280982
Tomlinson P C 060284
Wardle R N 100684
Drury F D F *BSc* 021084
Rylands J M C 081084
Smith N M *BA* 081084
Allen R *BSc(Econ)* 010285
Haugh K T 050285
Thornell A D 050285
Barlow G P 090685
King P J *BA* 090685
Davis R 071085
O'Hare T D 040286

Lieutenants

Marsh J *BA* 110483
White A C 070884

2nd Lieutenants

††Tomlinson J M *BSc(Hons)* 051082
†Toyne R C *BA* 060985

Quartermasters

Stafford W R *Capt* 010479
Stacey P D *Capt* 010481
Venus S J *Capt* 010483

Special Regular Officers

Majors

Steevenson A F R 300985

Captains

Edmonds J J 071085

The Prince of Wales's Division – continued

Lieutenants

Chedham F J	070884
Gray S D	060885

Short Service Officers

Captains

Freelove T J	290782
Millard E A	250384

Lieutenants

Hobbs A (*A/Capt* 010985)	140782
Hicks R G *MBE*	051082
Mullings P J	220183
Biddulph C S *BSc*	080883
Higgs R D ph	121283
Lister M J *BSc(Hons)*	090484
McCarthy C P *BA*	090484
Wilson W H C *BSc*	090484
Dennis P	060885

2nd Lieutenants

Heald C A	081284
Brain N S	130485
†Clements P N	060985

THE LIGHT DIVISION

Comprising..The Light Infantry (3 Regular Battalions, 3 Volunteer Battalions)
The Royal Green Jackets (3 Regular Battalions, 2 Volunteer Battalions)

Divisional Headquarters.......................Sir John Moore Barracks, Andover Road North, Winchester, Hants, SO22 6NQ
(*Tel No:* 0962-885522 *Ext:* 4207)

Colonel Commandant..........................Lt Gen *Sir* David Mostyn *KCB CBE*..310783

Divisional Brigadier.............................Brig C C Dunphie *MC*..050685

The Origins of amalgamated Regiments which are now included in The Light Division are as follows:—

THE LIGHT INFANTRY

On 6 October 1959

The Somerset Light Infantry (Prince Albert's) (13) and
The Duke of Cornwall's Light Infantry (32 and 46) amalgamated to form:
The Somerset and Cornwall Light Infantry

On 10 July 1968

The Somerset and Cornwall Light Infantry (13, 32 and 46)
The King's Own Yorkshire Light Infantry (51 and 105)
The King's Shropshire Light Infantry (53 and 85) and
The Durham Light Infantry (68 and 106) amalgamated to form:
The Light Infantry

THE ROYAL GREEN JACKETS

On 7 November 1958

The Oxfordshire and Buckinghamshire Light Infantry (43rd and 52nd) was redesignated:
1st Green Jackets (43rd and 52nd)

The King's Royal Rifle Corps was redesignated:
2nd Green Jackets (The King's Royal Rifle Corps)

The Rifle Brigade (Prince Consort's Own) was redesignated:
3rd Green Jackets (The Rifle Brigade)

On 1 January 1966

1st Green Jackets (43rd and 52nd)
2nd Green Jackets (The King's Royal Rifle Corps) and
3rd Green Jackets (The Rifle Brigade) amalgamated to form:
The Royal Green Jackets

THE LIGHT INFANTRY (13, 32, 46, 51, 53, 68, 85, 105 and 106)

A Bugle Horn, stringed, in Silver. The Sphinx superscribed Egypt. A Mural Crown superscribed Jellalabad. *Aucto*

Splendore Resurgo. Cede Nullis. Faithful

Gibraltar 1704-5, Dettingen, Minden, Nieuport, St Lucia 1796, Tournay, Dominica, **Corunna,** Rolica, Vimiera, Martinique 1809, Talavera, **Fuentes d'Onor, Salamanca, Vittoria, Pyrenees, Nivelle,** Nive, **Orthes,** Toulouse, **Peninsula, Bladensburg, Waterloo,** Ava, Aliwal, Sobraon, Ghuznee 1839, **Affghanistan 1839,** Cabool 1842, Mooltan, Goojerat, Punjaub, Alma, **Inkerman, Sevastopol,** Reshire, Bushire, Koosh-ab, **Persia, Lucknow, New Zealand, Pegu, Ali Masjid, South Africa 1878-9, Afghanistan 1878-80,** Tel-el-Kebir, Egypt 1882, Nile 1884-5, Suakin 1885, **Burma 1885-87, Modder River, Paardeberg, Relief of Ladysmith, South Africa 1899-1902**

The Great War– **Mons, Le Cateau,** Retreat from Mons, Marne 1914, 18, **Aisne 1914, 18,** La Bassee 1914, **Messines 1914, 17, 18,** Armentieres 1914, **Ypres 1914, 15, 17, 18,** Hill 60, Gravenstafel, St Julien, Frezenberg, Bellewaarde, **Hooge 1915,** Loos, Mount Sorrel, **Somme 1916, 18, Albert 1916, 18,** Bazentin, Delville Wood, Pozieres, Guillemont, Flers Courcelette, Morval, Le Transloy, Ancre Heights, Ancre 1916, 18, Bapaume 1917, 18, **Arras 1917, 18,** Vimy 1917, Scarpe 1917, 18, Arleux, Hill 70, Pilckem, Langemarck 1917, Menin Road, Polygon Wood, Broodseinde, Poelcappelle, **Passchendaele, Cambrai 1917, 18,** St Quentin, Rosieres, Avre, Lys, Estaires, Hazebrouck, Bailleul, Kemmel, Bethune, Scherpenberg, Marne 1918, Soissonnais-Ourcq, Tardenois, Amiens, Drocourt Queant, Bligny, Hindenburg Line, **Havrincourt,** Epehy, Canal du Nord, St Quentin Canal, Beaurevoir, Courtrai, Selle, Valenciennes, Sambre, France and Flanders 1914-18, Piave, Vittorio Veneto, Italy 1917-18, Struma, **Doiran 1917, 18,** Macedonia 1915-18, Suvla, Landing at Suvla, Scimitar Hill, Gallipoli 1915, Rumani, Egypt 1915-17, Gaza, El Mughar, Nebi Samwil, **Jerusalem,** Jericho, Tell'Asur, Megiddo, Sharon, **Palestine 1917-18, Tigris 1916,** Sharquat, Mesopotamia 1916-18, NW Frontier India 1915, 16-17, Aden, Archangel 1918-19

Afghanistan 1919

The Second World War– Kvam, **Norway 1940,** Dyle, Defence of Escaut, Arras counter attack, St Omer-La Bassee, **Dunkirk 1940, Normandy Landing,** Villers Bocage, Tilly sur Seulles, Odon, **Fontenay le Pesnil,** Cheux, Defence of Rauray, Caen, **Hill 112,** Bourgebus Ridge, Cagny, Troarn, Mont Pincon, Souleuvre, Le Perier Ridge, St Pierre La Vielle, Noireau Crossing, Falaise, Seine 1944, Antwerp, Hechel, **Gheel,** Nederrijn, Le Havre, Antwerp-Turnhout Canal, Lower Maas, Opheusden, Venraij, Geilenkirchen, Venlo Pocket, Roer, Rhineland, Cleve, Goch, Hochwald, Xanten, Rhine, Ibbenburen, Lingen, Aller, Bremen, **North-West Europe 1940, 44-45,** Syria 1941, Halfaya 1941, Tobruk 1941, Relief of Tobruk, Gazala, Gabr el Fachri, Zt El Mrasses, Mersa Matruh, Point 174, **El Alamein, Mareth,** Sedjenane, Mine de Sedjenane, El Kourzia, **Argoub Sellah,** Medjez Plain, Gueriat el Atach Ridge, Si Abdallah, Tunis, Djebel Bou Aoukaz 1943, North Africa 1940-43, Landing in Sicily, Solarino, **Primosole Bridge, Sicily 1943, Salerno,** Salerno Hills, Cava di Tirreni, Volturno Crossing, Monte Camino, Garigliano Crossing, Minturno, Monte Tuga, **Anzio,** Campoleone, Carroceto, **Cassino II,** Trasimene Line, Arezzo, Advance to Florence, Incontro, Gothic Line, Gemmano Ridge, Carpineta, Capture of Forli, Cosina Canal Crossing, Defence of Lamone Bridgehead, Pergola Ridge, Rimini Line, Cesena, Monte Ceco, Monte Grande, Sillaro Crossing, **Italy 1943-45,** Athens, Greece 1944-45, Cos, Middle East 1942, Sittang 1942, Donbaik, **North Arakan,** Buthidaung, Ngakyedauk Pass, **Kohima,** Mandalay, **Burma 1942, 43-45**

Kowang-San, Hill 227, **Korea 1951-53**

Regimental Marches

Quick Marches..(i) Light Infantry (ii) Regimental Double Past 'The Keel Row'

Agents..Lloyds Bank PLC Cox's & King's Branch

Regimental Headquarters......................Sir John Moore Barracks, Andover Road North, Winchester, Hants, SO22 6NQ
(*Tel No:* 0962 885522 *Ext:* 4220)

Alliances

Canadian Armed Forces........................The Royal Hamilton Light Infantry (Wentworth Regiment)
Le Regiment de Maisonneuve
The North Saskatchewan Regiment

The Australian Citizen Military ForcesThe Monash University Regiment

New Zealand Army................................2nd Battalion (Canterbury and Nelson, Marlborough and West Coast)
Royal New Zealand Infantry Regiment

Pakistan Army..11th Battalion The Baluch Regiment
13th Battalion The Baluch Regiment

Kenya Army..1st Battalion The Kenya Rifles

Mauritius..The Mauritius Special Mobile Force

Colonel in Chief...................................HM QUEEN ELIZABETH THE QUEEN MOTHER

Deputy Colonel in Chief.......................*HRH Princess* Alexandra *the Hon Mrs* Angus Ogilvy *GCVO*

Colonel..Maj Gen B M Lane *CB OBE*..100782

Deputy Colonels....................................Brig R B MacGregor-Oakford *OBE MC*..........................201279
Brig J Hemsley..100782
Brig B J Lowe *OBE* ret pay..100783
Brig R St C Preston *OBE*..010885

Brigadiers

MacGregor-Oakford R B *OBE MC* rcds jssc psc 300676
Hemsley J *MPhil FBIM* nadc df psc psc(IND) 300680
Makepeace-Warne A *MBE* rcds psc I 300682
Preston R St C *OBE* ndc psc 300684
Regan M D *OBE* psc 300685

Colonels

Lees B M *LVO OBE BA FBIM* ptsc 300678
Crawford R W H *OBE MA* psc 300679
Bevan T D V psc 300684
Fyfe A I H psc osc(NIG) 300684
Kendall J E *MBE* sq 300685

Lieutenant Colonels

McMurtrie D H (SL) *MBIM* psc 300673
Holworthy R psc osc(NIG) 300676
Bennett A C H (SL) *FBIM* ndc psc 300677
Chetwynd Stapylton R G H psc(a) 300680
Dru Drury M H *MBE* psc(a) osc(ZIM) 300680
Kaye C M S *OBE* odc(AUST) psc 300680
Nicholas R D *OBE* sq 300680
Farrant D K W psc 300681
Barker T M *OBE BA MSc MBIM* ndc sq 300682
Elliott B M *MBE* psc 300682
Watts M A G *MBE* psc 300682
Brown A D psc 300683
Deverell J F *MBE* psc(n)† 300683
Draper R A *OBE MPhil* psc 300683
Goddard P A sq ph 300683
Vellacott R D psc 300683
Williams J G *MA* psc(n)† 300683
Anderson L J C sq 300684
Cohen R S J *MBE BEng MSc* psc jsdc 300684
Parker J W *BA* psc 300684
Deedes C G psc† 300685
Estcourt R M psc† ph 300685
Garrett R J M psc 300685
Marsham J K psc 300685
Sale R A psc 300685

Majors

Rowe N C *MBE* ptsc (*L/Lt Col* 010380) 140762
Rowe A P 080265
Eller S P sq 060266
Arundell E R sq 311267
Bower D A sq tt 311269
Wilcocks J C F 311269
Firbank S C sq 300670
Reynolds O psc 300670
Vyvyan-Robinson R *MBE* sq 300670
Charlesworth J B sq 300672
Saunt G A C *MBE* sq 300672
Taylerson R J R sq 300673
Deedes C M J psc 300674
Poett S E N H sq 300674
York J H H *BA* psc 300674
Simmons A St C 300675
Hemsley J R psc 300676
King N A *MBE BA* sq 300676
Wykeham P J psc 300676
Harris T sq 311276
Rice C M 311276
Penny A H sq 300677
Eustace D W sq 300678
Tyndale J G sq 300679
Lewis N P C *MBE BA BSc* psc 311279
Philp M H psc 311279
Stephenson D H R psc 311279
Burt C *BSocSc* psc(a)† aic 300980
Gaskell N P sq 300980
Kench N R sq 300980
Peters R D 300980
Sawers I J psc 300980
Seear M H 300980
Whistler M H L sq 300980
Wynne Davies D A psc 300980
Cousens R P psc 300981
Downward C A *MC* 300981
Eliot D psc 300981
Gilbert A A *MBE BA* psc 300981
Hinde P N *BSc* psc† 300981
Jones N A de C sq 300981
Grubb M J W *BSc* 300982
Lerwill A T D 300982
Notley C J M 300982
Phayre R D S *BA* psc 300982
Rescorle M J psc 300982
Robertson-Mann D *BA BSc CGIA* psc(PAK)† 300982
Brims R V psc† 300983
Burns R I *MA* psc 300983
Harris R A 300983
Matheson R M B 300983
Stacey N W 300983
Weeks T F L psc 300983
Armstrong R R C psc 300984
Badgery J *LLB* 300984
Elcomb C M G *BA* psc 300984
Ogden C H D *BA* psc 300984
Sharland P R psc 300984
Daplyn T J psc 300985
Davenport N J 300985
Floyer-Acland R S psc 300985
Garner P G *BA* psc 300985
Lloyd-Williams R C 300985
Mackain-Bremner C M F psc 300985
Mortimer A M W 300985
Thomas D P 300985

Captains

Ottowell C M S (*A/Maj* 240585) 040878
Gregson T J *BA* 051078
Amber A *BSc(Eng)* 130279
Rollo-Walker R M J 090379
Hodson R M R *MBE* 301279
Simmonds R C F 090980
Spencer J N L 090980
Vincent M S R 090980
Montagu M C D *BA* 261280
Whitmore G *LLB* 230381
Blue R A 090581
Booth C C S 080981
Nichols D 281281
Rose A C C 281281
Martin T J *MA* 250482
Flecchia M D 080582
Williams R G *BA* 090882
Laidler S (*A/Maj* 180385) 060982
Oliver K A 071182
Bacon A P *BA* 010283
Tolhurst R J *BSc* 010283
Lynch-Staunton C H C 070283
Barry B W aic 110683
Jacob I M 110683
Trelawny A R 110683
Homan A C *BA* aic 050983
Malins-Smith J C *BA* 031083
Skipworth-Michell D J 081083
Harris C E R 060284
Montagu R J *BA* 130284
Johnson K F 081084
Bendall J P F R 050285
Sartain R P 050285
Chambers G P 090685
Kellett P A *BSc* 030985
Coward D 071085
Turner J W S *BSocSc* 231285
Hogg P *BA* 040286
Mills S C D 040286

Lieutenants

Hamilton-Briscoe A E W (*A/Capt* 260385) 120482
Payne M J C (*A/Capt* 220885) 090882
Topham C M E 090882
Wood D J (*A/Capt* 051085) 090882
Middleton A C (*A/Capt* 060186) 110483
Smith R R *BA* 110483
Trythall P J A *BA* 110483
Davies E P *BA* (*A/Capt* 101285) 090484
Gwinn C H S L *BSc(Econ)* 090484
Hall J W *BA* 090484
Lyman R M 090484
Shircliff M J B *BA* 090484
Dougan N J R *BA* 070884
Evans T P 070884
Humphreys C R 111284
Hardy J C 090485
Tricks W T F 090485
Woollard R J 090485
Turner E G E 070486

2nd Lieutenants

††Shields H E *BA* 030982
††Adams M M B 020983
††Barrett J P *LLB(Hons)* 020983
†Robertson H M *BSc(Hons)* 051084
McMurtrie T D 081284
Cummings J R 130485
††Hazlitt S C 240985

Quartermasters

Brynolf J G *MBE* 010476
Lt Col 230485
Hall R W *MBE* 010478
Maj 221180
Bevan R T 010479
Maj 100486
Burnett H R 010479
Maj 011283
Hassall B *Capt* 010480
Watkins G B 010481
Maj 141185
Grindley M R *Capt* 010482
Hardy P D *MBE* *Capt* 010483
Luxton P C *Capt* 010484
Blackburn G *Capt* 121184
Crook D R *Capt* 010485
Smith E *Capt* 010485
White M D *Capt* 010485

The Light Division — continued

Special Regular Officers

Majors

Carrington Smith N A	311277

Lieutenants

Wooldridge N C	131282
O'Hanlon M J (*A/Capt* 190286)	110483

Short Service Officers

Captains

Simmonds J E	110882
Wharton P *MM*	020483
Pelly R S H *BA*	030385
Shuttleworth P A *BSc*	030385
Richardson R W	050985
Jones R A W	311085
Stevenson W	230186
Leeming A S	250186

Lieutenants

Walls G	240282
Williams A R	150482
Pidgeon N R *BA* (*A/Capt* 300885)	070682
Taylor P A	281182
Humphries R S *MISM*	010283
Cockroft N E *BA*	110483
De Vos J P *BSc*	080883
Arkell N H M *BSc*	090484
Davies P J M	090484
Harris S A *BA*	090484
Montague P A J *BA*	090484
Radford T B *BA*	090484
Russell D F D *BA*	090484
Huxley H G R	111284
Bishop G R T	090485
Bruce-Smythe A C	070486
Hughes R N	070486
Waight R E C	070486

2nd Lieutenants

Ainsworth P H P	040884
Wigram T P H	081284
Chapman J M	130485
Hooper R J	130485
Savage M T	130485
Sibbald P E	130485
Keville P M	100885
McLean H D A	100885
Nicholl A R	100885
†Miller R H *BA(Hons)*	060985
††Pointing W J	060985
†Scarff M T *BA(Hons)*	060985
Arliss S E T	141285
Thompson J A	141285
†Baker I C *BA*	060186

Short Service Volunteer Officers

Lieutenants

Phillips G M	310785

2nd Lieutenants

O'Brien J	100684
Tait-Harris J H	120885

THE ROYAL GREEN JACKETS
(43rd and 52nd, King's Royal Rifle Corps, Rifle Brigade)

A Maltese Cross inscribed with selected battle honours thereon a Bugle Horn stringed and encircled with the title of the Regiment all within a wreath of Laurel ensigned with the Crown resting upon a Plinth inscribed "Peninsula" across the Tie a Naval Crown superscribed "Copenhagen 2 April, 1801" all in Silver

Louisburg, **Quebec 1759,** Martinique 1762, Havannah, North America 1763-64, Mysore, Hindoostan, Martinique 1794, **Copenhagen,** Monte Video, Rolica, Vimiera, **Corunna,** Martinique 1809, Talavera, Busaco, Barrosa, Fuentes d'Onor, Albuhera, Ciudad Rodrigo, **Badajoz, Salamanca, Vittoria,** Pyrenees, Nivelle, Nive, Orthes, Toulouse, **Peninsula, Waterloo,** South Africa 1846-47, Mooltan, Goojerat, Punjab, South Africa 1851-53, Alma, **Inkerman,** Sevastopol, **Delhi 1857,** Lucknow, Taku Forts, Pekin 1860, New Zealand, Ashantee 1873-74, Ali Masjid, South Africa 1879, Ahmed Khel, Kandahar 1880, **Afghanistan 1878-80,** Tel-el-Kebir, Egypt 1882-84, Burma 1885-87, Chitral, Khartoum, **Defence of Ladysmith,** Relief of Kimberley, Paardeberg, Relief of Ladysmith, South Africa 1899-1902

The Great War— Mons, Le Cateau, Retreat from Mons, Marne 1914, Aisne 1914, 18, Armentieres 1914, **Ypres 1914, 15, 17, 18,** Langemarck 1914, 17, Gheluvelt, **Nonne Bosschen,** Givenchy 1914, Neuve Chapelle, Gravenstafel, St Julien, Frezenberg, Bellewaarde, Aubers, Festubert 1915, Hooge 1915, Loos, Mount Sorrel, **Somme 1916, 18,** Albert 1916, 18, Bazentin, Delville Wood, Pozieres, Guillemont, Flers-Courcelette, Morval, Le Transloy, Ancre Heights, Ancre 1916, 18, Bapaume 1917, 18, Arras 1917, 18, Vimy 1917, Scarpe 1917, 18, Arleux, Messines 1917, 18, Pilckem, Menin Road, Polygon Wood, Broodseinde, Poelcappelle, Passchendaele, Cambrai 1917, 18, St Quentin, Rosieres, Avre, Villers-Bretonneux, Lys, Hazebrouck, Bailleul, Kemmel, Bethune, Drocourt Queant, Hindenburg Line, Havrincourt, Epehy, Canal du Nord, St Quentin Canal, Beaurevoir, Courtrai, Selle, Valenciennes, Sambre, France and Flanders 1914-18, Piave, Vittorio Veneto, Italy 1917-18, Doiran 1917, 18, Macedonia 1915-18, Kut al Amara 1915, Ctesiphon, Defence of Kut al Amara, Tigris 1916, Khan Baghdadi, Mesopotamia 1914-18

Archangel 1919

The Second World War— Defence of Escaut, **Calais 1940,** Cassel, Ypres-Comines Canal, Normandy Landing, **Pegasus Bridge,** Villers Bocage, Odon, Caen, Esquay, Bourguebus Ridge, Mont Pincon, Le Perier Ridge, Falaise, Antwerp, Hechtel, Nederrijn, Lower Maas, Roer, Ourthe, Rhineland, Reichswald, Cleve, Goch, Hockwald, Rhine, Ibbenburen, Dreirwalde, Leese, Aller, North-West Europe 1940, 44-45, Egyptian Frontier 1940, Sidi Barrani, Beda Fomm, Mersa el Brega, Agedabia, Derna Aerodrome, Tobruk 1941, Sidi Rezegh 1941, Chor es Sufan, Saunnu, Gazala, Bir Hacheim, Knightsbridge, Defence of Alamein Line, Ruweisat, Fuka Airfield, Alam el Halfa, **El Alamein,** Capture of Halfaya Pass, Nofilia, Tebaga Gap, Enfidaville, Medjez el Bab, Kasserine, Thala, Fondouk, Fondouk Pass, El Kourzia, Djebel Kournine, Argoub el Megas, Tunis, Hamman Lif, North Africa 1940-43, Sangro, Salerno, Santa Lucia, Salerno Hills, Cardito, Teano, Monte Camino, Garigliano Crossing, Damiano, Anzio, Cassino II, Liri Valley, Melfa Crossing, Monte Rotondo, Capture of Perugia, Monte Malbe, Arezzo, Advance to Florence, Gothic Line, Coriano, Gemmano Ridge, Lamone Crossing, Orsara, Tossignano, Argenta Gap, Fossa Cembalina, Italy 1943-45, Veve, Greece 1941, 44, 45, Creta, Middle East 1941, Arakan Beaches, Tamandu, Burma 1943-44

Regimental Marches

Quick Marches .... (i) Arrangement of 'Huntsman's Chorus' and 'Italian Song'
(ii) Regimental Double Past 'The Road To The Isles'

Agents .... Lloyds Bank PLC Cox's & King's Branch

Regimental Headquarters .... Sir John Moore Barracks, Andover Road North, Winchester, Hants, SO22 6NQ
(*Tel No:* 0962-885522 *Ext:* 4215)

Alliances

Canadian Armed Forces .... The British Columbia Regiment (Duke of Connaught's Own)
Princess Patricia's Canadian Light Infantry
The Queen's Own Rifles of Canada
The Brockville Rifles
The Royal Winnipeg Rifles
The Regina Rifle Regiment

Australian Military Forces .... Western Australia University Regiment
Sydney University Regiment
Melbourne University Regiment

New Zealand Army .... 1st Battalion, Royal New Zealand Infantry Regiment
6th Battalion (Hauraki), Royal New Zealand Infantry Regiment

Fiji .... The Fiji Infantry Regiment

Affiliations

2nd King Edward V11's Own Gurkha Rifles (The Sirmoor Rifles)
6th Queen Elizabeth's Own Gurkha Rifles

Colonel in Chief .... THE QUEEN

Colonels Commandant .... Gen *Sir* Frank Kitson *KCB GBE MC* ret pay 010179
*Gen *Sir* Roland Guy *KCB CBE DSO* 010781
Gen *Sir* James Glover *KCB MBE* 010684

*Representative Colonel Commandant for 1986

The Light Division — continued

Brigadiers

Cornell J R *CBE* nadc jssc psc 300682
Foley J P *OBE MC* psc 300682
Karslake A E K *MA* odc(FR) psc† ptsc osc(FR) 300683
Dunphie C C *MC* psc 300685
Henshaw C L G G *CBE MBIM* psc 300685

Colonels

Mogg J N B *MA* psc† 300682
Berry A E *OBE* psc 300684
Owen C C L O *LVO OBE* psc 300684
Treneer-Michell P *OBE* psc 300684
Harrisson C J M *OBE* psc† ph 300685
Prideaux N M odc(US) psc 300685
Robertson M J C *MC* psc(n)† psc ph 300685
Taylor J M *MBE* psc† 300685
Wallace C B Q *OBE* psc 300685

Lieutenant Colonels

Simmons C St C (SL) psc 300672
Holroyd C J (SL) psc† osc(NIG) 300673
Drew A S G *MA* psc 300681
Williams D A B psc 300681
Beddard J P O *MBE* psc 300682
Chamberlin P G psc 300682
Dewar M K O *MA(Hons)* psc† 300682
Vyvyan C G C *MBE BA* psc 300682
Lyddon P J *MBE* psc 300683
Pringle A R D *MBE BSc* psc† 300683
Smythe G F *OBE* sq 300683
Adams N H H *MPhil* psc† 300684
Gamble R M psc 300684
Godsal D H *MBE BA* psc jsdc 300684
Hayes G de V W psc 300684
Innes D J psc 300685
McKinley S D G *OBE* psc 300685

Majors

Shelley A T R psc 120267
Keyte J V *MBE* sq 300668
Francis J D psc† 300675
McGrigor A D sq 300675
Rimmer R J psc 311276
Gutteridge R H S sq 300678
Hearn S C psc 311278
Ross-Hurst R W K sq 311278
Babington Smith H *BA* sq 300980
Carter J S psc 300980
Heyman C F sq 300980
Jackson W N B *BSc* sq 300980
Jenkins R N R *MA* psc 300980
Manners-Smith M C H psc 300980
Pearson A J psc 300980
von Merveldt J-D M psc 300980
Corry T W 300981
Hamilton-Baillie T R *BA* psc† 300981
Jackson A J R psc† 300981
Jacques P H psc 300981
Luard P J psc 300981
Mangnall N J 300981
Palmer A M D psc (*A/Lt Col* 060186) 300981
Poole-Warren J A sq 300981
Stanford-Tuck S R psc(CAN) 300981
Browne P D *MBE* psc 300982
Daniell J A psc 300982
Smith M *MC* psc 300982
Balfour J M J psc 300983
Carroll A M *BA* psc 300983
Coles I A M 300983
Cottam N J *BA* psc 300983
Willing H C G psc 300983
Churcher R A *BA* 300984
Day D C 300984
Fairgrieve P B psc† 300984
Snagge C E M psc psc(AUS) 300984
Steel R A psc 300984
Durcan J M P *BA* psc 300985
Kitchin M A 300985
Martin R C J 300985
Mieville C J 300985
Pentreath P J 300985
Smith M B D *MBE* 300985

Captains

Schofield P J F (*A/Maj* 101083) 080379
Gardiner A W M 090379
Mostyn P J *BA* 030380
Matters R P 100580
Parker N R 100580
Prichard R R P (*A/Maj* 010585) 100580
Beattie C E I *MA* 010880
Wright T G *BA* 010880
Taylor G C A *CGIA* psc† (*A/Maj* 201285) 291280
Carrow R J 080981
Knight J C (*A/Maj* 230386) 080981
Leeming J M A *BA* ph 080981
Blackmore C D *BA* 050182
Tobey D M *MA* 010282
Chavasse N R G 080582
Athill J A 060982
Jackson J T 060982
Baverstock N A C *MA* 010283
Wilson A H M *BSc* 010283
Brown D W 070283
Russell J A N 070283
Bolton R L S *BA* aic 050383
Webb-Bowen M E *BSc* 010883
Magan J H *BA* 031083
Reid N J *BSc* 081083
Chitty C C M *MA* 010284
Haddock N J R *BA* 010284
Gladstone J R E *BA* 040284
Gordon J H 060284
Caton R W *MA* 200384
Vyvyan-Robinson J C 100684
Davies-Scourfield N G *MA* 010884
Ramsbotham J D A *BA* 010884
Carter N P 081084
Cunliffe J R 081084
Homer D St J 081084
Molesworth-St Aubyn W 090685
Roberts P P L *BA* 250885
Morgan-Grenville R T 071085
Plastow J I S 071085
Dawson R J H 040286
Luckhurst P 040286

Lieutenants

Winser R P (*A/Capt* 051184) 081281
Taylor W T *BA* 120482
Worsley A E H (*A/Capt* 230386) 120482
Winsloe M R (*A/Capt* 010385) 090882
Emck T H *BA* 110483
Schute J C C (*A/Capt* 050584) 080883
Bedford S E R 090484
Mangham M D W *BA(CombHons)* 090484
Wrightson G D G 060885

2nd Lieutenants

††Adams M J *BA(Hons)* 030982
††Constant R A M 020983
††Bryson J R B 230984
††Doran M J 101084
Trustram Eve N D P 130485
††Maciejewski J C W 240985
Cornell M R D 141285

Quartermasters

Hill B 010478
Maj 010479
Taylor W J *MBE* 010478
Maj 300882
Chapman L A 010479
Maj 101184
Conway D R *Capt* 010482
Hunt D *Capt* 010482
Bradford A E *Capt* 010483
Gray K *Capt* 010483
Lacey A B *Capt* 230884
Hill M P B *Capt* 010485
Stanger R E *Capt* 010485

Special Regular Officers

Captains

Bright E *MM* 010482

Lieutenants

Bowden J N G (*A/Capt* 160385) 120482

Short Service Officers

Captains

Nicholson D 011184
Evans G N 250285
Thompson R P R *LLB* 030385
Harwood C S P *BA* 030985
Potter K G 160985
Trower L R *MBE* 020186
Casey W J 200186
Crook P A J 170286

Lieutenants

Byrne T P 140182
Gleeson M F 150682
Foucar A C 090882
Fortune R F 080982
Condon J J 010183
McGarrigle M J 290183
Hibbert S J *BA* (*A/Capt* 140386) 110483
Hudson S D *BA* 110483
Day S C (*A/Capt* 221185) 080883
Butler E A *BA* 090484

Drax C R *LLB*	090484
Evelegh E J (*A/Capt* 021285)	090484
Moberly J P	090484
Whiteside M C *BSc FRICS*	090484
Maxwell A J C *BA*	200784
Purvis A J H *BA*	070884
Shipton W K	070884
Balls P J A	111284
Smith P R J	090485
Buxton R A	060885
Eadie P A	061085
Hunter C S P *BA*	141285
Mackie A A	070486
Watson A W	070486

2nd Lieutenants

Newall R I N	040884
Chaplin R H M	081284
Cooper W J R	081284
Murray Threipland T L	081284
Gard J W	130485
Bloomer A L C	100885
Fleming M V	100885
Parker E B	100885
†Carter C C P	060985
†Daniel R J A *BA*	060985
†Downing N A *BA*	060985
†Ingham S E C *BA*	060985
†Normand A J C *BA*	060985
†Salwey R P *BSc*	060985
†Stewart-Wilson A J O *BSc*	060985
†Watson E T *BSc(Hons)*	060985
Thicknesse R T	141285
†Black J J *BSc*	060186

THE PARACHUTE REGIMENT

Upon a spread of wings, an open parachute: above the Royal Crest

"Utrinque Paratus"

The Second World War— **Bruneval, Normandy Landing,** Pegasus Bridge, Merville Battery, **Breville,** Dives Crossing, La Touques Crossing, **Arnhem 1944,** Ourthe, **Rhine, Southern France,** North-West Europe 1942, 44-45, Soudia, **Oudna,** Djebel Azzag 1943, Djebel Alliliga, El Hadjeba, **Tamera,** Djebel Dahra, Kef el Debna, North Africa 1942-43, **Primosole Bridge,** Sicily 1943, Taranto, Orsogna, Italy 1943-44, **Athens,** Greece 1944-45

Goose Green, Mount Longdon, Wireless Ridge, **Falkland Islands 1982**

Regimental Marches

Quick March..Ride of The Valkyries
Slow March..Pomp and Circumstance

Agents..Holts Branch, Royal Bank of Scotland PLC, Lawrie House, Farnborough, Hants

Regimental Headquarters.....................Browning Barracks, Aldershot, Hants (*Tel No:* 0252-24431 *Ext:* 643/642 (Montgomery))

Alliance

Australian Military Forces....................8th/9th Battalion, The Royal Australian Regiment

Colonel in Chief....................................*HRH The Prince of* Wales *KG KT GCB AK QSO ADC*

Colonel Commandant ....Gen *Sir* Geoffrey Howlett *KBE MC*....................311283

Deputy Colonel Commandant.............Lt Gen *Sir* Michael Gray *KCB OBE*....................211285

Regimental Colonel..............................Col E A J Gardener

Brigadiers

Morton P S *OBE* psc jsdc	300684
Bowden C J *OBE* jssc psc	300685

Colonels

Southerst R G ndc psc	300680
Farrell G D *MBE* sq	300682
Beaumont P M *MBE* psc	300683
Brierley G J *OBE MBIM* psc osc(GH) osc(US)	300683
Coates K psc	300683
Charles D M G psc	300684
Gardener E A J ndc psc osc(NIG)	300684
Benjamin M A *BA* psc†	300685
Chaundler D R *OBE* psc†	300685
Pike H W R *DSO MBE* odc(US) psc	300685
Smith R A *OBE QGM* psc	300685

Lieutenant Colonels

Jenkins R J (SL) *MBE* psc(a)	300672
Ashley E (SL) psc	300674
Orr J A (SL) *OBE* psc	300677
Wood P E *MBE* ndc sq	300678
Loden E C *MC* psc	300680
Jackson M D *MBE BSocSc* ndc psc	300681
McLeod I *OBE MC* ndc psc† (*A/Col* 061285)	300681
Tudor M *MBE*	300681
McGregor J A *MC* psc	300682
Winter J Q *LVO* psc	300682
Hill S A S psc	300683
Parker D C psc†	300683
Roberts D L *MBE* psc	300683
Stratton M *OBE* ndc psc	300683
Clark A H psc	300684
Farrar-Hockley C D *MC* psc	300684
Keeble C P B *DSO* sq jsdc	300684
Patton R C sq	300684
Marsh T A *MA* psc†	300685
Miller R P *BA* sq	300685
Reith J G psc	300685

Majors

Butterworth P J sq	310766
Porter-Wright J sq	300668
Higginbottom D L *BA* sq	300674
Brinton R C J *MBE* sq	311274
Conn W P *MBIM* sq aic (*A/Lt Col* 040286)	300675
Nicholls M A G sq	300676
Milton R R P sq aic	300677
Chapman I L sq	311277
Hanmer D N F sq	300678
Hodgson B B psc†	311278
Martin B K *BSSc* psc	311278
Crosland J H *MC* sq	311279
Gullan P H *MBE MC*	311279
Hoyle R M *BA* psc	311279
Osborne H M sq	311279
Argue M H *MBE MC* sq (*L/Lt Col* 080684)	300980
Campbell D J psc aic	300980
Collett D A *MC* sq ph	300980
Davidson M A *MBE* psc(AUS)	300980
Dennison P E sq	300980
Mackay D G *DipEd AIPM MBIM MInstAM MISM MITD*	300980
Neame P sq	300980
Poynter D G	300980
Rolfe-Smith B P S psc	300980
Rowlatt M H	300980
Smith T H P aic	300980
Snook A W psc	300980
Llewellin R D psc†	300981
Easton J H psc	300982
Poraj-Wilczynski J J P	300982
Pullinger J R W psc	300982
Riddell A J	300982
Burls T W *MC* psc	300983
Davies G G	300983
Fletcher H M *LLB* psc	300983
Gallagher J C *BSc* psc(a)†	300983
Hicks C F psc	300983
Houghton M G psc	300983
Keenan D H	300983
Kershaw R J *BA(Hons)* psc(GE) (*L/Lt Col* 021285)	300983
Mallett K *MBE*	300983
Robertson D W	300983
Trigger R W *MBE* psc	300983
Arthur R R psc	300984
Freer A R psc	300984
Ibbotson J R *BA*	300984
Kennett A W J	300984
Lewis T K	300984
Martin J R	300984
Russell P S *BSc* psc	300984
Butler P R	300985
Carruthers H G	300985
Gandell M P psc	300985
Malkin A V I	300985
McFall G J J psc	300985
Pape J S aic	300985

Captains

Gash R H *BSc*	090279
Edwards W T	080379
Farrar P R *BSc*	170379
Benest D G *BA CGIA*	100979
Akister P G	090980
Barry S J	090980
Davidson I R D ph (*A/Maj* 070285)	090980
Mason A J (*A/Maj* 310784)	090980
Parkinson D C	090980
Hollins P D T (*A/Maj* 230985)	291280
Ford M J	060481
James J G *BA*	090581
Young J A *BSc(Eng)*	010881
Baird J N *BSc*	290981
Mackay H E	281281
Connor C S *MC BA*	150882
Worsley-Tonks M S H	060982
Finch C J *BA PGCE*	280982
Ketley P A (*A/Maj* 060985)	070283
Pearson M C	070283
Smedley R F V	110683
Chapman C *BA*	270983
Fletcher H M *LLB*	031083
Shaw J D *BA*	031083
Mason A D	081083
Leigh D M	111183
Robertson A B	021283
Smith I W	060284

Page J D *BA*	040384
Ramirez M R R *BA*	270884
Kennett A C P *BA*	021084
Baillon R J F	081084
Handford J D	081084
Holt R J	081084
Buckley W H *BA*	011184
Lister T P H	050285
Limb D M *MBE BA*	280285
Orpen-Smellie G R	071085
Ward A L	071085
Willis C G *BA*	131285
Marshall S W ph	040286
Greeves P D	180286

Lieutenants

Cooper D A	090882
Weighell G R (*A/Capt* 170585)	101182
Barrett J M (*A/Capt* 230885)	131282
Wallis G (*A/Capt* 060985)	131282
Chesterton G L *BA*	110483
Coe M A (*A/Capt* 181185)	110483
O'Neil M C (*A/Capt* 130985)	110483
Reilly T B T *BA*	110483
Waddington C C	110483
Needham-Bennett C P A (*A/Capt* 151185)	080883
Lowe M P *BA*	090484
Lorimer J G	111284
Chiswell J R	090485

2nd Lieutenants

††Stankovic M R V	030982
††Wilson A P F *LLB*	030982
Thomson R J	040884
Boyns C R	090984
Turpie P	251084
†Clayton-Jolly F B	060985
††Williams R J E	240985
††Haslam S W	091085
Sutton C M G	141285
†Dowie A L *BSc*	060186
†Grant M P *LLB DipLP*	060186
†James S J F *LLB*	060186

Staff Quartermasters

Williams J S *MBE DCM MBIM*		010474
	Lt Col	241285

Quartermasters

Geraghty P A *MBE BEM*		010477
	Maj	010282
Menzies N E *MBE*		010478
	Maj	190784
Godwin T	*Capt*	010479
Collier A J	*Capt*	010480
Henderson J A	*Capt*	010480
Brown G		010481
	Maj	110883
Lewis R	*Capt*	010482
Middleton T B	*Capt*	010482
Bell G	*Capt*	010483
Smith M L *MBE*	*Capt*	010483
Ashbridge L	*Capt*	010484
Simpson M *MBE*	*Capt*	010684
Wilson J J	*Capt*	010485

Directors of Music

Maycock R E W	*Capt*	160885

Special Regular Officers

Majors

Condie W T *DCM*	300679
O'Hara G *MBE*	300980
Andrews B	300983
Schwartz Von Megyesi T P C	300984
Churchouse J E	300985
Jenner R D	300985

Captains

Starkey E A B	281281
Adams P G	010883
Heslop R G (*A/Maj* 130984)	010484
Kennedy P	070685
Edlin K	011185

Short Service Officers

Captains

Munn M	020976
Carruthers J G	151081
Goldspink R I	161181
McVitie A	070182
Holborn J D (*A/Maj* 010784)	240182
Fox C	160382
Allen D M	040882
Seale M J *BEM* (*L/Maj* 041282)	010483
West A N *BEM* (*A/Maj* 130285)	010484
Harvey T *BEM*	010685
Newbould F C	310885
Oates M R *BSc*	071085
Reid R J A *BA AIL*	071085
Knox R	071185
Vaughan H L G	190386

Lieutenants

Angus N C *BEM* (*A/Capt* 010784)	010182
Burke S J *BSc(Econ)*	120482
Griffin C W *BSc*	120482
Hutton N A *BSc*	120482
Bell T A (*A/Capt* 080285)	080782
Copson P F	041182
Seekings K V (*A/Capt* 040585)	041182
Fairbairn J R *BEM* (*A/Capt* 011285)	301182
Aitken A *BSc*	110483
Merry D M	120483
Powles B (*A/Capt* 081285)	150583
Turnbull W C (*A/Capt* 181185)	180583
Farr J A	010683
Etherington M R *BA*	080883
Bolus D B (*A/Capt* 220186)	121283
Clucas M R	121283
Bashall J I *BA*	090484
Crawley I *BSc*	090484
Eaton R H	090484
Eland D J *BA*	090484
Birtles S D *BA*	070884
Marnoch A *MA*	070884
Snowball C H	070884
Wilford J G	111284
Bennett N J	070486
Davies D A	070486

2nd Lieutenants

Dobson S P J	040884
James H M	040884
Hannon A D	100885
Matthews P J	100885
†Faulkner D E *LLB(Hons)*	060985
†Warner D M *BA(Hons)*	060985
Gladston P C	141285
†Charlton A *BA*	060186
†Harrison-Pope M A W *BSc*	060186
†Stratta A M *BSc*	060186
†Waugh O M *LLB*	060186

Short Service Volunteer Officers

Lieutenants

Castle W G	020186

THE BRIGADE OF GURKHAS

Major General .... Maj Gen T A Boam *CBE* 010685
Brigadier .... Brig J H Edwards 020985
Brigade Major .... Maj T J O'Donnell *MBE* 10 GR 080185

Alliances

Australian Military Forces .... The Royal Australian Regiment
Canadian Armed Forces .... Queen's Own Rifles of Canada

2nd KING EDWARD VII's OWN GURKHA RIFLES (THE SIRMOOR RIFLES)

The Plume of the Prince of Wales. The Royal and Imperial Cypher of King Edward VII. Granted a Truncheon for distinguished service at Delhi, 1857.

Bhurtpore, Aliwal, Sobraon, Delhi 1857, Kabul 1879, Kandahar 1880, Afghanistan 1878-80, Tirah, Punjaub Frontier

The Great War— **La Bassee 1914, Festubert 1914-15, Givenchy 1914, Neuve Chappelle, Aubers, Loos,** France and Flanders 1914-15, Egypt 1915, **Tigris 1916, Kut-Al-Amara 1917, Baghdad 1915,** Mesopotamia 1916-18, **Persia 1918,** Baluchistan 1918

Afghanistan 1919

The Second World War— **El Alamein,** Mareth, **Akarit,** Djebel el Meida, Enfidaville, **Tunis,** North Africa 1942-43, **Cassino I,** Monastery Hill, Pian di Maggio, **Gothic Line,** Coriano, Poggio San Giovanni, Monte Reggiano, Italy 1944-45, Greece 1944-45, North Malaya, **Jitra,** Central Malaya, Kampar, **Slim River,** Johore, Singapore Island, Malaya 1941-42, **North Arakan, Irrawaddy,** Magwe, Sittang 1945, Point 1433, Arakan Beaches, Myebon, **Tamandu,** Chindits 1943, Burma 1943-45

Affiliated Regiment

The Royal Green Jackets

Allied Regiment of Commonwealth Forces

Royal Brunei Armed Forces

Regimental Marches

Quick March .... Lutzow's Wild Hunt
Slow March .... God Bless The Prince of Wales

Agents .... Holts Branch, Royal Bank of Scotland PLC, Lawrie House, Farnborough, Hants

Colonel in Chief .... *HRH The Prince of* Wales *KG KT GCB AK QSO ADC*

Colonel .... Lt Gen *Sir* John Chapple *KCB CBE* 020185

Brigadiers

Duffell P R *OBE MC* psc 300683

Colonels

Smith M J psc osc(US) (*L/Brig* 200682) 300681
Jackman B C *OBE MC* psc(a) 300685

Lieutenant Colonels

Rose H (SL) psc 300674
Lalbahadur Pun *OBE MC* psc 300680
Little P A *MA* ndc psc jsdc (*A/Col* 020486) 300680
Beauchamp V J ndc psc (*A/Col* 060985) 300681
Haynes N M *MBE* psc 300682
Scotson F D psc 300682
Brewer J S *MBE* sq 300684
Venning R M psc 300685

Majors

Ward C J R C psc 300670
Burlison J J sq (*L/Lt Col* 141084) 300673
Smart J B (*L/Lt Col* 250282) 300676
Fraser C N sq 311276
Covernton P L G sq 300678
Gates H S psc† 311279
McNeil A psc† 311279
Rambahadur Gurung 311279
Davidson C J L sq 300980
Kaye J W sq 300980
Lavender C P psc 300981
Attwood T 300982
Harrop J R 300982
Shakespear J N W *BA* 300982
Shuttlewood W F psc 300982
Coleman R H 300983
Ormsby R M C 300983
Bejoy Moktan 300984

Captains

Wylie-Carrick N D 090379
Hinton N J H *BA* 100979
Rae I F *LLB* (*A/Maj* 120984) 021080
Richford J M 291280
Sessions S L 291280
Crane S D *MA* 280982
Duncan A J 081083
Haines C G *BSc(Eng)* 081083
Barber R A H *BSc* 291183
Clesham B P 080684
Bowman J D L 071085

Lieutenants

Kendall C J V (*A/Capt* 151185) 081281
Blackwell N G M *BA* 120482
Forman M L R (*A/Capt* 141284) 090882
Haskard J D S 090484
Rigden I A 070884
Ranson M 111284
Bowring P J 060785

2nd Lieutenants

††Lawrence J C 020983
††Dawson J C 081084

Quartermasters

Cox R C B *MBIM* 010473
Lt Col 250983
Peacock L *Capt* 010482

Directors of Music

Parker R J *FTCL ARCM* psm 071177
Maj 071185

Special Regular Officers

Majors

Yambahadur Gurung	300983
Rogers A J B	300984

Captains

Bhakta Bahadur Gurung	210774

Short Service Officers

Captains

Bergin A	150486

Lieutenants

Lacey G J (*L/Capt* 200585)	040782
Rawlinson T S *BA*	110483
Kennedy A C C	070486

2nd Lieutenants

Mitchell-Heggs C C B	040884
Scott-Bowden P W	040884
Barton-Smith P C	081284
Howard D C	081284
Maynard J P G	081284
Dunlop B D H	100885
†Lamond J M *BA*	060985
Bulloch R I	141285

Gurkha Commissioned Officers

Majors

Narbu Lama *MBE*	141269

Captains

Kharkabahadur Gurung	011181

Queen's Gurkha Officers

Majors

Lalbahadur Thapa *MVO*	010684
Yembahadur Thapa	150684
Dikbahadur Rai	290385
Kishansing Gurung	010485
Debbahadur Pun	051185
Chandrabahadur Pun *MVO*	081185

Captains

Resambahadur Thapa *MM*	291077
Bhokbahadur Gurung	011278
Yambahadur Burathoki	130379
Kajiman Gurung	250379
Rumbahadur Pun	210180
Ganesh Gurung	111080
Jaibahadur Gurung	051280
Ranbahadur Gurung	180381
Danbahadur Burathoki	250381
Ramprasad Pun *MM*	041181
Manbahadur Gurung	181181
Lachhiman Thapa	191181
Debiparsad Ghale	141281
Takbahadur Thapa	300182
Belbahadur Gurung	230482
Haribahadur Gurung	240482
Dhaniram Thapa	141282
Karnabahadur Roka *BEM*	300583
Satyabahadur Pun	031283
Dalbahadur Rana	231283
Manbahadur Gurung	100284
Toranbahadur Gurung	120584
Indraprasad Gurung *BEM*	020684
Narbahadur Thapa	210984
Khembahadur Thapa *BEM*	131184
Karnabahadur Gurung	201184
Jangbahadur Rana	160485
Chhetraman Thakali	100785
Sirbahadur Thapa	230785
Dalbahadur Pun	010985
Shriparsad Gurung	051185
Kharkasing Pun	061185
Meghbahadur Gurung	071185
Gobind Gurung	081185

Lieutenants

Khilbahadur Thapa	170480
Utimbahadur Gurung	040181
Guptabahadur Gurung	260381
Jaibahadur Gurung	010581
Ekbahadur Ale	011181
Lalbahadur Rana	111181
Ajiman Gurung *BEM*	300182
Bhupalsing Thapa	130382
Netrabahadur Gurung	230482
Buddhakumar Gurung *BEM*	020682
Indrabahadur Gurung	301182
Magankumar Chhetri *BEM*	301182
Tambahadur Pun	011282
Benbahadur Rana	081282
Krishnabahadur Rana	101282
Ramprasad Pun	111282
Gokarna Thapa	121282
Bhimbahadur Pun	180383
Bharatsingh Chhetri	230383
Narbahadur Thapa	010583
Tilbahadur Chhetri	300583
Kumbahadur Gurung	120883
Lyangsong Lepcha	011183
Bhisansing Gurung	021283
Bajirman Gurung	031283
Dhanbahadur Gurung	061283
Prembahadur Gurung	061283
Yambahadur Gurung	091283
Hirabahadur Chhetri	231283
Krishnabahadur Gurung	100284
Surjabahadur Gurung	200484
Yeknarin Gurung	150584
Kumar Thapa	170884
Dipakkamal Chhetri	191084
Lalbahadur Gurung	201084
Lalbahadur Gurung	211084
Maitalal Gurung	131184
Chandrakumar Basnet *BEM*	011284
Deobahadur Rana	071284
Lalbahadur Pun	081284
Krishnakumar Ale *BEM*	091284
Manbahadur Gurung	190485
Lachhimiparsad Gurung *BEM*	130685
Bombahadur Thapa *BEM*	100785
Krishnajang Shah	230785
Prabin Gurung	270985
Ramkaji Gurung	051185
Hirasing Rana	071185
Hombahadur Gurung	081185

6th QUEEN ELIZABETH'S OWN GURKHA RIFLES

Two Kukris in saltire, thereunder the figure 6, the whole ensigned with the Crown, all in silver.

Burma 1885-87

The Great War—
Helles, Krithia, Suvla, Sari Bair, Gallipoli 1915, Suez Canal, Egypt 1915-16, Khan Baghdadi, Mesopotamia 1916-18, Persia 1918, North-West Frontier, India 1915

Afghanistan 1919

The Second World War— Coriano, Santarcangelo, **Monte Chicco,** Lamone Crossing, Senio Floodbank, **Medicina,** Gaiana Crossing, **Italy 1944-45,** Shwebo, **Kyaukmyaung Bridgehead, Mandalay, Fort Duffiren,** Maymyo, **Rangoon Road,** Toungoo, **Sittang 1945, Chindits 1944, Burma 1944-45**

Regimental March

Pipes
Quick March..Queen Elizabeth's Own

Regimental Band
Quick March..Young May Moon

Agents..Holts Branch, Royal Bank of Scotland PLC, Lawrie House, Farnborough, Hants

Affiliated Regiments

14th/20th Kings Hussars
The Royal Green Jackets

Colonel..Lt Gen *Sir* Derek Boorman *KCB*..300483

Colonels

Bullock C J D *OBE MC MBIM* psc	300684

Lieutenant Colonels

Pettigrew P D ndc psc†	300680
Whitehead M L psc	300680
Richardson-Aitken R F sq	300683
Anderson J A psc† jsdc	300685

Majors

Duncan R H	300668
Akalsing Thapa	311271
Whitehead T E K sq ph	300676
Gopalbahadur Gurung *MBE*	311276
Mackinlay J C G psc	311276
Briggs D H M *BSc* psc†	300679
O'Bree B M psc	311279
Davies G L	300980
Underhill P A T	300980
Gouldsbury P P A	300981
Bushell I P	300982
Bhagwansing Thapa	300983
Collett N A *MA* psc	300984

Captains

Groves A S R (*A/Maj* 091085)	180379
Manikumar Rai	030580
Harman M A J	090980
Lys G D	070283
Jarvis D A	100684
Baugh D M *BSc*	120684
Griffith A P M	071085

Lieutenants

Bradly D L *LLB*	110483
Buckeridge J C M (*A/Capt* 080486)	110483
Toyne J D *BA*	090484
Lowe T R	090485

2nd Lieutenants

††O'Keeffe G M	230984
Maclean D N	100885

Special Regular Officers

Lieutenants

Bulbeck D F P	080883
Latter C M	090484

Short Service Officers

Lieutenants

Gibb W M P (*A/Capt* 311085)	090882
Brade J J *BA(Oxon) FRGS*	110483
Grant P M A *BA*	110483

2nd Lieutenants

Stevens N J H	081284
†Thomas I N A *BA*	060985

Queen's Gurkha Officers

Majors

Jaibahadur Gurung *MVO*	210482
Gyanbahadur Gurung	061184
Bhimbahadur Pun	201185

Captains

Purnabahadur Rana	210978
Chintabahadur Gurung *MVO*	020480
Tulbahadur Gurung	300480
Bombahadur Gurung	261180
Tejbahadur Gurung	161181
Birbahadur Gurung	011281
Damberbahdur Shrestha	141281
Lalbahadur Thapa	220383
Sukbahadur Thapa	230383
Tejbahadur Chhetri	240383
Minbahadur Gurung	070284
Narayanbahadur Chhetri	240384
Ramparsad Gurung	300984
Narkaji Gurung	061184
Narbahadur Thapa *BEM*	041284
Taubahadur Gurung	121185
Tekbahadur Gurung	211285
Jagbahadur Gurung	140286
Navinkumar Sahi	150286

Lieutenants

Ganeshbahadur Gurung	161281
Amarbahadur Gurung	171281
Chandraprakash Tamang	101282
Chinbahadur Gurung	111282
Dholbahaur Gurung	310183
Paul Newar	010283
Durgabahadur Gurung	220383
Kamalbahadur Gurung	030583
Kharkaman Gurung	291183
Gumansing Rana	070284
Nandabahadur Thapa	210284
Dhankumar Chhetri	230384
Udaikumar Pradhan	151084
Jaganparsad Gurung	041284
Premser Lama	030585
Shamsher Thapa	300785
Padambahadur Gurung	190985
Khusiman Gurung	121185
Tobdengyamtso Bhutia	091285
Gangabahadur Gurung	211285

7th DUKE OF EDINBURGH'S OWN GURKHA RIFLES

Two Kukris points upwards the handles crossed in saltire the cutting edges of the blades inwards, between the blades the numeral 7 and ensigned with the Cypher of HRH The Duke of Edinburgh.

The Great War— Suez Canal, **Egypt 1915, Megiddo, Sharon, Palestine 1918,** Shaiba, **Kut al Amara 1915, 17, Ctesiphon, Defence of Kut al Amara, Baghdad, Sharquat, Mesopotamia 1915-18**

Afghanistan 1919

The Second World War— **Tobruk 1942,** North Africa 1942, **Cassino I,** Campriano, **Poggio del Grillo, Tavoleto,** Montebello-Scorticata Ridge, Italy 1944, **Sittang 1942, 45,** Pegu 1942, **Kyaukse 1942,** Shwegyin, **Imphal, Bishenpur, Meiktila,** Capture of Meiktila, Defence of Meiktila, **Rangoon Road,** Pyawbwe, Burma 1942-45

Falkland Islands 1982

Regimental March

Quick March..Old Monmouthshire

Agents..Holts Branch, Royal Bank of Scotland PLC, Lawrie House, Farnborough, Hants

Affiliated Regiments

The Cameronians (Scottish Rifles)
Queen's Own Highlanders (Seaforth and Camerons)

Allied Regiment of Commonwealth Forces

The Pacific Islands Regiment Papua New Guinea

Colonel..Brig J Whitehead *MBE* ret pay..101082

Colonels

Hunt-Davis M G *MBE FBIM* psc psc(CAN) (*L/Brig* 020685) 300684

Lieutenant Colonels

Robinson K G (SL) psc osc(BLD) 300674
Furney M C (SL) psc 300676
Blackford T G psc 300678
Powell-Jones E D *OBE* psc (*L/Col* 210286) 300680
Morgan D P De C *OBE* psc (*A/Col* 091085) 300681
Dawson W J psc 300683
Warren N R St J psc 300684

Majors

McCausland C M 300669
Eyres R C odc(FR) psc osc(FR) 300672
Maniprasad Rai 311272
Willis R L 300673
Stewart A R C sq 300676
Mallal Gurung 311276
Davis W P 300678
Forestier-Walker A D sq aic 311278
Kefford M H *FRGS* psc 311278
Couldrey R C psc jsdc (*A/Lt Col* 250386) 300679
Gay P H sq 300679
Lewis T A J *BA* 300980
Mossop R N C psc 300980
Whitehead R B 071180
Bicket G C 300982
Pearson G C J L psc(CAN) 300982
Willis D R D'A *MA* psc 300983
Hayes D G 300985

Captains

Gouldstone M P H 090581
Price A N *BA* 280982
Spencer C B *BA* 280982
Crowsley S J 070283
Palmer J C 050285

Lieutenants

Holley L A (*A/Capt* 190580) 190582
Redding J P (*A/Capt* 051283) 090882
Oates Q E (*A/Capt* 270885) 131282
Morris T D E 080883
Dewing S J M (*A/Capt* 020985) 121283
O'Leary T D P 090484
Smith G R *BA* 090484
Harman D J 060885
Lillingston-Price M M 060885

2nd Lieutenants

††Speakman A G 020983
††McConnell-Wood T I 011084

Quartermasters

Wynne J G 010478
Maj 010882

Special Regular Officers

Majors

Tekbahadur Gurung 300985

Captains

Bijaykumar Rawat 110284

Short Service Officers

Captains

Lupton I C 050984
Bulbeck J W *BA* 030985

Lieutenants

Pritchard R M 070884
Lunn G J 070486
Sanders N D 070486

2nd Lieutenants

Hamlin N D 040884
Robinson J G 081284
†Jones T S *BA(Hons)* 060985

Gurkha Commissioned Officers

Quartermaster

Rambahadur Gurung *MBE BEM* 221175
Maj 300383

Queen's Gurkha Officers

Majors

Rupman Thapa *BEM* 010284
Pratapsing Limbu *MVO* 111284
Kaluman Rai 210685

Captains

Dayaparsad Limbu 170180
Belbahadur Pun 030380
Naraiprasad Rai 070380
Amaraj Rai 160480
Dalbahadur Sunwar 230480
Manbahadur Mall 011180
Gagansing Thapa 241180
Hombahadur Gurung 220481
Bhuwansing Limbu *MVO* 160981
Sankhabahadur Limbu 011181
Belbahadur Rai 121181
Bhagirath Limbu 141181
Harkabahadur Rai 141281
Khagendrabahadur Limbu 150483
Harkabahadur Rai 160483
Dalman Golay 150883
Nandakumar Thapa 021283
Siriprasad Gurung 220584
Chandrakumar Pradhan 020884
Sange Tamang 200984
Tekbahadur Limbu 111084
Bhimbahadur Gurung 111284

The Brigade of Gurkhas — continued

Budhibahadur Rai	210385
Rabichandra Rai	050485
Chambahadur Rai	210685
Dikbahadur Rai	220785
Nainbahadur Thapa	280785
Taraprasad Gurung	150985
Narsing Chhetri	011085
Ashokkumar Thapa	281085
Mahendrasing Thapa	011185
Nayankumar Rai	221185

Lieutenants

Lokbahadur Gurung	140480
Hangsaraj Magar	021280
Tilakchandra Thapa	030481
Manbir Limbu	100481
Basantkumar Rai	150481
Ratnasher Rai	170481
Ranbahadur Rai	160981
Ratnabahadur Gurung	011181
Motibahadur Limbu	121181
Maniparsad Rai	131181
Hariprasad Limbu	141181
Kamalkumar Limbu	151181
Ramsing Limbu	101082
Kritiman Rai	201282
Bishnuprasad Shrestha	310583
Dalbahadur Rai	170683
Bhupalsing Thapa	110983
Kulbahadur Limbu	151183
Damarbahadur Gurung	021283
Indrabahadur Rana	031283
Ombahadur Chhetri *BEM*	150184
Jagandhoj Limbu	020884
Dillikumar Gurung	200984
Jitbahadur Newar	111084
Subhraj Rai	071284
Chhumbetshering Lama *BEM*	081284
Narbu Sherpa *BEM*	111284
Jasbahadur Gurung	210385
Kirtiman Limbu	220385
Moncheong Lepcha	050485
Dhaniram Ghale	270585
Prem Rai	220785
Sherbahadur Limbu	280785
Himal Rai	270985
Shivakumar Limbu	221185

10th PRINCESS MARY'S OWN GURKHA RIFLES

A bugle horn stringed interlaced with a kukri fessewise the blade to the sinister, above the kukri the cypher of HRH the Princess Mary (The Princess Royal) and below it the numeral 10

The Great War– **Helles, Krithia, Suvla, Sari Bair, Gallipoli 1915, Suez Canal, Egypt 1915, Sharquat, Mesopotamia 1916-18**

Afghanistan 1919

The Second World War– Iraq 1941, Deir ez Zor, Syria 1941, **Coriano, Santarcangelo,** Senio Floodbank, **Bologna,** Sillaro Crossing, Gaiana Crossing, Italy 1944-45, Monywa 1942, Imphal, Tuitum, Tamu Road, Shenam Pass, Ltan, Bishenpur, **Tengnoupal, Mandalay, Myinmu Bridgehead,** Kyaukse 1945, **Meiktila,** Capture of Meiktila, Defence of Meiktila, Irrawaddy, **Rangoon Road,** Pegu 1945, Sittang 1945, Burma 1942-45

Regimental March

Quick March..Hundred Pipers

Agents..Holts Branch, Royal Bank of Scotland PLC, Lawrie House, Farnborough, Hants

Affiliated Regiment

The Royal Scots (The Royal Regiment)

Colonel ....Maj Gen G D Johnson *OBE MC* 230285

Brigadiers

Pike C J *DSO OBE* ndc jssc sq 300683

Lieutenant Colonels

Allen M G ndc psc (*A/Col* 300985) 300677
Lees C A *LLB* ndc sq 300679
Cook M T psc 300681
Newton Dunn C T psc 300683
Worthington N R psc 300685

Majors

Cooke P N *GM* 300668
Watt A J J sq 300675
Madankumar Subba 311275
Narendra Kumar Rai 300676
Nima Wangdi Lama 311278
Gregory L S J T psc 300679
O'Donnell T J *MBE BA* sq 311279
Jeffery C E sq 300980
Litherland R psc 300980
Patchett J M 300980
Purves J J *MBE* psc 300982
Lewis R N A 300984
Trueman M J ph 300985

Captains

Roe M T psc (*A/Maj* 040386) 100580
Pearson P T C 080582
Stannard S J *BA* 280383
Glanville G R J 081084
Rowe N D J 050285
Hutchings M R C 090685

Lieutenants

White A J B (*A/Capt* 191284) 110483
Holt T J 060885

2nd Lieutenants

††Warrington T C St J 020983
Wombell C D 100885

Staff Quartermasters

Garman P F 010475
Lt Col 210385

Quartermasters

Buffine J J P *BEM* 010478
Maj 140882

Special Regular Officers

Lieutenants

Hughes G A (*A/Capt* 120785) 081281

Short Service Officers

Lieutenants

Archer S A (*A/Capt* 161184) 081281
Ashford T E 040782
Buckle R C M 220882
Prentice M V G *BA* 090484
Stanford H G W *BCom* 090484
Main Thompson J D 070884

2nd Lieutenants

Austin M H 040884
Corden-Lloyd N C 081284
†Maddox J K M *BA(Hons)* 060985
†Mitchell R V L *LLB* 060985

Gurkha Commissioned Officers

Captains

Karnabahadur Rai *MBE* 231181

Queen's Gurkha Officers

Majors

Manbahadur Rai 290185

Captains

Dhanbahadur Rai 011180
Asbahadur Limbu 041281
Amekmani Rai 210482
Himraj Gurung 310383
Judhabir Rai 220483
Manbahadur Rai 020583
Sukbahadur Rai 060583
Jagatram Rai 070583
Ganeshbahadur Gurung 111083
Deopal Rai 010584
Dendi Sherpa 020584
Angphurba Sherpa 141284
Siriprasad Limbu 120185
Kisnabahadur Rai 290385
Machindrabahadur Rai 050485
Nirbahadur Rai 190885
Harkabahadur Rai 241185
Pasangdhendup Lama *BEM* 070386

Lieutenants

Abiratna Rai 161281
Juktiman Rai 010182
Biswanath Rai 310383
Bhaktabahadur Limbu 220483
Harishanker Rai 020583
Aggaitshering Lepcha 030583
Ramprasad Rai 111083
Sarbahadur Rai 121083
Krishnabahadur Rai 090484
Krishnabahadur Limbu 010584
Padamkumar Limbu 020584
Lakpa Tamang 191084
Narendrakumar Rai 051184
Parsuram Rai 011284
Chandraparsad Limbu 141284
Kharkaparsad Limbu 120185
Tulbahadur Sarki 290385
Suman Limbu 050485
Indrabahadur Rai 051285
Bishnukumar Rai 061285
Ambarbahadur Limbu 071285

THE QUEEN'S GURKHA ENGINEERS

Two kukris points upwards the blades crossed in saltire, their cutting edge outwards, surmounted by the Royal Engineers' grenade, over the handles a scroll with the motto "Ubique". The whole surrounded by a wreath of laurel surmounted by a Queen's crown thereon issuant from the wreath a scroll: The Queen's Gurkha Engineers

Regimental Marches

Pipes
Quick March..Far O'er the Sea

Military Band
Quick March..Wings

Affiliated Corps

Corps of Royal Engineers

Colonel ....Gen *Sir* George Cooper *GCB MC* ret pay 121181

Lieutenant Colonels

Cook P W RE odc(US) psc† 300682

Majors

Stack D J R *BSc(Eng)* RE psc 300678
Walker D A *BSc(Eng)* RE psc† 300982
Wheeley J F RE psc 300983
Eagan S M R RE 300984

Captains

Botting M I RAPC 230382
Wright I D *BEd* RE 090882
Harking A D *BSc(Eng)* RE 070283
Souter A M *BSc(Eng)* RE 070283
Wood C R *BSc* RE 050983
Daniel P M *BSc(Eng)* RE 081084
Cockerill C M *BSc* RE 071085
Freeman M A *BSc* RE 260186

Lieutenants

Moody N C *BSc* RE 110483
Butler G T RE 271283

Quartermasters

Flower D H RE *Capt* 010480
Davies A J *MBE* RE *Capt* 010181

Garrison Engineers (Construction)

Winship D *MBE* RE *Capt* 070480
Cross R J RE *Capt* 301082

Garrison Engineers (Mechanical)

Nicholls R A *MBE* RE *Capt* 220179

Special Regular Officers

Majors

Powney R T *BA MITO* RAEC 191175

Captains

Smith P RE 060284

Short Service Officers

Captains

Francis D C *BSc* RE 140785

Lieutenants

Prowse C J *BSc* RE 080883
Jones D M *BSc* RE 090484

2nd Lieutenants

Hayes A M RE 130485

Queen's Gurkha Officers

Majors

Sunar Gurung *MVO BEM* 100283
Indrakamal Tamang 210584

Captains

Jamansing Rai 060280
Kharkajang Gurung *MVO* 010381
Manikumar Prodhan 020381
Jogindrasing Gurung *MBE* 241181
Bhaktabahadur Gurung 010584
Jahansing Rai 020584
Kharkabahadur Limbu 030584
Milanchandra Gurung 010185
Hukumraj Thapa 020185
Lakpatshering Bhotia 010985
Surjabahadur Thapa 010186

Lieutenants

Haribahadur Thapa 011281
Kumarsing Rai 050382
Durgaprasad Gunung 011282
Birbahadur Limbu 190483
Chitrabahadur Thapa 010783
Motiram Gurung 160484
Manilal Thapa 010984
Dalbahadur Gurung 010585
Dilkumar Limbu 200885
Kulbahadur Tamang *BEM* 221185
Chandrabahudur Gurung 011285

QUEEN'S GURKHA SIGNALS

In front of the figure of Mercury, holding a caduceus in the left hand, on a globe, all in silver, supported in his dexter hand. The Crown in Gold, two kukris in saltire the blades upwards and inwards also in silver, thereunder a scroll inscribed *"Certa Cito"* and below nine laurel leaves.

Regimental March

Quick March..Scotland The Brave

Affiliated Corps

Royal Corps of Signals

Colonel ....Maj Gen R Benbow *CB* 310186

Lieutenant Colonels

Neeve J E, R SIGNALS psc† osc(NIG) 300683

Majors

Thomas W P B, R SIGNALS 311270
Cartwright M J, R SIGNALS sq 300675
Alden M J M, R SIGNALS sq TE 311277
Adams H M *MBE*, R SIGNALS sq 300980
Noble N B RAPC 300980
Richardson T E M, R SIGNALS psc† 300983

Captains

Fletcher J L, R SIGNALS 080981
Crane A P *BSc*, R SIGNALS 010285

Lieutenants

Smith G M *BSc*, R SIGNALS 090882
Wadey T C *BA*, R SIGNALS 090882
Pratt D M *BSc*, R SIGNALS 110483

2nd Lieutenants

Jones T M, R SIGNALS 141285

Quartermasters

Simpson A J, R SIGNALS 120775
Lt Col 010584

Richardson C H, R SIGNALS 060378
Maj 151179

Technical Officers in Telecommunications

Brown D *MBE*, R SIGNALS 010974
Maj 050682
Tanner L, R SIGNALS
Capt 300985

Traffic Officers

Price R D, R SIGNALS 130677
Maj 130685

Special Regular Officers

Majors

Pilley D V *LRAM* RAEC 030377

Short Service Officers

Lieutenants

Davis E A *LLB(Hons)*, R SIGNALS 110483

Gurkha Commissioned Officers

Captains

Balbahadur Gurung *MVO* 310382

Queen's Gurkha Officers

Majors

Chandru Rai 221185
Shyambahadur Pun 221185

Captains

Girbahadur Rana 271180
Meherman Limbu 210482
Dilbahadur Rai 290482
Krishnakumar Thapa 011282
Balkrishna Rai *BEM* 250383
Indrabahadur Adhikari 021283
Lilbahadur Gurung 270484
Gambahadur Buduja 221185
Pirthibahadur Gurung 231185

Lieutenants

Santabahadur Gurung 031181
Ratnabahadur Pun 290182
Santoshkumar Rai 130382
Narain Rai 210482
Narbahadur Pun 290482
Madankumar Gurung 011282
Narbahadur Gurung 250383
Dinakar Mall 061283
Chandrakumar Shakya 010184
Dilkaji Gurung 240284
Khimpratap Mall 250284
Mohanbahadur Thapa 270484
Ratnaman Pradhan 270784
Rambahadur Gurung 150884
Tekbahadur Gurung 050485
Chaubahadur Gurung 221185

GURKHA TRANSPORT REGIMENT

On the eight-pointed Star in silver a Scroll inscribed *"Gurkha Transport Regiment"*. Issuant therefrom a wreath of laurel all in gold over all two kukris in saltire also in silver handled gold ensigned with the Royal Cypher also in gold.

Regimental March

Quick March..Wait for the Wagon

Affiliated Corps

Royal Corps of Transp

Colonel ....Brig R M Llewellyn *OBE*..010284

Lieutenant Colonels

Winarick M J RCT psc 300684

Majors

Hale J C RCT t 311272
Smetham A J M RCT osc(MAL) sq 300677
Clough J H *BSc(Eng)* RCT 300984
Marvin E W RCT 300985

Captains

Alberry P E RCT 060284
Brown P J RCT 090685
Searles T E D RCT 040286
Woodman T G W RCT 040286

Lieutenants

Copeland I M RCT 081281
Alexander I C RCT (*A/Capt* 080385) 090882
Cook D E RCT 090882
Morgan N D RCT 090882
Little M R RCT 080883

Quartermasters

Owens R *BEM* RCT 280279
Maj 010484
Chadwick M RCT *Capt* 110681
Stocks R D *AMInstTA* RCT *Capt* 121285

Special Regular Officers

Lieutenants

Randall P C RCT 131282

Short Service Officers

Lieutenants

Mayo D J RCT 121283

Gurkha Commissioned Officers

Captains

Balkrishna Rana 011181

Queen's Gurkha Officers

Majors

Yambahadur Khan *MVO* 111282

Captains

Dipakbahadur Gurung *MVO* 080476
Motiparsad Ale 241176
Sukbahadur Pun 151279
Pembadorje Sherpa 090480
Jasbahadur Gurung 031280
Partapsing Gurung *MBE* 111282
Yemprasad Gurung 300383
Pembawangdi Lama 160984
Mekbahadur Gurung 141284
Tejbahadur Gurung 151284
Ramprasad Gurung 280585

Lieutenants

Girmansing Rana 041281
Harkabahadur Pun 111282
Kajiman Limbu 300383
Tenduptshering Lama 181084
Krishnabahadur Newar 141284
Balasing Gurung 151284
Manbahadur Limbu 280585

231

SPECIAL AIR SERVICE REGIMENT

A winged dagger striking downwards with the motto "Who Dares Wins"

The Second World War— **North-West Europe 1944-45, Tobruk 1941, Benghazi Raid, North Africa 1940-43, Landing in Sicily,** Sicily 1943, Termoli, Valli Di Comacchio, Italy 1943-45, Greece 1944-45, Adriatic, Middle East 1943-44

Falkland Islands 1982

Regimental March

Quick March..March du Regiment Parachutist Belge

Alliances

Australian Military Forces....................The Special Air Service Regiment
New Zealand Army..............................1st New Zealand Special Air Service Squadron

ARMY AIR CORPS

A laurel wreath surmounted by The Crown: within the wreath, an eagle

Regimental Marches

Quick March..Recce Flight
Slow March..Thievish Magpie/Doges March

Agents..Lloyds Bank PLC Cox's & King's Branch
Corps Depot..Army Air Corps Centre, Middle Wallop, Nr. Stockbridge, Hants
(nearest railway station Andover Junction)
(*Tel No:* 0264-62121)

Alliance

Australian Military Forces....................No 16 Army Light Aircraft Squadron

Colonel Commandant..........................Gen *Sir* Martin Farndale *KCB*..010180

Brigadiers

Volkers M R *OBE* rcds psc ph(cfs) pl 300682
Canterbury D E *MRAeS* psc(a)† psc ph 300684

Colonels

Eccles R G sq ph(cfs) ph(i) pl 300683
Everett-Heath E J *MRAeS* psc pl(i) ph pl 300683
Hathaway K J *OBE* psc(a) ph 300683
Lytle S W St J psc† ph 300684
Robson K S psc ph 300684
Abbott R J *MBE* osc(NIG) sq ph 300685
Ralls D J *OBE DFC* psc ph 300685

Lieutenant Colonels

Legg P F (SL) *MC* pl(cfs) ph(i) pl(i) pl 300672
Corner A C (SL) *MRAeS FBIM* ph(cfs) ph(i) ph pl 300673
Edgecombe G J B (SL) *AFC* ph(cfs) ph(i) ph pl 300673
Williams H D (SL) ph(i) ph pl tp 300674
Canning R sq ph 300675
Swan D W A (SL) psc ph pl 300675
Deakin M F (SL) odc(US) sq ph 300676
Andrews M F psc† ph 300679
Harrison P G ndc psc† ph 300679
Mallock G R *AFC* psc ph(i) 300679
McMeekin G B *BA* psc ph 300680
Orwin M A psc(a)† osc(NIG) ph 300680
Tait E C psc† ph 300680
Fox D W *MBE MC MRAeS* psc† ph 300681
Pickup C J *OBE* psc† ph 311281
Moss W J H *MBE* psc ph 300682
Nathan S R psc ph 300682
Orde J R psc ph(i) ph 300682
Esson F J M psc ph(cfs) ph(i) ph 300683
Walker M R psc(a)† ph 300683
Cranston D A psc† ph 300684
Hyde-Smith C S psc ph(i) ph 300684
Reid K E *MRAeS* ph(cfs*) ph(i) ph tp 300684
Wilson D J *MBE* psc ph 300684
Hughes J C M *MBE* psc† ph 300685
McQueen P D P psc ph 300685
Perry M A psc ph(cfs) ph(i) ph 300685
Sharp D G *AFC* odc(US) sq ph 300685
Steward W *DipRMCS* gw ph pl tp 300685

Majors

Mason D J sq ph pl 090264
Wastie C F L sq ph pl 311267
Holtom A C S *AFC* ph(cfs) ph 300668
Wheeler J H sq ph(cfs) ph(i) ph 300668
Little M G psc† ph 300672
Cox B J ph(cfs) ph(i) ph 311272
Payne N G A sq ph(i) ph 311272
Pettigrew S W G *BSc* psc† ph 311274
Jerrard A C ph(cfs) ph(i) ph 300675
Castlemaine *The Lord MBE* psc ph(cfs) ph 311275
Prentis P M sq ph 300676
Wood P L W psc ph(i) ph 311276
Smith-Rewse C B sq ph 300677
Baynes R C K *MBE* sq ph 311277
Morley D G V sq ph(cfs) ph 311277
Wawn F M sq ph(cfs) ph(i) ph 300678
McMahon W A psc† ph pl 311278
Middleditch J E sq ph 311278
Blount C ph(cfs) ph(i) ph 300679
Denley J ph(i) ph 300679
Fogden S N L *BSc(Eng)* psc† ph 300679
Hall N S C *MBE* sq ph 300679
Sibun C S psc(IT) sq ph 300679
Skinner D J ph 300679
White I P pl(i) ph pl 300679
Gick A P ph 300980
Goodsir J *MBE* ph 300980
Hewetson M J T ph(i) ph 300980
Lees A W *BA* psc ph 300980
Scott-Hopkins R M sq ph 300980
Buck M S ph 300981
Burdett W F *BSc* psc(a)† ph 300981
O'Donoghue M psc† ph(cfs) ph(i) ph 300981
Schofield M psc ph 300981
Stirk W J Q sq ph(i) ph 300981
Thursby N D D ph 300981
Andrews R M *BSc* psc† ph 300982
Bourne J A ph 300982
Southgate R L *AFM* ph 300982
Stubington M psc ph 300982
Webb M D ph(i) 300982
Wilton C J A ph 300982
Leslie J psc(PAK) ph 300983
Parker N P ph 300983
Westcott A psc† ph 300983
Joyce D K psc ph 300984
Lawrence C ph 300984
Munro R M ph 300984
Sinclair-Kemp B psc ph 300984
Cranston K D psc† ph 300985
Gibson A M ph 300985
Husband D *BSc* ph 300985
Norrie D J ph 300985
Simkins A J N ph 300985
Webb A K *BSc AMRAeS* ph tp 300985
Welsh I M ph 300985

Captains

Twist R W *BA* ph 280878
Miller G D ph 080379
Webb-Bowen R I ph 080379
Slessor A J R *BA* ph 010879
Adams P G ph(i) ph (*A/Maj* 200484) 100979
Bourne A P ph 100979
Rowland-Jones S D ph 301279
Thorpe R W ph 301279
Walch C W ph (*A/Maj* 250385) 110280
Coward G R ph 090980
Emmerson K M ph 090980
Greenhalgh J G *DFC* ph 090980
Whitfield P G ph 090980
Pople K R *BSc* ph 021080
Maclaine D C ph 291280
Folkes R P D *BA* ph 010281
Mackie I D ph 060381
Fitzpatrick E W H ph(cfs) ph 160381
McDonnell J M P ph 090581
Roberts P C ph 090581
Edwards P A W ph 080981
Wright P J ph 080582
Hogan C D ph 060982
Oatts A R B ph 060982
Lawless P ph 180283
Caplin N J *BSc* ph 040683
Manning C W ph 110683
Sivewright W J ph 110683
Goble T J L *MA* ph 100883
Tanner S R S ph 081083
Parish J B *BA* ph 010284
Baulf C H G ph 060284
Rutter J W ph 060284
Thomson I R ph 060284
Sheeley G J ph 090584
Aungiers R G ph 100684
Winser J P ph 100684

Lieutenants

Hindley R J W *BSc* ph 120482
Sharpe A P *BSc ARCS* ph 110483
Spink G E *BSc* 080883
Wiley A G C *BSc* ph 080883
Daly J H ph 090485

2nd Lieutenants

††Meeks G P	230984
Houlton A V	130485
Taylor J E S	100885
††Enticknap D	240985
††Illingworth J T E	240985
††Sexton N D	240985

Quartermasters

Barnham R C		251174
	Maj	251182
Valler D		010377
	Maj	010385
Wilkinson V	*Capt*	061078
Anderson E M	*Capt*	030879
Taylor B J	*Capt*	160181
Cross J R *MInstAM MISM MASMC*	*Capt*	161181
Skingley R	*Capt*	020185
Moore A N	*Capt*	011285
Rowe R R	*Capt*	011285
Joicey R A	*Capt*	030386

Technical Aviation Instructors

Overy N C ph(cfs) ph(i) ph pl		011174
	Lt Col	211084
Markham A *AFC* ph(cfs)		100677
	Maj	100685
Duncan J S ph(cfs) ph		010180
	Maj	141281
Patterson D I *AFC* ph(cfs)	*Capt*	050181
Wiles A G *AFC* ph(cfs) ph	*Maj*	011082
Cornall I L *AFC* ph(i) pl(i) ph pl	*Maj*	011083
Morrish P ph(cfs)		010484
	Maj	010584
Bailey K V ph(cfs) ph	*Maj*	011084
Stockley P J *AFC* ph(cfs)	*Capt*	011285

Special Regular Officers

Majors

Law N J *AFC* ph pl	311274
Stafford G W *MBE* ph	300981
Wilson P M *MBE* ph(cfs) ph(i) ph pl	300981
Murray-Twinn S *AFC* ph(cfs) ph(i)	300982
Drennan S M *DFC* ph(i) ph	300983
Gater-Smith H ph(i) ph	300984
Hayhurst A J ph(i) ph tp	300984
Lawes R J ph	300984
Taylor-Roberts A B ph	300984
Board B R ph(cfs) ph(i) ph	300985
Hartley R ph(cfs)	300985
Slade S W ph(cfs) ph(i)	300985

Captains

Kennard J L ph	050376
Taylor P J *MBE* ph	310776
Byrne I B ph	070280
Mace T K C *BSc(Eng)* ph	010880
Welch S N *BSc* ph	040980
Tracy R H ph	161181
Wilson J C ph	080582
Northam H C ph(cfs) ph(i) ph	060982
Wilson C S *BEM* ph(cfs) ph (*A/Maj* 250784)	050183
Woods D R C ph(i) ph	050183
Lay J D *AFC* ph(cfs) ph	090383
Ryan J N ph(cfs*) ph(i) ph	310383
Hogg J R M ph pl	060284
Fagg D A ph	170885
Dawson N H ph	010186
Floyd H A ph	280386

Lieutenants

Holland G R N *BA* ph	040881
Morgan D A J ph	070486

2nd Lieutenants

Walker D A	141285

Short Service Officers

Captains

Finch V G E	011282
Young G L ph(i) ph	020983
Wordie A J K *BSc* ph	050983
Barratt P ph(i) ph	180285
Manklow P D ph	180385
Ball E N M ph(cfs) ph(i) ph	020985
Collett C *MA* ph	040286

Lieutenants

Tinker D A ph (*A/Capt* 030785)	051281
McCorquodale D N B ph	081281
Davies A J ph(cfs) ph(i) ph	010382
Harrison C W ph(i) ph (*A/Capt* 141085)	210382
Sapirstein M *BSc* ph	120482
Scotting D ph(cfs) ph (*A/Capt* 221084)	220482
Borrows D A ph(cfs) ph	050582
Jarvill M K ph (*A/Capt* 051184)	050582
McLachlan W K (*A/Capt* 141085)	010682
Marshall W B W	040782
Arbuckle I D *BEM* (*A/Capt* 010186)	010383
Holland A J	020383
King C A S *MISM*	020383
Thayer R J	020383
Burton I R	280383
Ions C J	020483
Presland P J *BEM*	070483
Rowe J A	070483
Ward J	010583
Bell D J (*A/Capt* 181285)	180683
Bell I J ph(i) ph	060783
Blyth J R	060783
Dunscombe C J	060783
Hoal W J ph	060783
Phillips R J	060783
Richie P J ph(i) ph	060783
Millett T D	150783
Haig A J ph	080883
Miley P G *BA* ph	080883
Smith P H *BSc*	080883
Meyer D H *BSc*	090484
Nicholas D A G *BA*	090484
Price J C E ph	090484
Tosh A J *BSc*	090484
Gaukroger P A	270484
Burdett J R *BSc*	070884
Fergusson A *BLE*	070884
Watts N J I ph	111284
Long G F ph	090485
Keith A R K ph	101285

2nd Lieutenants

Geal A ph	040884
Griffiths T Y	081284
King I P	130485
Mason-Smith R	130485
Snell I M	130485
Naylor R E H	100885
†Ford G J *BSc*	060985
Bentley G H J	141285
Hermon P J	141285
Smith W R I	141285
†Crighton S H *BSc*	060186
†Locke D J	060186
†Stevenson H R M	060186
†Whitcombe M J	060186
†Wood W M *LLB DipLP*	060186

ROYAL ARMY CHAPLAINS' DEPARTMENT

Upon a wreath of laurel and oak a Maltese Cross. In the centre a quatrefoil voided with a circle inscribed with the motto *"In this Sign Conquer"*. The whole ensigned with The Crown

For Jewish Chaplains

Upon a wreath of laurel and oak a Star of David. In the centre of the Star, a circle containing a quatrefoil voided. The whole ensigned with The Crown

Regimental Marches

Quick March..Trumpet Voluntary
Slow March...Trumpet Voluntary

Agents..Holts Branch, Royal Bank of Scotland PLC, Lawrie House, Farnborough, Hants

Alliances

The Canadian Armed Forces...............Chaplain Branch
Australian Military Forces....................The Royal Australian Army Chaplains' Department
New Zealand Army...............................Royal New Zealand Chaplains' Department

Chaplains are appointed by the Parliamentary Under-Secretary of State for the Armed Forces, on the nomination of the following accredited representatives of the various denominations, and in their religious ministrations to the troops are under the oversight of these representatives respectively:—

Church of England..The Chaplain-General, Ministry of Defence, Chaplains (Army), *Bagshot Park, Bagshot, Surrey, GU19 5PL*

Jewish..The Secretary, The Jewish Committee for H M Forces, *Woburn House, Upper Woburn Place, WC1H 0EP*

Methodist Church..The Secretary of the Methodist Royal Navy, Army and Royal Air Force Board, *Central Buildings, Westminster, SW1H 9NH*

Presbyterian Churches:—

Church of Scotland......................................The Convener, Committee on Chaplains to H M Forces, *42 Melville St Edinburgh, EH3 7HA*

Free Chuch of Scotland..............................The Representative on the Interdenominational Advisory Committee, *Offices of the Free Church of Scotland, 13 Kingsborough Gdns, Glasgow, Strathclyde, G12 9NH*

Presbyterian Church in Ireland...................The Representative on the Interdenominational Advisory Committee *8 Altnagelvin Park, Londonderry, N Ireland*

Presbyterian Church of Wales....................The Representative on the Interdenominational Advisory Committee *53 Richmond Road, Cardiff, CF2 3UP*

Roman Catholic Church.......................................Roman Catholic Bishop-in-Ordinary to H M Forces, *Bishops Oak 26 The Crescent, Farnborough Park, Farnborough, Hants, GU14 7AS*

United Navy, Army and Air Force Board comprising:—

Baptist

United Reformed Church............................The Secretary of the United Navy, Army and Air Force Board, *3 Hazel Gardens, Edgware, Middlesex, HA8 8PD*

Note:— Chaplains of the Church of Scotland, and the Presbyterian Church in Ireland are distinguished by the letters [C of S], Chaplains of the Free Church of Scotland and Presbyterian Church of Wales by the letter [P], Roman Catholic Chaplains by the letters [RC], Methodist Chaplains by the letter [M], United Board Chaplains by the letters [UB] and Jewish Chaplains by the letter [J].

Chaplains with no distinguishing letter belong to the Church of England

Chaplain General ranking as Major General

The Ven Archdeacon W F Johnston *CB MA QHC*..010780

Deputy Chaplain General ranking as Brigadier

Rev J Harkness *OBE QHC* [C of S]..010185

Principal Roman Catholic Chaplain (Army) ranking as Colonel

Rt Rev Mgr J N Williams..180585

Chaplains to the Forces (1st Class) ranking as Colonels

Pugh *Rev* W B 010882
Robinson *Rev* T H *MA* 010882
Thomas *Rev* J N *BA* 011284
Roblin *Rev* G H *OBE AKC* 010185
McIver *Rev* D T [RC] 180585
Cross *Rev* J S *MA* 021185
Hynd *Rev* R S *BA* [C of S] 060486

Chaplains to the Forces (2nd Class) ranking as Lieutenant Colonels

Wright *Rev* M M *BA* 120273
Beattie *Rev* H *MBE* [RC] 141273
McGee *Rev* S I *MA* 010578
Abram *Rev* P R C *MA* 040778
McNaughton *Rev* J *BA* 040778
Clemett *Rev* P T *BA* 310879
Carruthers *Rev* A C 010780
Laird *Rev* R G 240880
Denton *Rev* P B 151080
Parkinson *Rev* F W *BA* 080581
Mears *Rev* P A [M] 010981
Barrie *Rev* J A 070981
Hall *Rev* G H *BA* 260182
Slegg *Rev* J E *MA* 151082
Dean *Rev* A *BA DipTh* 011282
McDowall *Rev* R A *AKC* 011282
Bolton *Rev* J R [M] 200483
Dodd *Rev* P L *MBE BA* 200483
Rich *Rev* P M 010783
Watts *Rev* G S S 010783
Appleby *Rev* A R N *AKC* 010884
Vernon *Rev* J C *BSc(Eng)* 010884
Crosbie *Rev* M J [RC] 020884
Mallon *Rev* J L [RC] 311084
Griffin *Rev* A J [RC] 041184
Hiney *Rev* T B F *MC* 010585
Poole *Rev* A [RC] 180585
Bayley *Rev* P [M] 010685
Dobbin *Rev* V *MBE MA MTh PhD* [C of S] 010785
McAllen *Rev* R 010785
Holliman *Rev* J J *BA* 011085
Tomlinson *Rev* C C [M] 011085
Williams *Rev* R E *BA* 011085

Chaplains to the Forces (3rd Class) ranking as Majors

Ryall *Rev* M R *MA* 150771
Marshall *Rev* P J 060673
Berrow *Rev* P R 250973
Robertson *Rev* M *LTh* [C of S] 010774
Craig *Rev* P T *BA* 081074
Smith *Rev* A J *AKC* 210175
Small *Rev* D B 281075
Coates *Rev* J D S *BA* 210176
Pratt *Rev* B D 070776
Meager *Rev* P *BD MA* [C of S] 050177
Macfarlane *Rev* P T *BA* [C of S] 280477
Webb *Rev* J C R *FCA* 110577
Andrews *Rev* J G W 060777
Bass *Rev* G M 060777
Bailey *Rev* D G 050478
Heagerty *Rev* A J *BD MA* 050978
Jones *Rev* D R *MA MBIM* 050978
Jones *Rev* H L 050978
Murray *Rev* J A [UB] 050978
Sherrington *Rev* J B *BA BD CertEd* [M] 050978
Walters *Rev* D M T 050978
Smith *Rev* A *LTh MA* [C of S] 241078
Ward *Rev* C J W 090179
Clayton-Jones *Rev* R F *AKC* 250479
Cribbin *Rev* K M *BA BD* [M] 290879
Wilson *Rev* C M 290879
Stevens *Rev* R W *AKC* 030979
O'Hara *Rev* J [RC] 271179
Brooke *Rev* P M 030980
Macadam *Rev* J F [M] 030980
Blackburn *Rev* J *BA* 300182
Hadfield *Rev* G F *BSc* 020982
Rose *Rev* A J *BD* 020982
Shields *Rev* J M *MBE* [C of S] 020982
Cattermole *Rev* P G *BD MA* [UB] 150283
Heaver *Rev* D C *BTh* 150283
Price *Rev* A H 150283
Whitton *Rev* J P *BD MA* [C of S] 020683
Brown *Rev* A J *MTh AKC* 140683
Blakey *Rev* S A *BSc BD* [C of S] 310883
Howson *Rev* P J *BSc MA* [M] 310883
Cable *Rev* P J *AKC* 140284
Tickner *Rev* D A *AKC* 140284
Louden *Rev* S H *BA* [RC] 050984
Cosgrove *Rev* L J [RC] 311084
Bryan *Rev* L H 130285
Price *Rev* J R 130285
Dailly *Rev* J R [C of S] 300885
Vasey *Rev* K [RC] 300885

Chaplains to the Forces (4th Class) ranking as Captains

Masterson *Rev* M K [RC] 220780
Mitchell *Rev* R M 290880
Wells *Rev* C P 290880
Wilkes *Rev* D E [M] 290880
Hayes *Rev* A T [RC] 050980
Blair *Rev* J W *BSc DipTh AIIM* ae 010783

Short Service Officers

Chaplains to the Forces (3rd Class) ranking as Majors

Coombs *Rev* R J *BD* 061076
Symonds *Rev* J H 011079
Mead *Rev* D J [RC] 030681
Keat *Rev* R L S 221081
Stockbridge *Rev* A C *MA* (*L/2nd Class* 240785) 010982
Ward *Rev* J F [RC] 091182
Lenihan *Rev* T P [RC] 080283
Maclagan *Rev* H B *MBE* [UB] 140284
Jones *Rev* M F 160784
Mosley *Rev* E P 010984
Bunce *Rev* J M [RC] 081284
Elliott *Rev* B *BA* 010185
Pillar *Rev* K J 130285
Bunnell *Rev* A 010785
Brace *Rev* S 300885
Springford *Rev* P F A 300885
Cameron *Rev* R N [C of S] 011185
Finch *Rev* A F [UB] 190286
Gibbs *Rev* C W 190286
Knox *Rev* R A *LTh MA* [C of S] 190286

Chaplains to the Forces (4th Class) ranking as Captains

Nicholson *Rev* E C [M] 290880
Potts *Rev* G A [UB] 290880
Broadbridge *Rev* J A *BD* [M] 110881
Hooley *Rev* J P 010981
Makings *Rev* T J [RC] 010981
Robson *Rev* W *FCCA FCIS* 010981
Smith *Rev* N [M] 010981
Pearson-Miles *Rev* D 220282
Davidson Kelly *Rev* T A *BD MA* [C of S] 050782
Keen *Rev* C J J [RC] 010982
Dear *Rev* G F 270982
Boyd *Rev* A J *BSc CBiol MIBiol FSA(Scot)* 040183
Palmer *Rev* D J 210283
Richards *Rev* B [UB] 110483
Carter *Rev* N A 010683
Hewitt *Rev* D J 290683
Owen *Rev* R A 040783
Alker *Rev* J S [RC] 260783
Cook *Rev* J C D *MA* 010983
Murdoch *Rev* J A H [C of S] 010983
Hutchison *Rev* G J 190983
Spencer *Rev* M J B [UB] 190983
Wray *Rev* K 190983
Bretel *Rev* K M 200284
Bryce *Rev* M A G 200284
Burtt *Rev* A K 200284
Carter *Rev* P M 200284
Ingham *Rev* A W *LTh BPhil* [RC] 050384
Jolly *Rev* A J [C of S] 010684
Kerr *Rev* A *BD* [C of S] 010684
Knights Johnson *Rev* N A *BA* 010684
Rose *Rev* L S 020784
Broadbent *Rev* R A *BD AKC* 160784
Loveday *Rev* J M 160784
Savage *Rev* K G [M] 010984
O'Gorman *Rev* P A *BSc DipEd* 030984
Prince *Rev* K V [RC] 030984
Willey *Rev* M C A [RC] 030984
Woodward *Rev* A J *BSc* 030984
Pollock *Rev* D J M *QGM BCombStuds* 010585
Hart *Rev* D A E 010785
Sussex *Rev* G B [UB] 150785
Mills *Rev* D F 090985
Rutherford *Rev* P M *MTh DipTh* 090985
Warden *Rev* R J *BA(Hons)* 041185
Jones *Rev* R T 170286

ROYAL CORPS OF TRANSPORT

On a Star of eight points in Silver within a Scroll terminating in Sprigs of Laurel and inscribed ROYAL CORPS OF TRANSPORT all in Gold encircling the Garter proper on a Crimson ground the Royal Cypher also in Gold ensigned with the Crown also in Silver

Regimental March

Quick March..........Wait for the Wagon

Agents..........Lloyds Bank PLC Cox's & King's Branch

Corps Headquarters..........Buller Barracks, Aldershot, Hants (*Tel No: Aldershot* 24431 *Ext:* 2789)

Alliances

Australian Military Forces..........The Royal Australian Corps of Transport
New Zealand Army..........Royal New Zealand Corps of Transport
Indian Army..........Army Service Corps of India
Pakistan Army..........Army Service Corps of Pakistan
Sri Lanka Army..........The Sri Lanka Army Service Corps
Malaysian Armed Forces..........The Malaysian Service Corps

Affiliated Regiment

Gurkha Transport Regiment

Colonel in Chief..........*HRH Princess* Alice *Duchess of* Gloucester *GCB CI GCVO GBE*

Colonels Commandant..........*Maj Gen W Bate *CB OBE DL* ret pay..........010174
Maj Gen V H J Carpenter *CB MBE* ret pay..........010175
Maj Gen P Blunt *CB MBE GM* ret pay..........010176
Maj Gen P H Benson *CBE* ret pay..........311278
Maj Gen F J Plaskett *CB MBE* ret pay..........070681
Maj Gen D H Braggins *CB* ret pay..........010186

Brigadiers

Dixon A K *ADC* ndc psc psc(n) 300681
Colley D B H *CBE* jssc psc (*A/Maj Gen* 010386) 300682
Blakey G G *FCIT* ndc psc† TN 300683
Boyd C M psc 300683
Carrington C E G *CBE* rcds ndc psc 300683
Baxter I S *CBE* rcds ndc psc 300684
Palmer P I *OBE MCIT AInstTA MBIM* psc 300684
Turner M H *LLB MCIT* psc† 300684
Carey C J *AIPM MBIM* psc pl 300685
Marzetti P J psc 300685
Meier A L *OBE* ndc nadc psc 300685
Pitt J K *OBE MCIT MBIM* psc t 300685
Winn M psc† TN 300685

Colonels

Bidmead J D *CBE* sq 300681
Payne J D sq TN 300681
Barker W R *CBE* ndc psc 300682
Mears P S *MCIT* sq 300682
Reger P B sq ph pl 300682
Swan A J *FCIT FInstAM* psc† 300682
Baugniet M L A odc(US) sq 300683
Betts M W *MCIT* ndc psc 300683
Cooper D W *FCIT MBIM* sq t 300683
Macdonald J D *OBE MCIT MBIM* ndc psc 300683
Whall D C psc 300683
Allen W E J psc osc(NIG) 300684
Daniel P E B ndc psc 300684
Evans P B *MA MBIM* psc(a)† osc(GH) 300684
Hollins P F *AMInstTA* psc TN 300684
Lewis E A *MBIM* psc osc(NIG) 300684
Webb F M psc† 300684
Bartlett G E *MBE* ndc psc† 300685
Bullock R M ndc psc 300685
Cooke *Sir* David *Bt BA FCIT AMInstTA MBIM* psc t 300685
Coombes J S *MBIM* psc 300685
Kinnear D T *OBE* ndc sq 300685
Newcombe J A psc 300685
Ronald D W *BA FCIT MBIM* ndc psc† TN 300685
Sellars C J *BA MCIT* ndc psc 300685
Trinkwon B B *MBIM* sq t 300685

Lieutenant Colonels

Donnison D G (SL) sq 300673
Wellings M J (SL) psc† 300673
Bulpin P S (SL) t 300674
Mallon J J (SL) *FIQA MCIT* psc† t 300676
Tanner C E (SL) psc 300676
Wills R E (SL) sq 300676
Young M H G (SL) psc 300677
Flood J M psc lcc 300678
Horsfall W J psc† 300678
McAllister C D sq 300678
Sherburn J R (SL) *MBE* sq 300678
Tapp A R psc lcc 300678
Coles B H R (SL) *MCIT MBIM* sq t 300679
Hain J E T (SL) *MCIT* sq t 300679
Harding D J sq 300679
Hellberg I J *OBE* ndc psc (*A/Col* 011185) 300679
Stewart R F *MCIT MBIM* sq t 300679
Stormer A E W *MCIT* psc osc(ZIM) 300679
Arlidge R P sq 300680
Colston B E sq 300680
French P A *OBE* odc(GE) osc(GE) 300680
Harban B J *MBE MCIT* sq t (*A/Col* 200985) 300680
Lucas J C *OBE* psc† (*A/Col* 070286) 300680
McCartney M R U psc 300680
Merrylees D L (SL) *MBIM* t 300680
Sankey D J M *MCIT MBIM* sq 300680
Vaughan G E psc(a) 300680
Allum A R (SL) sq t 300681
Armstrong J E S *MBE* psc lcc 300681
Branch M W H *OBE* sq t (*A/Col* 251085) 300681
Bridger A L (SL) 300681
Connaughton R M *MCIT FBIM* psc 300681
Felton R J *BSc(Econ)* sq 300681
French P I *MBE MCIT MBIM* sq t 300681
Muddiman N *OBE* ndc psc (*A/Col* 151285) 300681
Ridgway T H (SL) t 300681
Smith R C *MBIM* psc† 300681
Taylor R H McF *MCIT* sq t 300681
Winter T B *MBE BA* psc† 300681
Bush F A ndc psc† ph pl 300682
Clementson J *MCIT* psc 300682
Collins R E osc(GE) sq I* t 300682
Colvin C A *MSc MCIT* t 300682
Cowan M (SL) psc 300682
Gilbert N E L ndc sq 300682
Grevatte-Ball R F psc pl 300682
Hambleton J G *MBE MCIT* t 300682
Haste S F *BA* psc 300682
Massey A C *MBE* odc(US) psc† 300682
Shipway D G *MCIT MBIM* sq t 300682
Brown L H *MBE MCIT* sq t 300683

*Representative Colonel Commandant for 1986

Butterfield C A psc lcc 300683
Crawley R A psc owc t 300683
Dadswell R H psc 300683
Green D B odc(US) sq ph 300683
Kevans G L *MBIM* sq t 300683
Lake C M psc 300683
Lee J B *MCIT* ph pl t 300683
Morgan R *MBE* sq t 300683
Stephens H V C *MCIT* psc 300683
Turner D J t 300683
White M S psc† aic 300683
Williams G D *BA(Hons)* sq 300683
Adams A R McC *MBE MCIT* sq t 300684
Bentley-Marchant H psc t 300684
Bloxwich W R *MCIT MBIM* sq t 300684
Blyth M J psc 300684
Constable C J *MCIT* sq 300684
Duxbury C J *MBE* sq owc 300684
Ewer G A *MBE* psc 300684
Hardaker G G psc 300684
Irvine D A psc jsdc 300684
Maxwell R *MBE* sq ph 300684
Osborne I N *MBE* ndc psc 300684
Robinson P K *MCIT* psc 300684
Simms S A G *MBE MCIT* t 300684
Skidmore R P *BA* psc 300684
Tarvit J sq 300684
Taylor C D *MIPDM* t 300684
Winarick M J psc 300684
Beard N H G *MBE BSc(Eng)* psc† jsdc 300685
Burgess B J *MCIT AMInstTA MBIM* sq t 300685
Carver M B sq 300685
Cawthorne J R sq 300685
French J P *MBE BA* psc lcc t 300685
Grieve G M J sq 300685
Hall O T sq ph 300685
Macartney T M psc† 300685
Ponikowski M A psc 300685
Sims M C sq 300685
Squire M J sq t 300685
Vaughan-Stanley R *MCIT MRIN* sq lcc t 300685
Yeoman G J *MBE* sq lcc 300685

Majors

Barton R H G *MBE MBIM* TN 220763
Parkin A R 041264
Macro J A *MCIT* TN 220765
Strange T E L t 010865
Wallace R C 010865
Ottley R T 110865
Beail D F 060266
Nicholas J R G 250366
Huthwaite J M psc 310766
Soulsby M H 310766
Wade E R L 051266
Arnold R E *MCIT MBIM* t 120267
Forster W A 120267
Murray J G L *MBE* sq 120267
Quick P C *MCIT* t 120267
Stevens H B *MCIT MBIM* t 030367
Randall D M G *MCIT MBIM* t 020467
Macbeth A C ptsc sq 020667
Bowcock D J *MBIM* t 311267
Clarke J N *MCIT* sq t 311267
Eaton L R *MBE* t 311267
Garner T H *MCIT* t 311267
Kearney M t 311267
Bond D M *MBE MCIT MBIM* t 300668
Edwards G C W *MMS* lcc 300668
Taylor J M *MBE MBIM* sq 300668
Burgess J F E t 311269
Casperd I L t 311269
Chilton J *BA MCIT AMInstTA* 300670
Collar J A 300670
Locke D J *MBE* 300670
Moss W P B *MCIT MBIM* t 300670
Nuttall F M *MCIT* t 300670
Hastings R S *MBE* 311270
McGuirk N F t 311270
Hayes J F T sq lcc t 300671
McAllister R C A sq 300671
Swain A R lcc 300671
Ottewell A B *MSc* sq 101171
Gwinn J N sq 311271
Potter B *MBIM* t 311271
Emmett A T t 300672
Hammett D G *MBE MCIT* lcc t 300672
Hale J C t 311272
Case A V 300673
Hutton-Dunton D P t 300673
Lucas B A 300673
Jones O M lcc 311273
Leeson A H t 311273
Whyte P *MCIT* psc t 311273
Campbell-Collins A I *AMInstTA FBIM* psc† 300674
Hope J O sq t 300674
Humpherson M J G C *MCIT* t 300674
Streatfield C M *BSc* sq t 300674
Todd A sq lcc 151074
Carolan P M *MCIT* t 311274
Gordon D S M t 311274
Rawlinson C E sq lcc 311274
Stevens M R psc 311274
Crabbe A sq 300675
Derry P D sq ph (*A/Lt Col* 270186) 300675
Lawrence A F psc† ph pl 300675
Lenton B P *BA MCIT MInstTA MBIM* sq t 300675
Notman A L J sq 300675
Rawlingson Plant D *MCIT MBIM MIPDM* t 300675
Barrett E L *MBE* psc (*A/Lt Col* 240685) 311275
Cubitt M F I *MBE MCIT* sq ph t 311275
Gunn I R t (*A/Lt Col* 151185) 311275
Paterson D K 311275
Pepperell D G sq t 311275
Somerville G W sq (*A/Lt Col* 201185) 311275
Fitzgerald J N psc t 040376
Arymar J R *MCIT MBIM* lcc t 300676
Baker D M A psc 300676
Davies J S psc† lcc 300676
Matthews F C sq ph t 311276
Watson R B psc 311276
Austen J T *BSc(Eng) MCIT* sq t 300677
Butters C 300677
Edwards R B 300677
Froehlich C V psc† ph 300677
Heal G N *MCIT* t 300677
Peterson N V t 300677
Smetham A J M osc(MAL) sq 300677
Belcher A C *MCIT* t 311277
de Marco M P *MCIT* t 311277
Glynn-Riley P D t 311277
Lewis J E C *BSc MCIT* sq t 311277
Moore H C *MCIT* sq t 311277
Osmond W G *MSc MCIT* sq t 311277
Paine M J *BA* sq 311277
Reason L C W *MCIT* t 311277
Shipway R A B *MCIT* ph t 311277
Britton-Johnson H sq 300678
Cox P R *MCIT* t 300678
Fisher D G *MCIT MRIN MNI* lcc t 300678
Miseroy P E sq 300678
Paterson A McL lcc 300678
Rennie A A t 300678
Roach M G *MSc* t 300678
Saunders E P t 300678
Saville D *MCIT* t 300678
Weatherly J M *MCIT* psc† t 300678
Dover W G psc 051178
Collins J P B sq lcc 311278
Fraser P sq 311278
Gardner R C *BSc FRGS MCIT* psc jsdc t 311278
Morrison A G *MBE* sq jsdc 311278
Neeves B C psc 311278
Searle S J sq 311278
Snow W A B *MCIT* t 311278
Edwards G J *MCIT MBIM* t 300679
Green C R C *CGIA* psc† aic 300679
Jewell W K owc 300679
May P G *MCIT* owc t 300679
Morling P W *BSc(Eng) MSc MCIT* sq t (*A/Lt Col* 021285) 300679
Palmer E F *MISM* owc 300679
Shipley A J 300679
Snowden D I *MCIT* t 300679
Stewart I H *MCIT* t 300679
Thomas P K *MCIT* t 300679
Birrell D R 311279
Brown D W 311279
Cairns D P C sq 311279
Ellison D M *MCIT* sq t 311279
Everingham P J 311279
Fielden J D *MBE* sq jsdc (*A/Lt Col* 010486) 311279
Fraser J A sq 311279
Graham M J B sq t 311279
Henderson P J *MBE BBS* psc 311279
Hoare J D *BSc(Eng)* psc† aic 311279
Jackson A R N psc 311279
Jones H R G *BA* psc 311279
Macfarlane D S psc (*A/Lt Col* 041085) 311279
McAleese M J sq 311279
Merritt J B sq 311279
Morris B sq 311279
Rowbottom K J 311279
Thompson T M 311279
Treasure J J psc† (*A/Lt Col* 230885) 311279
Wood N 311279
Anderson A B *MBE* 300980
Barr S J *BSc(Eng)* psc† aic 300980
Bowles J M *MBE* t 300980
Bray M P sq 300980
Burchill R t 300980
Burtenshaw P J t 300980
Carter D J 300980
Couzens A P owc 300980
Crawford H J 300980
Davidson A 300980
Evetts R sq t 300980
Gout J J R sq 300980
Hall J C G *MCIT* t 300980
Harrison R I 300980
Hopwood G *BA* t 300980
Hutt R A 300980
Keen M R sq 300980
Lilley G D sq 300980
May J M psc 300980
Moore M J C 300980
Murray T H sq 300980

Royal Corps of Transport – continued

Nowosielski-Slepowron W E *BSc* psc† aic 300980
Paton G *BA MCIT* sq ph t 300980
Poole P M *MBE* 300980
Ratazzi R E psc (*A/Lt Col* 251185) 300980
Rendall R P M 300980
Smith A R M psc 300980
Tait J H S t 300980
Upchurch C J sq 300980
Budworth G M 300981
Campbell R G C 300981
Chambers C R *BSc(Econ) MCIT* t 300981
Corani G *BSc(Eng)* 300981
Croslegh R C 300981
Cross A G 300981
Evans P A D *MBE* psc† 300981
Farmer M J *CGIA* psc† 300981
Fisher A J C *MBE* psc† 300981
Forrest J A t 300981
Gilham P A C 300981
Haig G J psc 300981
Harvey C sq 300981
Hawkey C *MCIT* t 300981
Hodson M G R 300981
Neville I H R lcc t 300981
Partridge D G 300981
Richards M J 300981
Shearer J P *BSc* 300981
Syms M E A *MBE* psc 300981
Thompson N L t 300981
Tutt K M *BA* psc 300981
Verge P D 300981
Wilmshurst N R t 300981
Ballinger B W *BSc(Eng)* psc† 300982
Barnes J R *BSc(Eng)* psc† 300982
Boyle G P psc 300982
Chaganis P psc(a)† 300982
Davies G G psc 300982
Dowdle M *MBIM AMITD* psc 300982
Draper C F R psc 300982
Forrest D E *BA* psc 300982
Fox G B L psc† 300982
Fraser G C 300982
Gosling P psc 300982
Harper P W 300982
Howard-Williams I R *BSc(Eng) MSc* mvt sq 300982
Johnson D L *BSc(Eng)* psc† 300982
Lawson D N 300982
Lewis R T A 300982
Logan D B *MIPDM* 300982
McCallum J Y 300982
Miller A J 300982
Pleasants D J 300982
Robertson P A psc 300982
Rust M J sq 300982
Swallow M P t 300982
Alexander M C S 300983
Cummings P B G 300983
Ferguson D F B 300983
Firth P psc 300983
Gethin R J St L *BSc(Eng)* t 300983
Hird C W 300983
Knowles J E *MCIT* t 300983
Longland J psc 300983
Mathew A M 300983
Mole R L *BA MInstPet* 300983
Newman-Carter J S t 300983
O'Brien P E C 300983
Thornton G psc 300983
Bell P H 300984
Clough J H *BSc(Eng)* 300984
Graham S *MBIM MIPDM* t 300984
Harris C D M 300984
Hemming-Tayler D J *MBIM MIPDM* t 300984
Kilpatrick R I *MCIT* t 300984
Maggs P J T psc† 300984
Marks C T *BTech MSc MCIT* dis 300984
Morrison R J 300984
Ormerod I S *BA DipTD* 300984
Steirn C M psc 300984
Webb G W 300984
Wilkins R t 300984
Jeffrey D R *CGIA* psc† 300985
Macfarlane I C *BA* psc† 300985
Marvin E W 300985
Morrison N D 300985
Muat G R t 300985
Palmer P t 300985
Plowright C J *MIPDM* 300985
Plowright N R 300985
Preston K N 300985
Reehal P S 300985
Shorer J M lcc 300985
Speight A M 300985
Sturgeon P R 300985
Sutherland A W 300985

Captains

Dawson J A 250177
Wilkie P B owc 060778
Whittaker K *BSc* 010279
Gilderson R P D ph(cfs) ph(i) ph 050279
James M R P owc 080379
Wright D N psc lcc (*A/Maj* 100186) 080379
Barton A B 090379
MacArthur I W 090379
Selley R J psc† (*A/Maj* 161285) 100979
Toms M R 100979
Bromham D I 271279
Attwood N J R *AInstTA* t 301279
Baker R M 301279
Brady S N lcc (*A/Maj* 221085) 301279
Stirling T 160380
Appleton N I F 170380
Wallace J R *BA* 130880
Chester M *BA* 090980
Garrick R S 090980
Harding D F 090980
Hay J M 090980
Kirkbride P L 090980
Lanham M R 090980
McCarthy D J 090980
Nelson J R 090980
Ward M A 090980
Humpherson N P *BA* 101280
Pope N S *BA* 090481
Beattie R 090581
Fitness G A *BSc(Eng)* 090581
Harding A N 090581
Kneale G D *BSc(Eng)* 090581
Philpott T G *BSc(Eng)* 090581
Price B S *BSc* 090581
Campbell I S ph 080981
Hunter E J *BSc(Eng)* 080981
Jones A L *BSc* 080981
Kane J M *CGIA* 080981
Little J J 080981
Norton D J 080981
Marlow S *BSc* 170981
Maginniss C H *BA* RLY 290981
Martin D J R *BSc AMBCS* 111081
McMahon P 091181
Murray C J 281281
Warwick P 281281
Witt M J *BSc MCIT FPWI* RLY 300182
McCulloch J A 080582
Parrott A J *MA* 010882
Abbott I W *TEng(CEI) AMIMI* 170882
Murley G W 210882
Collinson G T 060982
Cowlam S P 060982
Graham M G 060982
Hooper R J 060982
Lilley M R 060982
Morris J K 060982
Start N T 060982
Cole C F *BA AIPM* 280982
Gilroy R J *BA* 280982
Raby P D *BSc* 111282
Govan S 040183
Rees M S 070283
Robinson R F *BSc* 280383
Hudson M R *BA* 260583
Mosedale I R 060683
Bray A J 110683
Flint R M 110683
Haslam A T *BSc* 110683
Mould P L 110683
Anderson K B 080883
Howard R N *BSc* 150983
Bragg S D 081083
Brook P C *BSc(Eng)* 081083
Byrne D R 081083
Cowling A P 081083
Lowe J G O 081083
Phillips A W 081083
Williams J M *BSc* 081083
Alberry P E 060284
Hurley I M owc 060284
Varley M J 060284
Devonshire R M *BSocSc* 060484
Wymbs E J 090484
Duncan P A 300484
Taylor A S 100684
Dirkin M P A *BA* 180784
Newis-Edwards J P RLY 190784
Bedborough L R ph 081084
Canning N P 081084
Goodall J A *BSc* 081084
Harvey C J 081084
Littlechild G R 081084
Orr M J 081084
Pettet G F 081084
Rosher P M 081084
Russell M H F 081084
Taplin A P 081084
Thorpe P J *BSc FLS* 081084
Bacon R J 050285
Barkes C J *BSc* 050285
Bates P J 050285
Croxford D J owc 050285
Denning T M 050285
Dixon-Warren R A 050285
Frankland D P 050285
Heil B 050285
Laden R St L *BSc* 050285
Prince C R 050285
Stark J P *BSc* 050285
Askew J G *MHCIMA* 300485
Downes J A S *BA* 300585
Bower L A 090685
Brown P J 090685
Lawson M M 090685
Rowe A G 090685
Scully C F 090685
Smith N A 090685
Smith N T 070785
Bicknell D J *BSc(Econ)* 010885
Broadway J C H *BSc* 030985
Neal A J *BA* 030985
Bane S J *BSc(Eng)* 071085
Brimacombe P B 071085
Brown J 071085
Cox P G *BSc* 071085

Davies A L *BA* 071085
Fleet S J 071085
Gray J E 071085
Green C M 071085
Grocott P J *BA* 071085
Kirkham S J F 071085
O'Grady P A *LLB* 071085
Pepperday D R 071085
Underhill M C H 071085
Wyse W P P *BSc* 071085
Ball J D 301085
Bird P R C *BSc* 040286
Borrill D F ph 040286
Castell R G A 040286
Chapman N S 040286
Crossen E H *BSc* 040286
Ferrier J McD *BSc(Hons)* 040286
Grier A G 040286
Parsons S A *BEd* 040286
Redding J M *BSc(Eng)* 040286
Searles T E D 040286
Warden P A *BSc(Eng)* 040286
Woodman T G W 040286

Lieutenants

Copeland I M 081281
Smith P M 081281
Beavis R G *BEd* (*A/Capt* 140286) 120482
Carlisle W M *BA* 120482
Mathie R A 120482
Roberts S R 120482
Rowley R K 120482
Vickers M D 120482
Wiggins D A 120482
Alexander I C (*A/Capt* 080385) 090882
Cook D E 090882
Cooper L A 090882
McMahon M J 090882
Morgan N D 090882
Peters S E *BSc(Eng)* 090882
Butterworth P M (*A/Capt* 031085) 131282
Hood A M (*A/Capt* 300484) 131282
Lampshire D M (*A/Capt* 010385) 131282
Libbey R W 131282
Aspin B D (*A/Capt* 150685) 110483
Brandwood M 110483
Brown J J 110483
Hain C J T *BCom* 110483
Heaton S (*A/Capt* 160885) 110483
Jordan T J *BA* 110483
Lewis A J *BSc* 110483
McKend I G *BA* 110483
Reeve D W 110483
Baker P J A 030683
Little M R 080883
Robinson P J F 080883
Baxter M R 090484
Jones P A 060684
Barker T J *BSocSc* 070884
Coxon I G *BSc* 070884
Farquharson D J A 070884
Shilton A R *BA(Hons)* 070884
Bryan L J 090485
Hemsley S A B 060885
Martin J D V 101285
Gardner C D A 070486

2nd Lieutenants

††Parrott W J 030982
††Forster A W *BA(Hons)* 020983
††Gilday I R 230984
††Shirley S J 300984
Caldwell S J 130485
Tysoe A R 130485
Graham G P 100885
Mosedale T J 100885
Walker C P J 100885
†Kelly D A *BA(Hons)* 060985
†Lee B H *BA(Hons)* 060985
††Newman M E 240985
Pomroy G A 141285
†Arnold P J *BSc* 060186
†Brown E M *BA(Hons)* 060186
†Jennings A D *BA* 060186

Staff Quartermasters

Nelson T E 150674
Maj 300882

Quartermasters

Goold S 231072
Lt Col 310183
Blythe G O McM *AMInstTA MISM* 081272
Maj 020481
Main J L 301073
Maj 150579
Lambert A M *MBE* 050474
Maj 250482
Shiel N H *AMInstTA* 140674
Lt Col 240983
Burr P 010774
Maj 031082
Vaughan V H *MBE BEM* 170874
Lt Col 080585
Lambdon R W *BEM* 270974
Lt Col 180584
Boot D *AMInstTA* 151274
Lt Col 201185
Walling J G 010175
Lt Col 150384
Groom G N *MBE* 140175
Maj 131180
Bartlet J A 200175
Lt Col 081283
Brett M B 120375
Maj 110282
Sweeney G 200675
Maj 030783
Honeysett T W 011075
Maj 130582
Webster B R 021175
Maj 050281
Armitage D A 111175
Maj 070483
Waldis J E 150376
Maj 070384
Griffin D A 290376
Lt Col 071084
Surridge V E W *AMInstTA* 040776
Maj 120284
Burke J P J *AMInstTA* 050776
Maj 030682
Little R H 260177
Maj 170385
Gray W B 160577
Maj 101282
Stretton J H *MInstTA MASMC* 170677
Maj 060383
Knowles S G 180777
Maj 070483
Cuming T W 050877
Maj 080184
Johnson R M 250877
Maj 250885
Gower R G 100977
Maj 131183
Bunting T E 101077
Maj 030684
Myers P M 281277
Maj 270185
Matthews J A 010278
Maj 020181
Edington W 310578
Maj 170383
Thompson C N 010778
Maj 081285
Haynes A R 140778
Maj 290784
Robinson R 031078
Maj 131183
Ravenscroft K *Capt* 261078
Owens R *BEM* 041278
Maj 010484
Pickford R 221278
Maj 110885
Poyntz J D P 130479
Maj 200183
Batty A R J 160479
Maj 021284
Weir D I 010679
Maj 081285
Allen D A 160679
Maj 021284
Lambert M G 010779
Maj 290784
Tucker L R 021079
Maj 130486
Ames R J R 090180
Maj 050185
Gissing B P *AMInstTA MISM*
Capt 100680
Murrell S C 170680
Maj 150985
Blyth A D *Capt* 220680
Howard J *Capt* 120880
Le Cheminant D J 060181
Maj 230386
Cruickshank R H 020281
Maj 110885
Ferbrache D *Capt* 010681
Chadwick M *Capt* 110681
Houlston W 080981
Maj 130486
Hobson R B *Capt* 281181
Etheridge B J *Capt* 201281
Urch C G *MMS* *Capt* 250182
Prince G H *Capt* 080482
Brack M J *AMInstTA* 110482
Maj 120583
Kane A J *Capt* 150482
Clover J A *Capt* 290582
Hilditch A D *Capt* 220682
Douglas P L P *Capt* 010782
Lukes R A *AInstTA* *Capt* 130882
Carter R W *Capt* 170982
Taylor R *Capt* 310183
Price I W *Capt* 070283
Jackson D J *Capt* 120483
Proctor T H B *Capt* 140483
Lodwig T *Capt* 280483
Sherman D *Capt* 300483
Hunt J 070583
Maj 081285
Balding M P *Capt* 280783
Gray J M *Capt* 010883
Coles R D T *Capt* 121283
Thomas M R *Capt* 200184
Owen D J *Capt* 180284
Mutch A J *Capt* 090384
Roberts D P *Capt* 150384
Bunting R *Capt* 010484
O'Riordan F T *AMIWO*
Capt 010484
Dolan L R *Capt* 180584
Meiklejohn A McC *Capt* 230884
Hadlow B R *Capt* 061284

Royal Corps of Transport – continued

Meek J W	*Capt*	210285
Grimes J P	*Capt*	160385
McGuire M	*Capt*	310385
Montgomerie H R	*Capt*	310385
Sadler J W	*Capt*	080585
Dow W	*Capt*	010685
Clarke L W	*Capt*	160885
Musgreave A	*Capt*	310885
Streeter I	*Capt*	190985
Robinson J F	*Capt*	251085
Broadfoot T P	*Capt*	011185
Henderson G *MBE*	*Capt*	171185
Marrison G C	*Capt*	191185
Stocks R D *AMInstTA*	*Capt*	121285
Barlow M F	*Capt*	180186

Directors of Music

Kenny T A J *ARCM* psm	010570
Maj	010479

Special Regular Officers

Majors

Greene W L P	300674
Francombe D	300679
Robyns P J *MCIT* lcc	300679
Forbes A R M *AInstTA*	300980
Lloyd-Jones E K	300980
Tull A R	300982
Cook G T *AInstTA MBIM MISM MIPDM*	300983
Blease K W	300984
Cubbon D M	300984
Goymer N t	300984
Hinton R C *AMInstTA*	300984
Meys T C M *MInstTA*	300984
Mottram W L	300984
Quinn-Hall D R aic	300984
Richards F T	300984
Warnock S D J	300984
Myatt P W *MBIM*	020785
Oliver P C lcc	300985

Captains

Broad R P	100771
Rossetter M J B	291171
Mathias D A t (*A/Maj* 310186)	300777
Tilt S C lcc (*A/Maj* 051184)	080379
Dorrington N J	100979
Griffin N A t	080781
Brown H M *BA* t	230781
Jenkinson T	200382
Card R G *BEM* (*A/Maj* 140284)	030782
Beech R	230483
Handley-Greaves P L lcc	230483
Ponting K T	200683
Hughes A J	020783
de-Roeck P E	060883
Pickup G *AInstTA MISM*	060883
Morley C J M lcc	100983
Mutch H M	081083
Campbell N	271183
Oates M N	060284
Lebeter J	130284
Glossop D J	120384
Murray T	160984
Flack C	050285
Wood A J	180285
Wright I K	090685
Bate S D	300685
Hollas D I	071085
Taylor J P	040286

Lieutenants

Dawson L I M owc (*A/Capt* 140283)	120482
Mahanty A *BSc* (*A/Capt* 130186)	120482
Martin F A S (*A/Capt* 300985)	120482
Randall P C	131282
Teitge A D G	140683
Mence R J	090883
Gartside M J	121283
Key G J F	300884
Stockdale P T	151084
Fay A S J	101285
Jones W I M	101285

2nd Lieutenants

Ashmore S A	040884
Griffiths A I	081284
Heath A N	100885
Marshall P A	100885
Jay R E	141285
Kelly S M	141285
Ridd S	141285

Short Service Officers

Captains

Nicholson R L	170677
Thomson D A	060578
Baker D K	050579
Whiteley K	250879
Brown T	150979
Armstrong K J	301180
Crisp P W *BA*	211081
Cogar R M *BA*	261181
Coulson N	080582
Fenton S	190383
Kinghan C	230483
Clayton P J	100983
Tong J E	100983
Fessey L A	070184
Robson K W	270284
Lawrie I M *BA*	190484
Carter R J	290484
Fuller D J	190884
Maskell J M	300984
Shouesmith D J *BEd*	081084
Smith T K *BSc FLS*	251084
Murray J D	200185
Mckay D W	220485
Russell G	220485
Clayton A	190585
Loasby S M	140785
Jupp B K	050885
Davies C M	220985
McMinn T A W	061085
Claessens R H B *BA*	071085
Thomas R *BA*	071085
Underwood T M R *BSc*	071085
Willis R A E	071085
Grey M B	211085
McGrath P T	271085
Brownbridge J E *BA(Hons)*	281185
Atkinson R F *BSc*	040286
Bennett P S *BSc*	040286
Venables J	240286
Byrne T C	140386
Kennedy P A C	200386
Walkinshaw J R	220386
Bell E W	050486
Havard W J	050486
Carter J M	260486

Lieutenants

Lee N J	091280
Woof N M *BSc* (*A/Capt* 080385)	220181
Duma P N *BA*	040881
Card R S *BSc(Econ)* (*A/Capt* 040186)	250881
Brunjes K G *BA*	030981
Paterson K R (*A/Capt* 050684)	301181
Woods R (*A/Capt* 060684)	301181
Chambers T M	081281
Dixon G W *AMInstTA* (*A/Capt* 180784)	251281
Hornsby P M *BSc*	120482
Rooney N W *BA*	120482
Wensley C J *BA*	120482
Winkle D J A	160482
Collier J L (*A/Capt* 261084)	180482
Morgan G A	010582
Webster R E J *AMInstTA* (*A/Capt* 091184)	010582
Lovelock N E (*A/Capt* 271184)	160582
Barbone A W *BSc*	090882
Atterbury R S (*A/Capt* 080385)	220882
Fyfe N C (*A/Capt* 080385)	250882
Cavender T J (*A/Capt* 260585)	261082
Jones M C (*A/Capt* 310585)	261082
Stableford P W (*A/Capt* 070685)	261082
Coppin T M	241182
Battersby N M	131282
Jurgens D	171282
Everton M W	010183
Jones R	110183
Parry-Jones J (*A/Capt* 300785)	150183
Bessey P W (*A/Capt* 060985)	280283
Gibson J A	060383
Griffiths R A (*A/Capt* 211085)	200383
Williams P M *MBE* (*A/Capt* 030186)	200383
Ash J P	110483
Connell S L	110483
Doherty C M *BA*	110483
McNair R W L *BSc*	110483
Tidy P M *BSc*	110483
Clark R G	150583
Summerfield R D *BEM*	190583
Farmer G	030783
Battley A J	070783
Meakin K E	070783
Butcher M A	080883
Cave R A *BSc(Econ)*	080883
Deas A J *BSc*	080883
Farquhar D G	121283
Mayo D J	121283
Terrett E P G ph	121283
Abraham C M	090484
Brook S W *BSc*	090484
Bush R B *BSc*	090484
Mee J B *BSc*	090484
Parker A G	090484
Rendall J S	090484
Robinson L M *BSc(Hons)*	090484
Stark I G	090484
Tower M L (*A/Capt* 250186)	090484
Allcock C D	070884
Hickson M G	070884

Peek N M	070884
Rainforth P M J *BA*	070884
Underwood M J	070884
Keating C T	280884
Crutchley D W	051284
Lewis J W	111284
Stannett P R *BA*	111284
Stevenson A C	111284
Lappin A S	131284
Bennett A J	090485
Lewis H V	090485
Raynes A S	090485
Ciotti M	060885
Roberts S I	060885
Coward E N	101285
Sowden R M	101285
Pashley S J G	070486

2nd Lieutenants

Edwards I J	040884
Heselton J M	040884
Hill S J	040884
Moore R W	040884
Webber J	040884
Cadogan M K	081284
Donovan P J	081284
Doughty R A	081284
Hounsell S L	081284
Morley C J	081284
Abbott M J	130485
Dixon S J	130485
Ferrie A S	130485
Geller J S	130485
Griggs C J	130485
Lawton S P W	130485
McDonnell I M	130485
Dickson W R	100885
Gibson R A	100885
Hardy I M	100885
Judge R E G	100885
Male R J	100885
Scott N G A	100885
Stanhope-White J P	100885
Woodford D R	100885
†Dilnot J E *BA*	060985
†Dixon C M *BA*	060985
†McLeod A B *BA*	060985
†Millen D A J *BA(Hons)*	060985
Lane P J I	141285
Marsh A J	141285
Marshall A D	141285
Wilson S	141285
†Ashcroft D N *BSc*	060186
†English S N *BA*	060186
†Hall L P *BSc*	060186
†Ruddick G K D	060186

Short Service Volunteer Officers

Captains

McGuigan P J *BA*	020983

Lieutenants

Macintyre B H	110285
Kent A E *BSc*	211185

ROYAL ARMY MEDICAL CORPS

The Rod of Aesculapius the Serpent in Silver within a wreath of Laurel all gold thereunder a scroll inscribed 'IN ARDUIS FIDELIS' in silver the whole ensigned with the Crown in Gold

Regimental Marches

Quick March..........Here's a Health unto His Majesty
Slow March..........Her Bright Smile Haunts Me Still

Agents..........Holts Branch, Royal Bank of Scotland PLC, Lawrie House, Farnborough, Hants

Corps Headquarters..........Millbank, London, SW1P 4RJ (*Tel No:* 01-834-9060 *Ext:* 263)

Alliances

The Canadian Armed Forces..........Medical Branch
Australian Military Forces..........The Royal Australian Army Medical Corps
New Zealand Army..........Royal New Zealand Army Medical Corps
Pakistan Army..........Army Medical Corps
Sri Lanka Army..........The Sri Lankan Army Medical Corps
Zambia Army..........Zambia Army Medical Service

Colonel in Chief..........*HM* QUEEN ELIZABETH THE QUEEN MOTHER

Colonels Commandant..........*Maj Gen R N Evans *CB* ret pay..........261181
Col F A C Hine *MBE* ret pay..........011282
Maj Gen T S Hart *CB* ret pay..........260984
Maj Gen J P Crowdy *CB* ret pay..........070885

Brigadiers

Bray D W *QHS MB BS FFCM MRCS LRCP DTM&H FBIM* psc 300377
Robinson R G *QHS MB ChB MFCM DTM&H* 310378
Worsley D E *QHP MB FFCM DPH DIH DTM&H MFCM FFOM MFOM* 040581
England N W J *QHP MB ChB BSc FRCPEd FRCPath* 220681
Macphie D L *QHS MB ChB* 130883
Coakley P K *MCh MB BAO FRCS FRCSI* 300983
Swinhoe P H *OBE QHP MB BChir MRCS LRCP DObstRCOG DTM&H MFCM* 021283
Abraham P *FRCPsych MRCS LRCP DPM DTM&H* 010484
Beale P J *BA MB BChir MRCP MRCS DTM&H* 280185
Weeks D C *MB ChB MFCM DTM&H* ndc 150385
Billinghurst A O *MB BS FRCGP* 010885
Brown M *MB BS BSc FRCP FRCPEd MRCP DTM&H* 010885
Crawford I C *CBE MB ChB FRCPEd* 010885
Coull J T *MB ChB FRCSEd* 310386
Scott R *MCh BM FRCS DTM&H* 310386

Colonels

Quin N E *MB ChB MFCM* 140773
Brown T W *MB ChB FRCOG MRCS LRCP DObstRCOG DTM&H* 231073
O'Kelly J F *MAO MB BCh FRCOG DObstRCOG* 130174
Sim-Davis D *MRCS LRCP DTM&H* 090474
Kirkpatrick W A *MB BCh BAO FRCOG DObstRCOG* 201074
Youngson R M *MB ChB DO DTM&H* 011075
O'Rorke C M J *MB BCh BAO* 190176
Rees-Jones T G *MRCGP MRCS LRCP DCH DObstRCOG* 170876
McEwan J *MB ChB FFARCS* 191076
Johnstone G M *MB ChB FRCOG DObstRCOG* 021176
Goodall T M *OBE MB ChB MFCM* 050777
Leddy P P *MSc MB BCh FFR DMRD* 240777
Blackburn R F *MB ChB FFCM DPH DObstRCOG FBIM* 031277
Iffland J F *MB BS FRCS* 200678
Sanderson T A *MB ChB DObstRCOG DTM&H AFOM* 011178
Booth A I *LRCPI&LM LRCSI&LM DA* 260579
Treneman R H W *LRCPI&LM LRCSI&LM* 060779
Stewart A W C *MA MB BCh BAO FRCPath DipBact DTM&H* 240779
Macmahon P *MB BS* 071079
Printer K D *MB FRCOG* 010180
Garrett C J *MB ChB FRCP DTM&H* 220180
Humphreys T V *OBE MB BCh BAO* 310180
Bradshaw J *MA BM BCh FRCOG DObstRCOG* 240680
McDermott B C *CBE MB BS FRCS LRCP* 290680
Fitzpatrick D C B *MB BCh BAO FFARCS DA DTM&H* 030980
Mummery M B *MB BS MFCM DTM&H* 091080
Carter J W *MB BS FRCS FRCSEd LRCP DTM&H* 221180
Brasher P F *MB ChB FRCS DLO DTM&H* (*A/Brig* 310386) 150181
Michael A McG *MB ChB MRCOG DObstRCOG DTM&H* 060381
Peters N H *MB BS FRCS* 140381
Williams H A *MB BS MRCGP LMSSA DTM&H AFOM* 070581
Messent D O H *MB FRCS* 010681
Harwood A G *MB BS FFCM DPH DIH DTM&H MFOM* 090881
McCahon I A *MB BCh BAO FRCSEd* 170881
Blackburn P J *MA MB BCh BAO DPH DIH DTM&H FFCM MFOM* 180881
Carson J *MB ChB FRCP DTM&H* 080981
Ross D I *MB ChB* 031081
Robson D C *MD ChB* 051181
Jackson M B A *MB BS FRCOG MRCS LRCP DObstRCOG DTM&H* (*A/Brig* 190385) 150182
Bradford D E *MSc MB ChB FRCPEd DTM&H* 160182
Lewthwaite C J *BM BCh FFCM DPH DIH DTM&H MFOM* 010482
Governor I S *MB BS FRCOG DObstRCOG DTM&H* 030682
Robinson W M *MB BCh BAO FRCPEd DTM&H* 200782
Gardner P T *MB ChB FRCOG DObstRCOG* 130882
Restall J *MB BS FFARCS* 150982
Holmes-Smith J G *MB BS FRCP MRCS DCH DObstRCOG DTM&H* 270982
Bernstein S *MB BCh BAO FRCGP MBIM* 181082
Crawford I P *GM FFCM MRCS LRCP DPH DIH DTM&H MFOM* 311082
Mayes F B *MB BS FRCS* 141282
Forsythe-Jauch W E I *OBE MB BChir MFCM MRCS LRCP DTM&H FBIM* 201282
Dickson A S B *MB ChB* 070183

*Representative Colonel Commandant for 1986

Chapman B A E *MB ChB MRCOG DObstRCOG* 020283
Johnston W G *MB ChB FRCSEd DTM&H* 120283
Lees L A *MB BS FRCOG MRCS LRCP DObstRCOG* 150283
Ticehurst A C *MB BS MFCM MRCS LRCP MBIM* ndc psc 030383
Somerville G *MB ChB DTM&H* 210383
Coombe D H *MSc MB BS MFCM MRCS LRCP DTM&H* psc 150683
Spicer A J *MB BS FRCP MRCS DCH DTM&H* 060783
Daly M H *MB ChB FFARCSIrel DA* 200783
McGregor W S P *OBE MB ChB FRCSEd* 290783
Mason H C *MB ChB FRCGP DTM&H* 290983
Parry E S *MB ChB DTM&H* 020284
Deacon R C *MB ChB DTM&H* 240284
Hamer-Philip J M *MB ChB DA MBIM* 070384
Barry N A *LRCPI&LM LRCSI&LM* 060484
Penketh H V *MB ChB DTM&H* 240784
Ali S H *MB BS DPH DTM&H* 060285
Dowson J *MB ChB FRCS DO* 130685
Stock D G *MB BS FRCS LRCP* 270985

Lieutenant Colonels

Rao S C *MB BS DTM&H* 191274
Bell J D *MB BCh BAO MRCGP DCH DTM&H* 030675
Leach W H *MB ChB FFR DMRD DTM&H* 031076
Crosse J O *MB BChir MRCS LRCP DTM&H* 281076
Puszet J *MB BS MRCOG DObstRCOG* 200177
Thomas M J G *MB BChir LMSSA DTM&H* 310177
Callum D M *MRCPsych MRCS LRCP DPM* 040577
Hardie R H *OBE MB ChB* (*A/Col* 221084) 040877
Cowan G O *OBE MB ChB FRCP FRCPEd DTM&H* 060877
Depasquale J F *MD MRCOG* 100977
Anderson J *MB ChB* 021077
McMillan C R *MB ChB* ndc (*A/Col* 180385) 220378
Craig R P *MB BS FRCS* 150778
Eustace J W H *MRCPI MRCGP LRCSI&LM DTM&H* 030878
Bouchier-Hayes T A I *FRCGP LAH DObstRCOG* 170878
Flindell C R *MB BS MRCOG MRCS LRCP DObstRCOG DipVen* 030978
Longwill J A R *MB ChB MRCGP DCH DObstRCOG DTM&H* 030978
Stephens K Macg *MB BS FRCSEd* 130978
Haywood I R *MB BS FRCS LRCP* 291178
Weir G J S *MB ChB* ndc (*A/Col* 040684) 170279
Mifsud E *MD DipDerm* 130579
Hartley D I *MB BS MRCGP DObstRCOG* 290679
Lutter P F *MB BS MRCGP DObstRCOG* 270779
Graham T *MB ChB MRCPI DCH* 020879
Edgington K *MRCS LRCP DAvMed MRAeS MFOM* f ph (*A/Col* 020185) 080879
Warsap A J *BM BCh FRCGP* (*A/Col* 240685) 090879
øHannah H B *MB ChB FFARCS DA* 101079
Foxley J M *MB BS MRCPath MRCS LRCP* 060180
Tamlyn R S P *MBE MB BS FFARCS MRCS LRCP* 150380
Callow C G *OBE MB ChB DPhysMed* psc (*A/Col* 010785) 020480
Brown J R *MSc MB BCh DCH AFOM* 010780
Oldrey T B N *MB BS FRCP MRCS* 030780
Swanston J S K *MB ChB* 140780
Tinsley M J *MB ChB BSc MRCGP DObstRCOG* jsdc 270780
Houghton I T *MB BChir FFARCS LMSSA* 071080
Creamer I S *MC MRCS LRCP MBIM* psc (*A/Col* 120785) 061180
øCurran A *MB ChB MRCGP DCH DObstRCOG* 121180
Payne M J *MB BS FRCSEd LRCP* 181280
Ratcliffe G E *MB BS MRCPI MRCS* 120181
Pain P *MB* 180181
Short W R *MB ChB* psc 260281
Garnett R A F *PhD MB ChB BSc DPhysMed* 270281
Digges C N O'N *MB BCh DMRD FRCR* 110781
Johnston J H *MB ChB MRCP* 050881
Richardson J C *MB BChir MRCGP MRCS LRCP DRCOG* 041081
Anderson R M L *MB ChB MRCPsych* 221181
Brennan D T M *MRCS LRCP DObstRCOG* 231181
Wilson E M *MB BCh BAO* 150182
Ismaili N A *MB ChB FRCS* 300582
George R D *MB BS MRCGP DObstRCOG* 300682
Lynch P *MD ChB MRCP(UK) DObstRCOG* 060882
Conroy M D *MB BCh BAO MRCGP DCH DObstRCOG* 080882
Hannigan B G *MB BCh BAO MRCP* 041182
Bencini R A *MD MRCGP DCH* 130183
Ahern M D *MB BCh BAO DRCOG* 220283
Jolliffe D S *MB BS MRCP(UK) MRCS* 070783
Menzies R C *MB ChB MRCPath DMJ DMJ(Path)* 150783
East J A *MBE MB BCh BAO DAvMed MFOM* psc 280783
Cantlay L S *MB ChB MRCPsych* 040883
Hopkins G O *MB BS MRCP(UK) MRCS DPhysMed* 140883
Hargreaves R J *MB ChB FFARCS* 020983
Sewell P F T *MB BChir FRCSEd* 080983
Winfield C R *BM BCh MRCP(UK) DCH* 110983
McCarthy D O'B *FRCS* 011283
Mackay B G *MB BS MRCGP DObstRCOG* 221283
Grieve D K *MB BS FRCR MRCS LRCP DMRD DCH* 301283
Adams F T *MB BCh* 160284
Brown P M *MB BS FRCS LRCP DO* 080384
Youell A G *MB BCh BAO* 010784
Henderson D V C *MB BCh BAO* 290784
Wright D H *MB BS* psc 040884
Faithfull-Davies D N *MSc MB BChir MRCPath* 110884
Gordon E *MB ChB LMSSA DPhysMed* 280884
Ryan J M *MB BCh BAO FRCS* 120185
Lillywhite L P *MBE MB BCh* psc 020285
Reilly M J *BM BCh MRCP MRCS DObstRCOG* 100285
Millar K N A *MB ChB* psc 030885
Lyon Dean C W *MB ChB MRCGP* 040885
Smith D W *MB ChB MRCGP DRCOG* 040885
Macdonald R J M *MB ChB FRCSEd* 070885
Gray N *MB BCh BAO FRCSEd* 200885
Gauci C A *MD FFARCS* 071285
Thompson S G *MRCGP MRCS LRCP* 010186
Barber T S *FFARCS LRCSI&LM DA* 080186
Le Mesurier R T *BM BCh FRCS DO* 140286

Majors

Kumarasena H A D *MB BS FRCS* 010278
Symon T *MB ChB* 190578
Attard G J *MD FRCSEd* 270578
Coogan J S V St R *MB BCh BAO MRCPsych DPM* 040778
Orchard C J *MB ChB MRCOG* 210778
Croker G H *MB ChB* 280978
Lovegrove J E *MB BS FRCS LRCP* 100279
Grundy-Wheeler N J *MB BS MRCGP MRCS LRCP DA* 220279
Inglis S T *MB BS FFARCS MRCS LRCP* 110479
Box C J *MB BS DRCOG DAvMed AFOM* 150579
Carley R H G *MB BS MRCS MRCS LRCP DRCOG* 230679
Hannon C *MB BCh MRCGP DRCOG* 030779
Young K R *MB BS MRCOG* (*L/Lt Col* 110485) 220779
Batty C G *MBE MB ChB FRCSEd FRCS(Glasg)* 070879
Lansley P H *MB ChB MRCGP DRCOG* 100879
øDuggan E J *MB ChB BSc FRCS* 051279
Lantos H W G *MB BCh* 091279
Brookstein R *MB BChir FRCS* 100180
Wetherill M H *MB BS FRCS* 130180
Macmillan A H M *MB ChB* psc 070280

Royal Army Medical Corps — continued

Jackson D S MB ChB FRCS 210280
Thompson M C MB ChB FFARCS DCH DRCOG 100480
Durnford S J MB BS MRCGP MRCS LRCP DAvMed ph 300480
Saggar S N MB ChB FFARCS DA 030580
Shepherd A F I MB ChB BAO FRCSEd 110580
Myles R W MB BCh BAO MRCOG 300680
Cogbill K L MB ChB DRCOG 020780
Milligan G R MB ChB MRCGP DRCOG 250780
Guy P J MB ChB FRCSEd 280780
Thornton R MB ChB DIH DAvMed MRAeS MFOM ph 280780
Green A D L MB FRCSEd 310780
Atalla A E MB BCh MRCOG 020880
Simon J W BM BCh MRCP MRCS 080880
Pampapathi M R 031280
Chowdhury C R MB BS FRCSEd 170181
Borthwick-Clarke A MB FRCR 190181
Goel R K MB BS FRCS DO 210381
Parnell C J MB BS FFARCS MRCS LRCP 010481
Jowitt M D 260481
Freeman K MB BCh MRCP MRCS LMSSA 060781
Rasor P A MB BS FRCSEd LRCP 060781
Braithwaite M G MB ChB DRCOG ph 070781
Henderson A MB BMedSci MRCP 200781
Davies T W MB ChB 050881
Clarke J R MB BS FRCS(Glasg) DO 060881
Miller S A St J MB BChir MRCGP DRCOG 060881
Ward A B MB ChB BSc MRCP 060881
Johnston B MB ChB MRCOG 090881
Mellor S G MB BS FRCS 090881
Lloyd J S MB BS MRCP(UK) 110881
ØHeah J T C F MB ChB MRCOG 181081
Waring A J MB ChB MRCGP 261181
Finnegan T P MB BS psc 311281
Heap B J MB BChir 210182
Griffiths C L MB BS FRCS LRCP 010282
Johnson N A MB BS LMSSA 010282
Kempster S J MB ChB 010282
Surtees P FRCSEd 010282
Vyrnwy-Jones P MB BS DAvMed ph 010282
Hodgkinson C R ee 200682
Lyon A J MB BCh MRCP(UK) 120782
ØBergman B P MB ChB FRSH 140782
Mumford J D MB ChB MRCPsych 150782
Fairley I M MB ChB DMRD FRCR 200782
Aitken R H MB ChB BSc MRCOG 310782
Sharma A MB ChB DTM&H 010882
ØWells J M MB ChB DRCOG 010882
Chapman P MB ChB FRCSEd 050882
Galbraith K A BM BCh FRCS 090882
ØLodge L H MB ChB 010982
Forber R K J MB BChir FRCS 270982
Hayes G J 081182
Freeland W A MB ChB 091182
McPherson J S MRCS LRCP DRCOG 130183
Mikhael M S H MB BS FFARCS 230483
Groom A F G MB BS FRCSEd LRCP 110783
Pailthorpe C A MB ChB FRCSEd 120783
Tully A M MB 250783
Hobbs N J MB ChB FRCS 010883
McCullough A M MB ChB BAO MRCOG MRCS LRCP 010883
Stirling R W MB ChB MRCPath 020883
Lawrenson G W MB ChB DRCOG 040883
Raby N D MB ChB MRCPEd 070883
Whiteoak R MB BChir MRCP(UK) 080883
Allen J C MB ChB 240883
Boreham J J C MRCS DRCOG 200983
Deans J A J MB BS MRCS LRCP 010284
Jones R L D MBChB MRCGP DRCOG MRCGP 010284
Keech J P MB BS MRCS LRCP DRCOG DTM&H 010284
Strowbridge N F MB BS DA 020484
Donaldson J G LRCP 200484
Sloss J M MB BS BSc 100684
Ineson N MB BS MRCP(UK) 310784
Graham J T MB ChB BAO 010884
Sibson J W MB ChB 010884
Kutarski P W MB BS 280884
de Mello W F MB BS DRCOG 290884
Burgess J E MB BS MRCGP MRCS LRCP DRCOG 011184
Henderson L MB ChB 131284
Page I J MB BS MRCS LRCP 080185
Crate I D MB BS MRCS LRCP 010285
ØBoxer C M MB BS 190285
Jefferson T O MB DRCOG MIL MRCGP 310785
ØCory P MB BCh 010885
Von Bertele M J MB BCh ph 010885
Maciver D K MB ChB 260885
ØGlen L M MRCS LRCP 010985
Navein J F MBChB MRCGP MRCS LRCP 010985
O'Brien L S MBChB MRCPsych LRCP 010985
Ward P J 010286

Captains

Edmondson-Jones J P MB ChB 010881
Matthews S J E MB BS MRCS LRCP 010881
Phillips C J MB ChB 010881
Royle C A J P MB BS 010881
Thorp T A S MB ChB LRCP 010881
Hoad N A 070881
Miles D M MB ChB 310881
Brooks T J G MB BChir LMSSA 091081
Chinneck P J E BM 250182
Hawley A MB ChB 010882
Barker G J MRCS LRCP 011182
ØAnderson R C MB ChB 011183

Administrative Officers

Brigadiers

Francis B L 030386

Colonels

O'Neill C 091184
Banks G 020285
McCaffery A M BEM MBIM MRSH RGN 030386

Lieutenant Colonels

Whitfield D M MBE MBIM (A/Col 251085) 010981
Cooper-Tydeman T R MBIM 060782
Dempsey M J MBE 191082
Davis F E A RGN 011183
Hilton G 020384
Egan J OBE MBIM MChS 091184
Croxon R BEM MBIM 010285
Forsyth R M MBIM 010285
Mason T D MBIM MInstAM 010285
Strain I MacK 010285
Ward J W 010285
Old H K DCR(R) 020285
Morrison F S 300985
Sunderland G A 300985

Majors

Bayley B K MCSP (A/Lt Col 290186) 300678
Darroch P L K (A/Lt Col 130985) 300678
Willman A P RGN (A/Lt Col 010186) 300678
Kibbey S J MSRG MCSP 311278
Ratcliffe M J MBIM DCR(R) sq (A/Lt Col 160985) 300679
Thayne R C sq (A/Lt Col 211085) 300679
Town C J DCR(R) 300679
Cameron A J D 311279
Leitch R A MBE RGN psc 311279
Clarke L G A MBIM LRSH MAMS (A/Lt Col 200985) 300980
Dadds E M 300980
Foster B J (A/Lt Col 010785) 300981
Grainger M W 300981
Holmes R J RGN 300981
Brooks P E 300982
Harrison A J RGN 300982
Kane L 300982
Magee T J RGN 300982
Baker P B 300983
Langham A R J DN RGN 300983
Martindale K DN RMN RCNT 300983
Cobley G R 300984
Fram R F 300984
Graves A 300984
Pope T F 300984
Powrie C P T BSc MBIM im 300984
Newell R J RMN 300985

Captains

Pitcher T S *RGN* 170881
Coombe P A (*A/Maj* 220785) 040182
McGrory J D (*A/Maj* 251185) 230582
Norris S (*A/Maj* 030985) 230582
Vincenti G E 010882
McCarthy J B (*A/Maj* 200186) 090882
Howe S C *RGN* 301182
Lowe D (*A/Maj* 180985) 020183
Newcombe A 020183
Turford R J (*A/Maj* 270985) 020183
Morris D J 050183
Dickinson C J 100684
Martin K L 050185

Lieutenants

Millwater C A (*A/Capt* 130583) 280182

2nd Lieutenants

Jordan A P 040884

Nursing Officers

Majors

McNeilly B J *MRSH MRIPHH RGN RCNT* 020678
Gruber E E *ARRC RGN* 031280
Lyne A *ARRC RGN* 130582
Ashworth J E *RGN* 220583
Botting F G *RGN* 111183
Tate R *ARRC RGN* 180984
Devlin M D *RGN* 310385

Captains

Clarke W M *BEM RGN* (*A/Maj* 170286) 230578
Mackenzie R D T *RGN* 160879
Quinn J D F *RGN* 091279
Price R J *RGN GNCE* 160580
Gac S J *RGN* 160880

Quartermasters

Morris T R V 101071 *Maj* 280682
Wickings R F W 250773 *Maj* 280682
Casey J P *MISM* 261273 *Maj* 170185
Ward C J *FIMLS* 180974 *Maj* 010385
McHugh M 260974 *Maj* 111084
Davies G C 181074 *Maj* 100386
Kavanagh J J *Capt* 200575
Lee P *RMN* *Capt* 130176
Stewart E *RGN* 260776 *Maj* 010479
Harvey J W A *FIMLS* 270976 *Maj* 100386
Thomsett P A *Capt* 030477
Jones L A B *Capt* 250578
Jacobs R F *Capt* 291078
Nunnen J A *Capt* 070179
Pargin M E *RGN* *Capt* 160479
Green J A *MASMC* *Capt* 300579
Hair B F *Capt* 070380
McHale M J *MBE* *Capt* 050780
McCann C J *Capt* 061280
Hall D L *Capt* 070881
Mullen C P *Capt* 240881
O'Meara S J *Capt* 020981
Ward M B L *Capt* 260482
McFaulds R R *Capt* 140782

Non-Medical Officers

Everest R C *MInstPS* 091269 *Maj* 260779
Morris J W A *RGN* 260570 *Lt Col* 060384
Howard E B J 020672 *Maj* 020680
Long J M *MRSH DCR(R)* 110174 *Maj* 110182
Bench D J 150376 *Maj* 020779
Byott W G J *MInstPS* 130976 *Maj* 020680
Baxter J 060378 *Lt Col* 011085

Special Regular Officers

Colonels

Noone V *LAH DA* 020580

Majors

Amberton M A P S 300981

Pharmacists

Captains

øYates J *MPS* 240882

Administrative Officers

Majors

Campbell D A *MInstAM* 300679
Foreman R 040581
Harper B K *MISM MIWSP MAMS* 300981
Bettany D R 300982
Noble A S *MISM RGN BTACERT* 300982
Windess R J *AMRSH MAMS* 300982
Shepherd R C *RMN RGN* 010383
Deck P E 300983
Garland D W *MInstAM* 300983
Hardwick P R 300983
Howarth W 300983
Taylor E I *FIMLT* 300983
Acton N B 300984
Alderson C C 300984
Bowen T J 300984
Flower D R 300984
McKnight W *MBIM DCR(R)* 300984
Rose F 300984
De Bues C V R 300985
Reece-Russel B K 300985
Phillips J A 311285

Captains

Moir B J *DCR(R)* (*A/Maj* 060385) 050874
Seddon R K 091176
Yates D R *MBCS MASMC* adp (*A/Maj* 291084) 150980
Livingstone G J (*A/Maj* 071085) 201080
Jones D J (*A/Maj* 280385) 090381
Jose R A (*A/Maj* 310185) 090381
Reeves T A (*A/Maj* 030984) 090381
Sowka L R 121081
Foster T R (*A/Maj* 240185) 230582
Cherry D A (*A/Maj* 281085) 250582
Best M C 050184
Hives B 050184
Lock A J 050184
Murthi J R 050184
Young K D 040584
Ainsworth J R 050185
Baines C 050185
Bate C D *MISM* 050185
Evans J E F 050185
Holmes T K 050185
Housley R J *BEM MAMS* 050185
Lloyd J C 050185
Medland H J 050185
Nash N T 050185
Burns G H Q 030585

Lieutenants

Nobbs C G *AIMLS* 121082
Pemberton M V 261182
Waller R D *DCR(R)* 270285

Nursing Officers

Majors

Neaves D G *RGN* 280680
Keogh J P *RGN RCNT* 230982
Morgan D R P *RGN* 210183
Millard S G F *RGN* 190583
Cubbin A S *RGN* 050983
Dwyer P A *RGN RCNT* 061183
Lynn C *RGN* 151183
Pocock P A *RMN RGN EN(G)* 080584
McAllister E *RGN* 141184
Insley D C *RGN EN(G)* 291185

Captains

Saunders J E *RGN* 050975
McMillan J M *OND RGN* 240779

Technical Officers

Majors

Hammond W *AIMLT FIMLS* 300983
Ingram R K *FCR(R) DCR(MU)* 300983
Miller L J *MIEH* 300983
Simpson D M M *MIISM MRSH MIEH* 300983
Wantling L *FIMLT* 300983
Towersey B L 300985

Captains

Broadbent A N (*A/Maj* 010884) 201080
Armstrong C I *FRSH MIEH* (*A/Maj* 260285) 090381

Royal Army Medical Corps — continued

Rattenbury R L *MIEH* 020183

Non-Medical Technical Officers

Majors

Stevens P W *FIMLT* 130180
Warnock K J *MInstPS* 300984

Short Service Officers

Lieutenant Colonels

Irani B S *MBBS DA* 010183

Majors

Bhaskaran U *FRCS(Glasg)* 220279
Fouad S Z *MB ChB FFARCS DA* 011179
øMowat E *MB ChB MRCGP* 040780
Sinha R K *MB BS FRCSEd* 010880
Kingscote A D *MB ChB MRCPsych* 030880
Evans I D *MB BCh MRCP(UK) MRCGP DObstRCOG* 080980
Pani C K *MBBS DA* 270980
Zaklama M S *MB BCh MRCOG* 011180
Van Lare J P *MB ChB MRCP MRCS DPM* 060281
Herberts P J D *BM BMedSci BS* aic 080781
Kusre P *MB BS* 270182
Padwell A 030282
Skipworth J F *MBChB* 030282
Carabot P A *MD DipVen* 060482
Ghosh D *MB BS* 250482
Ghattas B F A *MB ChB DA* 010582
Manus N J *MB ChB FFARCS* 010582
Oak M K *MB BS MRCOG* 010882
Chinn R E *MB ChB MRCPsych* 070882
Kabuubi J B L *MB BS MRCP MRCS* 081082
Gamble D S C *MB BCh MRCPsych* 301082
Kocan M K *MB BCh FFARCS* 271282
World M J *MD BS MRCP MRCS* 070183
Fabricius P J *MB BS MRCP* 010283
Sahi S P *BM ChB MRCP* 100283
Jenkins J H *MB BS BSc MRCPsych MRCS LRCP* 180583
Melia W M A *MB BCh MRCP MRCPI* 190683
Grieve J H K *MB ChB* 010883
øHodgson B H *MB ChB MRCGP DRCOG* 010883
Little J F M *MB BS* 120883
Gillham A B *MB BChir MRCP(UK) MRCGP* 150983
Thomas J *MBBS MB BS* 261183
Denton M *MB BS* 121283
†Bhatt B M *MRCP(UK)* 160284
†Carter M L *MBBS FFARCS* 160284
†Hosni A A *MB BCh FRCSEd* 160284
†Moorthy B 160284
†Yoganathan S 160284
Milner S M *MB BS FRCSEd LRCP* 180284
Subramaniam S *MBBS* 020384
Abdul-Aziz L A S *BM ChB MRCPI* 120484
Titley J V *MB BS* 260484
Bosanquet H G *MB ChB* 230584
Stone M J *MB ChB DRCOG MRCGP* 080684
Bonnici W *MRCS LRCP DCH* 240684
Houghton M W *MB BS MRCS LRCP* 010884
McDonald J D *MB ChB BSc* 010884
Needham V H *MB BS MRCGP DRCOG* 010884
Sheardown J *MB BS DRCOG MRCGP* 010884
Cumberland N S *PhD* 010984
Price B A *MB BS FRCS FRCSEd LRCP* 030984
Johnston I G *MBChB DA* 040984
Lowe D M *MB BCh FFARCS* 060984
Fyvie A D *MB ChB* 290984
Graveston N H *MB BS FFARCS MRCS LRCP* 291084
øPiper M E *LMSSA* 031284
Griffiths M F P 161284
Mackay P M *MB BS MRCS LRCP* 220285
Maung H M *MBBS* 170385
Neville W T *MB BS* 300485
Murphy G R *MB BS* 310785
Bates B J *MB ChB* 010885
Bendelow K *MB BS MRCGP* 010885
Fawcett R L *MB BCh BAO* 010885
Worsley S D *MB ChB DRCOG* 010885
Gallagher C J *MB BS* 040885
øFoot V H 070885
Hands C A H *MRCS LRCP* 130885
†Buchanan N M M *MB ChB MRCP(Glasg)* 150885
Srinivasan M *MB ChB MRCS LRCP* 190885
Rowley P D *MB BS* 310885
Sidebotham C F *MB BS BSc MRCS LRCP* 310885
Gluckman P G C *MBBS FRCS* 010985
Jones K D *MB ChB* 010985
Stevenson P R *DRCOG* 010985
Savundra J E P *MB BS MRCS LRCP* 031185
Bennett J D C *MB ChB* 131185
Kennedy P M D *MB BS MRCS LRCP DRCOG MRCGP* 010286
Kane L J *MB ChB* 160386

Captains

†Ansah-Boateng Y *MB ChB* 270481
North R F *BEng* 020781
Brownhill D K *MB ChB* 010881
Coulson T J 010881
Golding M J 010881
Hughes S J *MB BS MRCS LRCP* 010881
Power R A *MB BS* 010881
Scott A W *MB ChB* 010881
øGrisewood H L *MB ChB MRCS LRCP DRCOG* 030881
øKelly S M *MB BCh BAO* 210881
Hodson C A J *MB BS* 310881
øMantell A J *MB ChB MRCS LRCP* 010981
Dowling J M *MB BS MRCP MRCP(UK)* 131081
Anderson R G W *MRCS LRCP* 020282
†Khan A M *MBChB MB ChB* 100282
Thomson A D *MB ChB* 210282
Whelan T R *BA* 170582
øBenson E M *MB ChB* 010882
Burge T S *MB ChB* 010882
Burnett G R M 010882
Candlish W 010882
Carr R G 010882
øHargreaves R E 010882
Knight M J M *MB BS* 010882
Lockett W J *BM BMedSci* 010882
McCutchan J D S *MB BCh* 010882
McPeake J J *MB ChB* 010882
Moore S P G 010882
øNiemiro L A K *MB BS* 010882
Sinclair D G *MB ChB* 010882
øTravis P J 010882
Donnelly M B *MB BCh BAO* 030882
McCulloch I W L *MB ChB* 030882
Hargreaves M D *MB BS* 050882
Dunlop B N B 060882
McCorkindale J W *MB ChB* 100982
øCunningham M B *BM BCh* 120982
Ford G R *MB BS* 201182
Barr D B *MB BCh* 050183
øClarkson M F *MB ChB* 080283
Drysdale S F *MRCS LRCP* 140283
Parker C J R *MB BS* 240283
Barrell J P *MB BS* 010383
†Jackson C J *MB BS MRCS LRCP* 240683
Allan G M 010883
øBroadbent J A *MB* 010883
Claydon R J 010883
Corps D J 010883
Elder J B *MB ChB* 010883
Gilbert P H *MB BCh* 010883
Grant J J H *MB BS* 010883
Green R E 010883
øGrossmith C M 010883
Harvey P R *MB BChir* 010883
Hill P J *MB BCh* 010883
Kidd A G *MB ChB* 010883
Mabin D C *MB ChB* 010883
øMoore S D 010883
Redman J H *MB ChB* 010883
Rixom J A 010883
Taylor N J J 010883
Thornton D M *MB ChB* 010883
Walker R T A *MB BS* 010883
Wichert S A *MBChB* 010883
øWoodhouse A M 010883
øAngus R A 020883
Bellamy D C *MB BS* 020883
Hall I M *MB ChB* 020883
Horsman G *MBBS* 020883
øSmylie C A *MB BS* 060883
Gillespie P N *MB ChB BAO* 080883
Mills A S *MB BCh BAO* 110883
Grant I B *MB ChB* 270883
Salmon J B *MB BChir* 310883
Bisset R J 010983
Craig G R *BM MB* 010983
Colvin A P *MB ChB* 110983
øGrummitt C C *MB BS* 110983
Grummitt W M *MB BS* 110983
McCallum J D *MB ChB* 110983
øPeters E B *MB ChB* 041083
Lowe P J *MB* 010284
Menzies A R 010284
Sadler R S *MB ChB* 170384
Abrines M J 010584
Atkinson S N *MB ChB* 010884
Cade S J *MB ChB* 010884
Connell B C 010884

Daykin S M 010884
Dowler J G F 010884
Gadd M C 010884
Grant S C D 010884
Hull J B 010884
Jackson T M *MB ChB* 010884
øJames B L *MB ChB* 010884
Johnson P A *MB BS* 010884
Jones T J *MB ChB* 010884
Jones H G *MB* 010884
Keeling J D *MB BS* 010884
Leach A J *MB ChB* 010884
Livesey J R 010884
øMacKellar S E F *MB BS* 010884
Manners T D 010884
Martin S A *MB ChB* 010884
McClure N 010884
McCurdie I M *MB BS* 010884
Nainby-Luxmoore J C *MBBS* 010884
Pounder R 010884
Sharples P E 010884
Singer B R *MB ChB* 010884
øTullberg H T W L 010884
Williams A N 010884
Evans D G R *MB BS* 060884
Timothy H R *MB BS* 060884
Morton I N *MB BS* 080884
Thorpe M A *MBBS* 090884
Barratt J A *MB BS* 100884
Crabtree J *MB ChB* 100884
Barker P G *MB BS* 140884
Stone C M 140884
Simpson R G *MB ChB* 210884
White S T *MB ChB* 010984
Gill R M F *MB BS* 100984
øDennis S E W 110984
Field J M *MB BS* 291184
øAllen P A *MB BS* 010285
Fernando A M 010285
Richards S D *MB BChir* 010285
Baker B C *MB ChB* 100285
Hooper R W H 150485
øBaker S M 190785
øMatthews S M 190785
Baggaley M R *MB BS* 010885
Baker D 010885
øBarnett A J 010885
øGoddard D 010885
Hepburn N C *BSc* 010885
John M R *MB ChB* 010885
Lapham G P 010885
McCall A W 010885
Morgan-Jones D J *MB BS* 010885
Nash S R 010885
øParker S F 010885
Trew G H *MB BS* 010885
øWeir K M 010885
Whitehouse D P 010885
øWilcox K E *MB BS* 010885
Williamson R H B 010885
Wilson R J T 010885
Crabbe R W 020885
Kenny T J W 020885
Grevitt M P 050885
øO'Connor J L 080885
Sharma S K *MB BSc* 080885
øStanley J J *MB BMedSci ChB* 150885
Bunbury M C de St P 200885
O'Kane C A J *MB ChB* 050985
North J P 141085
øLoveden L M 010286
Reggler J G *MB* 010286
Reynolds C D 010286
†Croft A M J *MB BS* 160286
ø†Ferguson D J M *MBChB* 160286
†Smith J H J *MBChB* 160286

Lieutenants

Donohoe J 020783
†Coghill D R 270783
øMyers S R 020784
Muir G H 090784
ø†Collins H F 150784
†Blewett K A *MB* 070185
ø†Laing-Morton P A *MB ChB* 200685
†Moate R D C 200685
†Bedford T A 250685
†Binns N D 260685
†Tyrer M 280685
†Taylor N P 010785
†Dennis M J 030785
†Fielding P D 040785
†Khan K M 080785
†Kay J L 100785
†Robinson D N 100785
†Parker P J 110785
†Bailey R D 150785
ø†Fenton T J 150785
ø†Horrocks C L 150785
ø†Jude B M 150785
ø†Kenyon S E 150785
†Littlewood C R 150785
†Malyon A D 150785
†Morrison S J 150785
†Ohri S K 150785
ø†Stanley J E 150785
ø†Young J J 150785
†Bowyer G W 230785
†Morris J R L 251185
†Hart J D 261185
†Terrell A G 161285
†Davies C 070186
†Firth M 070186
†Leigh-Howarth M 070186
†Ross D A 140186
†Roberts M J 280186

2nd Lieutenants

††Moffat G M 010982
††Jacks A S *BSc* 240683
ø††Abdy S 010983
††Bentley R M 010983
††Bhabutta R K 010983
††Bisson J I 010983
††Bowen J R C 010983
††Buttar P S 010983
††Collins O D G 010983
ø††Dolan C M 010983
††Driscoll J M 010983
††Etherington J 010983
††Hodgetts T J 010983
ø††Hughes S J 010983
††Kane G G *BMedSci* 010983
††Mackie S 010983
††Marshall J A G *BSc* 010983
††Peck D J 010983
††Pritchard I P 010983
††Robertson D G 010983
††Ross G G 010983
††Sandy C J 010983
††Schenk C P 010983
††Shanks T 010983
††Timothy J R *BSc* 010983
††Warwick N G 010983
††Weeks R V 010983
ø††Bentley P C 110184
††Clasper J C 110184
††Cook A S 110184
††Farrar M J 110184
††Gemmell I M 110184
††Wheatley G 110184
††Williams D 110184
††Allingham J P 010984
††Bailey D J W 010984
††Barrett P D 010984
††Beardsworth S A D A 010984
ø††Beardsworth S J 010984
††Bennett N J 010984
ø††Bentley-Walls C A 010984
ø††Bowes S N *BA* 010984
††Brett S J 010984
††Bricknell M C M 010984
††Byers M 010984
††Cooper A J 010984
††Harrison-Smith M K *GradRSC* 010984
††Haworth S R 010984
††Hendrickse A D 010984
††Hobbs C M 010984
††Howe A D 010984
††Jones S H 010984
ø††Kennedy S J 010984
††Kent A W 010984
††Mannings R A D 010984
††McPherson R J E 010984
††Monaghan S P 010984
††Morris C D 010984
††Rea A J 010984
ø††Robertson H M 010984
††Slade J A N 010984
ø††Sydenham J E B 010984
††Timmins B C 010984
ø††Corby J A 210984
ø††France P A 010185
††Kennedy D 010785
††Longden P 010785
††Owers R C 010785
††Smith M P 010785
††Wilcockson A Q 190785
††Sadler P J 200885
††Bramley R J 010985
ø††Brittenden J 010985
††Calcott C P S 010985
††Charlson M J 010985
ø††Dunn R M 010985
††Eaton M D *BMedSci* 010985
††Edwards D P 010985
††England M H 010985
ø††Holden L G 010985
††Hudson S J 010985
ø††Jarrams C E 010985
††Langston C J 010985
††Miller J H 010985
††Nicol A M 010985
†Paley M R *BA* 010985
††Rooms M A 010985
††Russell I D 010985
††Streeter-Smith G H 010985
††Vogwell P C 010985
††Winn J H 120985
††Price-Thomas S P 130985
††McCubbin A T G 190985
††Weir M J S 190985
††Rossiter N D 300985
ø††Lloyd-Davies S V 010186
††Francis A C 070186
††Russell I P 070186
††Taylor A R 070186
††Cook E J 280186

Pharmacists

Captains

Eadon B F J *MPS* 200884
øHannis J A *MPS* 250885

Royal Army Medical Corps — continued

øInkester S E *MPS*	080985
øSkeer K P *MPS*	260985

Administrative Officers

Captains

Manktelow D W	040584
Jones D K	050185
Newbound H P	050185
Newey C G	050185
Stephens M J	050185
Archer G J *BEM*	200585
Clarke A J	200585
Field R	200585
Paine S L	200585
Green J F	020186
Hiscoke B R	020186
Jones C *BEM*	020186
Sanford A	020186
Sharp M J	020186
Sterba M A	020186
White D A	020186

Lieutenants

French M T (*A/Capt* 020784)	111181
Gardner J (*A/Capt* 240386)	111181
Stone H (*A/Capt* 020784)	111181
Tennuci B S	111181
Thomson J C *MBE MISM* (*A/Capt* 240386)	111181
Chapman R (*A/Capt* 141085)	040782
Durbauree A R	040782
Frary M K	040782
Hockram P J	040782
Johnston S J	040782
Lequelenec A C	040782
Read I G *BEM*	040782
Selkirk B *BEM* (*A/Capt* 090985)	040782
Whyte P	040782
Bright P E	301182
Dagg E R	301182
Dobson A	301182
Hawkins A L	301182
Oxley B J	301182
Brogan H P	020783
Clunn J A S	020783
Davies A C *BEM*	020783
Groom R G A	020783
Harrison R W *MISM*	020783
James J L W	020783
Mann D J	020783
Sharp R S	020783
Tredget F S	020783
Williams E D	020783
Grant M E	040484
McIntosh J H	070884

2nd Lieutenants

Fasham D G	040884

Nursing Officers

Captains

Penn W D *RGN*	230578
Houston W J *BEM RGN*	020179
Dunn C *BEM RGN*	050180
Green M	070181
Hoy D M *RGN*	050281
Johnson D C *RMN RGN*	050481
Higham C J *RMN RGN*	010781
Davy K R *RGN*	180881
McCulloch D B *RGN RCNT*	230282
Gray M *MRSH*	240682
Bellwood M *RMN RNMS RGN RNT*	160782
Gunter P V *RGN*	161082
Harris M D	201282
Parrish J R *MISM MRSH RGN SFN*	070883
Mills D P *RMN RGN RCNT*	271283
Payne R G E	150884
Sokolow P J *RGN*	010185
Zissler M J *RGN*	010185
Bonfield C D V	140285
Payant K *RGN EN(G)*	240285
Keel M L *RSCN RGN*	250485
Eldridge M	130685
Craig T J	220885

Lieutenants

Childerley P	120682
McDonald I S	190882
Banks A J	251082

Technical Officers

Captains

Cooper T K N	031177
Stoker T H *MIEH* (*A/Maj* 160484)	090381
Forbes J R	191081
Pearson J E	020183
Chessell R A	210483
Bartlett M J *MCSP*	100783
Naylor J D	100783
Baronne A J	050184
Rolfe D M	050184
Spencer S C	050184
Pullen R W	040584
Membery B G	110584
Whittingham J T	050185
Ayscough D H *DCR(R)*	200585
Gault D F *FIMLS*	200585
Harmer L R W *DCR(R)*	200585
Jordan D *FIMLS*	200585
Wilson M	200585
Goundry D *HDCR*	020186
Robinson J A *FIMLS*	020186
Sayer N G	020186
Smith P E	020186

Lieutenants

Lindsay R	111181
McDonald A	111181
Rasell G J *FRSH MIEH*	111181
Brooks R	010482
Brunton M C	040782
Drake B W	040782
Gisborne B D *MBE*	040782
Moodie R H	040782
Shackleford D K	040782
Wardley A K	011182
Bogunovic M	301182
Wyeth C F	301182
Jackson S G	020783
Lyons A W	020783
Milne P J	020783
Pashen T J	020783

Technical Officers

Hart B *BEM FRSH MRIPHH*	021165
Maj	021276

Short Service Volunteer Officers

Captains

Chapman C J	011085
Whitton A D C *DRCOG*	011085

ROYAL ARMY ORDNANCE CORPS

The Arms of the Board of Ordnance within the Garter surmounted by the Crown

"Sua tela tonanti"

Regimental March

Quick March.......................................The Village Blacksmith

Agents.......................................Holts Branch, Royal Bank of Scotland PLC, Lawrie House, Farnborough, Hants

Corps Headquarters.......................................RAOC Secretariat, Blackdown Barracks, Deepcut, Camberley, Surrey (*Tel No: Blackdown Military Ext:* 514)

Alliances

Australian Military Forces.......................................The Royal Australian Army Ordnance Corps
New Zealand Army.......................................The Royal New Zealand Army Ordnance Corps
Indian Army.......................................Indian Army Ordnance Corps
Pakistan Army.......................................Army Ordnance Corps
Sri Lanka Army.......................................The Sri Lanka Army Ordnance Corps
Malaysian Armed Forces.......................................Malaysian Ordnance Corps

Colonel in Chief.......................................THE QUEEN

Colonels Commandant.......................................Maj Gen P J O'B Minogue ret pay.......................................010180
Maj Gen M Callan *CB* ret pay.......................................010181
*Gen *Sir* Richard Trant *KCB*.......................................010184
Maj Gen W L Whalley *CB* ret pay.......................................010186

Brigadiers

Brown H G *CBE* rcds sowc psc 300681
Istead P W E *OBE GM FBIM* rcds psc ato 300682
Turner J A *ADC FBIM FInstPet* psc pi 300682
Hulme J A jssc psc 300683
Paviour A J ndc psc ato 300683
Forshaw P *CBE FBIM* psc† ato 300684
Parker D S *FBIM* ndc sq s 300684
Jackson J A *MBE GM FBIM* psc ato 300685
Man D A ndc psc 300685
Owen M C *MBIM* psc ato 300685
Van Orton C E psc† pi 300685
Symes P W *CBE MBIM* ndc psc ph 311285

Colonels

Bowden R B im 300680
Underhill P M *OBE* ato tt 300680
John M F *AFInstPet* psc† osc(NIG) pi 300681
Porter D J *FBIM* sq 300681
Botting D F E *CBE* psc† ato (*A/Brig* 061185) 300682
Parry-Davies E M *MBIM* ndc psc† osc(GH) tt 300682
Pickard C R *QGM FIQA MIExpE* psc† ato 300682
Camilleri P F J psc 300683
Fox B R *OBE BSc CEng MRAeS* sq ato gw 300683
Hendy C M G *OBE* ato im 300683
Mathams M L *OBE* psc ato 300683
Mullins K A *BA(Hons) FBIM CBiol MIBiol* ndc sq 300683
Sharland J F F *MBIM* psc† ato 300683
Watts J M *OBE FBIM* s 300683
Baughan D *OBE* psc† ato 300684
Bewley W P *MBCS FBIM* psc† dis sq 300684
Cook J F G odc(AUST) psc osc(NIG) 300684
Curtis K E *FBIM* s 300684
Dickinson R H *AFInstPet* psc† pi 300684
Gillberry G K *FInstPet* pi 300684
O'Dea M J M *OBE* psc 300684
Willis M G D psc† ato 300684
Burden D L ndc psc 300685
Field P J M psc osc(ZIM) 300685
Guy L *OBE CEng MIProdE MBIM* sq ato gw im 300685
Hall M D *OBE GM* psc† ato 300685
Manuel W J ato im 300685
Walton P S psc 300685
Ward A A *OBE* sq 300685
Watt D C sq im 300685

Lieutenant Colonels

Barrett D J (SL) sq ato im 300674
Smith C A (SL) *OBE MBIM* psc† 300674
Janes J R J (SL) 300676
Weatherburn P (SL) 300676
Archer E G sq ato im 300677
Cannons R M *AFInstPet* pi 300677
Hogg M D (SL) im s 300677
McCulloch B D *FBIM MIIM* psc† 300677
Seddon J A F ndc psc osc(NIG) pi 300677
Stones N (SL) sq ato 300677
Cantrell F (SL) *MBIM LRSC MIExE* ato 300678
Eddison J N *AFInstPet* sq pi (*A/Col* 230885) 300678
Ford W V tt 300678
Gane W I (SL) *MBIM* im 300678
Hambly J R (SL) 300678
Knipe A G *MBIM* psc† ato 300678
Rees J A S *DMS FBIM MInstPS* sq im 300678
Allen B *MBIM* ato im (*A/Col* 151085) 300679
Cary G D (SL) pi 300679
Harris D F ndc psc (*A/Col* 131285) 300679
MacColl D J S 300679
Marshall M A pi 300679
Miles E B (SL) *MBIM* sq im 300679
Owen J R psc† ato 300679
Smith A C F *MBIM* ato im (*A/Col* 251085) 300679
Brady O P psc 300680
Cowell G F V *OBE FBIM* ndc sq ato im (*A/Col* 070386) 300680
Eaton J A *MCIT MBIM* sq im 300680
Evans J J (SL) *FBIM MInstAM MInstPS MIL* ato 300680
Ewens M *BA FBIM* psc† ph (*A/Col* 201285) 300680
Goad K J W ndc psc† psc ato 300680
Heap H G sq ato im 300680
Matthews C P (SL) *MBE* 300680
Neale J W *MBIM* im tt 300680
Owen T B *MBE* ato 300680
Ridley T C K *OBE* sq ato im (*A/Col* 311085) 300680
Williamson B F ato im 300680
Bradley W I R *MBIM* im 300681
Chapman G D *FInstPet* sq pi 300681
Chilcott M J P (SL) im 300681
Cooke C P sq 300681
de Wolf S G *MBIM* sq ato im 300681
Elliott D W M im 300681
Fleming P K *MInstAM* 300681
Green C D psc pi 300681
Hudson H D sq ph 300681
John L P *MBIM* sq ato im 300681
Keating J T s 300681
Norman-Bailey A *FInstPet* psc† pi 300681
Putt D M im 300681
Royle J A N R psc (*A/Col* 300885) 300681
Smith M J *MBIM* im (*A/Col* 100386) 300681

*Representative Colonel Commandant for 1986

Royal Army Ordnance Corps — continued

Wallace A S 300681
Woodliffe J A tt 300681
Allkins A M psc 300682
Bedford C R *MBIM* im 300682
Browning G R s 300682
Ford D B H *MBIM* 300682
Furness-Gibbon D N *MBE MBIM* ato 300682
Gerdes G S *MBIM* sq ato im 300682
Haden A P *BA(Mus)* ndc psc pi 300682
Holt G (SL) 300682
Jones B 300682
MacDougall G D ndc psc 300682
Portman S H pi 300682
Shore R G *BA DPhil MBIM* im adp 300682
Baines J F sq 300683
Braithwaite D M *MBIM* 300683
Forrest R G 300683
Gilbertson M A *MBE* psc ph 300683
Grant W D ato 300683
Inshaw I P sq ph 300683
Jeffrey E B *FInstPet* im pi 300683
Kirby R H T psc ato 300683
Lawton R A *MBIM* im 300683
Smith G *MBE* 300683
Stobie D M M sq s 300683
Waddell D B *FInstPet* psc† pi 300683
Chambers P A *MBE BA* psc 300684
Coeshott P M D *MBIM* psc 300684
Courtney-Green P R *MBE* sq ato 300684
Davy R J sq im 300684
Dickson B J *FBIM* psc† ato jsdc 300684
Falle F R sq im 300684
Flanagan P A *MA* psc† 300684
Hodgens D A *MBE* sq ato 300684
Hourahane R D *MBIM* sq ato im 300684
Jiggens M L C *BSc MBIM* psc† im 300684
Lennox R N psc† psc ato 300684
Mitford T A B *MA* psc 300684
O'Kelly K P psc† osc(ZIM) ato 300684
Regan J S *MBIM* im 300684
Rhodes R C J *MBIM* im 300684
Welch A C D psc 300684
Attrill R W sq s 300685
Bennett S L psc 300685
Butterworth A psc† aic 300685
Byrd T sq im 300685
Collis A C psc† ato 300685
Dalby-Welsh T psc 300685
Doyle P R *MA* sq im 300685
Hawkins J R sq ato 300685
Jennings R P *MBE QGM* psc† ato 300685
Lawson R J *MIMH* ocds(SP) sq aic 300685
Pollard A W sq 300685
Roberts M N sq pi 300685
Tennant C B *GM BA* ato 300685
Turner F R *BSc MBIM* pi 300685
Wall P M sq ato 300685
Wallace-Stock P P psc 300685
Warnes D W H *MSc* dis sq 300685
Wilson-Ing A H sq im jsdc 300685

Majors

Phillips C J ato 030864
Campbell J *MIQA MIRTE MBIM* ato tt 160965
Cooper K A ato im 300965
Williams D N tt 011065
Wheeler D D C 310766
Ford J H ato 211066
Pratt R W 051266
Cole B M B 260367
Boulton R B L pi 300667
Muston A J *FInstPet* pi (*L/Lt Col* 110283) 300667
Rose J H *MBIM MInstPS* tt 300668
Cosgrove T M *MBIM* ato 300669
Cutchey M C J s 300669
Downing J H s 300669
Hammond T J *MBIM* ato 311269
Brett B L *MBIM* 300670
Fitzsimmons R H ato 300670
Harris M J T s 300670
Hunt B J ato im 300670
McKinnon I A *BA FInstPet* pi 300670
Schranz A s 300670
Vitali G C L sq o 300670
Arliss R T 311270
Fleming H E s 311270
Bebbington R B ato 300671
MacLagan R J *MBIM* s 300671
Eccles D J *BSc* psc† t* 070971
Dobie J *AMIMI MBIM* tt 311271
Ahearne C J *MBE MBIM MInstAM AIExpE* ato 300672
Bracken R N *MBIM FInstPet* im pi 300672
Hodge M S s 300672
Scott G *MBIM* sq ato im 300672
Avery D G im (*A/Lt Col* 150186) 311272
Steele J H *MBIM* s 311272
Wallis R P R sq ato im 311272
Thompson J J ato 010373
Craven A S s 300673
Pike M A ato 300673
Walker I C s 300673
Hatton D J ato im 311273
Hill M S *MIDPM* (*A/Lt Col* 200186) 311273
Livingstone J im 311273
Brown R J tt 300674
Browne G J *MBE MBIM* ato 300674
Catt R L tt 300674
Clouter A I *GM* sq ato 300674
Coote C R sq 300674
Mills B B C ato 300674
Hollingworth L *MBE* ato 260974
Inman P G *MBIM* im 311274
Stewart M F *MBE MBIM* sq ato im 311274
Grainger J im (*A/Lt Col* 041085) 300675
Markham D *GM* ato 300675
Tregarthen R C s (*A/Lt Col* 220384) 300675
Turner M H *BA* odc(GE) osc(GE) ph (*A/Lt Col* 041185) 300675
Brown J J (*A/Lt Col* 020186) 311275
Cowan T *MBIM* im 311275
Gordon J J ato 311275
Hanington R K G *BSc* 311275
Holtorp P J sq ato 311275
Hortop J M D 311275
Williams J R psc† ato 311275
Bradshaw H ph 300676
Brown L sq im 300676
Thomas G M A ato 300676
Woodward A N W H sq 300676
Newman M E im pi 311276
Price R P sq 311276
Ross I M im pi 311276
Stacey M F *GM* sq ato 311276
Swindley R A *MBE* ato 311276
Thomas R E *BA* im (*A/Lt Col* 270985) 311276
Wright J B s 311276
Ambridge R J o 300677
Ashcroft G M s 300677
Hacon Williams R K *MIQA FAAI MBIM MIExpE* ato im 300677
Lance D C im 300677
Powell R J 300677
Smith R B P *FInstPet* im pi (*A/Lt Col* 230885) 300677
Tweed R W G *MBIM* 300677
Brightman C J sq 311277
Coleman I 311277
Conway-Hyde R H *MBIM MIPDM* s 311277
Edwards J H s 311277
Farey R H im 311277
Ironside N sq im 311277
Kime D C H im pi 311277
Mullins K R 311277
Pearce F R *BSc AIPM MBIM* psc† im 311277
Swift A F s 311277
Thornton S F sq im owc 311277
Williams L M im 311277
York R J *FBIM* sq im 311277
Bayley C A G ato im 300678
Bird R G *MIMH* sq ph s 300678
Dexter A W C s 300678
Hall R F sq aic 300678
Harris M J *AFInstPet* sq im pi (*A/Lt Col* 130985) 300678
Hastings J B ato im 300678
King M T *BSc* sq ato 300678
Nevill J D *BA* im 300678
Roberts S E im 300678
Bensaid R K V *FInstPet* pi 311278
Byles A P s 311278
Collins K N sq s 311278
de Foubert N O H s 311278
Glen T A *BSc AMIMI AIPM* aic I im 311278
Gunson J N *MBE GM* sq ato 311278
Jones S sq adp 311278
Lampard N A ato im 311278
Lyons A W psc (*A/Lt Col* 230985) 311278
McCormack H D *GM* ato 311278
Norris J M F S *MBIM* sq im pi 311278
Patrick A G *BSc MSc* sq ato gw 311278
Staples J E sq ato 311278
Steer F R *MBE CGIA* psc† ato (*A/Lt Col* 041185) 311278
Von Zugbach de Sugg R G L *BA PhD MBIM MMS ACP* im 311278
Woodley P A o 311278
Aitken E B C psc 300679
Bicknell R W ato o 300679
Brice P M *FInstPet* pi 300679
Clare D M owc s 300679
Geddie G K im 300679
Hazlerigg A R T s 300679
Marks D R s 300679
McDermott R *MSc* sq ato im 300679
Wraight C P ato 300679
Beaumont C H *MA* psc† ato 311279
Bentley A D 311279
Butterworth F A *MBE MBIM* sq im 311279
Buxey M J *MSc* sq im 311279
Ewers T J 311279
Ginn R G psc pi 311279
Jackman C H sq ato im 311279
Oldham R C *BSc* psc† ato 311279
Page G A ato 311279

Scourfield-Evans S H sq ato 311279
Simpson A E R *MSc* dis sq ato 311279
Townsend D W *MBIM* ato im 311279
Wylde N N *QGM* psc(a)† ato 311279
Aggett A J H *MSc* im 300980
Boryer R D *MBIM* sq o 300980
Bowen A F s 300980
Chilton D G psc o 300980
Dalley M J *MInstAM MInstPS MITD* o s 300980
Ells D R im 300980
Ewart J V *BA* s 300980
Field C *GM* psc† ato 300980
Foxton P D psc o pi 300980
Furneaux-Harris E A 300980
Gray R C *MSc FInstPet* sq im pi 300980
Greenwood T B s 300980
Griffiths D J P psc pi 300980
Ham F A o 300980
Harness B *AMRSH* owc s 300980
Hawkins P J *MSc* im 300980
Jarman R *BSc* sq im 300980
Jones H A *BSc(Eng) MSc* aic im 300980
Laceby A J psc(a)† ato 300980
Laird J o s 300980
Lamb P F *FRGS MIIM* im o 300980
Marshall I *MSc* ato im 300980
Mendham R F *GM MSc AMBCS* sq ato im 300980
Mobley B G *MASMC* sq im 300980
Mundy H J tt 300980
Neill J R *LLB* 300980
O'Brien P M *MSc* ato im 300980
O'Connell P o s 300980
Overton T W P *MInstAM* o (*A/Lt Col* 130186) 300980
Rees D T sq 300980
Stone A T J sq o s 300980
Taylor A J *QGM* ato 300980
Thompson B D o 300980
Tillotson G *BSc* psc(a)† ato 300980
Vickers J *BSc* psc† ato 300980
West J J G *MSc AMBCS* dis sq ato im 300980
Wilson I R psc† ato 300980
Wright D A *MSc* im pi 300980
Wyborn R T im s 300980
Atherton G S ato im 300981
Bugler R W *MA* psc 300981
Burr L S psc s 300981
Davison M J *MBE* ato im 300981
Den-McKay C A sq aic 300981
Dyer C N psc aic 300981
Fisher K A 300981
Gibson A F *MBE* psc(n)† ato o 300981
Glasby A V *GM* ato 300981
Gunson J B ato 300981
Hardcastle J K s 300981
Harris G W pi 300981
Ingram M D psc ato 300981
Jordan R J ato 300981
Maynard P C *MBE MSc MBIM MIExpE* ato im 300981
Medley R G im o pi 300981
Morgan J W im 300981
Nimick B E *MSc* im 300981
Rapple T B *BSc* psc(n)† ato im 300981
Rowland C R *DMS DipRMCS* s 300981
Taylor A psc ato 300981
Taylorson P J *FInstPet* pi 300981
White C H *MSc* im 300981
Withers J W s 300981
Wood L M pi 300981
Ramsden N St J D o 250682
Airdrie T C *MSc* aic im o 300982
Allington M W psc 300982
Atkey R J *MSc* dis ato o 300982
Bean L E ato 300982
Bridges A *MSc* aic im o 300982
Burrow C C o pi 300982
Carey R C ato o 300982
Carman R T im 300982
Carter P *BSc* aic im 300982
Coward R S psc o pi 300982
Dexter I R J *BSc(Econ)* psc o 300982
Elliott R o pi 300982
Frazer V C M *MSc* im o pi 300982
Graham C J M o pi 300982
Hewlett K J *MBIM MInstAM* 300982
Morley A J *MSc* ato gw o 300982
O'Leary C J *MSc MInstPet* im o pi 300982
Parsons J D o 300982
Paton G W ato o 300982
Postance A J *MSc* im o pi 300982
Ritchie J D M *MSc* aic im o 300982
Rook R psc† ato o 300982
Sharman P M *BA MSc* ato im o 300982
Shute P J o 300982
Southworth R J o pi 300982
Walcroft E G aic o 300982
Wilson T S psc† ato o 300982
Bell N S ato o 300983
Bradley C R im o 300983
Brewer F R W psc ato 300983
Cox G ato o 300983
Cross T *MSc* psc† ato gw 300983
Crowe S J ato o 300983
Eccles R A C o s 300983
Gaskin W J o 300983
Gillott G *BSc* psc† 300983
Hannaway G E M im o pi 300983
Hicks S M o s 300983
Kemp A D sq o pi 300983
McNally N J *BSc MInstPet MIPDM* o pi 300983
Murray T J *BSc* psc im o 300983
Rees I D O *BSc* psc im 300983
Rollason J F *BSc AIExpE* psc† ato 300983
Roycroft M J *MSc* psc† dis o 300983
Timothy P ato 300983
Wilcox M E ato o 300983
Addy S N o pi 300984
Barrow J L S aic im o 300984
Blatherwick M ato o 300984
Caldwell D R ato 300984
Claughton P M pi 300984
Doherty D B ato 300984
Hawthorne G 300984
Henwood P A ato o 300984
Kerley M *QGM* psc† ato 300984
Kerr D J *BSc* ato 300984
Littlewood D 300984
Monk S C 300984
Moules K A *BSc* psc ato 300984
Noutch R 300984
O'Hare J H *BSc* psc(n) ato 300984
Oliver M R ato 300984
Owen S F o 300984
Parle M E ato o 300984
Shackleton R A 300984
Simonds R G psc pi 300984
Southworth M S *MSc* ato im 300984
Tracy M s 300984
Burnett M J ato 300985
Callan P G M *BSc* o 300985
Campbell J S *BA* psc aic 300985
Coombs G R *BEM* 300985
Elderton C R psc† ato o 300985
Ford P M *TEng(CEI)* o 300985
Frere J S B *BA* 300985
Harris P C o pi 300985
Hazeldine D P *BSc* ph 300985
Inman J P *BSc* psc† im 300985
Josling N B *BSc* psc aic 300985
Kay R 300985
Kerr J S s 300985
McGhie P W o 300985
Murphy M G o s 300985
Pearson W E ato o 300985
Pepperell L H o 300985
Ritchie B D *BSc* ato im 300985
Tayler T 300985
Thompson M A W *BSc* im o 300985
Thwaite M C s 300985
Williams A P ato 300985
Wood M D *MA* psc aic 300985

Captains

Stafford-Curtis R G o (*A/Maj* 080285) 181276
Ball P A o 161278
Lloyd C o pi 161278
Hanlon P R ato o 080379
Lamb J S pi 090379
Parrott D E *BSc MIQA MBIM MIExpE AIExpE* ato im 090379
Simpson P A *BSc* psc† ato (*A/Maj* 201285) 090379
Walsh P M psc† ato (*A/Maj* 201285) 090379
Lewington M H o pi 100979
Stanton W E *BSc* aic o 100979
John S E *BA* o s 031079
Boyd A T ato o 301279
Buchanan M H P ato 301279
Carr J M *MBE* ato 301279
Fenwick M A pi 301279
Hewitt C A *CGIA* o pi 301279
Osborne P G pi 301279
Cartwright A M ato o 010380
Jones I A ato 010480
Emmett C N P o pi 100580
Lloyd-Jukes E *BA* 100580
Rees N D *BSc* ato 100580
Thompson D H s 100580
Whale N G P *BA* s 160780
Jackson K A s 030980
Banks N A 090980
Law A R *BSc(Eng)* ato o 090980
Patrick R J ato o 090980
Singer A J ato 090980
Smellie N A ato 090980
Wharmby M J ato o 090980
White T M ato (*A/Maj* 010985) 090980
Wiseman W H o 090980
Oldham R W J ato o 291280
Smyth-Pigott R M o 291280
Stein R S *BSc(Eng)* ato 291280
Storey C A *BSc* ato im 291280
Morrison J G *BCom* ato o 010281
Lodge C G *BSc* ato 030381
Wilberforce J F G pi 100381
Ellis R *BSc* pi 090581
Smith G P E ato o 090581
Wickham M C *QGM* ato o 090581
Cassidy I S J 080981
Duff S J ato (*A/Maj* 110486) 080981
Freegard P L *BSc* ato 080981
Hall S C *BSc* im 080981
Harris P *QGM* ato o 080981
Ward K M P ato o 080981
Phillips F S *BSc* 290981

Royal Army Ordnance Corps — continued

Clarkson S J ato o 281281
France I C aic o ph 281281
Medcalf M F ato 281281
Williamson P ato o 281281
Simmonds P J *FRGS* ph 301281
Crossman P C *BA* o pi 280282
Standfield P C *BA* ato 010482
Shilston M L ato o 080582
Slade S H o s 080582
Abson R S *BSc* ato 060982
Collins D J ato 060982
Hurst W M *BSc* ato 060982
Lloyd N P o pi 060982
Maginess M R ato o 060982
Stamps P F s 060982
Wallace A R ato o 060982
Wilson P *BSc* im o 060982
Hutton W L o pi 220982
Evans M G ato 280982
Wiggell J F ato 200183
Carins J E *BSc* ato 070283
Couch T pi 070283
Groves B N s 070283
McDowall R C ato o 070283
Owen C L *BSc* ato 070283
Roberts L R ato o 070283
Bean P ato 060383
Arnold P A 110483
Biddle I B ato o 110683
Ward R S D pi (*A/Maj* 230885) 110683
King S J o s 270683
Whiteley A D *BA* o 010883
Bagnall-Oakeley M A *BA* o 050983
Inions A o s 150983
Heron C A ato 081083
Hopps D J ato o 081083
Jobbings T N ato o 081083
Lloyd A R ato 081083
Perks F R *BSc* 081083
Saunders G C *BSc* 081083
Sunderland K S J *BSc(Hons)* im 081083
Walker C I *BSc* pi 081083
Heath M D *MBE* 121083
Wilson G G 121283
McCallum R G o s 271283
Beerling P D ato 060284
Cole W O 060284
Gwilliam C J ato o 060284
Hazlewood G A ato 060284
Inshaw D C ato o 060284
Sturges I J *BSc* pi 060284
Nunn I P ato 150284
McKeegan R D s 240284
Grieveson M W *BCom* ato o 050384
Blaber P W G 040584
Morgan C G *BSc(Econ)* pi 060584
Martin R H D s 080584
O'Sullivan G A *QGM* ato 100684
Brant I S *BSc BSc(Eng)* ato o 081084
Parry S J o pi 081084
Goldie A N *BSc* im 101084
Tonkins W C *BEM* 050185
Dade R o 050285
Dyer P C *BSc* ato 050285
Elwell R S 050285
Fox A S aic 050285
Mouat T N ato 050285
Noakes A D *BSc(Eng)* ato 050285
Redwood J E S o 050285
Smith J C D *BA* ato 050285
Whittaker K N 050285
Winchcombe P P 050285
Ough R J 200385
Galt J D A pi 260385
O'Byrne R N ato 120585
Davis M J ato o 090685
Seymour T D ato 090685
Turner D P ph 090685
Peacock R *BSc* 030985
Simon A H *BA* 250985
Argyle G W 071085
Blackwood B W ato o 071085
Dolamore M I *BSc* 071085
Gosney P J *BSc(Hons)* im pi 071085
Malin L J *BA* ato 071085
Wilson S P *BSc* 071085
Arkinstall J *BEM* 311085
Green A M ato 081285
Newell D ato o 070186
Greathead R F 040286
Simpson J P *BSc* 040286
Edwards R K ato 070486

Lieutenants

Blake S L (*A/Capt* 161184) 271181
Tween K N ato (*A/Capt* 121283) 081281
Whitaker J M ato o (*A/Capt* 101284) 081281
Simpson M C (*A/Capt* 231184) 160382
Cousins D M 120482
Lawrence R H ato (*A/Capt* 101284) 120482
Scurfield R W S *BSc(Eng)* (*A/Capt* 150785) 120482
Phelan D 280682
Farrow A D *BSc(Eng)* (*A/Capt* 010186) 090882
Hobday M E *BSc* (*A/Capt* 100685) 090882
Marshall S A 090882
Ruddock I D *BA* ato (*A/Capt* 120286) 090882
Saddleton P R ato (*A/Capt* 101284) 090882
Burton A W (*A/Capt* 180685) 170882
Nixon A C 151082
Vernon P S 231182
Bouch M C ato (*A/Capt* 170286) 131282
Bristow A D (*A/Capt* 261184) 131282
Crosby A pi 131282
Hirst A M ato (*A/Capt* 121283) 131282
Le-Var R W (*A/Capt* 070185) 131282
Lee C N D ato (*A/Capt* 050285) 131282
Wilkinson A E A (*A/Capt* 290985) 131282
Scott H J 180283
Albon A R ato (*A/Capt* 100386) 110483
Blong C 110483
Davies D C *BSc* 110483
Gee A G *BA* 110483
Hardy M R 110483
Ness T J 110483
Herring R J 090783
Hook M H J 020883
Marshall A J 080883
Maxwell R J C ato (*A/Capt* 070185) 080883
Stevens A D 080883
Dunn M L 301083
Bazire M H (*A/Capt* 050285) 121283
Evers T J M (*A/Capt* 190885) 121283
Farrington S T 121283
Reddick A J ato (*A/Capt* 170286) 121283
Douglas J M 090484
Dowe S P ato (*A/Capt* 170286) 090484
Harris M E *BSc(Econ) PGCE* 090484
Hodder C H ato (*A/Capt* 100286) 090484
Pepper M E *BSc* 090484
Sanderson C J H 090484
Simpson P W H 090484
Snaith C 090484
Bird D 070884
Gibbons D A H 070884
Grinstead J S *BHum* 070884
Moxon E N *BSc* 070884
Selling N pi (*A/Capt* 181185) 070884
Sims J M *BSc* 070884
Young M A 070884
Nash C A 121084
Smith R J 111284
Botto C J 120285
McGarr G *MMS* (*A/Capt* 140285) 140385
Goodman A J 020485
Cooper S R 090485
Gilbert J M 090485
Maybery R L 090485
Wilkes N C B 090485
Kendrick M P J 050685
Forster T P M s (*A/Capt* 020985) 060885
Leece S R 240985
Bolton N G 101285
Wicks D C 070486

2nd Lieutenants

††Hawthorn N R M 030982
Seddon R H 040884
Underwood M J 040884
Wilding H M 040884
††Jones J P 230984
Cooper M O 130485
Kavanagh C J 130485
Sharman A T M 130485
Short N P 130485
Berragan N B 100885
Dixon M W 100885
Lawrence G J 100885
Scoley P G 100885
†Harrold P A *BSc(Hons)* 060985
†Poole C A *BSc(Econ)* 060985
†Towndrow D W *BSc* 060985
††Anderson G C 240985
††Clack G C 240985
††Tyler D P 240985
Lewis P R 141285

Staff Quartermasters

Budge R W 040272
Lt Col 011182
Burnip W 150174
Lt Col 140484
Humphreys J A J 290675
Maj 140683
Allan W D *MBE MInstAM* 290975
Lt Col 110783
Twitchett H R *MInstAM* 010376
Lt Col 010885
Masterson W P 241276
Maj 050782
Matthews D *BEM MInstAM* 300377
Maj 080483
Smith G *MBE* 300377
Lt Col 010885

Murray J W *MBE MISM* 160977 *Maj* 130484

Granger R E 100478 *Maj* 280382

Berridge R W *BEM MBIM* 011078 *Maj* 130583

MacEwan L N A 111278 *Maj* 151182

Minchinton H A *Capt* 280579

Casbolt B D *MBE MBIM MInstAM* 140981 *Lt Col* 301184

Ordnance Executive Officers

Buck E *BEM* 021071 *Maj* 251079

Smith B P 150273 *Maj* 150281

Jordan L W 031273 *Lt Col* 010484

Symons R D 241273 *Maj* 241281

Adams W C 271273 *Maj* 010479

Simpson S 110574 *Maj* 110182

Lawrence S *MBE BEM* 130574 *Lt Col* 280683

Harris M 230674 *Maj* 230682

Brunt J 070175 *Lt Col* 270784

Houseman J *MBCS* 240775 *Maj* 180278

Page B A *BA MBIM MInstPS* 150875 *Lt Col* 280784

Wynn J H 200875 *Lt Col* 230486

Boucher B J 290975 *Maj* 220279

Larrard L A W 181075 *Maj* 050982

Triggs D 171175 *Maj* 041183

Bell D *MBIM* 081275 *Maj* 040777

MacKay D M 121275 *Maj* 221182

Mayne D E 070276 *Maj* 020983

Brown W P R 260276 *Maj* 250382

Taylor A T *GM* 130376 *Maj* 020983

Keane T A T *BEM* 240476 *Lt Col* 011284

Connelly J P 040676 *Lt Col* 030784

Binns K M 150676 *Maj* 260883

Whitwham P M 100776 *Maj* 230781

Young K 230976 *Maj* 130184

Vaughan H A *MBE* 260976 *Lt Col* 061184

Hoe C E R adp 301176 *Maj* 290483

Crawford J R 250177 *Maj* 051282

Stewart M A W 270177 *Maj* 260982

Reid R 260377 *Lt Col* 121085

Bull A 300377 *Maj* 270884

Lentz M J 300377 *Maj* 270884

Ore J B 300377 *Maj* 110584

Bolt J E *MBE* 240677 *Maj* 010479

Course A R 030877 *Lt Col* 011185

Pincher S 020977 *Lt Col* 220486

Dorning N 150977 *Maj* 161184

Graham P A *MBE* 201077 *Maj* 100585

Longmoor R D 300378 *Maj* 300386

Miller R L 300378 *Maj* 020385

Noblett M G *BEM* 300378 *Maj* 060186

Auton W 030478 *Maj* 021283

McGrellis J A *MBE* ato 090578 *Maj* 130583

Kilbride D 010678 *Maj* 210183

McGrellis G 100678 *Maj* 010479

Fuller C M *MMS* 130678 *Maj* 180383

Munce A R *MInstAM* 290678 *Maj* 111085

Veal P E 300678 *Maj* 080285

Callaghan N 010778 *Maj* 050186

Bartle G *MBE MInstAM* 290778 *Maj* 011185

Lilley C H *BEM MInstAM* 030978 *Maj* 060184

Wood T *MBE* 080978 *Maj* 201183

Griffiths J 100978 *Maj* 110283

Train B K *MBE MInstAM MISM MASMC* 110978 *Maj* 310585

Anderson D M 011078 *Maj* 010181

Knight M W 111078 *Maj* 050882

Rowe D G 201078 *Maj* 010181

Wheeler J A E *Capt* 281178

Moughton F W *DMS MBIM* im *Capt* 301178

Wilkinson R C *Capt* 181278

Westbrook R C 241278 *Maj* 141284

Morling J W *Capt* 010479

Moore A D 180479 *Maj* 040283

Parry A 240479 *Maj* 200784

Hedley J *Capt* 010579

Harcourt G W *MInstAM MISM* 190579 *Maj* 280486

Atkinson P C *Capt* 200679

Dale J E 010779 *Maj* 270184

Sheridan P J 100779 *Maj* 070185

Hart M J 300779 *Maj* 171183

Bridle N J 030879 *Maj* 050185

Haycock B A *MInstAM* 250879 *Maj* 030386

Glendenning I *BEM* 020979 *Maj* 090484

Brown A *BEM* *Capt* 050280

Mitchell K W *Capt* 100380

Hickey J A *MASMC* *Capt* 010480

Moody M *Capt* 010480

Willox R G 010480 *Maj* 280984

Edge R G 020480 *Maj* 160386

Brown A J 090480 *Maj* 060186

Young A *MInstAM* *Capt* 110480

Jenkins B L 140480 *Maj* 180383

Curtis R A W 250480 *Maj* 080285

Hinchliff C E *MBE* *Capt* 020580

Grant J G 140580 *Maj* 020684

Halsall J L 010680 *Maj* 140984

Print J W *MMS* 220680 *Maj* 140984

Gower A J 010780 *Maj* 060186

Parsons M E 200880 *Maj* 300983

Miller M E 310880 *Maj* 010384

Goodswen G *Capt* 010980

Palmer M W 200980 *Maj* 251183

Buckle C G o 051180 *Maj* 130484

Downes B A *MIMH* *Capt* 211280

Cooper R F *Capt* 060181

Marshall G D R *Capt* 240181

Brant A *Capt* 230281

Clark D J *Capt* 030381

Foster J T *Capt* 300381

Hawkins T P *MInstAM* *Capt* 300381

Pedley A E *Capt* 300381

Jelly A N B 010481 *Maj* 100284

Lill T R *Capt* 020481

Wafforne I D *Capt* 260581

Priestley R 010681 *Maj* 080285

Davies D G *Capt* 060681

Park T C *BEM* *Capt* 280781

Hammond T T *Capt* 120981

McCabe M *Capt* 121081

Oldham W D *GM* *Capt* 171081

Mackey P *Capt* 031181

Hampton W J *MBIM MInstAM* *Capt* 271181

Walker E J *MBE* *Capt* 281181

Whitaker K W *Capt* 231281

Palin T *Capt* 010282

Wood J R *Capt* 010282

Ward A 010582 *Maj* 260485

Redfern E J *BEM* *Capt* 040582

Allen M C *Capt* 130582

Wilson B P *Capt* 140782

Hillan E C A *Capt* 180782

Kenwright J F *Capt* 140882

Bennett J *MBE* *Maj* 230982

O'Shaughnessy A F *Capt* 111082

McGill J B *MBE MInstAM* *Capt* 121182

Robinson C *BEM* 291282 *Maj* 080483

Kitwood J 301282 *Maj* 030383

Gill R *QGM* ato 311282 *Maj* 190485

Royal Army Ordnance Corps — continued

Name	Rank	Date
Stephenson F *MBE*	*Capt*	311282
McCusker R W		070483
	Maj	080785
Jones H D	*Capt*	100483
Pitchforth E R *MInstAM MISM*		120483
	Maj	180185
Fripp D R	*Capt*	250483
Alford J A *MMS MASMC*	*Capt*	050583
Hartley M J	*Capt*	090683
Hewitt D C ato		150683
	Maj	291185
Hudson W S	*Capt*	170683
Ball R W *MISM*	*Capt*	020783
Henty D M J	*Capt*	170783
Walton J	*Capt*	080883
Hendy T	*Capt*	250883
Davenport C F	*Capt*	290983
Jackson B D *MBIM*	*Capt*	051083
Fagg L J	*Capt*	151083
Jay K C	*Capt*	071183
Crisp R B *BEM*	*Capt*	081183
Starrett E P	*Capt*	091183
Mallett G J	*Capt*	101183
Prior-Sanderson R J	*Capt*	311283
Talakuli M	*Capt*	311283
Trebble R	*Capt*	311283
Chisholm R	*Capt*	010484
Garrod M E *MBE*	*Capt*	010484
Auger C B *BEM MInstAM*	*Capt*	030784
Toland R E	*Capt*	030784
Walch A C	*Capt*	270784
Kennedy C V *MInstAM MISM MASMC*		300884
	Maj	140685
Banfield W R ato	*Capt*	211084
Denholm G J	*Capt*	211084
Lowe M	*Capt*	211084
Drew I W	*Capt*	221084
Turrell P M	*Capt*	231084
Moore P J	*Capt*	221184
Cook E J *BEM*	*Capt*	281184
Greenaway D *BEM*	*Capt*	281184
Longley D J	*Capt*	011284
Matthews M D	*Capt*	120185
Pugh M R	*Capt*	220185
Walls R G	*Capt*	280185
Cook E G	*Capt*	070285
Shepherd B R	*Capt*	080285
Haugh D T *BEM BA*	*Capt*	040385
Underhill W J *MIQA*	*Capt*	020485
Snow P	*Capt*	080485
Nanovo A T	*Capt*	010585
Harmon S P	*Capt*	050585
Sowerby P E	*Capt*	060585
Tait T N	*Capt*	210685
Collett B I N	*Capt*	010885
Timms D J	*Capt*	010885
Beaton W	*Capt*	210885
Langridge B A	*Capt*	220885
Burke T *MISM*	*Capt*	230885
Prior J W *MBIM MInstAM MISM*	*Capt*	300985
Greig D J *MIQA*	*Capt*	011085
Lawrence G J	*Capt*	121085
Knight M J	*Capt*	011185
Hubbard J R	*Capt*	101185
Barker N	*Capt*	301185
Johnson W S *MISM MASMC*	*Capt*	301185
Charlesworth A M *BEM*	*Capt*	020186
Lawrence F	*Capt*	010286
Bush R C *BEM*	*Capt*	150286
Ottley G S	*Capt*	170286
Barron D L	*Capt*	190286
Barraclough D M	*Capt*	260286
Garratt G W *BEM MISM*	*Capt*	010386
Bowes F T	*Capt*	010486

Directors of Music

Name	Rank	Date
Price D E psm	*Capt*	140480

Special Regular Officers

Majors

Name	Date
Daykin J G	300676
Goldring S	300678
Icely D A	300981
Roberts B	300981
Evans A G	300982
Bourton J R o s	300983
Clark D M o	300984
Dunn J J *BEM*	300984
Greenshaw R M *BEM*	300984
Guest D G M ato o	300984
Lillington R E F	300984
Brown A o	300985
Byrne R J o	300985
Hillier C	300985
Martin W A s	300985
Morgan J B	300985
Turner I W *MInstAM*	300985
Tweddle W *BEM*	300985

Captains

Name	Date
Hutchinson R D *BA*	070877
Hughes P B *BSc* aic	011179
Manners I R (*A/Maj* 090485)	060180
Brehaut N F G	291280
Briggs T A P o	250881
Smethurst C R ato	080981
Sturdy A J	080981
Smith S P *BA* ato o	290981
Scott P *BSc* o s (*A/Maj* 160985)	090282
Watkins M K *GradIISEC MIExpE* ato	250382
Griffin A G *GM*■	060582
Emerson S J ato (*A/Maj* 191185)	200582
Dey G (*A/Maj* 310186)	190882
Ginn S R T	281082
Johnson B J (*A/Maj* 280286)	181182
Lear R B	300383
Worrall J R *BEM*	300383
Errington-Weddle B A o	081083
Brace B N	121083
King W J M	121083
Thomson G *BEM*	121083
Tuck A C	121083
Wood G	121083
Anfield A *BEM*	121283
Donoghue J A *BEM*	010284
Johnston J A	010284
Knoll P R	010284
Liddell D	010284
Eagle M R G *BSc MPS* ato	060284
Homewood D M	040584
Weeks H E E ato	310884
Dudley A F	111084
Irvine W D	111084
Tidmarsh J *BEM*	111084
Carey M o s	050285
Le Sueur M R o	050285
Robinson R	160585
Bondsfield M	120885
Gregory R	311085
Jenkins S G	101285
Bruce R V *GM*	020486
Crossland G	020486
Myers S	020486
Quigley B J	020486

Lieutenants

Name	Date
Reid C I	120981
Mapstone P J (*A/Capt* 040685)	071081
Gallagher M A	201081
Greenwood V	011181
Patterson S J aic (*A/Capt* 200985)	081281
Davies D K L (*A/Capt* 100185)	100182
MacLaren A S	020282
Goff R (*A/Capt* 010885)	080482
Roberts T (*A/Capt* 090585)	080482
Stuart E K (*A/Capt* 080485)	080482
Farbrother J T ato (*A/Capt* 030284)	120482
Brooks R G (*A/Capt* 310585)	300582
Stacey R A P ato	200682
Philpott P W	040782
Bates M	300882
Mitchell P *MBE QGM*	091082
Adam G C	131082
Elliott G I (*A/Capt* 011285)	131082
Laing I H *BEM* (*A/Capt* 161185)	161182
Menzies W S	270283
Bond R J E	050583
Ryder D *BEM*	270683
Watkins L H	080883
Gowans T A	111083
Burnham D	090484
Donaldson J K	111284
Slater G W	111284
Songhurst N D	111284
Storey G E	111284
Armstrong S R	240485
Cameron R B (*A/Capt* 060186)	060885
Dawson C P (*A/Capt* 161285)	101285
Haines S R	101285
Coole D	141285
Carter S J	070486
Clayburn R R R	070486

2nd Lieutenants

Name	Date
Richmond S J	040884
Lynch M D	080984
Holmes M R	081284
Salmons A N E	081284
Smith D A	081284
Redwood P A	130485
Ruff D B	130485
Davis G E A	100885
Wilson P A	100885
†Oxborough R J *BSc PGCE*	060985

Short Service Officers

Captains

Name	Date
Howard G	201181
Lillystone D F *BA* o pi	050583
Royle K	230683
Edwards M B *BA*	130983

Lacis M *BSc* pi 031083
Curtis M E *BA* 071084
Bamford C H W pi 071085
Kearns P T *BSc* 040286
Mollison K *MA(Hons)* 040286

Lieutenants

Jones R S
(*A/Capt* 021285) 040881
Millward P D *BSc* 030981
Harrison R
(*A/Capt* 021184) 021081
Ling R pi
(*A/Capt* 161184) 081281
D'Souza P J A
(*A/Capt* 271284) 271281
Munro I C 020182
Simmons P F 020282
Davis R S 080482
Challis N P *BSc* 120482
Donovan C J *BA* 120482
Woodyear C D J *BA* 120482
Bulmer E D
(*A/Capt* 040785) 040782
Watts P J
(*A/Capt* 040785) 040782
McIntyre A D *MISM* 010882
Guild R T 080882
Bevan J D 090882
Currie D T *BSc* 090882
Goodwin N J *BA* 090882
Mead W *BSc* 090882
Crabbe D 270882
Nicholson K *MBE BEM*
(*A/Capt* 270885) 270882
Smith P D
(*A/Capt* 010985) 010982
Hagen R W M 031082
Arkle A
(*A/Capt* 091085) 091082
White C R 091082
Coull P
(*A/Capt* 161185) 161182
French W R *RVM*
(*A/Capt* 271285) 201282
Marsh D W
(*A/Capt* 211285) 201282
McPhee M J
(*A/Capt* 260186) 260183
Callan R R 010283
Gray D
(*A/Capt* 010386) 280283
Ockleton D R 020383
Towers-Clark D 160383
Gibson A M *BA* 110483
Jones A R *BSc* 110483
O'Shea J *BSc* 110483
Paramore A 110483
Patchitt B
(*A/Capt* 110486) 180483
Bragger B W 210483
Matthews J P *MISM* 210483
Bradley D C
(*A/Capt* 111185) 080583
Sandison A G 020783
Wolfe D W 090783
Kennedy A J *MISM MASMC* 200783
Mardon L D 060883
Allen J R *BSc* 080883
Quinn K A 270883
Kelly D A 100983
Michael P 140983
Sutterby P 210983
Beagle P R
(*A/Capt* 280585) 121283
Hayward L M 121283
Rushworth C 121283
Astley N I 090484
Clydesdale A N *BSc* 090484
Coveney R M 090484
Gooderham C J B ato 090484
Hawkins J H A 090484
Hazou J N 090484
Cree R 070884
Jones R C 070884
Poffley M W *BA* 070884
Urch M J S *BSc ARCS* 070884
Allen T H 111284
Gliniecki M *BSc* 111284
Grogan J A 111284
France T G 060885
Fisher T M J 101285
Cieslik N P 070486
Hodgson A 070486
King P R 070486
Levene G A 070486

2nd Lieutenants

Bligh R A 070484
Pope M C 070484
Duncan A J 040884
Neville R C 040884
Porter S S 040884
Campbell A 081284
Dickinson D C 081284
Myers D S 081284
Carter D A 130485
Davies R C 130485
Greenall W J 130485
Dean P R 100885
Gallagher P J P 100885
†Ascroft J R *BSc(Hons)* 060985
†Roberts J M *BSc(Econ)* 060985
Bond C N 141285
†Lonsdale G R A *BA* 060186

CORPS OF ROYAL ELECTRICAL AND MECHANICAL ENGINEERS

Upon a lightning flash, a horse forcene gorged with a coronet of four fleur-de-lys, a chain reflexed over its back and standing on a globe. Above, a crown upon a scroll bearing the letters "REME"

Arte et Marte

Regimental Marches

Quick March..........Lillibulero and Aupres de Ma Blonde
Slow March..........Duchess of Kent

Agents..........Holts Branch, Royal Bank of Scotland PLC, Lawrie House, Farnborough, Hants

Corps Headquarters..........The Corps Secretariat REME, Isaac Newton Road, Arborfield Cross, Reading RG2 9LN

(*Tel No: Arborfield* X 760421 *Ext:* 220)

Alliances

Canadian Armed Forces..........Land Electrical and Mechanical Engineers
Australian Military Forces..........The Corps of Royal Australian Electrical and Mechanical Engineers
New Zealand Army..........The Corps of Royal New Zealand Electrical and Mechanical Engineers
Indian Army..........Corps of Electrical and Mechanical Engineers
Pakistan Army..........Pakistan Electrical and Mechanical Engineers
Sri Lanka Army..........The Sri Lanka Electrical and Mechanical Engineers
Malaysian Armed Forces..........The Malaysian Electrical and Mechanical Engineers

Colonel in Chief..........Field Marshal *HRH The Prince* Philip *Duke of* Edinburgh *KG KT OM GBE QSO*

Colonels Commandant..........Lt Gen *Sir* Richard Vincent *KCB DSO*..........040281
Maj Gen J V Homan *CB* ret pay..........280282
*Maj Gen P H Lee *CB MBE* ret pay..........140283
Maj Gen T B Palmer *CB*..........010486

Brigadiers

MacLauchlan A *ADC BSc(Eng) CEng MIMechE MIEE* psc† psc ptsc 300682
Tyler C *MA CEng FIMechE FRAeS FBIM* psc† ae 300682
Chown R H *CEng FIMechE FRAeS FBIM* ndc nadc psc† 300683
Winchcombe P *BSc(Eng) CEng MIMechE FBIM* ndc psc 300683
Gardner M A *BSc(Eng) CEng FIMechE* ndc psc† 300684
Shaw D *CBE BSc(Eng) CEng MIMechE* rcds ndc psc† osc(GH) 300684
Till J G *BSc(Eng)* ndc sq 300684
Weston R A *CEng MIMechE MRAeS* sq ae 300684
Higson R S *BSc(Eng) CEng MIMechE FBIM* psc† 300685
Hutchinson G M *MA* psc† 300685
Johnston J F J *CBE BSc(Eng) CEng FIMechE FBIM* rcds psc† 300685
Stubbington G R *BSc(Eng)* ptsc 300685

Colonels

Tinkler J R *MA CEng FIMechE FRAeS FBIM* ndc psc† ae 300680
Turner B S *CEng MIMechE MBIM* sq 300680
Gotts B D *BSc(Eng) CEng MIMechE* psc† 300681
Inman T M V *BSc FBIM* psc im 300681
MacPherson R I C *BSc(Eng)* psc 300681
Roberts S J *BSc CEng FIMechE CBIM* psc† 300681
Bidwell D *BSc(Eng) CEng MIEE FBIM* psc† 300682
Dennis J *BSc(Eng) CEng MIEE* psc† 300682
Lord M T A *BSc(Eng) CEng MIMechE* psc† osc(NIG) 300682
Nitsch C J B *BSc(Eng) CEng MIMechE* psc† 300682
Staniforth A G *BSc CEng FIMechE FBIM* psc† 300682
Webber S T *CEng MIEE MIERE* sq ee (*A/Brig* 221085) 300682
Appleton J R *BSc(Eng) CEng MIMechE* ndc psc(a)† 300683
Craxford S C *MA CEng MIEE MINucE MIERE MBCS* psc† 300683
Fleming B *MBE BSc(Eng) CEng MIMechE* psc† ae 300683
Heath M S *BSc(Eng) CEng MIEE MIERE MBIM* ndc psc† aic ee 300683
Quirke G J *CEng MIMechE* psc† (*A/Brig* 210286) 300683
Simpson G B *BSc CEng FIMechE MRAeS* sq ae 300683
Slater G R *OBE BSc(Eng) CEng MIMechE MIProdE FBIM* ndc psc† (*A/Brig* 240186) 300683
Axson D R *BSc(Eng) CEng MIMechE* sq 300684
Briggs R M G *BA CEng MIMechE* psc† 300684
Derbyshire C J *BSc(Eng) CEng MIMechE ACIS* psc† 300684
Elkins T L *BSc(Eng) CEng MIEE MBCS MBIM* sq ee 300684
Glass P P *MBE CEng MIMechE MBIM* psc† 300684
Graham J A psc† osc(NIG) 300684
Lucas R *BSc(Eng) CEng MIMechE MBIM* ndc sq 300684
Porter B D *BA CEng MRAeS* sq ae 300684
Smithson N McC *MA CEng MIMechE* ndc psc† ae 300684
Campbell M *CEng MIMechE MBIM* sq 300685
Carey M H *BSc(Eng) CEng MIEE* psc† ee 300685
Holdsworth R A *CEng MIMechE* sq ae 300685
Palmer W K *BSc(Eng) CEng FIEE* psc† 300685
Rush D J K *CEng MIMechE MBIM* psc† aic 300685
Skinner R J *BSc(Eng) CEng MIProdE MBIM* psc† 300685

Lieutenant Colonels

Hemsley P R (SL) *BSc(Eng) CEng MIMechE MRAeS* sq gw 300674
Martin J A A (SL) *OBE CEng MIMechE MBIM* 300674
Clothier N A E (SL) *BSc(Eng) CEng FIProdE MBIM* 300675
Kirby R V G (SL) *CEng MIMechE MBIM* sq 300675
Mabbett E W *BSc(Eng) CEng MIMechE MBIM* psc† (*A/Col* 200985) 300675
Bidgood J F S (SL) *BSc(Eng) CEng MIEE MBIM* 300676
Cowl P E (SL) *BSc(Eng) CEng MIERE* ee 300676
England S W *CEng MIMechE MBIM* sq 300676
Ivey V M (SL) *BSc(Eng) CEng MRAeS* sq ee 300676

*Representative Colonel Commandant for 1986

James D L *BSc(Eng) CEng MIEE* psc† ee 300676
Moore J P (SL) *BSc(Eng) CEng MIMechE* 300676
Morton A *CEng MIMechE MIProdE FBIM FInstAM MIIM* psc† 300676
Neilson D N *MIMechE* psc† 300676
Stroud A F (SL) *BSc(Eng) CEng MIMechE MBIM* 300676
Wall W E *CEng MIMechE* psc† 300676
Crouch W J *BSc(Eng) CEng MIEE MIERE MBIM* ee 300677
Hastings C D W (SL) *CEng MIEE* sq gw 300677
Kenyon N O (SL) *BSc(Eng) CEng MIMechE MIERE* ptsc ee 300677
Towler J J *BSc(Eng) CEng MIMechE* sq 300677
Durn S V *CEng MIMechE FBIM MIIM* me (*A/Col* 070984) 300678
Nobbs C K F *BSc(Eng) CEng MIEE* sq 300678
Preece R (SL) *CEng MIMechE MRAeS* ae 300678
Stevens C R L *CEng MIMechE MIProdE MRAeS* psc† ae 300678
Terry A J *BSc(Eng)* psc† 300678
Woodall J A *BSc(Eng) CEng MIMechE FBIM* psc† 300678
Abate S J *BSc(Eng) MSc CEng MIEE MBIM* psc† sq gw 300679
Bonnor-Moris D E *BSc(Eng) CEng MIMechE CDipAF* psc† 300679
Courtnell T I *BSc CEng MRAeS* psc† ae (*A/Col* 070685) 300679
Cox P J (SL) *BSc(Eng) CEng MIMechE* 300679
Hancock R M (SL) *CEng MIMechE* ae 300679
Lyon A R *BSc(Eng) CEng MIERE* ee 300679
Ross B F *MBE CEng MIMechE* sq ae 300679
Soar A A *BSc(Eng) CEng MIProdE MBIM* (*A/Col* 200985) 300679
Stevens R D C *BA CEng MIMechE MRAeS* ndc sq ae (*A/Col* 100685) 300679
Tarsnane R *CEng MIMechE MBIM* sq 300679
Wessendorff P J C *CEng MIMechE MBIM* psc† 300679
Wood W H D *BSc(Eng)* sq 300679
Reavill B *CEng MIEE FIERE FIProdE MBIM* sq ee 130580
Ayscough R M *CEng MIMechE* sq 300680
Calderwood R J A *BSc CEng MIEE MIERE MBIM* sq ee gw 300680
Cooper B R *MA CEng MIEE* psc(a)† ee (*A/Col* 101284) 300680
Dolby C R *BSc(Eng) CEng MIEE* sq ee 300680
Harvey H J S ndc sq ee 300680
Lemon M D *BSc(Eng) MSc CEng MIMechE* psc mvt 300680
Newby M R *BSc(Eng) CEng MIMechE* sq ae (*A/Col* 220186) 300680
Squires C J *BSc(Eng) CEng MIEE* psc† 300680
Steel R *BA BSc(Eng) CEng MIMechE MIERE MBIM* sq ee 300680
Drew J R *BSc(Eng) CEng FIEE FBIM* psc† ee 240481
Corp P J G *MA CEng MIMechE* psc† 300681
Davey J W *BSc(Eng) MSc CEng MIEE* sq ee gw 300681
Heggie C A *MA CEng MIMechE MBIM* psc† 300681
Le Quesne J E *BSc(Eng) CEng MIEE* psc ee (*A/Col* 151185) 300681
MacDonald R O *CEng MIMechE* sq 300681
McArthur I *CEng MIMechE* sq 300681
Osman K J A C *MBE BSc(Eng) CEng MIEE* psc† ee adp 300681
Ost P L *BA BSc(Eng) MSc CEng MIERE FBCS* dis sq ee 300681
Pullen C J *BSc(Eng) MSc* odc(US) mvt sq 300681
Ray J B *CEng MIMechE MBIM* sq 300681
Rodgers K W A *BSc(Eng) CEng MIMechE* psc† 300681
Sharman A G *CEng MIMechE* psc† (*A/Col* 141085) 300681
Steel K W *CEng MIMechE MBIM MIIM* psc† osc(NIG) (*A/Col* 181085) 300681
Varney J E *BSc(Eng) MSc CEng MIEE* sq ee gw 300681
Widdowson J *CEng MIMechE MBIM* sq 300681
Bellis R H sq 300682
Curphey E H *BSc(Eng) CEng MIEE* psc ee 300682
Fines B J *CEng MIMechE MRAeS FBIM* sq ae 300682
Gibson P H *BSc(Eng) CEng AMIEE MIERE* psc† ee 300682
Jones G P sq 300682
Lipsett R M *BSc(Hons) AMIEE MBIM* sq ee 300682
Meagher A G P *BSc(Eng) CEng MIMechE* sq 300682
Millington A H *BSc(Eng) CEng MIMechE MBIM* sq 300682
Osborne N J L *BSc(Eng) MSc CEng MIEE* sq ee gw 300682
Platt A G *BSc CEng MIEE MRINA* psc ee 300682
Potter A J *BSc(Eng) CEng MIMechE MRAeS* sq ae 300682
Rawlins G J *OBE BSc(Eng) CEng MRAeS* psc ae (*A/Col* 270386) 300682
Sleight D W *BSc(Eng) CEng MIMechE* psc† 300682
Unwin R H *BSc(Eng) CEng MIMechE* sq ae 300682
Yeomans J R *BSc(Eng) MSc CEng MIEE* sq gw 300682
Booth F *CEng MIMechE* psc† 300683
Brown C P T *BSc(Eng) CEng MIEE MIERE* sq ee 300683
Hawxwell J A E *BSc(Eng) MSc CEng MIEE MBCS* psc† 300683
Hitchcott M *CEng MIMechE MBIM* sq 300683
Jones R Mc *BSc(Eng) CEng MRAeS* psc† ae 300683
Kay P H *BSc(Eng) CEng MIProdE* sq me 300683
King D E *BSc(Eng) CEng MIEE* psc† ee 300683
Roberts D H *CEng MIMechE* psc† osc(NIG) 300683
Selby M P *BSc(Eng) MIEE* psc† ee 300683
Shepherd J H *BSc(Eng) MSc* dis sq ee 300683
Shields R J *MA* psc† ee 300683
Soar T R *BSc(Eng) MSc CEng MIMechE MIProdE* sq gsd 300683
Watson J P *CEng MIMechE MBIM* psc† 300683
Curran L D *MA CEng MIEE* psc† ee 300684
Darby R G *BSc CEng MIMechE* sq ae 300684
Davidson P C *BSc(Eng) MSc CEng MIEE MBIM* psc† dis ee 300684
Derwent I P G *BTech MSc MIEE* sq ee gw 300684
Hodgkiss B J *BSc(Eng) MSc* sq ae gw 300684
Holland N J *MA CEng MIMechE* sq jsdc 300684
Mullin R W P *BSc(Eng) CEng MIMechE* psc† 300684
Short L W R *CEng MIMechE MBIM* 300684
Wildman M L *BSc(Eng)* psc 300684
Wood J R *MA CEng MIMechE* psc(a)† 300684
Wright D J *MA MSc CEng MIMechE* mvt sq 300684
Ardrey G T *MA CEng MIMechE* sq 300685
Ball A D *MA CEng MIProdE* psc† aic me 300685
Besgrove P V R *BSc(Eng) CEng MIProdE* psc ee jsdc 300685
Crook D *BSc(Eng) CEng MIEE* sq ee 300685
Heathcote R G *BSc(Eng) MSc CEng MIMechE* mvt sq 300685
Joy R M A *BSc(Eng) MIEE MIERE* psc(a)† ee 300685
Major P G *MA* sq 300685
Shorthose R J *BSc(Eng)* 300685
Sibbons M E *BSc(Eng) CEng MIEE MIERE* sq 300685
Skaife D J *MA CEng MIProdE* sq 300685

Majors

Cornish G S C *CEng MIMechE* 270365
Gould N A 310766
Sinclair B G *MBIM* 310766
Griffiths J D C *BSc(Eng) CEng MIMechE MIERE MBIM* 270467
Davies T *BSc(Eng) CEng MIMechE* ae 311267
Hooper I R *CEng MIMechE* sq ae 311267
Williams K S *CEng MIMechE MBIM* ae 311267
McManus D L 300669
Murdoch N L *MSc(Eng) CEng MIEE MRAeS MBIM* sq gw (*L/Lt Col* 040584) 300669
Gilmore S B *BSc(Eng) CEng MIMechE MRAeS* ae 311269
Strong M R *CEng MIMechE MRAeS* sq ae 300670
Britton P J A *CEng MIMechE MBIM MIIM* 311270
Kennett P H *MBE CEng MIMechE MRAeS MBIM* 311270
Anderson W J *MBIM* sq 300671
Bennett R W *BSc(Eng) CEng MIMechE* sq adp 300671
Hunter K E G *CEng MIMechE* ae 311271

Corps of Royal Electrical and Mechanical Engineers — continued

Broughton R *CEng MIMechE* sq 300672
Cameron K S *MSc AMBCS* dis sq 300672
Thompson C M P *CEng MIMechE* 311272
Elkins M J *BSc(Eng) CEng MIEE* ee 280674
Bennett D J *MA* sq ae 300674
Finnamore H J *CEng MIEE MIERE* 311274
Houldsworth K F *CEng MIMechE MRAeS MBIM* ae 311274
Loader R J *CEng MIERE MBIM* ee 311274
Semmons J M W sq ae 311274
Godfrey L W D *BSc(Eng) MSc CEng MIMechE* sq 300675
Norman J P *BSc(Eng)* sq ee300675
Park A L *CEng MIMechE MBIM AIIM* sq 300675
Taylor A H *CEng MIProdE MBIM MIIM AMIMS* 300675
Johnstone I A *BSc(Eng)* 300676
Knox B T *CEng MIMechE* sq 300676
Stewardson J K *CEng MIMechE* 300676
Tandy R H *CEng MIMechE MIMarE* sq 300676
Edsor A W D *BSc(Eng) CEng AMIEE MRAeS* ae 311276
Riley J B sq 311276
Brett R A *BSc* sq aic ee 300677
Young J *BSc(Eng)* EM 300677
March R L 031277
Calbreath J A *BSc(Eng) MSc CEng MIEE* sq ee gw (*A/Lt Col* 201285) 311277
Campbell A M *BSc CEng MIMechE* sq 311277
Griffin A R *BSc CEng MIMechE* sq 311277
Jackson-Smith E C *BSc(Eng) CEng MIEE MBIM* sq ee (*A/Lt Col* 130186) 311277
Bonser K G *BSc(Eng) MSc CEng MIERE* ee gw 300678
Campbell J A *BSc(Eng) MSc CEng MIEE MBCS* dis ee 300678
Filmer J W *BSc* sq 300678
Heavey P J *CEng MIMechE* 300678
Jenkins S N *CEng MIMechE* psc 300678
Platt R D *BSc(Eng) CEng MIEE* sq ee 300678
Capper M J *BSc(Eng) CEng MIMechE* psc† jsdc me 311278
Dorward M C *MBE MIProdE MBIM* 311278
Hutchins B G J *BSc(Eng) MSc CEng MIEE* gw 311278
Jaram P E *BSc(Eng) CEng MIEE* sq ee 311278
King A A *BSc(Eng)* psc ee (*A/Lt Col* 130186) 311278
Mount R A sq ae 311278
Postgate K G *BSc MBIM* mvt sq (*A/Lt Col* 140386) 311278
Scotcher C J *BSc(Eng) CEng MIMechE* psc† me 311278
Allen M R *BSc(Eng) MSc* mvt sq 300679
Andrews D W *BSc(Eng) MSc CEng MRAeS* psc† ae gw 300679
Broad P E *BSc(Eng)* sq me 300679
Deacon C G *BSc CEng MIMechE* sq 300679
Garland P M *BSc BSc(Eng) CEng MIMechE* sq 300679
Harrison W G *BSc* psc† ae 300679
Jarvis H R *BSc(Eng) CEng MIEE* ae ee 300679
Jessop J E *BSc(Eng) CEng MIEE* sq ee 300679
Mills I F 300679
Gange P A *BSc(Eng) CEng MIEE* psc† ee 311279
Jagger R L *CEng MIMechE MRAeS* sq ae 311279
McManamon D G *BSc(Eng) MSc* sq ee 311279
Owen R G *BTech* sq me 311279
Peregrine R B *BSc(Eng) CEng MIMechE* psc† me 311279
Ross N D *BA* ae 311279
Wildbur M S *BSc(Eng)* ae aic 311279
Brookes M G *BSc(Eng) MSc* dis sq ee 300980
Chuter J W *BSc(Eng) MSc CEng MIEE* psc† ee gw 300980
East G R *BSc(Eng)* sq me 300980
Flower A F *BSc(Eng) MSc CEng MIEE* gw 300980
Hall A D *BSc MIMechE* sq 300980
Maddison D *BSc(Eng)* psc† ee 300980
McMahon J B J *BSc(Eng) CEng MIMechE* sq me 300980
McNab I D *BSc(Eng) MSc CEng MIEE* sq ee gw 300980
Middleton S G *BSc(Eng)* psc† ae (*A/Lt Col* 170186) 300980
Morgan P *BSc(Eng) AMIEE* psc† ee (*A/Lt Col* 230985) 300980
O'Connor T P *BSc(Eng) MSc CEng MIEE CDipAF MBCS* dis sq ee 300980
Paskell C W *BA* psc† me 300980
Powell A R *BSc(Eng)* 300980
Snodgrass J D *BSc(Eng)* me 300980
Walmesley-Cotham D B *BSc(Eng) CEng MIEE* sq ee gw 300980
Watson A M *MSc CEng MIMechE* dis sq me 300980
Roberts M D *MRAeS* 120681
Arthur D M *BSc(Eng) AMIEE* psc† aic ee 300981
Cochran A N *BSc(Eng) MSc CEng MIEE* ee gw 300981
Craig J A *BSc(Eng)* psc† me 300981
Croucher R J *MA GRADIMechE* psc† me 300981
Graham I P *BSc(Eng) CEng MIMechE* sq me † 300981
Lamb K I F *BSc(Eng)* me 300981
Lawrence I G *MA* me 300981
Leigh P G *MA* me 300981
Morgan J C B *BSc* psc(n)† me 300981
Palmer K G *BSc(Eng)* ee gw300981
Ravn J T *BSc(Eng)* sq me 300981
Yeoman M P L *BSc(Eng) CEng MIMechE* ae 300981
Blair-Pilling I C D *BSc(Eng) CEng MIMechE* me 300982
Booth A A B *BSc(Hons)* ae 300982
Crabbe M J *CEng MIEE* 300982
Figgures A C *BA* psc† me 300982
Fredericks M R *MBE BSc(Eng) GRADIMechE* psc† me 300982
Haverson J *BSc(Eng) CEng MIMechE* sq me † 300982
Hulmes R J *BSc(Eng)* ee 300982
Huntley M *BSc* psc† 300982
Judd D L *BSc(Eng) CEng MIMechE* psc† me 300982
Loweth J R *BSc(Eng) CEng MIMechE* me 300982
Oswald C J R *CEng MIMechE* me 300982
Palmer J B *BSc CEng MIMechE* psc† me (*A/Lt Col* 111285) 300982
Slater R J *BSc(Eng)* 300982
Spires C E J *BSc(Eng)* ee 300982
Thompson S R *BSc(Eng) CEng MIMechE* 300982
Bowles M D *BSc(Eng)* 300983
Cameron S J S *BSc(Eng) CEng MIMechE* ae 300983
Campbell J C *BSc(Eng) CEng MIMechE* psc† me 300983
Collins I G R *BSc(Eng) CEng* me 300983
Cort P C *BSc(Eng)* psc† me 300983
Creighton F J *MA MIMechE* psc† me 300983
Gray P A *MA CEng MIMechE* me 300983
Hardy S F *BSc(Eng) CEng MIEE MBIM* ee 300983
Knudsen N P *BSc(Eng) MIMechE* psc† ae 300983
Manson S H *BSc(Eng)* me 300983
Nutt B *BSc(Eng) CEng MIEE* ee 300983
Pickford A J *BSc(Eng) CEng MIMechE* me 300983
Rickard R I B *BSc(Eng) CEng MIMechE* psc† me 300983
Smart P *BSc(Eng)* psc ae 300983
Soanes D R *BSc* 300983
Willman A G *BSc(Eng)* 300983
Ashley W A *BSc(Eng)* psc† 300984
Bradley P P *BA BSc CEng MIMechE GRADIM* ae ee 300984
Cameron H R *BSc(Eng)* ae 300984
Garratt M J *BSc CEng MIMechE* psc† me 300984
Goldsack A H *BSc(Eng)* me 300984
Graham W H *BSc* me 300984
Kemp H A *BSc(Eng)* psc† 300984
Laidler R J *BSc* 300984
Marlow E D *BSc CEng MIEE MBIM* ee 300984
Merrett D G *BSc(Eng) AMIRTE* me 300984
Morris A D *BSc(Eng) CEng MIMechE* psc† me 300984
Pearse M J *BSc(Eng)* 300984
Perks T W *BSc* ae 300984
Philp A R *BSc(Eng) CEng MIMechE AMRAeS* ae 300984
Rodger D J *BSc(Eng) AMRAeS* ae 300984
Sandison J P *BSc(Eng)* me 300984
Thomson A F *CEng MIMechE* psc ae 300984
Usher L J *BSc(Eng)* me 300984
Wright D M H *MSc MIEE* psc† ee gw 300984
Bethell J J *BSc(Eng)* 300985
Carruthers S J *BSc(Eng)* ae 300985
Drapper C J *BSc(Eng)* ee me 300985
Ducker C J E *MSc CEng MIMechE* psc† dis me 300985
Eveleigh T H *BSc(Eng)* me 300985
Jarman D J R *MA CEng MIEE* psc† ee 300985
Leadbetter N A *MBE BSc(Eng)* me 300985
Matthews S C *BSc(Eng) CEng MIMechE* psc† me 300985
McCarthy P T *BSc(Eng)* me 300985

McPherson A M *BSc(Eng) MIMechE AE* 300985
Milne T D *BSc(Eng)* psct me 300985
Moll R G *BSc CEng MIMechE* me 300985
Phipps A *BSc(Eng)* ee 300985
Richley M C *BEng* ee 300985
Rudd M A *BSc(Eng)* me 300985
Sharpe P R *BSc(Eng) AMIEE* 300985
Thompson J A De M *BSc(Eng) CEng* ae 300985
Tyler T N *MA* psct ae 300985
Waugh P L *BSc(Eng) AMIEE* 300985

Captains

Watson-Walker M A *BSc(Eng)* ae 181276
Jackson P W *BSc(Eng) CEng MIMechE* ae 300777
McCavitt G *BA BSc(Eng)* ee 300977
Brown A W *BSc CEng MIMechE* ae (*A/Maj* 020985) 250278
Slade S E E *BSc(Eng)* ae 140478
Peters A J *BSc(Eng)* me (*A/Maj* 170284) 010678
Paine A P *MA* ee 010279
Opie M D *BA BSc(Eng) CEng MIERE* ee (*A/Maj* 020284) 070279
Matheson D D *BSc(Eng)* me (*A/Maj* 171284) 120279
Burch A J *BTech CEng MIMechE* me 050379
Cooke D J *BSc(Eng) CEng AMRAeS* ae (*A/Maj* 260985) 080379
Jarvis S A M *MA* ee (*A/Maj* 300983) 080379
Rotchell L R *BSc(Eng)* ae (*A/Maj* 070386) 080379
Ward C *BSc(Eng)* ee (*A/Maj* 201285) 080379
Bayliss M W E *BEng MA* me (*A/Maj* 190785) 090379
Hall P C *BSc MIMechE* ee me 090379
Marsden P J *MA* (*A/Maj* 180486) 030479
Drayton N R *BScTech* 050979
Oldnall M W D *MA* ee 050979
Barclay W J R *BSc(Eng)* ee 100979
Becker S I *BSc(Eng)* ae 100979
Dixon M F *MA* me 100979
Lower M R H *BSc(Eng) CEng MIMechE* ae 100979
Robertshaw P S *BSc(Eng)* me (*A/Maj* 030585) 100979
Bowman M F *BSc(Eng)* ae (*A/Maj* 110185) 301279
Lewis C J *BSc(Eng)* me (*A/Maj* 250185) 301279
Mackay R C *BSc(Eng)* ee 301279
Macpherson A B *BSc(Eng)* ee (*A/Maj* 011084) 301279
Sparks N R S *BSc(Eng)* me 301279
Topp A E *BSc(Eng)* (*A/Maj* 310385) 301279
McNinch H H *BSc(Eng)* ae 030480
Thorpe D A R *BSc(Eng)* me 100580
Ferguson K E *BSc* me 010880
Green D M *BSc(Eng)* 080980
Burnett B A J *MA AMIEE* ee 090980
Crittenden G J *BSc(Eng) CEng MIMechE* me 090980
Eldon R J *BSc(Eng)* ae (*A/Maj* 270285) 090980
Hughes G *BSc(Eng) CEng MIMechE* ae 090980
Musgrove P T *MA* me (*A/Maj* 270186) 090980
Ross I W *BSc(Eng)* me (*A/Maj* 190785) 090980
Welsh A K *BSc(Eng)* ae 090980
Coleman R N *BSc* me 021080
Steadman V R *MA* 091180
Bulmer M R *BSc(Eng)* 291280
Mathew T C *BSc(Eng)* ae 291280
Horsfield P J *BSc AMIEE* ee 140281
Peall K R *BSc(Eng)* ee 090581
Clements N *BSc* me 280781
Hooper N R *BSc(Eng)* ae 010881
Ellis G R *BSc(Eng) CEng MIMechE* 080981
Frostick M C *BSc(Eng)* 080981
Gould N *BSc(Eng) CEng MIMechE MIRTE* 080981
Jones B A *BSc(Eng)* 080981
MacDonald I R *BSc(Eng)* 080981
Scarlett T Y *BSc(Eng)* 080981
Tudor M J *BSc(Eng)* 080981
Egan D H *MSc CEng FIProdE* 160981
Tetlow S J *BSc* 151081
Bowhay D M *BSc(Eng)* 281281
Colling S J *BSc(Eng) AMIEE* 281281
Moore G P *BSc(Eng)* 281281
Palmer B *BSc(Eng)* 281281
Davies N K H *BTech CEng AMIEE MIProdE* ee (*L/Maj* 070486) 280282
Brown G S *BSc(Eng)* 080582
Andrews S M *MA AMRAeS* ae 060982
Anthistle A *BSc(Eng)* 060982
Clatworthy J A G *BSc(Eng)* ae 060982
Gallier N P *BA* 060982
Martin R A *BSc(Eng) AMIMechE* 060982
May N C *BA* 060982
Williams N T S *BA* 060982
Cahill F J *BSc* 250982
Curry P C *BSc* 280982
Moore N *BSc* 280982
Freeman R D *BSc(Eng)* ae 141082
Crawford J P *BSc(Eng) AMRAeS* ae ph 070283
Edwards J M *BSc(Eng)* 070283
Louth P N W P *BSc(Eng)* 070283
Pead A N *BSc(Eng)* 070283
Phillips P D *MA AMIMechE* ae 050383
Sinclair T F *BSc(Eng)* ae 020483
Tugby M *BSc(Eng)* ae 100483
House R M *MA* 050583
Langley-Poole A I *BSc(Eng)* 110683
Dale I C *BSc(Eng)* 080783
Roy T J *BSc GRADIMechE* 090783
Gilbert J P *BSc(Eng)* 081083
Hemmings R K *BSc(Eng)* ae 081083
Lister B J *BSc(Eng)* 081083
Mulroy J *BSc(Eng)* 081083
O'Sullivan S T *BSc(Eng)* 081083
Phillips A G *BSc(Eng)* 081083
Philpott G R *BA* ae 081083
Ransom M *BSc(Eng)* ae 081083
Warwick M B *BSc(Eng) AMIEE* ae 081083
Williams S M *BSc(Eng)* 081083
Millson A J *BSc(Eng)* ae 141183
Barker M *BSc(Eng)* 060284
Feldmanis E C *BSc(Eng)* 060284
Jones N J E *BSc(Eng)* 060284
Sowray S T *BSc(Eng)* ae 060284
Walker J D *BSc(Eng)* 060284
Young K T *BSc(Eng)* ae 060284
Bartlett D M *BSc(Eng)* ae 100284
Hayle M P *MA CEng MIProdE* 030484
Curry N R *BSc(Eng) GRADIMechE MIProdE* 100684
Wells R E *BSc(Eng)* 100684
Saville J R C *BSc(Eng)* 010884
Wilson A S *BSc(Eng)* 220884
Duncan I W *BSc* 260884
Churchman C P *BSc(Eng)* 081084
Maclean M D 081084
McCall B W *BSc* 081084
Nevill A L 081084
Parsons R J *BSc(Eng)* 081084
Riley P F *BSc(Eng)* ae 081084
Robertson G A *BSc(Eng) AMIEE* 081084
Rouse J F *BA GRADIMechE* 081084
Walker A C C *BSc(Eng)* 081084
Crook R *BSc(Eng)* 050285
Griffiths P J *BSc(Eng)* 050285
Holliday S H *BSc* 050285
Duncan A D *BSc AMIEE* 230385
Hughes M A *BSc* 010885
Smith A E *BSc* 010885
Davies J G 060885
Croft R R *BSc* ae 071085
Horder R D ae 071085
Laborda M A *BSc* 071085
Metcalfe C W *BSc* 071085
Pearson M R *BSc* 071085
Shimmings M R *BSc* 131085
Longmore P 011285
Chenneour M *BSc* ae 040286
Harper J L *BSc* 040286
Marshall A C *BSc* 040286
Miller P H K *BSc* 040286
Packham K C *BSc* 040286
Simpson I S *BSc* 040286
Tarlton I J *BSc* 040286

Lieutenants

Ripley M E *BSc* 040881
Nowak A M P 080981
McMurdo D J *BSc* 081281
Tuson M C 081281
Wyld G V *BSc* (*A/Capt* 210286) 081281
Birrell A M *BSc(Eng)* 120482
Byers P R *BSc(Eng)* (*A/Capt* 070386) 120482
Bywater J J *BSc(Eng)* 120482
Hill J A *BEng* (*A/Capt* 210286) 120482
Mills T *BSc* ae (*A/Capt* 161285) 120482
Mortimer A D 120482
Parsons I M *BSc* (*A/Capt* 240186) 120482
Smale D S *BSc(Eng)* 120482
Wyatt R G P 120482
McAreavey J O 200482
Bailey D N 090882
Boswell M J *BSc(Eng)* (*A/Capt* 190386) 090882
Dixon R S *BSc(Eng)* 090882
Fairclough I P 090882
Groves C P 090882
Law L R 090882
Leedham D A *BSc(Eng)* 090882
McKenna P A 090882
Webber A T B C 090882
Wright G S *BSc(Eng)* 090882
Laurie R N F 131282

Corps of Royal Electrical and Mechanical Engineers — continued

Wormington J C 131282
Powell A T 311282
Burgess D C 140183
Brown A R *BSc(Eng)* 110483
Bush D L *BSc(Eng)* 110483
Hutton P *BSc* 110483
Judd J C *BSc* 110483
Mackenzie A C W 110483
Martin A S *BA(Cantab)* 110483
Moult S R *BSc(Eng)* 110483
Pashen D M *BSc* 110483
Shewry P A *BSc(Eng)* 110483
Taylor S J *BSc AMIEE* 110483
Teare A D *BSc(Eng)* 110483
Thorley A C *BSc(Eng)* 110483
Thornton D W *BSc(Eng)* 110483
Williams R C *BA* 110483
Mitchell R J 200583
Millar D 030883
Kelly W R *BSc* 080883
Mitchell P G 080883
Oakes M C 080883
Oxford J J 080883
Stuart J S 080883
Weatherall S P *BSc* 080883
Ensor J A 180883
Martin P D 151183
Chambers M 121283
White S R 121283
Barnard S 090484
Betteridge A J *BSc* 090484
Condliffe M I 090484
Crummack I J *BSc* 090484
Deverill P A *BSc* 090484
Dykes R J *BSc* 090484
Henderson J M R *BSc* 090484
Preston A D *BSc(Eng)* 090484
Tucker A V 090484
Went A C *BSc* 090484
Kinsey G J 030584
Wiles A C 300784
Armstrong M A 070884
Frendo E 070884
Lay J B *BSc(Eng)* 070884
McArthur A 070884
Thorpe R P 070884
Woolgar N A *BSc(Eng)* 070884
Lugg M H 111284
Brittain J R 090485
Case R H 090485
Easton D W 090485
Fitzgibbon S P 090485
Frendo S P M 090485
Frostick P C 090485
Golding S P 090485
Howe R C 090485
Waters M C 090485
Wilson M C 090485
Baker D H 060885
Bearcroft E P C 060885
Coxon N J 060885
Downes A S 060885
Flynn P J 060885
Jaques P W 060885
Armstrong P J 101285
Bowen P F 101285
Mackay E A C R 101285
Morris A W 101285
Parker N B 101285
Smith R D 101285
Evans C M 070486
Fram R C 070486
Joels B D 070486
Miller P 070486
Sherman J A 070486

2nd Lieutenants

Ellis J A
††Champion D L *BTech* 040981
†Marsh D J *BSc(Hons)* 040981
††Brown P I *BSc(Eng)* 030982
††King A F *BSc(Hons)* 020983
††Nitsch R M B 020983
††Thompson M A 020983
††Millar F J 031083
††Preece R M H 031083
††Morgan K J 081083
Salisbury C S 101283
Court M L 070484
Gyorffy T A 070484
Holborn B R 070484
Mitchell G I 070484
Astbury R P 040884
Braham D C 040884
Burton C A 040884
Collett J C E 040884
Cotter A F J 040884
Hogg N M G 040884
Ingram P J 040884
Murdoch C J 040884
Perrett R C 040884
Ringrose M C 040884
Smith J S W 040884
Young R J 040884
††Price S N 230984
†Rogers M T 230984
††Soar A J 051084
Allen A A 081284
Munday M N 081284
Thomas S J 081284
Welsh R P 081284
Angel S R 130485
Cosgrove R P 130485
Gaunt M J 130485
Golding D H 130485
Hopkins D R D 130485
Bols P H C 100885
Gibson I P 100885
McGown R G C 100885
†Abate J R *BSc(Eng)* 060985
†Robinson A T *BSc* 060985
††Cowan W D 240985
††Howard A C S 240985
††Jones P M 240985
††McNeil I N 240985
††Williams R D 240985
††Aspray R J 300985
††Dale A J 071085
Crichard G 141285
Jones C O 141285
Power J 141285
Purnell M J 141285
Snape M G 141285
†Thwaites J M *MSc* 060186

Staff Quartermasters

Anderson E C 011073
Lt Col 260284
Ellis C E 010475
Lt Col 010385
Bly D *BEM* 010676
Maj 090984
Barr K *BA* 310377
Maj 050382

Quartermasters

Hannaford M P S 160375
Lt Col 011185
Bowman R G 070475
Lt Col 200185
Kent E D 300476
Maj 141180
Wright K *MInstAM* 010776
Maj 260282
Kyle G 290478
Maj 140183
Derricutt J C 011079
Maj 191182
Lindsay T *Capt* 160680
Reynolds F J 300980
Maj 041182
Hallett D 081081
Maj 180485
Slater B D *MISM* 130282
Maj 040584
Webster A W 220282
Maj 040584
Maguire P J 060382
Maj 131185
Eagle M W 061282
Maj 270184
Emblen R H *MInstAM*
Capt 010283
Hill P J *MInstAM MISM*
Capt 010283
Parkes G P *MInstAM MISM*
010283
Maj 240585
Kufluk-Thackery B G
Capt 081283
Smith C P *MISM* *Capt* 010284
Pittaway P *Capt* 160684
Claypole G W *Maj* 121284
Featherstone G P *MISM*
Capt 121284
Gogin T *Capt* 250185
Hart C I *MISM* *Capt* 010485
Berrystone P J *MInstAM*
Capt 160685
Dunn J *Capt* 280885
Chown T G *Capt* 281285
Brown G A *Capt* 030486

Electrical and Mechanical Assistant Engineers

Daykin P A 300672
Lt Col 140182
West D 011173
Lt Col 190583
Gibbens R A *MBE TEng(CEI) MBIM MIE* 290375
Lt Col 290485
Bartlett E P *TEng(CEI)* 280475
Lt Col 091284
Brown A F E 010575
Lt Col 121284
Fermor T J 010775
Maj 200778
Minard R E *TEng(CEI) MIMGTechE*
010875
Lt Col 100184
Woods J B *TEng(CEI) MIE* 010875
Maj 200281
Beadle R R E *MIRTE* 011075
Maj 010279
Fenn M 011075
Maj 010479
Flambard M A *FBIM* 011075
Maj 010380
Hendy R B *TEng(CEI) MIRTE MISM* 091075
Maj 010380
McGowan A 010476
Maj 260282
Jeffery D K 010776
Maj 220282
Jackson B G 081076
Maj 010479
Le-Var M W *TEng(CEI)* 061276
Lt Col 100984
Hewton R J *MIE MIMGTechE*
140277
Maj 251182

Leeder R L *TEng(CEI) AMIRTE MIE* 010377 *Lt Col* 050485

Sanford T E 010377 *Maj* 010380

Reed A J *MBE FSERT MBIM MIIM TEng* 310377 *Maj* 191182

Stacey B D *MIE* 020577 *Lt Col* 201085

Shotliff B *MBE* 300877 *Maj* 021082

Burdon A D *TEng(CEI) MICE MISM MIE* 011177 *Maj* 010380

Warner G B *BEM* 011177 *Maj* 010479

Hartley A C 011277 *Maj* 191182

Maxwell P J *TEng(CEI) AMIRTE* ph 011277 *Maj* 240183

Stubbs R P *TEng(CEI)* 070278 *Maj* 191182

Collins P W G *TEng(CEI) AMIRTE MBIM* 010378 *Maj* 141180

Gregory R F *TEng(CEI) AMIMI* 250378 *Maj* 191182

Hunter A T K 030478 *Maj* 141083

Morton A J *MBE TEng(CEI) FSERT* 270478 *Maj* 261181

Nottage R S 120578 *Maj* 200281

Barlow P *FSERT* 310578 *Maj* 031183

Garrow I A *TEng(CEI) MRAeS MIRTE FBIM* 010678 *Lt Col* 280885

Tully G R H 140778 *Maj* 141083

Fox M F *TEng(CEI) MBIM MIE* 310778 *Maj* 280883

Cook G R 010878 *Maj* 260282

Turnbull B *MBE* 290978 *Maj* 050382

Bevan H W 011178 *Maj* 020384

Bush A J 071178 *Maj* 200281

North P A 141178 *Maj* 030383

Symonds L A *TEng(CEI) AFSLAET FSERT* 261278 *Maj* 300983

Coates C W 120279 *Maj* 141083

Williams J C 130279 *Maj* 170982

Townsend F W W *TEng(CEI)* 280279 *Maj* 141181

Harris G E 310379 *Maj* 030383

Walker D R O *TEng(CEI)* 010479 *Maj* 071082

Griffin J G *MBIM MIIM* 020479 *Maj* 191182

Stone G A *TEng(CEI) MIE* 100479 *Maj* 141181

Robbins D A *TEng* 010679 *Maj* 030383

Cassidy J M 050679 *Maj* 040584

Blofield A G *TEng(CEI) MIMI* 130779 *Maj* 141083

Watson W G C 150779 *Maj* 040584

Fisher A R G 011079 *Maj* 021184

Hay M 011079 *Maj* 141083

Powell J L *TEng(CEI) MIMI AMIMI* 011079 *Maj* 141083

Hassell C P *MISM* 010180 *Maj* 141181

Johnson K *TEng(CEI) FSERT* 010180 *Maj* 020280

Newman G M *TEng(CEI) MIMI MIRTE MIIM* 010180 *Maj* 141181

Weedon W D 090180 *Maj* 131280

Hoskins B D 020480 *Maj* 031183

Hunter A S *AMIMI* 140480 *Maj* 240585

Pritchard M H E 160580 *Maj* 030383

Sargent D D *TEng(CEI) MIRTE* 180580 *Maj* 040584

Mawdesley R *BEM* 270580 *Maj* 200984

Greenall W 070680 *Maj* 030383

Pickworth D G 310880 *Maj* 021184

Bennett F C *TEng(CEI) FSERT MISM* 170980 *Maj* 141083

Hill D J 011280 *Maj* 191182

Bradshaw T P *MIRTE* 041280 *Maj* 240585

Platt W H *MBIM* 010281 *Maj* 260282

Iveson J *TEng(CEI) MISM* 010481 *Maj* 160983

Orchard C A *BA* *Maj* 010481

Swinburn G A F J 010481 *Maj* 030383

Watkins G G 010481 *Maj* 021184

Young C A 010481 *Maj* 191182

Cass H T J 060481 *Maj* 200784

Weekes P E 050781 *Maj* 121185

Chalmers A G *TEng(CEI) MIRTE* 010981 *Maj* 040584

Jeffery C J *TEng(CEI) MITE* 010981 *Maj* 131185

Lockyer P J 010981 *Maj* 240486

Fraser T *Maj* 270981

Lawry B 031181 *Maj* 020384

Major D A *TEng(CEI) AMIRTE* 041181 *Maj* 021184

Memmott D A 181181 *Maj* 141083

Tyrrell R P *TEng(CEI) AMIMGTechE* 011281 *Maj* 260282

Mead G J *TEng(CEI) AMIMI* 081281 *Maj* 200583

Costanzo M V *TEng(CEI) FSERT* 020482 *Maj* 240585

Delf M sq 020482 *Maj* 031183

Stanford D H J *TEng(CEI) MIRTE* 040482 *Maj* 131185

Mason P J J *TEng(CEI) AMRAeS MSLAET MISM* 111082 *Maj* 020384

Bunyard T I 251182 *Maj* 251182

Crowson R C 081282 *Maj* 110584

Kane V J 081282 *Maj* 240486

Botelle B T C 110383 *Maj* 141083

Higgins J L R *Capt* 130483

Sands G C 300483 *Maj* 131185

Cosh J L *Capt* 190583

Harris R F G *TEng(CEI) MITE* *Capt* 040683

Wyng J W 260683 *Maj* 240585

Brown A E J *TEng(CEI) MIE MIMGTechE* *Maj* 050783

Beeken P G *TEng(CEI) FIMI* 070783 *Maj* 141083

North P H 250983 *Maj* 031183

Williams B J *Capt* 250983

Ireland E *MIMGTechE* *Capt* 011083

Tomlinson E J *TEng(CEI) MIE* *Capt* 021083

Carroll K E *BEM* *Capt* 091083

Mason N A R *Capt* 211183

Dolphin P *Tech(CEI) AMIMI AMIRTE* *Capt* 090184

Smith N S *Capt* 160184

Hunter R M *TEng(CEI) MIRTE MIE* *Capt* 250284

Mears A R *Tech(CEI)* *Capt* 060484

Beard P F 010784 *Maj* 131185

Dixon A C *MIMGTechE* *Maj* 160784

Kellam R W 140884 *Maj* 131185

Churcher L *TEng(CEI) MIRTE MBIM* *Capt* 011184

Keymer D *TEng(CEI) FSERT* *Capt* 011184

Chadwick D J *Capt* 101184

Paul R D J *Capt* 301184

Gatward R F *TEng(CEI) MIE* *Capt* 081284

Dickson R W *Capt* 111284

Chapman R *Capt* 121284

O'Rourke M T *Capt* 190185

Trengove E H *Capt* 260285

Nickson R A *Capt* 310385

Sargent E V G *MBE* *Capt* 050485

Tyler B T *TEng(CEI) MISM MIE* *Capt* 140485

Davis M J *AMIRTE MISM* *Capt* 180485

Waterman P J *Maj* 210485

Barnard N C H *Capt* 290485

Brotheridge R *MISM* 010585 *Maj* 131185

Thwaites R R *Capt* 010585

Corps of Royal Electrical and Mechanical Engineers — continued

Brotherton R M *Capt* 130585
Greaves B *TEng(CEI) AFSLAET* *Capt* 050685
Holman J R *Capt* 120685
Hurren D B *Capt* 240785
Moore E *MISM* *Capt* 010885
Maloney A L *Capt* 220885
Hind H E 100985 *Maj* 240486
Moss A J *Capt* 201085
Kempson D E F *TEng(CEI) MITE TEng* *Capt* 011185
McHenry R R *TEng(CEI) FSERT FSX-RayT* *Capt* 311285
McIntyre J *Capt* 230186
Strachan B G *Capt* 110286

Directors of Music

Ross C J *ARCM* *Capt* 020381

Special Regular Officers

Majors

Waight P D ee 300675
Kemp J F *AMIMI MCIT* 311275
Read A E *MBE CEng MRAeS* ae 300676
Savage F E J 311276
Ellis P *BA TEng(CEI) FIMI MBIM* 311277
Howlett D 311278
Walker J *TEng(CEI) MIMI AMIMI MIRTE* 311278
Dempster M M sq 300980
Kempson C A 300980
Summerton M *AMRAeS* ae 300980
Tonks R T 300980
Kitchener B I H *MBE* 300981
Nixon T E *TEng(CEI) FSERT* 300981
Olley B A *TEng(CEI)* 300981
Powell M J *CEng MIERE* 300981
Pinder K ee 300982
Dewdney N F *TEng(CEI) FSERT* 300983
Ord R *MIElecIE* 300983
Calder H C 300984
Hart-Ives N J *MIIM MIElecIE* 300984
Kemp A J *TEng(CEI) MIMGTechE* 300984
Stanyer J 300984
Wing A P H 300984
Allcock K E 300985
Allen G J P *Tech(CEI)* 300985
Braham M E *MIE MIMGTechE* 300985
Evans P H M *BSc(Eng) AMIEE* 300985
Glasspool J K *TEng(CEI)* 300985
Hincks G W *Tech(CEI) AIRTE* 300985
Johnson D A *BSc AMIEE* 300985
Marwaha T S *BEng* 300985
Neale K F *TEng(CEI) MISM MIMGTechE* 300985
Roberts B 300985

Captains

Emsley P A M ee 210879
Byrne W P J 240480
Cleasby I W J *TEng(CEI) FSERT* (*A/Maj* 190785) 111181
Shearsmith P F 111181
Clutson M J *TEng(CEI) MIE* 280482
Guignard B E *TEng(CEI)* (*A/Maj* 271085) 280482
Roach P F (*A/Maj* 070185) 280482
Shephard R J *TEng(CEI)* 280482
Storey J P 280482
Bull C 031182
MacQuarrie N 031182
McDonald I D *Tech(CEI) MIE* 031182
Barker S *TEng(CEI) FSERT* 260483
Charman M J 260483
George B W *MBE MISM* 260483
Mills B J 260483
Piper T L *MIRTE TEng* 260483
Tanner G F *BA* 260483
Hamilton B W *BSc* ae 050983
Baskeyfield A 011183
Chaszczewski V J *AMIRTE* 011183
Coward S C *BEM* 011183
Ferguson W D *BSc CEng MIERE FSERT* 011183
Foad J E *TEng(CEI)* 011183
Frobisher G *TEng(CEI) FSLAET* 011183
Hollingsworth E *TEng(CEI) MIRTE* 011183
Illingworth K G *TEng(CEI) MISM MIE* 011183
Layhe R E *Tech(CEI) AMIE* 011183
McQuilton K C 011183
Smith M D (*A/Maj* 240386) 011183
Swinton I A *MISM MIE* 011183
Poole B 260484
Eyre M D *BSc(Eng)* ae 300484
Powell D *TEng(CEI)* 151184
Bowles A P *BSc* ae 181184
Callun M P *BSc(Eng)* ae 050285
Heelis M C 250485
Hutton D J 250485
Powell C R 250485
Taylor W G 250485
Gedge P F *BSc(Eng)* 071085
Fox J R *MIQA MIMGTechE TEng* 141185
Garner S A *TEng(CEI) MISM MIElecIE* 141185
Kellie J I 141185
Ungi S V *TEng(CEI)* 141185
White I *MIMGTechE* 141185

Lieutenants

Dymmock P *TEng(CEI) MIMGTechE* 140581
Nicholls B J 140581
Mackenzie J S (*A/Capt* 291184) 301081
Oldfield P *AMIRTE* 301081
Oliver M W *AFSLAET* 301081
Perry S M *BSc(Eng)* 131281
Noakes P V 070582
Barry S K *BSc(Eng)* (*L/Capt* 061285) 090882
Armitstead C J *BSc* 090484
Eke D M 070884
Dorset S 060885

2nd Lieutenants

Hygate M W 040884

Short Service Officers

Captains

Chattin D W *TEng(CEI) MISM MIE* 090181
Jones A T *TEng(CEI) MISM* 090181
Cole S J *BA BSc* ae 290382
Chewins D *TEng(CEI) MIRTE* 280482
Glossop B M 280482
Kitchin C H 280482
Logan R J *TEng(CEI)* 280482
Scriven A L 280482
Southall S 280482
Storey M A *TEng(CEI) AMIMI MISM MIE* (*A/Maj* 011185) 280482
Barber J M C ee 031182
Millman D I *MIMI AMIMI* 031182
Morris D 031182
Fuller H V *MIQA* 260483
Maddy W P 260483
McCann G C *AMIRTE MIMGTechE* 260483
Pover J 260483
Stoker A E 260483
Taylor J 260483
Thompson R C A 260483
Washington R J *BEM AMIMI* 260483
Howes A R *TEng(CEI) AMIMI MIMI* 011183
Stephenson E 011183
Walker T 011183
Baxter K L 260484
Brodrick D T *Tech(CEI) MISM MIE* 260484
Phelps R M J *TEng(CEI) MIRTE* 260484
Wareham R A 260484
Dollimore R F 151184
Fairbanks A M 151184
Gibson M R 151184
Golder S V 151184
Haynes D J F P 151184
Le Tiec L N 151184
Brooking C C *TEng(CEI) AFSLAET* 250485
Feast J P D *AFSLAET* 250485
Poffley M A *TEng(CEI)* 250485
Stevens B R 250485
Todd P R *AMIRTE AMIE* 250485
Tozer K M *TEng(CEI) MIRTE* 250485
Ward J J 250485
Davison J M *BSc* 210885
Stott C D *BSc* 071085
Cooke R A *TEng(CEI) FSERT MIElecIE* 141185
Doherty D 141185
Gower A G *TEng(CEI) FSERT* 141185
Kemp F B 141185
O'Kelly B V A *AMIRTE* 141185
Willcoxson J D 141185

Lieutenants

Brown M G (*A/Capt* 011184) 301081
Clarke D 301081
Clutson D P (*A/Capt* 051184) 301081
Dryland A R (*A/Capt* 191284) 301081
French M C *TEng(CEI) MIMGTechE* (*A/Capt* 010684) 301081
Law M J *MITE TEng* (*A/Capt* 011284) 301081
Martin H 301081
McEwan A (*A/Capt* 010684) 301081
Morgan A R W 301081

Murray M K (*A/Capt* 291184)	301081
Pearson M E (*A/Capt* 011184)	301081
Shipton R I *MIElecIE TEng* (*A/Capt* 291184)	301081
Stewart T L (*A/Capt* 080684)	301081
Sutton M K (*A/Capt* 080285)	301081
Wadner A F (*A/Capt* 050684)	301081
Twycross M J *BSc*	120482
Davison M	190582
Harris-Deans P G *MIMGTechE TEng* (*A/Capt* 210585)	190582
Jennings A *AMIRTE* (*A/Capt* 170685)	190582
Jones C S (*A/Capt* 181284)	190582
Kennett M (*A/Capt* 211284)	190582
Kneebone M A (*A/Capt* 090185)	190582
Lancaster V J (*A/Capt* 171284)	190582
Larkins M J W *BA TEng(CEI) MIERE FSX-RayT* (*A/Capt* 040785)	190582
Leslie K J (*A/Capt* 211284)	190582
Longhurst R M (*A/Capt* 110185)	190582
O'Keefe P C *TEng(CEI) MIMI* (*A/Capt* 211284)	190582
Plumb J *BA TEng(CEI) AFSLAET*	190582
Plummer P M (*A/Capt* 130585)	190582
Saul C M M (*A/Capt* 211284)	190582
Scollard-Kerr D (*A/Capt* 250285)	190582
Snaddon J *MISM* (*A/Capt* 211284)	190582
Steiner D S *FSERT*	190582
Wadsworth M D	190582
Williams P L (*A/Capt* 211284)	190582
Miller C L *BSc*	090882
Anderson G M (*A/Capt* 270985)	291082
Chisholm A *Tech(CEI) AMIRTE MISM* (*A/Capt* 070685)	291082
Cleland K M (*A/Capt* 010685)	291082
Dimmock R G (*A/Capt* 010985)	291082
Eaton K J *BEM* (*A/Capt* 290585)	291082
Fyffe D	291082
Hammond D *MIRTE* (*A/Capt* 270585)	291082
Hawkes P S J *FSERT* (*A/Capt* 081185)	291082
Henderson W G (*A/Capt* 291085)	291082
Hirst G (*A/Capt* 010985)	291082
Kearley W J (*A/Capt* 070685)	291082
Leech A R (*A/Capt* 010985)	291082
Marven J F *TEng(CEI)* (*A/Capt* 270985)	291082
Merry R E	291082
Palmer J G (*A/Capt* 070685)	291082
Pollin R S	291082
Powers N	291082
Smy B S *MISM MASMC*	291082
Spaul M B *TEng(CEI) AMIMGTechE*	291082
Stinchcombe D J (*A/Capt* 310585)	291082
Ulyatt J W (*A/Capt* 070685)	291082
Williamson S *BSc*	071182
Abbott J P J F *BSc*	110483
Hull D E *BSc(Eng)*	110483
Knowland P R *BSc*	110483
Richards P *BA*	110483
Baker A R	180583
Eva R F (*A/Capt* 161285)	180583
Gardner J K	180583
Hinds P A *BA*	180583
Holding M J *ASERT*	180583
Jefferies C H	180583
Miles K A *TEng(CEI) AIRTE MIMGTechE*	180583
Powell M J *AFSLAET TEng*	180583
Sadkowski D *TEng(CEI)* (*A/Capt* 060186)	180583
Soper L J	180583
Tonkin V P (*A/Capt* 080186)	180583
Kelly P B (*A/Capt* 131285)	090683
White J N *BSc*	080883
Belgum G R *BSc*	090484
Bennett R N H	090484
Coveney M J *BSc(Eng)*	090484
Gurney D M *BSc*	090484
Hendry D J *BSc*	100484
McClean B C W *BSc TECH(CEI) TMIMGTechE*	070884

2nd Lieutenants

†Heathman J R *BEng*	060985
†St John O P *BSc*	060985
†Wilson P A *BSc*	060985

Non-Technical Administrative Officers

Captains

Scott T	260484
White J	260484
Cullen A W	250485
Gills A V *MISM*	250485
Heffernan P K M *FIMS*	250485
Payne J E	250485
Rogers D J	141185
Workman A	141185
Anderson A E	060286
Foreman J A	060286

Lieutenants

Jordan R W (*A/Capt* 011085)	301081
Deane J C B (*A/Capt* 211285)	180583
Hilton R J (*A/Capt* 160386)	180583
Truluck V S *MISM*	180583
Twine P J	180583

CORPS OF ROYAL MILITARY POLICE

Within a laurel wreath, the Royal Cypher with Crown above. Beneath, a scroll inscribed "Royal Military Police"
"Exemplo Ducemus"

Regimental March

Quick March..........Regimental March of The Corps of Royal Military Police (The Watchtower)

Agents..........Lloyds Bank PLC Cox's & King's Branch

Corps Headquarters..........RHQ/RMP (PM5), Roussillion Barracks, Chichester, West Sussex
(*Tel No: Chichester Mil Ext:* 238)

Alliances

Canadian Armed Forces..........Canadian Forces Security Branch
Australian Military Forces..........The Royal Australian Corps of Military Police
New Zealand Army..........Royal New Zealand Military Police
Pakistan Army..........Corps of Military Police (Pakistan)
Sri Lanka Army..........The Sri Lanka Corps of Military Police
Malaysian Armed Forces..........Malaysian Military Police

Colonel in Chief..........THE QUEEN

Colonel Commandant..........Gen *Sir* James Glover *KCB MBE*..........230783

Brigadiers

Thomas B *CBE* sq 300683

Colonels

Allen N C *OBE* ndc psc 300683
Hanglin P J *MBIM* 300683
Taylor G A psc 300685

Lieutenant Colonels

Curtin J P *MBIM* 300678
Theis R J *MBE LLB* 300678
Squier P H M 300679
Williams P M 300679
Bland R E psc 300680
Hewlett-Smith P B ndc psc 300680
Ramsey M G 300680
Rawlings B A 311280
Hughes-Jones W B 300681
Bell A R *MBE* psc
(*A/Col* 270386) 300682
Bonell J K psc 300682
Watkins C W 300682
Murray A R ph 300683
Cameron I psc jsdc 300684
Wright B *MBIM* 300684
Hodges J A psc 300685
Murray L *MBE MBIM* sq 300685
Tilston R J 300685

Majors

Surtees P H *MC* 150167
Lane A N *BA* 300673
Graham J 300674
Field R A sq 311275
Manger D C 311275
Mirehouse G E W R 300676
Scriven T G 311277
Wonson D W 300678
Townsend P E *MBE* 311278
Ridd J 300679
Baber J H 300980
Fulton I W 300980
Nelson J A J 300980
Thompson G A C 300980
Watson M P 300980
Barton I R 300981
Farley C J 300981
King-Evans R E 300981
Nugent M psc† 300981
Backler J A A 300982
Collyer M N 300982
Farrelly P E 300982
Figg A J 300982
Lanham J W 300982
McLean S C 300982
Blackford J R 300983
Lovell-Knight R E *BA* 300983
Walters N H C 300983
Batten K M 300984
Leigh R C *QGM* psc 300984
Powell G L 300984
Palmer R W 300985

Captains

Evans R J 040878
Findlay C A *BA DipEd CGIA* 271079
Atkinson W A N
(*A/Maj* 171285) 301279
Boyd S F *LLB* 130280
Barnard N M B 090980
Collins A P
(*A/Maj* 280685) 090980
Evanson G W *MCFA*
(*A/Maj* 040486) 291280
London J E S
(*A/Maj* 041085) 090581
Giles D C N *LLB* 280282
Wood W *BArch* 280282
Oughton R A B *BA* 090882
Blackmore G R 270383
Marshall K G o s 170983
Cuthbert-Brown M 060284
Edwards G R *LLB* 130284
Ridout N J 130284
Faithfull L 270984
Baillie P F *BA* 071085
Tiley D J *BTech* 071085
Watton T P 071085
Standish A K *BEd* 040286

Lieutenants

Mackay R M 070481
Green J T 090882
House P C *BA*
(*A/Capt* 210286) 090882
Waters I
(*A/Capt* 160484) 131282
Stenning I A R 110483
Forster-Knight E O *LLB(Hons)*
090484

2nd Lieutenants

Borrows J C 040884
Bower M W 130485

Quartermasters

Manning S C 080976
Lt Col 191184
Woodiwiss W G *MBE* 231280
Maj 260484
Pemberton T *Maj* 221182
Jonas W 160683
Maj 280285
Kinnersley K E W *MBE*
Capt 160683
Quigley F G *Capt* 011085

Special Regular Officers

Majors

Friend P J 300679
Page D E 300981
Pangborn A F 300981
Bacon K T 300984
Collins J J *MBE BEM* 300984
Copland M F 300984
Dawson J C 300984
Hayes S G 300984
Loftus R J 300984
McIntosh J H 300984

Captains

Boothby F R C 011181
Gallagher J P 090482
Calder R *BEM MInstAM* 011282
Pike J J 010583
Bamber P N 270783
Russell S J 060284
Prosser I E 100684
Foy E G 010784
Hollingsbee T P 151084
McIvor P A C A 050285
Williams C G *MM* 150285
Bishop R T M 250785
Davies B 050985

2nd Lieutenants

Mason J P A 040884

Short Service Officers

Captains

Ditchfield R	090878
Kitchen M S	010980
Mansergh J D	020181
Taylor L	030981
Barry T R F T	220683
Hall J	021183
Ward D A	151084
Peel D	150285
Abbott J	031085

Lieutenants

Glover E M (*A/Capt* 280884)	220282
Haskins S M (*A/Capt* 140285)	220282
Lindop F M (*A/Capt* 171284)	220282
Meek F W (*A/Capt* 070984)	220282
Seaward A J (*A/Capt* 081084)	220282
Wilson J M	220282
Miller C R (*A/Capt* 280984)	200382
Stacy-Marks R A *BA*	120482
Hardy M A	280283
Long R B (*A/Capt* 160985)	280283
Silk R W	280283
Slater A (*A/Capt* 160985)	280283
Campbell-Smith R H	270383
Moore R M	090583
Evans P C W *BSc*	080883
Douglas J C	090484

2nd Lieutenants

Williamson M A	081284
King J V	141285
†Westcott M P *BA*	060186

ROYAL ARMY PAY CORPS

The Royal Crest in Gold thereunder a Scroll inscribed FIDE ET FIDUCIA in silver

Regimental March

Quick March....................Imperial Echoes

Agents....................Lloyds Bank PLC Cox's & King's Branch

Corps Headquarters....................Worthy Down, Winchester, Hants (*Tel No:* Winchester 880880 *Ext:* 2435)

Alliances

Colonial Forces....................Pay Section, Royal Hong Kong Defence Force

Fiji....................Army Pay Corps

Colonels Commandant....................Maj Gen O J Kinahan *CB* ret pay....................010983
*Maj Gen J J Stibbon *OBE*....................270485

Brigadiers

Fullerton B V H *CBE ADC FCCA FBIM* sowc psc† pfc 300679
Bowen B M *FCCA FCMA* ndc psc† sq pfc (*A/Maj Gen* 030386) 300682
Conibear P K *FCIS FBIM* psc† sq pfc 300683
Bray P S *AIDPM ACIS* ndc psc† sq pfc 300685

Colonels

Nicholson J *MBIM* pfc 300677
Brenchley P J *MBCS ACIS* pfc 300678
Bingle B C *FBIM* pfc 300682
Bunney D *ACIS MBIM* sq pfc 300683
Davis J A *FCIS FBIM* sq pfc 300683
Edwards M G H *BA FCMA FCIS* pfc 300683
Gadd G M *FBIM* 300683
Johnstone M D *OBE MBCS MIDPM* 300683
Ramsey R D 300683
Wilcox R sq 300683
Adams A A S sq 300684
Cauchi G E *FAAI FCIS MBIM* sq pfc 300684
Crossley A B *ACIS* pfc 300684
Rea A J A *MBE ACIS* pfc 300685
Roberts F *MBCS ACIS* psc† sq pfc 300685
Ropes J J *MIDPM ACIS* pfc 300685
Smith D E *FCA FCMA* pfc 300685

Lieutenant Colonels

Oldfield J C F *FCCA FCMA MBIM* pfc 300672
Chattock B N *MBIM* pfc 300674
Graham-Hill P *ACMA ACIS* pfc 300675
Bennett R J *ACIS* pfc 300678
Townsend R J M 300679
Turnbull G *ACIS* sq pfc 300679
Churchill J C sq 300680
Lloyd B A *FCMA* pfc 300680
O'Meara S M B *MIDPM FBIM* ndc psc I pfc (*A/Col* 140386) 300680
Wadham M W 300681
Ahl C J F 300682
Bush A E *MBIM* pfc 300682
Dowey D J T *MBE FCMA ACIS CBIM* psc† sq pfc (*A/Col* 070386) 300682
Evans S F E *ACIS* ae pfc (*L/Col* 070486) 300682
Geal C *OBE FAAI ACIS MBIM* psc† sq pfc (*A/Col* 280286) 300682
Hannam D G *AIDPM* 300682
Scott W E R *ACMA ACIS* pfc 300682
Shaw P *MBE ACIS* sq pfc 300682
Cook J A *FCCA FCMA FCIS MBIM* sq pfc 300683
Entwisle I J *ACIS* pfc 300683
Mills A *MBE FCMA FCIS AIB* pfc 300683
Morgan B *BA FCCA FCMA MBIM* pfc 300683
Pollock W G *MBE ACIS* pfc 300683
Thomas R J *MBE FCMA* pfc 300683
Walshe C B H *MIDPM ACIS* sq pfc ph 300683
Clark R F *MBIM* 300684
Cowley D *FCMA FCIS* 300684
English T H *FCIS* sq pfc 300684
Mardles P J *FCMA* pfc 300684
McMillen C P *FCIS* sq pfc 300684
Overton S G *FCIS MBIM* sq pfc 300684
Pollock C D C *TEng(CEI) MIPlantE MBIM* sq tt 300684
Power J F B *ACIS* pfc 300684
Whittaker J I 300684
Bennett P A *ACMA* pfc 300685
Brooke-Webb A T *ACIS* G pfc 300685
Burt D J L *FCMA ACIS* pfc 300685
Jackson C N M J W G *ACIS MBIM* pfc ph 300685
Lee T W R *MBE* 300685
McDowell T P *FCMA* 300685
Reay T M *ACIS* pfc 300685
Southwell G pfc 300685

Majors

Foulis J A *MC* 161262
Scott A T J 090264
Stump A G S s 070366
Notley N D 310766
Dickinson E *FAAI* 040268
Ferguson J L 040268
Harper J S *MBIM* 300668
Meadmore J R C *ACIS* pfc 300668
Bennett J R 250768
Moore A S *AAAI FICM MBIM* 161268
Field A J 250369
McGimpsey A R 280769
Reed T N 050570
Lawrence D H 080670
Thirsk A F *ACIS* pfc 300670
Ward B H *ACA ABAA MBIM* 041170
Parry-Evans D C pfc 201270
Stanton R C *FAAI MBIM* 090571
Dromard D L 300671
Sankey C J *ACIS MBIM* pfc 090971
Connell T W P *MIDPM ACIS* sq pfc tt 191271
Cross R S 190172
Sharp R J G *ACIS* pfc 261072
Good C P 190373
Nelson I F 060573
Ward J C C 300673
Taggart N L *MBIM* pfc 230773
Trubody R T *ACIS* pfc 230773
Turner-Cain M G 161273
Clarke I C pfc 290774
Lonsdale-Hands G A M 290774
Drake R M W tt (*A/Lt Col* 280286) 010874
Anthony R W B pfc 040974
Rawlinson M S sq 011174
Barron P R A pfc 221274
Langrishe R D *BSc(Eng) AIDPM ACIS* pfc 221274
Ball R A pfc 040375
Hickie C C W 250375
Simmonds E W *BA* 300675
Hazel W T ph 040875
Conder R S *AIDPM ACIS* pfc 211275
Prince J R B *ACIS* pfc 211275
Sant E W *FCMA ACIS* pfc 211275
Stangroom R W *AIDPM ACIS* pfc 270476
North N O P *ACIS* pfc 201276
Yates S J 160177
Cates R P *MIDPM ACIS* pfc 130277
Lowndes E pfc (*A/Lt Col* 220286) 050377
D'Arcy-Irvine C K A ph 060377
Billson J T *BSc* adp 300677
Guthrie M D *BCom* sq 310777
Parry-Evans M P D sq adp 010977
Budd C F *MIDPM* sq pfc adp 291177
Freeman J D *FCMA* sq pfc 181277
Blackwell R G *ACIS* pfc 160178
Mackereth N A *ACIS* pfc 030478
Lees A J *BSc* 150678

*Representative Colonel Commandant for 1986

Addison J P G G	300678
Bowen A D pfc	100778
Atkinson R J B	300778
Boulton A D *MSc MBCS* dis sq pfc	300778
Stoneham F T *AMBCS* sq adp	300778
Tugwell R	300778
Watterson I *ACIS MBIM* psc pfc (*A/Lt Col* 270985)	300778
Young D H *MIDPM* sq	300778
Binks R J *ACIS* pfc (*A/Lt Col* 131285)	171278
Mills G H *ACIS* pfc (*A/Lt Col* 070286)	171278
Ward M L psc pfc pl (*A/Lt Col* 210286)	171278
Lynch M *ACIS MBIM* pfc	270179
Fyfe G A	080279
Peerless D J *MSc* dis sq	130279
Lear P M *FCMA* psc jsdc (*A/Lt Col* 060186)	310379
Brand C N *ACIS* sq pfc	200579
Howard R G	040679
Andrews F R	300679
Cooper S E *ACMA*	290779
Drake T C L *MA* sq	290779
McConkey H L ph	290779
Cox G H *ACMA*	300779
Weaving B E *ACMA*	100979
Rawlinson P A *AIDPM ACIS* pfc	031279
Spiers W J pfc	031279
Barrett P J *AMBCS* sq adp	161279
Bone C W *ACIS* pfc ph	161279
Corbett R J pfc	161279
Oakley C T G(a)	161279
Kirkwood D pfc	110280
Ball R R *BA* sq pfc	280280
Taylor C D R psc† pfc	270380
Johnston J *ACIS* pfc (*A/Lt Col* 100186)	100680
Kerridge M R psc	100680
Latham L P *MIDPM* adp (*A/Lt Col* 210985)	300680
Nicholls V J *FCMA MBIM* pfc (*A/Lt Col* 160885)	090780
Pannett M H G	280780
Powell M G *BSc ACIS* sq	280780
Duncan J S *MA*	050880
Ambrose J D	300980
Holtam P G *MCIT MBIM* t	300980
Myatt P J	300980
Noble N B	300980
Brown R F *BA AIDPM*	081180
Moralee S C adp	151280
Walker M J	151280
Walker T R	010481
Duncan M H *AIDPM* sq	120481
Jones D A psc	010881
Pearson C R J *BSc(SocSc)*	300981
Robinson A N M	300981
Cross I M S	201281
Drinnan D R ph	201281
Llewellyn M R *ACIS* pfc	201281
Homewood A M	020582
Lake R P	250782
Oddie D A P *MBE FCMA*	060882
O'Donnell T E *BA FCMA* pfc	030982
Evans M R	220982
Brown N	191282
Head C G J	310183
Yardley L E *ACEA*	050483
Embrey I G *AIB* pfc	270583
Sheehan P S D	250783
Cameron E C	310783
Gershon N D G	310783
Goodison R L	310783
Rutherford D M	310783
Snowdon J R *BSc*	310783
Kearns J N M *BA*	100983
Culton J W	300983
Stuart R C *FCMA* pfc	141083
Cassie A S *BSc*	111183
Rust D J	051283
Chisem D M aic	181283
Stewart R L	060284
Craig M W	270384
Dennison P M *BSc* im	270484
Dibley R G	080584
Winstanley W D	300784
Leighton R *BSc*	221084
Wee T G	070285
Say R *ACMA ACIS* pfc	140285
Donovan C G	140485
Carter J H L B	300985
Case D R	300985
Eckett B L	300985
Horsman G P	300985
Jamieson J S	300985
Keating P G J	300985
Lane S A *AIB*	300985
Lock M J	300985
Lowry T	300985
McNeill W I *FAAI*	300985
Morris R G	300985
Mullarkey A J	300985
Petry G A	300985
Roberts M D	300985
Strong G I M	300985
Wilkinson P K *BA CGIA*	300985

Captains

Sharpe D W	090476
Quinn H J *BAcc*	011278
Hutchison G J S aic	090379
Howard Harwood A G G(y)	090679
Willis P L D	310879
Braybrook T J *ACMA* (*A/Maj* 131285)	100979
Lane R D	100979
Tedridge A	100979
Farrington A	230180
Kingshott M J	090480
Martin J	300480
Ryder D J *MA* ee	090980
Worts R C *BSc(Eng)*	090980
Vearncombe B J	230381
Kemp C S	040881
Robinson P G	090981
Hyams R M *BSc*	290981
Jeffery C D	200182
Dransfield N	240182
Botting M I	230382
Fairclough A R	180582
Walker A J	070283
Renfrey A T	110483
Wolsey J N	081083
White P D H *BSc(Eng)*	060284
Truelove N	100684
Bedford C J H *BA*	161184
Holder K J	300685
Holt M J *BA*	050985
Brown A	051285

Lieutenants

Ayling K S *BA*	220982
Ward S G *BA*	110483
Beaumont C J	090485

2nd Lieutenants

†Freedman R E J *BA(Hons)*	060985
Gallagher M J	141285
†Gibson D A *BA(Hons) AIB*	060186

Royal Army Pay Corps – continued

Assistant Paymasters

Kilburn P W *MIDPM*		231069
	Maj	231069
Willoughby A		241069
	Maj	040980
Chappell D P		181070
	Maj	141082
Wilkinson P		280471
	Maj	110778
Minns W G *MBCS*		011071
	Lt Col	160186
O'Brien J J		221271
	Maj	030981
Jackson H		010572
	Maj	110175
Andrews A R		030572
	Maj	201083
Butler F R W		280672
	Lt Col	230381
Coleman D R		310772
	Maj	150977
Hathaway K W		260972
	Maj	280679
Graham J G *MBIM*		270972
	Maj	161082
Russell P R		131172
	Maj	050480
Douglas R McI		190473
	Maj	291080
Trinder G V D		010573
	Maj	240381
Ponting R A *MBCS MIDPM*		010474
	Maj	230681
Stewart-Smith G		080474
	Maj	031084
Young R		011074
	Maj	110675
Howells H M		181274
	Maj	280276
Crosfield W N M *MInstAM*		150475
	Lt Col	040581
Esgate H J *MBE MInstAM*		230475
	Maj	031084
Howard W		220575
	Maj	031084
Ballard B F W		100775
	Maj	021085
Collier C E		210875
	Maj	300583
Darlow K I		201075
	Maj	200981
Kaye H		100176
	Lt Col	011185
Meakin R S		260376
	Maj	071178
Wilson P B J		260376
	Maj	270278
Hughes M		100476
	Maj	021085
Barnham E R		031076
	Maj	080284
Bott G G		031076
	Maj	180484
Tupper J		060377
	Maj	010479
Tweedie C		290377
	Maj	300179
Slater J		300377
	Maj	010479
Turnbull R	*Capt*	230577
Cornwall B		010677
	Maj	030981
Widgery R D M		270777
	Maj	280679
Burrows R		021077
	Maj	290385
Love F		021077
	Maj	310185

Royal Army Pay Corps – continued

Milne R *Capt* 051277
Woodhams M G 020478
Maj 040980
Thomas D W *MBE MInstAM*
Capt 060678
Dangerfield K R 100978
Maj 070186
Tideswell A 100978
Maj 091285
Woodcock A E 100978
Maj 210286
Stringer A 170978
Maj 010479
Earle D R *MBE* 020479
Maj 040980
Smith W *Capt* 170679
Armes-Reardon A A A A
Capt 220879
Brady D V *Capt* 211079
Blundell J A *Capt* 010680
Lockwood M J *Capt* 230481
O'Keefe D W *Capt* 010184
Cox M G *Maj* 010984
Baddeley M W *Capt* 090386

Special Regular Officers

Majors

Johnson E *BA* 050868
Clark A J 300675
Davies W R 300677
Glendinning P H 311278
Moignard Howarth M S SVY
311278
Mahony R C S 300679
Metcalfe G B *MIDPM* adp 300679
Castell K S *FCCA FCMA ACIS* owc
300680
Pendlebury N *FCMA* 300680
Booth B W 300981
Bowden D A 300981
Day J E 300981
Duckworth V J 300981
Eborn R A C *MBCS AIDPM* 300981
White R J 300981
Crickmore R B *MBCS AIDPM*
300982
Rylance R C 300982
Hamilton S W 300983
Hillier D A 300983
Turner P E 300983
Howells E G 060984
Ambrose M C 300984
Clifford J C *AAAI* 300984
Samphier M 300984
Allan L H 300985
Bamforth P F 300985
Chandler M *ACMA AIDPM* 300985
Dainty A *MIDPM* 300985
Dunn R K 300985
Evans G J L 300985
Gallager T 300985
Gill F H J 300985
Hackney B *MBIM* 300985
Hargreaves A *ACMA* 300985
Higginson W S 300985
Hill M E 300985
Irvine J W 300985
Jones P E 300985
Layton L 300985
Lewing A C 300985
Moses A P 300985
Palmer D D J 300985
Reed J R 300985
Roriston D C *ACMA* 300985
Smith J W G 300985
Tetlow M D *ACMA* 300985
Thompson R W 300985
Torrens R J *AIDPM* 300985
White S P 300985

Captains

Whale P J 081270
Clancy P D 030974
Paskin K J 110376
Iremonger G J 080679
Chapman D C *BA* 010879
Cross T M 021079
Evans R
(*A/Maj* 010485) 021079
Hugill C F 021079
Maroney T J *BSc* 220480
Minns L R 100980
Winter J T 100980
MacAllister A R *BPhil* 030181
Clarke W T 160981
Jackson M J 160981
McCall R 160981
Goddard P 150882
Beale K L F *BEM* 140982
Bishop G L T 140982
Carroll T P J J 140982
Dollery N *ACMA* 140982
Griffiths D A 140982
Lane D C 140982
Round P 140982
Burton G 130983
Morris R 130983
Robinson G 130983
Robinson J T 130983
Wiltshire W 130983
Caswell J D 081083
Curl J J M 081083
Smith S A 081083
Taylor J C 081083
Boyd J D 120984
Brooks M 120984
Grist L A 120984
Hutchison A B 120984
Jones G E 120984
Walton P R 120984
Pool M G 081084
Coombes R W 110985
Downing P J N 110985
Eacock D A G 110985
Loughlin S L *MBE* 110985
Thompson P C 110985
Lodge M A 071085
Holmes R V 040286
Thornton A T 040286

Lieutenants

Stafford K
(*A/Capt* 071284) 011181
Cronin K T
(*A/Capt* 150485) 250582
Godber G R
(*A/Capt* 111285) 231284
Meldon P 101285

2nd Lieutenants

McCallum A S 100885

Short Service Officers

Captains

Stevens J A E 130576
Smart A 240578
Dawson R W *BA* 280578
Coulthard W 031078
Beach A D R 160981
Cavaye N P *MA* 280383
Iles G H 130983
Broad D C *BA* 050384
Bayes N 120984
Nash M R 120984
White T W 120984
Baillie J A 110385
Fish R J 110985
Gartside C 110985
Last C H *MInstAM* 110985
Minns D 110985
Montgomery C D 110985
Morse R J 110985
Sketchley I R 080486

Lieutenants

Bright J
(*A/Capt* 040684) 081081
Death P H
(*A/Capt* 080684) 081081
Franklin D
(*A/Capt* 070684) 081081
French R H
(*A/Capt* 110684) 081081
Fryer I *BEM*
(*A/Capt* 040684) 081081
Kellett P D
(*A/Capt* 160684) 081081
Macdonald Evans V J
(*A/Capt* 080684) 081081
Megarry R 081081
O'Callaghan P M
(*A/Capt* 040684) 081081
Rosenhead R A *ACIS*
(*A/Capt* 080684) 081081
Wright M A
(*A/Capt* 120785) 260182
Dobbs G L A
(*A/Capt* 050485) 270782
Dunn I F *ACMA*
(*A/Capt* 220385) 270782
Fairclough P C
(*A/Capt* 220385) 270782
Farrington W H
(*A/Capt* 150385) 270782
Johns S R L
(*A/Capt* 220385) 270782
Markham P P D
(*A/Capt* 250385) 270782
Morris J K
(*A/Capt* 150385) 270782
Nixon J R
(*A/Capt* 180385) 270782
Parish P C
(*A/Capt* 220385) 270782
Paulin G J
(*A/Capt* 190385) 270782
Rutherford D F
(*A/Capt* 170385) 270782
Spry T R
(*A/Capt* 220385) 270782
Squirrell P R *ACMA*
(*A/Capt* 150485) 270782
Young K J
(*A/Capt* 220385) 270782
Barker D A
(*A/Capt* 190785) 110483
Abbott M 090983
Goult D F 090983
Grimmer K M 090983
Kingston B N 090983
Macdonald J C *MInstAM* 090983
Gleed S M
(*A/Capt* 270685) 140983

ROYAL ARMY VETERINARY CORPS

The Figure of Chiron in Silver within a wreath of Laurel thereunder a Scroll inscribed ROYAL ARMY VETERINARY CORPS the whole ensigned with the Crown all gold

Regimental March

Quick March..........Regimental March of The Royal Army Veterinary Corps (Arrangement of "Drink Puppy Drink" and "A Hunting We Will Go")

Slow March..........."Golden Spurs"

Agents..........Holts Branch, Royal Bank of Scotland PLC, Lawrie House, Farnborough, Hants

Corps Headquarters..........Ministry of Defence (AVR), Government Buildings, Worcester Road, Droitwich, Worcester (*Tel No:* 0905 772323)

Alliance

Pakistan Army..........Pakistan Remounts, Veterinary and Farm Corps

Colonel Commandant..........Lt Gen *Sir* Brian Kenny *KCB CBE*..........230783

Hon Colonel Commandant..........Brig J R Spurry *CBE* ret pay..........210679

Brigadiers

Clifford R J *QHVS FBIM MRCVS* 300683

Colonels

Moffat S C *BVMS NDA MRCVS* 300683
Durrant G R *MBE NDA NDD BVSc MRCVS* 300684

Lieutenant Colonels

Thompson B J *MBE BVetMed MBIM MRCVS* 300683
Forgrave B T G *BVM&S MRCVS* 300684
Carding N H *MBE BVM&S MRCVS* 300685

Majors

Horne A W *BVSc MRCVS* 040269
Corrigan R B *MVB MRCVS* 010477
Jepson P G H *BVSc MSc MRCVS* 010480
Warde A S *BVetMed MRCVS* 010480
Roache A H *BVSc MRCVS MRCVS* 040881
Davison P J *BVSc MRCVS* 101281

Captains

Cooksley A *BVetMed MRCVS* 060481
Coulson N M *BA VetMB MRCVS* 260682

Quartermasters

Roffey P A 220675
Maj 010183
Beldham W E G 040879
Maj 170384
Hepworth P W *Capt* 240284

Special Regular Officers

Majors

Rossell T E 300985

Short Service Officers

Majors

øKneale J A *BVM&S MRCVS* 290184

Captains

Martienssen A B *BVSc MRCVS* 080781
Hutton T C *BVetMed MSc MRCVS* 260682
Graham T S *BVM&S MRCVS* 160782
Revell M D 011082
Pilling A M *BVSc MRCVS* 270783
MacDonald D A *BVM&S MRCVS* 300983
øGallard A S *BVetMed MRCVS* 050484
Carver J F A *BVetMed MRCVS* 010585
†White D S *BVMS MRCVS* 041185
†Southerden P *BVSc MRCVS* 060186

Lieutenants

Angwin R J *MISM* (*A/Capt* 050485) 011082

SMALL ARMS SCHOOL CORPS

A Vickers Machine Gun, thereon a pair of crossed rifles with bayonets fixed, a crown within the angle formed by the rifles above the machine gun; the whole within a laurel wreath; on the wreath scrolls inscribed on the left side "small" on the bottom "arms" and on the right side "school"

Regimental March

Quick March..Regimental March of The Small Arms School Corps ("March of the Bowmen")

Agents..Lloyds Bank PLC Cox's & King's Branch

Corps Headquarters..............................The School of Infantry, Small Arms Wing, Warminster, Wilts, BA12 0DJ
(*Tel No:* 0985 214000/Mil *Ext:* 2397)

Colonel Commandant ....Gen *Sir* Roland Guy *KCB CBE DSO ADC Gen* 060481

Advisers Infantry Weapons

Name	Rank	Date
Evans D J		011174
	Lt Col	070885
Stockley A E		011174
	Maj	100881
Dolling J R		011275
	Maj	270682
Stephens A		011275
	Maj	300982
Hutchings R J		011176
	Maj	291182
Mills D E		010377
	Maj	010983
Harvey G H		011177
	Maj	230384
Wilson A *MBE*		011177
	Maj	080384
Daborn K R		080278
	Maj	080286
Chater R F	*Capt*	301078
Whyte T	*Capt*	091178
Dawes A	*Capt*	170479
Bona M J	*Capt*	230779
Brown M E	*Capt*	151079
Cooke L A	*Capt*	010480
Ford A S	*Capt*	010480
Muir G	*Capt*	071281
Hixson N P	*Capt*	010482
Major M J	*Capt*	010482
Wilson R K *MBE*	*Capt*	010482
Blenkin K J	*Capt*	010483
Teasdale A R	*Capt*	010483
Williams R	*Capt*	010483
Silk R	*Capt*	010484
Harverson A	*Capt*	141184
Noonan M F	*Capt*	010485
Ryan J M	*Capt*	010485
Turner J E J	*Capt*	060985

MILITARY PROVOST STAFF CORPS

The Royal Cypher ensigned with the Crown thereunder a Scroll inscribed MILITARY PROVOST STAFF CORPS all gold

Regimental March

Quick March..."The Metropolitan"

Corps Headquarters..............................PM(A), Room 321, Lansdowne House, Berkeley Square, London
(*Tel No:* 01-499-8040 *Ext:* 7384)

Colonel Commandant ....Lt Gen *Sir* Norman Arthur *KCB* 010983

Quartermasters

Name	Rank	Date
Carroll J J		250476
	Maj	130984
Andrews P *MBE MInstAM*		100378
	Maj	060282
Harris G P *MBE*	*Capt*	081178
Humphries W	*Capt*	290379
Goddard P J	*Capt*	311080

Short Service Officers

Captains

Name	Date
Russell M J	010785

ROYAL ARMY EDUCATIONAL CORPS

A fluted flambeau of five flames thereon a crown and below the crown a scroll inscribed "RAEC"

Regimental March

Quick March..Regimental March of The Royal Army Educational Corps ("Gaudeamus Igitur" and "The Good Comrade")

Agents..Holts Branch, Royal Bank of Scotland PLC, Lawrie House, Farnborough, Hants

Corps Headquarters..............................Eltham Palace, Court Road, Eltham, London, SE9 5NR (*Tel No:* 01-859-2112)

Alliances

Australian Military Forces....................The Royal Australian Army Educational Corps
New Zealand Army..................................The Royal New Zealand Army Education Corps

Colonel in Chief.................................*HRH The Duchess of* Gloucester

Colonels Commandant...........................Gen *Sir* Richard Trant *KCB*..011079
*Maj Gen L Howell *CBE* ret pay..011082

Brigadiers

Lee J S *MBE MA* psc 300684
Manson J J N *MA* 300684
Thwaites D E *BSc(Econ) MA* psc† 300684

Colonels

Davies C R *MA FBIM* 300679
Underwood D V *MA* 300680
Reeves B *MA DipPhysEd* psc 300682
Gibbons G E *BSc(Econ) MA* 300683
Kinvig C A *MA* 300683
Sherry T C *OBE BA* 300683
Oxley D H *MA* psc 300684
Petrie A F P *MA* 300685
Prince J H *MA MIL* 300685
Russell C J F *DA MBIM* 300685
Silvey G H *BSc* 300685
Tuffnell P A *BSc(Econ) MSc* psc 300685

Lieutenant Colonels

Reese P H L *MA MPhil DipEd* 300674
Bradley J W *MA DipEd* 300675
McClean J L *BA DipEd* 300675
Adams T A A *MA* psc 300676
Goodman G S *BA ACIS MIL* 300676
Greenwood W R *OBE BA* 300676
Goodban D C J *MA* 300678
Hurn B J *BA MBIM* psc 300678
Ellams J J P *MA DipEd FITD* 300679
Glover G W D *MA* 300679
Pennick P B *BA* 300679
Cullens D K *MA* 300680
Paxton J G *BA* 300680
Stythe M G S *BA(Hons) MA DipEd* 300680
Wishart J G *BSc MBIM* psc† 300680
Fitzsimons W H P J *BSc BSc(Econ) MA DipEd* 300681
MacFarlane J M *MA* 300681
Cockram J M *BSc(Econ)* psc† 300682
Haworth-Wood J M *BEd MBIM MICO* 300682
Maughan B F *BA MSc* 300682
Thompson A D *BSc* psc 300682
Eldred D E *MA* 300683
Griffiths R P *BSc MA* 300683
Lowe D *MA* 300683
Mackay A I *BSc MA DipEd* 300683
Millsop K *BA* 300683
Newman N J *BA(Econ) MA* 300683
Wilson P L *BSc MA* 300683
Coupar W A *MA MLitt* 300684
Drewe R C *MA* 300684
Hardwick W K *MBE BA* 300684
Horsfall C F P *MA MSc* psc 300684
Jones R G *MA* psc 300684
Kirkwood R W *BSc MA* 300684
Smith P M *MEd ATD(Birm) DA(MANC)* 300684
Trewhella T M J *MSc NDA* 300684
Ward R W *MA* psc 300684
Anderson W R G *MA* 300685
Beard C B *BSc(Soc) MSc MITD* 300685
Burton B M *BA MSc(Econ)* 300685
Clamp S P *MA* 300685
Harrison D A *BA MSc(Econ)* 300685
Hoyal N R C *MA* 300685
Payne T W *BSc MA* 300685
Sjogren F G N *BA MSc(Econ)* 300685
Thomas N B *MA* 300685

Majors

Gurney J M *BSc(Eng)* 260367
Gibby J B *BA MSc(SocSc) DipEd MBIM* 290368
Millar A C *MA DipADEd* 100569
Andrews J E *MA* 031170
Surtees W *MA* 301170
Morgan J F *MA* 110171
Matthews C E *BSc MA* 201171
Huggins J M *BSc(Econ) MEd* 030972
Abnett K E B *BA DipEd* 040173
McKinnell J *BSc* 290373
Dixon P B *BA MBIM MITD* 110973
Gill P *BA MIL* 030374
Deans T *MA* 120574
Rashid P A *DipEd* 210674
Ashton G W *MSc DipEd* 010974
Bradley F A *BSc MA* 010974
Edwards D G *BA DipEd* 010974
Fox K O *MA MPhil MSc* 010974
MacIntosh E *MA MSc(Econ)* 010974
McMahon K *BA DipEd* 010974
Mills J *BSc DipEd* 010974
Nicoll W *MA DipEd MBIM* 010974
Preston R T *MSc* 010974
Smith B V B *BSc(Eng) MSc* 010974
Wade M *BA* 010974
Bedding D G *BA MSc* 200275
Birkbeck J *BA MA(Ed)* 010375
Milway A C *MA DipEd* 010375
McManus M J *MA MLitt* 290475
Gent R M J *BSc(Eng) MEd* 100675
Nichols D J G *BA DipEd* I 010376
Thornborough S G *BSc* 080876
Gilders J L *BSc MA* 030976
Eddie E F *BSc MA DMS* 040976
Hunter C I *BA MEd* 040976
Fletcher R G *BSc MSc(Econ)* 160976
Williams T *MA MSc DipEd MIL* 071276
Egan P *MSc* 231276
Miller G *MA* 010377
Norman P D *BA MSc* 010377
Cummings S G *BA DipEd CDipAF* (*A/Lt Col* 210386) 100377
Slater N T *MA MSc* 300877
Carstairs R D N *BA MEd CertEd MBIM AMITD* 010977
Philpott A *BSc* 020977
Howie D *MA* 170977
Ranson M F *MA* 311077
Howitt J R L *BA BSc MA* 091277
Hendry J S *MA MSc(Econ) DipEd* (*A/Lt Col* 270186) 240278
Thackaberry D G *BA DipEd* 010378
Dever D M *LLB* 260778
Flower-Smith M A *BEd MSc* 260878
Taylor G C *MA MSc* 020978
Parker G J *MA* psc 070978
Esmonde-White J L P *MA* 111178
Calver J R O *BSc* G 171278
Pugh J A *BSc(Econ) MSc* 020279
Taylor J F *MSc DipEd* dis sq 290379
Jenkins J H *BSc(Hons) MSc MBIM MITD* 250479
Madders R J *BA* 260479
Harron S M B *BSc MA* 190579
Thomas P R *MA* 030679
Cunniam M D *MA* 040679
Sales J B *BA* 290779

---

* Representative Colonel Commandant for 1986

Royal Army Educational Corps — continued

Johnson P S *BA(Econ) MEd DipEd MITD* 110879
Hughes D E *BSc MEd* 180879
Forster A D *BSc* 010979
Murray P S *MA* 080979
Roberts H G *BA BSc* 250979
Bowman D K L *BEd MSc(Econ)* 101179
Clare J J *BSc(Eng) MA* 161279
Field-Smith R A *MBE BA* psc 240180
Bartle R A *BA MSc(Econ)* 030380
Beaglehole R G *BA MSc* psc 030380
Dana D K *BSc(Eng) MSc* dis 030380
Pittendreigh D W *MA MSc MITD* 050380
Jones I R *BA MPhil* 110380
Maley T *BA MSc(Econ)* 220480
Edwards-Major L C *BSc MSc(Econ)* 060780
Aitken D *MSc* dis 280780
Denson H W I *BA MSc(Econ)* 310880
Watts P N P *MA MSc MBIM* 310880
Blackwell I O *MA* 080980
Lewis P J *BEd MA MSc MITD FCOLLP* 110980
Kerly B L E *BSc(Econ) MA DipEd* 311080
McCarthy T J *BEd MA* 031180
Powell T B D'E *MA* 190281
Simmonds J S *MA* 020381
Bradbury G *BA* 050781
Magee D W M *BA MSc* 020881
Booker R M *BA* 010981
Harwood V P G *BA MEd* ph 020981
Thomas A G *BA* 030981
Boden R D *BA* 060981
Wilkinson M V A *BSc(Eng)* 051081
Laird R A *MA MSc(Econ) DMS* 091181
Simmonds G M *MA* psc† 161181
Martindill C J *MA MEd* 290182
Stephens C J *BA(Econ) MSc* 010382
Wilson G H *BA DipEd* psc 290382
Boulter K A *MA* psc 090482
Lawson K G *MSc* 040582
Parkes M C *BA* 030782
Wright M J *MSc* 020882
Winfield K O *MA* psc 130882
Arnold K J *BA* 010982
McWilliams V F *MA MEd DipEd* 090982
Morrison R K *MEd* 081182
Atkins B M *BSc MA* 040183
Edwards R *BA MEd MITD* 040383
Wells P F *BSc* 020583
Hack C *BA* 280683
Stockill J A *MA* 310783
Harvey W J *MA MSc(Econ)* 120983
Marley C W *BSc* 300983
Burgess S C *MSc* dis 061083
Tustin W J *MA* 271083
Clarke J A L *BA* 111283
Hughes S C *BA* 181283
Moore T C R *BA* 181283
Telford W G *BEd MSc* 040284
Fraser G T *BA* 280284
Hannan J P *MA* 270484
Cain A *BSc(Econ)* 250584
Swalwell S G *BA MSc* 300784
Bradbury A *BA* 030984
Douglas A *BA DipTechEd* 070984
Green S I *BA* 021084
Hopkins I N *BSc* 040385
Cousins T E *MA* I 050385
Mitchell P W *BEd* 250485
Hall R C M *BSc* psc 200585
Willcox-Jones P W *BEd* 050785
Bacon G A *BEd* pl 270785
Brister A W E *BA* 040885
Wither J K *BA MSc(Econ)* 120885
Higson R P S *MA* 040985
Filler M St J *BEd* psc 050985
Rawlings A A *BA* 090985
West J W *BSc CBiol MIBiol* 290985
Wareing F *MA* 161285
Lewis-Cooper C *BSc* 130286
Keenan A W *BSc DipEd* 040386

Captains

Clifton S J P *BSc* 021079
Cardy A J *BA* 031079
McIlvenna M F *BA* 130280
Danchev A *MA PhD* 260280
Ciaglinski R Z A *BA* 280280
Gilbert H S *BEd* 290280
Viviani G J *MEd DipTechEd AMIMGTechE* 070380
Lawrence F E *BA* 270380
Avery A P *MA* 280380
Standish M P *BEd* 290380
Bell D R S *BA* 020480
Hopwood D *MA* 150880
Caswell C J *BA* 290980
Bristow C D *BEd* 021080
Wakefield M I *BA(Econ)* 280381
Burn D F *BEd* 030481
Dickins M A *BA* 030481
Rees B W *BA* 130881
Moss M P *BEd* 290981
Munro A A C *MA* 031081
Owen C D *BSc* 031081
Allender C J J *BEd* 151081
Jones M W *BSc* 010282
Hanlan C G *BSc* 130282
Shepherd D A *BA* 280382
Rigg W P *BEd* 290382
Johnson J P *MA* 020482
Leach G W *BEd* 020482
Mackenzie N N *BSc* 020482
Walker E P *BA MSc* 070482
Douglas R W *BEd* 140482
Williams T G *BA(Hons) MA* 140682
Daykin L *BA BA(Hons)* 140782
Hargreaves G N *BA* 031082
James D A *BSc* 291182
Thomson A J *BSc* 160283
Rabbitt A J *BA ALCM PGCE* 030483
Howells R T *BA MSc(Econ)* 120483
Collins R J *BMus LTCL PGCE LRSM LGSM* 130683
Russell P M *BEd* 071083
Denny S J *BA* 081083
Holgate M J 130284
O'Connell S H *BEd* 030384
Wilkinson B R *BSc* 010884
Ayo P B *BA* 071084
Douglas C *BA DipEd* 081084
Draper G *BSc* 081084
Dolan A *MA* 050285
Hazledine D W *BEd BEd(Hons)* 150285
Thomson B G *BA* 220785
Iles J K *BA* 071085
Carolin R *BA* 121085
Schofield R K *BSc* 121085

Lieutenants

Reames R M T *BA* 090484

2nd Lieutenants

††Ford L K 240985

Special Regular Officers

Majors

Lewins M J *BA* 160368
Fender J N 041170
Hoskins G F J 010171
Moss B V *BA* 230171
Marray D *BA* 010271
Drew P P 220671
Barker R P 190872
Jackson J C *BA* 011172
Bruckshaw A T 090173
Brown G *MA* 160373
Woodhouse C J M *BA* 170373
Beet C L 200373
Fry B W 190873
Pearce C C *AIL* 051173
Crump H G *BA* 120274
Goldthorp E N *MA DipEd* 030574
Lord M J W *BSc* 310874
Bell D R F *BA* 010974
Brooks P *BA MSc(Econ) DipEd* 010974
Storey C B *BSc* 010974
Walters M J *BA MBIM MInstAM MITD* 030974
Brown M *MA* 031274
Scott R D *BA* 071274
Patch R J *BA* 050175
Horne G R *BA* 270275
Lougher G *BA(Hons) MA* 010375
Marshall B *BA MSc* 030375
Barnard J F *BSc* 031075
Powney R T *BA MITO* 191175
Isaacs A L *BA* 021275
Walker A C *BA* 021275
Woodcock R W *BA MBIM* 060376
Smith J R *BA* 030776
Gillingham J P *MA DPhil ATD NDD* 260976
Mahon M J *BA(Hons)* I 141176
Omer J G 071276
Hutchinson R P D *MA DipEd* 060177
Beaman D H *AIL* 010377
Pilley D V *LRAM* 030377
Dutton C *MSc* dis 050377
Hughes D *BSc DipEd AIL* 011077
Wickens D J *BA* 141077
Sparrow A M *BSc DipEd* 181077
Kerslake W B *BEd FRGS* 280278
Handy D A *BSc DipEd* 010378
Tuckwell M C *BA MEd* 010378
Moore J K *MA* 210378
Hilton A W *BA* 040478
Marston R *BA MSc(Econ)* 170478
Earle J C *BA* 040878
Walters C *BA* 180978
Young R K *MA(Ed) DipEd* 180978
Dotchin T S C *BSc DipEd* 181278
Murgatroyd D *MA DipEd* 030479
Hayward M S *BA MSc DipEd* 260679
Mahoney D J *AIL* 210879
Wilson R *BA MA* 081079
Butler K D *CEng* 251079
Foster G J *BA MBIM* 050180
Jones R E E 060180
Littlewood P F *BA MEd* 110280
Morris D H 150880
Booth M *BA MIL* 281080
Croucher A R *BSc(Eng) MSc* 191280
Moverley L L *BA MEd* 020381
Syme D C *MA* 020381
Holloway D 110881

English J A *BA* 040981
Stuart R R *BA MSc* 010182
Wilkie W D *BSc DipEd* 010382
Thompson B F G *BEd* 080382
Griffith J D *BSc(Eng) ARSM* 140582
Eman J M *MBE* 040183
Martin B 040183
Morris M A *DipTechEd* 040183
Nash J W 040183
Whiteley G *BA MEd MSc(Econ)* 040183
Taylor B K *BA* 050283
Rea W *BA MSc* 010383
Bevan T O 040383
Wildgoose A 080783
Halligan S *BEd* 050983
Cunningham R J *BA* 091183
Fison W G C *BA MEd* 180184
Waters F G *FIERE MIIM* 040284
Nowell C B *MBIM* 020285
Capel C N D 280285
Dobbie M M *BSc DipPhysEd* 260485
Johnston J D *MA DipEd* 120885
Doyle C M *BA* 010286
Norton P W 010286
Wheeler C P *BA MSc* dis 010286
Aylett D J *BSc MIL* 220286

Captains

James C B *MBE MA DipEd* 090771
Harold M T 010879
Higgins J C 010879
Rudall A G *BSc* 060180
Barnard B C N *BEd TEng(CEI) FSERT* 120780
Englishby C *BA* 120780
Gordon K F *BA TEng(CEI) FSERT TEng* 120780
Wheeler W *BA TEng(CEI) FSERT* 120780
Lyne A R B *BA MIL* 160780
Hughes R F *BA* 280980
Rose M P J *BA(Hons)* 301080
Dempsey T P A *BPhil* 031180
Green C G 310181
Arter D J L *DEF DMS* 020281
McBirnie D *BA* 030481
Gilmour R J *BA* 160781
McMahon M J 160781
Quilter D R *BA* 160781
Griffiths A D 010881
Kyte N J *BA* 130881
Wingate N C *BA* 130881
Bufton R A *BSc* 021181
Bott M L *BA DipTRG* 191181
Wilson J H *BA* 150282
Davis C *BSc ARCS* 260482
Braithwaite R A *BEd* 140682
Akbar R A *BA* 140782
Chown D W 140782
McAlwane J E *BA* 140782
Power C *MIL* 140782
Roberts M G *MIL* 140782
Wilkie D R E 140782
Rumbles M J *BEd* 280982
Davis J A *BEd* 301082
Coy J E *BSc(Hons)* 200283
Hughes B J 200783
Joseph A *BA* 200783
Kitching D R 200783
O'Conor D L *BA* 200783
Waterhouse D J *BA* 200783
Cartwright N E *BEd* 130883
Butler P H *BA* 150384
Pickles K M *BA AIL* 160884
Woods A B *BEd* 071084
Evans D M *BA AIB* 081084
Whitfield A D T *BEd* 150285
Wright E J *BSc PGCE* 150285
Cummings B J *BA TEng(CEI) MIElecIE* 150885

2nd Lieutenants

†O'Connor M *BA* 200885

Short Service Officers

Captains

Beaumont M P 140177
Miles B *BA BEd MITD* 290381
Robertshaw A P *LLB* 030481
Preston M D *BA DipRSA* 020781
Barnes A D *BA* 160781
Hamilton E M 160781
Manuel R M *TEng(CEI) AMIMI AMIRTE* 160781
Parkinson R *BSc* 090282
Carson M B *BEd* 020482
Ellis D G *BA* 140782
Shelby-James J M *BEM* 140782
Eve J A 280882
Lee-Wood R S *BTech* 280982
Rentell M E *BA AIL* 230383
Wilkinson I *BA* 060683
Barnett M 200783
Colbeck P G C 200783
Craig P G B 200783
Crane A P *MSRG* 200783
Norman D 200783
Trenam R *BA* 200783
Wilde G 200783
Nadin R 011183
Hunter C J *BEd* 051283
Earle J C R S J *BA* 170284
Kemp J C R *BEd* 030484
Barrow I D S 160884
Bornstein D *BA* 160884
Griffin W T 160884
Watts L J 160884
Worrall J M 160884
Savage M S *BEd* 190984
Davie R J *BSc* 081084
Butterfield A W *BSc* 091084
Gibson G C *BA* 121084
Gordon R D B *BA* 050285
Murphy P J *BSc PGCE* 150285
McKenna P G *BEd* 050385
Newton J L *BSc* 020485
Buxton A *BEd* 100685
Wilson N J *BEd(Hons) FRGS* 100685
Bridgman R W *MA* 080785
Knight C J *TEng(CEI) MIMGTechE* 150885
Tognarelli W G *BSc* 071085
Heritage E *BA* 121085
Pell-Ilderton N C *BSc* 121085
Lawson M C *BA* 040286
Bailey M S *BA* 090286
Cartwright D T *BSSc* 090286

Lieutenants

Yarrien P A *MInstAM* (*A/Capt* 281085) 150281
Alexander D W 260182
Gambrill R M 260182
Harrison R H 260182
Lister D C *BA* 260182
Robinson A 260182
Short D S *BA* 110482
Nash J P *BEd* 120482
Naylor R *BA* 090882
Craig D A *BA* 111082
Holloway D J *BA* 111082
Lambert P J *BSc* 110483
Williams S F *BA* 110483
Vickery D A *BEd* 080883
Hopkins K W *BSc* 090484
Lewis N R *BSc* 090484
†Hobbs J H 250785
†Rose C D 250785
†Williams P 250785

2nd Lieutenants

†Payas S F *BEd*
†Warren D J L *BA* 101284
†Armstrong B S *ARCM* 200885
†Buckley P J P *BSc(Hons)* 200885
†Gibb D M *BSc PGCE* 200885
†Moore E L *BA* 200885
†Rodgers A H *BA(Hons) PGCE* 200885
†Romans N M *BA(Hons)* 200885
†Willcock C P *BA(Hons) PGCE* 200885
†Beer J M *BA(Hons) MA PhD* 041285
†Maher N *BA BA(Hons) PGCE* 041285
†Smith P J *BSc PGCE* 041285
†Tarrant P M *BEd* 081285

ROYAL ARMY DENTAL CORPS

Within a Laurel wreath a dragon's head and sword; beneath a scroll bearing the motto "Ex dentibus ensis"
The whole surmounted by a crown

Regimental March

Quick March.."Green Facings"

Agents..Holts Branch, Royal Bank of Scotland PLC, Lawrie House, Farnborough, Hants

Corps Headquarters..............................Headquarters and Central Group RADC, Evelyn Woods Road, Aldershot, Hants (*Tel No:* 0252-24431)

Alliances

Australian Military Forces...................The Royal Australian Army Dental Corps
New Zealand Army..............................The Royal New Zealand Dental Corps

Colonels Commandant.........................Maj Gen E J Bowen *CB* ret pay..........020182
*Brig G Smith ret pay..........311283
Hon Colonel Commandant.................Col G L Howe *TD*..........031075

Brigadiers

Coulthard E *QHDS MSc BDS FBIM* 280482

Colonels

Charlton T *BDS* 210274
Heap C V *LDS* 250177
Docherty R *QHDS MSc LDS FBIM* 010577
Newell M J *BChD FDSRCSEng DOrth* (*A/Brig* 300384) 191078
Fletcher W P *LDS DDPH FBIM* 100579
Taylor R R *BDS MGDSRCSEng* 190779
Lervy W K *FDSRCSEng LDS DOrth* 101179
Richards F L *LDS FBIM* 281179
Smith E *BDS* 240480
Jack D R *MSc BDS* 090680
Scarborough A D *LDS* 030880
Ashenhurst F E *MSc BDS FBIM MInstAM* (*A/Brig* 161184) 210880
Brocklehurst J I *BDS* 290581
Halford R S *BDS LDS* 030981
Trezona J D *LDS* 311081
Smith D H *BDS* 121281
Newlyn C P *BDS FDSRCSEng* 200182
Potts R W *BDS* 030882
Smart R A *BDS FDSRCSEng DOrth* 051082
Masterson L J *BDS* 130283
Boulton D *BDS FDSRCSEng FDSRCPSGlas* 170384
Kessel L J *BDS FDSRCSEng* 080484
Parkinson C D *LDS* 070984
Craven J A *BChD* 010485
Bhabutta R L *BDS* 280585
Sewell W A *BDS* 210685
Potts R E *BDS MGDSRCSEng* 130985
Royle M *LDS* 081285

Lieutenant Colonels

Higham R F *LDS* 010170
Dhupa D V *LDS* 280770
Morrey A M *LDS* 291271
Lee D W *BDS* 160974
Mumford A S *BDS* 181074
Douglas D S *BDS DDPH MBIM FRSH* 041174
Pickard R L W *BDS* 210775
Willis E H *BDS MGDSRCSEng* 260676
Brocklebank M R *BDS* 170776
Clements J S *BDS MGDSRCSEng* 050976
Roberts C *BChD* 180377
Frost D A *BDS* 111177
Fleet J D *MBBS BDS FDSRCSEng MRCS LRCP* 141277
Deere E G *BDS FDS FDSRCSEng FDSRCSEd DOrth* 211277
O'Regan P K *BDS* 070478
Lettington E D *LDS* 080878
Edwards J D E *BDS MGDSRCSEng* 120878
Boyle J A *BDS* 040179
Jeffrey R S *BDS* 140379
Montgomery J I *BDS DRDRCS(Ed)* 300379
Fleming-Jones D P *BDS MGDSRCSEng* 120879
Hopkin B A *MSc BChD* 290979
Hawkes A J *BDS DDPH FRSH* 011279
Thomas F D *BDS FDSRCPSGlas* 191279
Horobin P R *BDS MGDSRCSEng* 221279
Hunt B G *BDS* 240680
Miller S F N *BDS MGDSRCSEng* 030780
Lee C H W *BDS* 170880
Davies B M *BDS* 120980
Jones E G *BDS* 271280
Cheetham W A *BDS MGDSRCSEng MGDS(Edin)* 180481
Purkis C M *BDS* 010781
Townsend M R *MSc BDS MGDSRCSEng* 120781
Watt K A C *BDS* 181281
Phillip R M H *BDS FDSRCPSGlas* 080182
Bradley J R *MSc BDS* 080282
Forsey K C *BDS* 240482
Atkins C A *BDS MGDSRCSEng* 270482
Poole S J *MSc MGDSRCSEng MGDS(Edin) LDS* 210782
Mathews R *BDS* 040982
Gamon J A *BDS MGDSRCSEng DRDRCS(Ed)* 010183
Hardy J H *MSc BDS MGDSRCSEng MGDS(Edin)* 060183
Goulbourn A J *BDS* 090183
Lover J *BDS* 240683
Tinlin W R *BDS* 290683
George A G *BDS* 200783
I'Anson R C *BDS* 141183
Watson F *BDS MGDS(Edin)* 260784
Holloway F E *BDS MRCS* 110185
Aitken J F *BDS* 140785
James C M *BDS* 050885
Reynoldson H P *BDS* 070985
Barlow D A R *BDS* 010186
Crapper H J *BDS* 290386

Majors

Barclay B *BDS* 100778
Sims A P T *BDS FDSRCSEng* 020179
Wills J G N *LDS* 050179
Lyall J B F *BDS FDSRCSEd* 030779
Lomax S P *BDS MGDS(Edin)* 101279
Clarke W H F *BDS* 280780
Harper J R C *BDS* 161280
Coles J P *BDS* 090281
Elstub M J *BDS* 240381
Long G K *BDS* 260481
Woodward-Court P *BDS* 090781
Monk S R *BDS* 050881
øCunningham H J *BDS* 311281
Pretsell I A *BDS* 311281
Revington P J D *MSc FRCS FDS* 040182
Gaw D A *BDS* 010782
Bryan D C *BDS FDSRCPSGlas* 120782
Stuart K G *BDS* 140882
Anderson J Q *LDS* 111082
Daniell L R *BDS* 091083
Newell S L *BDS* 311283
øReece J M *BDS LDS* 311283
McCormick R J *BDS* 020884
Rush C S *BDS* 171284
Pearson M H *BChD* 190385
Simpson S H *BDS* 040885

Captains

Pilcher R *BDS* 250681

---

* Representative Colonel Commandant for 1986

Guest S M *BDS* 030282
Carmichael E B *BDS* 140782
Holmes J P *BDS* 150982
Colquhoun R K *BDS* 131282
Heath S P *BDS* 080783

Quartermasters

Williams R T 160275
Maj 110784
Parsons R C *Capt* 150876
Croman D J 010280
Maj 010286
Thomson D H *Capt* 170780
Taylor R R *Capt* 170281
Fannan P P M *Capt* 100581

Special Regular Officers

Lieutenant Colonels

øAshworth R C *BDS* 300980
Newton D A *BDS* 091180
Emanuel O T *BDS* 210782
øPower A J *BDS* 260784

Majors

Rogers P *BDS* 170481
East C M *BDS* 160981
Cox S R M *BDS* 280183
Young N M *BDS* 230184
Herdman C D *BDS* 030784
Isherwood S J *BDS* 030984

Short Service Officers

Lieutenant Colonels

Jones W F *LDS* 250680

Majors

Cohen J B *MGDSRCSEng LDS*
150980
Fairclough J *BDS* 150980
Pughe J W *BDS* 231081
Jones J R *BDS* 281281
øCrinson B *BDS* 230182
Haigh B *BDS* 120982
Davies J A *BDS* 140283
Collins G J *BSc BDS* 010583
Diggins M H *BDS* 151283
Loftus S F *BDS* 040585
Hathway R *BChD* 230685
øMitchell A J *BDS* 260785
Tyrrell H R M *BDS LDS* 290785
øGilpin H A L *BDS* 040885
øMcComb S A F *BDS* 251085
øNuttall S M *BDS* 120186
Parkin J C *BDS* 220186
Wilkinson A J *BDS* 270286
øBlenkinsopp R C *BDS* 180386

Captains

Allan J C U *BDS* 270781
Fisher R W *BDS* 270781
øWillett R E *BDS* 030881
Fullerton K A 170881
Partridge S *BDS* 040981
øBolt D J *BDS* 260981
MacEachen W R J *BDS* 191181
Sergeant P L *BDS* 151281
øSimpson J *BDS* 181281
øHaslam A B *BDS* 160182
Bentley C R *BDS* 030282
Byfield S D E *BDS* 030282
øCompsty I B *BDS* 030282
Mitton J M 110382
Bryant D G *BDS* 010782
Gallier S M *BDS* 080782
øAldridge J B *BDS* 140782
øBrooks I *BDS* 140782
øFisher K M C *BDS* 160782
Nicholson K *BDS* 250782
Black W C *BDS* 150982
Craig G H *BDS* 150982
øPreston S *BChD* 150982
Williams M D *BDS* 131282
McIntosh R C *BChD* 171282
øDeeves S A *BDS* 090283
øTrepess L M *BDS LDS* 170383
Sloss D R *BDS* 140783
øParkes J M *BDS* 211283
øCopson A M *BDS* 311283
Morris S R *BDS* 030784
Poznansky J B *BDS* 100784
Mulford A *BDS* 170784
Nuttall B V *BDS* 271284
Pilcher R L *BDS* 271284
San M G *BDS* 271284
øHorner G P *BDS* 311284
Burrows P *BDS* 140285
Jones G W *BDS* 140285
øNoble R E *BDS* 140285
øEllingham H K *BDS* 170685
Clark M A *BDS* 161285
Moore R A *BDS* 191285
Ramsden A J *BDS* 191285

2nd Lieutenants

††Brooks R G 010983
ø††Iffland T J 010983
††Dixon R 010984
††Lane I B F 010984
ø††Mindak M T M 010984
††Boulcott M N 010985
†Dobson J E *BSc(Eng) MSc CEng MRAeS* 010985
†Heath G C 010985
ø†Hiscock J E 010985
†Preece J M R 010985

Non-Dental Officers

Lieutenants

Roots K V 211181
Marshall R J 080282
Sellars J B 080282

ROYAL PIONEER CORPS

Two Pioneer axes crossed in saltire beneath their heads and surmounted on a Pioneer sword and laurel wreath below the same a scroll inscribed Royal Pioneers and the whole ensigned by a Royal Crown all argent

Regimental March

Quick March..........Regimental March of The Royal Pioneer Corps ("Pioneer Corps")

Agents..........Lloyds Bank PLC Cox's & King's Branch

Corps Headquarters..........RPC Training Centre, Simpson Barracks, Northampton (*Tel No:* Northampton 62742)

Colonel in Chief..........*HRH The Duke of* Gloucester *GCVO*

Colonel Commandant..........Maj Gen J J Stibbon *OBE*..........010186

Hon Colonel Commandant..........Brig A F Mutch *CBE* ret pay..........031183

Colonels

Buck T N *MIPM MBIM* cl	300682
Hickman H J *OBE AIPM MBIM* cl (*A/Brig* 190385)	300683
Higginbotham D R *GradIPM* cl	300685

Lieutenant Colonels

Telfer C *MIPM* cl	300681
McDonald R F *AIPM* cl	300682
Piper G E *MIPM MBIM* cl	300682
Baird P D N cl	300683
Everett C R B *MBIM MInstAM* psc	300684
Le Masurier M C osc(MAL) sq	300684
Hill G ndc sq	300685
Ingle D C *GradIPM*	300685
Wither R *AIPM* cl	300685

Majors

O'Dea W J M cl	040268
Stacey L J *AIPM* cl	311276
Sievier J B cl	300677
Stott R W *MA MBA*	300678
Bright T R sq	210579
Spears C D *AIPM MBIM* cl	300679
Cooper G R *AIPM MIMH* cl	311279
Buesnel A J *GradIPM* cl	300980
Nicholson P J *GradIPM* cl	300980
Rayner J R M cl	300980
Tyson-Carter A H *AMITD* l	300980
Allen J F J *MBE*	300981
Homewood I M	300981
Milne I A cl	300981
Powell T S *MBA* cl	300981
Crook G F	300982
Downey G M	300983
Hunting M J	300983
Dickson R N	300984
O'Connor N *BA MSc(Econ)*	300985

Captains

Jones I E *BA*	010281
Shaw A T *GradIPM* cl	170681
Hardy C G	281281
White M *BA*	090282
Mapstone M R J	070283
Gregori L S J *BSc*	081083
Rainey W D *BA*	081083
Starling J A *BSc(Eng)*	060284
Moody R E	100684
Clayton R J	081084
Kershaw G B *BSc*	081084
Wilde P A	090685

Lieutenants

McNulty P J	120482
Code C R *BSc*	090882

2nd Lieutenants

Glynn S D	
Hughes D M	040884

Quartermasters

Read J S	201173
Lt Col	140282
Lineham G F	120682
Maj	260982
Fleming P J *MISM MIMH*	
Capt	020283

Special Regular Officers

Majors

Moody B *MBE*	300679
Corrigan A J F	300981
Kedda R J	300981
Featherstone M J	300982
Morgan D E *BEM*	300983
Bingham M J *BA MBA* cl	300984
Ferguson H E	300984
Spalding G	300984
Aveyard B	300985

Captains

McNaught P J	130273
Warren G D *BSc AIIM LRSC*	050181
Webb R C	090581
Faux A C H (*A/Maj* 150285)	020781
Stock G	230781
Coffey J G *Tech(CEI) MHTTA MISM*	300781
Monkley H P	070881
Paterson J T	310382
Tunnicliffe D	010982
Campbell J M (*A/Maj* 011184)	030982
Hall E I	051082
Wilson M G	210183
Smith J H *FRGS*	260183
Doran J T *BEM*	230283
Atkinson C N	160383
Langford C D	110683
Ralph P J D	110184

Lieutenants

Sanders R J	111284

Short Service Officers

Captains

Turquand J N	190580
Yeo L J *BSc(Econ) DipEd*	290980
Crawford O J *TEng(CEI)*	010582
Tonks J	040882
Graham D J	110882
Salmon F	071082
Humphreys E S	120183
Sharp A	160283
Johnston C J J	200583
Mealing P C	130783

Lieutenants

Downey J S G	081281
Smith M D	030682
Grant A B	060682
Cochrane D C	030483
Hardie F J *MBE*	150483
Pratchek N D S *BA*	070884
Robertshaw S N	060885
Belgum C	101285
Buckingham M B J	101285

2nd Lieutenants

Tully S W	100885
Whitworth B J	100885
†Bennett M J *BA(Hons)*	060985
†Gascoine R J *BSc*	060985
Duggan M D M	141285
Everitt A C	141285
Evetts S N	141285

INTELLIGENCE CORPS

A Union rose within two branches of laurel surmounted by a crown; below the laurel a scroll inscribed "Intelligence Corps"
"Manui Dat Cognitio Vires"

Regimental Marches

Quick March..."The Rose and the Laurel"
Slow March..."Trumpet Tune (and Ayre)"

Agents...Lloyds Bank PLC Cox's & King's Branch
Corps Headquarters.............................Templer Barracks, Ashford, Kent
(*Tel No:* Ashford 25251 *Ext:* 243)

Alliances

Canadian Armed Forces.........................Canadian Forces Intelligence Branch
Australian Military Forces.....................The Australian Intelligence Corps

Colonel in Chief...................................Field Marshal *HRH The Prince* Philip *Duke of* Edinburgh *KG KT OM GBE QSO*

Colonel Commandant ....Maj Gen C R L Guthrie *LVO OBE*..010386

Brigadiers

Crawford A K rcds ndc psc 300685

Colonels

Ford M P *BA* sq (*A/Brig* 090386) 300682
White R A S psc† 300682
Sloan H M *MA MBIM* odc(FR) psc osc(FR) 300683
Venn D J *OBE* psc 300684
Durman M D *BA FBIM* psc 300685
McMullen J J *OBE* psc(a) 300685

Lieutenant Colonels

Landolt J D psc 300677
Redler L M *FBIM* psc 300679
Terry B J *OBE* sq 300679
Dobson A J *AIL* sq 300680
Grace C B T sq 300680
Ridger A F sq 300680
Reece D A ndc psc 300682
Springfield E P O *BA* psc 300682
Burrill D M *BA MBIM FITD* psc 300683
Parr C D *OBE* psc 300683
Van-Orden G C *MBE BA* psc 300683
Jackson W M W *MBE* sq 300684
Langstaff R A psc 300684
Messervy-Whiting G G *MBE MBIM* psc(a) jsdc 300684
Whitehead J M B *MA* psc 300684
Abbott A J *MBE BA* psc 300685
Head M A W *MBE BA(Hons) MA(Hons) MBIM* psc 300685
Hughes-Wilson J N psc 300685
Snell P W *MBE* sq 300685
Williams A *MBE* sq 300685

Majors

Richards R A U 220763
Shears J B ptsc sq 120267
Shaw R W M *BA* 300669
Johnston P T *MIL* sq 311269
Ashley P R *MBE* sq 300670
Hughes C B *BA* psc (*A/Lt Col* 270985) 311277
Box A M *BSc* sq 300678
Walker M P psc (*A/Lt Col* 050785) 311278
Randell R G O sq 300679
Eccles R A sq (*A/Lt Col* 140386) 311279
Holtom C G psc 311279
Muir N B *MC* sq 311279
Webb H P sq 311279
Hewitt C W *MA* sq 300980
Kerr J G *QGM MA* 300980
Mercer E G psc 300980
Venn I psc 300980
Barclay K P A I* 300981
Laurie M I *BSc(Eng)* psc 300981
Newell N J 300981
Payne G S *BA* 300981
Bassnett S A *MBE BA* 300982
Dover G D *BA* psc 300982
Lamidey J *MA* 300982
Wardley M C *BSc(Econ)* psc(GE) 300982
Wyllie W H *BA* 300982
Brokenshire P J R *BA* 300983
Gregory-Smith R L *BSc(Econ)* 300983
Levack W D M 300983
Morrison J P 300983
Adams R J *BSc* 300984
Andrews R I H *MBE* 300984
Berry J R *AIL* 300984
Haydock D L *MBE* psc 300984
Hill M K *AIL* 300984
Marshall R *MBE* 300984
Nebel M A 300984
Tobias J W *MBE* 300984
Cronin M J *MA* I 300985
Cunningham P 300985
Dysterre-Clark N F *BA* 300985
Gosnell J D *MA AIL* 300985

Captains

Russell M S *BSc* aic 280878
Campbell-James J *BA CGIA* 161278
Davies P N *BA* 080379
Cox P L *BA* 090379
Walker J W *BEd DipEd* 010879
Hildyard N D *BSc(Eng)* (*A/Maj* 010485) 100979
Baker C *BSc* 090980
Suggit J R *BA* 090980
Bullivant G *BSc* 011080
Baird Fraser R I *MA* (*A/Maj* 220286) 021080
Nelson W 051180
Brown S R *MBE* ato 291280
Stevens T E *BA* 120281
Charters D S 090581
Terrington C J L *MA* 120881
Richards J R *BSc* 080981
Longhorn R W 281281
Sanderson C *BA* 281281
Barron A J L *BA* 010282
Lander J C *BSc(Econ)* 010382
Corbett G J *MA* 100482
Edge T D J *BA* 010882
Everson P F 060982
Munns R P D *BA* 060982
Lawton C P 170982
Bailey M *BA* 031082
Collinson C J *BA* 211082
Bunker B J *BA* 191182
Watts I F 070283
Innell N F *BA* 080483
Millar W G E *BA* 050983
Tomlinson T C *BSc* 050983
Fox N R H 081083
Baynham S C D *BA* 060284
Dean G L *BA* 060284
Pugh R 290284
Hopkins M J *MA* 070484
Jefferies I D *BA* 190484
Keightley M D 100684
Lincoln S G 100684
Fullerton P *BA* 050285
Holland A C H *BSocSc* I 050285
Berger A J E *BSc* 240485
Stringer P J *BA* 090685
Reeve G W *BA* 130685
Donovan M J *MBE* 221085
Hyden J S *LLB MA* 280286

Lieutenants

Orr R R J *BA* 071081
Franks A H T 081281
Baston S J *BSc* 120482
Hannam R B *BA* 120482
Jeynes R P *BA* 120482
Miller S N *BA* 120482
Bird C B *BA* 110483
Fairclough G J *BSc* 110483
Le Fevre G R *BA* 110483
Tozer J I *BSc* 110483
Petrie N R (*A/Capt* 220285) 080883
Carroll J P 121283
Denyer C *BA* 090484
Edwards P W D *BA* 090484
Hack E H J *BSc* 090484
Woods I W I 090484
Barton D M A 060684
Munns S C 161084
Dakin N J 090485
Whiteley J 090485
Britton N J 070486

2nd Lieutenants

††Hockenhull J R *BA(Hons)* 030982
Hallas M J 070484

Intelligence Corps — continued

Nash M J R 040884
Adair S A 300984
Phillips F J 081284
Tunnicliffe I P 081284
Rawdon-Smith R J 130485
†Hodkinson R A J *BA(Hons)* 060985
†Weale A J *BA* 060985
††Hazel J M E 240985

Quartermasters

Davis A *BA* 170377
Lt Col 300683
Spencer D J 011279
Maj 140484
Greenfield A J *MBE* *Maj* 040784
Woolmore J D *BEM*
Capt 230785
Ward W *Capt* 040486

Technical Duty Officers

Hedison J 010871
Lt Col 290485
Dawkins M D 161075
Maj 010479
Welch P W 020579
Maj 041182
Henderson I F G 011083
Maj 190985
Stevenson A D C *MBE* 101183
Maj 151184

Special Regular Officers

Majors

Hodges P J 300678
Jarvis J M 300678
Haynes J S sq 311278
Haylor L C *BEM* 300679
Jackson H 300679
Dixon C J T sq 300980
Groves J adp 300981
Jubb G W 300981
Ashford P F 300982
Duncan D I *BEM MIL* 300982
Baker L T *MBE* 300983
Burry P *AIL* 300984
Crawley D A 300984
Goodall J E *BEM* 300984
Harrison C *MIL* 300984
Lewis J 300984
Taylor R C W 300984
Thomas A G sq 300984
Thorp D J 300984
Barnes A 300985
Bone J F 300985
Boothman R P 300985
Cant P T 300985
Lewer A H J 300985
Nash A P 300985
Sevier J C R 300985
Thorpe M T 300985

Captains

Courage M J
(*A/Maj* 170284) 230278
Mobbs P A 221278
Titchener A R *MInstAM* 300379
Devoti P J J 300979
Gallichan J P
(*A/Maj* 201285) 060280
Little M F adp
(*A/Maj* 051084) 060280
Kett R E 030780
Giddings D M *MBE BEM*▪ 040182
Williams G V A *MBE* 170382
Brewer R E I
(*L/Maj* 010486) 230582
Ogglesby J M
(*A/Maj* 260386) 150982
Babington-Smith J *BA*
(*A/Maj* 130186) 190982
Hagger M J *MBE* 181282
Dicker S R I
(*L/Maj* 291185) 050183
Hammond L R 100383
Jacobs A *MBE* 021183
Child A N
(*A/Maj* 310186) 110184
Roberts A 260484
Richardson P A *MBE* 040185
Vigrass C J 040185
McMullen T M 180285
Murphy H 180285
Hollinshead D E 050485
Knought G A *BEM* 050485
Simpson P J 030585
Hogg W A 260885
Noeken J C *BEM* 260885

Short Service Officers

Captains

Maunder R D 010581
Carr C R I 300682
Ryles J A *BEM* 311082
Smith R A 100284
Lawson A G W *BEM* 150384
Hammond L G 020484
McCrindle R S *BEM* 081084
Eaton H 040185
Westbrook M S D 040185
Boughton M P R 150785
Chambers A G P *MBE* 260885
Peaks D C 260885
Hills D J *QGM* 101085
Downey K J *BA(Hons) MA MBIM MInstAM MISM MITO* 171085
Romanis T A 141185
Dales K J 201285
French M *MBE* 201285
McGinily M G D 201285
Wright R G 201285
Greaves G H 250186
Wilkinson R T 020486

Lieutenants

Biles J A *MBE*
(*A/Capt* 100485) 280282
Flanagan T
(*A/Capt* 010186) 280282
Foley T A P
(*A/Capt* 120785) 280282
Hopkins P
(*A/Capt* 160985) 280282
Luttrell T W 280282
Parsons R G
(*A/Capt* 211284) 280282
Whitney S H
(*A/Capt* 010685) 240382
Gillion G P H 290482
Eaton G P 050682
Livermore I N
(*A/Capt* 090185) 200682
Gray A 030782
Carpenter J A
(*A/Capt* 040285) 010882
Wood F C
(*A/Capt* 290485) 060882
Hughes B 210882
Cohen M
(*A/Capt* 260685) 161182
Hall G A *QGM BEM*
(*A/Capt* 251085) 161182
Smith M S
(*A/Capt* 160585) 161182
Ansell I C
(*A/Capt* 230785) 090183
Gaw A A
(*A/Capt* 150785) 090183
Poole M A 090183
Anley R J *MBE*
(*A/Capt* 290785) 250183
Langham D A
(*A/Capt* 230885) 060283
Leggat P M R *QGM*
(*L/Capt* 110386) 010583
Pearcy D J
(*A/Capt* 161285) 110683
Elliott C J 100983

ARMY PHYSICAL TRAINING CORPS

Crossed swords surmounted by a crown

Regimental March

Quick March..Regimental March of The Army Physical Training Corps ("Be Fit" words from "Land and Sea Tales" by Kipling)

Agents..Lloyds Bank PLC Cox's & King's Branch

Corps Headquarters..........................The Army School of Physical Training, HQ and Depot APTC, Queens Avenue, Aldershot, Hants (*Tel No:* Aldershot 24431 *Ext:* 2132)

Colonel Commandant.........................Gen *Sir* Nigel Bagnall *GCB CVO MC*■..050281

Commandant......................................Brig R J Baddeley..250486

Masters at Arms

Name	Rank	Date
Gelder G W		220272
	Lt Col	160284
Gardiner J *BEM*		071074
	Maj	071082
Glynn D J		050575
	Lt Col	020785
Hargraves P *MSRG*		300575
	Lt Col	301185
Hammond T F *MBE*		140476
	Maj	011283
Duxbury A		120776
	Maj	120784
Flood A G		230776
	Maj	120583
Foster D A		011176
	Maj	080784
Martindale D J *MSRG*		050177
	Maj	050185
Sears D C		280377
	Maj	040984
Knight T C		040577
	Maj	030385
McBurney D E *MSRG*		
	Capt	030578
McCombie F J	*Capt*	170578
Carr A	*Capt*	180578
Hellicar T A D *MSRG*		
	Capt	110978
Hughes D T	*Capt*	201178
Pollock J	*Capt*	260379
Macaree T	*Capt*	010679
Morris G	*Capt*	280780
Lyons P L	*Capt*	010980
Quare T *MSRG*		301081
	Maj	210782
Allen A	*Capt*	040182
Goulding T J	*Capt*	160382
Slater R B	*Capt*	210682
Monk R F	*Capt*	060982
Jennings J	*Capt*	290783
Carraher D	*Capt*	010883
Carter K G *BEM*	*Capt*	010485
Hepton S J *BA*	*Capt*	010485
Parker T	*Capt*	010485
Lillywhite B	*Maj*	040685

Short Service Officers

Captains

Name	Date
Steel R A *MSRG*	180684
Stallard M P *BA*	210285
Clay D N	121285

Lieutenants

Name	Date
McNeish S G	021081
Fisher A J (*A/Capt* 091084)	100382
Crawford L	030682
Larkham J V (*A/Capt* 080385)	140782
Pickering K *BEM* (*A/Capt* 140385)	140782
Miskimmin J (*A/Capt* 030785)	121082
Smith R J (*A/Capt* 071085)	121082
Spree R (*A/Capt* 170785)	241282

ARMY CATERING CORPS

Within a circle inscribed "Army Catering Corps" an ancient Grecian Brazier beneath a scroll bearing the motto "We Sustain" The whole surmounted by a crown

Regimental March

Quick March..........Regimental March of The Army Catering Corps "Sugar and Spice"

Agents..........Holts Branch, Royal Bank of Scotland PLC, Lawrie House, Farnborough, Hants

Corps Headquarters..........St Omer Barracks, Aldershot, Hants (*Tel No:* Aldershot 24431 *Ext:* 2612)

Alliance

Australian Military Forces..........The Australian Army Catering Corps

Colonel in Chief..........Hon Maj Gen *HRH The Duchess of* Kent *GCVO*

Colonels Commandant..........* Gen *Sir* Geoffrey Howlett *KBE MC*..........041181
Brig R K Hudson *CBE* ret pay..........010486

Brigadiers

Maddy R N *MHCIMA* lc 300685
Paterson M J *FBIM FHCIMA* lc 300685

Colonels

Barnett A F *OBE MBIM FHCIMA* lc 300683
Bloxham J B *MHCIMA* lc 300685
Nash N S *MBIM MHCIMA LRSH* 300685
Procter M *MBIM FHCIMA FRSH* lc 300685

Lieutenant Colonels

Paget G V R *FHCIMA FCFA HCITB-INSTR* lc 300677
Drewett P A *OBE MBIM MHCIMA MRSH* lc 300678
MacDonald E J *MBIM MHCIMA* lc 300679
Apperley R W *FBIM* 300680
Bannister J J *MBIM MHCIMA MCFA MRSH* lc 300681
Dickinson M J 300681
Cowley V G *BA MBIM MHCIMA* 300682
Atkinson A B lc 300683
Giles R M *MHCIMA* 300683
Hathorn D McF *MBE* lc 300683
Stringer R J *MBIM MHCIMA* 300683
Wilkinson G lc 300683
Monk A C *MHCIMA* 300684
Smith H J *MBE HCITB-INSTR* 300684
Collins R M L *FHCIMA* 300685
Denham S C 300685
Fisher A 300685

Majors

Prince E B *ACT(Batt) MHCIMA* 311271
David B J (*A/Lt Col* 210386) 311276
Saunders D C 311276
Pearce I L 300677
Quinton B D 300677
Cadman F W 311277
Marshall M S *MBE* 310578
Giles S 300678
Hirst P T 300678
Johnson B J 300678
Macfarlane G C 300678
Hellard A C *MHCIMA* 300679
Hatton N H *MBIM MHCIMA AMRSH* 311279
Mansell-Ward G M psc lc 311279
Torrington W S 311279
Walker G S *BSc* 311279
Edwards J S A *BSc MHCIMA* 300980
Jones P A *BSc MBIM MHCIMA ACP* lc 300980
Legrove M *MHCIMA* lc 300980
Murphy M K 300980
Noons C H 300980
Rossiter P R 300980
Carlile J lc 300981
Hampson A *BSc MHCIMA* lc 300981
Hill R A 300981
Robertson D S *BSc MHCIMA* 300981
Dickinson P M lc 300983
Cooper P H lc 300984
Dyer E J G 300984
Henwood J D *BSc MBIM MHCIMA FRSH* 300984
Lowe M R J *MHCIMA* 300984
Fairbrother B N lc 300985
Morgan J F M *MHCIMA* 300985
Parsons C H *MHCIMA* lc 300985

Captains

Lindsay-Scott P *MHCIMA* (*A/Maj* 300184) 170379
Withers W G lc (*A/Maj* 251185) 090980
Cooke N P lc 080981
Cheeseright J C lc 100981
Miller J C *MHCIMA* lc (*A/Maj* 250185) 051081
Williamson B I *MHCIMA* 281281
Vincent W E *LHCIMA AMRSH* 260182
Budd P V *MHCIMA* 081083
Hemingway C J 081084
Herriott M W *MHCIMA* 081084
Marchant N F *MHCIMA* 081084
Spoors M L 050285
Smyth G F 090685
Dunlop C S 071085
Barsby N I *AMRSH* 220186

Lieutenants

Beardsell M L (*A/Capt* 070685) 081281
Pearce G R (*A/Capt* 291085) 150282
Clacher A D C (*A/Capt* 041185) 180582
Auger G J 090882
Johnston A K B 131282
Field J A (*A/Capt* 101085) 110483
Russell C N M 121283

Quartermasters

Smith W J 040171
Lt Col 011184
Clegg H 010871
Lt Col 291285
Dyson B S 100175
Maj 280881
Walker R W *MHCIMA MCFA* 210275
Maj 010479
Clewes F 010578
Maj 171081
Allen R G *MHCIMA* 130878
Maj 281181
Sillett T 250878
Maj 021282
Earl J A *Capt* 010978
Melody M J 031078
Maj 051181
Carr J G *Capt* 011079
Humphreys C A *MHCIMA HCITB-INSTR* 011079
Maj 210783
Mitchell D J H 011079
Maj 101085
Murison G *Capt* 011079
Borrett D A *Capt* 170680
Jagger H A 050980
Maj 180785
Hann M C *Maj* 160481
Raby C A *Capt* 040781
Wood D *Capt* 031082
Fitch D E *MBE MHCIMA* *Capt* 190183
Cooper P W M *Capt* 310183
Carson J G *MBIM MHCIMA* *Capt* 010783
Anspach A J *MHCIMA* *Capt* 300883
Howes G *Capt* 310184

---

* Representative Colonel Commandant for 1986

Nutter D W *Capt* 300984
Elrick I W *Capt* 141084
Swan S G J *Capt* 011184
Bettsworth D G *Capt* 010485
Fuller K R *Capt* 010485
Sinclair D I *Capt* 010485
Warburton G G *Capt* 010485
Wells G B *MHCIMA MCFA* *Capt* 010485

Special Regular Officers

Majors

Wallace J 311278
Roberts W F 300980
Fisher W J 300985
Morin M H 300985

Captains

Young C 031079
Usborne J E 040681
Major M R *MHCIMA* (*A/Maj* 100186) 010482
Barlow J T 010582
Dick M 010782
Barnes A J *MBIM MHCIMA* 010683
Bell D W 010683
Ryde T C K 010683
Reddings T J 200783
Shearsmith R A 200783
Dowson S J 060284
Blake M 280684
Ratcliffe J S 280684
Murray C S P 240585

Lieutenants

Appleton M R 081282

Short Service Officers

Captains

Oytaben J A 020177
Beard G M 010881
Whitley J E S 010582
Shanks R I D 010683
Harrold D 200783
Graham S 010685
Hymers B 010685
Taylor E 300985
Hotson N G M *BA* 071085
Cheesman D L *MBIM MISM MHCIMA MCFA* 030186
Read C E J 240486

Lieutenants

Godwin C B (*A/Capt* 200285) 020182
Gardiner R E 300182
Lund J R (*A/Capt* 040185) 300182
Singleton R G (*A/Capt* 270285) 060282
Larke N G 030382
Moorey J 010482
McCall P J *BA LHCIMA* 120482
Yates T A *BSc* 120482
Norton J A (*L/Capt* 170685) 010682
Kingston P R 090882
Norris D R *HCITB-INSTR* 121082
Barlow H H (*A/Capt* 010286) 151082
Knowles J M S 151082
Morgan P E S (*A/Capt* 110486) 151082
Sheriff T M *BEM HCITB-INSTR* 151082
Tall M A 151082
Whale J (*A/Capt* 281185) 151082
Miller K A 071282
Woolger G M 110483
Amis S A 280583
Fitzgerald N D 080883
Oliver P J 261084
Easdown K J 210685
Furey P C 060885
Chappell J 101285

2nd Lieutenants

Barnett M G A 100885
Sinclair P J 100885

ARMY LEGAL CORPS

The Figure of Justice superimposed upon the Globe surmounted by The Royal Crest. Behind the Globe Crossed Swords with blades uppermost on a black ground within a circle inscribed "Justitia in Armis" On a Scroll below "Army Legal Corps"

Regimental March

Quick March......................................"Scales of Justice"

Corps Headquarters............................ALS1, Empress State Building, London, SW6 1TR

Alliances

Canadian Armed Forces......................Office of the Judge Advocate General of The Canadian Armed Forces
Australian Military Forces...................The Australian Army Legal Corps

Colonel Commandant..........................Lt Gen *Sir* David Mostyn *KCB CBE*....................170983

Brigadiers

Boyle D A *LLB (Solicitor)* 300681
Fugard M T *(Solicitor)* 300683

Colonels

Clarke M H F *(Barrister)* 300682
Selwood D H D *(Solicitor)* 300682
Pugh O L *LLB (Solicitor)* 300683
Taylor J *BL (Solicitor)* 300683

Lieutenant Colonels

Barclay J N *BL (Solicitor)* 030277
Murray J *BL (Solicitor)* 230880
Hawley D C *LLB (Solicitor)* 010481
Norris A P *OBE MA (Solicitor)* 010481
Rogers A P V *OBE (Solicitor)* 010481
Wright T B *(Solicitor)* 010481
Glynn T *LLB (Solicitor)* 050581
Davis T J *(Solicitor)* 010682
Mitchell J H *(Barrister)* 070383
Risius G *(Solicitor)* 280883
Bryant P J *LLB (Solicitor)* 270485
Garraway C H B *MA (Barrister)* 090985

Majors

Venn J K *BA(Hons) BA(Hons) MA (Barrister)* 110977
Spencer R E P *BA (Solicitor)* 010481
Price C P *MA (Solicitor)* (*L/Lt Col* 160784) 260881
Moon J J E G *MBE (Solicitor)* 021181
Swabey J C M *(Barrister)* 111282
Howell D V *LLB (Barrister)* 190383
Howell D M *MBE LLB (Barrister)* 220983
Lampitt D J *(Solicitor)* 220284
Paphiti A S *LLB (Barrister)* 180685
Lozynski P M *LLB (Barrister)* 161085
Vowles S G *BA (Solicitor)* 051285
McEvoy P D *LLB (Solicitor)* 070286

Captains

Lever J *LLB (Barrister)* 090680
Adams G A R *LLB (Solicitor)* 271082
Scott A R *BA (Solicitor)* 201182
Reddin D G *LLB (Barrister)* 250684
Bowman J C *LLB (Solicitor)* 300985
Bullough C G J *BSc(Econ) (Barrister)* 300985
†Morrison A M *LLB(Hons) WS* 300985
Peters W J S C *(Solicitor)* 251185

Non-Legal Officers

Lever A 010978
Maj 020785

Short Service Officers

Captains

Lewis R D *MISM (Barrister)* 100380
Jones N J H *LLB (Barrister)* 210981
Mason P D A *(Solicitor)* 040582
Kerce J A *BA* 210583
Greasley C *BA (Barrister)* 211183
øSullivan R 100784
Conway M D *LLB (Barrister)* 021084
Webster L *LLB (Barrister)* 251185

QUEEN ALEXANDRA'S ROYAL ARMY NURSING CORPS

The Cypher of HM the late Queen Alexandra combined with the Dannebrog, the whole within a laurel wreath inscribed with the Corps motto "Sub Cruce Candida" surmounted by a crown. On the lower portion of the wreath a scroll inscribed "QARANC"

Regimental March

Quick March..."Grey and Scarlet"

Agents...Holts Branch, Royal Bank of Scotland PLC, Lawrie House, Farnborough, Hants

Corps Headquarters...........................QARANC Training Centre, The Royal Pavilion, Farnborough Road, Aldershot, Hants, GU11 1PZ (*Tel No:* 0252 24431)

Alliances

Australian Military Forces...................The Royal Australian Army Nursing Corps
New Zealand Army..............................The Royal New Zealand Nursing Corps

Colonel in Chief..................................*HRH The Princess* Margaret *Countess of* Snowdon *CI GCVO*

Colonel Commandant.........................Col K Grimshaw *RRC* ret pay...310781

Brigadiers

Hennessy M B T *MBE RRC QHNS RGN RM* 311284

Colonels

Grieve J V *RRC ARRC RGN* 231179
Smith V J *RRC ARRC RGN RM* 140681
Morrison C *ARRC RGN RM* 240582
Stewart M M *ARRC RGN* 011083
Anderson D G M *RRC ARRC MTD RGN RM* 300484
Braisby N M *MBE RRC RGN RM* 250485
Johnson R E *RRC MTD RSCN RGN RM* 301085
Field J M *ARRC RGN* 030286
Clune M J *ARRC RM* 010486

Lieutenant Colonels

Russell M C J *ARRC RGN RM* 310379
Smith M J *ARRC RGN* 210681
Cooper S M *ARRC RGN RM* 010182
Agate M A *RRC RMN RGN* 010483
Tasker B *RRC RGN RM* 280384
Nesbitt M A *RRC MTD RGN RM* 300484
Timms R *RGN RM* 040884
Challis K M *RGN* 070884
Gillies J B *RGN* 300884
Taggart M A *RGN RM RCNT* 220385
Taylor K M *RGN RM* 250485
Scott S *RGN RM* 090985
Dixon-Nuttall H S *ARRC RGN* 030286
Mulhern M E *ARRC RGN* 010486

Majors

Rutherford P L *ARRC RGN RM* 100767
Daly M *RGN RM* 060170
Reynolds E P *RSCN RGN RM* 051070
Lynott M B *RGN RM* 261070
Curran M V *RGN RM* 070271
Tansley B D *ARRC RGN RM* 071073
Hudson M G *RGN* 051173
Rushby M B *ARRC RGN RM* 130874
Humphries J *RGN RM* 181174
Lang J D *RMN RGN* 260375
Houghton T S M *RGN RM* 170475
Pimble P V *ARRC ONC RGN RM* 050176
McGilp P *RSCN RGN RM* 030276
Ayers C M *RGN RM* 120476
Fitzpatrick S M *RRC RGN RM* 020976
Machin J *RGN* 081276
Parke J *RGN* 300177
Marsh E E *RGN* 050777
Ogden C E *MTD RGN RM* 270777
Emerson P M *RGN RM* 280777
Scannell M A *RGN* 070877
Russell M *RGN* 280877
Storrie I S *RGN RM* 081277
Beckett R *RRC HV RMN RGN RM* (*A/Lt Col* 101284) 171277
Cushen J I *RGN RM* 171277
Lowes C E *RGN* 310178
King C M *RGN RNT* 120278
Slattery M M *SRN RM* 230278
Hamilton S E *RGN RM* 050478
Sandilands M E *RGN RM* 010578
McAulay S L *ARRC RGN* 051278
Pringle S B *RGN RM* 130279
Arigho J M *ARRC SRN* 160279
Kennedy J B *RFN RGN* 061079
Easey M A *RGN RM* 030180
King S J *RGN RM* 280580
Meaden E A A 050980
Murray L J *RGN RM* 141080
Kerr A *RSCN RGN* 191080
Sloman M J *ARRC RSCN RGN* 231080
Viner E J *ARRC RGN* 021180
Bandy M *RRC RGN RM* 131180
Oddy R Z *RSCN RGN* 060181
Parks R C *RGN RM* 060181
Watson M W *RGN* 260381
Morton Mason S R *RMN RGN RM* 070481
Watson P M *RGN* 110881
Pyott Cooper M C *RGN* 040981
Leith-Macgregor I M *RGN RM* 200981
Anderson A M *RGN* 200182
Marsh M A *RGN RM* 020282
Pillay J N A *RGN* 200482
Broughton T A *MTD RGN RM* 010582
Mumford-George M M *RGN* 051082
Paterson M *RGN* 191082
Numbers L M *BSc(Hons) RGN RGN RNT GNCE* 010583
Moody P J *RGN RM* 131083
Kneale S J *RGN RNT* 051283
Murtagh I T *RGN RM* 131283
Quarington D M *RGN* 010184
McEvilly B C *ARRC RGN* 240184
Wood A R C *RGN RM* 180284
Woolridge S D *RGN RM* 030484
Grimwood P A *HV RGN RM* 111084
Simmonds S J *RGN* 121284
McElligott D M *RGN RM* 120185
Evans J M *RGN RM* 290485
Foster M K *RGN RM GNCE* 250585
Hobbs A M T *ARRC RGN RM* 230685
Barclay M E *RGN RM* 130885
Gilmour M *RGN RM* 111285

Captains

Bland K *RGN* 280478
Wideman J *RGN RM* 120778
Quickfall M A *RGN* 010978
MacDonald M M *ONC RGN RM* 201178
McKay P A *RGN* 020879
Webster S L M *RGN* 081280
Wells L M *RGN* 250681
Doresa M J *RGN RCNT GNCE* 071282

Non-Nursing Officers

Majors

McCombe M H 271184

Special Regular Officers

Majors

Brimley N *RSCN RGN* 091078
McGrath M A *ADM RGN RM* 260379
Reakes M A *RGN* 290880
Scotchbrook D E *RGN* 121080
Bradley G *RGN RMN RM* 310881
Daly S E *RGN RM* 290982
Thornton G C *RGN RM* 161082
Ward A *RGN* 160483
Jackson C D *RGN RGN RM* 250683

Queen Alexandra's Royal Army Nursing Corps — continued

Name	Date
Jones H M *DN RGN RNT*	101183
Pitt B J G *RGN RM*	130284
Cowie J M *RGN RM*	160684
Pauley G P *RMN RGN*	150785
Ashton P J *RGN RM*	051285
Mills S E *RMN RGN RM*	220286

Captains

Name	Date
Curwen L *RGN RM*	050179
Alexander J *RGN RM*	250879
Ripley J M *RGN RM*	090880
Horton P J *RGN*	100681
Nardi J P *RGN RM*	200981
Conway P A *RGN*	301281
Crooke S J *OND RGN*	020583

Non-Nursing Officers

Majors

Name	Date
Liggat R	250483
Pettit C M *EN(G)*	021084
Yarnold B M	250385

Captains

Name	Date
Kerr M	140282

Short Service Officers

Captains

Name	Date
Bruce L *RGN RM*	300678
Verow S J *RGN*	111078
Henshall G M *DN RGN RNT*	031178
Downie C M *RGN RGN RM RNT*	161178
Cytrynbaum S R *RSCN RGN*	260679
Holder S R *RGN RM*	201079
Fisher W S *RGN*	110180
Shapland E M *RSCN RGN*	310180
Hodgins S A *RGN RM*	010380
Skidmore S *RGN RM*	080380
Moffat M L M *RGN RGN RM*	230880
Hawkins J P *RGN RM*	270880
Heneghan M S *RGN RM*	291080
Hubble G A *RSCN RGN RM*	051280
Findlay S *RGN RM RCNT*	060381
Crummack P J *RGN RM*	180381
Bee E J *RGN*	130681
Hugonin S M *OND RGN*	280681
Lee M C *RGN RM*	290681
Cozens S A *RGN RM*	210781
Bailey R E *RGN EN(G)*	270781
Hudson M S *ONC RGN*	280781
Stones C D *RGN*	300781
Southerden M J *RSCN RGN NNEB*	130881
Stacey D M *RGN RM*	160881
Copeland E R *RGN RM*	180881
Gray C C *RGN RM*	260981
Morgan M P *RGN EN(G) RM*	031081
Edwards J P *ADM RGN RM*	141081
Clewley D J *RMN RGN RM*	151081
Roberts S *RGN*	211081
Sutton C *RGN*	011181
Parker S *RGN RM*	241181
Sulima C *RGN*	181281
Mathieson A E *RGN RM*	261281
Morris V *RGN RM*	291281
Oliver C M *RGN*	291281
Bannan J M *RGN*	170182
Barker J W *RGN RM*	190182
Kenworthy J M *RGN*	020382
Brown J C *RGN RM*	190382
Bryant J A *RGN*	050482
Herington K L *RGN*	110482
Washington L *RGN*	230482
Cox P A *RGN*	290482
Thomas M L *RGN RM*	100582
Goodman A *RGN*	120582
Edmonds M *RGN RM*	230582
Reason S J *RGN RM*	160682
Edgar E M *RGN*	050782
Green B A *RGN RM*	230782
McGrath J M *RGN RM*	260782
Field K M B *RGN*	270782
Mendez M K M *RGN*	140882
Roberts D *RMN RGN*	170882
Gallagher M C *RGN RM*	310882
Griffin G D *RGN*	070982
Naylor R J *RGN*	080982
Alun-Jones S J *RGN*	190982
Smith A P *RGN*	210982
Wood V F *RGN RM*	011082
Campbell G D *RSCN RGN*	261082
Bane I P *RGN*	271082
Barbour J *ONC RGN*	291082
Hopkins S A *RGN*	301082
Hitchen M S *RGN*	161182
Shallcross J *RGN*	301182
Hope L A *RGN*	111282
Stockport S M *RGN RM*	241282
Harding C A *RMN RGN*	160183
Ball J E *RGN RM*	260183
Rammell R A *RGN*	300183
Hart S J *RGN*	020283
Conn U M E *RGN RM*	260283
Duffin J *OND*	080383
Friedrich L D *RGN*	100383
Bower B L *RGN*	080483
Williams S A *RGN*	100483
Murray J L *RGN*	220483
Whaites C A *RGN*	220483
Brown G R *RGN*	270483
Boylett S A *DN RGN GNCE*	070583
Kingdon R S *RGN*	130583
Rich J F *RGN RGN*	150583
Blundell B *RGN RM*	050783
Reynolds S E *RGN RM*	270783
Hair D *RGN*	010883
Castle R A *RSCN RGN*	020883
Seaton F E *ONC RGN RM*	190883
Smith C D M *RGN RM*	270883
Marvin B E *RGN RM*	050983
Dickinson J *RGN RM NNEB*	060983
Warburton A P *RGN RM*	220983
Stone D J *RGN RM*	011083
Donaldson M A *RGN*	071083
Roach D L *RGN RM*	251083
Pears R D *RMN RGN*	201183
Harper B *RGN RM*	211183
Spencer W J *RGN*	021283
Hoskins J S *RGN EN(G)*	031283
Long Y S *RGN*	131283
Ensor C H *RMN RGN*	171283
Tilt B S *RGN*	271283
Hutton S A *RGN*	160184
Full S J *RGN RM*	170184
Martel H J *RGN RGN*	190184
Meeke S *RGN*	040284
Collie F M *RGN RM*	150284
Steele G *RGN*	180284
Greenwood J J *DN RGN*	030384
Hunter J *RGN RM*	040384
Devine B M *RGN*	050384
Covill A Y *RGN RM*	140384
Yates J E *RGN RM*	230384
Topham S E *RGN*	120484
Brown K *RGN*	200484
Lowry N *ADM RGN RM*	200484
Browne A C *RGN RM*	210484
Robinson L I *RGN RM*	260484
Davies D J *OND RGN RM*	040584
Poulten C M *RGN*	100584
Nicol S G *RGN RM*	110584
Greed V J *RMN RGN*	130584
Ryan J M *RGN RM*	300584
Deacon L E *RGN RM*	050684
Robson A M *RGN*	100684
Boden N S *RGN RM*	140684
Sharp L *RGN*	240684
Allibone E M B *ONC RGN RM*	140784
Gregg K *RGN*	160784
Winter E J *RSCN RGN*	270784
Tranter S A *RGN RM*	120884
Jones L J *RGN*	140884
Smart S *RGN*	150884
Hobbins C S W *RGN*	230884
Brearley K H *RGN RM*	240884
Castledine J A *RGN*	270884
Dallimore M S *RGN*	270884
Banford R H *RGN*	010984
Harvey S E *OND RGN RM*	020984
Harper E P *RGN RM*	111084
Yates F J *RGN RM*	151084
Wright G O *RGN*	201084
Morris G *RGN RM*	211084
Tidd G E *RMN RGN*	021284
Strickland J D *RGN RM*	041284
Mullin L E *RGN*	051284
Rowbottom A M *RGN*	051284
Wright L A *RGN*	071284
Hooper A G *RGN RM*	141284
Jerman M G *RGN*	141284
Bowditch L M *RGN*	311284
Bateman C M *RGN*	010185
Ladley A C *RGN*	010185
Sharp S *RGN RM*	020185
Sparks S M *RGN RM*	090185
McArthur D J *RGN RGN*	200185
Greene A Y *RGN*	120285
Millar J E *RGN RM*	150285
Robinson T	180285
Laverick S H *RGN*	190285
Baker H P *RSCN RGN RM*	210385
Morshead C *RGN RM*	230385
Horwood E M *RSCN RGN*	060485
Hughes J *RGN RM*	120485
Lacey M *RGN*	120485
Marshall G D *RGN RM*	180485
Sloane A M *RGN*	260485
Eaton J M *RGN*	300485
Staines J M *RSCN RGN*	010585
Fergusson T *RGN RM*	080585
O'Sullivan C S *RGN*	080585
Hulse W P *RSCN RGN NNEB*	160585
Callaghan M I *RGN*	280585
Smithers P J *RGN RM*	050685
Stuart H M M *RGN*	230685
Ward L M *RGN RM*	240685
Kennedy L A *BSc RGN RM*	300685
Evans Y B *RGN RM*	060785
McMillan E J *RGN RM*	060785
Taylor J *RGN*	160785
Bicknell S A *RGN*	170785
MacBeth C J *RGN RM*	200785
Martindale C A *RGN*	200785
Taylor P J *RGN*	290785
Malcolm A *RGN*	300785
Bowers L M *RGN EN(G)*	040885
Hedley E A *RGN RM*	170885
Icely K B *RGN*	230885
Davis G M *RGN*	270885
Murray F H *ONC RGN*	270885
Roberts A *RGN*	300885
Webber A C *RGN RM*	060985
Harrison S M *RGN*	160985
Street K L *RGN*	160985
Holme A R *RGN RM*	170985
Thompson S K *RGN*	260985

Kennedy F S *RGN RMN* 051085
Parmiter S J *RGN* 051085
Thorne J M A *RGN RM* 051085
Robinson A K G *RGN EN(G)* 111085
Whittaker H M *RM* 201085
Driscoll C *RSCN RGN* 241085
Williams E C *RGN* 021185
Lessing-Turner G H S *RGN RM* 031185
Molland J S F *RGN RM* 031185
Shrimpton S D *RGN* 041185
Plowman J M *RGN RM* 161185
Whitehurst S J *RGN RM* 211185
Wadlow M E *RGN RM* 301185
Maltby J *RGN RM* 021285
Smith C I W *RGN* 051285
Wilson E A *RGN* 071285
Attwood J K *RGN* 121285
Northcott N J 181285
Moore A J *RGN* 191285
Garner K E *RGN* 231285
Johnson K E 251285
Selby K *DN RGN RM* 301285
Pitt P A *RGN RM* 100186
Cant C A *RGN RM* 120186
Scanlan B *RGN* 130186
Sinclair D M *RGN* 150186
Thompson F M *RSCN RGN* 270186
Brodie L A *RGN* 280186
Medley C J *RGN* 290186
Kitching P J *RGN* 310186
Pooley C A *RGN* 070286
Scrivens G F *RSCN RGN* 220286
Wilson H A *RGN RM* 120386
Haycock P A T *RGN* 170386
Vasey C *RGN RM* 220386
Morris S L *RGN* 020486
Grant D J *RGN* 030486
Exley S H *RGN RM* 080486
Chesworth-White A C *RGN* 150486

Lieutenants

Neyton C D *RGN* 030482
Davies C H *RGN RM* 050482
Underwood S *RGN RM* 160482
Brown C S *RGN RM* 170482
Smith M M *RGN* 050582
Randall C M *OND RGN* 080582
Paterson E D *ONC RGN* 190582
Johnson H R *RMN RGN RM* 240582
Coxon D E *RSCN RGN* 150682
Hammond D J *RGN* 180682
Ford S M *RM* 210682
Wilson V *RGN* 220682
Belej L A *RGN* 250682
Richmond A A C *RGN* 030782
McCall R M *RGN RM* 290782
Emmett S *RGN* 050882
Eccleston C E 060882
Beardsell P E *RGN* 070882
Smith C *RGN RM* 120882
Timperley K H *RGN* 130882
Grove S J *RGN* 180882
Palmer S E *RGN* 180882
Saunders K *RNMS RGN* 180882
Maddicott P J 240882
Elton J *RGN* 280882
Weaversmith L *RGN* 310882
Britton S M *RGN* 090982
Poulton E H *RGN RM* 110982
Rigg C A *RSCN RGN* 170982
Hemphill D C *RGN RM* 200982
Higgins B G *RGN* 290982
Rutherford C *RGN RM* 290982
Rigby T A *RGN RM* 051082
Moffat A *RGN RM* 171082
Gough F V *RGN* 211082
Jones H J *RGN RM* 011182
Hawkesford K *RGN RM* 021182
Marsh A J *RGN* 121182
Street K M *OND RGN RM* 151182
Foyster A C (*A/Capt* 260783) 221182
Bertram V S *RGN* 071282
Osborne S L *RGN* 081282
Pavett D J *RMN RGN* 101282
Jenkins Y A *RGN* 111282
Johnson K D *RGN* 151282
Riddett S J *RGN* 161282
Armstrong J M *RGN EN(G)* 171282
Baugh J M *RGN* 181282
Harrison S L 191282
Alexander M *RGN* 211282
Murray L J *RGN RM* 231282
Lea C *RGN* 241282
Tuffin R P *RGN* 251282
Pike G F *RGN RM* 030183
Elliott E A *RGN RM* 120183
Smith S M *RGN* 140183
Henry J E *RGN RM* 180183
Adamson B G *RGN* 190183
McDougall P J *RGN* 200183
Irving C E *RGN RM* 260183
Burton C J *RGN* 070283
Fisher A E *RGN* 080283
Rolley J S C *RGN* 080283
Bridgland J *RGN* 110283
Watson F A *RGN RM* 130283
Mackey M W *RGN* 160283
Macdonald-Holland J *RGN* 120383
Blackledge J F 240383
Crittenden J N *RGN* 250383
Epplestone C A *RGN* 250383
Macleod D *RGN* 250383
Cowley S M 270383
Pratt S J *RGN* 300383
Reddihough E A *RGN* 030483
Green E M *RGN* 110483
Parker L A 110483
Dodson C P A *RGN* 190483
Lee S *RGN RM* 200483
Everett C J *RSCN RGN* 220483
Stocker A J 140583
Horstman S J *RGN* 180583
Anderson C A *RGN* 250583
Allen A E *RGN* 030683
Roberts G A *RGN* 030683
Close C *RGN* 060683
Willdridge A *RGN* 070683
Snell J M *RGN* 140683
Croft Y *RGN* 150683
Piskorowskyj A *RGN* 150683
Kidd B C *RGN RM* 180683
Lloyd S M *RGN* 210683
Mann L J *RGN* 010783
Rowe K J *RGN* 010783
Woodmore C A *RGN* 010783
Thompson J M *RGN RM* 080783
Kerr E J *RGN RM* 150783
Morrison C *RGN* 270783
Browne D M *RGN* 300783
Forster-Knight S C *RGN* 020883
Macdonald S A F *OND RGN* 050883
Holmes K M *RGN* 110883
Sherratt J *RGN* 110883
Harper D *RGN* 120883
Bye D P *RGN* 240883
Evans S K *RGN* 020983
Macpherson J M *RGN RM* 140983
Cliffe D M *RGN* 180983
Canty J S *RGN* 210983
Goode V J *RGN* 210983
Walton E M *RGN* 210983
Chapman G *RGN* 250983
Braithwaite A L *RGN* 081083
Orton E *RGN* 101083
Rogers S E 111083
Gill S R *RGN* 141083
Slade S L *RGN* 141083
Ellwood W *RGN* 251083
Foley S J *RGN* 251083
Green L A *RGN* 231183
Porter S W *RGN* 231183
Clarke S J *RGN* 251183
Morris L 301183
Turrell C J *RGN* 301183
Gibson A M *RGN* 011283
Ranson J E *RGN* 071283
Pickard R C *RGN* 091283
Higgs J D *RGN* 080284
Thorpe T J *RGN* 170284
Jordan P L *RSCN RGN* 200484
Rotheram J C *RGN* 310584
Whent L J *RGN* 140684
Rickcord F C *RGN* 240784
Cornwell B J *RGN* 250784
Davis S *RGN* 260784
Judd J A *RGN* 140884
Sanders D G *RGN* 230884
Vick D A *OND RGN* 160585

Non-Nursing Officers

Captains

Ashpitel A H 060981
Phelps G A 010386

Lieutenants

Watson S (*A/Capt* 141085) 200282
Ellis M J T *EN(G)* (*A/Capt* 011185) 020782
Wilcox S J *DCR(R) DSR(T)* (*A/Capt* 070486) 060486

2nd Lieutenants

Mawdsley S M (*A/Lt* 010485) 040884

WOMEN'S ROYAL ARMY CORPS

A laurel wreath surmounted by a crown; within the wreath a lioness rampant
Suaviter in modo, fortiter in re

Regimental Marches

Quick March.....Arrangement of "Lass of Richmond Hill" and "Early one Morning"
Pipe Air.....The Nut Brown Maiden
Slow March.....Greensleeves

Agents.....Lloyds Bank PLC Cox's & King's Branch

Corps Headquarters.....Womens Royal Army Corps Centre, Queen Elizabeth Park, Guildford, Surrey (*Tel No: Aldershot* (0252) *Ext:* Guildford 283)

Commandant-in-Chief.....*H M* QUEEN ELIZABETH THE QUEEN MOTHER

Controller Commandant.....Hon Maj Gen *HRH The Duchess of* Kent *GCVO*

Deputy Controller Commandant.....Brig A Field *CB* ret pay 051184

Brigadiers

Meechie H G *CBE ADC MA* ndc psc 300682

Colonels

Nield S P *BA* 300682
Robertson N R *MBE* 300682
Smith A J *BA* ndc psc 300684
Hutley F E *BSc* psc† 300685

Lieutenant Colonels

Marriott C A 300682
Ramsey G K *MBE* sq 300682
Robinson E A ndc psc 300682
Kelly A A ndc sq 300683
Brown A K *MBE* sq 300684
Johnstone J E *MBE AIDPM* sq 300684
Lawson J L *MBE* 300684
Bolland C R psc jsdc 300685
Wing M S sq 300685

Majors

Ashplant M R jsc 231165
Heath N L 311274
Tye E 300677
Watson A C *BSc MEd* 230978
Rook M J *MHCIMA AMRSH* sq 311278
Hawkins S P 300679
Patrick R D 311279
Smith E A *BEd MA MSc(Econ)* 310180
Bishop S M sq 300980
Cornwell R E sq 300980
Flake J A 300980
Ganter L M sq 300980
Harwood M A sq 300980
Purves P S *MA* psc 080181
Batchelor V 300981
Chilton R A 300981
Elliott E D *MBE* 300981
Harvey G R 300981
Weaver C V M *BA* 300981
Halliday D L *BSc* 300982
le Gassick W A 300982
Park R M *BSc* psc† 300982
Roulstone J M 300982
Trehern A *BA* 300982
Trout V E 300982
Webb S J B 300982
Burwell S *BA* psc 300983
Freebairn J A *MA* psc 300983
Henderson R E R 300983
Johncey S I F 300983
Randall M *BSc* pi 300983
Reynolds S E *BSc* psc† 300983
Smith J C A 300983
Walker S J G 300983
Davies D F psc 300984
Short G A *BA* adp 300984
Westlake S J 300984
Wright V L 300984
Lindsay J A 300985
McCord I M *BA* psc 300985
Relph L A 300985
Simpson P M 300985
Walthall F A *BSc* 300985

Captains

Brighton V M *BA* (*A/Maj* 260485) 060478
White G A *MA(Hons)* (*A/Maj* 010486) 270979
Samson P J (*A/Maj* 220984) 181079
Sherring P S *BA* 261079
Staples C M (*A/Maj* 241283) 090280
Ridley-Jones J P R *BEd* 050980
Gold P J 101080
Hetherington P A 101080
Lewis-Taylor C D *MISM* 101080
Isaacs A J 150281
Jones V H *BA* 210381
Canham F E 190681
Rollo S J o 190681
Dunn E A H *BSc* 210981
Jenkins C J 101081
Johnson P M adp 101081
McGregor L W I 101081
Suart C 101081
Lauder M F *BSc* 160182
Gurney L C 140282
Hay D 140282
Walters E M 140282
Boram P A *MA* 290382
Palmer C G 060482
Ransom J L 290582
Perks G M *BSc* 110782
Colmer H E *BEd* 160982
Dathan J A 151082
Ewan A E 151082
Lebeter B M *BEd* 091182
Newnham E A *BA* 130183
Holden S L 120283
Woodcock C *BEd* 160383
Merrington-Rust C H *BEd* 130783
Gibson G M *BSc* 210983
Kitchener C J 250983
Howell A M J 151083
Paxton C R *BA* 040284
Dowson J 260584
Barry J 260784
Cooper S E 071084
Armstrong D J *BA* 081084
Flint C B *MA* 081084
Stevens S J *BA* 081084
Boileau A M *BSc* 050285
Blake L 180585
Foster D 180585
Cartman B A *BA PGCE* 071085
Grafton J E 020286
Lambert S J *BSc* 040286

Lieutenants

Coates J A (*A/Capt* 150785) 030482
Buckley C S *BA* (*A/Capt* 060186) 120482
Murdoch N A (*A/Capt* 140583) 070882
Archer R *MHCIMA* (*A/Capt* 191084) 210383
Hewitt C A *BSc* 110483
Grundy F J (*A/Capt* 121085) 080484
Pendlenton C M E *BA* 090484
Frost F E 050885
Rose F A 050885
Stewart T 070486

2nd Lieutenants

Edwards A K 040884
†Oberheim D J *BEd* 230985
†Tilford G A *BScTech* 270985

Quartermasters

Carroll T M *MBE* 170271
Maj 090180
Haynes H R 271075
Maj 210584
Pratt S *Capt* 060481
Maskens-Mcintyre A *Capt* 010484

Special Regular Officers

Majors

Ball J M 300981
Morgan R *MA AIPM* psc† 300982
Lucas S M 300984
Smith L B 300984
Kennedy C C *BD* 270385
Binnie P A *BSc* 020885
Duddridge D M H 300985

Captains

Bellingham-Smith H *MMS* 301277
Davies L E 190681

Ryder D 090682
Rogers V 120982
Dixon J R 270583
Patrick L M *BEd* 170783
Corrigan I J B A 140983
Wilson E M 151083
May L P *BEd* 210384
Walton R E *BA* 071085
Lewis C J M s 020286

Lieutenants

Bates S E (*A/Capt* 120885) 020881

Short Service Officers

Captains

McMahon B O 240578
McKay E A *LLB MA* 030980
Howes M M *BA* 180781
Pearce V R *BEd* 200981
Jackson F M 221181
Ashton J D *BSc(Econ)* 090282
Fisher M C *BA* 310382
Beadle A E *BA* 060482
Bacon C D *BSc* 130183
Foggin D J *BSc* 130183
Marriott S B *BSc(Econ)* 160183
Jackson E K *BA* 210383
MacKinnon L A *BA* 210383
Simpson T 110583
Borthwick J A *BEd* 210983
Eckersley S A J *BSc* o s 210983
Curtis J P *BEd* 051083
Wildman H *BA ALA* 040284
Jenkinson A M *MA* 060284
Quinlan S J *BA* 210384
Russell D E *BEd ASTA* 120484
Aungiers S T *BSc* ae 040884
Fullerton A *BA* I 071084
Wing G F *BSc* 071084
Harris M L *BEd* 081084
Lee C L *BA* 081084
Oak-Rhind P A *BA* 081084
Harper J F *BSc MICE* 121084
Davies-Stewart L E *BEd* 201084
Elliot F E 191184
Gordon I M 040285
Hogg E C 040285
Turpin J C 040285
Crosse P J *BEd* 050285
Gait S C J *BA* 050285
Mundill Wood S J *BA(Hons)* 050285
Pollington D L *BEd* 080285
Robertson D B 210385
Curry V J 180585
Cunningham E E 130685
Merry A C 130685
Shiel A J 130685
Aitken S M *BSc DipEd* 060785
Armstrong W C 220885
Piers M G E 170985
Adams R A 051085
Dando J A 051085
Salmon J A 051085
Warwick E J 051085
Caddick C A *BA* 071085
Ewing N J *BSc* 071085
Gibson F J *BA* 071085
Greenhalgh J E *BEd* 071085
Loudoun S E *BA* 071085
Porter D L *BSc* 071085
Pyatt P A *BEd* 071085
Reed S K *BA* 071085
Rundle S G *BA* 071085
Smith D E *BA* 071085
Williams B I *MA* 071085
Reaney S J L *BA* 081085
Stone S E *BSc* 091085
Forsythe L N R *BA* 121085
Gardner S P *BSc* 121085
Martin V J *BA* 121085
O'Nians C S 121285
Forster E P 171285
Bedborough J L 020286
Bownass L J 020286
Crittenden E A 020286
Moore F A S M 020286
Vincent S L 020286
Crook M T *BSc* 040286
Fincham P M F *BEng* ae 040286
Greig J K *BA* 040286
Hatherell A S *BA* 040286
Ronan C *BSc* 040286
Sawford K P *BA* 040286
Wilde L M *BA* 040286
Jackson A M *BA* 090286

Lieutenants

Bailey C R V (*A/Capt* 051184) 020881
Phillips M A S *BCom* (*A/Capt* 230784) 040881
Bettison K J (*A/Capt* 240286) 141181
Scott K L 141181
Maltman G A *BAcc* (*A/Capt* 220386) 301181
Harrison G (*A/Capt* 120983) 061281
Stewart M R L (*A/Capt* 211085) 061281
White H V (*A/Capt* 100386) 111281
Walton J A (*A/Capt* 120885) 251281
Michelli A M L (*A/Capt* 011282) 150382
Brodie-Murphy J E *CSS* (*A/Capt* 161285) 160382
Briggs C M 090482
Mann A P *BSc* 090482
Thackery R A L *MA* 110482
Currie S F *BEd* 120482
Donaldson A K J *MA(Hons)* 120482
Evanson A *BA(Hons)* (*A/Capt* 030984) 120482
Humphreys A *BSc* (*A/Capt* 170585) 120482
Johnson C S *BSc* 120482
Lodge R C *MA(Hons)* 120482
Madsen S *BA* 120482
Martin K J *BA* 120482
May S *BSc* s (*A/Capt* 290885) 120482
Mohan C C *BA* (*A/Capt* 300985) 120482
Mollison E R *BA* 120482
Pratley M S *MA* (*A/Capt* 141285) 120482
Emery H C (*A/Capt* 310383) 070882
Miller D H (*A/Capt* 090484) 070882
Raine V (*A/Capt* 010984) 070882
Turner L J (*A/Capt* 140384) 070882
Vye C J 070882
Jones K D *BA MLitt* 080882
MacDonald M I *MA(Hons)* 090882
Phipps T J *BEd* 090882
Roberts M R *BSc* 090882
Pritchard Y *BA* 150982
Taplin A H *BSc(SocSc)* 260982
Mapley D *MBE* 011082
King C D (*A/Capt* 100984) 111282
Woods R E A I (*A/Capt* 300485) 111282
Platts K E *BA* 020283
Trainor J 190283
Dunn J M (*A/Capt* 011284) 090483
Law J A (*A/Capt* 120585) 090483
Morris S E 090483
Thornton-Berry B J (*A/Capt* 160784) 090483
Wood D E (*A/Capt* 160985) 090483
Wright P F (*A/Capt* 140185) 090483
Billson S *BA BSc* 110483
Blackburn K J *BSc* 110483
Clinch M C *BA* 110483
Dougherty L C *BA* 110483
Gregory J P *BA* 110483
Hamilton F E *BA* 110483
Harrill C E S *BSc* 110483
Hindmarsh S V *BA* 110483
Keir A J *MA(Hons)* 110483
Lush L G *BA* 110483
Morrison W V *BA* 110483
Payter N J *BA* 110483
Short S K *BEd* 110483
Stevenson K M *MA* 110483
Tognarelli D M *BSc* 110483
Wells C S 230683
Cox J L (*A/Capt* 130884) 090783
Clegg H A (*A/Capt* 030984) 070883
Grimmett V A (*A/Capt* 071085) 070883
O'Meara R (*A/Capt* 210186) 070883
Saunders A (*A/Capt* 150385) 070883
Scott-Fox L J (*A/Capt* 100885) 070883
Searight L M (*A/Capt* 280884) 070883
Bruce F *MA* 080883
Fesemeyer G A *BA* 080883
Haigh C *BA* 080883
Hands J *BA* 080883
Hurford-Dawson J K *BSc* 080883
Lester C *BSc* 080883
Ogden-Swift K A *BSc* 080883
Robins S E *BSc(Hons)* 080883
Rye P R *BSc* 080883
Munnoch K M 211183
Craven-Griffiths C E 021283
Bevan C A 111283
Chambers J C (*A/Capt* 170186) 111283
Davies B (*A/Capt* 210386) 111283
Marshall N J 111283
Taylor L A (*A/Capt* 200485) 111283
Winchester A R (*A/Capt* 281085) 111283
Mawby S A (*A/Capt* 070885) 200384
Perks A J 080484
Brown A K *BA* 090484
Burrows J V H *BSc* 090484
Bushell G M *BA(Hons)* 090484
Clarke S M *BSc(Eng)* 090484
Cole G D *BSc(Hons)* 090484
Garnett N A *BScEng(Civil)* 090484
Glasse A E *BA* 090484

Women's Royal Army Corps — continued

Hathaway D A 090484
Howling C J 090484
Jones S M *BA* 090484
King M S *BA* 090484
May J S *BSc* 090484
McCausland H E J *BSc* 090484
Potts G A *BA* 090484
Redman D J *BA* 090484
Sutcliffe T J *BSc(Hons)* 090484
Wollacott J C *BSc LHCIMA* 090484
Cooper J A 070684
Baylis H L 060884
Boxell F J 060884
Ostacchini M H 060884
Dullam E J *BSc(Hons)* 070884
Knipe C S *BA(Hons)* 070884
Procter J J M *BSc(Hons)* 070884
Skipper D C *BSc* 070884
Wilkerson S D *BA(Hons)* 070884
Williams V K *BSc(Hons)* 070884
Hayes J J 091184
Morgan K S s
(*A/Capt* 270885) 190385
Bobbitt W L 080485
Smith P L 080485
Turner J M V 080485
Atkinson C R 050885
Bower J 050885
Deasy S 050885
Hill D 050885
Lucas P A 050885
Wood V M 050885
Allen D M 070486
Chesworth A S 070486
Holt S A 070486
Parks S M 070486
Pevalin J E 070486
Wilson S M 070486

2nd Lieutenants

Davis D D 040884
Gow C A 040884
Hall A D 040884
Kirkpatrick F A 040884
Ogden D J 040884
Palmer J C 040884
Taylor D J 040884
Wilmshurst-Smith L A 040884
Wilson C M 040884
Bright V S 130485
Daly K L 130485
Deans J M 130485
Dickens P J 130485
Fifield V A *HCITB-INSTR* 130485
Gavin J 130485
Nation T M 130485
Spanner C A 130485
Taylor B J 130485
Vickers N G H 130485
Weir J C 090585
Hyde A V F 100885
Jones H L 100885
Small N J 100885
Wheeler A J 100885
Wilkes S 100885
Woolford T J 100885
†Attfield K M *BA* 230985
†Charlesworth S M *BSc DipEd* 230985
†Dixon S P *BSc(Hons) PGCE* 230985
†Dunn E A *MA* 230985
†Hart A C *BSc(Hons)* 230985
†Horton L S *BA(Hons) PGCE* 230985
†Bamber X R *BA* 270985
†Bradley A J *BSc(Hons)* 270985
†Collier-Jackson N A *BSc* 270985
†Davison S *BSc(Hons)* 270985
†Donald J *BA(Oxon)* 270985
†Frearson C *BSc* 270985
†Gardner F H *BA(Hons)* 270985
†Ireland G E *BSc(Hons)* 270985
†Kingham S M 270985
†Moffat N P *BA(Hons)* 270985
†Pulverman K E *BSc* 270985
†Tait M L *BA(Hons)* 270985
†Thomas F M E *BSc(Hons)* 270985
†Thomson I *BSc(Hons) MPS* 270985
†Tindall A J *BSc(Hons) ARCS* 270985
†Venner A *BSc(Hons)* 270985
†Ward G M *BA* 270985
†Watson S H *BA(Hons)* 270985
†Griffiths R C *BSc SRD* 240186
†Henry J A *BA(Hons)* 240186

Short Service Volunteer Officers

Lieutenants

King E J 180984
Storey E F *BA* 070185

2nd Lieutenants

Winder P J 040285

GENERAL LIST

Lieutenants

Smeaton I B (*A/Capt* 060186) 120482

2nd Lieutenants

††Roberts J S *BA(Hons)* 230984
†Rayment S C W *BSc* 060186

Short Service Officers

Captains

Cheng Kam Chuen 130981
Wong C K 260583
Lui Kam Chuen 090983
Wu Fai 010384
Chung P K 140984
Chu Cho Min 240984
Leung Hing Chuen 280385
Chau Yat Keung 031185

Lieutenants

Li Nai Chung 010282
Chan Wing Yau 140982
Kwan Yiu Wah 140982
Lo Wong Yin 140982
Lee Chuen Bun 241282

2nd Lieutenants

†Bavin C A N *BSc* 060985
†Blofeld N J *BA(Hons)* 060985
†Ling G J *MSc* 060985
†Beard A P C *BSc* 060186
†Burgoyne M J *BA(Hons)* 060186
†French H G *BA(CombHons) MSc* 060186
†Lai T J *MA* 060186
†Robottom R *BA* 060186
†Spearing M J *BSc* 060186
†Wright K P *BSc* 060186

SECTION IV

TERRITORIAL ARMY

ROYAL MONMOUTHSHIRE ROYAL ENGINEERS (MILITIA)

The Prince of Wales plume, cornet and motto *'Ich Dien'*, surmounted by a crown, on either side of the plume the letters 'R' and 'E', below a scroll inscribed *'ROYAL MONMOUTHSHIRE'*

Hon Colonels ....*HRH The Duke of* Gloucester *GCVO*

Lt Col E D Smeedon *DL* ret pay...010472

Colonels

George A F *TD*▪ *BA BSc LLM* 150984

Lieutenant Colonels

Lee B C A 010785

Majors

Pope R J *TD*▪▪ *MA MIMC* 190775
Dowle J R *TD* sq(v) 010779
Golland A P *MBE TD*▪ *BSc CEng MICE MIHT MBIM* 181183

Captains

Barton S F *TD MA* 010778
Hoyle R A *TD BA AHA* (*A/Maj* 021284) 010479
Hennessy H *TD* 011179
Lakeland S J *BSc* 150280
Kent R H (*A/Maj* 160985) 050980
Page N E 010483
¶James L G *TD* 110483
Earey D A *BEng MICE* 270483
¶Campbell W 060683
¶Llewellyn G 300683
Havercroft M P 010884
Munson D G 011184
Browning A P *BVSc* 110585
Denman T D 010386

Lieutenants

Frankish O J *BTech* (*A/Capt* 010882) 080579
Critchlow C (*A/Capt* 060685) 040881
Zmuda R C *LLB* 180682
Hodgson G J 191182
Charles J E 010483
Coulson M G *BA ARICS* (*A/Capt* 310784) 220783
Edwards A A (*A/Capt* 310784) 080883
Salmon P F E 021283
Brode N D 110184
Cooper S J 070884
Farmer J R 310785
Spencer J H 211185

2nd Lieutenants

Down K H 290784
†Noble C 160685
†Bates J N 070785
†Stark P G 280785
†Thompson I C *BSc(Hons)* 280785
†Turner C D 280785
†Lawes B D 051285

Quartermasters

Wright D S *Capt* 130583
Moore B *Capt* 100985

THE HONOURABLE ARTILLERY COMPANY

Artillery

An old fashioned cannon with a scroll above inscribed 'HAC' and a scroll below inscribed *'ARMA PACIS FULCRA'*; the whole surmounted by St Edward's Crown

Infantry

A grenade with monogram *'HAC'* on the ball

Regional Headquarters......................Armoury House, City Road, London, EC1Y 2BO (*Tel No:* 01-606-2521)

Captain General......................THE QUEEN

Colonel Commandant......................Gen *Sir* Richard Trant *KCB*......................010984

Regimental Colonel......................Col S A Sellon *OBE TD*......................160185

Colonels

Sellon S A *OBE TD* 160185

Lieutenant Colonels

Kay B A *TD*■■ 010976
Godbold G E *TD* 300984

Majors

Walter P F *MBE MC*■ 140963
Richards A T G *TD* 140780
O'Hagan A R *TD* 010982
Raven G A *TD BA* 010982
Ring M S H *TD* 010982
Neil G M *ARICS FRVA* 010483
Blomfield R H L *TD LLB* 220683
McCall I V *TD* 281183
Spooner D P 010184
Coulton D M 010584
Davies T L *TD* 011284
Webster M S *TD* 150585
Peters R N *TD*■ 100286

Captains

Adams P G *TD* 191180
Edmunds H T (*A/Maj* 011284) 010481
Dobbin A M C 010981
Close-Smith R H (*A/Maj* 011084) 010982
Cox C H 261182
Purnell-Edwards P 010983
Jones P R *BSc FRICS* 011083
Lalor S F N 160484
Huleatt-James R M 210884
Brown G R *BSc(Econ)* 011084
Packer R 010485
Jackson R J 200485
Fowler S C T 100785
O'Gorman M P 260985
De Margary G D M *AICS* 011085
Hunt W G 111185
Gabb A H S 071284
Wingate O J 010185
Lloyd-Jones J R 140385
Steele C C 190385
Graham R S 290385
Vyvyan-Robinson P D C 241085
Ferguson J M *BA* 010286
Kerr D F *BSc ARICS* 010286
Todd H W M 010286

Lieutenants

Quayle W 080975
Gordon D P 221176
Walker J F S (*A/Capt* 010781) 080678
Ramsdale R W 110379
Pengelley R B 300679
Nuthall C J F 291079
Beaumont H E S *BSc* 111179
Squires M T D 141279
Cox P C 290680
Wynter Bee P F (*A/Capt* 011084) 010881
Bullivant G A 151181
Maitland-Jones G H 240183
Jones R J R 160383
Morpeth I C S 310383
Heaton T F 020483
Spicer H W 280483
Navin S W H *LLB MA* 300384
Westman P M A *FCA* 310884
Cranfield R W L *MA* 141084
Snowden J F H 301184
Hampshire M R 011284

2nd Lieutenants

Baldwin B 011081
†Mellor A J 181283
†Clarke G R 200584
†Clitherow B C T 200584
†Lawson-Smith N 070785
†Young S J V 061185
†Bailey C J W 281185
†Cox S F T *MA(Cantab&Oxon)* 021285
†Wright J C W 101285

Quartermasters

Blackwood D J *Capt* 011082
Bassett-Cross R S *FCA* *Capt* 191083
Freeman J R *FRSA* *Capt* 131284

Directors of Music

Boulding K R R *LRAM ARCM* psm *Maj* 040782

HOUSEHOLD CAVALRY

THE LIFE GUARDS

Captains		*Lieutenants*			
Harbord J J	181178	Cayzer *The Hon* H R	220776	Cayzer *The Hon* C W	060879
				Hoare J A	010981
				Bell M L W	310882

THE BLUES AND ROYALS (ROYAL HORSE GUARDS AND 1st DRAGOONS)

Captains		*Lieutenants*			
Lingeman M H	250579	Bagge A J S	100375	Everard R A S	190277
				Bagge T P	080377
				Voorspuy T M	100879

ROYAL ARMOURED CORPS

1st THE QUEEN'S DRAGOON GUARDS

Majors

Wood A S *TD* 150182

Captains

Rosier F D S *MA* 300480
Baird I D V 010782
Wisher P S 010782
Mullins R G 011083
Farquharson J J F *BA* 010684

Lieutenants

Larminie O R C *MA* 100974
Daniell A H *BSc* 201174
Roe A F J *BA* 041178
Watterson A G 060879

THE ROYAL SCOTS DRAGOON GUARDS (CARABINIERS AND GREYS)

Captains

Gillington R J F *TD FRICS* (*Bt/Maj* 310577) 211070
Pocock M D A 010679
Potter J L 010782
Lancaster R J 010685

Lieutenants

Murray J M D *BA* 291078
McFall C W H *BA* 191180

4th/7th ROYAL DRAGOON GUARDS

Captains

Bennett J A 180679
Forbes P P S 290879
Milner J E G 011083
Nicholls M W *BA* 010685

Lieutenants

Brown T C 111278
Wheeler R S *BA* 271278
Gordon R C P R *LLB* 040380
Bell M G 081281
Page M J 070183
Brown R S R 110883

5th ROYAL INNISKILLING DRAGOON GUARDS

Captains

Vigors P M D *BSc ACA* 010782

Lieutenants

Baker O R H *BA* 040979
Allerston M F 070481
Young K P 061281
Milligan D F S 180882

THE QUEEN'S OWN HUSSARS

Captains

Parker M J *MBE* 290768

Lieutenants

Ratner R A *TD BL LLB* (*Bt/Maj* 010285) 131270
Lodge O A W *BSc* 300478
Ward S C R 200382
Bampfylde M H W 160684

THE QUEEN'S ROYAL IRISH HUSSARS

Captains

Morris J J *BA* 220678

Lieutenants

Duckworth H M 101175
Bidie T C *BA* 060177
Lucy W W *BA* 060479
Thorman J P 010779
Wolstenholme A W L *BSc* 040979
Fee A J 071279
Weston-Baker C E T A 021084

9th/12th ROYAL LANCERS (PRINCE OF WALES'S)

Captains

Bulleid P J *TD MA ALI* (*Bt/Maj* 090784) 010877
Peaver R H *TD MA MIL* (*Bt/Maj* 090784) 010877
de Salis *The Count TD BA LLB* 010679

Lieutenants

Lewis P J *BA* 240179
Crawshay W J J *BA* 171080

THE ROYAL HUSSARS (PRINCE OF WALES'S OWN)

Captains

Coates O H F *BSc* 010383
White *The Hon* L R 011083

Lieutenants

Holford-Walker E A *BA* 260776
Fowle C S *BSc(Hons)* 090279
Forrest P A A 060879
Troughton E T A *MA* 030381
Crewdson W A H *BA* 070481
Farquhar P C E *LLB* 180681
Atkinson C D B 121182
Arkwright M P V 081183
Rogers M S 010585

13th/18th ROYAL HUSSARS (QUEEN MARY'S OWN)

Majors

Bindloss C O A tt 190681

Captains

Walsh W N F *TD MA* 011174
Trigg M G 011083
Cameron E G *LLB* 010685

Lieutenants

Filmer C P N 081281
Scaramanga A T 081281
Hussein *HRH Prince of* The Hashemite Kingdom of Jordan 051083

14th/20th KING'S HUSSARS

Majors

Davis M G S tt 070583

Captains

Dashwood *Sir* Richard 010478
Baines J F T *BSc* 020678
Symons J N 010383

Lieutenants

Pownall-Gray H D 270278
Lawrence P J 080481

15th/19th THE KING'S ROYAL HUSSARS

Captains

Anderson J P P 010877
Bullard J G 010480
Barne A R 201080
Ellis R A *TD* (*Bt/Maj* 090784) 010383
Wilton J P 010685

Lieutenants

Bampfylde R I D 070878
Jones-Warner C M 180979
Jessel G E 111280
Barkes G W N 141281
Fox W P 090682

16th/5th THE QUEEN'S ROYAL LANCERS

Majors

Prout C J *BA DPhil* 010785

Captains

Kayll M P 010480
Tetley C M 010782
Evetts J M I 080782
Kenney-Herbert H C 010685
Stow R J S 010685

Lieutenants

Goodwin C H A *BA* aic 151075
Reid M G F 300977
Hepburn I F 251177
Clifton T D 230279
Ward N E 220382
Cuthbert M J 090882

17th/21st LANCERS

Captains

Marriott C J W *TD ARICS* 020371
Kerr A N 011083

Lieutenants

Lowes T N 080377

ROYAL TANK REGIMENT

Majors

Messenger C R M *MA* psc† 020980
Fieldhouse A W *TD*▪▪ 010483

Captains

Baker R C C aic 060677
Molyneaux D C *TD* 010679
Roberts W R *BA* 010480
Chetwynd M C *BSc* 010782
Stockdale W J *TD MA FCA* 010782
Colton J H E *BA* 010383
Palmer A J *BA* 010383
Atkinson N 010783
Clifford W D S *BSc* 010783

Lieutenants

Biggs A J *BA DipEd* 280375
Rackley T M *MA MICE* 070575
Planterose R M *BA BL LLB* 100377
Shaw C B H *BSc* 141180
Hewson G P R 231181

Colonel Commandant Yeomanry ....Lt Col (Bt Col) *The Visct* Ridley *TD DL* 151182

THE ROYAL YEOMANRY

Associated Regular Regiments

(Royal Wiltshire Yeomanry) Squadron ....The Royal Hussars
(Sherwood Rangers Yeomanry) Squadron ....17th/21st Lancers
(Kent and Sharpshooters Yeomanry) Squadron .....Household Cavalry
(North Irish Horse) Squadron ....5th Royal Inniskilling Dragoon Guards, The Queen's Royal Irish Hussars
(Westminster Dragoons) Squadron..........................2nd Royal Tank Regiment
Band (Inns of Court and City Yeomanry) ....Household Cavalry

Regimental March

Quick March..The Farmer's Boy

Alliance

Colonial Forces ....The Royal Hong Kong Regiment (The Volunteers)

Royal Hon Colonel..H M QUEEN ELIZABETH THE QUEEN MOTHER

Dep Royal Hon Colonel..*H R H Princess* Alexandra *the Hon Mrs* Angus Ogilvy *GCVO*

Hon Colonel ....Maj Gen J G R Allen *CB* ret pay 151182

Hon Colonels of Squadrons

A *(Royal Wiltshire Yeomanry) Squadron* ....Maj *The Hon* J I Morrison *TD DL* 151182

B *(Sherwood Rangers Yeomanry) Squadron*..........Maj R F Abel Smith................................011079

C *(Kent and Sharpshooters Yeomanry) Squadron* .Lt R Leigh-Pemberton (*HM Lord Lieutenant Kent*) 010579

D *(North Irish Horse) Squadron*..............................Lt Col *The Lord* Dunleath *TD DL* 010781

HQ *(Westminster Dragoons) Squadron*
Maj Gen J G R Allen *CB* ret pay 111082

Band (Inns of Court and City Yeomanry) ....Col G D Thompson *MC TD DL* (Sponsor Officer)

Colonels

Hunt J C V *OBE TD ADC* 140283

Majors

Brooking Thomas I C *TD* 011074
Stanley D A *TD* 010178
Radcliffe J G Y *MA* 010179
Yates C J 010181
Santry N 300981
Winstanley C J 010182
Lapworth G B S *TD* 150183
Arkell J R 260983
Pollock *The Hon* R C S *TD MA* 060285

Captains

Frost D S C *TD* 011176
McDonald C R *TD BSc MICE* 010678
Kemp D E *MA* (*A/Maj* 211084) 010179
Parkes T C *BA* (*A/Maj* 031184) 011180
Bendix T M De R 190681
Charman A (*A/Maj* 011184) 230981
Kennerley P D *BA* 281081
Boyd J J *TD* 010882
Robinson N J M *BSc(Eng) ARSM* 140982
Bennie C H A R 140683
Orme J G 011083
Colville R M L 160584
Doughty G E J A *BA* 031184
Windsor-Clive G F 010385

Lieutenants

Lawson-Cruttenden A T *TD* 300975
Field R A K *BA* 020676
Schlesinger J F *BA* 190477
Stark R C *BA* (*A/Capt* 011184) 120677
Bryant M E P 060877
MacNamara J J *BA* 231177
Emary R H *BA* 200179
Dennison C M W *BVM&S MRCVS* 260179
Lower A M 190579
Raschen H D *BCom* 270180
Smith A M 080780
Wingfield A N B 080780
Meyrick T F 030581
Ferris J R (*A/Capt* 010485) 040881
Giddins G E B 011081
Mills W L (*A/Capt* 201185) 051081
McIlwaine C D 071281
Hanson P A 180282
Denee P 090882
Smith B R 300882
Crewdson G W M 251182
Beattie M J 140583
Clutterbuck F W H 240484
Whitamore C C W 060684
Bogle J S L 210784

2nd Lieutenants

Grant D J T 200584
†Coleman R A 151284
Carpenter C J 270185
†Coulter A R 290385
†Barr J A L 180485
†Charlton-Jones J A *BA(Hons)* 070785
†Tougher N C 210985
†Ashton-Johnson P J 011285
†Hughes M C 011285

Quartermasters

Annett J W *Capt* 121176

THE ROYAL WESSEX YEOMANRY

Associated Regular Regiments

(Royal Wiltshire Yeomanry) Squadron ....The Royal Hussars (Prince of Wales's Own)
(Royal Gloucestershire Hussars) Squadron.............The Royal Hussars (Prince of Wales's Own)
(Royal Devon Yeomanry) Squadron ....3rd Royal Tank Regiment

Hon Colonel ....Maj *The Hon* J I Morrison *TD DL* 151182

Hon Colonels of Squadrons

(Royal Wiltshire Yeomanry) Squadron ....Maj *The Hon* J I Morrison *TD DL* 151182
A&C (Royal Gloucestershire Hussars) Squadron ...Lt *His Grace The Duke of* Beaufort 070684
(Royal Devon Yeomanry) Squadron ....Maj Gen *Sir* John Acland *KCB CBE* ret pay 311283

Lieutenant Colonels

Ayshford-Sanford D R *TD DL* 010778
Hills J E B 010784

Majors

¶Barrington Browne D S 010871
Clifford P R H 010676
Jenkins R L *LVO* 121281
Chamberlain O J H *MRAC ARICS* 010883
Penley J F *TD* 010184
Wilson R M C 011284
Walcot J H *MA* 300985

Captains

¶Humberstone B T *MBE* 280582
Lees C J *BSc* 010883
Hodson A D F *BA* 011183
¶Mertens D G 010484
¶Walton W M *MBE* 010484
¶Mitchell G J 030484
Ponsonby R C 011084
¶Hoddinott A J 040285
Selby Bennett J S 251085
Tokeley-Parry J A F 271085

Lieutenants

Hankin G A N *BA* 130378
Mullings R R 221080
Arundell R J T 210181
Gardner T J 210181
Wirgman R W 040881
Widdicombe P E 270182
Ranson L C A 130683
Doherty M J W 011284
Hart S A 230185
Fortescue A W 290185

2nd Lieutenants

†Harwood O H F 121083
Polglase A P 181184
Bowles S B 270185
†Martin A J O 260585
†Rothwell M J R 011285

Quartermasters

Shepherd A J J *Capt* 010983

THE QUEEN'S OWN MERCIAN YEOMANRY

Within a strap inscribed *'QUEENS OWN MERCIAN YEOMANRY'* a double headed eagle ensigned with Saxon Crown, the whole surmounted by St Edward's Crown

Associated Regular Regiments

(Warwickshire and Worcestershire Yeomanry) Squadron
The Queen's Own Hussars
(Shropshire Yeomanry) Squadron.............................1st The Queen's Dragoon Guards
(Staffordshire Yeomanry) Squadron ....16th/5th The Queen's Royal Lancers

Colonel in Chief ....THE QUEEN

Hon Colonel ....Maj Gen P B Cavendish *CB OBE* ret pay 310382

Lieutenant Colonels

Appleby P G *TD*▪ 281085

Majors

Pitt A W H *TD*▪ *BSc MEd DipEd CBiol MIBiol* 020973
Boote C R M *TD*▪ sq(v) 010274
¶Edwards C J 010780
Evans T M *BSc ARICS* 020382
Cotterell R C R 250485
Carver B J I 281085

Captains

¶Castle E E *MBIM*
¶Stratton P J 160381
Bunch W A L 311281
Wharton R *TD* (*A/Maj* 010485) 010282
Farquharson D J H (*A/Maj* 010486) 020583
English J R S 250683
Seccombe P S *ARICS* (*A/Maj* 230985) 250683
¶Tucker T W 020783
¶Sibson J H 220584
Payne B P 030486

Lieutenants

Largue S D *BA BSc* 160581
Leigh D L (*A/Capt* 010485) 060482
Pippen B I B 251083
Bailey P J M 150584
Robotham R J 010784
Weir C F 230185
Clarke P S 220585
Skirving M T 220186

2nd Lieutenants

Sheppard J M A 200584
Miles C P C 181184
†Caddick-Adams A P 010385

Quartermasters

Tetlow D *Capt* 031185

THE QUEEN'S OWN YEOMANRY

A fox in silver, in a scroll inscribed *'QUEENS OWN YEOMANRY'*

Associated Regular Regiments

(Queen's Own Yorkshire Yeomanry) Squadron......4th/7th Royal Dragoon Guards
13th/18th Royal Hussars (Queen Mary's Own)

(Ayrshire Yeomanry) Squadron......The Royal Scots Dragoon Guards (Carabiniers and Greys)

(Cheshire Yeomanry) Squadron......5th Royal Inniskilling Dragoon Guards
16th/5th The Queen's Royal Lancers

(Northumberland Hussars) Squadron......15th/19th The King's Royal Hussars
9th/12th Royal Lancers (Prince of Wales's)
4th Royal Tank Regiment

Regimental March

Quick March......D'ye Ken John Peel

Hon Colonel......Lt Col G Sparrow *MC TD*......010386

Hon Colonels of Squadrons

Y *(Queen's Own Yorkshire Yeomanry) Squadron*..Col *The Hon* R N Crossley *TD*......081281

A *(Ayrshire Yeomanry) Squadron*......Col D C Greig *TD DL*......010477

C *(Cheshire Yeomanry) Squadron*......Lt Col G Sparrow *MC TD*......010781

NH *(Northumberland Hussars) Squadron*......Col *Sir* Ralph Carr-Ellison *TD HML*......010386

Colonels

York E C *TD ADC* 010881
Brooks A D B *ADC DL* 010583

Lieutenant Colonels

Collins J W H *MA* 070783
Thompson D R B 240784

Majors

Maclean R W B 310779
Sowler T R H *TD MA* 010180
Price M W T 060680
Hawke E G *TD ARICS* 010182
Mitchell-Rose C M *BSc* 010582
Kennedy P N B *TD CA* 160782
Dalrymple-Hamilton N J F *MA* 081182
Speke I B 011183
Westminster *The Duke of* 010185
Mather P L *BSc* 160885

Captains

Churton D N V *MBE* 220578
Hay G A *TD LLB* (*A/Maj* 010785) 010879
Sample C J 010781
Maitland J A C 261181
Nickell-Lean J R 010182
Callander R *FRICS* 081182
Barkes R J N (*A/Maj* 010284) 010583
Bingham J W W *BSc* 010985
Blackett J S 011085

Lieutenants

Pritchard-Barrett T J 120977
Fife J A (*A/Capt* 241285) 081177
Barne W M *BA* 190278
Arkwright A M G (*A/Capt* 010284) 310179
Royds J C 011080
Watson T P 091280
Hutchinson-Smith C R (*A/Capt* 010185) 211081
Harrison C J 300182
Owen J L 160282
Scott M D'A B 060482
Hunter Johnston J W *BSc* 090882
Wyrley-Birch N R 090882
Allsop E P C 271082
Forsyth A J M 010383
Cormack M V S *LLB* 110883
Beckett *The Hon* R D 011083
Egerton R N 220585
Glazebrook N C 120685

2nd Lieutenants

†Moir J M H 240485
†Reynard C W 070785
†Shires P M 070785
†Cooper P M 011285

Quartermasters

Donohue A J *Capt* 060477

THE DUKE OF LANCASTER'S OWN YEOMANRY

A rose within a wreath, laurel on left, oak on right; a scroll inscribed *'DUKE OF LANCASTER'S OWN'*, the whole ensigned with a ducal coronet

Associated Regular Regiment
14th/20th King's Hussars

Regimental March

Quick March .... John O'Gaunt

Colonel in Chief .... THE QUEEN

Hon Colonel .... Lt (Hon Col) S Towneley *JP* 220279

Lieutenant Colonels

Hewitt F E *TD MEd*	010483

Majors

Fowden B J *TD*	010175
Thompson G D *TD*	070978
Collis J S	120379
Eastham J *TD LLB FRICS ACIArb*	010481
Steiger M T *LLB*	020581
Hammersley A J *TD BA*	011283
Laing H C D	010185
Tustin J	151185

Captains

¶Sheen E *MBE*	211180
Berry A P	051081
Walker J R G	010482
¶Stocker B G	020682
¶Lovell T H	010483
¶Colborne V L	140483
¶Escott J J	020983

Lieutenants

Norman S G J	010382
Koss R A	251083
Fulton G O TE TEM	010185
Bowring T G	010285
Cowan I R *MA*	170485
Hargreaves C	120685
Ryder E N	211185
Boardman J M	220186
Garewal J	220186
Hankinson C	220186

2nd Lieutenants

Brookes B J	200584
†Hewitt D E M	151284
†Jolleys R H *BA(Hons) PGCE*	280785

Quartermasters

Steven J D	*Capt*	010683

DISBANDED YEOMANRY REGIMENTS

SUCCESSOR SUB-UNIT

The Leicestershire and Derbyshire Yeomanry (Prince Albert's Own)
Former Associated Regular Regiment
9th/12th Royal Lancers (Prince of Wales's)

The Leicestershire and Derbyshire Yeomanry (Prince Albert's Own) Company, 7th (Volunteer) Battalion The Royal Anglian Regiment

The Queen's Own Lowland Yeomanry
Former Associated Regular Regiment
4th Royal Tank Regiment

225 (Queen's Own Lowland Yeomanry) Squadron 154 (Lowland) Transport Regiment Royal Corps of Transport (Volunteers)

The Highland Yeomanry
Former Associated Regular Regiment
4th/7th Royal Dragoon Guards

239 (Highland Yeomanry) Squadron, 153 (Highland) Artillery Support Regiment Royal Corps of Transport (Volunteers)

Inns of Court and City Yeomanry
Former Associated Regular Regiment
Household Cavalry

68 (Inns of Court and City Yeomanry) Signal Squadron, 71st (Yeomanry) Signal Regiment (Volunteers)

Hon Colonel:
HM QUEEN ELIZABETH THE QUEEN MOTHER

The North Somerset and Bristol Yeomanry

6th Battalion The Light Infantry (Volunteers)

The Pembrokeshire Yeomanry

Amalgamated into 4th (Volunteer) Battalion The Royal Regiment of Wales (24th/41st Foot)

The West Somerset Yeomanry

6th Battalion The Light Infantry (Volunteers)

ROYAL REGIMENT OF ARTILLERY

Hon Colonels .... *His Majesty Olav V* King of Norway *KG KT GCB GCVO (Hon Col* 100 *(Yeo) Field Regt RA (Volunteers))*

Lt Col J A Bailie *OBE DL (Hon Col* 102 *(Ulster and Scottish) Air Defence Regt RA TA)* 010181

Lt Col J W Dowdeswell *MC TD JP DL (Hon Col* 101 *(Northumbrian) Field Regt RA (V))* 070581

Lt Gen *Sir* Richard Vincent *KCB DSO (Hon Col* 100 *(Yeo) Field Regt RA (Volunteers))* 051282

Col A C Roberts *MBE TD JP DL (Hon Col* 269 *(West Riding) Observation Post Battery RA (TA))* 150483

Col J M A Gunn *OBE TD DL (Hon Col* 307 *South Nottinghamshire Hussars Yeomanry RHA Battery RA (Volunteers))* 041183

Maj Gen A G E Stewart-Cox *DFC (Hon Col* 289 *Commando Battery RA (Vols) TA)* 131183

Brig G W Hutton ret pay *(Hon Col* 266 *Gloucestershire Volunteers Artillery Battery RA (TA))* 071283

Maj Gen M J Tomlinson *CB OBE (Hon Col* 104 *Air Defence Regt RA (Vols) TA)* 010185

Col R Squires *OBE TD JP (Hon Col* 103 *Lancashire Artillery (Volunteers) Air Defence Regiment RA (Volunteers))* 011083

Colonels

Hardie D D G *TD■ DL* 011276
Orchard-Lisle P D *TD■ ADC* 010479
Ingham J E *OBE TD■* 261081
Taylor M J E *TD■ LLB MA MIPM MBIM* 221182
Cawse M G *OBE* psc ptsc G 011083
Stevens D E *OBE TD■* 011284
Porteous W R *TD■■ MSc DipEd FRSC* 011185
Lloyd T D C *TD■ ARICS ARVA* 080286

Lieutenant Colonels

Paterson D J *ERD TD* 011171
Steele J M *OBE TD■■■ BSc* 010778
Lloyd P J *MBE TD■ BSc ARICS ARVA* 010379
Glenton A A E *MBE TD■* 180384
Shedden R C psc 010484
Sainsbury J D *TD■■* 011284
Jolley E A *TD* 130585
Chambers T H *TD* 010186
Cameron D J *TD* 010486

Majors

Suthers J D *ERD■ TD■ CEng AMInstF MCIOB* 191165
Morrish P H *MBE TD■■* 011168
Parker I K *TD■* 011169
Proctor J T 250770
Craig-Cooper F H M *CBE TD■■* 310171
Newman J M W *TD■■* 310171
Howard J A *TD■■ BA* 210271
Thurgood W P C 210271
Mitchell A J *TD■■ MA* 280371
Fordyce M M *MBE TD■■* 010472
Cowan J M *TD■ AIB* sq(v) *(Bt/Lt Col* 010682) 010173
Richardson W T *TD■* 010173
Ridley N R N *TD* 011273
Spurr I J *TD■ MA* pl 011273
Johnston A *TD■* 010874
Bianco A A *MBIM* 311274
Blackmore J A *TD BSc MA* 010175
Boyce A C psc 170375
Oliver A J *TD■* sq(v) 010475
Evans K G C *TD■■* 240475
Bruce A J *TD■■ MA FRGS FRMetS FRSA* 010675
Cox T J L *TD■■* 010675
David A M *TD ARICS* 010675
Doyle G W *TD■■ AIB* 010675
Graham H J M *TD■* 010675
Hartgill J C *TD■■* 010675
Moore I O W *TD■* 010675
Moss A P *TD■ MA MICE MIHT* 010675
Naylor R M W *TD■■* 010675
Vere C M N *MBE TD MA* 010675
Winterton M A C *TD■■ MA* 010675
Cox J C *TD■* 030476
Barnes M *TD■* 010876
Gurd J N *TD■■* 091076
Rodale P H A *TD■■ DMS* 091076
Wilson T A K *TD■ BDS* 091076
Lindsley R M *TD■■* 121076
Fryer G M *TD■■ BSc PhD* 010177
Herron E R C *TD■* 161077
Dorward A G *TD LLB NP* 111177
Shaw B R *TD LLB MA* 140178
Hughes T J *TD* 030778
Saunders P A *TD■* 190778
Jones H B C *TD* sq(v) 280778
Lovegrove M L 010878
Smith R M G(a) 080878
Hill C P R *TD* 010179
Shergold J R S *TD BA* 010179
Bucknall R M *TD■* 010279
Headey P G *TD■■* 260280
Irvine R A N *TD■ LLB* 050380
Kirkham D J *TD* 101180
Gornall R E *TD■* 111180
Good M F *TD* 010481
Kobine N J G 040881
McVicker W B J 051081
Armstrong K M *TD* 300382
Pritchard S C G *TD■* 140582
Morriss R E F *TD* 300682
Hall R E 200782
Redfern C P *TD■ FCA* 290782
Moffat A D *TD LLB* 010882
Richmond T S *MBE TD FCA* 010882
Hill S *TD BSc CEng MIMunE* 011282
Walker A J *TD BA ARICS MRTPI* 011282
Clarke D G *TD BA* 131282
McLean I S *TD* 010183
Lithgow-Smith D *TD BSc MA* 100183
Ventham P R *BA* aic 010483
Best K L *TD MA* 110683
Mount P *TD* 180983
Moore R G *TD* 081183
Doyle F T M *TD■* 211183
Munro P A D *BSc* 011283
Treseder H S 200184
Lucas C W *TD■ ACII* 010484
Cracknell S T G 120484
Harvey-Jamieson R R *TD LLB WS NP* 010884
Kelly R D *TD■* 030884
Griffiths D J *TD BSc* 121084
Reid J F *TD BSc GRADIMA* 221084
Llewelyn-Davies J D ph 261084
Vaughan R D G ph 121184
Allder C P R *TD■ MRAC* 011284
Bain D K *TD LLB LLB(Hons)* 011284
Baron J H *TD■ AIB* 011284
Biggins J A 011284
Dornan P A *TD* 011284
Thompson P G N 011284
Eleanor N J R *TD BA(Hons)* 031284
Seal-Coon R F M *TD■* 010185
Muse J M *TD■ ACA ACA* 190185
Hancock R D *TD* 050285
Houldsworth J 230285
Stubbs G M *TD* 230285
Stone P R *TD■* 260585
Halliwell M J A 010685
Lewis D A 010685
Phillips S B *TD AIL* 010685
Heap P *BA* 010885
Tomlinson D I *TD■ MA* 010885
Wallace M C R 010885
Scott A D *TD BSc(Eng)* 010985
Relph G C N sq G 011185
Syred R 091185
Morris B H *LLB* 100286
Norrington N C *TD* 100286
Ventham I R 100286
Worrall R D *TD* 010486

Captains

Smith J *TD* 121069
Robson A B B *TD MISM FInstPet FInstSMM* 311071
Downham R E *TD■■* 011171
Pocklington M *TD■* 010472
Taffs J D *TD BSc(Eng) CEng MICE* 300972
Aldridge G E *TD* 010573
Jackson W H *BSc* 010773
Seal D M *TD BA* 010874
Walton J A S *TD* 010475

¶Lake G R 130975
Stoney I M *BSc* 010276
¶Norton G W A 160876
Bevan S J P *TD FCA* 010477
Horwill C *TD BSc(Eng) CEng MIEE* 150477
Chambers C J 010677
Nell M J R *TD BSc* 011077
¶Pauley F J 010178
Long M J *TD AIB* 010378
Gilbert D C 130678
Baldwin K W 010778
Jordan P A *TD BA* 010778
Ball M J 280778
Murphy D J *TD* 280778
Walters D G 010978
Donaldson A S *BA* 030978
¶Logan P 301178
Loder J F *MA* 010179
¶Ferry D J C 020179
¶Campbell W J 260179
Mackenzie N M *TD BSc DMS MInstPS* 010279
Orton P C *TD BSc CEng FRINA* 010279
Righton D J *AIB* 010279
Anwyl-Hughes D W 010379
Blair J M G *LLB* (*A/Maj* 011085) 050379
Kelly D R 010479
Barton P A F *TD BSc* 010579
Connew R A *TD* 120579
Vivers A G C *BSc* 010879
Lamplugh D M 270879
Aiken R D *BSc* 150979
Dixon T M *BSc(EstMan) ARICS* 200979
¶Phillips R W 161179
¶Smith P G W 021279
Barrow P G 010180
¶Cormack D P 010180
Nolan J P *TD BA* 010180
Wherrett R J *TD BSc* 010180
Tatton H M *BSc* 210180
¶Lines J T 290180
Dines A J *LLB* (*A/Maj* 060985) 190280
Crowther J R 010480
Burn I *TD* 010780
White R A *TD* 030780
¶Tetlow L E 170780
Houghton C 010880
White R D *TD BA* 010880
¶Goldthorp F 151080
Gibson A E 011180
McClintock B T 111180
Janes P R *MSc* 251280
¶Myford R 010181
Anderson T J *BSc* 010281
¶Warner O R 110281
Baldry A B *BA LLB* 180281
Porter S E *TD* 010581
¶Inkster H K 160581
Hearn C *MSc* gsd 150681
Irwin S (*A/Maj* 011085) 140881
Boyd W W *BA* 220981
Gracie W T *TD* 051081
Talbot G J 051081
¶Guite H 231081
Comport C E 261081
Walsh P F 091181
Walshaw P A *AIB* 201181
¶Hurlock T H *OBE* 150682
¶Kerslake J G 120782
Bryson G R *LLB MA* 010882
Hall A D A S *LLB WS* 010982
Churchhouse G M *BA* 261182
Doughty P T 261182
Hutt R W F *BSc ARICS* 261182
Fox J S *BSc PhD* 010183
Lemon W J *BA* 010183
Guest J A 180283
Boyce P J *BSc* 010383
McCabe C N *MSc RCNC* 260383
Meres J T 100483
MacFarlane A E *MA ACCA* 180483
Lidbetter R S J 260483
Abrams R L *DMS* 130783
Cooper R A N 010883
Edge A R 250983
MacVicar S D *BA* 011083
¶Munro D 011083
Anderson R C R 051083
Jefferson I D *BA BSc* 121083
Burton R *ACMA* 211183
Wyche P *BA* 211183
Pickles D M 011283
Daniel N A *BA* 010184
Constable J C *BSc* 010584
Taylor M H *MA ACA* 140584
¶Cross W H E 210584
Doherty I J V *BA* 230584
¶Gittos R M J 140684
Blake R P M 180884
¶Harriman R E 030984
Carnegie J W G *BSc* 110984
Barrett J A 011084
Britten P R *LLB(Hons)* 011084
¶Davies J H *MBIM MITD* 011084
Dowty J M S 011084
Wright J S *BSc(Eng)* 011084
Cunningham C I 041184
Fielding M W 041184
Harriman J W F *BA(Econ) BSc* 041184
Fitzsimmons F J 091184
Wilson I A *BSc* 101184
Boorn D C 271184
Lomas D 011284
Manson F P L *TD MBA FCCA* 011284
Dowdney N F 010185
Gleave C *MSc PhD* 230285
Thompson H E G 230285
Long M G G(a) 280285
Partridge W M J 140385
Cowan-Martin A P D F 310385
Rylands H J J 010585
¶Shaw R J sq G 140585
Price S L 010685
Cummins J P F *MA* 010785
Davenport J H *MA PhD* 010785
¶Ross M 010985
Kennedy W R 011085
McFerran J 011085
Walters T R J 011085
Paget D W 121085
Parkinson A J 121085
Harris D 221085
¶Potter J D 291085
Mills R J 101185
¶Bristo R T 161185
Kirk R 131285
¶Richards T 160186
Durrant J L A *BSc PhD* 120286
MacLeod I M *BA* 120286
Nuttall P J 130286
Docherty J S 010386
Haggerty J H 010386
Gibson B G *FInstLEx* 010486
Kennington R 010486
McClements T *MBE TD*▪▪ 010486

Lieutenants

Young D R J *TD* (*A/Capt* 011074) 110571
Douglas-Osborn P E *BSc CEng MIMM* 040975
Hearne C J *BSc(Econ) MSc FRSA ACIS MBIM* 150776
Lycett-King I R *BA* 081276
Cookes H N 250578
Smalley P H 260679
Buckels P N *BA* (*A/Capt* 080983) 280879
Varley J C *BA* 150680
Cockroft S D *BA* (*A/Capt* 010284) 180181
Hilton R S 210181
Armitage J A D 220181
Whyte J W *BA DipEd* 270281
Irwin-Houston D F (*A/Capt* 021284) 010681
Sadler S N S (*A/Capt* 010186) 120681
Mellor E 260781
Turp J R *BA* 240881
Salloway P C *BSc* 060182
Brotherston D J (*A/Capt* 131285) 300182
Kinloch S A 090882
Arnold-Forster D O 271082
Trezise-Hardinge D A 271082
Edgar C M *MA ARICS* 231182
Royle N S *BSc* 040183
Reed C D 090283
Wells N B *BSc* (*A/Capt* 131285) 010383
Foote M B 050483
Hall J S 050483
Gough A J E 110583
Gravatt A S 190583
Bulmer D C 240583
Bird C J E *BA* 150683
Etches S J *BSc* 260683
Humphrey D A *BA* 310783
Stewart J G 080883
Williamson M *MA DipEd* 080883
Whitta S J 081083
Webb M A P *BA(Hons)* 131083
Maxton N J 021183
Smith A 151183
Eyre G R 090284
Reed G 240384
Hall P R (*A/Capt* 010885) 090484
Mountford S G 090484
Owen D R 090484
Cox G E 250584
Jackson J E 310784
Comport C A 070884
O'Connor M J 070884
Anthony B P *BA* 110984
McKibbin R 211184
Kirk F (*A/Maj* 010185) 010185
Keet J C M *MInstFF* 110285
Motteram E B 010385
Tanzey D C 010385
Farrell R P 010485
Ramshaw D S 020485
Brocklebank M G *BEng MICE* 080585
Grice P E 220585
Hodge M J 220585
Campbell J 120685
Smith A M 310785
Hughes N J H 011185
Sweeting D A *BA(HonsCantab)* 140286
Sparks J N 010386

2nd Lieutenants

Bletchly F E J *BSc AIWSC* 051280
†O'Connell M J 200582
†Angus H D W *LLB DipLP* 011183
White J V 211183

Territorial Army, Royal Regiment of Artillery — continued

Drake C W *LLB*	221183
†Rumbold S O	080384
Baker E D	200584
†Boyd W A	240584
†Ferguson T R	240584
Cummings G	100684
Horton D C	100684
Jelf S C	100684
Knox D E	260784
Hare S J *ACIS MBIM AMITD*	290784
Pearson M H	010884
Roberts J A	010884
†Law I M	011184
Bramley M J	181184
Paige M S	181184
Suthers J W D	181184
Gault M T H	141284
†Berragan H N *BA(Hons)*	270185
Charlish D N	270185
Jones I	270185
†White G	270285
†Henry S P	260485
†Honnywill C G	060585
†Harcourt M	140585
†Powell D J	140585
†Verney A C	150585
†Mills S S	260585
†Walters R C	260585
†Dobbs M J	160685
†Harrison J G	160685
†Jeffers S D	160685
†Keyte M K	160685
†King M J	160685
†Harvey R A M	070785
†Higgins J R C	070785
†Sadler J F	070785
†Smith T H M	070785
†Clark D I	110785
†Begg J	280785
†Hicks T M	280785
†King R G F	280785
†Middleton D	280785
†Rengger P E P	280785
†Saunders A D *ACA*	280785
†Simpson N H	280785
†Summerfield J D	280785
†Watson K A	280785
†Shepherd P H	031085
†Beddows P A *BSc ARICS*	011285
†Gallico M K *BA(Hons) MSc*	011285
†Randall P N	011285

Quartermasters

Gamble W *TD*		240671
	Maj	160284
Smith D		120280
	Maj	120185
Blackwell C W	*Capt*	170883
¶Dorey A	*Maj*	060285
Hesketh E L P *TD*	*Capt*	010485
Sloan E *MBE*	*Capt*	101185

Technical Instructors in Gunnery

Perry D H *TD*		010467
	Maj	010479

CORPS OF ROYAL ENGINEERS

Hon Colonels

Col G P Jones *TD DL JP* 010774
Col D N Spratt *CBE TD DL* 010676
Maj Gen P C Shapland *CB MBE* ret pay 271179
Maj Gen P J M Pellereau ret pay 150480
Col J B Timmins *OBE TD DL* 010480
Maj J P Rettie *TD* 010482
Maj J A de M Greeves 010483
Maj Gen G B Sinclair *CB CBE* ret pay 010584
Maj Gen E W Barton *CB MBE* ret pay 140784
Col P D W Vaughan *MBE TD* 010185
Maj Gen M Matthews *CB* ret pay 080885
Brig L F H Busk 010486

Colonels

Carter A J *OBE TD■* 050878
Evans J G *CBE TD■■ ADC* 010479
Miall R C *TD■■ BSc(EstMan) FRICS* 150780
Williams P E *TD■■ ADC FRICS AMRSH ACIArb* sq(v) 160881
Moore J *TD■■ MIMunE MIHT DL* 011282
Perks J *TD■* 010484
Terry A A F *TD■ ADC CEng MIMunE MIHT* 120484
Scott D A *OBE TD■* 010685

Lieutenant Colonels

Jordan R L psc 130475
Rose E P F *TD■■ MA DPhil FGS MIWES* 010478
Bettridge J S *TD■ FIPHE* 010479
Ewen R *OBE TD■ MA* 300979
Ayling L J A *TD■ MA MIMechE MBIM FInstPet* 010483
McLeman L *TD■ MCIOB MBIM* sq(v) 010483
Williams D W *TD■* sq(v) 010483
Pagan C W *MBE TD■ BA LLB FBIM WS NP* 161283
Watkin G *TD■* 010284
Garside F J *TD■ BSc ARICS MIOB FICW MBIM* sq(v) 010384
Watson M H *TD■■ MA CEng MIGasE MCIOB MIMC* 010484
Turver K E *TD■■ BSc PhD FRAS CPhysFInstP* 010884
Hillard D H 160984
Udall R D *TD■ CEng MICE MIMunE MIHT* 011284
Edwards G F *TD■ DipTE MICE FIPlantE MIHT MBIM* 010585
Eyre R S *BSc(Eng) DMS MICE MIMunE* 050286
Page I L R *MIStructE MIMunE MIHT FPWI* 010486

Majors

Kemp R M TN 300668
Mitchell D S *TD■ MA FCIS* 010469
Wrathall D *TD■■ FICE MIMunE FIHT MBIM* 010771
Ewing J D *MBE BSc(Eng) MICE MBIM* C 120472
Jones G C *TD■■ MSc MIQ* 011072
Parker M J M *ACIS MBIM* 111272
Rowell D EM 010173
Weeden M H D *TD* 010473
Spark A J *TD■■* 010673
Balme J G *TD BEng MICE MIHT* 151273
Jones C D *TD BSc MBA* 010474
Carmichael R *MBIM* sq(v) 250175
McCabe L *TD* 010275
Campbell D A 260375
Hobbs J M *TD■ FIQ MIAT MITO* 010475
Thompson W F *TD■ MBIM* 010276
Holt S *TD MICE* 010476
Whitten B S R *TD■ BSc(Eng) CEng MICE* 010476
Whatley N J *BSc(Eng) CEng MICE MBIM* C 020776
Williams H D B *TD■■ BSc(Eng) CEng MICE MBIM MIWES* 151076
Fitzgerald P O *TD* 011176
Simpson A D *TD MICE MIHT* 120377
Davies D W *TD■ BSc(Eng) MA MSc CEng MIProdE MBIM* 010477
Gardiner B J *TD■ FHTTA MIAT* 010477
Hope H C G *TD■ LLB* 030677
Hough D *TD■■* 010777
Bell W J *TD TEng(CEI) FHTTA* sq(v) 140877
Hawley J C A *TD BEng CEng MICE* 011077
Williams N D O *TD DMS MBIM* sq(v) 010178
Travers M C *CEng MIMechE MIEE* EM 090278
Kirkpatrick D J *TD* 060578
Burgoyne F D *TD■ LLB* 010179
Murning I H *TD LLB ARICS MBIM* sq(v) 250379
Clarke J L *TD■ BEng BSc MICE MIHT* 010479
Ford J *TD■ BSc CEng MIChemE* 010479
Jordan R C 090479
Mould D J *TD■ BSc* 040779
Goodwin R A C *TD BSc MICE MBIM* 010879
Dobbie R O M *BSc(Eng)* SVY 050879
Bennett R H B *TD■ BSc CEng MICE MIHT* 011179
Rooth S L *MBE* 271279
Hunter D Mc *TD■ BA MICE MIMunE MIHT* 010480
Jack R L *TD■ MA MICE* 010480
Henry S K J *TD* 010580
Campbell J S *TD* 091180
Campbell Ellen B 020181
Taggart H G R *MIPlantE AMIRTE MBIM FInstPet* 080281
Ritchie D J *TD* 290381
Kendrick R J *FRSA FBIM* 010481
Selby-Boothroyd R G *TD■ MBCS* 010481
Bootland E T *TD LLB* sq(v) 051081
Johnston W A *BSc(Eng)* 271081
Paige C D *TD■ MBIM MInstM* 011181
Rogers S A 301181
Hunter R D *TD■* 010382
Allison M R *MA MIEE* 010482
Angwin C A *TD MA AICS* 010482
Harrison C B *MA MBA MICE* 010482
Nichols D J *BSc(Eng) CEng MIGasE* 300482
Simpson J T F *TD BSc MICE* 030682
Webster S *TD BSc* 010782
Wilson S J T 010982
Manley J R 100982
Lewis D W *TD* 130982
Pickles R 250982
Dodman J W *TD■ BSc MICE MIStructE* 011082
Chegwidden G *TD MSc MICE MIWES* 011182
Wells I J *TD MA MSc* 141182
O'Ballance M *TD MA* 010283
¶Nye A E 230383
Marsh G R *TD BEng MICE MIHT MBIM ACIArb* 010483
Masterman M *TD BA BSc CEng MICE* 010483
Holden J C *TD* 010683
Murray I S *TD■ BA MIL* 010883
Burgess D R *BSc CEng MIMechE* 010983
Stringer C *BSc MIPlantE* 010983
Hopkins J L *BSc(Eng) CEng MICE* C 031083
Kirkwood S C *TEng(CEI) MIPlantE FSCET* 091083
Lloyd D F *TD BSc* 081283
Scott D *TD BSc AMIQ* 010284
McNair I J *TD BSc FGS CEng MICE* 100284
Kingsford M F *TD FRICS LIOB FIH* 130284
Proud I P S *TD■ MA* 150284
Underwood I D *BSc* 160284
Jones P D *TD CEng MIStructE* 010484
Vest A V *FRICS ACIArb* 010484
Paynter W G *TD■ ARICS* 120484
¶Huggett S *MBIM* 020584
Holt N A C *BArch DipTP DipArchCons ARIBA MRTPI* 060584
Hall C J *TD MA FCA* 010684
Boult J D L *TD BSc ARICS* 031084
Miller P A 021184
Mason J A *BSc(Hons) MSc PhD CEng MINucE CPhysMInstP DIC CPhys* 111184
Sowerby A P *DMS MCIOB* 161284
Greenwood N D *BSc* 171284
Tear B 171284

Territorial Army, Corps of Royal Engineers — continued

Lain P B BSc PhD CEng AMInstF 010485
Feketey P A TD BSc MICE MIMunE 010585
Benson D TD 010685
Baggs M J TD CEng MICE MIMunE 010386
Ferrier A G TD■■ 050486
McMahon W D J TD ARICS 130486

Captains

Reid R C T TD■ FInstPet (A/Maj 010685) 170967
Klewin L M TD■■ 011167
Davies G S TD■ BSc DMS MICE MIHT MBIM 011268
Rodger D C TD■■ ARTCS CEng MIMechE AMIISO (Bt/Maj 010778) 070169
Rawlinson J C TD■ MCIOB MIPHE (A/Maj 010385) 280769
Amy R F MBA FBIM (A/Maj 010483) 301070
Austin E E TD 040272
Marshall D L BA DMS MBIM MRSH 240573
Goodall G R BA MSc 011173
Sawyer J H TD ARICS 070474
Caldwell-Nichols C J TD MA PhD CEng MIEE 200974
Boult P D TD 051074
Gallagher M H 280675
Cairns A J 310875
Macfarlane G R TD 010975
Wilkie J M BSc CEng MICE 221175
Cook S C TD 010376
Rigby C S MBE TD BEd MBIM LRSC ACP (A/Maj 010183) 070376
Peck C J TD BSc(Eng) MICE MIWES 010476
Clunie K E FRICS 010576
Woodford-Brown D J 190676
McGregor T 011176
¶Mellett B A E MISM 131176
Snowden D J S TD 201276
Hodgson G W TD TEng(CEI) MIHT FHTTA 180477
Oldfield B 010977
Chown D A BSc 240977
Pulley J A TD BSc(Eng) CEng MIMechE 011177
¶Whittaker R 070178
Cheetham S TD BSc (A/Maj 101084) 150378
Burkill P J TD ARICS AFAS 010478
Parker N M BEng 010478
Waters H (A/Maj 190684) 070678
Lain A W CEng MIMechE AMRAeS 010978
¶Wright H A 111278
Crawford I F BSc CEng MIERE (A/Maj 010485) 190379
Brookes E J N BA(Hons) MA CEng MIMechE 010479
Waters D I TD FIPM 010479
¶Godsmark R J 070679
Kermack J A BSc(Eng) 220679
¶Carnie A M 050879
Turner A R TD BEng MSc CEng MICE 200879
Long M G BSc CEng MICE (A/Maj 010186) 010180
Chesney G C (A/Maj 011285) 240180
Gay P A BSc 050280
Hawthorne J C TD TEng(CEI) FSCET 010380
Barr R D BSc 060380
Brownlie D K TD FBIM MInstAM MInstM 010480
Maley E M BSc(Eng) MBA MIMechE 010480
Schofield D R B LIOB 010580
Evans D W MA MBA 010780
¶Pickering J MISM 250880
Sutherland J G M BSc(Eng) CEng MICE MIMunE MIHT (A/Maj 010884) 090980
¶Banks A J 021080
Anslow A C 141280
Parkinson A P BSc 151280
Smyth B R BA 020181
¶Jury R 020281
Byrne V J BSc 010381
Billings A D 280381
¶Batty B 060581
Jones P D BTech 110581
¶Moore D 100681
Irvine T D TD (A/Maj 011285) 140681
James D F (A/Maj 010384) 190681
Carter J H B TD 270681
¶Gailey I B TD■ sq(v) 010781
Ward I (A/Maj 150386) 010781
Barker W R BSc MICE 011181
Cartwright J D C 181181
Hollerhead P TEng(CEI) 010182
Smith D S 010182
Jack N B S BA 010282
Paisley J I BA 010282
Gardiner C A BSc 100282
Price A C R MA CEng MICE 080382
Cashyap M M BSc 010482
Peace G A P MSc FGS 010482
Penn C R MA PhD 010482
Pallister J FRICS 170482
Metcalfe S BSc(Eng) 210482
Mellor R J 010582
Gowen S 010982
Purvis E J BSc 010982
Nevill W E P BAcc 011082
¶Philpot R L S 011082
Brennan J F 121082
Macandrews T J J ACA 011182
Cordon J S 021182
Eames R J BA MSc 121282
Mumford A M 020283
Smith A M MIPHE 030283
Brown R H BSc MICE MCIT AFPWI CDipAF 010483
Davis J A S BSc AIB 010483
French D J AIDPM 010483
Kramer N A BA 010483
Moodie D R BSc AMIMechE 010483
Richardson R A 020783
Sargeant D R AIB 020783
¶Scott J B 060783
Brown P K 120783
Murfin R W 150883
Hunter B T 160883
Glass W J 010184
¶Prestwood J TD■ BSc CEng MIMechE 030184
Morrison T M 010284
Stewart J S 010284
Skilbeck A K 220284
Crossland I B 010484
Harvey N J BSc 010484
Jones J N S BSc MICE MIStructE MIWES MIPHE 010484
¶Veck R E MBE MBIM MISM 080484
Reid J V S 100484
Lavender D J MA (A/Maj 160684) 150684
Robinson R J S 190684
Rice S 070984
Catterall S E BSc 150984
Weir S C BSc(Eng) 280984
Coughlan J P 011084
Carlisle R W 011184
Lee C J 011184
Thomson R D 011184
¶Nicholls J 201184
¶Fairbairn G 211284
¶Williams W F 030185
¶Ashurst H E MInstAM 060285
Carruthers D R BSc MEng 010485
Jones A F J TEng(CEI) MITE MIEEE 010485
Englishby C J 250585
Lee C A 250585
Oliver G J H BSc PhD FGS 010685
¶Allison K 080685
¶Curtis F G 030785
¶Bennett D M 130885
¶Downey G P 020985
Fairclough D 110985
¶Hambrook S D GM 021285
¶Reilly G T 161285
Hamilton R A 010186
Bridges J M BSc 010286
Lockyer J E B 010286
Mann G C MChS 010286
Shacklock N A BSc 010286
Anderson E G 010386
Larcombe R J 010386
Scott A G 010386

Lieutenants

Arkle A
Arthur M A MICE MIMunE
Farr D
Rice S
Sumpter J A
Edeleanu H R BEng MA (A/Capt 070181) 070576
†Oliver S M BSc 071076
Dodds R A BSc 210277
Halsey A N 120977
Rivers J C M MA MICE 170278
Moore M W BSc (A/Capt 010785) 110179
Huxtable B (A/Capt 011184) 260179
Rigby S G 060879
Hodgson C W BSc(Eng) (A/Capt 010284) 220280
Taylor I D (A/Capt 010382) 020480
Sharp A M BSc (A/Capt 010985) 200480
Barker R J 250480
Peart M BSc 130880
Greer J M 171280
Macleod J A 040281
Harrison M T (A/Capt 010985) 280281
Thompson P A BEng 080381
Facchini M A 250381
†Hickman S J 250381
Creighton M A BSc 200781
Robinson D 011081
Harvey B P 051081
Ringshaw T J 071081
Court W J 251181
Taylor S D 011281
Chambers C N 071281
Carson N W L 270182
Griffiths D S BA 030382
Mason P N 280482
Anderson W G 250582

Mayer D 250582
Mitchell J A 070682
Robinson T M *BA* 090682
Murphy S J 011082
Howie E M *BSc(Hons)* 071082
Rogers C W *BA* 131082
Kirkdale B G 271082
de la Fuente C *BSc* 101182
Gurney D N 161182
Butcher J M 120183
Dye G R
(*A/Capt* 130183) 120183
Wilkinson K *BSc(For) MSc* 180383
Smith J W G 110483
Hudson M
(*A/Maj* 120483) 120483
Horner M R 080883
Waddell C Q O 080883
McAlinden B P 130983
Cooper C M *BSc(Eng) MIMINE ARSM* 251083
McGill D W 251083
Parker-Smith H M E 261083
Wilson A S *BSc* 261083
McCarron B L *BSc* 011183
Hawkins C A
(*A/Maj* 171183) 171183
Bates P R 241183
Jones S A
(*A/Capt* 071283) 071283
Birkett-Wendes J H 200184
Stewart I R *BSc(For)* 220184
Munro A R L
(*A/Capt* 010484) 090484
Heyes T P O 240584
Camp M C 020684
Saunders M J *BA* 250684
Devlin J 070884
Glaister G W 070884
Smith L M 070884
Squibb S M 070884
Stevenson G J 070884
Angus M J *BSc*
(*A/Capt* 141184) 131184
Wilks M D *BSc* 151184
Farthing S J 211184
Thomas P D 211184
Robinson M C 230185
Craven N R 030285
White P J *BA RIBA*
(*A/Maj* 100485) 100485
Walker R G 130585
Howie C R 220585
Teeling M P 220585
Greenshields T H 230585
MacGregor R C A 230585
Rosenbaum M S *BSc DIC ARSM PhD FRGS FGS CEng MIMM* 120685
Liddell R A 310785
Moxon P 310785
Watson H N 290885
Bland G
(*A/Capt* 060985) 060985
Rawcliffe S A
(*A/Maj* 170985) 170985
Campbell A 151085
Hoolihan D 151085
Merrick D 151085
Russell J F 151085
Sawyer W J 151085
Emsley M D 211185
Goodhew T *BSc(Hons)* 211185
Ogden M G 211185
Underwood M V 211185
Webster I 211185
Whalley A G 211185
O'Coy A D 220186
Redgate T C W 220186
Roylance C J 010486

2nd Lieutenants

†Larmett E F *MIAS MIBCO* 271153
†Geere R G *BSc* 271078
†Salmon A J 310180
†Manson G E *BEng* 270782
†Foster M S *MA PhD* 131082
†Wild P D 120683
Bennett R D C 221183
†Shore S J 150584
Eaton J C 200584
Henry J G 200584
Ogston P 200584
Rabone P S 200584
Rhodes K M 200584
Shepherd D J 200584
Williams T C 200584
Wilshin D C 200584
†Young W G M 200584
†Topping P B 240584
†Maclean H D *BSc* 310584
Best K 100684
Briggs P W *BEng* 100684
Cairns R *BSc* 100684
Coe P W 100684
Davidson I C 100684
Jenns C A 100684
Nell P G R
(*A/Capt* 110685) 100684
Smith D J 100684
Elvidge R D 120784
†Clapham N H 290784
Cosgrove G B *BSc* 290784
†Gramaglia S 290784
†Plews R L 290784
†Smith C C 290784
†Willmott E P 290784
†Queen G T 301084
Bailey I G 181184
†Broomhead S C 181184
†Lakin C V 261184
Stewart J D 140185
Holland R T 270185
Mauer P J 270185
Murphy D P 270185
Ritchie D 270185
Thompson J M 270185
†Topliss A 270185
Pegg A M 150285
†Moult J *BSc* 250585
†Cox R F *BSc(Hons)* 260585
†Walker H 160685
†Webb L E S 160685
†Collins R W M 070785
†Johnson I A E 070785
†McLean A J *BSc(Hons)* 070785
†Peters S C 070785
†Tate R H *MA* 070785
†Webster R A 070785
†Baines M L 280785
†Illingworth M A 280785
†Spreull J L 280785
†Gavin J J 210985
†Maybin F J 031085
†Kay M G *BSc(Hons)* 011285
†Marris J *BSc(Hons) MICE ACIArb* 011285
†McGlen S D 011285
†Rogers P S 011285
†McGrath K W 100186

Quartermasters

Adams D *TD* 041271
Maj 181079
Raybould I R 180376
Maj 040983
Brown W J 010476
Maj 111083
Campbell S C *Capt* 270477
McKenna K G 140478
Maj 100285
Tepper R E *FISM FInstSM MIP* 201278
Maj 130984
Bailey K G *BEM* *Capt* 010680
Hawkins-Brown A B *Capt* 010680
Anderson N A D *Capt* 041080
Wood T H *AMIRTE* *Capt* 130481
Bernard M *MISM MIEEE* *Capt* 210481
Burrows J H *Capt* 140781
Morrow R B *Capt* 270781
Blades G P *Capt* 120182
Jones N C *Capt* 140182
Smith D *Capt* 230182
Hawkins D R *Capt* 100282
Procter M J *Capt* 110282
Piper B R *Capt* 210782
Final W T *Capt* 010183
Wood J *Capt* 070283
Erskine E *Capt* 070383
Benson H *Capt* 230383
Schofield R *Capt* 110583
¶Davis R E J *BEM* *Maj* 310583
Heal M S *MIPlantE* *Capt* 030683
Murray M M *Capt* 040683
Morrison W J N *Capt* 010983
Hobley R A *Capt* 050983
Lowbridge E *Capt* 140983
Sharman D L *Capt* 051183
Sharman L P *Capt* 051183
(*A/Maj* 051183)
Snelgrove R *Capt* 051183
(*A/Maj* 051183)
Watts W D F *Capt* 051183
Edwards V *Capt* 071283
Wheal K A *Capt* 221283
Howle L *Capt* 080184
Donnelly A G *Capt* 190484
Robertson M R *Capt* 190484
Dodd G A *LIOB* *Capt* 020584
Forshaw W J *Capt* 010784
Robinson K E *Capt* 010884
Couch B M *Capt* 070984
Greenwood J *Capt* 231184
Barker M J A *TEng(CEI)* *Capt* 150285
Middlemass J B *Capt* 160285
Binning A H *AIIM* *Capt* 190385
Godfrey D M *Capt* 030485
Marchant A T *Capt* 100485
Russell R T *MISM* *Capt* 220585
Cook A D *Capt* 281185
¶Lloyd L A *Capt* 010486
Lucas J *Capt* 030486

POSTAL AND COURIER SECTION

Hon Colonel..........Maj J H B Cantley..........270485

Colonels

Mackay J W *TD*▪ *MA* 010583

Lieutenant Colonels

Whittall D E L *TD*▪ 011176
Gratwicke E M *MBIM* 010483
Hawley M *TD*▪ 010483
Pain D A *TD*▪ *MBCS* 010483
Cockburn W *TD*▪ *CDipAF* 010484

Majors

Johnston R M *BA MSc FIPM MBIM* im 220572
Wiltshire A D *TD*▪ 010476
King R V *TD*▪ *MInstM* 210576
Elmy S G *TD*▪ 120676
Disney R *TD* 151176
Pawson C C M *TD* 120177
Brown A M *TD* 010477
Morrow E M *TD* 110777
Fitton J A F *TD* 010479
Griffiths W K *TD* 210579
Barker J K *TD* 010481
Rosser R A *TD* 010481
Clatworthy R E *TD BA* 180182
Wharrier H *TD* 010482
Fish S M *TD BA* 190482
Campbell J *TD MBCS* 010483
Forrester P F *TD* 010483
Gill R F *TD* 010483
Doe J C *TD* 010484
Jayes M S *TD AIPM* 010484
Brewer N *MA* 010784
Baker C *TD MBCS* 010485
Cruickshank J I *TD* 010485

Captains

Logan D E *TD* 010473
Evans K R G 300775
Haworth G M *TD* 010476
Cheal V R *TD* 010477
Frost T D *TD BSc* 010477
Woods D *TD* 011277
Ferry D J *TD* 140378
Bintliff J M *MA* 010479
Evans B J 010479
Fisher K T 010479
Mulligan W J 010479
Woodland N *BSc* 010479
Reid D T 010480
Tracey G K 010480
Howett F A R *FRICS FIQS ACIArb* 010481
Whittaker J F 010481
Zaczek M P 010481
Manning G R 240182
Snart R D 010482
Hunt A R *BA* 010483
Nosowski G M *MA MSc* 010483
Blake K H 010484
Hignett A R *BA* 010484
Jack A 010484
Perriton D G 010484
Shanks G J 010484
Seabourne M *MInstAM MISM MIWO* 010485
Tiffin J B 010485
Gisby J D E 010486
Inman D T 010486
Madeley A S 010486
Weller M A 010486

Lieutenants

Doyle D J P 220783
Norman A D 220783
Peters N J *BA* 150484
Norman M J 050584
Billinghurst B J 101184
Collis M F *BA DMS MBIM* 101184
Marsden C 071284
Wilmowski W P 240185
Domican J A *BA* 100685
Lundberg P F 250785
Deeney J E 200186
Prout J H 220286
Atkinson R S *DMS* 160386
Pollard G A 160486

2nd Lieutenants

Roberts P J S 070185

ENGINEER AND TRANSPORT STAFF CORPS

Costain House, Nicholsons Walk, Maidenhead, Berks, SL6 1LN

Hon Colonel..........Maj Gen M E Tickell *CBE MC* ret pay..........230783

In Command

Wyatt C T *BSc(Eng) FICE FIStructE* 010586

Colonels

Freeman *Sir* Ralph *CVO CBE MA FICE FCIT* 160263
Coode D C *CBE FICE* 170669
Laing *Sir* Kirby *JP DL MA FICE* 170571
Bonham-Carter J *CVO DSO OBE ERD* 120971
Robson A E *OBE FIMechE FCIT* 250972
Turner S *FCIT* 120973
Jones S *CBE PhD BSc(Eng) FIEE FIMechE* 021073
Harris *Sir* Alan *CBE BSc(Eng) FICE* 291173
Campbell I M *CVO BSc FICE* 010874
Williams J T *OBE BSc FICE* 040276
Stringer D A *OBE FCIT* 170276
Lunch E P J *CBE VRD FCA FCIT* 120576
Lisle P R *OBE FICE* 200676
Stanbury J F *FICE* 120178
Bowick D M *CBE FCIT MBIM* 301178
Oakley H R *CBE MSc FICE* 150480
Reed E C *OBE DFC FICE FBIM* 301080
Cox P A *BSc FICE* 090781
Maxwell W W *MA FIMechE FIEE* 220781
Wyatt C T *BSc(Eng) FICE FIStructE* 091084
Gardiner I D *BSc(Eng) FIMechE FIEE (Hon Col RCT(TA))* 111184
Purbrick M C *BSc FICE* 181184
Oakes J S *MA FIMechE FIEE* 180385
Dale K W *OBE TD FCIBS FInstF* 140186
Haseldine J M *MA FICE MIMechE* 140186
Yuill W G *BSc FIMM* 140186

Lieutenant Colonels

Harrington J L *OBE* 150856
Hearn S G *CVO OBE FCIT* 150856
Granter E *BSc FICE* 250257
Cantrell A H *OBE ERD BSc FICE* 180965
Miller T C B *MBE FIMechE* 140269
New D H *ERD BSc FICE FIMechE* 211069
Dytch A K *FIMechE* 010172
McMurdo A W *MBE ERD BSc FICE* 010172
Reynolds W O *OBE FCIT* 090172
Tyler J F H *BSc FIEE* 070573
Triggs R L *BSc(Eng) FICE* 010874
Gillespie J H H *OBE BSc FICE* 010775
Ordman N N B *BSc FICE* 040276
Scott K F *MC FICE* 170276
Binnie D S *OBE* 200676
Daniels R A *MC* 130478
Lefeaux J M *MIMechE FBIM* 020979
Little A L *BSc(Eng) FICE FIStructE* 261079
Chastell L E *MIMechE* 301080
Jackson H W *MIMechE* 061280
Stein J M *BSc FICE* 020181
Austin W T F *BSc FICE FIStructE* 090781
Williams G *OBE MA FGS FInstPet* 220781
Drew E A *OBE BSc FICE FIWE* 200881
Bartlett J V *CBE MA FEng FICE FIE AUST* 210782
Pugh A T 070882
Green D J *FIMechE FInstPet* 130183
Taberner J P *MA FICE FIHE* 160183
Hobden S C L *TD ERD MICE MIHE* 110184
Addyman O T *TD FICE FIWES* 091084
Taylor K *OBE FIMechE FIEE* 091084
Weeks R J *BSc(Eng) FIEE FIMechE* 091084
Soane L J *OBE MICE* 111184
Hall A P *TD FICE FCIOB* 181184
Lee D J *BSc FICE FIStructE* 181184
Hogbin W *MA FICE* 010185
Loten A W *CB MIMechE FCIBS* 180185
Currie D S *FICE MIMechE* 020285
Owens P G T *BA FCIBS* 180385
Bond R H *MA FIMechE* 140186
Casey M V *BSc FIMechE* 140186
Lawrence L S *FIEE* 140186
O'Brien J J 140186

Majors

Edwards R H *ERD FICE* 050956
Townsend C E C *TD BSc(Eng) FICE* 250166
Matthewson-Dick T *FIMechE FIEE* 290966
Emerson A H *FIMechE FIEE* 020168
Cuthbert E W *OBE MSc FICE* 150174
Knowles A E *MBE MIGasE* 090774
Manson J B *BSc(Eng) FICE* 170775
Martin P L *CBE FIMechE FInstF* 120178
Smith S F *MA FIMechE* 010478
Shepherd G T *CBE BSc FIMechE FIEE* 190779
Dunford G I *MRAeS MRIN* 070380
Jones D *BSc FICE FCIT* 150480
Francis H W A *CBE FEng FICE* 011182
Barwell D R M *FIMarE FRINA* 250483
Quarmby D A *MA PhD FCIT* 100583
Kirby D D *MA FCIT* 030883
Deuce T L G *FEng FICE FIHE* 090883
Slater R J *BSc FICE FIWES* 160983
Hennessy J R *MA FICE FIWES* 010284
Spokes F K *MRAeS* 270384
Sage R J *TD MIMechE* 040484
Moir A H M *FIMechE FCIB* 170884
Pygall G F P *FCIT FWRI* 220884
Japes M D *FICE MIWES* 120984
Osborne A *BSc* 120984
Douglas R H R *BSc FICE* 021184
Sallitt T W B 061184
Edwards R J G *BSc MSc MICE FGS* 081184
Rothwell R W *MA FICE* 121184
Whitehead G O *BSc MICE* 151184
Cameron J C *MICE FCIT* 190885
Lace J H 270885
Stoner R F *BSc FICE* 270885
Gurney T J R *MA MICE* 280885
Everett P *BSc* 290885
Brown P A *BSc FICE FIStructE* 060985
Paterson A C *BSc FICE FIMechE FIStructE* 291085
Holleywood J *FICE FCIT* 191185

ROYAL CORPS OF SIGNALS

Hon Colonels		
	Lt Col (Bt Col) *Sir* John Wills *Bt TD JP*	130575
	Col M B Haycock *TD DL*	010280
	Capt M C Stanley *MBE*	040281
	Col R M Stewart *OBE TD DL*	230381
	Maj (Bt Lt Col) P R H Dixon *TD*	010481
	Col J A D Francis ret pay	080981
	Lt (Hon Capt) J E Wilson *OBE*	160382
	Maj Gen *Sir* Roy Redgrave *KBE MC* ret pay	010483
	Col D J MacIntyre ret pay	010483
	Capt N F Althaus	080783
	Capt (Hon Capt) P F Orchard *CBE*	311283
	Brig N A Butler *CBE* ret pay	010485
	Col M H Seys-Phillips *TD DL*	200785

Colonels

Eversfield J C *ERD*■ *TD* 011076
Craig J M *TD DL* 111278
¶Brown K D *OBE TD ADC DL* 011279
Greenhill J *TD*■■ *MBIM* sq(v) 011180
Jolliffe P F *TD*■■ *MPS* 010781
Hawksworth A H *TD*■■ *ADC MA MIPM* 010482
Illingworth A W *TD*■ *MIPM MBIM MInstAM MMS JP* 010483
Casstles D S *TD*■■ *ADC MA MIMC RGN DL* 011083
Thompson P R H *OBE TD*■ 011283
Myhill R P *OBE TD*■ *MIERE* 281085

Lieutenant Colonels

Petrie A S *TD*■■ *MITO* 100976
Mather P J *TD*■■ *MBCS AIB* sq(v) 201179
Allan W I M *TD*■■ 131080
Titterington R G *TD*■ *BEng CEng AMIEE MIERE* 201182
Upson M V *TD*■■ *MA MSc* 020283
Henwood P N *TD*■ *BA MEd* 010484
Mitchell G C *TD MA DPhil* 231184
Cunningham A C *TD*■ *BSc(Eng) CEng MIEE* 011284
Gale C D *TD*■ *MA DMS CEng MIMarE* 231185
Stenning C P *TD* 161285

Majors

Hall G C *TD*■■■ *BSc* 020864
Showell R G D *TD*■ *CEng MIMechE MIProdE* sq(v) 011171
Bedford J F *TD AIB* sq(v) 011271
Webster J *TD*■■ *MSc MIISM FITD* 011271
Branch M F *TD BEng* 010472
McCulloch I C *TD* 011172
Motteram B M *TD* 011172
Sutherland E R McG *TD*■■ 301172
Sharp M P *TD*■■ 010573
Groves A P *TD*■ *BSc MScTech* 010773
Grove J A R *TD BA* 011173
Baldwin J D *TD*■■ 010774
Jenkins M L *TD*■■ *AMIEE* 010874
Allmond M M *TD*■ *BA MIPM FHCIMA* 011074
Thorpe D J *TD*■ *MA* 011174
Vokes M G *TD*■■ 071174
Squance E H *TD BSc(Agr) PhD* 010175
Harrison G W *TD FCIS* 050175
Atkinson R B *TD*■ 010475
Rowe B H *MBIM ACII* sq 120475
Lamb D A A *TD BSc AMIEE MIERE* 010975
Harvey N R *TD*■ *AIB* sq(v) 011175
Hallchurch T T *MBE* 260276
Hedgecoe R 160376
Scott J A H *TD* 010476
Stevens J R *TD BA* 010476
Byrom C E 160676
Goulding K G *MBIM* 310776
Reynolds-Jones C *TD*■■ 011076
Broomhead R A *TD*■ *MA* 121176
Davies D M *TD*■■ 011276
Harvey K R J *TD*■ 010177
Paden R S *TD MA PhD* 010177
Rhynas J W 010177
Sutherland A K *TD*■ 010177
Collins A S *TD* 010477
Geddes N *TD* 031077
Douglas J A K *TD MA CEng MIEE* 241077
Sutherland P *TD BSc CEng MIEE* 241077
John D L R *TD* 011177
Leech A C *TD* 011177
Webber C B J *TD* 091277
Grocott D J *TD MA* 010178
Foxon B N T *TD*■ 080178
Sexton M E *TD* 010478
Barnes R E 010678
Smith D L *TD*■ *MA* 140778
Milne W D *TD* 041078
Bailey *The Hon* C R *BA* 240279
Chrystie I L *TD BSc PhD* 010379
Gibson A 010479
Ivison J B *TD*■ *DMS* 160579
Darrah B E 010679
Whittle P D *TD* 010879
Hardy D G *TD* 300979
Hatfield T M *TD* 011079
Pinkerton J W D *TD* 011179
Bodycombe D A *TD*■ *ACIS MInstAM MMS* 021179
Scholes R T *TD* 010180
Mackenzie F S *BSc(Eng)* 090280
Wright M W R *TD MIERE MITE* 310380
Clarke-Lomas H R E *TD*■■ *MInstM* 130580
Johnson B J 010680
Giles G W 121080
Verey A P *TD* 151080
Oxford P S *TD* 021280
Flint A M *TD*■ *LCSI* 010181
Haysom R N *TD* 010281
Phillips T J *BA MEd DipEd* 010281
Renecle P N *TD* 010281
Henderson I G *TD BSc MSc(Econ)* 310381
Clark C J B *TD* 010481
Keane J W W *TD*■ 010481
Williams R *TD*■ 220581
Morris W G *TD BSc* 190681
McLay D *TD* 130781
Cobbold I A *TD BSc(Eng)* 280781
Wing D B *TD BSc* 020881
Allan J C *TD*■ *BSc* 011081
Bosley M J *TD BTech PhD* 011281
Burgess J E *TD* 230382
Hill R V *TD MInstAM* 300482
McNaught R M G *TD* 010582
Taylor B V *MA* 010582
Heath R S 050782
Mill J D G *TD CA* 150982
Lea T E *TD* 011082
Tebbutt D L 011082
Smith D E 261082
Cartwright S J *TD* 011282
Duxbury R P G *TD* 010183
Arkless P D *TD* 010283
Bartlett D *BEd* 130683
Acda P W 010783
Fisher I M *TD LLB* 010783
Laurence C J *TD*■ *BVSc* 010783
Bland C G *TD MA* 170983
Mote C C *MRO* 191083
Ives R R *TD BSc* 141183
Kirkham F G *TD BEd* 180384
Kerr D *TD LLB* 010484
Thomson I H *TD BSc* 010484
Stafford P *TD BA MEd* 030484
Touchin M G *TD MA* 211084
Hartill R F *TD* 011284
Skipper M C *TD* 010185
¶MacHeath R A 120185
Barnes W A *MISM MASMC* 210285
¶Kinkead H R *TD* 210385
Luing M A *TD BA* 010485
James J T 010985
McConnell D C *TD* 130985
Armstrong A I 121185
Frost S H *BA ACA* 011285
Benbow A J *TD* 010186
Maude A A *TD BSc* 160186
Carter R J 010286
Watson J P *TD* 010486

Captains

Oates A K *TD*■ *BA* 010462
Jewell A J T *TD*■ 011067
Boocock T W *TD*■ 010469
Dennis C J P *TD*■ 010569
Adams T *TD* 210969
¶Johnson C G 111269
Walsh P J 310170
¶Hall T E 260470
Cree D J *TD*■ *BSc(Eng) CEng MIEE* 010671
Insley J H (*A/Maj* 310385) 070971
¶Mully D P 200372
Crothers J H *TD MA* 010673
¶Esson R 200973
Malone W J *TD MIWSP* 010175

Mainwaring-Taylor J E *TD BA* 010375
Cresswell J 010575
¶Nicholas D *MISM* 190675
Cansfield P *TD* 010875
Widgery E F *TD* 011275
Smith C J 270176
Keith E J B *TD BSc(Eng) AMIEE* 010476
¶Thompson R P 300676
Lucas M J *TD BSc GRADIM* 011176
Simpson J *TD BSc* 011176
Woodhead P A *TD BSc(Eng) CEng MICE* 010177
McMahon M D 170577
Dohoo J E *TD BSc CEng MIMechE AIIM* 250677
Forster J P W *TD* (*A/Maj* 020685) 270877
¶Hatton J B 010977
Gransbury R C *TD AIB* (*A/Maj* 140185) 030977
MacLeod J B M 041077
¶Esson J A *MBE* 020178
Geake J H *TD MA MBA* 220178
Buston R *TD LLB MBIM* 010378
¶Filder E S 060378
Lechmere J M C *BSc(Eng)* 010578
Davis R E C *BSc FSMC FBOA* (*A/Maj* 161282) 010678
¶Garratt J R *MBIM* 070878
Eskell C L *TD LLB* 010978
Hill C J *BA* 180978
Matthews W J *TD BSc* 011078
¶Naismith W J A 260179
Zaremba-Tymieniecki M W 260179
McConnell R A *TD BSc(Eng) ACGI CEng MIChemE* 010479
Derrick B W 010679
Majury S F *BSc* 010679
Puddy I G *BSc GRADIMA* 310779
Murray I J B *BSc(Eng)* 070879
Trayers D *TD* 200879
Bruce-Smith K J *BA* 260979
Foakes S P *TD AIB* 011079
Heathfield B J *TD* 011079
Turner A A *TD BEng MICE* 311079
Walker P R *TD* (*A/Maj* 010385) 011179
¶Meyer R C 041279
Jones R A *MISM* 080380
Wilkinson R A *TD* 100380
Payne G *AMIEE* 010580
Etherton D J 270580
Deighton M *TD BSc PhD MRSC* 010780
Harrison B *TD* 010780
Briant A M *AIIM LRSC* 010381
Piper J W 050381
¶Tidey P D 240381
Langan J *TD* 020481
¶Smithard R E 030481
May R N 010581
Stewart M T H *TD* 010581
¶Roy D S *AMISM AMITD* 010881
¶Burns A *MASMC* 010981
Harris R C 010981
Slaughter C 010981
Clifford R V *TD* 090981
¶Bell A H 011081
Berncastle A *BA* 011081
McKeown D F *BSc FRSA CEng MIEE MIRSE* 011081
Rhodes A P 011081
Lapsley A C C (*A/Maj* 011084) 011181
Blake D M A *LLB* 031181
¶Carney B M 031181
Clough D R *BSc* 181181
¶Hill A R 211181
Quayle S 010282
O'Beirne M J 200582
Jepson F 010682
Wells I *BSc* 170682
Harvey S G *BD* 010782
Fleming G R 010882
Ramsay B 130882
Ludlow R N *BA* 280882
Dunlop A J *MA PhD* 180982
Parkes N G *BEng* 011182
Anson D J 261282
Cummings C *BSc* 010183
Kennedy B S *TD BSc* 010183
¶Webb C S 060483
Cornish A J *BSc* 010583
Redrup P B *BA* 010583
McKee J K *BSc* 050583
Davison M F L 010783
¶Henry D *MISM* 230783
Keleher N M *BSc(Eng)* 010883
¶Shakespeare D 160883
Denning N H *MA* 250883
Hinson L P 100983
Barber J R 011083
¶Lemon J M 031083
¶Upstone H W 301083
¶Hawley G T *MISM MIMH* 021183
¶Kay R W 161183
King A R *BSc* 010184
¶Bradbury M E 170184
Hunt R *TD* 010284
MacGillivray A C W 160284
Hewer D J 180384
Woods W J 290484
Beacom N C 010584
Jack S 010584
Robson S W *AIB* 010584
¶Salmon N H 030584
Davenport R 010684
Leviseur N T *MA* 270684
¶Bonner G G *TEng(CEI) AMIRTE* 020784
White D B *BA* 130784
¶Radford J 170884
Baxter G D 011084
Ellison R J *BEd* 011084
¶Derrick K P 191084
¶McMorris W C 011284
Webber I J *BA* 011284
Adams A E C 010185
¶Handley J G 070485
Kyle I H 220485
¶Devine G F 200585
Deaves N W 010685
Fickling K J *BSc CEng MIEE CDipAF* 010685
Penfold P F 010685
¶Hawkesford D R 010885
Mitchell P S 010885
Ruske J W 141185
Hamilton J G 011285

Lieutenants

Stobo A J *LLB* (*A/Capt* 010486) 110478
Cull J P W *BSc* (*A/Capt* 010283) 110678
Cummins M A *ARICS* 101079
Townsend N D 110280
Crackett J *BA* 120680
Brown W D L *MSc* 241080
Mackesy W P 191180
Wilkinson R K (*A/Capt* 170883) 150181
Fidler C C I (*A/Capt* 181085) 130381
Moore P W *BA* 010581
Clarke S J 050681
Tucker D L 140681
Lane W G *BSc(Eng) AMIEE* (*A/Capt* 010486) 190681
Spencer A *BSc* 190681
Reeve P H 011081
Ahmed S *BSc ARICS* (*A/Capt* 160284) 171081
Welsh-Harding P J M 211081
Whitworth C J E 231181
Miles G 050182
Bretton M J *BSc(Econ) MBA MIEx(GRAD)* 230282
Hill R N 060482
Geddes J F 010582
Ball R S 250582
Harvey D A (*A/Capt* 060186) 250582
Potter S J 180682
Stuart C A 011082
Swithenbank S *BSc PGCE* (*A/Capt* 010985) 011082
Morant N D 111082
Morrison G G *BA BA(Hons)* 171082
Jones M K *BSc* 021182
Bannigan P A 161182
Sampson W S 161182
Lenanton J P 191182
Thomas N A 070683
Crowther J M 150683
Kingston R D 120783
Irvine J *BSc* 081083
Keogh T W 011283
Grindrod A M 010184
Jones H E 260184
Donald C *BSc* 280284
Manifold R H 090484
Wright P D *BSc* 090484
Dyball C W 280484
Evans M D *BSc* 260584
Harty P H 040884
Abell J F *BSc* 051184
Atkinson M G P 141184
Dudley A G (*A/Capt* 200685) 211184
Wreford-Brown G C 211184
Mehta P 020385
Cummings M O 220385
Hills R E 010485
Barron W A 220585
Fathers P C (*A/Capt* 181085) 220585
Gilfether B P 220585
Green M *ASVA* 220585
Hannam D A 220585
Hornsby G S 220585
Scott R J 230585
Bryan G M *BSc* 120685
Hammal R 060785
Posnett A 271085
Fern J 151185
Blagden S P 211185
Hill P A 211185
Thompson N S *BSc AMIEE* 211185
Hall I T 220186
Lambton J A 220186
Tomlinson J H 220186

2nd Lieutenants

†Sawyer R S H 090682
†Bardell-Cox T A 241183
Blemings W J 200584
Bracey R H 200584
Rose A D 200584
Brown I D *BEng AMIEE* 250584
†Appleyard J P 100684
†Blewett W J 100684
Watson S 100684
Allen R J *BEng* 290784
†Brocklebank T J 290784

Territorial Army, Royal Corps of Signals — continued

Name	Rank	Date
Fallows J W		290784
Lavery K S		290784
Meikle C B		290784
Whittle A J		290784
Willmott P N		011084
Brown G P F		181184
Hassell P H		181184
Strachan I B		181184
†Cadman M		151284
Holder S M		270185
†Reid B		150585
†Luke S J *BA(Hons)*		260585
†Wooler P R		260585
†Sowerby B M		160685
†Brown R D		070785
†Given D T		070785
†Gregory J D		070785
†Kerr G M		070785
†Langley G E		070785
†Parsell R J *BSc*		070785
†Petty M D		070785
†Burns R G		280785
†Conlen M		280785
†Payne A R *BSc PGCE*		280785
†Stiles H C		130985
†Duggan J R S Q		210985
†Almond J M		011285
†Harrison E N		011285
†Mills S R		011285

Quartermasters

Name	Rank	Date
Miller R L *TD*		190570
	Maj	190582
Wilson F	*Capt*	281077
Gray P L	*Capt*	070679
Greenwood J B	*Capt*	170979
Knowles R W	*Capt*	290280
Mitchell J	*Capt*	011080
Hawkins D A *TD CEng MIERE*		
	Maj	280781
Haywood V L	*Capt*	160881
Dillon J	*Capt*	250582
Robson J	*Capt*	240782
Evans W F	*Capt*	010982
North H	*Capt*	280383
Muxworthy P	*Capt*	140483
Gallacher J S	*Capt*	110883
Skinner P J	*Capt*	160484
Lafferty A P	*Capt*	031085
Tinker G E	*Capt*	311085

Technical Officers in Telecommunications

Name	Rank	Date
Cottage S *MBE TD■■*		170759
	Maj	170771
Lovell A *TD■■*		180962
	Lt Col	270584
Fowler J T *TD*		260170
	Maj	260182
Ward F W		150770
	Maj	160782
Wall H J B *TD■■ JP*		131171
	Maj	131177
Toft R F *TD MIERE*		210372
	Maj	050983
Baxter D G W *TD MBIM MIIM*		
		150872
	Maj	150884
Roberts J W *TD BA CEng MIERE*		
		010475
	Maj	010481
Williams R F *TD*		240776
	Maj	090685
Knowles K J	*Capt*	200178
Treharne D G E	*Capt*	230578
Everett M E	*Capt*	310179
Hinds L W		010879
	Maj	120885
Burton P A	*Capt*	110980
Moorhouse C	*Capt*	010481
Watt D	*Capt*	090482
McGowan I	*Capt*	150384
Southall T G	*Capt*	020484
Fredericks P A	*Capt*	050784
Thomas I R *MSc*	*Capt*	271084
Lythgoe W J	*Capt*	010385

Traffic Officers

Name	Rank	Date
Bridgwood W A *TD■*		200761
	Maj	200773
Graham C S J *TD*		011063
	Lt Col	170985
Seymour B T *TD*		010466
	Lt Col	010184
Purkis R V *TD*		131071
	Maj	140480
Hughes R D *TD*		200972
	Maj	270481
Beckett D H *TD■■*		010274
	Maj	061075
Lott M C *TD*	*Capt*	180574
Moore R J		140974
	Maj	100385
Newell D A		070375
	Maj	140283
Lewer J A	*Capt*	270276
Back M R	*Capt*	141180
Fahey A	*Capt*	070182
Griffiths D	*Capt*	080783
Turner J A W	*Capt*	140184
Rigley D *MBIM*	*Capt*	190284
Findlay G	*Capt*	230684
Lingard J R	*Capt*	280885
Graham J B	*Capt*	051285

THE SCOTTISH DIVISION

52nd LOWLAND VOLUNTEERS

Upon a Saltire, thistle within a circulet inscribed *'MEMO ME IMPUNE LACESSIT'*

Regimental March

Quick March..Scotland the Brave

1st Battalion 52nd Lowland Volunteers

Hon Colonel..Col C H K Corsar *OBE TD JP* 301175

Majors

Turner W S *MC* psc 231076
Pearson G D *TD* nadc 010182
Gebbie J D 010183
Quar J N *TD LLB* 010684
Fisher D B 011084
Wright J P 011084
Grieve A G 010985

Captains

¶Aitken J 260177
D'Inverno J G 100382
Short G R *MA DipEd* 010682
¶Martin E 220883
¶Colclough A J 100983
¶McDonald J J M 170983
¶Rodger C J 041183
Stewart J A 010684
Munley A J *BSc PhD* 011084
Flemington J W R 010285
¶Skinner N M 010485

Lieutenants

Taylor M J *MA* 011183
Bell R W S 090484
Grant J 230584
Glancy D C *LLB* 310584
Lindsay R B *LLB DipLP* 040585
Milroy C J A 120685
Daisley A 011185

2nd Lieutenants

Tweed D J 200584
Wood J T 200584
Macdonald M 100684
Murray R M 100684
†Doyle R 260585
†Welsh A A 260585
†Lawrie G M 070785
†Carroll P J 280785

Quartermasters

Stewart G C *Capt* 010682

2nd Battalion 52nd Lowland Volunteers

Hon Colonel..Maj Gen *Sir* John Swinton *KCVO OBE DL* ret pay 220483

Majors

Percy W R V *TD*▪ *BCom MA* 040574
Hamilton S *TD MA CA* 011074
¶Wood D *MBE* 010375
Connell J D *TD* 240776
Tait J F G 010479
Corkerton D J P 020682
McDiarmid D W *TD BA* 280284
Young A W *TD* 280284

Captains

Corsar G K D 010482
Tait G M G *TD* 010682
¶McKeen R 190983
¶Jones J *MBE* 011083
Jack A C O 310184
Tosh G C 010384
Maxwell J G *BArch BSc* 011084
¶Westhead J A 121184
¶Nicol D 090185
Smiles E 301085

Lieutenants

Tait W R G 060780
Douglas D R *BSc* 240583
Douglas D W 240583
Fraser C G 241283
Marsh N D 230584
McKay J K 070884
Robb G J M 211184

2nd Lieutenants

Conaghan A P 200584
†Terris A A B *BA(Hons)* 260585
†Burrows J D *BSc(Hons) PhD* 050685
†Mann T J P 070785

Quartermasters

Nicholls G J *Capt* 121083

Extra-Regimentally Employed

Lieutenant Colonels

Stavert of Hoscote A W psc 150182
Williamson I W psc 011082

Majors

Brownlee J T *TD* 010473
Tweedie H J *TD*▪ sq(v) 011173
Cowie G K *TD* 010174
Smout F D J *TD*▪ 060775
Leighton B V *TD*▪ 010678
Hudson N E *BSc PhD* 010481
Mitchelson K R H 190584
Waltham G N *TD* 011284
McCance N A D 020285

Captains

Oswald R R *TD* 010474
Downie A F *BSc* 010484
Dear A G W *TD LLB MA* 080785

Lieutenants

Scott W B 020285
McCallion G S T 090285
McCrow R T R (*A/Maj* 010286) 090285
Thomson R 091285

2nd Lieutenants

†McKay D 211182

51st HIGHLAND VOLUNTEERS

Upon a Saltire, a stags head above a scroll inscribed *'CUIDICH'N RIGH'*

1st Battalion 51st Highland Volunteers

Hon Colonel..........Lt Col (Bt Col) D Carnegy-Arbuthnott *TD DL*..........010480
Dep Hon Colonel..........Col A D Anderson *TD DL*..........011183

Majors

Hastie K *TD* 011177
McRae J R *MBE* 091177
Roberts P A J *BA* 070783
Scott-Barrett N H *MA* 120385
Ritchie D M *AMBCS* 010485

Captains

Henwood S H *BA ACMA* (*A/Maj* 021181) 011077
Gavin M 100979
Barton J O *ALIA* (*A/Maj* 010983) 080180
Wilberforce R W *BA AIB* 010281
Tournay R N A J 050281
Peggie A L *BA* 010781
Glen M T A *BSc* 011181
¶Loudon J 200982
Pearson K J 011182
¶Johnson R M 030583
¶Miller J R 010683
Campbell J A M B 091283
Rankin-Hunt D 010684
¶McGonnigle J *MISM* 170984
¶Dorsett E T *BEM TEng(CEI) FSERT* 120885

Lieutenants

Holmes C S 070982
Ludlow M W H *BSc(Econ)* 280284
Storr J A 180884
Allen G L 220585
Gibson G M 220585

2nd Lieutenants

†Lennox-Warburton A C 061283
†Hardie F A G 200584
Hall A G 310584
†Beecher M E *BA(Hons)* 181184
McAdam G *BSc* 270185
†Lamont D N 260585
†Burnett R S 280785

Quartermasters

Rose R I *TD* 240470
Maj 120181

2nd Battalion 51st Highland Volunteers

Hon Colonel..........Col D H W Brown *MC* ret pay..........150483

Lieutenant Colonels

Johnston G S *OBE TD*▪ *CA DL* 051183

Majors

Hewitt M R *TD*▪▪ *BSc(Eng) MSc PhD MIMechE FInstR* 010470
Dickson R C *TD* 011076
Young R M D *TD LLB NP* 230580
Oag A C *TD* 151081
Mackay A S *TD* 021181
Balfour R A C *TD*▪ *LLB MA MLitt* 010884

Captains

McKen G *TD* (*A/Maj* 161283) 021181
Willis A J S *MInstM* 060482
Anderson J E M *BSc PhD* 200582
Duncan W 101082
¶Longstaff M 010983
¶Moyse R A 010983
McGregor J K *BEM AIB(Scot)* 150983
¶Macpherson E C 220484
¶Wright L T 220884
¶Taylor L *MISM* 110385
Bentley P J *BSc* 011085

Lieutenants

Prentice P C 250582
Gordon A W *BSc LLB* 161182
Rose E (*A/Capt* 010185) 240583
Donald R E *ATD* (*A/Capt* 070284) 161083
McArthur R 011183
Macleod M M 031183
Purser D H *MA(Hons)* 230584
Black D M 220585
Trevillion E A *PhD MRSC* (*A/Capt* 010985) 220585
Thain N G 211185

2nd Lieutenants

Headridge E R 100684
Thornton-Kemsley I S 010984
†Henderson I R R *FIMLS AIMLS* 170685
†Cabrelli P 280785
†Morrison N S *LRSC* 011285
†Munro E 150186

Quartermasters

Prati C G A 180778
Maj 100186

3rd Battalion 51st Highland Volunteers (The Argyll and Sutherland Highlanders)

Hon Colonel............Lt Col G P Wood *MC* ret pay............260685

Lieutenant Colonels

Ostman E J *TD AIB(Scot)* 010885

Majors

¶Lowrie A C 010578
Bell A D *TD* 140579
Douglas W H S 300980
Steele R L 300980
Buchanan A A 011181
Steuart-Corry M C *TD MBA DMS* 180682
Elliot D G *TD LLB WS NP* 010184
Edmunds D F 011085

Captains

¶Price R C 010378
Macnair C N *LLB* 191180
¶McNeill R J F ae 200982
Doherty D J *TD* 010783
¶McGurk B 010883
Macintyre A K 010184
Ronnie S P 010184
¶Wheatley A 190184
¶Parker A S *MBE TD* 010884
Robertson R *BA* 091284
Linney G K R *MIAS MIBCO* 010186

Lieutenants

Hall R D J *LLB* 190582
Robertson S A *MA(Arch) DipArch* 171083
Seaton G R *BSc* 310584
Aitken D H A 220585

2nd Lieutenants

McLeod G 100684
†McNeil D R 150585
†Doyle J 260585
†Ponsonby N L 260585
†Dunbar S 280785
†McCulloch A J K *BDS* 280785
†Thomson M G 280785

Quartermasters

Stirling W *Capt* 110284

Extra-Regimentally Employed

Colonels

Sim I A *TD*▪ *MBA AIB(Scot)* 011082

Lieutenant Colonels

Murdoch A *TD*▪ *FCIS* 011181
Davidson C G *TD*▪ 010483

Majors

Wilson J S *TD*▪▪ *LLB MA NP* 100769
Young J A L *TD*▪▪▪ 010471
Conners J J B *TD*▪ 121271
Holliday R D *TD*▪ *BSc(Eng)* 010372
Muir D D *TD*▪▪ *MA* 230673
Rutherford-Young N R *TD*▪ 011174
Walker S T *TD* 161274
Duggan S V *TD BEd* 240476
Hewitt J A B *TD* 161176
Taitt M P 311277
Gibson E M *MBE TD DL* 201078
Lindsay M W *TD* 071179
Kennedy J N *TD LLB* 240380
Brimage M 060181
Macleod J C *TD MSIAD* sq(v) 010481
Stewart I F 300981
Ross M N B N aic 010385
Layden P J *TD LLB* 031285

Captains

Evans D S *TD* 280475
Taylor C D G 010482
Robinson R H *BA* 310183
Walker G 010185

Lieutenants

Sheehan T C J *BA* 040379
Hillman D A 220180
Elliot I D (*A/Capt* 010285) 180982
Robertson F K 011082
Key B S 221082
Bullard W A 160384
Paine J R 090484
Wood J F M *TD* 120185
Gordon-Rogers A M *BSc PGCE* 240285
Allardyce C G M 010385
Palmer J R W 010385
Sclater N W L (*A/Maj* 300585) 140585
Abernethy R N *TD* 010885
Mackenzie C S *BL* 240885
Kean M S T psc 010985
Macrae J N 101285

THE LONDON SCOTTISH

Hon Colonel............*HM* QUEEN ELIZABETH THE QUEEN MOTHER

THE QUEENS DIVISION

5th (Volunteer) Battalion The Queen's Regiment

Hon Colonel............Col *HH Prince* Georg *of* Denmark *KCVO*............290475
Dep Hon Colonel............Col J B Ogilvie *OBE TD DL*............290383

Majors

Parkinson C F G *TD BA* sq(v)	050877
Wooles S E	020981
Argent C L *FCA ATII*	280583
Gibson G E	310384

Captains

¶Bass J R	160577
McDermott T N *BA*	141077
Harper W P T *TD* (*A/Maj* 260585)	010678
Benson T *TD*	020879
McCardle P S F	031281
Thompson S J C (*A/Maj* 010885)	031281
Oyler T J (*A/Maj* 011284)	010482
Rumsey M S	030482
Conroy W F	010982
¶Newman P A	010483
¶Lynch T J	260483
McGhie M W	010683
¶Scripps B M	291083
Milne W D	010184
¶Robb J *MBE*	140185

Lieutenants

Kelly N J (*A/Capt* 021178)	110977
Pike G W D	260679
Leonard C N	291179
Wilson R M	050880
McMahon S A *BSc* (*A/Capt* 250386)	210581
Redfern J A (*A/Capt* 070286)	270182
Taylor M P (*A/Capt* 010684)	270182
Maccariello E J G *BSc*	250582
Wilson D	050483
Barlow S M	230185
Pilkington M T A	120685

2nd Lieutenants

†Scoones S J *BSc*	040583
†Mackenzie M D	050783
†Mason R A	190784
Fields N	181184
†Houston D D M	181184
†Moore P A	210985
†Phillips M L	210985
†Sage B G	210985
†Steel-Jessop M W	210985
†Stretton J C	210985

Quartermasters

Gawler W E	*Capt*	010185

6th/7th (Volunteer) Battalion The Queen's Regiment

Hon Colonel............Col R R St J Barkshire *TD JP*............010886

Lieutenant Colonels

Lowans R E *TD MITD MICO* sq(v)	010486

Majors

Salter A J D *TD BEd*	160675
Hall R A *TD MSIAD*	040578
Hurd C K *TD*	011080
Roche T O G	010785
Ross J H D	010286

Captains

¶Marnoch D C	010178
Guthrie C J S (*A/Maj* 010486)	060880
Gibson P *BSc PhD RGN* (*A/Maj* 011185)	160383
¶Medcalf T J *MInstAM*	110483
¶Carrol P T	020683
¶Parker E S *MISM*	220783
Day J *LPRI*	010484
Harwood D	070884
¶Weaver J C	060984
¶Green R A	040185
Partridge R H	010486
Robertson F	010486

Lieutenants

Plowman S J F (*A/Capt* 011185)	191078
Robertson A	120480
Guthrie A P *BSc*	201280
Haynes T J *BA*	130381
Durston G J	161081
Copley S W *BA MSc*	241081
Clement A M *BSc*	160782
Carter K I A	011082
King M J *BA* (*A/Capt* 010785)	271082
Muir G I	161182
Horwell N C *BA*	131282
Dalby A H B *ACA* (*A/Capt* 010484)	050483
Sparks G J *BA*	050483
Windmill S M	160983
Asplin M G	291183
McNamara J A	211185
Strachan N A	211185

2nd Lieutenants

†Lindsay C M *BSc BSc(Hons) PhD MRSC*	100684
†Hoffman S R	210985

Quartermasters

Chapman P J	*Capt*	080884

Extra-Regimentally Employed

Colonels

Ogilvie J B *OBE TD■ DL*	010476
Dudding M J *ADC ACIS MBIM* psc	301181
Putnam J R G *TD FRICS*	020484

Majors

Harrington P G *TD■*	010169
Dineley G *TD■■*	190469
Evans G W *TD■*	010472
Carte B A *TD*	011073
Wright G H *TD■■*	240974
Adler M F H *TD FRGS TFA*	180575
Bingham A J *TD■■ ARIBA*	160675
Haigh A P *TD■ BA DipEd*	260975
Stocks A G H *TD■*	010476
Gardner A F *TD*	030876
Mercer M C *TD*	120978
Prior A W *TD LLB*	010180
Meldrum A J *TD AAAI ACIS*	050880
Storie-Pugh P A D *TD*	050880
Thornton R G C *TD■*	121180
Broadbent P M P	230381
Sinclair-Lee R	010483

Captains

McInerney J P	010380
Leonard A J	150881
Blausten S A *BSc ARICS*	010182
Marchant A A (*A/Maj* 010482)	010482

Lieutenants

Rogers A A P N *TD AMIEE*	250368
Doyle P *MA*	180779
Brett M R G	100680
Whelan M G A *BScTech*	171280
Lacey S A (*A/Capt* 010485)	271082
Chattle P A	211185
Gilpin R D *TD*	260286
Bunce C R C *ACIS* psc	060386

5th (Volunteer) Battalion The Royal Regiment of Fusiliers

Majors

Carruthers R J *TD*■ 140776
Robertson A J 010880
Lee E *TD BSc* 011280
Coulter P P J 160683
Booth R G 010883

Captains

¶Sandland D 130376
Thomson J R (*A/Maj* 010684) 010977
Gale R S *TD BSc AIB* 010478
Smith T F *MA* 010478
Railton H M *BSc AMIMechE* 010880
Andrews I C F *BSc* 020381
Smith A N 160282
Bromley S D E *BA* 290682
Crook P L C 210982
¶Sutton A T 210883
¶Ogrady J 130184
Hughes-D'Aeth W J *BA* 011184
Keegan G L *BA* 160185
¶Nash J 020485
¶Wilkinson J T 021085
Ainsworth A R 080486

Lieutenants

Preece M L 261077
Murphy D H G 080878
Bartlett J C (*A/Capt* 010785) 250582
Jeffreys A P *MA* 120682
Conway A L 181082
Brennan D 250384
Gibbs A (*A/Capt* 010785) 090484
Clarke R M A 180784
Lancaster J R *BA* 070884
Vickers M C *BSc* 070785
Matthews A C 220186

2nd Lieutenants

†Peden C A 270185
†Pickersgill J 260585
†May S L 210985
†Edwards G 111185
†Owen D C 011285

Quartermasters

Wooldridge L R *Capt* 240784

6th (Volunteer) Battalion The Royal Regiment of Fusiliers

Hon Colonel..........Capt (Hon Col) *The Duke of* Northumberland *KG GCVO PC TD JP DL FRS*..........010475

Majors

Alderson J S 010576
Smail D J R *TD* 010478
Fry A A S Q 200880
Festing R M *MA* 010781
Knightley E B 301183
Mannings M E 111283
Cawthorn E O 011184

Captains

¶Calvert F A *MBE TD* 261063
Smyth P C 011081
Rowe S I (*A/Maj* 020985) 010482
Wilkinson A R 090982
¶Lerpiniere L A W 010483
¶McAllister J 010483
¶Perring B R J *MISM* 010483
¶Smith H J 010583
Earl S *BA* 010185
Liddell-Grainger I R P 010185
Simpson G C 010185
Ridley P 120485

Lieutenants

Parker J C (*A/Capt* 010982) 230780
Robertson-Mcisaac J W (*A/Capt* 010185) 180781
Marshall P S (*A/Capt* 010185) 271082
Scott W J *LLB* (*A/Capt* 010186) 050483
Ferguson A 090484
Duran J F 070884
Burbridge D J *BSc* 011184
Smith I P 121184
Ellis P J *BSc* 220585
Hobbs J L 310785

2nd Lieutenants

†Cowen J R *BA(Hons)* 260585
†Heron G T 260585

Quartermasters

Potts S W *Capt* 260383

Extra-Regimentally Employed

Colonels

Robinson P J C *ADC DL* 010783

Lieutenant Colonels

Turnbull R G *TD*■■ 010884
Burton P J *TD*■ *BA MRIPHH* 021084

Majors

Manvell P P *MBIM* psc 311269
Webb J C M *TD*■ 010573
Cariss R L *MBE TD*■ 010475
Bewley C A *TD*■ 131176
Baldwin S *TD*■ 011277
Butler R C *TD BSc* 010278
Bayldon R *MBE* sq 230485

Captains

Harland T A 121175
¶Simmonett W T 140176
Auld C J D *BA* 010878

Lieutenants

Edmundson L W 311076
Bond A E *BSc* 050483
Hill S T 070884
Turvey M J (*A/Maj* 010985) 180485
Carnell M A *BSc(Eng)* 310785
Hall G W 200985

THE ROYAL ANGLIAN REGIMENT

D Hon Colonels ....Maj D W F Willard *TD JP*
The Royal Anglian Regiment (Northamptonshire) TA 010480
Col G C P Morgan *DL* ret pay
The Royal Anglian Regiment (Essex) TA 010480
Col R G Wilkes *OBE TD DL*
The Royal Anglian Regiment (Leicsestershire) TA 290981
Brig W C Deller *OBE* ret pay
The Royal Anglian Regiment (Suffolk) TA 050283
Col W J Gleadell *TD ADC*
The Royal Anglian Regiment (Lincolnshire) TA 010484
Maj R A Shervington *TD*
The Royal Anglian Regiment (Cambridgeshire) TA 010484
Maj J P Wetherall ret pay
The Royal Anglian Regiment (Bedfordshire) TA 010484
Col P W Raywood *TD DL*
The Royal Anglian Regiment (Norfolk) TA 310385
Capt J Lowther *CBE (HM Lord Lieutenant Northamptonshire)*
The Royal Anglian Regiment (Northamptonshire) TA 180586

5th (Volunteer) Battalion The Royal Anglian Regiment

Majors

Horrell P G R *TD*	030881
Chissel A D	020482
Inch J D R	011182
Gregory A C *TD*	010484
Huggins J E	220985

Captains

¶Petch A W M *TD*▪	091180
Alexander C A F *TD AIQS*	191180
Thomas C A F (*A/Maj* 010785)	010882
Warr T	010882
¶Albany C S *TD*	010683
Marsden D K *LLB*	010883
Crampton R A	011083
¶de Bretton-Gordon L J	230484
Peakall G A *BA*	230684
Walton G P	230684
¶Aylin C G P	210784
¶Fisher D H	010485
Card S	011285
Wilson J R	011285
Darlington N E *BA*	010386

Lieutenants

Ostacchini S R *BA*	080781
Hawkesbury J J	230284
King A P	240584
Laughton H R I	300684
Dixon S G	010385
Vince C P	230585
St John C J	220186

2nd Lieutenants

Jones N G	200584
Ridley T J *ARICS*	200584
†Baker M A	240784
Parker K J	290784
†Pattison R W T	290784
Meads R G *BA*	270185
†Dormer T *BA(Hons)*	230785

Quartermasters

Eden R	*Capt*	180585

6th (Volunteer) Battalion The Royal Anglian Regiment

Majors

Prince W T T psc	301173
James R P *TD*▪ *BSc CEng*	010774
Lucas W D *TD ARICS*	010275
Haslam D R *TD*▪▪▪ *ACII*	011176
Davidson J S	010282
Raybould J L	010282
Spearing A L	020883
West R J C *TD*	010684

Captains

¶Milward J F	280277
Veal M R	010483
¶Grosch A J P	060483
¶Thompson A T	160583
¶Gandon G A J	010683
Lopes J D *BSc*	020883
Denson D S (*A/Maj* 010485)	021083
¶Davidson D	180584
McArdle A D W *BA*	010884
¶Page M J	021284
Herriot R G H	010585

Lieutenants

Stewardson J A *BA*	011080
Adey R M	211081
Clapham N G	090882
Tusa J H A	150683
Thurkettle V	090484
Overton C H	070884
Palmer R J	070884
Wakely A	070884
Rogers J R D	310785
Wawn C J N	310785

2nd Lieutenants

Wardle I P (*A/Capt* 040485)	040484
Fik C F *DMS MBIM AIIM*	181184
Revell C I R	181184
Kirk A P	270185
†Cameron G I F	260685
†Keron R W	070785
†Snaith N J S	070785

Quartermasters

Burch D P	*Capt*	160982

7th (Volunteer) Battalion The Royal Anglian Regiment

Lieutenant Colonels

Harris D K *MBE TD*▪ *LLB* 231084

Majors

Chell L A 270175
Honnor F *MSc* 210677
Marshall E W *TD* 020280
Hemmings A M 010782
Williams P D 010883

Captains

Smith A L 010176
Hunt R G *BSc* 010678
Mee M R *TD* (*A/Maj* 010283) 011278
¶Ashton J B ptsc EM 140180
Darbyshire P J *BA* 280780
Newmarch G W C (*A/Maj* 211085) 160982
Chandler D 071082
¶Amos A T 010483
¶McNaughton P *OBE DPA FBIM MASMC* 010483
¶Bruton K S 300483
¶Dawe M N J 051083
Hyde J G 011084
Livingstone D A 150785

Lieutenants

Elliott E I B *MA* 200477
Robinson A 280581
Smith G J C *BSc* 160383
Szabo C L W 050883
Mallett C A 090484
Sweeney D 060784
Cox D A P 230185
Howe J A 310785
Slatter K C 310785
Howard P A 211185
Stanley R J 211185
Watson J F 211185
Barber B J 220186

2nd Lieutenants

†Mitchell I M 250684
†Page N B 290784
†Pennington R N 290784
Fielder M R 181184
Clarke I M 270185
Stanton J P 270185
†Alcock A M T 070785

Quartermasters

Taylor G T *Capt* 101281

Extra-Regimentally Employed

Lieutenant Colonels

James D W *OBE TD* 070381

Majors

Churchill J D *MC* 060266
Stewart C A S *TD* 010870
Freeman B D *TD*▪ 010472
Barnett G R sq 050473
Gardner C W 010176
Young D A 150676
D'Alton A C 010479
Standley S 150980
Elsey A E *TD FInstLEx* 101080
Kelsey N H *TD MA* 010481
Wild T P *TD* 010781
Reed D W *TD BSc PhD* 201282

Captains

Taylor A H 010777
Cordy P B *MRTPI* (*A/Maj* 010386) 061082
Green M M *BA* 011182
Reeves R E 010984

Lieutenants

Roads C H *MA PhD* 090155
Woodward A F 011271
Wesson R J J *BSc FGS AMIGeol* 220377
Godfrey M H 240583
McNicoll I D G *BSc(Eng) MA* 010684
Rivett K H 010884
Evans D 011284
Pryce-Howells A J J *MBE TD*▪ 230585
Smith G N 230585
Taylor J D 230585
Wood A 240585
Beckett J C 080885
Shalders P C 160186

2nd Lieutenants

†Paling N J 201083

THE KINGS DIVISION

4th (Volunteer) Battalion King's Own Royal Border Regiment

Hon Colonel.........Lt Col (Bt Col) A Matthew *OBE DL*.........101282

Majors

Charlton M *TD ACIS*	151277
Diss M G *TD BSc*	110380
¶Houston H J	310381
Metcalfe J R A	190782
Weighman J	230585
Carney P J *TD*	010186

Captains

Lewis N D *BSc*	041178
¶Gabbott E J *TD*	110880
¶Taylor P *MBE*	250880
Mills J	010681
Chandler A P	011182
Mitchell N W *BA*	190383
¶Hopper J A	260483
¶Regan A	051083
Brandwood P M H	010186
English R M	010186

Lieutenants

Blendall A J (*A/Capt* 010583)	221080
Chaldecott M S	010781
Barr-Richardson D C	140882
Byrne J S *MRSC*	010784

2nd Lieutenants

Stonebridge J M	270183
Ashurst M J	200584
Irvine M	200584
†Dand D G	260585
Pendlebury-Green J	070785

Quartermasters

Slater T D *BEM*	*Capt*	060482

Extra-Regimentally Employed

Lieutenant Colonels

Messenger E W *TD*■	170380

Majors

Bradburn P R *BA*	020485

Lieutenants

Ferguson J H	011085

5th/8th (Volunteer) Battalion The King's Regiment

Hon Colonel.........Lt Col (Bt Col) *The Earl of* Derby *MC DL*.........010474

Majors

Duff L T *TD*	010680

Captains

¶Clarke H *MBE*	010475
Thomas D M *BA MInstPS* (*A/Maj* 010985)	220780
Hilton P J *BA*	160481
Ratcliff C A W	160481
Atkinson M J (*A/Maj* 011184)	010981
Hayward K C *BA* (*A/Maj* 010486)	010981
Pybus G H	010882
¶Jobes J J	020683
¶Meredith C	020883
¶Goldman D J	170983
¶Corkery D A	011083
Riley C W *BSc*	150684
Williamson J G	081284
Davies R M	150185
Clarke S R	010285

Lieutenants

†Dickinson C G *TD BSc* (*A/Capt* 010485)	100772
Marley M B *BSc AIMLS*	290981
Reynolds J K *BSc*	160282
Dowson A S *BEd(Hons)*	170583
Byrne G	260484
McMahon E G (*A/Capt* 010485)	071284
Mullin P	230185
Fogarty P D	220186

2nd Lieutenants

Brown C W	200584
Sankey I *BA(Hons)*	200584
Turner A J *BA*	100684
Nanson P A E	290784
†Keleghan P S	261184
†Mooney P H	220585
†Gerrard T R	260585

Quartermasters

Nuttall F J	*Capt*	050979

Extra-Regimentally Employed

Colonels

Wilson P F *OBE* psc	031077

Majors

Ormiston J A *MBE TD*	060568
Chadwick D P W *TD BSc AIPM*	031075
Riley I L *TD BSc*	011077
Sayle J *BA*	020280
Holmes C P W *TD*	010983
Machin L G *TD*	070285

Lieutenants

King L J	010185
McGuire P D	010285

2nd Lieutenants

†Shelton R L	090685

Quartermasters

Platts T *ARCM*	*Capt*	010981

4th (Volunteer) Battalion The Queen's Lancashire Regiment

Hon Colonel........Col A J Smith *OBE*........010486

Lieutenant Colonels

Stam G B psc	290385

Majors

Felton S A psc	260579
Goodwin P *BSc* sq(v)	010481
Nesbitt T	010481
Holland W F	101083
Barston R P *MSc(Econ)*	011085
Hart D R *BSc*	010286

Captains

¶Rayner A J V	
¶Weir J	020975
Webb D M (*A/Maj* 010285)	010481
Harris C T J *BA* (*A/Maj* 010485)	011281
¶Kewley J W *MBE*	300783
Crompton G R *MA DipEd*	010484
Roberts S G *BEng*	261184
Haworth W	010485
¶Ball H	090585
¶Bartaby R C	011085

Lieutenants

Kinnaird B A	210581
Fitton L	070884
Myers J	070984
Smith D T	120685

2nd Lieutenants

†Speakman T P	060385
†Shorrock A C	070785
†Crowley D	181285

Extra-Regimentally Employed

Lieutenant Colonels

Brooks R W	100982

Captains

Boyce J	010485

Lieutenants

Rees-Pedlar T J	220186

YORKSHIRE VOLUNTEERS

The White Rose of Yorkshire, ensigned with St Edward's Crown, below, a scroll inscribed *'YORKSHIRE'*.

Regimental March

Quick March..........Ilkley Moor

Hon Colonel..........Hon Maj Gen *HRH The Duchess of* Kent *GCVO*..........070568
Hon Regimental Colonel..........Lt Col C J Tattersall *TD*..........011184

1st Battalion Yorkshire Volunteers

Hon Colonel..........Lt *The Rt Hon The Earl of* Scarborough *DL*..........011275

Lieutenant Colonels

Gaynor A E 020785

Majors

Dunning R W *TD FCA* sq(v) 011077
Smalley G B *TD AIB* 221179
Podmore A J *TD* 290980
Fox J *LLB* 291183
Tovey W J *BA* 021283
Bettney R 060285

Captains

Camp J P *BA* 270181
Radford A M *BA* 010281
Hastings S J *MSc ARICS* (*A/Maj* 131085) 010881
Tickell R M *MA* 290981
¶Hoyland K 010483
¶Wallace J H 010583
¶Goodger M 170583
¶Rees D F 100783
Hopkins D E *BA* 050983
Hall R C S *BA(Hons)* 061183
Garrad C S *BSc* 160384
Jones C E *MA* 010584
Farquhar N H *FRICS* 310784
Hackston D J *BSc(Econ) IPFA* 091084
Wood R 011284
Hughes D *MBE* 160385
Richardson B D 220585
Bramley D 021185
¶Edmonds W D *MBE* 030486

Lieutenants

Brown K J 040683
James M P 151183
Temke A G 011283
Leigh W T *JP* (*A/Capt* 011185) 051084
Hinchcliffe R A 220585
Almsteier S L 211185
Clarke P 211185
McHale I A 211185

2nd Lieutenants

†Swanson A *MA* 301084
Butler-Gallie S *LLB(Hons)* 121284
†Thacker K B 260585
†Marshall I 030685
†Greenwood H J 070785
†Sullivan A M 070785
†Frolish R A *BA(Hons)* 280785
†Gardner J A 011285

2nd Battalion Yorkshire Volunteers

Hon Colonel..........Capt (Hon Maj) The Rt Hon *The Lord* Middleton *MC JP DL*..........310376

Lieutenant Colonels

Frais A D *TD*▪ *BA* 010983

Majors

Wharton A C P *DL* 071277
Oliver R W 010183

Captains

Lill J A *TD*▪▪▪ 131254
Pearson D *TD AMIEE MMS* 011276
Wood C J M (*A/Maj* 231182) 010279
Watson D J *BA* (*A/Maj* 091183) 010579
Tasker D 011279
Bell A N 010580
Postill J P S (*A/Maj* 010983) 090980
Spilsbury J E M *BA* 010981
¶Newton J M 181181
Molesworth P J N *BSc* 210282
¶Harrison F 010683
Somers D F 200683
Booker R M 010983
Wadforth G S 011083
¶Kirk S H *MBE* 020284
¶France J W A *BEM* 070984
Woodall P 071185

Lieutenants

Beech N (*A/Capt* 010585) 270381
Brunyee P F (*A/Capt* 010585) 081181
Murfin M 090882
Clarke N L 240583
Potter D *BSc* 120683
Gajowskyj J B 251083
Crawford D 090484
Fewster F 061184
Wilson S J 120685
Manging A C P 240985
Critchlow R P 211185

2nd Lieutenants

†Whitney W P 221184
Willis H M 270185
†Johnson D J 260585

Quartermasters

Cockerill D T *Capt* 010285

3rd Battalion Yorkshire Volunteers

Hon Colonel......Gen *Sir* Martin Farndale *KCB*......231183

Majors

Armitage S M *TD* 010379
Massey D G 010379
Newcombe T R *TD* 221081
Ault E D *TD*■ 011284

Captains

¶Dunell A 010578
Robinson B *GradRSC* 150180
Dunston D R 010281
Croft I 010482
Rushworth M 010283
¶Bailey H B 040783
Walker M H *BTech* 020883
¶Hill C 020983
¶Stanley D W *MISM* 101083
¶Hamp P G *BEM* 011183
¶Melia P B 020784
Beaumont P (*A/Maj* 130385) 010984
Harris B M 020984

Lieutenants

Danilewicz C J *MA* (*A/Capt* 070985) 010279
Winterbottom A (*A/Capt* 090985) 220585
McDonald J R 211185
Flanagan K M *BA* 260186

2nd Lieutenants

Laycock P A 240584
Fovargue S G 290784
Kelly I G 181184
†Birdsall M J 160685
†Rhodes D K 160685
†Sissling E H M 160685
†Bramham R D *AIB* 280785

Quartermasters

Carey D *Capt* 190183

Extra-Regimentally Employed

Colonels

Wilson J M *TD* 010482
Tattersall C J *TD*■ *BSc FRICS* 010485

Lieutenant Colonels

McClay A J *TD*■ 050680
Mortimer P J *TD*■ *MA* 010481
Elliott R J *TD*■ *LLB* 010485

Majors

Bagguley N J *TD*■ 010473
Garnett R M F *BA* 010974
Pickard M De B ph 010775
Hall J J *TD BSc* 010777
Hawley M *TD* 160977
Cross D G *TD BMet* 151278
Lamb M E *TD BSc MEd MRSC* 150579
Hardy S M 010880
Newton M P *TD* 010880
Tetley N G 051183

Captains

Potter B J *TD BSc* 021075
Hendry J A 010181
Bown C J (*A/Maj* 011185) 230581
Dickson W 070885
¶Harding J H 011285
Neville M W 060486

Lieutenants

White J 220180
McGinlay D W 270182
Pickersgill T 280285
Kirby D 120785

2nd Lieutenants

†Thorne P M 210985

4th (Volunteer) Battalion The Royal Irish Rangers (27th (Inniskilling) 83rd and 87th) (The North Irish Militia)

Hon Colonels .... Col M E W Nicholl *TD* 010183
Maj Gen C W B Purdon *CBE MC CPM* ret pay 280386

Lieutenant Colonels

Elder S M *TD*▪ *DipPhysEd* 190186

Majors

Lee R T *LLB* 011180
Hassard J H 010883
McKeown W J *TD* 171084
Aitchison-Tait D A *TD FInstSMM* 010185

Captains

McClay J A *TD DMS MBIM* 010473
Leslie R B *TD FIMLS* 011178
¶Anderson J 160979
Crawford C E *TD* (*A/Maj* 191184) 131079
Cooper D I S *TD* 020581
Dunn M J 021082
Blair S J 240283
¶Shannon S T *TD*▪ 010683
Weir J F F 290683
Simpson P A 010883
¶Jordan J 111083
¶Barron D J 050284
Irwin C A *BA* 010984
Mooney J P *BA* 010185

Lieutenants

Chambers J P *BVSc MRCVS* 250680
Boles H W J (*A/Capt* 010984) 050581
Lyttle W D J 240582
Graham A J *BA* 011082
Logan G J 201183
Scott J *BSc* 030384
Fallis A D 070884
Perry N P *BA* 070884
Hopwood C C J 240285
Grugan J H 120685

2nd Lieutenants

Kenwell B P *BA* 290784
†Rankin S W G 290784
†Emerson R S 060984
†Keane K M W 290385
†Rooney K A 280785

Quartermasters

Ryan I *TD* *Capt* 180979

5th (Volunteer) Battalion The Royal Irish Rangers (27th (Inniskilling) 83rd and 87th)

Hon Colonel .... Col R G Madocks *CBE TD DL* 010476

Lieutenant Colonels

Trimble A P *TD* 050385

Majors

Maguire N F *TD* 010478
Quinn R N *TD* 120280

Captains

¶Smith R G 180377
Bell J G *TD* (*A/Maj* 011181) 110677
Owen R D J R 291078
Telford R J *TD BEd* (*A/Maj* 011184) 011178
Abbott G T N 011181
McAllister H K 141281
¶Espey S D 171281
Stewart D A *BA* 170782
¶Dodds G R 090583
Potter W R 010683
Arnold F R L *FLIA ALIA* 281083
Lynas B G 011085

Lieutenants

Whiteside C H (*A/Capt* 010584) 271081
Herron N H (*A/Capt* 010584) 090882
Hutcheson R L (*A/Capt* 010684) 240583
Davidson G M (*A/Capt* 010486) 070884
Mitchell L C *ATD* (*A/Capt* 010486) 070884
Kelly E C N 081284
McKillop J A 310785
Rooney W J 310785

2nd Lieutenants

Crawford R A 200584
Crozier J D 200584
Cree A 290784
Ewart C D 290784
†Sterritt W P 290784
†Woolnough P 290784
†Nelson P 290385
†McCoy W P 260485

Quartermasters

McNair D R *Capt* 121176

Extra-Regimentally Employed

Lieutenant Colonels

Reid A H *OBE TD* 130979
Baird G H *OBE TD* 011081
Twigg D W F 010685

Majors

Farnan M G *MBE TD BSc* 010479
Fallis J E *TD* 020482
Telford E R *TD BA* 020482

Captains

Price F W *MBE TD* (*A/Maj* 010578) 010473
McCarthy K P 010581
Phillips S J L *BSc* 010984
Vosper A W L aic 140285

Lieutenants

O'Malley J F G (*A/Capt* 180685) 061183

THE PRINCE OF WALES'S DIVISION

THE WESSEX REGIMENT (RIFLE VOLUNTEERS)

The Wessex Wyvern on a plinth inscribed *'WESSEX'*

Regimental March

Quick March..A Farmer's Boy

1st Battalion The Wessex Regiment (Rifle Volunteers)

"Their land to defend"

Hon Colonel..Maj Gen M J H Walsh *CB DSO* ret pay 011181

Majors

Bond M J A sq 300676
Parnham C H 160379
Tristram B J 010181
Booth P M *BSc* 010481
Cook M S O *MBE* 120582
Stanley P *TD* 070583
Brady G E 010883
Cundy A C *BEM* 150485

Captains

¶Foreman J F 020578
Cunningham I J G *BA* 151180
Heatley R D (*A/Maj* 010885) 240582
Fausset M C *BSc* 020682
Lawrence R N 170682
Oxborough T J 010183
¶Burt G R *MC* 060483
¶McMeeken G D 250483
¶Wallace R *MBE MInstAM* 220583
¶Barrow J A *MBE* 010783
Lawson-Lee R G *BA* 010883
¶Thomas G S *MBE* 021083
Ffitch N A 180884
Davidson-Houston S C O *BSc* 070685
¶Mitchell J 021085

Lieutenants

Simpson T *BSc* 280281
Summers G S *BA(Hons)* 041081
Barrett N T 200582
Young R K 260483
Shapland T C A 131083
Berry H 131284
Upshall I R 220585
Mereweather I T 220186

2nd Lieutenants

Sorge M W 230185
†Payne A D 070785
†Scott A L 250985

Quartermasters

Coleman R W *MBE MInstAM* *Capt* 200384

2nd Battalion The Wessex Regiment (Volunteers)

Hon Colonel..Lt Col *Sir* James Scott *Bt* 280485

Majors

Spanner J H *TD* 121177
Holmes E R *TD*■ *MA PhD* 230478
Fox J E 030381
Quant S P *BSc* 010183
Bateman R P 010185

Captains

¶Corrigan F
Pass G J 010781
Easton N P aic 040881
Pinchen G J 010982
¶Hope J R 020982
¶Roberts D F *MBIM* 301082
¶Arnold M J 031083
¶Blight G B *MBE FBIM* 010884
Protheroe C 011184
Twentyman W M 140285
Howman R E (*A/Maj* 021185) 241085

Lieutenants

Wolanowski P L (*A/Capt* 020386) 040278
Groves J M 310180
Walton J C (*A/Capt* 010186) 180281
Maxwell E P (*A/Capt* 311285) 011181
Goodall A J P 160383
Thiele R M C 230584
Curtis J M 080385

2nd Lieutenants

Farrimond C B 290784
†Quarterman W J C 290784
†Marshall A W 280785
†Pertwee L C F *BSc(Hons)* 280785

Extra-Regimentally Employed

Colonels

Buglass K R *TD* psc 011079
Stevens W H F *OBE ADC* 011081

Lieutenant Colonels

Grazebrook A M *TD*■ 010883

Majors

Jenkins R J E *TD*■ 010173
Rendle C G 160673
Ryan D C *TD*■■ 010873
Campbell J M *TD DipEd* 010474
Andre J E A 040774
Roger Smith E M *MIEE* 170177
Taylor I P B *TD*■■ *AIB* 151177
Wilkin A J *LLB* 010478
Bloomfield H F *TD BA* 010578
Lillies J C *MIPR* 190679
Miller G D *TD* 010181
Childs B D *MBCS* 010881
Hallett D G R 200182
George P V B *TD* 111082
McDine D J *OBE* 010984
Mills R N P *BSc* 100286
Mullen J F L *AIB* 010386

Captains

Morgan P G T 010475
Wills B M *TD* 211177
Rollin M J 100779
Bryan E W H 200781
Wedderburn H E A 020981
Keir L R 010882
Falkner J J 170983
Peel A R C *AIB* 021083

Lieutenants

Fuglesang C F (*A/Maj* 010184) 010982
Tucker D R 090982
Blake D J 280982
Petherick C 280982
Goad S P 151182
McElwee A J E 151183
Henry A J S 011185

2nd Lieutenants

†Green S G 181182
Metcalfe P G 310783
†Longrigg T J F 211183
†Watchman H D 160685

MERCIAN VOLUNTEERS

Double headed eagle ensigned with Saxon Crown

Regimental Marches

Quick Marches ....(i) Come Lassies and Lads (ii) Days we went a gypsying

1st Battalion Mercian Volunteers

Hon Colonel ....Col C J Baines *CBE MC TD DL* 210380

Majors

Lewis B P 010378
Garlick N P 220581
Brazier J M 140681
Boyd R A 141182
Phillips T E *TD* 011184
Biddulph A D *DMS* 010286

Captains

¶Dunn W P 280279
Nightingale C G M 180381
¶Bridges J H 220781
Williams A P (*A/Maj* 271085) 070382
Smith R B 090782
¶Kane B F *BA* 110583
McNeil C P 170783
Bridges D G 061283
Pickup M E C 060184
Crawford P W 010684
Hill G C 010684
¶Holden F P 190385

Lieutenants

McMillan S R (*A/Capt* 010285) 260380
Adams R J (*A/Capt* 271085) 190581
Strongman I M *LLB* 010981
Embley S D 101182
Farrow J A (*A/Capt* 011085) 090484
Szabo L S A 070884
Adams A I 200285
Loots D A 220585
Vukmirovic W E 211185

2nd Lieutenants

Morris W J E *BA TCERT* 181184
Sibbald P J 181184
Whitelegg D 181184
Worton J H 270185
†Wotton P J 280785
†Evans J P 210985
†Williams N J 210985

Quartermasters

Walker R *Capt* 131280

2nd Battalion Mercian Volunteers

Hon Colonel ....Col A B Griffiths *TD DL* 020679

Majors

James H P *FCIS MBIM* 011172
Jackson P H *TD*■ *BSc(EstMan) FRICS* 010980
O'Neill E J 270782
Noakes K W 200884

Captains

Scott R S (*A/Maj* 020585) 010680
Cox A E (*A/Maj* 011183) 010980
Machin R E *BA* (*A/Maj* 171285) 220881
Bramble I (*A/Maj* 310384) 010981
¶Carson R C 021083
¶Pearce F *MBE* 041083
Bloor D C *BScTech* 011183
¶Kendrick G A 230184
Leedham S C (*A/Maj* 010386) 010384
Rashid M 010584
Middleton S N 010784
¶McGilvray G *MBE MBIM* 051184

Lieutenants

Green R W 200179
Noble T H 230179
Harrison C J (*A/Capt* 011285) 271082
O'Brien P A 161182
Walton A C D (*A/Capt* 070186) 080883
Smith L E (*A/Capt* 230285) 220284
Russell J A T (*A/Capt* 181185) 211184
Cooper M A 220186
Sproson M D 220186

2nd Lieutenants

Smith D G 200584
†Barnes T C 100684
†Wood J T G 150684
†Bleasdale T J 270185
†Bell S M J 260585
†Darke G A 280785
†Leach V R 280785
†Bratton S A 011285
†Waller D 011285

Extra-Regimentally Employed

Colonels

Griffiths A B *TD*■■ *DL JP JP*010476

Lieutenant Colonels

Jeavons K H *TD ACP* 011182

Majors

Abell A K M *TD*■ 010672
Dodsworth E C *TD*■ 031072
Rainbow M S *TD MA DMS FBIM* 010573
Reid W E L *TD BA(Cantab) MA(Hons)* 030274
Clarke B L *TD BA MEd* 101176
Rhodes J N *TD MA PhD* 011078
Hudson B K *AIRTE* 091179
Sayers B D *AIB* 010980
Ricketts T H 160281
Bury N G D 021182
Etheridge S P *MBE TD FCII ACIArb FLIA JP* 050983

Captains

Kent H N *BSc* 010381
Kennison M D H *BA* 011181
Waterland R *MISM* 050486

Lieutenants

Rudge D J G *DipArchCons RIBA* 130974
Wright B J 200678
Graham A G M *ARICS* 261082
Price D A 080283
Carlton A J 030684
Garfield W J 070884
Featherstone J J 120585
Atkins D M 031185
Howells M J 031185

2nd Lieutenants

Evans H R

3rd (Volunteer) Battalion The Cheshire Regiment

Hon Colonel.........Col W A Bromley-Davenport *DL JP*.........010385

Captains

Wyllie R O *TD BEd* 130880
Connor R C *MISM* 010584

3rd (Volunteer) Battalion The Royal Welch Fusiliers

Hon Colonel.........Maj P C Ormrod *MC JP DL*.........171185

Majors

¶Lee H K 300672
Ellis-Jones W *TD BA* 311073
Ranson M B 171184

Captains

¶Hughes H J 130471
Atkinson-Willes G A *BSc* 010283
¶Blewitt R C 060783
¶Whitehouse W E 011083
Williams M G 011184
¶Stopforth B 021085

Lieutenants

Bednall J C P o 080282
Evans E R *AIMLS* 060482
Hill S G 070884
Roberts D A 070884
Beard N R 211185
Fanning M A 220186

2nd Lieutenants

Roszkowski J T *BSc(Hons)* 290784
†Snape D K 160685
†Northover A 070785
†Leader M J A 280785

Extra-Regimentally Employed

Colonels

Egan J N *TD*▪ *ADC* 010783

Majors

Thomas M *TD*▪ 020477

2nd Lieutenants

La Roche M J

3rd (Volunteer) Battalion The Royal Regiment of Wales (24th/41st Foot)

Hon Colonel.........Lt R Hanbury-Tenison *JP (HM Lord Lieutenant Gwent)*.........010482

Majors

Gooderson P L 010779
Cantlay D A *TD* 210381
Jones D C *LLB* 010585
Jones H T W *BSc* 011085

Captains

Rayer W F
(*A/Maj* 010384) 021277
Matthews J T 010381
¶Davies D M 140481
Wilson J D
(*A/Maj* 240684) 011081
Norris C R V 180882
Lucas R J 091182
¶Wilding J 020983
¶Freeman L D 181083
¶Reardon D J 010484
¶Crouch P F *BEM* 160784
Blagojevic P A 010186
Jenkins D C 010186
Pennell G D 010186

Lieutenants

Hart P M 040881
Neale G J 010485
†Brunsdon D J 290784
†Dyer H M 290784
†Sinnett D C M 290784
†Tatnell P J 290784
Petersen T J 181184
†Rock S E J 181184
†Burrow A P 151284
†Iles T J 120185
Warnes R A 270185
†Fish P L 280785
†McArthur D C 011285

2nd Lieutenants

Drummond-Hay R N 200584
Foster S D 200584

Quartermasters

Rock A E *TD*▪ 220170
Maj 210681

4th (Volunteer) Battalion The Royal Regiment of Wales (24th/41st Foot)

Hon Colonel..........Col W P Howells *OBE TD DL*..........210482

Majors

¶Williams R V	011079
Pugh R L *TD ACA ATII*	010681
Warner A J *AIM*	010284
Evans G B	010585

Captains

¶Webb D	011079
Blyth G L	010482
Jenkins G B *BA* (*A/Maj* 010585)	010482
Buckley S D	211082
Hall J B *BPhil MA*	211082
¶Middleton-Jones R *MBE*	190783
¶Williams R J	011083
¶Gill K	281183
Jones P R *LLB*	010284
Crowley D E *LLB*	010585

Lieutenants

Runnalls D	011082
Thomas J A	160884

2nd Lieutenants

Gay N S	100684
†Mann N G *BSc(Hons) PGCE*	280785

Quartermasters

Flower T J M *TD*	*Maj*	010485

Extra-Regimentally Employed

Colonels

John B T *CBE TD ADC LLB AIB*	010480

Lieutenant Colonels

Protheroe A H *MBE TD* (*Bt/Col* 061284)	010979
Mathias R M *TD*■	050785

Majors

Harry K R *TD*■ *BA MIPM MITO*	060271
Rees T J V	030771
Baldwin R W *TD*■ *BSc*	010574
Morgan D G *TD*■ *ARICS*	230975
Morgan T P C *TD FInstIC*	111175
Everett M J *TD*■	010479
Mason C R *TD BA*	010679
Kent I S A *BSc*	040680
Jones N A *TD*	010481
Martin W A	011081
Vosper K W	011081
Davies D	121281
Campbell J T	010784
Evans R D *TD*	110185

Captains

Stevens P A *MA*	291177
Warry T N (*A/Maj* 010885)	211178
Watkins D J M	280683

Lieutenants

Pugh G S A (*A/Capt* 011184)	010579
Edwards H G	050282
Tucker B J	010485

3rd (Volunteer) Battalion The Worcestershire and Sherwood Foresters Regiment (29th/45th Foot)

Hon Colonel..........Brig C E Wilkinson *CBE TD*..........010483

Lieutenant Colonels

Cullen C N *TD*■ *NP*	161084

Majors

Robinson B K *TD*■■	291075
Simpson M *TD*	020876
Hodgson J C *TD*	010378
Walton I *TD BSc*	011080
Fairman C H *TD*■■	030882
Sneath D R	051283
Garratt C R	011285

Captains

Freeman D J (*A/Maj* 161084)	011080
Banyard N K	020182
¶Magowan S *MBE BEM*	190782
Monks M F (*A/Maj* 010485)	010783
¶Walker T	200783
¶Gibbs D	230783
¶Meads J A	250783
¶Martin P *MBE*	100983
Nayer P R	120684
¶Cook R V *MBE*	081084
Brown T C E	010485
Webb A	010485
Brandrick A J *EdB*	020485

Lieutenants

Reilly M J *BA*	240681
Platt P J *LASI*	010981
Leckey M A *LLB*	211081
Turner N H (*A/Capt* 130184)	211081
Lawrence R C	250582
Abbott D M *BA ACA*	260582
Palfreyman S G	151183
Greenop R E	090484
Eden G P	230584
Mantle J D G	310785
Marshall B A	211185

2nd Lieutenants

Hancock R J	290784
†Fraser-Burton S	181184
Nilan J L	181184
†Smith S	280785

Quartermasters

¶Gillard D V	*Capt*	180182
Whitehead B	*Capt*	020483

Extra-Regimentally Employed

Brigadiers

Wilkinson C E *CBE TD*■■	010282

Colonels

Browne M E *TD*■	010185

Lieutenant Colonels

Ffinch T I M *TD*■	101080
Newell D R D	010186

Majors

Ward J R *TD*	101077
Graves R J *TD MA MSc DipEd*	020579
Parker M C *LLB*	160679
Peatfield M *BSc CEng MIM AICeram MIRE*	210582

THE LIGHT DIVISION

5th Battalion The Light Infantry

Hon Colonel......Col W P Cox *MBE MC TD JP*......010685

Majors

Crowther T J *TD*▪▪	100977
Barneby W H	110979
Turner J A	161081
Stedman-Jones R *TD BA*	011181
Peacock M A P *TD*	010482
Evans J R *TD FCA*	230383
Nicholls W R A *TD*	010184
Deighton A J *MA(Ed)*	010285

Captains

¶Love A R	020775
Conway D L (*A/Maj* 010486)	010180
Goodwin J	250880
Dee D J S (*A/Maj* 010184)	010181
Walters R K *BSc ARICS*	010181
Best M	010482
Huss C N	010782
Spry-Leverton H H S	101082
¶Marsh T	011182
¶Ackling R	010483
¶Chappell T A	010483
¶Wilson A J	210683
¶Worthen L E	010883
¶Wood V	021083
Adams M P *BSc*	301183
Lawrence K G	010285
Hodson J D T	010485
¶Harding C	030486

Lieutenants

Chapman P M *BA*	210279
Huss J P S	060879
Carney A	271183
Blanchard G K G	120685
Broadman L A	310785
Smith G S	310785
Woodward F K G	310785
Kelly D J	211185

2nd Lieutenants

Wright S C	290784
Jenkins R J	181184
†Priekulis B C	260585
†Galliers I	160685
†Mottershead R B	160685
†Houlston P S	070785
†Scott M L	070785
†Johnson A M	280785
†Ward C G	010985

Quartermasters

Matthews T A		301075
	Maj	251282

6th Battalion The Light Infantry

Hon Colonel......Lt Col G W F Luttrell *MC JP (HM Lord Lieutenant Somerset)*......010477

Dep Hon Colonel......Lt Col G T G Williams *DL*......221179

Majors

Bradley P sq	311274
French T G *TD*	270178
Corry M A *BA* ph	080479
Atkin N A S	170280
¶Peck J A	020780
Mortimer R E McK *TD*	270483

Captains

Lyng A S *BEd* (*A/Maj* 021085)	110678
Mortimer K A M *TD* (*A/Maj* 010885)	201080
¶Pascoe S W A	071083
Guest R J	191083
¶Dudart-Aberdeen J E	011183
Cole R A *BA*	010384
¶Albert G H W	010584
Gee H M *BA* (*A/Maj* 011085)	280584
¶Kirkham J W	110385
¶Herrington E W *MBE*	220685

Lieutenants

Jacobs A G (*A/Capt* 010885)	010879
Avenell J L P (*A/Capt* 011085)	180181
Downey T J *BA*	211081
Bateman C T *MPS* (*A/Capt* 021085)	090882
Coia J M	101182
Charlton-Taylor R S	230185
De-Pulford J C F S	120685
Jones C S	310785

2nd Lieutenants

†Butson P R	260585
†Chamberlain C S	260585

Quartermasters

Lang R D	*Capt*	090479
Mason H J	*Capt*	100282

7th Battalion The Light Infantry

Hon Colonel..........Lt Col *The Lord* Barnard *TD (HM Lord Lieutenant Durham)*..........011279

Majors

¶Tompkins G W 180573
Smiles J C *TD* 010479
Charlton A W 010782

Captains

¶Wackett D W 280476
Van Der Gucht M (*A/Maj* 011085) 011278
Barton N C *BSc(Eng)* (*A/Maj* 011085) 011279
Hedgley D *BPhil* 040381
Henry P *BSc* 010482
Latter M J (*A/Maj* 011085) 010782
Armstrong A *MIIM* 010982
¶Lynn A F 010483
Foster M 010983
Clutterbuck R E H *BSc(Eng)* 151083
Watson A J P *LLB* 010284
Jackson T J H (*A/Maj* 210285) 170984

Lieutenants

Wood F D A (*A/Capt* 010484) 270580
Hayward A P 200483
McLeod H N G (*A/Capt* 220884) 250783
Joyce N 260783
Johnson I C 230584
Kerford M S 120784
Milner K G 070884
Lustman A M 230585
Nicholson K P 120685
McLernon W B 310785
Tough R 310785
Wyer P E 220186

2nd Lieutenants

Wicks C G M 011284

Quartermasters

Finley H *Capt* 220485

Extra-Regimentally Employed

Lieutenant Colonels

Kent-Jones T D *TD*■ *LLB* 010782
Heron J R *TD*■ *BA* 171083
Allen D G 210185

Majors

Philpott D H *BSc(Eng)* C
Bryant J B *TD*■■ 011065
Bayley L R A *MBE TD*■ *BSc* 010169
Jackson J *TD* 150472
Hale C J *TD* 160575
Minton Beddoes S W *TD*■ 311275
Loader C F *TD* 011077
Bull C A *TD*■ 011277
Anthony P 260678
Besford G 311278
Peters W M *TD* 010479
Wheeler C A *DipEd* 010979
Kelly J J A *BA MBA PGCE* 080283
Peach W R *TD* 010883
Backhouse C L'E sq 150285

Captains

Tuhey K M F *TD BA* (*A/Maj* 010485) 010678
Nicholas G V F D W 010481
Friend P N 010282
Daly M A 011282
James H R 280584
Breeze C C 010784
Evans H 010884
Pack C I ph 081185
¶Robinson R *FInstAM* 231185

Lieutenants

Jones R 300772
Twentyman N G 080882
Wright R 010585
Moore A W 080585
Dodson M J 090585

4th (Volunteer) Battalion The Royal Green Jackets

Hon Colonel..Lt (Hon Col) *Lord* Holderness *PC DL*..010467

Majors

Johnson N A *TD* 180978
Crisp T A *TD BSc BS MB* 290180
Abrahams S A G 050984

Captains

Smith J A *TD*▪ *AIB* 010364
¶Lawless P 280475
Thomas I I G *BA* 270778
Asquith A M E *LVO BSc* (*A/Maj* 220784) 291278
Howell-Pryce J B (*A/Maj* 011283) 180480
¶Bye P L *AAAI MInstAM* 020883
Griffith-Jones J G *TD BA* (*A/Maj* 120384) 010983
¶Yates R B 010983
Chapman S C (*A/Maj* 100184) 011083
¶Hooton G R *MBE MISM* 041083
Long R L H 011183
Marvin A M D 011283
¶Brimmer R C 100184
Hogg J R G 100184
Poe A D 120384
Lanyon R C B *BSc* 180784
Askham A J 011084
¶Kearl D V 031085

Lieutenants

Ryan R K *BA* (*A/Capt* 011084) 290878
Hill C N C *BSc* 080379
Naismith I A *BSc* 230280
Barkes S R 191080
Glaister T A (*A/Capt* 050984) 211081
Darcy J J C 150882
Blackwell P B (*A/Capt* 120685) 250882
Brown E R (*A/Capt* 051285) 111182
Campbell L P K 241182
Sanderson D W J 050483
Matthews T J C 230584
Hudson R J 231084

2nd Lieutenants

†Wax J L 210584
†Gardner F R 230584
†Coade C C 290784

Quartermasters

Breckenridge D A *Capt* 270977
Macdonald I D *Capt* 150885

5th (Volunteer) Battalion The Royal Green Jackets

Hon Colonel..Lt Gen *Sir* Peter Hudson *KCB CBE DL* ret pay..010485

Captains

¶Beerman J 011085

Extra-Regimentally Employed

Lieutenant Colonels

Williamson E I *TD* 080782
Travers D E 011285

Majors

Field R J *TD* 010475
Wells W A A *TD* 180282
Halsey N G *FRICS* 011084
Fulton C C *TD* 120285
Vyvyan G J T 100685

Captains

Pease A M 151280
Bryden I A *BA* 310881
Edwards M J R (*A/Maj* 010485) 080185
Fowler E W W *MA* 131285

Lieutenants

Price J A J 030575
Jackson A O 060284

2nd Lieutenants

†Ferguson J D 210678
†Scoffield B T 290784
†Rogers H P 130285

THE PARACHUTE REGIMENT

Hon Colonels .... Lt Gen *Sir* Michael Gray *KCB OBE* 170284
Dep Hon Colonel .... Col B C F Arkle *MBE TD* 200485

Lieutenant Colonels

Christian J *TD*	260378
Ironside E A C *TD MBIM ACII*	010284
Harkon J A *MBE TD*	311085

Majors

Salmon R E A *TD*▪	260767
Hickman J F psc	130869
Hutton A H *TD*	010270
Dawson I M C	010470
Bastyan A E O	010572
Schulz R A *MBE TD BSc PhD MSc*	100673
Cazenove B M de L *TD*	271076
Ellis J E H *BA* psc	071176
Vaughan Payne R C *TD*	191077
Sissling H C *TD*	080478
Stancombe J G	090478
Wotton K *TD*	011178
Mackay D J	010280
Power J C *TD BA MRCGP MIEE FITE CDipAF FBIM*	010280
Tolliss C J	011180
Farrell M W *BSc MBA*	010381
Keane S *TD BSc(Eng)*	010781
Pickup B *BEd*	011081
Beattie R A *BA MSc MSc(Econ)*	010182
Tanous C D W *TD*▪	200182
Cuthbertson-Smith D M	111282
Moore R	151083
Fleming J W A *OBE* sq	121084
Dempsey P W W *AIB AIB(Scot)*	011284
Orpen-Smellie H J *OBE MBIM MInstAM* psc	230885
Cave S D *BSc*	261185

Captains

Brown A N W *TD*	010175
Whitley P J	020279
Dunning C F *BA* (*A/Maj* 010485)	010280
¶Grant A s	220280
Dixon A C (*A/Maj* 010784)	140780
Baron P G *BSc*	131080
Bellairs H M *MEd CertEd* (*A/Maj* 250682)	010381
Bowden P L *BSc* (*A/Maj* 010183)	010381
¶Bell W S	010681
Watson R M *FCII*	010881
Owen A D	010482
Rennie K J *CIMechE*	010482
Thomas B J	290482
Evans R R B	150982
Quarendon B L (*A/Maj* 020785)	261082
O'Brien A J *TD*	011182
Hardy J M *BA*	161182
Bellairs S J	221182
Crowther N M	110183
Bennett R P	070283
Luke T F (*A/Maj* 280384)	200383
¶Turner J G *MBE*	120483
¶Cowie V A J *TD*	010683
¶Hodgkinson P	010683
¶Edney M J H	080683
¶Boxall P R	130683
¶Wilsher J S	270683
Hodges N P (*A/Maj* 011284)	130783
¶Rowntree R F	270883
¶Tosh T	010983
¶Collier G	290184
Kerr J M	190284
Ellis D A	010384
¶Wood J E	020384
¶Harratt W J	010684
Murrell V J R (*A/Maj* 010785)	271184
Harris-Ward L	281184
Pollak T E	190285
Blackman S A F	010585
Maclean I S	170785
Hall P J	220885
¶Ades H T J *TEng(CEI) MCIT MBIM MIIM FISM*	230885
¶O'Hara H F	240985

Lieutenants

Marshall H L (*A/Capt* 010983)	030479
Shaw J A B *BSc* (*A/Capt* 040184)	270979
Waudby E G (*A/Capt* 141284)	031279
Hardisty A F	270580
Weatherald P B (*A/Capt* 311085)	080780
Whyte N F	050880
Burnikell B M	020381
Fava A J (*A/Capt* 010784)	190981
Manning D T	290981
Webster S *BA*	020382
McFadyen D Y A	250582
Platt N B	090882
Turner S V	131182
Antic A *BA*	050483
Irwin M D (*A/Capt* 010486)	050483
McLean J	040583
Watson M C	100683
Shugar N A	240683
Blunt F G	310783
Macdonald I L	130983
Hardie M G	251083
Wilson R P P	230584
George D	070884
Gregory D J	070884
Mike C J V	211184
Thomas C W	211184
Doggett A J	010285
Booth S A	220585
fitz-Gibbon S S	220585
Hardie A K	220585
Imossi A	220585
Sedgwick S B	220585
Stirling H A C	220585
Falconer R B	230585
Winter M G	211185
Guild K J M	220186
McKay N J *TD*	190286

2nd Lieutenants

†Cameron F T	
†Hall S J D	160383
Simmons C W	221283
MacAlpine-Downie C R	200584
†Weir R C	200584
Hodgson P MacG	310584
Smart W McD	100684
Mackie B C	290784
Gilhooly A S	261184
†Osborne J	270185
†Quaile S W	220485
†Evason P C	260585
†Stow D H	260585
†O'Hare J G	160685
†Mason K *BSc*	070785
†Ellis S E H	280785
†Sisson-Pell M W	280785

Quartermasters

Devlin R		121175
	Maj	271185
Browning E G	*Capt*	010381
Woodhouse W H	*Capt*	221184

SPECIAL AIR SERVICE REGIMENT

ARMY AIR CORPS

Majors

West J K ph	271274
Marpole D J ph(i) ph tp	011177
Stansfeld A H R psc† ph	300778
Voy D A ph	020379
Walker D A	020379
Nixey I D	151084

Captains

Pidcock F *TD* ph	310866
Ramsden R T ph(i) ph	271268
Short A G E ph	100771
Mutton C J ph	090372
Manning G ph	080972
Gordon A D ph(i) ph	221173
Warren M A *TD MCIOB LIOB*	010174
Cooke N J H ph(i) ph	260174
Black J T ph	170774
Green M A ph	150575
Jones M A ph(cfs) ph	151175
Snape C J	191176
Tutt J R ph	250577
Dove P L ph	191277
Scarratt W T *DFC* ph	100578
Scott J D *BEM*▪ ph(cfs)	310379
Talbot N *BSc* ph tp	040879
Graham C S	010480
Hampton C M F ph	180581
Green M L	260182
Cowie J A R ph(cfs)	310382
Collins T A ph	160982
Row N A ph	010783
Adams-Cairns I M ph	250484
Woods J D ph	090784
Le Moignan J ph	060285
Farrant B E pl	241085

ROYAL ARMY CHAPLAINS' DEPARTMENT

Chaplains to the Forces (3rd Class) ranking as Majors

Webb *Rev* R W J *TD*■■ [P] 230564
Belben *Rev* K F *TD*■ 030365
Hill *Rev* M *TD AKC* 130565
Hiles *Rev* J M *TD*■ *MA* 290765
Bolton *Rev* M *TD*■ *BA* [C of S] 140270
Prins *Rev* S V *TD BSc MA* 040570
Brown *Rev* E H *TD*■ 230770
Moore *Rev* E J *TD MA* 011073
Wall *Rev* D O 090774
Curley *Rev* R L [RC] 010375
McKelvey *Rev* R S J H *TD BA* 010476
Weisman *Rev* M *MA* [J] 080876
Lavery *Rev* E R *TD* 011076
Newnham *Rev* O J *BA* 300377
Main *Rev* A *TD BD MA THM PhD* [C of S] 240677
Lloyd *Rev* P J *TD* 300877
Heron *Rev* G D 290778
Johns *Rev* R C *BA* 200978
Smith *Rev* T G *TD MCSP RGN* 011178
Lucas *Rev* J M *TD* 190379
Samuel *Rev* R R *BSc BD* [C of S] 010479
Richards *Rev* E 180779
Duncanson *Rev* D J *BA AKC* 030979
Tomlinson *Rev* B L *LTh* [C of S] 280979
George *Rev* M W *TD BA BEd* 191079
Brunswick *Rev* R J 200280
Holdsworth *Rev* J I *BA MTh* 280181
Peach *Rev* E V [RC] 270581
Rouch *Rev* D V *RNMS RGN* 010681
Cocking *Rev* K N 011081
Fox *Rev* C G 120282
Cameron *Rev* P S G *TD*■ *MA* 070982
Hughes *Rev* A 200982
Salter *Rev* A T J *AKC* 211082
Herve *Rev* J A *BA* 011282
Lowe *Rev* D C *TD* 120183
Foskew *Rev* D [RC] 230183
Anderson *Rev* W C *LTh* [C of S] 010383
Worley *Rev* W 130583
Flux *Rev* B G 160284
Joyce *Rev* K R 080384
Funnell *Rev* B A [RC] 190684
Grey *Rev* R T *BA* 250784
Franey *Rev* A [RC] 030884
Firth *Rev* G A 171184
Pritchard *Rev* M O 130385
Barclay *Rev* I C *BD MA* [C of S] 180385
Punshon *Rev* K *MA* 230485
Handley *Rev* N 190685
Griffiths *Rev* R H 290885
Silcox *Rev* J R *BD* [C of S] 050985
Forbes *Rev* J W A [C of S] 060985
Rymer *Rev* D J T 181085
Vaughan *Rev* T 021185
Hathaway *Rev* D A G 260286

Chaplains to the Forces (4th Class) ranking as Captains

Humphreys *Rev* J R *BSc(Eng)* 220174
Harrington *Rev* J C 180276
Willcox *Rev* S H 030380
Woods *Rev* A G *FCCA* 060380
Corker *Rev* J A 180380
Sutch *Rev* C D 160480
McDonald *Rev* I H 220480
Beal *Rev* R D 150580
Campbell *Rev* R D M *BD FSA* [C of S] 300580
Crawley *Rev* D 030980
Wilkinson *Rev* S E *BA* 030980
Elmore *Rev* G M 050980
Wilson *Rev* P D [C of S] 180980
Kinch *Rev* D [M] 200181
Barker *Rev* A I *BSc MA* [RC] 260281
Taylor *Rev* J P [UB] 201281
Butterworth *Rev* J K *BCom BD* 040382
Hayes *Rev* R B M 060482
Hoare *Rev* P R A R *TD* 100582
Walker *Rev* D 040682
Bartlett *Rev* A M 140782
Torrance *Rev* I R *BD MA DPhil* [C of S] 260782
Farmer *Rev* K W 160882
Williams *Rev* D J *MSc DIC CBiol MIBiol* [UB] 230882
Scott *Rev* J P *BA(Hons)* 301182
Miln *Rev* P 131282
McCormick *Rev* A M [C of S] 301282
Forsyth *Rev* A R *MTh* [UB] 160283
Latimer *Rev* D [C of S] 240383
Mendel *Rev* T O 240583
Pugh *Rev* J H [M] 141183
Douglas *Rev* A V *BEd* 161183
Day *Rev* C I *BA(Hons)* 201283
Dick *Rev* C B 020384
Brawn *Rev* M J [UB] 120484
Kemp *Rev* B *MA* 130484
Smith *Rev* J [C of S] 110584
Calder *Rev* R P 041284
Bishop *Rev* H D *BA* 220585
Payne *Rev* R S 120685
McKinnel *Rev* N H P 020785
Noblett *Rev* W A 160885
Duddy *Rev* J [RC] 260985
Robbins *Rev* S 271185

Section B - Army Cadet Force

Chaplains to the Forces (3rd Class) ranking as Majors

Akers-Perry *Rev* E
Alton *Rev* K
Ashley *Rev* J M
Barnard *Rev* M G
Birmingham *Rev* P [RC]
Bolster *Rev* R F *CLJ* [C of S]
Boston *Rev* J B
Bowdren *Rev* D M [RC]
Briggs *Rev* M W
Buckett *Rev* J F
Burns *Rev* W G *MBE*
Clarke *Rev* E J A
Cooper *Rev* N M
Corfield *Rev* J B
Cornish *Rev* A
Dakin *Rev* R J B
Dickson *Rev* J C [C of S]
Edwards *Rev* P A *CF*
Edwards *Rev* G A
Evans *Rev* J M
Felix *Rev* D C
Glew *Rev* G W
Glover *Rev* B R
Gray *Rev* P *TD BA MA*
Gwyther *Rev* R L
Hatcliffe *Rev* C J W
Hibbert *Rev* R T
Law *Rev* K
Llewellyn *Rev* J H N
Ludlow *Rev* A P
Lynn *Rev* G
Mackay *Rev* H
Mark *Rev* R J
Martin *Rev* D A
Matthews *Rev* R I J
McMullin *Rev* J A [C of S]
Moore *Rev* W J F
Pearce *Rev* F
Pollock *Rev* T
Pomeroy *Rev* M J
Rathbone *Rev* R G
Rawson *Rev* J J [RC]
Richards *Rev* J F
Ritchie *Rev* W M [C of S]
Roberts *Rev* F F C
Robertson *Rev* J T
Robertson *Rev* E [C of S]
Robson *Rev* J [C of S]
Sanderson *Rev* F [M]
Secrett *Rev* I R
Seeds *Rev* C W
Shenton *Rev* B
Sims *Rev* A G [RC]
Smith *Rev* G K [C of S]
Steed *Rev* H E *MA DTH*
Steward *Rev* R E A
Stewart *Rev* W T A [C of S]
Stoddart-Seller *Rev* J S
Symons *Rev* J E *AKC CF*
Thomas *Rev* I R L
Tolland *Rev* J
Truman *Rev* J M
Tunbridge *Rev* D F [UB]
Turner *Rev* G R
Varney *Rev* W J G
Wakelin *Rev* A F
Warburton *Rev* R T *MBE*
Williams *Rev* P D [M]
Williams *Rev* M R J
Williams *Rev* D M R
Wood *Rev* F H

Chaplains to the Forces (4th Class) ranking as Captains

Anderson *Rev* M J A
Beck *Rev* J C
Bell *Rev* G B
Bennett *Rev* E J
Broughton *Rev* S R
Burt *Rev* R M
Carter *Rev* J H
Cheall *Rev* H F K
Collins *Rev* R H
Cripps *Rev* M C R
Daley *Rev* V L
Farnworth *Rev* M G F
Farquhar *Rev* R M [C of S]
Flynn *Rev* S J
Gatt *Rev* D W
Girling *Rev* D F C
Goskirk *Rev* J L
Gwyther *Rev* G D
Hagan *Rev* T J
Hartley *Rev* P
Hitchcock *Rev* D
Holloway *Rev* G E
Hughes *Rev* G B
Hughes *Rev* B [RC]
Hunt *Rev* P J
Jones *Rev* G T
Lea *Rev* N
Letford *Rev* P A
Lloyd *Rev* H J
Lynett *Rev* A M
MacDonald *Rev* J W
Mackle *Rev* G J [RC]
MacMillan *Rev* J A
McCormick *Rev* J A A
McKenna *Rev* M F [RC]
McPherson *Rev* N F W [UB]
Meredith-Jones *Rev* R
Monaghan *Rev* J *MBE* [C of S]
Mulcahey *Rev* A
Nash *Rev* D *BD*
Nicholson *Rev* N P
Noise *Rev* R A
Pargeter *Rev* P [RC]
Rees *Rev* O P D
Ridgway *Rev* D
Rogers *Rev* N D *TD*
Setchell *Rev* N W F
Snow *Rev* C M S
Spong *Rev* T J *CLJ*
Stacey *Rev* J R
Stone *Rev* P J
Strachan *Rev* S G *MA*
Sudbury *Rev* P J
Swann *Rev* A K
Thomas *Rev* G H
Thorpe *Rev* M W
Tyndall *Rev* J H
Wall *Rev* N J
Westmuckett *Rev* J S
White *Rev* P G
Whitehouse *Rev* B [RC]
Williams *Rev* M C [UB]
Withey *Rev* M J
Woods *Rev* M S

Territorial Army — continued

ROYAL CORPS OF TRANSPORT

Hon Colonels .... Col D E Gibbs *CBE TD JP DL* 010475
Lt (Hon Lt Col) *The Earl of* Elgin and Kincardine *KT JP DL* 010976
Col J A Creaney *OBE TD QC DL* 211080
Col R L Wallis ret pay 011280
Brig D Cardle ret pay 030681
Brig J G Starling *CBE MC DL* ret pay 010482
Lt Col I D Gardiner 301082
Sir Christopher Leaver *GBE JP* 010583
Brig B C Ridley ret pay 040884
The Rt Hon The Viscount Downe *DL* 200984
Brig R E L Jenkins *CBE* ret pay 010485
Col J R B Smith *TD* 010785

Colonels

Baldry P D *TD*■ 011078
Spate G T *TD* 140979
Heslop D W *TD*■■ *ACII* 270782
Falloon W E *CBE TD*■■ *ADC BA BSc* 010483
Emery B D *TD*■■ *MA FCIS FCII* 010783
Butler J A *MC TD*■ 270785

Lieutenant Colonels

Ahern C J *TD*■ 010178
Coates D B *TD*■ *MICE MIMunE MIHT* 011179
Spurr C L E *ERD*■ *TD* 011179
Gibb J D *TD*■ *AIB(Scot)* 011180
Jones D E B *TD TEng(CEI) FSCET FInstCES* 010482
Herbert C A *TD DMS MBIM MITO JP* 010782
Troman J J *TD*■■ 010782
Lockhart D A S *TD*■ *MA MSc PhD* 160782
Lynch J P *TD*■ *FRSH* 011182
Spackman S H *TD*■ 011182
Street R D *MCIT AIRTE MBIM MIPDM* sq t 010483
Douglas I M *TD*■ *CEng MICE MIHT MRSH* 221183
Clifford L *TD*■ sq(v) 011283
Durbin P C *TD* 290284
Heath J W *TD*■ 010484
Shawley G J *TD*■ 010484
Walters R I t 010484
Webber R E *BA* 210784
Sowden J A *TD AIB JP* 120984
Ainsley C H *TD MBIM FInstPet* 011084
Barkshire B F 010485
Mead D A *TD*■ 010485
Wandless P J *TD CEng MIMarE* 011185
Marshall W J *MBE TD*■ *BA DL* 031185
Milner-Williams C W M *TD ACIS* 010486

Majors

Lowndes J F L *TD*■ *BSc CEng FIMechE MIOB* 010970
Dawson F S *MBE TD*■ *AIB* 251070
Keir J M *TD*■■ *MCIT* 260571
Edwards A R *TD*■■ 020173
Innes J H *TD* 150973
Maddern A J *TD*■ 011173
Burns E J *TD BA MIPM MIIM* 151273
Knight M D R *TD*■■ *FRICS* 151273
Reeks D R *TD BSc* 151273
Jordan H A J *MBE FCIT* t 201273
Thomas J E *TD FCA MBIM* 020674
Whittard P J T *TD*■ *MICE MIHT* 020674
Botting K W *TD*■ *ACII* 010974
Campbell-Robson R L *TD* 011074
Maclean A D F *TD*■ 011174
Herbert M J *TD*■■ 021174
Blackman R H sq t 181274
Davies T A *TD* 011075
Trundell H K *TD*■■ 021175
Mitchell E B D *TD*■ 010676
¶Davidson R 090676
Russell B A F 110976
Barron R G *TD*■ *FCII* 011176
Unthank D R *TD*■ 011176
Oldfield J E *TD*■ *CEng MICE MIStructE* 041176
Tucker B *CEng MIMechE* 181276
Last G *TD*■ *FISM* 191276
Brown J S *TD*■■ 010177
Edwards D W *TD*■ 010177
Haywood S S *TD*■ *BSc DMS* 010177
Cameron J J *TD*■ 010577
Codd R H I A P *TD*■ 010577
Evanson-Goddard L M sq adp 300677
Stanley R M *TD*■■ 010877
Potton A E *TD*■ *BA MEd PhD* 011077
Gillham L S A *TD* 051277
Templar C H *TD*■ 010178
Graham J R *TD*■■ *MA* 010478
Turnbull J C *TD*■ *AMInstTA* 010478
Patten E M *TD* 010578
Stone R J *TD*■ 010578
Ward M C *TD*■ *BA* 010578
Webber M J *TD*■■ *BA* 010578
Reed J *TD* 130878
Jackson P V E *TD*■ 161078
McElwee N *TD* sq(v) 011278
Burton D R *TD AIB* 010179
McRobbie I W B 010179
Allcock R E *TD*■ *MSc MCIT MIPDM* 010379
Dempster I F *TD* 010479
Haynes C J *TD AIB* 010579
Stevens D W *TD*■ 010579
Saunders M B *TD BA MSc* 010779
Laing R M *TD BSc MCIT* 011179
Fletcher C *TD* 010180
Aindow P J *TD* 190180
Stockdale D R *TD BTech CEng MIMechE MIProdE MBIM* 110280
Mason C N *TD FRICS* 010480
Matthews-Maxwell C G *TD ACIS* 010480
Patton M A 010480
Wakley J E J *TD* 010580
Pool N W *TD* 040680
Carson R F *TD* 150680
Cross C *TD* 110880
Betts G A 300980
Stonestreet B F 300980
Bone A C W *TD*■ 011080
Dobson R H *TD*■ *AIB* 201080
Mansel A R *TD* 221080
Taylor R G *TD*■ *BSc* 101180
McMillan I *TD*■ 141180
Horne L W F *TD BSc* 010181
Hughes R D L *TD BA* 010181
Todd J *TD* 010381
Astbury J *BSc* 010481
Davies A E *TD* 010481
Lilley J M *TD*■ *ACIS MBIM AIB* 010481
Park J C *TD BSc* 040481
Rodgers R M *TD* 010781
Arnold G P *TD* 121081
Highton T C *TD* 121081
Cafe M C *GradRSC* 130382
Burn B T W *TD* 010482
Lardner G J *TD BEng* 010482
Wilkinson R M *TD* 010482
Marsland-Roberts P J *TD* 010582
Mount P J *TD* 010582
Sharp C E C *TD MBIM* 010582
Sutherland R J *TD* 240682
King P D *TD LLB MA AKC* 010782
Markwick W H *TD BSc* 010782
Burton F M *TD*■■ *BSc FRSC* 010882
Burkes A D 010982
Kane D J *TD* 021082
Adams A R W 240183
Bancroft R L A *TD* 130283
Aitken W *TD BA* 010483
Couper I S B *TD* 010483
Goodman G P *TD* 010483
Hughes M J N *TD BSc BSc* 010483
Hyde M P *TD* 010483
Orrell G W *TD*■ *BA* 010483
Pearson R V C *TD* 010483
Peterson J C *TD* 010483
West M J *TD* 020483
Waite E G *TD AIB* 220483
Sutherland A D *TD* 250483
Jesson A F *MLS MBIM ALA* 010683
Limmer J *TD AIB* 010683
Tambling W J F *TD BA DMS* 010683
Whalley P F *LLB* 200683
Macdonald A G 300683
Milligan D *TD* 300983
Siebert M L A *TD BSc MRSC* 201083
Naysmith P A R *TD AIB* 011183
Membry D A J *TD BSc* 141183
Colquhoun E S *TD* 011283
Durham D *TD MInstPet* 010184
Sanders D J *TD* 010184
Kinsman P F 010384
Laverick R *TD* 310384
Morgan D T *TD* 010484
Pow R A *TD* 010484

Santon R C *BSc(Eng) CEng MIChemE* 010484
Boulton A J *TD BA* 011084
Drewe A B 011084
Shiell C D S *TD* 011084
Pashby A J *TD* 061084
David R G E *TD* 131184
Finlay G C *TD*▪ 011284
Morrison W R *TD*▪ 010285
Westerby G G 150285
Naughton A C 040385
Severein P J *BSc(Econ) MInstPS* 080385
Soden F T *MBIM* t 180385
Harris L B 010485
Lees T *BA* 010485
Tarrant G J H *TD ACA* 010485
Warwick I J T 010485
Wilson J C *MBIM* 010485
Bradshaw D M *TD BSc DipTechSc* 010585
Butler J M *TD MSc* 010585
Sheridan P R *TD BA NP* 010585
Frame H R *TD* 100685
Wilding A D C 010785
Brownhill W H 180785
White W J *BSc* 060186
Barnard A J 180186
Lynch A S R *BSc(Eng)* 180186
Edmondston-Low G D 010486
Hales A R 010486

Captains

¶Pitt J
¶Woodruff J W pl 211054
James W J *TD* (*Bt/Maj* 010782) 010468
¶Birtles G S 011269
Marshall P 020670
¶Oliver R E *BEM* 040471
Feldman A S *TD*▪ 060571
¶Harding A 151271
Rawlings K J 010374
Harris R W *TD* 290175
Hinchcliffe P J *TD* 140275
Ferguson J K *DMS MBIM MIHORT* 310775
Neill J T *TD* (*A/Maj* 010484) 010975
Milne S A W *TD* 010476
Smith M A A *TD* 010476
¶Morgan C 070476
¶McKeever W B *MISM* 120876
Bottomley H E *TD* 011076
¶Oliver D 010277
¶Hadden A D 310377
Harrison T *MBE TD* 290477
Hagon A *TD*▪ *MCIT* 010577
Sutherland N M *TD* (*A/Maj* 011284) 150577
Mays B J *TD MSc MRSC* 080977
Raggett B G *TD* 091077
Cantlay L J *TD* 010178
Coggon S H *TD* 010478
Corcoran B M *TD* 010478
Lunt K C 110478
Duffell C G *TD BSc MICE* 010578
Stabb P R *TD IPFA* (*A/Maj* 050585) 110678
¶Davies D G F 011278
¶Ryan A 010179
Warner E W *TD MSc FSS LIDPM CBiol MIBiol* 010179
Marples P *BSc* 010279
Jefferson R *TD* 010579
Thoms R S *TD* 010579
Dunn M J 010879
Hamilton A A D (*A/Maj* 010685) 010879
Staves J *BSc PhD* 010879
¶Rooney E N 010979
Rouse I 151079
Bishop-King J R *TD* 010180
Page P R *TD* 010280
Patterson S R *LLB* 010280
Terrett W H *TD BEd* 010280
Watt W A *TD BA ACII* 010280
Baker-Munton R S *TD BSc* 010480
Standring G L *TD BDS* 010480
Steffen J M 010480
Strong J W F 010480
Naqvi R H *LLB* 040680
Braden S A *BSc(Eng)* 090980
Patterson I D 131180
Bennett J C 010181
Beveridge A J 010181
Smith P J D 010181
Montgomery D J 200181
Crawford J F 090381
Brown J A 010481
Parr D T 010481
Baker P W (*A/Maj* 130185) 110481
West D *TD* 110481
Young W M *BSc(Hons) CEng MIMechE ACIBSE* (*A/Maj* 140584) 010881
Adams A G C 250981
Sands N W H *BA* 250981
Cooper C J 021181
Sturrock J 091181
¶Orr R 300182
Coleman D B 180282
Conroy T J *BSc* 010382
Arnett E A 150382
Stewart J R *TD BSc MRSC* 010482
Williams H L 010482
Phillips J C G 010582
Stuart J R (*A/Maj* 071085) 040782
Watson P L B 010882
Dyer C A 080982
¶Gill P J 160982
¶Garwood J 180982
Darling A P 300982
Sutton A H *TD BSc(Econ)* 300982
Leeder J 011082
Brown R T *BSc* 211082
Sykes J P 010183
Ashman T J *BSc* owc 150283
Jeffery F L 010383
Woodthorpe P G 010383
Bartlett B S 140383
Aickin R M *BSc PhD FRSC ACII* 010483
Baker P G 010483
Chapman J M *MCIT* 010483
Charlton A A *BA MA MBIM FIMS* 010483
Holman S J *BA MSc* (*A/Maj* 010486) 010483
Mustow J *CEng MICE MIMunE* 010483
Sheen M J *BEd MA* 010483
Vaughan A 010483
¶Knight J C 010583
Sykes N C 010583
Burnell C M 260583
Davies L C 010783
Lyon G T *LLB* 010883
Page A 010883
Haworth S C 020883
Rayner R W 010983
Hood R A 150983
Kennedy I F 011183
¶Morley E *MBE* 071183
Stead K 010184
Waananen P J 010184
Doran P M 010384
¶Genever C B *MBE* 010384
McCall D *BSc* 010384
Nisbet K R 010384
Adams R J *MA* 010484
Clarke G D 010484
Girdwood D C B 010484
Melaugh M J 010484
Smith R J *TEng(CEI) MIMI AMIMI* 010484
Stewart T *TD* 010484
Westcott R 010484
¶Greenbrook C 120484
¶Herbert N D B ph pl 260484
Harkiss J W M 150584
¶Ryan M J 160784
¶Tucker I J pl 240884
Donaldson D 011284
Goble E 011284
Hamilton I D 011284
Hyden I 011284
McKay F 011284
¶O'Sullivan K *MBE* 181284
Meredith F F 010185
Goleczka J A *BA MIPDM* 190185
Moses N F 190185
Hambleton R C 100285
¶McDougall A G 170385
McCoig M J *ATD* 310385
Northover M A *ACA* 310385
Hardiman J W 010485
Lassiter C J 010485
Whitty W J *TD* 010485
Shaw K D 010585
¶Chisnall A D W *TEng(CEI) MIRTE MBIM MIIM* 020585
Dolan J 010985
¶Miller F J 180985
Hills J 011185
Heffron D *MBE* 021185
Openshaw D A 101185
¶Allen R H *AInstTA* 020186
McBride D I *MB BCh BAO* 060186
Blackman T A *MA* 010486
Clark D P T 010486
Foulkes W 010486
Palmer D M 010486
Spindler H M *BSc(Eng) MBIM* 010486
Weale T D *ASVA ARVA* 010486

Lieutenants

Docherty C G (*A/Capt* 010477) 150475
Parker M R G 121175
Vincent P *TD* 270176
Lovell D G 200477
Norman J R 251077
Poole D N J *BD MA FRGS* 260179
Bloom G W (*A/Capt* 010485) 260679
Davison G M *MCIT* 220180
Waller G R (*A/Capt* 010282) 220180
Taverner J H E *BSc* (*A/Capt* 150485) 070980
Galvin M P (*A/Capt* 310385) 301080
Cockbill P J 231180
Archibald G 220181
Crozier A (*A/Capt* 010284) 010481
Goddard G H M *BSc(Econ) FIA* 010481
Ireland G A (*A/Capt* 010784) 010481
Marguet J S (*A/Capt* 151184) 010481
Mantell P D K *BA(Hons)* 070481
Groves J N 150481

Territorial Army, Royal Corps of Transport — continued

Name	Date
Cinnamon R	040781
Taylor S J	211081
Twemlow-Krzempek D F	
(*A/Capt* 010485)	211081
Foster T P	310182
Curtis A G	120382
Martin J M	010482
Beaton K C *BA*	
(*A/Capt* 070985)	150482
Wilkinson D W	200582
Macpherson J S *BA*	250582
Ricketts A J	
(*A/Capt* 151184)	250582
Moynham D	180682
Holmes-Ievers R L	090882
Price J R	271082
Llewellin W O	161182
Sayers A G	
(*A/Capt* 010485)	121282
Matthews J R	
(*A/Capt* 010285)	240583
Palmer C S J	240583
Dodds J S	
(*A/Capt* 010885)	080883
Scott W C	080883
Hogan G R	060983
Smith M R	
(*A/Capt* 010985)	251083
Halus K F	311083
Storrie R S *BSc(Eng)*	210184
Burns P M G	
(*A/Capt* 010485)	300184
Elliott G H S	090484
McLennan R M	230584
McPeake G W C	
(*A/Capt* 011084)	230584
Nicholas W H M	230584
Gorringe E G A	240584
Turner T	240784
Barnes A F *BSc*	290784
Paterson G S	040884
Olney M	011084
Clarke P R *BSc*	201184
Stevenson C S	211184
York J	211184
Arthur K A E	280285
Coombes W A G	280285
Thompson D W L *TD*	
(*A/Maj* 040385)	040385
Finch A *TD*	200485
Galloway R L	200485
Pope J J B *MBE* sq	130585
Florance P J	220585
Jordan J A	220585
Starr P N M *BA*	220585
Field R J B	230585
Marsh S A W	230585
Lawson N G P	260585
Ellis I P	010685
Willoughby G N J	250685
Cowan N	010785
Cornmell T	050785
Gibbins D C	190785
Doherty P J	081085
Groome J C	111085
Holde E R	211185
Wilkinson N W	211185
Boden M J	220186
Gagen D M	220186
Stanford G F	220186
Haylock T	110486

2nd Lieutenants

Name	Date
†Martin P L	121182
†Sutton P R	011282
Fox R J	211183
Bennett S W	200584
Grear F D	200584
Logan A D	200584
Lynch B G	200584
Mortimer J H	200584
Thomas A B	200584
Bedwell D	100684
†Smith J	100684
Van Den Bergh M J	100684
Dillon M R S	290784
Edmonds P S	290784
James C P	290784
†Wilson J D	290784
Carmichael I L	181184
†Powell C C	151284
†Hogg R	050585
†Earl W H	150585
†Browne N P	260585
†Creedican P J W	260585
†Hassall M J	260585
†Jassal V B	260585
†Lucas J D	260585
†Morrison R E	260585
†Stuart B G	260585
†Killacky C *BSc(Hons)*	060685
†Manning D M	130685
†Austin W J	160685
†Fraser G M K	160685
†Picken A K	160685
†Blakey M C	070785
†Hughes J D	070785
†Morgan J D H	070785
†Gray J D H	280785
†Green K C	280785
†Ward J P	280785
†Fenton J G	011285
†Kitney W R	011285

Quartermasters

Name	Rank	Date
Smith R F		310375
	Maj	021082
Norman W J		130178
	Maj	260784
Roberts K		290578
	Maj	020785
¶Lipscombe E G *MInstAM*		080179
	Maj	170275
Brimacombe A K	*Capt*	010483
Burris J	*Capt*	210683
Colclough P	*Capt*	230883
Davey W A	*Capt*	140983
Grant S	*Capt*	210184
Edgeller T J	*Capt*	020284
Nisbet L	*Capt*	010384
Desmond C P	*Capt*	130584
Higgins J R	*Capt*	130584
Kelly J R	*Capt*	130584
Naisbett T E	*Capt*	130584
Togher M	*Capt*	160584
Rogers G J *AMInstTA*		
	Capt	260584
Mooney W J	*Capt*	010784
Livingstone A *MBE*	*Capt*	050784
Lowe A	*Capt*	010884
Jones S E	*Capt*	221084
Jarrett K J	*Capt*	291084
Jones J M	*Capt*	120485
Edwards A C	*Capt*	230685
Sears M A D	*Capt*	230685
Baldry D	*Capt*	130885
Selley R	*Capt*	250985
Hennon J A	*Capt*	011185
Goodenough H W	*Capt*	131285
Marriott K L	*Capt*	131285

ROYAL ARMY MEDICAL CORPS

Hon Colonels

- Lt Col H F Crawford *TD* 050178
- Col L G R Wand *TD* 140781
- Col T C Dow *TD* 140781
- Col J R Cross *TD* 011081
- Brig J N Ghika *CBE* ret pay 281081
- Lt Col J B Bridges *TD* 090282
- Col A McCalister 090282
- Col T K Burke *TD* 010482
- Col H G Brown *TD* 010482
- Lt Col H W V Charlton *TD* 150882
- Col J S G Blair *OBE TD* 191082
- Maj Gen N G Kirby *OBE* ret pay 161282
- Col D F Smith *MBE TD* 231282
- Maj Gen J D C Graham *CB CBE* ret pay 010483
- Lt Col R W S Miller *TD* 010483
- Col J D Evans *TD* 240284
- Lt Col G L Featherstone *TD* 040884
- Brig C D H Wilson 010585
- W A B Smellie 011185
- Gen *Sir* Peter Whiteley *GCB OBE* 221285
- Brig R G Robinson 010486
- Brig D C Wilkins *CBE* 020486
- Lt Gen *Sir* Alan Reay *KBE* 070586
- Col R A Goodhead *TD* 020686

Colonels

Edmond P *CBE TD MB ChB FRCSEd* 021176
Hall-Davies G *CBE TD■ MB ChB FFARCS* 011077
Burton R M *TD■ BSc MA MB ChB FRCS FRCSEd FRCOG MMSA* 011178
Sechiari G *TD MB BCh FRCP* 010479
Elder W M *TD■ MB ChB* 011079
Bremner A D *TD QHS MB ChB DCH DObstRCOG* 021179
Anderson J A D *TD■ MA MD ChB MRCGP FFCM DPH DObstRCOG DL* 130981
Daly P J *OBE TD■■ LRCPI&LM LRCSI&LM* 011081
Eakins W A *CBE TD■ MB BCh BAO MBIM MFOM* 191081
øClarke K *TD■ MB BS FFARCS DA* 010482
Tait I B *TD■■ MB ChB FRCS FRCSEd* 010482
Platt H S *TD■ QHP MD BS BSc* 011182
Smith G B *TD■ MB BS FFARCS MRCS LRCP DA* 011182
Howorth P J N *TD MD MSc MRCPath* 010483
Jones J J *TD MB ChB* 300983
Johnman L *QHP MB ChB MRCGP DObstRCOG* 011183
Austin T R *QHS MB ChB FFARCS DTM&H* 010184
Alexander J P *TD QHS MB BCh BAO MRCPI FFARCS FFARCS DA* 010984
Stenson K *MB BS MRCGP MRCS LRCP DObstRCOG* 010485
Briggs A P *TD■ MB ChB MRCOG MRCS LRCP* 011085
Thompson R A *MBE TD MB BS FRCP FRCPath MRCS* 011085
Tatler G L V *TD■ MRCS DMRD* 011185
Young C J *MSc MRCOG MRCS LRCP* 011185
Griffiths H E D *TD■ MB BS FRCS LRCP* 010486
Skene J R *TD■■■ MB ChB DObstRCOG* 010486

Lieutenant Colonels

Bridges J B *TD■■ BSc MD BCh BAO BSc* 010769
Humphreys J *TD■ ChM MB FRCS FRCSEd LRCP* 111169
Myles D M G *OBE TD■■ MB ChB* 010172
Bryson T H L *TD■■ MB ChB FFARCS DA* 010472
Connolly D P *LRCPI&LM LRCSI&LM AFOM LFOM* 080872
Holmes W *MB BS MFCM DPH DIH DTM&H FRIPHH AFOM* 240872
Bamford N E C *OBE TD■■ MB BCh BAO* 010173
Fisher M L *TD■■ MB BS MRCGP DObstRCOG* 010173
Young C H *ERD TD■ FRCS FRCSEd LRCP* 010473
Brookes J P C M *FFARCS LMSSA* 170673
Francis R C *TD MB BS FRCOG MRCS LRCP DObstRCOG DTM&H* 010574
Owen-Smith M S *MS MB FRCS FRCSEd LRCP* 170674
Carson D J L *TD■■ MD BCh BAO* 120375
Peacock G W *MRCGP MFCM MRCS LRCP DObstRCOG DTM&H* psc 061175
Loyn W G G *ERD TD MB BS FFARCS DA* 010476
Reed M F *TD■ MB ChB FRCOG* 010177
Clink H M *TD MB BS MRCPath MRCS LRCP DObstRCOG* 010477
Manuel H *MB BChir DObstRCOG DTM&H* 190577
Ferguson J J *TD■ MB ChB FRCGP CBiol MIBiol* 010777
Aitken R E G *MB ChB* 011077
Welch G S *OBE TD MB BS FRCS LRCP* 181177
Wakely D *TD■ MB BS FFARCS MRCS LRCP DA* 010178
Currie J C M *TD MChir MB FRCS* 010478
Green R J *TD MB BS MRCS LRCP* 010478
Hart D D *TD■■ MB ChB FFARCS DA* 140678
Calder I M *TD■■ MD ChB DMJ* 011178
Bradshaw C R *MB BS FRCR* 071279
Roberts J D A *MRCS LRCP MBIM* 290180
Worthy J A R *MB BS MFCM DTM&H* 010380
Nicol A G *PhD MB ChB MRCPEd MRCPath* 140281
Francis J G *TD MB BS FFARCS DA DObstRCOG* 060381
Kay N R M *TD FRCS LRCP* 210481
Aldridge M J *MB ChB FRCSEd* 010781
Brown G N *TD MB ChB MRCS LRCP DIH MFOM* 010981
Newsome D A *MB ChB MRCP(UK)* 011281
Day J B *TD MB ChB FRCSEd* 010282
Banks R *ARRC FBIM RGN* 010482
Feggetter J G W *MB BS FRCS* 010482
Jones G R B *TD MB BCh MRCPEd MRCS* 010482
McIntosh C S *TD■■ MD ChB MRCP(UK)* 010482
Muncaster J W *TD MB BS DObstRCOG* 010482
Sethi K B S *OBE TD MB BS MRCGP DLO* 010482
Sutton R N P *TD■ DM BCh FRCPath DCH* 010482
Tinckler L F *MD ChM FRCS LRCP DTM&H* 010482
Bracewell B F *TD MB ChB* 010582
Haslett W H K *TD■■ MB BCh BAO FFARCS* 010582
Low R A L *TD MB ChB FRCS(Glasg) FRCOG LRCPS* 020682

Territorial Army, Royal Army Medical Corps — continued

Stanworth P A *TD■■ BM BCh FRCS DCH* 010782
Hill J D *TD■ MB BS FFARCS DA* 011182
Howlett K A *MB BS FFR MRCS LRCP DCH FRCR DMRD* 011182
Scott J A *TD MA MB BChir MRCGP DObstRCOG* 020183
Selkon J B *TD■ MB ChB FRCPath DCP* 310183
Bushby D R P *TD MB ChB DObstRCOG* 010483
Chandler G P *MB ChB MRCOG* 010483
Lawrence P A *TD■■ MB BS MRCS LRCP DIH DObstRCOG AFOM* 010483
Shepherd W F I *TD MB BCh BAO FRCSEd DO* 010483
Gwynn C M *TD MB ChB MRCP(UK) DCH DObstRCOG* 010583
Strachan R *MB ChB MRCGP* 010983
Grant R W *MB ChB* 030983
Power D J *TD MB BCh BAO MRCPsych DPM DMJ* 011183
McLaren E H *TD MB ChB BSc FRCP(Glasg)* 021183
Hamilton A J *TD MB BS FRCS FRCSEd MRCOG LRCP* 011283
Hawkins T J *TD MB BS FFARCS DA* 161283
Hipkin L J *MD ChB FRCPath MRCS LRCP* 060384
Banerjee R K *OBE TD MB BS FRCS* 010484
Gilkison J N *MB ChB MRCGP DObstRCOG* 020684
Johnson M K *MB ChB FFARCS* 010884
Morgan J G *RGN EN(G) RCNT* 011084
Coleman J C *TD■ MB BS FRCPath MRCS LRCP FRCPath* 011184
Batson G A *TD MD ChB FRCPEd DObstRCOG* 010185
Wilson C R M *TD■ MB BS MRCPsych DPM* 040385
Green R L *TD MB ChB DAvMed MFOM* 010485
Herring D W *MB BS FRCS* 010485
Morriss G W *FFARCS MRCS LRCP DA DTM&H* 010485
Steen K C D *TD MB BS MRCGP MRCS* 010485
Robertson I G *TD MD ChB MRCOG* 100485
Dornan J D *TD MB BCh BAO MFOM* 010685
Davies C *TD MB BCh FRCPsych DPM* 010885
Colohan M D *MB BCh BAO* 140985
Gallagher L B S *TD■ MB BCh BAO FFARCS* 011085
Smith M F *TD■ ChM MB FRCSEd MRCOG* 011085
Stewart A I *MB ChB FFARCS* 011085
Hamilton J B *TD MB BCh BAO FRCSEd* 311085
Rowe B *TD MB BChir FRCPath DTM&H* 011185
Pusey R J *TD MB ChB FRCS* 010186
Moore E J H *MB ChB* 010286

Majors

Petrie R A N *TD■■ MB BChir MRCS LRCP* 100861
Thomson K F M *TD■ BM BCh DLO* 080362
Arbuthnot J H *TD■■ MB BCh BAO MRCGP* 100364
Hope A M *TD MB BS MRCS* 161064
Robinson E T *MB ChB MRCGP DObstRCOG* 130965
Robinson A P *TD■ MB ChB* 030666
Boulton T B *ERD■ TD MB BChir FFARCS DA* 010467
Cook P J *TD■ MB BS FRCS(Glasg) LRCP* 010467
Davies A *TD■ MB BS DObstRCOG FPDip* 010467
Gibson R M *ERD TD MD ChB FRCS FRCSEd* (*Bt/Lt Col* 101271) 010467
Hunting J B *TD MB ChB* 010467
McKay R H G *MBE TD LRCP LRCS LRFPS* (*Bt/Lt Col* 181084) 010467
Price E C V *TD■■ MB BS FRCSEd LRCP* 010467
Cross T W *TD MB ChB DPH DIH DObstRCOG MFCM MFCMI MFOM MFOMI* 120867
Townsend D C *MB BS FFARCS MRCS LRCP DA* 040868
Price J L *TD MB ChB FRCSEd FRCOG DObstRCOG* 261168
Bhattacharya P K *TD■ MB BS* 011268
Higham A *TD MB ChB FRCS FRCSEd* 011268
Pitt P C C *TD MB BS MRCPEd FRCS FRCSEd DTM&H* 010169
Dulake C *TD MB BChir MRCPath MRCS LRCP* 170169
Beeson A A *MB BS MRCP DPH* 070369
Flynn W A *TD■ MB BCh BAO* 060569
Kennedy B R *TD■ MB ChB FFARCS* 010370
Kenyon A R T *MB BS LMSSA* 070370
Kerr G D *TD■ MB ChB FRCSEd FRCOG DObstRCOG* (*A/Lt Col* 110479) 011270
Holmes-Ievers R J *TD MB LAH* 290171
Carter R *MB BS* (*Bt/Lt Col* 181084) 130271
Tyson J E *TD■■* 300471
Parry J W L *TD DM BCh FFARCS* 030571
Murray D P J *MRCP(UK) DipVen* 060571
O'Hanlon J N *TD■ LRCPI&LM LRCSI&LM* (*Bt/Lt Col* 181084) 120172
Ireland B J *TD■■ MB BCh BAO MRCGP DA DObstRCOG* 150172
Dundas C R *TD MB ChB FRCP(Glasg) FFARCS* 010472
Williams B M *TD MB ChB MRCPath* 120472
Drysdale W R *MB ChB MRCS LRCP DObstRCOG* 130672
Russell J D *MB ChB DMRD* 021072
Gibbons J R P *MBE TD■■ MB ChB FRCS FRCSEd MRCGP* 010173
Ferguson I R *TD MB BS MRCPath MRCS LRCP DipBact* 040173
McCracken R J *TD■■ BSc* 030273

øSkillen M M *TD■ MB BS MPS* 010973
Powers N *TD MB BChir* 240973
Lewis B R *MB BCh DObstRCOG* 281173
Fraser I R *TD MB BS FRCS LRCP* 280274
Leslie G J B *TD MB ChB DO* 110574
McCarthy D P J *TD■ MB ChB* 130574
Jones D N *MB BS FFR FRCR MRCS LRCP DMRD* 060674
Valentine B H *MB BS MRCS LRCP DObstRCOG* 280674
Spiers A S D *TD MD PhD BS FRCPEd FRACP FACP FRCPathA* 031074
May A R L *TD MB BS FRCS FRCSEd* 120375
Hunter D *MB ChB DObstRCOG* 200775
Solomon M *TD MB ChB MRCGP DIH* 090975
Catto J V F *MB BChir FFR FRCR MRCS LRCP DMRD DCH DObstRCOG* 011075
Aitkenhead I McA *MB ChB MRCPsych DPM* 131075
Brown K J A *MB ChB MRCGP* 181175
Cass M *MBIM* 030176
Owen T J *MB BS FFARCS MRCS LRCP DA* 160176
Anderson J T H *MRCS LRCP DA DObstRCOG* 160276
Pendlington M *TD MB ChB* 290476
Humphreys L M *TD BM BCh MRCP(UK) MRCS* 050576
Ware C F W *MB BCh BAO FRCSEd DO* 160676
McGill J O 010776
Grabau W J *MB ChB MRCP* 140776
Rosenberg B C *TD MB BCh BAO MRCOG DObstRCOG* 081076
MacIntosh K C *MB ChB FFARCS* 261076
Saunders D A *TD PhD MB ChB BSc FFARCS* 171276
Thomas I R *MSc MB BS* (*A/Lt Col* 010485) 170377
Bell J R *TD MB ChB FRCSEd* 300377
Ghosh A K *MB BS DTM&H DipVen* 190477
Washbrook R A H *TD MB ChB DPM DPM* 240477
Gray R *TD■* 280577
Darragh P M *TD MD BCh BAO MRCPI MFCM DCH LFOM* 060777
Frewin T H *MB ChB MRCS LRCP* 070977
Adkins R B *MB ChB MRCS LRCP DObstRCOG* 100278
Peyton J W R *TD BSc MD BCh BAO MRCP(UK) FRCSEd* 030778
McCluskie P J A *MB ChB* 030878
Bishop R *TD MB ChB* 160878
Dunbar J A *MB ChB MRCGP DMJ* 111078
Grieve A M *MB ChB MRCGP DObstRCOG* 141178
Sturrock R R *DSc MB ChB* 241278
Robertson B *MRCS LRCP* (*A/Lt Col* 011185) 110179
Campbell D L *TD BSc MB ChB MRCGP DRCOG* 240179

Miller D H *TD■ MInstSWM* 070279
Kotwall F B *MRCGP DO DO DA* 120379
Findley L J *MB ChB MRCP(UK) MRCS DCH DObstRCOG* 150379
Hindle W J *LRCPI&LM LRCSI&LM DObstRCOG* 150379
Weston-Davies W H *MB BS FRCS LRCP* 150379
O'Callaghan E G *MB BCh BAO DObstRCOG* 040479
Brewster B S 160579
Simmonds M J *TD MB BS MRCS LRCP DObstRCOG* 190579
¶Songhurst W D 300679
Furness P J *MB BS MRCS LRCP* 030779
Symonds R P *TD MD BS MRCP FRCSEd FRCR FSR(T)* 160779
Gallagher P *MB ChB BSc FRCS* 260779
Croton R S *MB ChB FRCS* 310779
Reid R J S *MB BCh BAO* 310779
Phalp C G A *MB ChB* 150879
Young J R *MB ChB FRCS DLO* 310879
Fearn C B D A *MB BChir FRCS FRCSEd* 231179
Barker G H *TD MB BS FRCS MRCOG* 200180
Lowerson B *MB BS* 020280
Lockhart J D F *MB BCh BAO DPH* 230280
Gibbs A R *MB BS MRCPath* 020380
Reid A R *MB ChB DIH MFOM* 010480
Messing H J *BM BCh DCH DObstRCOG* 150480
Nelson R E *TD■ AIMLT FIMLS* 110580
Feggetter G S *MB BChir MRCP(UK) MRCPsych* 150580
Ducker D A *MRCP* 090680
Rockley P A *MB ChB* 110680
Haines D H *BDS* 120680
Mukerji B D *MB BS FFARCS DA* 270680
Shaw J W *MB BCh BAO FFR DMRD* 210780
Park G R *TD MB ChB BSc FFARCS* 110880
øQureshi S A *TD MB ChB MRCGP DCH DRCOG* 110880
Charles R H G *BChir DPH DCH FRIPHH MFCM* 290880
Markby D P *MB BS MRCGP MRCS LRCP DObstRCOG* 100980
Cove P *LRCP LRCS* 180980
Olver J J *TD MB BS* 011080
Ackah K O *TD MB ChB BAO FRCS* 011180
Donaldson R A *MB BCh BAO FRCPI* 011180
Loan W B *MD BCh BAO FFARCS* 011180
Ide C W *MB ChB MRCGP DRCOG* 231180
Bolton J P G *MB ChB MRCGP DRCOG* (*A/Lt Col* 010485) 061280
Johns W A *MB BS MRCP MRCS DObstRCOG* 091280
Gardner D *MB ChB MRCS LRCP* 181280
Beeley J W *TD RGN QIDNC* 290181
Bonser J B *RGN RNT RCNT* 290181
Kinnear R C *MB ChB BAO* 300181
Eaton A C *MB BS BSc FRCS LRCP* 060281
Royle G C *FBIM MRSH RGN BTACERT RNT* 120281
Penny R A *RMN RGN* 210281
Gatehouse D *MB ChB FRCS* 240281
Petrie J C *RGN* 280381
Currie F *MB BCh MRCOG* 010481
Hartley C *LSSCh RGN* 230481
Akhtar M J *MB BS FRCPsych DPM DTM&H DipVen* 300481
Verity H J *MB BChir LMSSA* 020581
Mulhearn J F J *MB ChB LMCC* 150581
Macaskill I A M *MB ChB* 020881
Levack I D *MD ChB FFARCS* 130881
Arnold B *TD RGN* 190881
Lee-Cann I R *RMN RGN RNT* 100981
Seal M T *MB ChB BDS* 051081
Hedley G S *MB ChB DRCOG* 131081
Thilagarajah K *MB BS FRCS FRCSEd LRCP* 121181
Mansel R E *MB BS FRCS LRCP* 261181
øSymonds K E *MB ChB FRCSEd* 031281
McFarlane H W *MB ChB FRCS FRCSEd* 020182
Harris V G *MB BS MRCOG MRCS LRCP* 020282
øParish P *MBChB MRCGP* 020382
Drought T K 040382
Sydney D M R L *RMN RNMS RGN RNT* 110382
Clark N H *MB BCh MRCGP DObstRCOG* 210382
Panting G P *MB BS DCH* 020682
Summers A *TD RGN QIDNC* 160682
Graham E *RNMS RGN RCNT* 100882
Ford C D *MB ChB DObstRCOG* 240882
Wood J J *RGN RNT* 280882
Groves R C C *MB ChB MRCGP DRCOG* 160982
Haworth E *MB ChB MRCP(UK)* 210982
Richards C 021082
Ivey V *RGN* 051082
Dennis W J *RGN* 061082
Murray R S M 121082
Johns A M *MB BChir FRCS* 141082
Samaratunga K A *MS MB FRCS FRCSEd* 201082
Seiler E R *MB ChB MRCGP DCH DObstRCOG* 041182
Cave-Bigley D J *MB BS FRCS LRCP* 061182
Smith J 231182
Cope A R *MB BS FRCS MRCS LRCP* 011282
Richardson F I 221282
Baker P J *RMN RGN RNT* 230183
Buckley D A *RMN RGN* 260183
Gibson E *RMN RNMS RGN* 260183
Bowler G M R *MB ChB FFARCS* 010283
Robinson M J *TD BA MRCS LRCP* 010283
Kennedy A G *MB ChB* 080283
Argent V P *MB BChir FFARCS DA DCH DRCOG* 140283
øHeber M E *MB BS MRCP MRCS MASEE* 160283
Watson G A *RGN RNT* 250283
Seal R H *MB ChB FIMLT* 030383
Hogan J A *RGN* 180383
Harris D A *HDCR* 010483
Irving A G *MRCS LRCP* 170483
Smith W M V *MB BS MRCGP* 010583
Hodges A K 220583
Behan J T *RMN RGN* 290583
Gormlie H E C *RGN* 290583
¶Ball L 020683
McEwan M *RGN RMN RNT* 230683
Lowe J W *MB MRCP MRCP(UK) MRCPath* 260683
West C A *MB ChB* 110783
Saksena V K 130783
Martin J F *MD ChB MRCP MRCP(UK)* 040883
Howes J H T *ARRC RMN RGN* (*A/Lt Col* 010486) 270883
Stephenson R H *MB BS MRCS LRCP DObstRCOG* 270883
Murton M D *MB ChB* 080983
Brooman I C *MRCS LRCP* 130983
Daniel T M 011083
Strachan N *TD■* 151183
Byers A *TD■* 010184
Bennett J K *RMN RGN* 010284
Payne A E *RGN* 010284
Ross B A *BS FRCS* 140284
Billings J E *DN RMN RGN QIDNC* 170284
Evans D H C *MB BS FFARCS DObstRCOG DTM&H* 310384
Buchanan W *RGN BTA* 190484
Stabback D J G *MISM* 010584
Telford W A *FRSH RMN RGN* 030584
øSmith P A *MB ChB MRCS* 090584
Scott S D *MB ChB FRCS* 250584
Hedges J R *MB BS MRCS LRCP* 030784
Grimble I T *MB BS MRCP(UK) MRCS DCH* 070984
øDent C J *MB ChB* 150984
Kinchin C G J *MB BS MRCS LRCP* 061084
Salisbury N S *MB BS MRCS LRCP DObstRCOG* 101084
Mullins D G *RMN RGN* 011184
Parham A L S *BCh* 081184
Fawcett W G 011284
Jessop E G *BM BCh MFCM* 011284
Stubbs F S *RMN RGN* 011284
Greaves D N J *MB ChB DRCOG* 051284
Tallents C J *MB BS FRCS LMCC DO* 051284
MacKenzie D A *RGN* 301284
Grant T J *RGN* 050185
Houston R F *MB MRCP FRCR MRCP(UK)* 260185
Hawkins A K I *MB BCh* 020285
Mixer P R *MB BS MRCGP DCH DRCOG* 140285
Jones H M *MB BCh FFARCS* 060385
Pashby N L *MB BS* 060385
¶Allen R M *RGN* 010485
¶Crook D M *MBE* 010485
Hilton J J *LSSCh AMIHospE MBCHA MRSH RGN AASI* 010485
¶Price T *MBE* 010485
¶Tanner A J 010485
Hannam R C *MRCS LRCP BDS* 020585
øMorrish L H B *MB ChB FFARCS* 200585

Territorial Army, Royal Army Medical Corps — continued

Knock M A R *FRCSEd* 230585
Riley M D 100685
Morgan J G *RGN* 220685
Cameron M *RMN RNMS RGN* 010785
Jones K P *MB BS MRCS LRCP* 020885
Diack G A M *MB ChB DRCOG* 250985
ØClaydon S M *MB BS MRCS LRCP* 010186
Smith E T S *MB ChB FFR FRCR DMRD* 240186
Hetherington J W *FRCS FRCSEd* 080286
Capps S N J *MB BS BSc FRCS* 120286
Jones C *RGN* 060386
¶Maxwell R 010486

Captains

Caldwell P J *MB BS*
Gad G K *MRCPsych* (*A/Maj* 011084)
¶Horner C A
Jayaratne T W B B *MB ChB FFARCS*
Manders D H *TD*▪▪ (*Bt/Maj* 250783) 240366
Barnett K *TD*▪ 010372
Harris K N *RMN RGN* 140573
Stallard R *TD OND RGN* 310773
Spriggs W A *RGN RNT* 160674
Hunt K H *RMN RGN RNT* 251174
Biddulph L N *TD DipHEng* 011075
Clifford P C *MD ChB FRCP* 010276
Cox C W F M *MB BS FRCSEd MRCOG* 080576
Bane V *TD* 010676
Samuel P D *TD* 130876
†Palfrey E L H 011077
Hughes J L *MSc RGN* 050178
Beaumont G P *TD* 010578
Young B *MBIM RGN* 290778
Earl D N *RMN RGN* 150878
Nicolson I H *RGN* 280878
Hemmerman B 310878
Palmer K *RMN RGN* 020978
Thomson N S *MB ChB* 110179
Villar R N *MB BS BSc FRCS* 080279
Handbury N K *DN RNMS RGN RNT RCNT* 060879
Darby P *RGN RM RNT RCNT* 110979
Sutton D *RGN* 270979
Knowles D *RGN* 201079
Archer J V 011179
Sheikh N A *MB BS MRCP* (*A/Maj* 021281) 101179
Jones D A *RMN RGN* 090180
Monypenny I J *MB BChir FRCS* 230180
Sutton M L *BM BCh MRCP FRCR DMRT* 210280
Sauven P D *ChM MB FRCS* 290280
Barnard I 050680
Bhugowandeen R *RGN RMN RCNT* 130780
Lambert W A 310880
Phillips G *MB BCh MRCP(UK)* (*A/Maj* 230683) 221080
Dalal A *MB ChB FFARCS MRCS LRCP DA DRCOG* (*A/Maj* 010784) 240181
Ayyaswamy V K *MB BS FRCSEd FRCS(Glasg)* (*A/Maj* 010284) 030281
Usherwood T P *MB BS BSc MRCP* 030281
Buirski G *MB BS MRCP* 040281
Bristow A 010481
ØDurant E A *MB BS MRCS LRCP* 110481
ØMaher O 230481
Crowther G R *MB ChB BAO* 250481
ØJohnston H M L *MB BCh BAO FFARCS* (*A/Maj* 150684) 250481
Green M A *MB ChB MRCPath DCH DObstRCOG DMJ* (*A/Maj* 060683) 020581
Choudhury R *MB BS* 170581
Gupta R L 210581
Brown K *RGN RMN* 250581
Newton A 290581
Barker G R *MB BS BSc FRCSEd LRCP* (*A/Maj* 010184) 260681
Ashworth D A *MB ChB* 080781
Shorten W W J *MB BCh BAO MRCGP DCH DRCOG* 010881
Pope A J *BSc* 030881
Kennedy J H 050881
Bonser R S *MB ChB MRCP(UK) FRCS* 070881
White C 030981
Mehta R B *MB BS DPH* 180981
Weeder R G *MB ChB* (*A/Maj* 010884) 111081
Burns H J G *MB ChB FRCS(Glasg)* 171081
Jeffery W R *RMN RGN* 011181
Jackson R G *MB ChB MRCGP DRCOG* 071181
Saunders W P *RGN RNT* 281181
Leigh P R *RGN* 291181
Livingstone J S *MB BChir* 151281
Sparrow G E A *MB BS MRCP MRCP(UK)* 151281
Leeson P J 191281
Gleaves B J 231281
Gutkowski J A *RMN RGN* 240182
Bell H J T *MB ChB BSc* 300182
Maguire J *MB ChB* 300182
Rogers P N *MB ChB FRCS(Glasg)* 300182
James M T 010282
Hirani A 030382
Buist R *RGN RMN* 210482
Bailie R *MB ChB BAO* 080582
ØO'Sullivan E M *MB BS FRCR MRCS LRCP* (*A/Maj* 160885) 190582
Finch M E *MB ChB MRCGP DObstRCOG DObstRCOG* 260582
Platts B W *MRCGP DIH MFOM AFOM* 260582
Welch J D *AIMLT FIMLS* 230682
Mackway-Jones K C *BM BCh BS MRCP MB* 010882
Sneyd J R *MB BChir* 010882
Smith B A C *MB ChB FFARCS* (*A/Maj* 050984) 120982
Best B G *MB ChB BAO FRCSEd* 140982
McLean M *MD BCh BAO FRCSEd FFR* 140982
White D B 071082
Jaiswal A 121082
Galvin J F 261082
ØDutt S *MB BS* (*A/Maj* 191185) 021182
Freeman J W *MB ChB MRCP MRCP(UK) FFARCS* (*A/Maj* 190684) 031182
Williams N A *MB ChB* 031182
Williamson J D *MB ChB MRCGP MFCM DObstRCOG* 031182
Wilson S G *MD ChB MRCP(UK)* 061182
Stewart J C M 121182
ØLang D A *MBChB FRCPS(GLAS)* 131182
Baskett P J F *MB BCh BAO FFARCS* (*A/Maj* 150384) 171182
Paskins J R *MB BS FRCS* 191182
Shadwell R N 021282
Murphy R J *MB BCh BAO DA DRCOG* 081282
Greenhouse P R D H *MBBChir MRCOG MRCS LRCP* 101282
Rai B S 181282
Spires K A 241282
Smart R J *MRSH MRIPHH MIEH* 030183
Savundra P A *BM BCh* 140183
Weller R M (*A/Maj* 011184) 140183
McCrea W A *MB BCh BAO LRCPI LRCSI* 010283
Rowan J F 010283
Walker S J *MB ChB* 020283
Duffy B S C *RGN RCNT* 080283
Harris M L *RGN* 080383
Bragg A J D *MB ChB MRCS LRCP* 010483
Maguire M J 130483
Mawhinney I N 300483
Scott J N *MRCP(UK) MRCPsych* (*A/Maj* 060984) 300483
Hadden W A 040583
Somerville J J F *MD BCh FRCSEd* 040583
¶Booles R L D 130583
Gammon A W M *MB BS MRCS LRCP* 160583
Iddisah C B *DN BTA* 170583
Holt M F *RMN RGN* 200583
Dickson G R *MB BMedSci ChB FFARCS* 230583
Duke J D 030683
Wady G F *RMN RNMS RGN* 230683
Horsburgh M W *RGN EN(G)* 240683
Wheater A W *MB BS BSc MRCOG* 080783
Elliott M B *MCSP SRP* 010883
ØFoster E M *MB BS BSc* 010883
Miller J E *MB ChB* 010883
Uden S *BSc MB BS* 010883
ØBurdett-Smith M V *MB BS* 110883
Davies L A L *MB BS* 110883
Riley B *MB BS FFARCS MRCS LRCP* 130883
Weerakoon B S 200883
¶Parker J 010983
Aston N O F *MB BChir FRCS LRCP* 030983
Bhatnagar D 080983
Deahl M P *MBBS MRCP(UK)* 270983
Karran G P *FIMLS* 011083
Bretland N P *MB BS DRCOG MRCGP* 261083
Fuller G M 261083
Dendy R A *MB BS MRCS LRCP* 041183
Vassallo D J *MB MRCS LRCP* 101183
Mitra P M *MB BS* 241183
ØHoskins M C *MB BMedSci BS* 261183
¶Frost P J 071283

Campbell D A *MB ChB FRCS FRCSEd* (*A/Maj* 060385) 211283
Rich A J E *LLB* 100184
Carter S S C 110184
Kucharczyk W A J *MRCS LRCP* 110184
Ridley S A *MB BS* 130184
Ahmed K 170184
Mountjoy J H *MB DA DRCOG* 020284
Morgan I D P 070284
Bryson P N *MB BCh ChB BAO MRCPath DRCOG* 090384
Burns S A *MB ChB* 090384
Burton A E 010484
Doherty J A *BEM MInstAM MISM MIWO AMIWO* 030484
Chambers T L *MB FRCP FRCPEd MRCS DA DCH DObstRCOG* 060484
Kuber A 070484
Colville A *BA BM BCh* 110484
Lambert R G W *MBChB* 240484
Bloom S F *MInstAM* 010584
Bhatt R *MB BS* 140584
Ash P E *RGN RM* 250584
Richardson F J *MBChB* 310584
Steele A D *MB BS* 120684
Stone J M 270684
¶McSweeney D J 020784
Latty A J *MPS* 150784
Garner A 230784
¶Richardson P F 240784
Moss A Y D *MB BS* 310784
øWady E *MB BS* 310784
¶Barley A K 010884
Taulke-Johnson T D 010884
¶Doolan J A 140884
Purdy G M *MB BCh BAO* 060984
Stonebridge P A *MB ChB FRCS FRCSEd* 060984
¶Cross M F *MInstAM MAMS AMR* 021084
Magee A G 031084
Marshall S G 031084
Sharma R C *MB BS* 051084
Yearwood W A *MInstAM* 211084
Bamber M G 261084
Gray D C *MB ChB* 261084
Frayne J M *MB ChB FFARCS* (*A/Maj* 010186) 301084
Lynch A *PhD MB ChB* 301084
Ashton J R *MB ChB FRCP(Glasg) FRCS(Glasg) FRCPS(GLAS)* 141184
Ewart I C *MB BS* 141184
Mathams A J *MB BS FRCS LRCP* 141184
Kerr G R *MB BS* 151184
Anderson N W 131284
Gautam R *MBBS FFARCS DA* 290185
Naroz N A *MB BCh DRCOG DORCPI* 290185
øWise V A *MB ChB* 120285
Shambrook A S J *MB ChB* 150385
¶Emms J W 180385
Murray W 010485
Williams D G *MSc* 010485
Ackerley G C 120485
¶Rowan D 150485
Dennis M W *MBChB* 300585
Rajagopal C *MRCGP DCH* 060685
Godby C 130685
O'Neill H B 220685
McGhee T D 260685
Dunning J J *MB ChB* 300685
Meenz G *RGN RNT RCNT* 010785
Paterson R M 050885
Verma S K 190885
Landes A H L *MB BS FFARCS FFARCS LRPS* 240885
Edlin G P 100985
Bedi N P S 210985
Fear J D *MBChB* 210985
Heys S D 210985
Parkins D R J *MBBS* 041085
Collings A D 091085
Singh K S P N 111085
Clarke T 221085
Ryan P G 241085
Firth D A *MB ChB BSc MRCPsych* 311085
Hudson F D B 011185
Brinkley M A *MB ChB* 031185
Hughes J A 281185
Jones T N *RMN RGN* 080186
Connolly B 010286

Lieutenants

Crookes R J 160380
Towler B A 201181
Darragh E *RGN RM* 140482
Weeks K W *RGN* 061282
øHeybourne C M E *BSc MPS* 300484
Fairbanks R S *TDCR* 190185
øPrice H E *FIMLS* 190585
Owen J P 240685
Lavine M J *TD MB BS MRCS LRCP* 210785
Hughes A W 201285
øDoughty H A *MB BChir* 231285

2nd Lieutenants

†Liddell J C R *MPS* 011183
øPearsall S E *MCSP SRP* 230584
ø†Wilton K M *MPS* 310584
†Clauson J G 261084
†Faulkner P J 131284
†Preston M H *RGN* 280285
ø†Englishby V L 290385
ø†Roberts J M 010485
†Cooper J L *DCR(R)* 150885

Pharmacists

Majors

Asher D M *TD MPS AIPharmM* 010485

Captains

øMalins D R *MPS* (*A/Maj* 010486) 070681

2nd Lieutenants

ø†Taggart H M *MPS* 080285

Administrative Officers

Captains

Andrews G M 010485

Lieutenants

Fleming M *FIMLS AIMLS* 060985

Nursing Officers

Majors

Manning G A *RGN* 100780
Reed W J *TD MBIM RMN RGN* 011180
Grose W D *RGN* 250382
McCloskey J G *TD RMN RGN* 010183
Patterson A E S *TD RMN RGN* 010183
Stewart J A *RGN RMN* 110583
O'Brien S H *RGN* 010284
Darcy L M *RGN* 180384
Parker W H *RMN RGN* 240784
Ingram D J *RGN* 100884
Simm G *RGN BTA* 061084
Osborne A J *RNMS RGN* 050185
Carroll S J *RGN* 130185
Williams B *DN RMN RGN RNT RCNT* 180185
Reeves P C *RGN* 030485
Mackerill D J *RMN RGN* 180585
Hempton J A *RMN RGN* 181085
Durbin C G *RGN RNT* 211085
Moate P *DN RGN BTA RNT* 221185
Strange S R *RGN* 241285

Captains

Grazette H S *RMN RGN DNTC* 140776
Pointon T *RMN RGN* 030977
Whitaker P 081277
McCartney J *MRSH RGN* 010878
Dalby C R *RGN* 190878
Robertshaw B *RGN* (*A/Maj* 011184) 190878
McGarva J N *RGN RGN* 110978
Anderson C G *RMN RGN RNT RCNT* 031278
Tankard G *RMN RGN* 150179
Harris L *RGN RNT RCNT* 290179
Barnes L J *RMN RGN* 310379
Evans L R *RGN RNT RCNT* 220479
Strutt A F *RGN RNT DNTC* 220479
Purcell R *RGN* 300479
Battle P J A *RMN RGN* 130579
Maudsley D *RMN RGN GNCE* 201079
Ryan M J *RGN* 311079
Somers J C *RMN RGN RNT RCNT* 061179
Terry M H *DN RGN RNT* 131179
Winstanley K *RNMS RGN RCNT* 261179
Cross D J *RMN RGN* 031279
Hanlon T *RMN RGN* 100180
Li J H S *RGN* 220280
Rawlins P A *RMN RGN* 260380
Dunn R J *RGN RGN OHNC* 010480
Rendall R *RMN RGN* 030680
Orr J G *DN RMN RGN RCNT* 270780
Clark J A *RGN EN(G)* 240980
Ramdharry D D *RMN RGN* 020881
Erskine J G *RGN RMN RGN* 071181
Vayapooree K P *RMN RNMS RGN RNT* 190182
Murray W A E *RMN RGN RM* 130382
Howard M D *RGN* 120682
Hubbard K E *RMN RGN* 130782
Donald G M *RGN* 230982
Goodman L G *RMN RGN* 061082
Buckenham M A *RGN RNT* 150183
King S A *RGN* 170183

Territorial Army, Royal Army Medical Corps — continued

Spencer M *RGN RMN RNT RCNT* 140983
Lowry M *RGN* 011083
Holmes A J *RGN* 311083
Little T G *RGN* 281183
Goorwappa L 051283
Wilkinson B *RGN* 201283
Woolley E S *RGN* 020184
Vincent R *RGN* 070284
Hunter P *RGN* 020484
Nicholls C F *RGN RM* 220185
Morrissey F J *RGN* 050285
Downs P D C *RMN RGN* 110385
Beech R *RMN RGN* 060485
Thomson T B 100485
McMillan C S *RGN* 250485
Chater J *RGN* 140585
O'Brien J B 180785
Radford G I *RGN* 250785
Collins J *RGN* 070885
Goodship D A C *RGN RM* 281085
Taylor A R *RMN RGN OHNC* 240186
Ainscough J M *RGN EN(G)* 280386

Lieutenants

Woodhouse P J *RMN RGN GNCE* 130378
Bell A P 151180
Vernengo M V *RGN RM* 281281
Kennedy J W *RGN* 030282
Farrimond P A *RMN RGN* 030482
Cook J D *RSCN RGN* 280882
Stead W L 210982
Thomas A F *RGN* 310383
Brewer J E 260683
Jackson P *RGN RM* 020983
Siddle R G *RMN RGN* 210983
Hackett R M *RGN RMN* 270983
Perkins D A *RGN* 160484
Medway N B *RGN* 171284
Llewellin W T *RGN* 300185
Davies D J 270385

Technical Officers

Captains

Brown B T *BSc MPS* 030483
Windsor A M *MCSP SRP* 011183
Turner S *DCR(R)* 190384

2nd Lieutenants

†Lewin I *DCR(R)* 240784
†McLellan J H 040485
ø†Crook T C *MCSP SRP* 120585
ø†Davies M *DCR(R)* 300585

Non-Medical Officers

Lieutenant Colonels

Walker N J P *TD MB BCh BAO MRCGP* 010785

Majors

Talbot G N B *TD*▪ 010172
Andrews S C *TD* 011277
Barker F R 140980
Snaith F J B *TD*▪ 220582
McCarthy J F *MB ChB MRCGP DCH DRCOG* 030882
Freeman R *TD RMN RGN* 010183
Hardie R J *BA MB BChir MRCP(UK)* 010884
Bishop M J *BEM MISM* 081084
Horsfield T N R *TD*▪ *AIDPM FBIM* 141184
Griffiths H 101284
Williams R J W *MB ChB* 010485
Canning W J 040485
Allsopp T J *RGN RCNT* 200485
Hall W J *TD DCR(R)* 010985
Midford J T 011185

Captains

Gosling R C *TD*▪▪ (*Bt/Maj* 120380) 100669
Green M J *TD*▪ (*Bt/Maj* 210582) 220371
Ritchie P *TD* (*Bt/Maj* 010783) 010272
Bailey J R *TD MIEH* 160972
Bristow A F *TD* 241075
Thornton I W *TD RGN* 200276
Horsley D *RMN SRN* 180177
Shaw A F L *RGN* 310578
Young J S *RMN RGN* 310578
McEvansoneya S *RMN RGN* 200878
Lewis N J *MRCP MRCGP MRCS DRCOG* 160879
Patrick C J *TD BSc FCA* 010180
Sheppard G J 010480
Dickson R J 110580
Tame P A 010780
Rodgers R C 010880
Loades R P 011180
Baynham J H O *RNMS RGN* 080281
Partington J H *MCIT ACIS IPFA* (*A/Maj* 110184) 010481
Clark C V *MB ChB BSc FRCSEd* 010881
Grant F V *RMN RGN* 220981
Dowd C D P *RMN RGN RCNT* 251281
Allen M *RGN RNT RCNT* 250182
Scott R G V *RGN* 010282
Morgan M G *RGN* 270382
Corner N B *MB BS FRCS LRCP* 010882
Eliatamby S R *MB* 010882
Marshall A M *MB BS ChB MRCGP DRCOG* 040882
Davies A J *RGN RCNT* 240982
Tibbatts W P 040183
Gardiner J E R *RGN RCNT* 010483
McDermott G J *RMN RGN* 220483
Desmond R 030683
Garrett B *RMN RGN* 010783
McKinnon J S 240783
Cumiskey F *RGN EN(G) BTA* 030883
Tisshaw C C *RGN EN(G)* 280883
de Lusignan S 010983
Newton R G *RMN RGN* 121183
Watkins K S *RMN RGN* 240384
Humberstone C V *FIMLT* 010484
Strange F *RGN* 060484
Taylor N A 010684
Cowan M E *FIMLT* 230684
Gallamore R A J *MPS* 260684
Toy W M *RMN RGN* 300684
Notley C R *RMN RGN* 120784
Rickard N A S *RGN RMN* 140784
Austin M W *MB BCh* 010884
Hayward A P *MB BS* 010884
Lewis D J M *MB BCh* 010884
Phillips C W 010884
Watson M S *FIMLS* 011184
McLennan I D *RMN RGN* 021284
McGregor E D 010185
Griffiths N P *RMN RGN* 010485
Bish D M *AIMLS* 111085
Sharpe T H *RGN* 021185
Phimister D A *MSc FIMLS* 151185
øLeach U I *MCSP* 101285

Lieutenants

Derrett R V *RGN* 170580
Rew D A 130781
Strong P W 060282
O'Sullivan K M *MB ChB* 070782
McNally B F 080782
Nicoll N W *DCR(R)* 311082
Thomas M B *RMN RGN* 011282
Herbert J M E *RMN RGN* 021282
øMitchell S *MPS* 111282
McArthur D J *RGN RMN RGN* 240383
Barrie A S W *RMN RGN* 240583
Osborne M R *RMN RGN* 280583
Wynn C *RMN RGN* 210983
Davies K *RGN RGN* 231183
Worsley D J 111283
McKinnon A J *BSc FIMLS* 200484
Gregory T R 010784
Atkinson R M *DSR(T)* (*A/Capt* 010186) 180884
øGillespie S J *MCSP SRP* 190884
Hodges H 061084
Chue P 210185
øHead L 010285
Sharkey A J 020385
Cain P A *MB ChB* 200685
øHarris N M C *MBChB* 200685
Hughes P A *MB BS* 150785
Munson K M 230885
Copland B D B *MCSP* 020985
øBuckland S P 011185

2nd Lieutenants

†Tombs D G 031280
Inman J S *PhC MPS* 080783
McCarthy C A *MPS* 110184
Waring N E 110184
†Postlethwaite W T 270684
†Davies D E *AIMLS* 260784
†Huitson I 051084
Wales D A 121084
ø†Jewell C 141184
†Hardy G P S 050285
ø†Phillips S L 130285
†Ginnis J A 170385
ø†Kiltie A E 010985
†Fisher J 170985
†Soar R H *FIMLT* 031085
†Henley D M *DCR(R) DCR(MU)* 041085
†Morison D D *AIMLS* 111085
ø†Close V M 251085
ø†Thompson E 251085
†Bingham J R F 311085
†Haskew A E J *GradRSC AIMLT CBiol MIBiol* 311085
†Aitken W S 221185
†Horner L T 051285
†Knight B H 171285
†Henry W S 191285

Non-Medical Technical Officers

Captains

Rutherford I C *MCSP DipTP* 010884

2nd Lieutenants

Name	Rank	Date
ØHill M C *DCR(R)*		300784

Quartermasters

Name	Rank	Date
Winspear M L *TD*		231058
	Maj	240668
Graham D *TD*		220171
	Maj	210872
Foreman R K		140671
	Maj	140683
Pike M F E *MM TD*		210771
	Maj	051184
Lewis D B *TD*		190472
	Maj	260276
Walton J A *TD*		140771
	Maj	140783
Allan A G E *TD AIMLT FIMLS*		170871
	Maj	170877
Wolstenholme H	*Capt*	170772
Davidson J G *FIMLT*		170573
	Maj	170585
Willis A D *TD*		280174
	Maj	051283
Monaghan R A J	*Capt*	121274
Thompson I H *AIMLT FIMLS*	*Capt*	210275
Bibby W R	*Capt*	290375
¶Donachie D S		310375
	Maj	010485
Walters R J	*Capt*	010475
Hall C R *AIMLT FIMLS*		290875
	Maj	221185
Wilson H M	*Capt*	190975
Nason M R *TD*		011075
	Maj	220379
Duncan C G *TD*		010476
	Maj	060884
Milnes J W G	*Capt*	200976
Tunks R W		151076
	Maj	060483
Wright D G	*Capt*	010177
¶O'Neill W P		020377
	Maj	020383
Rennison R A *MSSCh*	*Capt*	010477
Pringle E M	*Capt*	050878
Paterson F D *MISM MIMS MASMC*	*Capt*	120878
Kerr R B McL	*Capt*	230878
Donaldson J A M *FIMLT*	*Capt*	210978
Scott W E		141178
	Maj	010485
Twells M	*Capt*	270379
O'Connor J C *MBE*	*Capt*	130180
Yates J H *TD*▪ *MBIM*		010280
	Lt Col	061084
Herbert W G *TD*	*Capt*	010181
Curry-Peace F	*Capt*	130882
Balmer H	*Capt*	100185
Smith E F *MBE*	*Capt*	011085

Non-Medical Officers

Name	Rank	Date
Donaldson A	*Capt*	210978
Jamieson J H	*Capt*	170279
Barrie K J	*Capt*	230380
MacDonald W G L	*Capt*	060381

Section B - Army Cadet Force

Majors

Agnew S A
Baker J H E
Glanvill T
Glover J E
Handley A J *MD MRCP*
Harris W H
Khan M M
McCaffrey J B
McConnell T J D
Nicol N T *OBE TD*
Parkyn J
Pembrey M R
Rowland C J
Scully J A
Singh A

Captains

Czaykowski A A P
Davison D W
Hallinan W M C *MRCS*
Harris A R W
Hart D P
Lavine M J
MacLeod I H
øOstler K M
Saeed A
Salmon R W
Thompson M E
Whitbread R P
Williams J T
Young W B M

ROYAL ARMY ORDNANCE CORPS

Honorary Colonels	Brig M J Short *CBE* ret pay	010482
	Lt Col P F Ryan	150584
	Col D S Strong *TD*	150584

Colonels

Strong D S *TD■ FIB*	050777
Walker W J *TD■■ MCIT MBIM FIPDM MIMH*	010481
Hall D S *TD■■ FIPDM MIMH*	010985

Lieutenant Colonels

Barton G R *TD■*	080982
Groves M P psc† psc ato	010485
Mundell R E *TD■*	010985
St Quinton E A *TD*	011085

Majors

Timpson T *TD■* (*Bt/Lt Col* 010177)	010470
Randerson R	311271
Bridges P J *TD BMet PhD PhD CEng FIM*	010475
Chadwick A B *TD■■*	010775
Bridges T W *TD■ MBIM LTI*	010476
Riley P F *TD■*	010776
Griffiths B O H *TD■■ MA ACII*	010277
MacDougall D J *TD MA*	010477
Woodford M N *TD*	050777
Wise A G *TD■■*	010178
Loynes S *TD■*	010978
Stafford G H *TD■ MBCS*	010978
Slater S M L A *TD*	010481
Buffham R L *MBE MSc FBIM* ato im	300981
Tyce C J *TD*	010482
Turner J P A J *TD*	010483
Bonney N A	010683
Phillips J M B *TD*	010883
Scott F M *TD BA*	010484
Carter G E *TD■*	010584
Campbell E W *MISM MIMH MASMC MIPDM*	011184
Duchart R N *TD MA*	011184
Nicklin E E *TD■*	011184
Perkins M L *AIB*	011184
Rowlands M *TD*	011184
Cook R A M *TD■*	190185
Cockerton G R *TD*	010485
Lynham R G *TD*	011185

Captains

¶Young D R	
Gamble C *TD*	291257
Nicholson A F *TD■■*	111159
¶Harmer A J	051066
Gannon B *TD■ BA MEd*	021167
Fussell C V	141171
McFadyen J *TD DipTechEd*	030475
Jones P D H *TD DMS DMA AIPM*	180576
Swain G E *TD AIB*	180576
Poll D C *TD BSc CEng MICE MIMunE MIHT*	011077
Storey R J *TD DMS*	011278
Quick M *MA*	161278
¶Coveney R A G	160479
¶O'Neill J A	020779
McElhoney J B	200180
McKay E M	200180
Gee M J *TD MInstFF*	310580
¶Cousins L J *MBIM*	010980
Holman E J *TD AIB*	010481
Smith B E	010481
Townsend B G	010481
Tunstall P A	010481
Wardle S D *TD AIB*	010481
Williams L J	010481
Pettit R ato	050481
Scholefield B	010781
Smart M A A	030781
¶Fellows J G L	020182
Grout R	010382
Grainger A D	010482
Lamping D	010482
Haslam M J	050782
Silver J A *BSc*	010982
Crotty J F	010483
Winter P H	010483
Rees S A	070783
Field M R *MIPDM*	010983
Hughes R E ato	010284
Beevers C A	010484
Doran C J L	010484
Garforth-Bles D J *MA ARICS*	010484
Lane R *FCII*	010484
¶Roberts W E	020684
Mosedale J F *LRSC*	011184
¶Pether M J o s	251184
Moore D M	011284
Schofield V T	011284
¶McDonald G D	200385
Agnew N R	080485

Lieutenants

Smith J C E *TD BSc*	151067
Mantle M A	010370
Storey K	150379
Kan K *BA MSc AMISM* (*A/Capt* 021085)	190579
Davies A (*A/Capt* 010484)	240180
Biddick A J P	160981
Livingstone G M	211081
Brown M F J	240882
Pocock R E (*A/Capt* 190485)	190484
Armstrong J A	230185
Caslaw D M	190585
Edge D R W *BEd ACII*	300585
Urquhart D G	281285

2nd Lieutenants

†Illsley R C	170377
†Davies D W J	160179
Vaughan G W	010580
†Newland B	190680
†Fairlie M H	061282
†White M	190583
†Jago D H	040684
†Lea A O *BEd(Hons) MA MPEA*	010285
†Barwick G P	070785
†Bellerby S W	280785
†Freer J E	280785
†Gilchrist D G	280785
†Harris R C A	280785
†Johnson I	280785
†Meeres B L	280785

Quartermasters

Ruck R J B	*Capt*	150481
Bartlett M A	*Capt*	080282
Twentyman D J	*Capt*	080282
Williams T	*Capt*	080282
Atherton K H	*Capt*	010483
Thompson A V	*Capt*	010483
Penrose G W	*Capt*	220983
Rawlins R A *BA MSc MIElecIE TEng*	*Capt*	010484
Tillotson M A	*Capt*	010484
Tuckey D P *TD MIMH*		010484
	Maj	020484
Wells G A	*Capt*	010484
Wood J W	*Capt*	010484
Marshall M J	*Capt*	190784
Callaghan K *GM QGM*	*Capt*	150884
Foster R E	*Capt*	201085

CORPS OF ROYAL ELECTRICAL AND MECHANICAL ENGINEERS

Hon Colonels .... Col D E Filer *TD* 010478
Brig A W Reading *OBE MC TD* ret pay 010481
Lt Col (Bt Col) A F Wilkinson *TD* 010481
Lt Col B Giles *TD* 010483
Brig G A Atkinson ret pay 010486

Colonels

Forrest D W *TD▪▪ CEng MIMechE MIPlantE MBIM* 010478
Linnett G O *TD▪▪* 010486

Lieutenant Colonels

Thorley S R *TD▪▪* 010478
Cooper W D *TD▪ BSc PhD MRSC* 070780
Morris C C *TD▪▪* 010481
Currier I B *MBE TD▪ BSc CEng FIEE* sq(v) 010483
Kelsey M E *TD CEng MIEE* sq(v) 200883
Milne A B *TD▪ BSc CEng FIEE* 010184
MacArthur C A *TD MSc MIMechE MIChemE MCIBSE* 010484
Kohn E F *TD▪ BSc CBIM FInstM* 311284
Bennett P G *TD▪ CEng MIEE* 010485
Matthews G B *BSc CEng MIMechE MBIM* 010485
Hardie J D *TD▪ BScTech* 010486
Whyman M W *TD▪ BSc CEng MIEE* 010486

Majors

Trumper K H *TD▪▪ CEng MIMechE* 010272
Evans M A *TD▪▪ MEng* 010473
Sewell T *TD▪ TEng(CEI) MIMechE* 010973
Lintin J B *TD▪* 010474
Mackereth R *TD▪ BSc* 011075
Smith M *CEng MIMechE* ae 010777
Edmonds M C *TD* 080278
Sykes F A *TD* 140378
Illingworth G R *TD▪ BSc(Eng) MIMechE* sq(v) 010478
Dean P W *TD▪▪ BSc CEng MIMechE AMIEE MIProdE* 010778
Gillanders T G E *TD▪ BSc BSc(Eng)* 010978
Storey J W *TD▪* 231078
Skeat M R S *MBE TD* 011178
Moorcroft D *TD▪ MSc DPhil MRSC* 011079
Fairclough G T *TD CEng MIM MIBE* 010380
Garden B *TD▪ BSc* 010480
Gardner R M *TD▪▪ BSc(Eng) MIMechE* sq(v) 010680
Anderson H *TD▪ AMIEE* 011280
Steele J R *MSc DMS CEng MICE MIMunE MIHT* 011280
Stephens J M *CEng MICE* 010981
Godwin R S 310182
Hardy P J *TD CEng MIMechE* 010483
McNab J G *TD BA* 010483
Brown G *DMS* 011083
Rae A *TD MIEE* 011283
Lee J W *TD MSc* 010184
Rogers C M C *TD BSc ASCA FCA ACA* 010484
Quine O A *TD BSc* 070584
Sheil A E *BSc(Eng)* me 300584
Barrett M *BSc MIMechE MIGasE* 011084
Brunt J H *CEng MIProdE FIIM* 111184
Evans J S *BSc CEng MIMechE MCIOB* 010185
Griffin R M *MSc CEng* 010185
Pitcher G E T 190185
Bridgeman J S *BSc FBIM* 010285
Armstrong P G *MSc CEng MIERE MBIM MIIM* gw 020285
Laird R J *BSc MIMechE CDipAF MIPC* 100285
Thomson G M *PhD* 150585
Wood A R *TD MA CEng MIERE* 010785
Gould D W *TD BSc DMS DMS MIMechE* 010885
Ross H M *TD CEng MIMechE* 010885
Boyle K *BSc CEng MIMechE* 120885

Captains

Chown J D B *TD BSc* 011272
Haxell J P N *TD BSc PhD DIC MRSC* 010874
Bridges R E *TD* 010475
Hitchings D G *BSc* 010476
Ashley F A *BA MIQA TEng(CEI) MRAeS MIMGTechE* 190877
Scott P J *TD BSc* 011177
McClay W *TD BSc* 010478
¶Cross J C H *AIIM* 160778
¶Hadfield K 091078
Edgerton D M *BSc* 070479
Huxford G G *BSc DMS* 010180
Tedbury J E 270181
Whitelock L A 270181
Haley J M *TD BSc MIMechE* 010281
Mifsud V J *MA PhD AIL* 010481
Rogers S G *BSc(Eng) MSc MIMechE AMRAeS MIOA* 010481
Rennie J S *DD* 010581
Leicester F G 010182
¶Wilson T E 010382
Ball M L *BSc* 100382
Dobbie D M *BEng* 270682
¶Jaggers A R L 021082
Harvey J L *BSc* 010183
Shepherd A *BA* 100283
Baxter J R *MInstAM* 060383
Telford S F 010483
Benger P D 010583
Morris A P *BSc CEng MIMechE* 010583
Smith A K *BSc* 010583
Willmott G F A *CEng MIMechE MIProdE* 010583
Fuller J D *BSc* 010983
Vousden B F 221183
Berry J M *BSc CEng MIMechE* 010184
Elliott S J 250184
Campuzano L J M 110484
¶Blackwell J P 250484
Reeves J E A M *BEng* 180684
Lloyd R C 150984
Hammond P L 301084
Tipping R H 011184
¶Brewster R E C 051184
Martin S E 121184
¶Dickinson R 020585
Buckright J P 010685
Pickard P W 090685
Porat A P 010885

Lieutenants

Gosney A K *CEng MIMechE MIPlantE* 180174
Campbell D J 190577
Moore J A 280779
Potts M F (*A/Capt* 010885) 280480
Hornung C S 211180
Murray S J (*A/Capt* 010284) 020681
Mulholland J F *BSc* 260482
Paterson C J *BSc* 190582
Lee S *BSc* 090882
Stuart P M 020982
Green P J *BSc(Eng)* 051082
Halford J K (*A/Capt* 291083) 260483
Richardson C E (*A/Capt* 121184) 240683
Craig I J 011183
Watters P H *BSc PhD AMIMechE* 080584
Bosley K J *BSc* 200584
Robinson N P *BSc* 310584
Frost W F 041085
O'Hanlon J L 051085
Jones A T 110486

2nd Lieutenants

†Slater I C 071280
McCarthy J T 160783
Fletcher P L 200584
Gilbert L G 210584
Ward J S *BSc PhD* 210584
†Gordon D M 240584
McDougall I G 090684
†Riches C J 250684
†Francis N J *BSc AMIMechE AMRAeS* 290784
†Hamilton R J 290784
†McCrirrick S A 270984
Philip M W 270185
Grime I S D 150285
†Forrester J R N 260585
†Kinloch J A B 260585
†Cameron A 160685
†Ferguson G 160685
†McNaughton A D 070785
†Cooke A G *BSc* 280785
†De Souza C A 280785

†O'Regan J 280785
†Russell-Floyd R S 280785

Quartermasters

White D T *TD*■ 010469
Maj 230675
Philpots D K *Capt* 160184

Electrical and Mechanical Assistant Engineers

Sterling M *TD MITE MIMI AMIRTE TEng* 080273
Maj 081082
Youngman R F *TEng(CEI) MIRTE MIIM MIE* 300773
Maj 021180
Boggis T W G *TD CEng MIMechE* 070274
Maj 010983

Cartwright C 300775
Maj 031082
Bensted N C 220776
Maj 310884
Elvin S 060577
Lt Col 150185
Brown I 070778
Maj 091285
Murray C G *MISM MIDIAGE*
Capt 070778
Stevens D G *Capt* 150180
Anderson A H *Capt* 200580
Simmons W *Capt* 020880
Jolley A G *Capt* 270181
Dransfield D W *Capt* 030482
Nicholson D *Capt* 160482
Howorth C R *Capt* 010982
Nicholas T *Capt* 070483
Eadie J D 210483
Maj 050584

Langley W E *Capt* 280483
MacFarlane A *Capt* 300483
Miles J R J *Capt* 050583
Gorse M *Capt* 210783
Rarity D I *Capt* 230883
Pearce R *Capt* 041083
Lloyd D *Capt* 090284
Burton D A *BSc* *Capt* 200384
Bannerman C J *Tech(CEI) MIIM DipSM AMIMI* *Capt* 240384
Beedall A W *MISM* *Capt* 220784
Irwin B K *Capt* 230884
Rust T J *Capt* 141284
Simpson D R *Tech(CEI) MIRTE*
Capt 120285
Spurling A *TEng(CEI) AMIRTE MIMGTechE* *Capt* 160785
Fanning D D *Capt* 261085
Laska F A *Capt* 221185

CORPS OF ROYAL MILITARY POLICE

Hon Colonel..........Capt O F Lambert *CBE* ret pay..........010984

Lieutenant Colonels

Brumhill R M *MBE TD* 010486

Majors

Kelly T B *TD* 011072
Hyslop M J *MBE TD* sq(v) 301173
Williams P K *TD* sq(v) 010474
Dugdale T B *TD* 010277
Burn D J *TD* 010280
Kyd D A *TD* 160681
Burr A J 010482
Hilton D G *TD* 110482
McKean D B 020384
Gill R S *TD* 240484
Soper G W E *DMS DMA ACIS MBIM* 130585
Foley B J N 310386

Captains

Wright G W H 210871
Mudford R J *RMN RGN* 200976
Mercer A M 010881
Grubb J M A 090882
Fothergill S D *AMIMI MIRTE* 230583
Ewing G 090983
Thompson P 230984
Crompton K J 010485
Winship P L 010685
McCutcheon B C 261085
Eggelton R L *MISM* 180386

Lieutenants

Kennedy D J *BSc* 201277
Matthews S R 091181
Bealey D G *BA* 150382
Hurley K B 170482
Peedle R A *MBIM MISM* (*A/Capt* 010485) 030384
Niland R T 180485
Graham S *FInstLEx* 011085

2nd Lieutenants

Driver P J 131183
†Johnston H C 140384
Gray J W 210584
Toms G W 030684
McBride C 290784
†Shaw I 290784
Short A D 290784
Jones S A 230185
†Wood G 140585
†Stephens M A 260585
†Hutchinson C F 011285
†Gillespie R M 181285

ROYAL ARMY PAY CORPS

Majors

Latham D *MBE ERD TD■ ACII* 230862
Dunbar N W *TD■■* sq(v) 011263
Smiles J R *TD■■■* 030467
Haywood J H *TD■ FCA* 010468
Hardy M S *TD■■■ MA* 010369
Osborne M F 060970
Smyth D A C *TD■ MBIM* 251070
Hurst M J *MBE TD AIB* 230171
Franklin R A *TD■ FIB* 260472
O'Connor L D *TD■■ MBIM* 310173
Rutherford W G *TD■■ AIB* 030374
Griffiths R *TD■■* 010474
Batchelor N G *TD■ MIRTE MBIM MIIM MInstSWM* 010775
Rees W H *MBE TD■■* 101275
Armitt H S *TD■* 010376
Greatrix J G TE 110976
Keith T J D *TD* 261176
Roberts P T *TD FICM* 011276
Straton T D *TD■■ CA ATII* 010177
Bond P M *TD■* 010477
Cuff B G *TD■ FIB* 010477
Dash C G T *TD■ AIB* 010477
Exton J B *TD* 010477
Kirkwood W J *TD■■ AIB* 010477
Malcolm J *TD■ BA MSc(Econ)* 010477
Palmer G T J *TD■* 010477
Simpson M *TD■ AIB* 010477
Sumner J E *TD■■ FCII* 010477
Voss M H *TD■* 010477
Owen J *TD■■ MCIT FMS* 010777
Black R A *TD■ AIB* 010877
Stephenson G D *TD* 240977
Edwards P *TD■* 011277
Gallagher P *TD■ AIB* 190278
Marsh C E *TD AIB* 140578
Page E N *TD■ MSc MRSC* 200878
Forrest J C G *TD■ AIB* 241078
Tasker R B L *TD■* 160279
Brady T J *TD* 010479
Brown A S *TD* 010480
Garrett K 160780
Barber D L *TD■ AIB* 020980
Magnay D E *TD■ AIB* 020980
Barrell J R 021080
Roberts T *TD■* 010181
Haycock A *TD FBS FBIM* 210181
Cameron J N H *TD■ CA FCMA FBIM MIMC JDipMA* 010481
Head R J *TD* 010581
Duchemin D F *TD■ BA* 240781
Patterson J D A *TD■* 010981
Scott A D *TD■ FCA ACIS* 061181
Deas D T *CA* 050582
Purdy G M *TD■■* 010682
Smith T K F B *TD FBIM MInstAM* 280682
Gaffney M A *MBE* 030982
Reid G B *TD AIB(Scot)* 130883
Shaw G A *TD■* 010983
Bell G *TD■ ACIS AIB* 011083
O'Farrell P *MBIM* owc 270184
Marcus A H M *TD■* 011084
Heppenstall J B *TD MBA MBA ACMA* 311084
¶Maclennan G *TD ACMA MBIM* 031284
Grainger S D A *TD■ AIB* 140185
Stiling G W *TD AIB* 140185
Lawson N L *TD* 110685

Captains

Harkin P A B *MBE TD* 240973
Turner R T *AIB* 010475
Melville W M 030975
Lanham C D *TD MInstAM AIB* 010476
Palmer W R *TD* 010677
Anderson L A *AIB* 011177
Wallace J P 010178
Finnegan F C *MBE* 050278
Kerridge B S *TD DMS AIB* 140278
Page N *FCCA ACIS AIB* 130378
Duthoit M R *AIB* 140378
Marsden J G *TD AIB* 170478
Richardson G R C *AIB* 170478
Butler J J *AIB* 010578
Wretham B R *AIB* 160678
Clark S *TD AIB* 010778
Wright J S *AIB* 011078
Povey A 101278
Bedder R J *AIB* 140579
Cole S P *AIB* 140579
Collis A N 140579
Snell M J M *AIB* 140579
Walker M J *BSc(Econ) AIB* 140579
Carr J A *ACMA* 010679
Watts R N (*A/Maj* 010985) 020380
Wilkinson D W 150680
Jones N L 280780
Kennedy P J B 220381
Guild D W 010481
Launchbury J B 101081
Wilkie J B *FCCA IPFA* 101081
Batty C J 230182
Brownrigg D J *AIB* 010382
Ballingall D B 200582
Paddock G A 260582
Parsons R S *AIB* 260582
House C M 040682
Lee D B *AIB* 010882
Olsson J A 221082
Hardy D 301082
Rillands T *MBCS AIDPM MInstAM* 071282
Conroy K 180183
Raper A 180183
Baird A 030283
Quinn N T V 080283
Searby D 080283
Thompson F T *BA* 040983
Rogers A F *MBE* 071083
Gregson E A 120184
Fiderkiewicz A J 020284
Leigh P S 300784
Mutch J 010984
Theobald F A *MBIM* 180984
Randerson T D 290984
Parkinson B S 101184
Aldhouse F G B 030285
Longstaff A R 030285
O'Donnell C 040585
Dearnley R J 260585
Hallam J L 010685
Ross J R 171285
Cullimore A R 221285
Holt N C *AIB* 200186

Lieutenants

Bridge P 020480
Muir T H 011083
Boardman R 090484
Garner G K 190584
Masters N H 280285

2nd Lieutenants

†Hulland M W 270385
†Lindsay A 010485
†Mahoney H 210985
†Brann R F 111085
†Rudder V A 211085

Quartermasters

Chambers J *TD* 010971
Maj 101282

ROYAL ARMY DENTAL CORPS

Colonels

Stafford G D *TD*▪ *QHDS(TA) PhD MSc LDS FBIM* 010482
Calder K D *TD*▪▪ *LDS DL* 010485

Lieutenant Colonels

Clarke P B *OBE TD*▪▪ *MB ChB FDS FDS FDS* 080671
Hindle M O *TD*▪ *MDS FDS* (*A/Col* 010685) 080677
Gallagher J P *TD BDS* 010282
Macfarlane S F *BDS* 010482
Laws I McO *TD MB ChB FDS* 060882
Shafford L T *BDS* 040784
Toms B V *FDS* (*A/Col* 010485) 150185
Bowman J C *TD BChD* 011085
Hough D A *TD BDS* 011085
Pendlebury M E *LDS* 010186

Majors

Richards J F *TD LDS* 010467
Van Den Berg J S *TD*▪ *LDS DDPH* 250368
Collins W J N *MSc FDS FDS* 010768
Morton J D K *TD BDS* 040669
Edwards A J *FDS DDPH* 311269
Fraser J F *BDS* 040770
Patton D W *FDS FDSRCPS* 010775
Jukes A R *BDS MBIM MInstAM* 070676
Harrison A *TD PhD FDS* 160676
Parkinson A D *TD LDS* 290876
Ford G B C *BChD* 260477
Hughes H J *BDS* 280477
Middlemass I M *BDS* 050877
Hudson G M *BDS* 080179
øLithgow-Smith D K *TD BDS* 070579
Francis J R *BDS* 211180
Hale L R O *MSc FDS DOrth* 170981
Caen A J *BDS* 010282
Harrop D R *BDS* 070482
Willey D L *BDS* 010682
Girdham D R *BDS* 281283
Gorst R C *BDS* 180384
øOlver Y B *BDS DOrth* 130684
Nelson M V B *BDS* 250784
Mason V P *BDS* 231084
øMillar S M *BDS* 200585
Thomasson P A *BDS* 080685
Stewart J W *BDS* 230785
Brace D M *BDS* 270785
Alston F *BDS DOrth* 200985

Captains

øPreston J *BChD* 070183
Beck A C *BDS* 290483
Vaughan A G *BDS FDSRCPS* 280783
McVicar I H 080983
Goldthorp W F 041083
Davies P *BDS* 061083
Tyrer G L *BDS* 061083
Day K J *BDS* 190184
Cuccio J J *BDS* 170484
Wilson M C D *BDS* 180984
øElliott S D *BDS* 290185
Latham G B *BDS LRSC* 030285
Bourne N D *BDS* 220285
Hood P W J 290385
Marshall I R 290385
Halliday C J 150585
Roberts G V *BDS* 200785
Atkins J D W 250785
Adey A J *BDS* 010985
Clark R R 051185
Cowell N P *BDS* 051285

ROYAL PIONEER CORPS

Hon Colonel..........Lt Col K J Broom *TD*..........041181

Majors

Heathcote T A *TD*▪ *BA PhD* sq(v) 010782
Blanch M D *TD BSocSc PhD AMA* 091283
Child F W *TD* 091283

Captains

Thornton B A *GradIPM* 021280
Gallyot B A *BSc DMS CEng MICE MIMunE MBIM* 010681
Burrow K N *MRTPI* 101283
¶O'Connell P J *MIPM MBIM MIMH* cl 040585
Keith J L 101085
Maling P V 101085

Lieutenants

†Lake M T *MA* 270177
Morgan R P 101180

2nd Lieutenants

Eames I W 290784
†Adams S J 210985

INTELLIGENCE CORPS

Hon Colonel .... Maj (Bt Lt Col) C J Workman *TD* 060177

Lieutenant Colonels

Gilbert D R *TD■ LLB MA* 010782

Majors

Fitzjohn B S *TD■ BA FIL* 011169
Mancey-Jones M *TD■ BA DipEd* 010674
Barbour R W C T *MBE TD* 010776
Wardle P L *TD■■ MA* 010479
Muckler J G *TD■ BSc(Econ)* 010579
Archibald T D R *MBE TD■* 010879
Newbold W T *TD MA FIPM DMS* 010180
Moss M *TD■■ FInstPet* 040880
Watson R T *TD■ MA* 010481
Field T H E *TD■ BSc(Econ) FCA* 270581
Watt C I *TD* 011081
Kaye R G *TD■ LLB* 010582
Robinson G W *TD■ BA* 140582
Orford K J 010982
Reide J L *TD■ LLB MA* 230982
Wiskin M C R 120583
Wardrop S McL 011183
White R M 011183
Hefferman K A J 010384
Fearn J N *TD BSc(Econ) MInstM* 011184
Jardine A T *TD■ DipArch ARIBA MBIM* 011184
White R L 011184

Captains

Mann P H *TD■■ FSS FIS* (*Bt/Maj* 260479) 010164
Kennedy A I *MBE MBIM* psc† 050465
Woff R A *TD■* 010668
Pepper E B *TD■ RIBA* 010169
Svendsen N K *TD■■ BSc(Econ)* ndc 230869
Cameron D C B *MBIM MIL* 310869
Williams G *TD■* 011169
Boggis-Rolfe N sq 180270
Hart G J *TD■ LLB* 061270
Eastgate J A 300671
Barlow P J *TD■ BA(Hons)* I* 010872
Fiteni R W *TD■* 010872
Booth R P *MA* 281272
Donnelly C N *TD BA* 010973
Rochester R *BPhil(Ed)* 301174
Thornback R K *TD BTech CBiol MIBiol* 010276
Wood D J 010876
Rutherford J *TD* 271076
Dick C J *TD BA* 010577
McLean G G *TD■* 010577
¶Oliver P J 010777
Devere D A L *TD* 010478
Takle E P *BA AIB* (*A/Maj* 011185) 010678
Elwell R S *BA MSc* ph 070279
Pope S M *TD* 011079
Walker D J *TD* 011079
Nutley P 170280
Davies T L 131280
Waters T R W *MA PhD MIL* I 010482
Nicklas-Carter C M *BA* 010582
Jay A C *TD BSc* 010782
Long J M *MA* 120882
Blair W 011282
Sheehan R H 011282
Howard M J *BSc(Econ)* 010183
Perry N E V *BA* 010483
Roe J N *BA* 010483
Erskine G D *BA* 010583
Weight R J 190783
Smith P *MA* 011283
¶Webb R G 121283
Swain N R 220284
Templeman R M 010484
Gyselynck R K *MA ACA* 230684
¶Alderton E P 250684
Mason D 200784
¶Mauger C J *BA AIL* 100984
¶Herring A J 110984
¶Patrick B D 011184
¶Black A E *MBE* 051184
Pattenden S J 010385
Cullimore J S 010785
Campbell B A 010985
Taylor G D 161185

Lieutenants

Nutine J F J G *BSc* 071076
Buchan A P *CBiol MIBiol* (*A/Capt* 010584) 260177
Billington R J *BA* 061077
Cooper P F *BSc* 261080
Hunt A P 051180
Villiers P J *MA* 300681
Sutch A L *MA* 270182
Potter J R *BSc(Eng) MSc PhD AMIEE* 120383
Constantine C A 080883
Dalziel S P C 270983
Rahman S *BSc AIB* 230584
Blair A R 081084
Brown A D 211184
Crichton W 220585
Nightingale M D H 210785
Bostock M A 310785
Parr T L sq 081185

2nd Lieutenants

†Gallo P A *LLB DipLP* 011183
†Macadie J J 200584
†Rodgers W D 200584
†Ghansah E 260585
†Philipps R D 070785
†Jefferies P R 150885

Quartermasters

Webster D *Capt* 180883

ARMY CATERING CORPS

Majors

Chilver G A *MHCIMA MCFA* 030183
Webster R L 010483
Veal E H *TD* 010284
Gaunt A N *MBIM MHCIMA MCFA MRSH* 010485

Captains

¶Brumfitt J L *MBIM MHCIMA* 020185

Lieutenants

Coleman P D 090185

2nd Lieutenants

†Herbertson D C 210584
Roberts J B *FHCIMA* 080884

Quartermasters

Walker J P *MHCIMA FCFA LRSH* 180376 *Maj* 180382
Gibbons J *TD* *Capt* 241077
Cornwall E R 161177 *Maj* 240883
Marshall P J *Capt* 100682
Wright P L *Capt* 180683
Beesley B E *Capt* 061283
Griffin J E *Capt* 240184
Scattergood M H S *Capt* 160384

GENERAL SERVICE CORPS

The Royal Arms

QUEEN ALEXANDRA'S ROYAL ARMY NURSING CORPS

Lieutenant Colonels

Daly P W N *ARRC TD RGN RM* 010482
Jackson W B *ARRC RGN* 010482
Scott S B R *TD RGN RM* 260482
Deerin H *RGN RM* 011082
Thompson J M E *RRC TD DN RGN* 141182
Williams M *RRC TD■ RGN* 010483
Hough C B *RRC TD HV RGN RNT* 020683
Taylor M *TD RFN RGN* 011083
Hinds H *RSCN RGN* 010485
Hughes E A *TD RMN RGN* 010485
O'Gorman M A *TD RGN RM* 010485
Turk P M *TD RGN RCNT* 010486

Majors

Hampshire M L *RRC■ TD■ HV FWT(HV) RGN RM* 150168
Blackwood J *TD RGN RM* 270168
Llewellyn R M *TD■ RGN* 130370
Murphy L F *TD■ RGN RM* 140470
White E M *RRC TD■■ RGN RGN RM* 190570
Cowan J M C *RGN RM* 260970
O'Sullivan G M *TD■ HV RGN RM* 200271
Owens P *TD■ HV RGN RM* 260471
Duncan C P *RRC TD■ RGN RM* 140571
Lattimore E A *RRC TD■ MTD RGN* 150571
Buchanan M *RRC TD■ RGN RSCN* 290772
Rigby J M *TD■ HV FWT(HV) RGN RM QIDNC* 110773
Keating M O M *TD HV MTD RGN RM* 221173
Russell G *RRC TD HV RGN RM* 090274
Houlison B *ARRC TD■ DN RGN RM PWT* 200474
Kidley R J *TD■ RGN* 120674
Jones J *TD■ RGN* 051174
Taylor J *TD■ RGN* 170375
Murray E M *BA RMN RGN RM RNT* 260375
Paley P M *TD RGN* 051075
Black K W *TD MTD RGN RM* 101075
Kiehne N P *TD SRN RGN RM* 190276
Melvin B *HV RMN RGN RM* 230476
Hargreaves C *TD HV RGN RM RNT HVTC* 250677
Herd M *TD DN RGN RM RCNT* 100877
Coleman A *TD RGN RM* 200877
Maxwell M *TD HV RGN RM* 061077
Bremner M A M *TD RGN RM* 081077
Glover G *TD RGN RNT* 281177
Woods E *ARRC TD RGN* 151277
Blackburn M *TD HV RGN RM* 140178
Morgan S A *TD RGN RCNT* 040278
Shaw M A *TD RGN RM* 290678
Sills G A *TD RGN* 200778
Naisbitt N *TD MTD RMN RGN RM* 291178
Chowdhury C *TD RGN* 011278
Davies B *TD HV RGN RM DNTC QIDNC* 060179
Rutledge A A *TD RGN RM* 060479
Moore J M *TD RGN RM* 190479
Smith I E *TD RGN* 100579
Pargeter K R *RGN RM* 050779
Parker L A *TD RGN RM* 160779
Walker R *TD HV RGN RM* 010879
Bartlett E A *RGN* 240979
Marks J I *TD HV RGN* 101079
Spence E M *TD HV FWT(HV) RGN* 101179
Culley A M *TD DN MTD RGN RM* 111279
Smyth G I *TD RGN RM* 160180
Strevens R E *RGN RM* 180480
Courtenay J A *TD HV RGN* 200480
Matthews M W *DN RGN RM RCNT* 220680
Campbell E J *HV RGN RM* 250780
Ballinger M E *OND RGN RM* 060880
Colgrave J E *DN RGN RM* 070880
Pringle M T *RGN RSCN RGN RM* 220880
Golding D *RGN* 240880
Young C A *TD RGN RM* 090980
Bell M M *TD RGN RM* 200980
Perkins J P *HV RSCN RGN RM* 240980
Johnston M A L *RGN* 051080
Young M A *MTD RGN RM* 191080
Jepson P A *OND RGN* 170481
Jupe N A *RGN* 220481
Martin A R *HV RFN RGN* 260481
Marsden K *TD DANS MTD RGN RM RCNT* 050581
Murray K *TD DANS MTD RGN RM RCNT* 050581
Macintosh V *RGN RM* 200581
Duncan A M *RGN RM RCNT PWT* 290581
Godfrey B M *TD RGN* 310581
McMillen P *RGN* 120781
Parsons V R *HV RGN* 160981
Thornberry D E *RGN* 251081
Lane M *RGN RM* 031181
Powell J M *RGN* 041181
Parry R A *TD HV RGN* 121181
Blackford D C *RGN* 051281
Greatrix E M *HV RGN RM* 300182
Eberhardie A C M *TD RGN RNT* 190282
Curran E A M *RGN EN(G) RM* 010382
Almonds M C *RGN RM* 190382
Barley A *TD HV RGN RM* 050482
Rennison W W H *HV RGN RM* 110682
Morrison E *RGN RM* 030782
Stafford J *RGN RM* 030782
Chapman K *RGN* 280782
Thornley K J *RGN RM* 210882
Owen M J *HV RSCN RGN RM RNT RCNT* 290982
Taylor K V *RGN RM* 061082
Weston R C *HV RGN RM* 061082
Storey J *RGN* 141082
Luckie M M G *RGN* 151082
Ritchie D E *RGN* 301082
Smith Price M T *HV RGN RM* 311082
Watson M *DN RGN RM* 231182
Cole M A *RGN* 011282
Gibson I M *RGN RGN RM* 031282
Collingwood M P *RGN RM* 091282
Cowen M *RGN RM* 161282
Quayle S N *TD RGN* 231282
Bordenkircher M *RGN* 220183
Moorhouse J *RGN* 260183
Cowell U M *TD MSc DN RGN RNT RCNT* 020283
Cameron J E *TD RGN* 060283
McAlpine O *RGN RM RNT* 150283
Abbott J *RSCN RGN RNT* 030383
Dickins B F *DN RGN* 150383
Taylor M I *TD RGN EN(G)* 210483
Kerr M *RGN RM* 220483
Loadman J *RGN* 220483
Cuming E *RGN RM* 060583
Dando R A *BA(Hons) MSc DN RGN* 070583
Green R E *MTD RGN RM* 130583
Cockerton M *RGN* 190583
Taylor H M E *RGN RM* 250583
Jenkins E *RGN* 050883
Kennett A S *RGN* 050883
Waller C *TD RMN RGN RNT RCNT* 100883
Moore M *MTD RGN RM* 220883
Parker B R *RGN RM* 090983
Burton A P *RGN* 121083
Fink C C *RGN* 181083
Edge S *RMN RGN* 131283
Starkey N *RGN* 191283
Bailey P *RGN RNT* 240184
Farley J C *RGN RCNT* 230284
Parker M H *RGN RGN RCNT* 270284
Colegate E A *RGN RM* 010384
Munro C *RGN RM* 160384
McWhinnie L P *RNMS RGN* 180484
Beggs F H *RGN RM* 300484
Robinson P B *HV RGN RM* 170584
Lewis M B L *RGN* 240584
Smith A C *RGN* 060684
Webber S A *RGN RM* 130684
Strange J *RGN* 040784
Burr E J *RSCN RGN RCNT* 050784
Roberts B V S *DN RGN* 050784
Jones J A H *RGN* 100884
Morris J A *RGN* 100884
McCabe M C *RGN* 040984
Payne S E *ONC RGN RNT* 230984
Sheldrake D A *HV RGN* 260984
Jones B N G *HV FWT(HV) OND RGN* 021084
Walsh C A *HV FWT(HV) RGN* 041084
Hunter R M *RGN RM* 061084
Humphreys M F *RSCN RGN* 011284
Clouston A *RGN RCNT* 030185
Gallop B J *HV RSCN RGN RM* 210285
Miller S J *RGN RM* 010385
Wilson B A G M *RGN RM* 050385
Allen M A T *RGN RM RNT* 290485
Brocksom A P *RCNT* 040585
Page P *RGN RM* 100585
Young G E *RGN RNT* 210585
Handysides H A *RGN* 050785
Spires K A *DN RGN RM RNT RCNT* 110985

Woodward V A M *RGN* 150985
Harrison B H B *HV RGN RM* 250985
Bentley C J *HV FWT(HV) RGN RM* 300985
Garway-Templeman C M *RGN* 101085
Howorth H M *RGN* 101085
McAllister M A *RGN* 271085
Rossaye J M *RMN RGN* 131185
Elton A *DN RGN* 110186
Gilson P A *RGN* 300186
Bloomer S L *DN HV RGN RM* 220486

Captains

Wright M V P *OND RGN QIDNC* 031273
Davies A R *RGN* 260974
Baker J C *RMN RGN RNT* 270974
Rai B K *MTD RGN RM* 080875
Hedley M D H *RGN* 081275
Smillie D E V *TD RMN RGN* 150476
Milne M O *RGN RM* 170576
Turner P J *RGN RNT RCNT* 270277
Jones C A *RGN RM* 250477
Broadhead G M *RGN* 050777
D'Souza L M *RGN* 240877
Hirst M I *RGN* 280977
Riley B M *HV RGN RM* 101177
Jubb S V *RGN RM* 170178
Evans B *RGN* 020278
Moore M E *RMN RGN* 260478
Bish L M *RGN RNT* 300478
Holmes A L *RMN RGN* 260578
Friend P A *HV RGN* (*A/Maj* 010985) 270678
Slade J A *DN RSCN RGN RM* 070778
Lall S A *HV RGN* 010878
Horrell V A *RGN* 070878
Robinson H *HV OND RGN* 080878
Whiting J M *HV RSCN RGN RCNT* 120878
Sutherland P J *RGN RM* 290878
Ness D E *RGN RNT* (*A/Maj* 011185) 020978
Craven E R *RGN RM* 201078
Caton J A *HV RGN RM* 051178
Maddock V A *RGN RM* 091278
Irwin M E *RSCN RGN* 020179
Howells A *RGN RM* 290179
Barclay C D *RGN RGN RCNT* 030279
Allen-Rice P J *RGN RM* 100279
Evans V E *SRN RGN RM* 110279
Davidson S *RGN* 040379
Hardie E M *BSc DN RMN RGN RCNT* 060379
Hubbard V A *HV FWT(HV) RGN* 240379
Swattridge S H *RGN RCNT* 250379
Robinson P J *RGN RM* 270379
Moore S G *RGN RM* 010479
Taylor M L *RSCN RGN* 030479
Marjoram B A *RGN* 140479
Green M *RGN* 020579
Purdy J *RGN* 110579
Smyth M J *RSCN RGN* 110579
Kalideen D P *RGN RCNT* 060679
Morrison M A *RGN* 190679
McPartlan C W *HV RGN RM* 260679
Fagan P *RGN RM* 270679
Robertson-Bell D M 270679
Meara E A *RGN RM* 040779
Briggs N *DN HV RGN RM* 050779
Green L D *RGN RM* 150779
Ashton P M *RGN* 060879

Fletcher S L *RMN RGN* 280879
Hill S M *RGN RM* 080979
Mears S B *RGN RCNT* 301079
Wilson C M *RGN* 071179
Frisby S D *RNMS RGN* 201179
Storton J *RMN RGN* 251179
Evans C A 281179
Minshull J *DANS RGN RM RNT RCNT* 021279
Dickson B *RMN RGN* 111279
Stewart G P *DN HV RGN* 230180
Scotton C *RGN* 240180
Docherty J *RGN* 300180
Averty J T *RGN RM* 250280
Underwood A C *RGN* 180380
Kelly V A *HV RGN* 280380
Clark A *RGN RM* 030480
Ahern E H *RGN* 300480
Green J M *RGN RM* 070580
Arkwright A A *RGN* 170680
Brough V M *RGN* 260680
McNeice F M *HV RGN RM* 300680
Clabby M 190780
Noall P F *RGN RM* 210880
Parsons R D *RGN RM* 250880
Rouine A *HV RGN RM* 260880
Andrew J L *RGN RM* 080980
Burgess C *RGN RM* 150980
Ritter S A H *MA RMN RGN* 161080
Gardner E R *HV RGN RM* 021180
Watson M B *RGN RSCN RCNT* 121180
Redpath A 141180
Ascott M *RGN* 211180
Powell J W *RGN* 211280
Wrapson R A *RGN BTA* 311280
Luckett D *RGN* 010181
Holmes A *RGN* 150181
Page M J *RGN* 250181
Cook J A *RGN* 280281
Cassidy E *RGN RMN* 020381
Carey-Harris J *RGN RCNT* 280381
Shannon H C *RGN* 300381
Browne N M *RGN* 050481
Shipp S *RGN* 160481
Deery E L *RGN RM* 300581
Johnson A *RGN RCNT* 310581
Cowling H E F *RGN* 090681
Bulley C C *HV RGN RM* 230681
Ratcliffe S P 070781
Castledine D M *RGN* 080781
Shaw S A *RGN* 080781
Ayscough E M C *RGN* 190781
Osborne B M *RGN* 260781
Lodge P J *RGN RM* 010881
Boyle M W *RGN* 170881
Brown U D *BSc DN RGN RNT RCNT DON* 100981
Collinson S F *RGN RM* 220981
Hird M *RGN* 220981
Ratcliffe P *RGN* 021081
Hoad P J *DN RGN* 131081
Kikerpuu L *RGN* 211081
McLoughlin J *RGN* 231081
Canning M A *RGN EN(G) RM* 281081
Duffy C A *RGN* 201181
O'Connor A G *RGN* 271181
Berry A *RGN RM* 011281
O'Hare M A *RGN EN(G)* 191281
Syddall P J *RGN* 100182
Lister E A *HV RGN RM* 010282
Smith E R *RGN RM* 020282
Glanville C M *RGN* 040282
Davis J E *RGN* 160282
Slater J J *RGN RM RDSA* 150382
McKibbin A *RSCN RGN RM* 220382
Booth A M *RGN* 300382
Kift L M J *RSCN RGN* 310382

Lee-Cann J A *RMN RGN RCNT* 070482
Stanton P A *HV RGN* 150482
Seth-Kosoko V M *HV ONC RGN* 240482
Chappell B A *RGN EN(G) RM* 250482
Brooks G I M *RGN RM* 040582
Crawford R M *RGN RM* 140582
Shirra M *RGN* 310582
Bowes S M 170682
Joseph E *RGN RM* 270682
Walmsley A M *RGN* 010782
Verow K J *RGN* 200782
Lee G R *HV RGN* 230782
Kennaugh A *RGN RM* 290782
Kennedy Y L *RGN RM* 310782
Kendall L *RGN* 010882
Horn P A *RGN RM* 070882
MacDonald A S *RGN RM* 070882
Johnson B *RGN* 110882
Thornton C M *HV RGN RM* 150882
Brookfield S M *RGN* 200882
Royle A J *RGN RM* 220882
Singh M *HV ADM RGN RM* 310882
Phillips N C J *RGN RNT RCNT* 060982
Finn M E *HV RGN EN(G)* 200982
Chandler S C *RGN* 021082
Grimes R E *RGN RM* 181082
McClure C 261082
Cocking J *RGN* 311082
Quainton S G D *RGN* 311082
Williams E H *RGN RM* 051182
Theaker E *RGN RM* 151182
Duggan M *RGN* 161182
Reeve S P *RGN* 291182
Bennett G M *RGN* 301182
Middleton L *HV RGN* 011282
Lennox A J *RGN EN(G)* 061282
Tatam S *RGN* 101282
Birch S G *RGN* 191282
Richards G *MTD RGN RM* 220183
Foster A B *RGN RM* 250183
Stephens S *DN MTD RGN RM* 080283
Semple J S *RGN RSCN* 170283
Crabb V G *RGN RM* 200283
Eaton E *RGN* 080383
Revill M A *RGN* 080383
Bailey D J *RGN* 150383
Bowyer S *RGN* 150383
Davidson L *RGN* 150383
Garner S E 150383
Barr D M J *RGN* 280383
Robertshaw J A *RGN RM OHNC* 290383
Court L A 010483
Thomas D S *HV RGN RM* 050483
Smith J M *RSCN RGN* 090483
Hughes D *RGN* 230483
Brown R M 060583
Poyzer J L 270583
Mansel C I A *RGN* 130683
Nelson G B *DN RGN RM RNT RCNT PGCE* 190683
Bragg D E *RGN* 200683
Luxton P J *HV RGN* 250783
Prince L J *RMN* 260783
Murphy S *RGN EN(G)* 310783
Jones H A *RGN BTA* 020883
Jenkins L J *RGN* 250883
Roe D A L *HV RGN RM* 310883
Robinson M S *HV RGN RM* 060983
Quinn C F *RMN RGN RM* 100983
Hogan E P *RGN* 180983
Dart A *ONC RGN* 190983
Home E M *RGN RM* 210983
Clowes N *RGN* 270983
Cheung S N *RGN* 111083

Territorial Army, Queen Alexandra's Royal Army Nursing Corps — continued

Wood A E *RGN* 111083
Holman J M *RGN* 131083
Davies V 171083
Mainds D M *RGN* 171083
Marshall P 171083
Boone J L 251083
Watson J E *RGN RM* 271183
Burgess P A *RGN RSCN* 281183
Martin I *RGN* 281183
Sloan P 021283
Cottrell N E *RGN* 151283
Nicholl H M *RSCN RGN RM* 151283
Pert C *HV RGN* 171283
Woods S 010184
Mitton A *OND RGN* 050184
Allan D H *RGN* 040284
Harries-Jenkins S *RGN* 100284
McClure P T *RGN* 240284
Cadogan R H *RGN* 190384
Clark E O *RGN* 230484
Hadnett C A *RGN* 290484
Davies N M *HV RGN* 010584
Hazlewood O E *RGN* 240584
Crame G E *RGN* 070684
Lawes S L *RGN* 160684
Uprichard S 230684
Brand M J 250684
Powis J *RGN* 300684
McConnell E J *DN RGN RNT* 150784
Wilson L 240784
Pottle B C *RGN* 300784
Hall H *RGN* 310784
Smith D A *RGN* 290884
Whittaker C *RGN* 290884
Murie R R *RGN RM* 110984
Davis S *DN RGN RM* 150984
Houston C A *OND RGN EN(G)* 131084
Mackay C A *HV RSCN RGN* 131084
Orr E C *RSCN RGN* 301084
Smyth V M *RGN* 311084
Shepherd M M *RGN RM* 011184
Walker H M *RSCN RGN* 151184
Gofton S *OND RMN RGN* 251184
Jarvis A M T *RGN* 261184
Muscroft Paylor C A *HV RGN RM* 291184
Nicholls J M *RGN* 011284
Parkin E J *RGN EN(G)* 011284
Ramuite D E 011284
Stoneham C M *RGN* 011284
Weedon K P *RGN* 031284
Richardson D M *RGN* 151284
Burton L E *HV RGN* 181284
Smith B *RGN* 070185
Farley V R *RGN RM FPDip* 110185
Wallace P I *SRN EN(G)* 230185
Ryan E A 250185
Russell P M *RGN* 310185
Cross C V A *HV RGN RM* 130285
Hollins G M *RGN* 110385
McGuigan S E *RGN* 190385
Purdy P A *HV RMN RGN RM* 270385
Atherton I *TD* 010485
Cadwallader D K B 010485
Bean D *RSCN RGN* 030485
Colley J E *HV RGN* 070585
Walsh A M *OND RGN RM* 270585
Evans A E *HV RGN* 060685
McKee E V *EN(G) CSS* 200685
Knight J A *RMN RSCN* 210685
Whewell C A *ADM RGN RM* 220685
Clift J A 020785
Goodenough E *RGN* 130785
Snaith K A 220785
Axup J E *RGN* 310785
West J H E *RGN* 010885
Broomhead J A *RGN* 070885
McLeod L *RGN MSTA ASTA IFSTA* 120885
Douglas F M *RGN* 170985
Whittlesey P F *RGN* 230985
Howells J B *RGN* 240985
Bromley C M *LSSCh RGN RM* 280985
Vinnicombe A *RGN* 061085
White J A M 181085
Walsh B C *RGN* 141185
Bott J C *OND RGN* 081285
Bretland J S *RGN* 151285
Stubbs C *ONC RGN* 020186
Tate B A *RGN* 030186
Twigge E *RGN* 040186
Cleghorn B L *RGN* 100286
Prictoe R M *ONC RGN* 310386
Durant A M *RGN* 060486
Notman A *RGN RGN* 100486

Lieutenants

Godsell E J *MICE RGN RM* 110378
Clarke H A *RGN* 200280
Marshall G T 201280
Conibere M P *RGN RM* 200181
Ogden P J *RGN* 130581
Hiscock E *RGN* 300781
Jackson J E 300781
Reid K J *RGN RM* 050881
Hamilton J S 100881
Eveson J A *RGN* 180881
Moore K M *RGN* 170981
Harteam A M *RGN* 271081
Fearon S A *RMN RGN* 011281
Wood S A *RGN RM* 091281
Knight J C *RGN* 040182
Hackney S A *RGN* 060282
Kaschewitz F *RSCN RGN* 070382
Ballard C T *RGN* 300382
Merrin V N *RMN RGN EN(G)* 010482
Wilson S J 160482
Mart R B L *RGN* 230482
Ingham P A *RGN* 030582
Mackeen J M *RGN* 090782
Bailey K A P *RGN* 160782
Bramley T H R *RGN* 230782
Carrington A D 230782
Lewis S *RGN* 080882
Gunningham S P M *RGN EN(G)* 160882
Hughes S M *RGN* 290882
Cunningham S M *RGN* 080982
Maxwell L J 100982
Maginniss M E *RGN RGN RM* 130982
Rogerson H M *RGN* 260982
Day S E *RGN* 131082
Johnston R J *RGN* 221082
McClements K A 221082
Corcoran D N *RGN* 241082
Valentine C E J *BN RGN* 261082
McVeigh J E 291082
Kane M M *ONC RSCN RGN* 161182
Shakespeare M 231182
Ashton D A *RMN RGN* 011282
Bough J A *RGN* 131282
Bowen S J 251282
Mitchell De Faria A *RGN RM* 281282
Brough S J *RGN* 030183
Butler N *HV RGN RM* 080183
Garner G K *RGN* 140183
Jackson E M I *RGN* 180183
Henderson I A *BSc(Hons) RGN* 290183
Houghton J *ONC RSCN RGN* 020283
Harkins E *RGN RGN* 220383
Forrai J E *RGN* 230383
Jarrett N A *RGN* 240383
Thomas J *RGN* 020483
Paxton K 110483
Pearson D *RGN RM* 270483
Carter S A *RGN* 300483
Dawson E *RGN* 240583
Gallagher S C *RGN EN(G)* 270583
Tong C *RGN* 040683
Klassa H C *RGN* 080783
Gardner K 170783
Standley M R K *RGN* 300883
Rees H M *RGN* 060983
Parrott M M *RGN* 180983
Lowes S *RGN* 260983
Shawcross A *RGN* 260983
Fletcher C *RGN* 031083
Greer E P J *RGN* 071083
Ebbrell A M *RMN RGN* 071183
Taylor J E 201183
Duhre K S *RSCN RGN* 010184
Stuart M J *RGN EN(G)* 250184
Bell J *RMN RGN* 040284
McNeill M L *RGN* 230384
Kendell K *RGN* 010484
Scholes H D *RGN* 010484
Barten C M *RGN* 230684
Jamison M J 260684
Leader R C V *RGN* 260684
Martin E E 260684
Convery C E 050784
Legge F V *RGN RGN* 130884
Round S J *RGN* 130884
Christie M M 250884
Hilton D L 080984
Lewis S P *RMN RGN* 190984
Burd K M *RGN* 011084
King A D *RGN* 211184
Lodge J M 101284
Lewis E V *RGN* 010185
Curry M 070185
Maiden V R *RGN EN(G)* 010385
Ward J A *RGN* 110385
Crozier A M 260385
Potts S J 010485
Smillie J D 070585
Clapperton C G *RGN* 010685
Ashurst S D 170685
Lightfoot S T *RGN* 140885
Martland J A *RGN* 230985

2nd Lieutenants

†Weber C W *MAMS* 050684

Non-Nursing Officers

Majors

Guyler J *BA MInstAM* 121080

Captains

Cordwell A *AIMLT* 300983
Bone L K 010485
Oxby J A *TD* 010485

Lieutenants

Skone E C 010684

2nd Lieutenants

†Martindale A E *BA* 120684
†Wallace M A 150385
Murton S I 170885

WOMEN'S ROYAL ARMY CORPS

Lieutenant Colonels

Blackwood J C *OBE TD*■ 210382

Majors

Squance E *TD* 010876
Notley A N *TD* 030380
Nicholson M J *TD BSc* 101180
Huggett P M 311280
Hindshaw J M *TD FCA* 210182
Howie K M 010482
Wymbs R D *TD DipEd* 010482
Gordon I M 010384
Howard K M 010584
Dakin S A 150584
Campbell E M 061184
Holroyd I M *BA* 010485
Wilson J J 011085
Maude S E *TD BSc* 010186
Homewood H E 160186

Captains

¶Carter E *TD* 180964
Hinds G A *TD* 270372
Mackintosh H R *TD*■ *BSc* 010472
White D 010577
Bell E H *BA* 291178
Hammersley M E *BSc* 010479
Wilson L A *TD BSc* 010479
Hedgecoe P J 010779
Henderson D M *LLB* (*A/Maj* 150285) 141179
Majury S F *BA* 221179
Millar C F B *MA* (*A/Maj* 010486) 011279
Rhind J M *TD* 010980
Tuhey R K *TD BA* 011180
White S A *BA* 231180
Edwards M J *TD BSc* 010281
Riley P J 250381
Williams H *BEd* 010481
Allan J A *MA* 010581
Peyton M E L *TD BSSc MSc* 010981
Freeman-Tozer V J *BEd* 160981
Fenney S *BSc* 190482
Haddow D M *BSc* 010582
Raggett E A *RGN RM RCNT* 130682
Walker J L *TD BA BSc* 010782
Maltman R E *BSc* 221282
Morters J 010483
Williams S R M 010483
Springman S M 270683
Shannon M E *BSc* 010783
Adams K M J (*A/Maj* 120186) 010883
Campbell C M 010983
Mohan S A 120983
Sanders A J *BA* 220983
Daly U M *BSc* 011083
Larsen-Burnett E C A *BEd* 011083
Monks S E 011083
Buckels J V 011183
Jones G H 011183
Weston H M R 221183
Mann G M 010184
Payne E R 210684
Mantle E *BSc* 010884
Smith S D 050884
Dunn F J 240984
Baird E A 011084
Appleby J A 251184
Guzkowska M A J 201284
Webber L F 010185
Solomon H M *BSc DMS* 010285
Pickles C P 010385
Eggington A *BSc* 010485
Oliver D M *MA* 010485
Morton A M 100585
Morrow D L 240585
Barnes J E *BA* 050685
Hancox A E 230785
Twinem C S 130885
Whittaker J C 010985
Sweeney A 210985
D'Inverno I J *MA* 011085
Maltman E M *BAcc CA* 311085
O'Hara H M 011185
Sowerby B M 141185
Quine K E *MA BA VetMB MRCVS* 150186
Mathieson C M M 300186

Lieutenants

Farnan P J *TD BSc* 280472
Payne J C *BSc* 011074
Neale S E *LLB* (*A/Capt* 220684) 190177
Lightbody R K *BA BSc* 120878
Hoskins C A 260679
Logan S R *BA* 160979
Reading S A 250979
Walker-Cull J *BA* 011079
Mullineux D S 021079
Ness G 041279
Dahl N V *BSc* 310180
Eaborn L J (*A/Capt* 191185) 090380
Hibbert S A (*A/Capt* 220584) 190480
Martin D N (*A/Capt* 140783) 071080
Thomis S P *BPharm MPS* (*A/Capt* 200883) 221080
Barkley S 180181
Hall B A *BA* 270281
Andrews M F 020681
Roy H M *BA* 240681
Rogers M E M G 290781
Creamer M 010881
Bound V A *BA(Hons)* 241081
Bogan P C (*A/Capt* 120186) 311081
Holland A C *BPharm MPS* (*A/Capt* 010285) 121181
Joyner S M (*A/Capt* 071284) 061281
Dawson H A *BEd* (*A/Capt* 020685) 221281
Davison P M 300182
Rhodes P A 300182
Lilley D A 100482
Stuart-Monteith S J 200582
Wormell V L 090682
Luke T J 220682
Freeman J E 130782
Cruickshank F M *MA(Hons)* 240782
Hutchinson V L 240782
Miles D A *BSc* 240782
Dunn H M F 310782
Fitton E R 180982
Richards A E 180982
Withers K M *BCom* 180982
Gann S J *BSc* 210982
Black J E *BSc PhD* 021182
Bowser C H *BA* 021182
Paige C D *BSc(Hons)* (*A/Capt* 010884) 121182
Sharp A D *BSc* 051282
Shaw A M *MA* 040583
Aitchison C A V 070583
Hughes D M 110583
Roberts P L *BA* 170583
Abbott J (*A/Capt* 020785) 300683
Vipond M *BA* 160783
Munley M L 220783
Clayton C R 300783
Francis Z M *BCom* 300783
Stenning A F M 300783
Cable G L 010883
Warren E D *BSc* 010883
Maychell C L 190983
Fathers J C *BA(Hons) PGCE* 210983
Giannini C F (*A/Capt* 010485) 021183
Hay H D *BSc* 021183
Varney A E 071183
McKee J H 261183
Hammond S 011283
Hutber M 240184
Berriman J *BSc* 260184
Carson S M 280284
Jepson V M 030384
Herkes R C 080384
Rose P A 030484
McClean J C 110484
Jones S L *BSc* 030584
James H E *BA* 240784
Marchant E G *BA AIMLS* 240784
Watson R E *BSc* (*A/Capt* 011284) 070984
Carroll A M 180984
Haywood G E S 180984
Watson M M *BA(Hons)* 241184
Rawson L *BSc* 161284
Aldred E M *BSc* 120185
Annison J B 310385
Dimond J H 010485
Ross F A F 280485
Hubbard J E 300785
Winter R M E 300785
Lynall P A 180885
Hall M A *BSc* 010985
Blake R L 020985
Berry K J 031185
Mudryk C M 131185
Armstrong F C 261185
Bell J *LLB* 261185
Jenkins C A 261185
Lloyd S E *BSc* 261185
Robb A J 261185
Wellbeloved P D 261185
Archer E K 010386

2nd Lieutenants

†Fletcher C *BSc* 260473
Sanderson A H *BSc PGCE* 020478
Harrison S R N 130381
†Johnson C M 010881
†Bassett M E 161081
†Standfield E F *BA* 170182
†McIntosh B A 310782
†Marsland L C 180982
†Pusey S L 261082
†Andrews D P S 031282
†Lucas C A 031282
†Agnew A M *LLB* 051282
†Murray K H *RSCN RGN* 051282

Territorial Army, Women's Royal Army Corps — continued

†Halsall L K	210483
†Argent C A	160783
†Ford K P *BCom*	300783
Roberts H A	300783
†Bloomfield J F	131083
†Frith J	021183
†Watson J M	011283
†Taylor K S	051283
†Allred S	131283
†Evans F E *BA*	260184
†Harcourt K J	260184
†Worrall S F V	150384
Blyth A	220484
†Steele S C	030584
†Turner C S G *BSc(Hons)*	150584
†Berriman G	240584
†Collier-Jackson T K	240584
†Smith A	240584
†Wilson M L	240584
†Bailey L M A	300584
†Walker C	300584
†Marnoch E C *NNEB*	310584
†Burton K A	250684
†Lawrence J A	250684
†Dickson L C	140784
Farquharson F	140784
†Pakenham-Walsh S F *BA*	140784
Barker S A	280784
Bowden F A	280784
†Brill H M	280784
†Day D	280784
Rothwell P J	280784
Matthews S L	290784
†Pallin E P	080984
Wakefield C V	100984
†Cooper S T	210984
Baynaro V A	220984
†Collins H A	220984
†Cunningham F J *BSc*	220984
†Hill C J	220984
†Stonehouse S A	250984
Davies C M M	011184
Payne N L	241184
Tudor S J	241184
†Coles C E	261184
Beattie S	220185
French S I	150285
Brennan J L *LLB(Hons)*	280285
†Dalby A J	280285
Broughton C Z	200685
†Lockton F J	210685
†Alcock J P	130785
†Barker S J	130785
†Bingham G M	130785
†Blair R M	130785
†Cameron W M	130785
†Ehlert K F	130785
†Fletcher L M *BSc(Hons)*	130785
†Harrison K M	130785
†Hastings J A	130785
†Hill K A L	130785
†Howard E J	130785
†Lee S	130785
†Macilwaine J H *LLB*	130785
†Nichols S C	130785
†Oliver M	130785
†Pascoe E J C	130785
†Skentelbery N A	130785
†Taylor H P	130785
†Turner J C	130785
†Aynsley S L	270785
†Collins L J	270785
†Dunn J L	270785
†Fitton J A	270785
†Gregg E L	270785
†Hargan J A	270785
†Holland A M	270785
†King J E	270785
†Owen C M	270785
†Ridler S A	270785
†Stocks J R	270785
†Terrell D A	270785
†Thomson C M	270785
†Wood C S	270785
†Bridle J M	210985
†Carson J E	210985
†Curry P D	210985
†Fenoughty T J	210985
†Fisher S B	210985
†Foster M R	210985
†Harberd K E	210985
†Hassall B	210985
†McClure G M M	210985
†McGowan S C	210985
†O'Rourke M C	210985
†Smith G K M	210985
†Wagner S J *LLB(Hons) DipLP NP*	210985
†Wallace V G	210985
†Carpenter E J	220985
†Nickell K P	031085
†Sutherland C R	031085
†Christensen L K	161185
†Darby J M	161185
†Gill K L	161185
†Gurney C C G	161185
†Harold N F	161185
†Manley B E	161185
†Sleigh P J	161185

Quartermasters

Verrinder S G M	*Capt*	130584
Mahoney D E	*Capt*	130785

OFFICERS TRAINING CORPS

ABERDEEN UNIVERSITY

Hon Colonel

Brig D W Anderson *CBE* ret pay 240182

Commanding Officer

Lt Col R W Grant RAMC TA 030983

BIRMINGHAM UNIVERSITY

Hon Colonel

Maj Gen R W T Britten *CB MC* ret pay 010878

Commanding Officer

Lt Col C J Eager RA 270186

BRISTOL UNIVERSITY

Hon Colonel

Lt Gen *Sir* Hugh Cunningham *KBE* ret pay 180377

Commanding Officer

Lt Col M E Kelsey *TD* REME TA 200983

CAMBRIDGE UNIVERSITY
"South Africa 1900-01"

Hon Colonel

Gen *Sir* Hugh Beach *GBE KCB MC* ret pay (*Vice Lord Lieutenant Greater London*) 010777

Commanding Officer

Lt Col N H H Adams RGJ 210784

CARDIFF UNIVERSITY

Hon Colonel

Maj Gen L A H Napier *CB OBE MC DL* ret pay 310385

Commanding Officer

Lt Col W E Strong RA 080885

EAST MIDLANDS UNIVERSITIES

Hon Colonel

Col S H Clark *OBE JP DL* ret pay 010583

Commanding Officer

Lt Col D R D Newell WFR TA 241285

EDINBURGH AND HERIOT WATT UNIVERSITIES

Hon Colonel

Field Marshal *HRH The Prince* Philip *Duke of* Edinburgh *KG KT OM GBE QSO*

Commanding Officer

Lt Col J W H Collins QOY 070783

EXETER UNIVERSITY

Hon Colonel

Maj Gen *Sir* John Acland *KCB CBE* ret pay 100980

Commanding Officer

Lt Col J N Alford RA 221084

GLASGOW AND STRATHCLYDE UNIVERSITIES

Hon Colonel

Col A S Weatherhead *OBE TD* 250182

Commanding Officer

Lt Col A P L Halford-MacLeod BW 011085

LEEDS UNIVERSITY

Hon Colonel

Maj Gen D E Isles *CB OBE* ret pay 200585

Commanding Officer

Lt Col K A Mitcheson RA 291184

LIVERPOOL UNIVERSITY

Hon Colonel

Maj Gen P A Downward *CB DSO DFC* ret pay 280280

Commanding Officer

Maj C A Herbert *JP* RCT TA 211083

UNIVERSITY OF LONDON

Hon Colonels

HM QUEEN ELIZABETH THE QUEEN MOTHER

Surg Capt M N Naylor *RD* RNR 180179

Commanding Officer

Lt Col J B Bennett RE 160985

MANCHESTER AND SALFORD UNIVERSITIES

Hon Colonel

Maj Gen D Houston *CBE* ret pay 280385

Commanding Officer

Lt Col C G Davidson *TD JP* 51 HIGHLAND 010483

NORTHUMBRIAN UNIVERSITIES

Hon Colonel

Col *The Visct* Ridley *TD* (*HM Lord Lieutenant Northumberland*) 010386

Commanding Officer

Maj R G Turnbull *TD JP* RRF TA 010884

OXFORD UNIVERSITY

Hon Colonel

Gen *Sir* Frank Kitson *GBE KCB MC*■ ret pay 210782

Commanding Officer

Lt Col J M Craster GREN GDS 310785

QUEEN'S UNIVERSITY BELFAST

Hon Colonel

Col W E Falloon *CBE TD ADC* 010683

Commanding Officer

Lt Col T H Chambers *TD* RA TA 011086

UNIVERSITY OF SHEFFIELD

Hon Colonel

Brig C D H Wilson ret pay 260685

Commanding Officer

Lt Col R J Elliott *TD* YORKS 200385

SOUTHAMPTON UNIVERSITY

Hon Colonel

Maj Gen M Matthews *CB* ret pay 250785

Commanding Officer

Lt Col I C T Ingall 5 INNIS DG 100884

TAYFORTH UNIVERSITIES

(St Andrews, Dundee and Stirling)

Hon Colonel

Lt Gen *Sir* Alexander Boswell *KCB CBE* ret pay 010182

Commanding Officer

Lt Col C W Pagan *MBE TD* RE TA 161283

ULSTER DEFENCE REGIMENT

A harp ensigned with crown in gold

Regimental Marches

Quick Marches......................................(i) Sprig of Shillelagh. (ii) Garryowen.
Slow March..Oft in the Stilly Night

Regimental Headquarters....................Magheralave Road, Lisburn, Co Antrim (*Tel No: Lisburn* 5111 *Ext:* 41157)

GENERAL LIST

SECTION A

Lieutenant Colonels

Powell W *TD* 180674
Iredale J A *TD*▪▪ 011178

Majors

Oliver J P J D *MBE* sq 241077
Somerville G C *TD* 010378
Hall D G S 020978
Vasa A *TD BA* 010780
Whitcombe G M V 080880
¶Bell H 030983
Clapton P T A 011284
Browne J E D De La V *MBA MSc MP* 010785
Bacchus A J 100286
Jenner-Fust R 100286

Captains

Bamber I G M sq 280865
Stewart-Liddon R J 150573
Greenwell J P 280776
Buckman C S (*A/Maj* 061083) 310776
Wood T A 200277
Koder P C *BVMS MRCVS* 310577
Colvill A J *BSc MA CA* 010677
Bleby J *BVetMed MRCVS* 280878
Lawrence C J D *BA* 061078
Juster D H 181178
Tittmar H *TD BA PhD* 010479
Hewitt S G B 010480
Bates J E N *BA* 130580
¶Cattle G A 010980
Oliver A R *MA* 080981
¶Webb K W 210981
Backett K B (*A/Maj* 010286) 011181
Rogers J S (*A/Maj* 040484) 010182
Skinner P N *LLB* 211282
Pegg K S *LLB AIL JP* 020483
¶Goodinson J 240583
¶Henderson W A B 120683
Anderson D J L F 280783
Philby P M 010883
¶Core G 200983
¶Watts D S 161183
Allen J V 011283
Menneer R C *BSc* 021283
Price B S (*A/Maj* 011284) 021283
Walker D M *BSc MICE* 021283
Avery J W L S *BA* 031283
¶Walkden J 100184
¶King J H 160184
Fleming J W (*A/Maj* 010185) 300184
Wood A J (*A/Maj* 010185) 010284
¶Irving D A *BEM* 010384
Balmer D *BScTech* 040484
Hoe A 020684
¶Watson A *MISM* 210684
Walker T 300884
Keating G J ph 110984
Fox R C 101084
French J R *LLB* 211084
¶Blake W 010285
Wrangham J (*A/Maj* 220485) 210485
Harrison S D C 010785
Daintry G M 090985
Baty P R A L 311285

Lieutenants

Conlin H L 020173
Rees P 051174
Sharp J F 231177
King S G *BSc* 271177
Miles I D 190579
Smith R F 130679
Kemp I D *BA* 090979
Mudge F B 240979
Orde J R 271079
Wright J F 240280
Broadfoot T K *BSc* 031180
Pay P I W *BA* 180181
Phillips N G 050481
†Taylor T A (*A/Capt* 310584) 230581
Gray G T 040881
Eliot-Slater J D 201081
Castle R J (*A/Capt* 010285) 131181
Stables R H (*A/Capt* 300984) 301181
Pritchard S J O 081281
Macleod A J *MA CEng* 020282
King W N (*A/Capt* 210683) 150282
Stenner A P (*A/Capt* 280183) 270183
Mortimer A F 010383
Newcombe R H J 110583
McDougall R J 080883
Ballard R E (*A/Capt* 010885) 030983
Parkes P J C 300983
Cook T R 250284
Young D W *BSc* 250684
Chalmers A E *BA LLB* (*A/Maj* 130784) 120784
David N P 150784
Adams N W 070884
Carne F C P 141084
McKeown R A M *LLB DipLP* 301084
Malik S C R *BSc(Hons)* 011184
Falkowski J P McM (*A/Capt* 010485) 211184
Cawthorne A C 210485
Connaughton A M 220585
Mahoney P F 010785
Gardner M J 310785
Graham W C (*A/Capt* 020685) 310785
Hannam I C 310785

2nd Lieutenants

†Baker M K
†Winkler E E *PhD* 310775
†Coleman J A 070576
†Sutcliffe A H W 241079
†Holman P F 120680
†Collins N E 010581
†Wile A M B 010581
†Blackburn J A 210681
†Thompson J P *MB BMedSci ChB* 130981
†Hicks J L 170182
†Penny S J 300182
†Milne C A 280482
†Robertson A B 280482
†Flanagan I M 190582
†Gibson A 230582
†Evans J 150682
†Campin R L 260982
†Collins A A 101082
†Grosvenor J M N S 261082
†Sullivan J D 011282
†Attard J P 081282
†Elliott O C 160383
†Mannion J P 190583
†Stubbs D T *BSc* 190583
†Cullingford P A 070683
†Hainsworth M 150683
†Jones J D 150683
†Jones M J P 150683
†Rawcliffe S W 150683
†Bland J M 220683
†Vause S J 220683
†Croft D C *BSc* 260683
†Gourlay F M 260683
†Brown S P 270683
†Large R E 270683
†Roberts G A 270683
†Tapp C D 270683
†Fraser W S *BSc* 310783
†Forer T J 131083
†Thomson K W *MA(Hons) DMS* 011183
†Raye D J 021183
†Nicholson C N L 201183
†Ponsonby W J C *MB* 271183
†Cran D J 011283
†Greenslade S P 011283
†Garcia A J 051283
†Phillipson A P 061283
†Bindley-Ross S M 131283
†Gray D M *ARICS* 270184
†Kay J S 070284
†Keeling C R 280284
Ransom D A C 010484
†Stanley N J 040484
†Maccariello M A 030584
†Thonger J C T 210584
†Spearing S M 220584
†Medcalf S P 240584
†Rigby D I 240584
†Walls K J 240584
†Musgrave T M *BSc* 310584
†Edwards R 050684
†Willis D 050684
†Fircks A J 090684
†Logan W S 110684
†Clouston E N 250684
†Edwards J P 250684
†Kumik P C 250684
†Parlour R S 250684
†Thompson C A J 250684
†Winthrop I S 080784
†Monk P C T 290784
†Sloan M A 080884
Dingemans J M 030984
†Ho D R 120984
†Harley S J 250984
†Payne S M 281084
†Sharp J B 281084
†Allan J C 301084
Sagan C Z 011184
†Collie J I 181184
†Hartland-Mahon M H F 181184
†Mackenzie C A 181184
†Tyler J M 181184
†Barnett A H 261184

†Conway S	261184
†Cornwell G E	261184
†Molley P M	261184
†Strong K J	261184
†Szembel N	261184
†Tooth D R	261184
†Dunn M P A	301184
†Manley J I	031284
†Thistlethwayte M E	061284
†Riley C P U	131284
†Vassallo N A	141284
†Beckley C P	151284
†Charles D P	151284
†Graham M A	151284
†Gregory P M	151284
†Jones I C	151284
†Lapslie R W	151284
†Marrett A P R	151284
†Powell D S *BSc(Econ)*	151284
†Green A J S	270185
†Howard I P	270185
†Rolande R S	270185
†Sheerin R J	270185
†Vingoe I P F	060285
†Briston S A	130285
†Clinton T R	130285
†Flett S K M	130285
†Anton A G	260285
†Edmond D J	260285
†Gourlay G	260285
†Gray A D A	260285
†Bailey S F	270285
†Austin J G S	280285
†Dymond M W	280285
†Salter R C	280285
†Shine K R	280285
†Fulton A H	080385
†Pugh-Cook R M	220385
†Allen R P *BA(Hons)*	240385
†Lovell W J	240385
†Perryer J P W	240385
†Simpson M R E	240385
†Vivian H C	300385
†Wynne D O W	220485
†Tweedie H J *BA(Hons)*	250485
†Nunan J J P	260485
†Atherton T E J	060585
†Grannan J K	060585
†James M S	060585
†McMillan D W	060585
†Sides A G	090585
†Knollys The Hon C E	110585
†Russell P D	150585
†Wakefield N E	150585
†Willey G J	150585
†Gray G A	160585
†Bamber R H	250585
†Corbett O R P	250585
†Blackwell W R	260585
†Jeffers J J	260585
†Rhodes C M	260585
†Griffin D R	030685
†Horthy L I	030685
†Brown M S	060685
†Burrows M D	070685
†Kent A S H	160685
†Clunie P J H	210685
†White A M	210685
†Goldstein S R	050785
†Davies G H	070785
†De Vater S R R	070785
†Griffiths J B	070785
†Skirrow F A	070785
†Brown M M	150785
†Canning S J	150785
†Sparshott N	270785
†Brookes J R	280785
†Marlow E H R *BA*	280785
†Sutton C M B	280785
†Wyatt R O	280785
†Yee R	280785
†Hughes D S C	290785
†Tusa J F T	310785
†Seeney D L	010985
†Richardson N J	030985
†Rooney J	040985
†Dunk S P	150985
†Beardmore L J	180985
†Williams A D H	180985
†Barden D	210985
†Bowden R J	210985
†Farrell D T	210985
†Koltonowski E T	210985
†Pratelli N J	210985
†Wheddon S W H	210985
†White M F	210985
†Perkins C J S	011085
†Brown C D	031085
†Etherington R C A	051085
†Heather W G	111085
†Edwards M F J	131085
†Bull R J A	161085
†McClement M I	181085
†Musgrave J B	281085
†Dunford J R	261185
†Firbank R C T	261185
†Stanford E J R	281185
†Swabey C E M	291185
†Chauhan D	011285
†Mason R	011285
†Prodger M J	011285
†Francois M G	181285
†Kelly N J F	181285
†Close C A	100186

SECTION B

COMBINED CADET FORCE

Captain General ....THE QUEEN

ABERDEEN GRAMMAR SCHOOL

Majors

Gray R

Captains

Lawrence G S

Lieutenants

øPaterson L

ABINGDON SCHOOL

Majors

Webber R J

Captains

Fox R *MBE BEM*

Lieutenants

Drummond-Hay J D E
Haworth T
Johnson T J
Jones D

ADAMS' GRAMMAR SCHOOL

Captains

Blore J D

Lieutenants

Moody M S
Thompstone B S

2nd Lieutenants

Halsey A G

ALDENHAM SCHOOL

Captains

Wilcockson M L

Lieutenants

Henderson K H

2nd Lieutenants

øWilcockson A J

ALLEYN'S SCHOOL

Majors

Randall E F *MBE*

Captains

Jones E M D

Lieutenants

Blyth J V
Collins W L
Lowry R J P
øScott E M
Temple J H
Wilkinson D J

ALLHALLOWS SCHOOL

Lieutenant Colonels

Preston A W

Captains

Gordon A J

Lieutenants

Willis J G

2nd Lieutenants

Clapp I A
Giles N J

AMPLEFORTH COLLEGE

Lieutenant Colonels

Trafford P H

Majors

Corbould M

Captains

Dean J J F
Wright T M

Lieutenants

Wright S P

ARDINGLY COLLEGE

Lieutenant Colonels

Elford T *OBE*

Majors

Hayes P A

Captains

Boothroyd M J
King T W

Lieutenants

Brooker T J
Ridd S M
Wolley D W

2nd Lieutenants

James H R
Moorhead T S N

ARNOLD SCHOOL

Majors

Collins E T

Captains

Poole J R

Lieutenants

Ashcroft J B
Miller D J
øRaby G
Watson S B

AUDENSHAW GRAMMAR SCHOOL

Majors

Thornton E K

2nd Lieutenants

Miller B
Nickson J H
Twigg J A

AVONHURST SCHOOL

Lieutenant Colonels

Jones B T

Captains

Jakeman R J

Lieutenants

Legg P H

BANCROFT'S SCHOOL

Captains

Bromfield J G

2nd Lieutenants

Macleod A P

BANGOR GRAMMAR SCHOOL

Lieutenant Colonels

Greenaway D B

Captains

Culbert J W

Lieutenants

ØWeir I S

BARNARD CASTLE SCHOOL

Captains

Farrar A R

Lieutenants

Braham P J
Kean S

BATLEY GRAMMAR SCHOOL

Captains

Dawson G

Lieutenants

Gott P H
Thomas B W

BEARWOOD COLLEGE

Majors

Narracott V A

Captains

Owen J P

Lieutenants

Hooper R L S

BEDFORD SCHOOL

Captains

Baker C
Wickens G J

Lieutenants

Marks M J
Phillips G N
Sochacki M F

BEDFORD MODERN SCHOOL

Lieutenant Colonels

Roberts D G

Captains

Sampson A J
Wilson A M

Lieutenants

Berry R
Christopher P E
Jackson P

BERKHAMSTED SCHOOL

Lieutenant Colonels

Glover W E

Captains

Charnock F

Lieutenants

Mowbray R K

2nd Lieutenants

Irvine K
Pullinger K M

BIRKENHEAD SCHOOL

Captains

Walton P G

Lieutenants

Gill S M
Whittel P A

BLOXHAM SCHOOL

Majors

Fletcher-Campbell C M

Captains

Cane M C V
Fiori J V *MC*

BLUNDELL'S SCHOOL

Lieutenant Colonels

Richards R B

Majors

Park D J

Captains

Wood B

Lieutenants

Brabban D H
Hall N R
Morgan T J R

BOURNEMOUTH SCHOOL

Captains

Thomas J R

2nd Lieutenants

Crockett G J

BRADFIELD COLLEGE

Lieutenant Colonels

Suffield-Jones N S

Captains

Buchanan J G

Lieutenants

Farrar-Bell C J
Marshall N A
Smallwood K L

2nd Lieutenants

Chaloner T H

BRADFORD GRAMMAR SCHOOL

Captains

Burnett S P D

Lieutenants

Davis H

2nd Lieutenants

Ratcliffe P

BRENTWOOD SCHOOL

Lieutenant Colonels

Hall M G

Majors

Best T M G

Captains

Foreman K
Thomas G

Lieutenants

Brown J R
Carr N J
Lawrence J E
Nuttall R N
Robinson A C

BRIDLINGTON SCHOOL

Majors

Moore A D

Lieutenants

Hargreaves J H
ØWhitehead J M

BRIGHTON COLLEGE

Majors

Hanson P D

Lieutenants

Orton S D W
Radojcic S
Wolley R

BRIGHTON & HOVE 6th FORM COLLEGE

Lieutenant Colonels

Smithies J A

Captains

Akers D F
Harman J

Lieutenants

Jones I

BRISTOL GRAMMAR SCHOOL

Majors

Hunt J

BROMSGROVE SCHOOL

2nd Lieutenants

Foord J T J
Simkin D E W

BURY GRAMMAR SCHOOL

Lieutenant Colonels

Bennett G B

Captains

Ferley J E D

Lieutenants

Bishop J
Newton P G

CALDAY GRAMMAR SCHOOL

Majors

Todd C R McL

Lieutenants

Nelson-Woods B J

2nd Lieutenants

Twist M

CAMPBELL COLLEGE

Lieutenant Colonels

Grant D E *OBE*

Majors

Gailey C F

Captains

Caves R E
Cowan C

Lieutenants

Corry C V
McGuffin M
McKinney H J
Oldfield D S
Semple J W D

2nd Lieutenants

Quigg S D

CANFORD SCHOOL

Lieutenant Colonels

Playfair H G L

Majors

Jarvis H A

Captains

Evans J D

Lieutenants

Boult G P
Bowen A J
Collison D V
Marriott M M
Owen M A

CATERHAM SCHOOL

Lieutenants

Howgego R J

2nd Lieutenants

Latham A M

CHARTERHOUSE

Majors

Clayton A R K

Lieutenants

Gordon-Smith R A
Smeeton R W

2nd Lieutenants

Georgiakakis N S

CHELTENHAM COLLEGE

Majors

George D B
Wright I D

Captains

Wright C C

Lieutenants

Cox S H

2nd Lieutenants

Grindel D J

CHELTENHAM GRAMMAR SCHOOL

Majors

Dray M J B

Captains

Salmon D A

Lieutenants

Buckland K *TD*
Roe P S

2nd Lieutenants

Clark P S

CHICHESTER HIGH SCHOOL

Lieutenants

Griffiths G M

CHRIST COLLEGE, BRECON

Majors

Crockett R J

2nd Lieutenants

Smith P W
Thomas S M K

CHRIST'S COLLEGE, FINCHLEY

Majors

Walden J I

Captains

Cliff J N

Lieutenants

Fuller B W
Smees C S
Tinch D L

CHRIST'S HOSPITAL, HORSHAM

Majors

Wyncoll N E

Captains

O'Meara D J

Lieutenants

Gunning A M

CHURCHER'S COLLEGE

Captains

Searle J C

Lieutenants

Broadhead R W

2nd Lieutenants

Stutchbury J H

CIRENCESTER SCHOOL

Captains

Perkins F

Lieutenants

øRoberts S M L

CITY OF LONDON SCHOOL

Majors

Clements M P

Captains

Woodhams F R
øWoodhams J A

Lieutenants

Whitmore P J S *MBE*

CLAYESMORE SCHOOL

Majors

Foot M E J

Lieutenants

Scott G

CLIFTON COLLEGE

Lieutenant Colonels

Barton R

Captains

Newhouse C B
Wright M P G

Lieutenants

Bailey R J
Cross G M

COLLYER'S SCHOOL

Captains

Palmer G E

Lieutenants

øStyles A M

COLSTON'S SCHOOL

Majors

Brace F E

Captains

Toase R C

Lieutenants

Finnigan A

COWES HIGH SCHOOL

Captains

Sutton R

Lieutenants

Seymour F A J

2nd Lieutenants

øLong L

CRANBROOK SCHOOL

Majors

Allison A C

2nd Lieutenants

Carter I C

CRANLEIGH SCHOOL

Majors

Ayers J M

Captains

Gowen B D

Lieutenants

Lowry J H

2nd Lieutenants

Henshall C M

DANIEL STEWART'S AND MELVILLE COLLEGE

Majors

Caton P A

Captains

Evans A L
McCulloch S J

Lieutenants

Barker A J

2nd Lieutenants

øThomson M

DEAN CLOSE SCHOOL

Majors

Burrows J R J

Lieutenants

Price J L
Ryall R P
Whitehouse D G

2nd Lieutenants

øWebster S J

DENSTONE COLLEGE

Captains

Duncan A R J

Lieutenants

Green N M

2nd Lieutenants

øMorris J R

DOLLAR ACADEMY

Lieutenant Colonels

Glasgow R J C

Majors

Torrance A R

Captains

Barber I B

Lieutenants

Collier G L

2nd Lieutenants

øEmbrey C A

DOVER GRAMMAR SCHOOL

Captains

Colman R C

DOWNSIDE SCHOOL

Lieutenant Colonels

More A V

Captains

Pountney A H

Lieutenants

Page A H *TD*

DUKE OF YORK'S ROYAL MILITARY SCHOOL

Lieutenant Colonels

Moorse A J

Majors

Hind R S

Captains

English J H
Pearce R J

2nd Lieutenants

Parsons D L

DULWICH COLLEGE

Majors

Jennings J R

Lieutenants

Cantrell P R
Crehan D A
Rutter G E

DUNDEE HIGH SCHOOL

Majors

Holmes D C

Captains

Steele R H

Lieutenants

Allen G H
Sim E S M
Spowart G W

2nd Lieutenants

Laidlaw D

DURHAM SCHOOL

Majors

Lee J S

Captains

Burgess J A
Clayton G

Lieutenants

Copeland P J N
Hind J R

EASTBOURNE COLLEGE

Lieutenant Colonels

Young M T

Majors

Wastie G F

Captains

Deighton A M
Watson T G *BEM*
Welsh D W

Lieutenants

Hodkinson D J
Kent B L
Pendry N G

EDINBURGH ACADEMY

Lieutenant Colonels

Wilmshurst P J

Majors

Boyce L D

Captains

Fenton J J C
Jack N J

Lieutenants

Williams P R

ELIZABETH COLLEGE

Majors

Rawlins-Duquemin I J

Captains

Hamilton R A
Mauger R

Lieutenants

Aplin B E H

ELLESMERE COLLEGE

Majors

Jagoe R R
Scorer J M

Captains

Morris J J
Wickson J L

Lieutenants

Elwell-Sutton S A
Nixon D J

2nd Lieutenants

Blott T D D

EMANUEL SCHOOL

Lieutenants

Thomson P F

EPSOM COLLEGE

Majors

Lees-Jones D R

Captains

Hampshire M
Huxter E A
Nash M A
Scadding A G

Lieutenants

ØHuxter K
Young D J

2nd Lieutenants

Baverstock C J
ØStebbing J E

ETON COLLEGE

Majors

Colquhoun N R

Captains

Galletly G T
Proctor H S J

Lieutenants

Fussey G D
Prior R G
Woodcock J M S

2nd Lieutenants

Manley P K

EXETER SCHOOL

Majors

Allen J D

Captains

Harris S J

2nd Lieutenants

Hanlon S P
ØHewitt G A

FARNBOROUGH 6th FORM COLLEGE

Lieutenant Colonels

Dyer R S G

Captains

Bunting J W

Lieutenants

Dunn R
Stych R I

2nd Lieutenants

ØHarnden J E

FELSTED SCHOOL

Captains

Down R C

Lieutenants

High J
Pockley T G
Shepheard A W C

FETTES COLLEGE

Majors

Clark N J *MC*

Captains

Murray A F

Lieutenants

ØCochrane F J A
Corvi P J
Foot J K
Hills J W
Ridley A N

FOREST SCHOOL

Captains

Little A L

Lieutenants

Buzzard P J
Capes P J
Lewis J C

FORT AUGUSTUS ABBEY SCHOOL

Captains

Haines H E M

Lieutenants

Morris G S

FRAMLINGHAM COLLEGE

Lieutenant Colonels

Kennon H W O

Majors

Ward N K D

2nd Lieutenants

ØWellman A J

GAYTON HIGH SCHOOL

Captains

Geear G D

GIGGLESWICK SCHOOL

Majors

Mussett N J

Captains

Batty R S

Lieutenants

ØMussett K M L
Peek M E
Shevill I

GLASGOW ACADEMY

Lieutenant Colonels

Plowman J R

Majors

Wright I

Captains

Littlefield R S

Lieutenants

Anderson G R M
Robertson W
Spike N T

2nd Lieutenants

Whyte J G

GORDON BOYS' SCHOOL

Majors

A'hearne P

Captains

Reynolds W T W

Lieutenants

Goodwin V
Robinson D H
Stapleton H

GRESHAM'S SCHOOL

Majors

Peaver R H *TD*

Captains

Ashby K

Lieutenants

ØBonham V A
Heaney R G
Moore S
Rowley J H
Runnalls M J
Worrall G B

HABERDASHERS' ASKE'S SCHOOL (ELSTREE)

Captains

Moore S F C

Lieutenants

Roberts A J

HAILEYBURY

Lieutenant Colonels

Sawbridge E H F

Captains

Bass R G
Hamilton F A L

Lieutenants

Bishop R H
Chamberlain P A
Ford-Robertson J De C
Nye H R

HAMPTON GRAMMAR SCHOOL

Captains

Xiberras M D

2nd Lieutenants

Montague D R
Tribbick J N

HARDYE'S SCHOOL

Lieutenant Colonels

Lacey D

Captains

Mactavish A J
Spriggs D W B

Lieutenants

Butt R H

HARROW SCHOOL

Majors

Beckett J R
Ingram J G K

Captains

Collins R G
Davis W A

Lieutenants

Crofts M A
Macpherson S F
Warfield P J

2nd Lieutenants

McKinney W J

HENRY MELLISH GRAMMAR SCHOOL

Captains

ØParker A

Lieutenants

Brockhurst D J

HEREFORD CATHEDRAL SCHOOL

Majors

Briggs N H P
Theakston D W

Captains

Morris A

Lieutenants

Dunn J E
Taylor J A

2nd Lieutenants

ØFowler V R

GEORGE HERIOT'S SCHOOL

Majors

McClure I G

Lieutenants

Copland I M

HIGHGATE SCHOOL

Lieutenants

Cobill D T
Short M J

2nd Lieutenants

Lunn N M

HULME GRAMMAR SCHOOL

Majors

Coulton I T

Captains

Wood P F

2nd Lieutenants

Galloway P

HURSTPIERPOINT COLLEGE

Majors

Bullock T H *MBE*
Mance M J

Captains

Perry R J

Lieutenants

Cooke R J S
Gowans J A

2nd Lieutenants

Edey N J

IPSWICH SCHOOL

Lieutenant Colonels

Le Mare J S

Captains

Clayton R L

Lieutenants

ØLe Mare R E

JUDD SCHOOL

Majors

Thorn N

Captains

Clarke K M
Stone R H

KELLY COLLEGE

Lieutenant Colonels

Mann J R K

Captains

Candlish R H

KELVINSIDE ACADEMY

Majors

Geddes G
Jenkins I S

Lieutenants

Duff J H
Mabon A

2nd Lieutenants

Alexander M G
McCulloch G

KIMBOLTON SCHOOL

Lieutenant Colonels

Coles G

Majors

Laflin K W

Lieutenants

Curtis K J
Guthrie P J

KING'S COLLEGE, TAUNTON

Majors

Sykes B

Captains

Bartlett J G

Lieutenants

Blagden J
Cole D J
Halford I
Yeabsley C G

2nd Lieutenants

Bell S C

KINGS COLLEGE SCHOOL (LONDON SW19)

Majors

Evans J A

Lieutenants

Kiddle D R
Storey P J

2nd Lieutenants

Grayson J T

KING'S SCHOOL, BRUTON

Majors

Passmore M B

Captains

Hastings R C F

Lieutenants

Chillcott R
Mullins T J
Neal J R *MBE*

2nd Lieutenants

Tomaszewski N A

KING'S SCHOOL, CANTERBURY

Captains

Vye M J

Lieutenants

Parker M R G
Poots I

KING'S SCHOOL, CHESTER

Lieutenants

Izzett P C S

KING'S SCHOOL, GRANTHAM

Majors

Kirkby W R

Captains

Caulfield J L
Dixon T E

Lieutenants

Brister P H
Divall J H

2nd Lieutenants

Broadbent D R
Page J L
Woodward P M

KING'S SCHOOL, ROCHESTER

Captains

Richter B W

Lieutenants

øBeaumont S C
Davies C J L
Humfrey D L P

KING'S SCHOOL, WORCESTER

Majors

Stacey A L

Captains

Davies S R

Lieutenants

Brown I
Griffiths B
Thompson P C

KING ALFRED'S SCHOOL, WANTAGE

Captains

Hardy T M

Lieutenants

Eggleshaw R A

KING CHARLES I SCHOOL

Captains

Lloyd N G
Stooksbury K I

Lieutenants

øGray E

2nd Lieutenants

Bullock I P

KING EDWARD'S FIVE WAYS SCHOOL

Lieutenants

Fellows P R

KING EDWARD VI GRAMMAR SCHOOL, CHELMSFORD

Majors

Retford L G T

Captains

Routledge P G

2nd Lieutenants

Colyer P J
øKitto S J

KING EDWARD'S SCHOOL, BATH

Majors

Phipps I D C

Captains

Currie W T

Lieutenants

Jones L D L

2nd Lieutenants

Rothnie N C

KING EDWARD'S SCHOOL, BIRMINGHAM

Captains

Dewar D C

Lieutenants

Bailey J D
Wills C J

KING WILLIAM'S COLLEGE

Lieutenant Colonels

Christian E C

Captains

Morton W D

Lieutenants

Christian J D B
Hannibal B

KINGHAM HILL SCHOOL

Majors

Chapman R H B
Craik-White R V

Lieutenants

Boyd R C

2nd Lieutenants

Shepton R L M
Sinclair A J

KINGSTON GRAMMAR SCHOOL

Captains

Ellen K V

Lieutenants

Church R A
Hedditch F A

2nd Lieutenants

øEllen G M
øNorton J L

KIRKHAM GRAMMAR SCHOOL

Majors

Sayer F W

Captains

Clarkson R M
Scott I M

Lieutenants

Gill R
øPiggott S
Willatt G P L

2nd Lieutenants

Partington I J

KNOX ACADEMY

Lieutenant Colonels

Wilkie S

Lieutenants

Macfarlane G L

LANCING COLLEGE

Majors

Lewis P E

Lieutenants

Tanner R S

LANGLEY SCHOOL

Majors

Osborne W A

Captains

Hadlett P W T

Lieutenants

Frost G A D
Overton R F G

2nd Lieutenants

Bujak P E

LEEDS GRAMMAR SCHOOL

Captains

Fuller K F

Lieutenants

Warren J F

LEYS SCHOOL

Lieutenant Colonels

Wiseman H H

Majors

Slatter H A

Captains

Woods R C

Lieutenants

Brown M A
Hurst B P

LIVERPOOL COLLEGE

Majors

Clarke W A *TD*

Captains

Davies A

Lieutenants

Hildick B G
Hughes D C

2nd Lieutenants

Bailey S M

LLANDOVERY COLLEGE

Lieutenant Colonels

Carew-Jones J

Lieutenants

Beck D S
Parkinson J
Rees A T

2nd Lieutenants

Jennings C N H

LORD WANDSWORTH COLLEGE

Captains

Taylor P F

Lieutenants

Baker J D

LORD WILLIAM'S SCHOOL

Captains

Anderson M W

Lieutenants

Stowell G H

2nd Lieutenants

McDonald J D

LORETTO SCHOOL

Majors

Whait R P

Lieutenants

Grainge D G
Shepherd P A

LOUGHBOROUGH GRAMMAR SCHOOL

Majors

Beazley H G

Captains

Horwood D R

Lieutenants

Field A J
Hall S
Jennings M R
Leese S

2nd Lieutenants

Steele D W

MAGDALEN COLLEGE SCHOOL, OXFORD

Lieutenant Colonels

Holmes R H

Captains

Cooper A C

2nd Lieutenants

Bates J N
Rollings N A

MAIDSTONE GRAMMAR SCHOOL

Lieutenant Colonels

Caley W J C

Captains

Coleman B E
Smith L

Lieutenants

Hardyman M K J
Rafinski A H

2nd Lieutenants

øKallend K T

MALVERN COLLEGE

Captains

Harriss F O

Lieutenants

Askew J
Chapman R C
Smith R A
Witcomb R G

2nd Lieutenants

Mensforth D L
Smith R S D

MARLBOROUGH COLLEGE

Majors

Heaton D A

Captains

Heffron P M
Kirk J P

Lieutenants

Brown A J
Foley A D
Lough P J

MERCHANT TAYLORS' SCHOOL, CROSBY

Majors

Wallace I

Captains

Whittles L T

Lieutenants

Irvine P A

MERCHANT TAYLORS' SCHOOL, NORTHWOOD

Majors

Colley G P

Lieutenants

Blight N G
Mayhew R J
Watkins G A

2nd Lieutenants

Parrock A W V

MERCHISTON CASTLE SCHOOL

Lieutenant Colonels

Melluish J R F

Lieutenants

Johnston C A K
Selby J K

2nd Lieutenants

Clark S C
Russel R J

MILLFIELD SCHOOL

Captains

Cheney K A
Sankey P E
Williams E J M

Lieutenants

Farley-Pettman K H
Page C I

MILL HILL SCHOOL

Majors

Bickerdike P S

Captains

Bowden P R

Lieutenants

Axworthy R L
Brownlie I C
Rees J D

2nd Lieutenants

Appleton S G

MILTON ABBEY SCHOOL

Lieutenant Colonels

Townsend C O

Captains

Hall S R D
Sale M J

Lieutenants

Clapper M S
Deane A J

2nd Lieutenants

Chesney J P S

MONKTON COMBE SCHOOL

Lieutenant Colonels

Marsden P D

Captains

Chorley D J
Potter M N

Lieutenants

Law A W

2nd Lieutenants

Jameson D R
Mallia J M

MONMOUTH SCHOOL

Majors

Jenkins D J R

Captains

Dennis-Jones P
Sealy R J F

Lieutenants

Adams D C
Francis A V
Townsend P V

2nd Lieutenants

Henderson M M

MORRISON ACADEMY

Captains

Hicks M D

Lieutenants

McCarra P F

MOUNT ST MARY'S COLLEGE

Majors

Jackson M P

Captains

Hopkins J D

2nd Lieutenants

Gill D J M
Krlic M
Turner S E
Wild P D

NEWCASTLE HIGH SCHOOL

Majors

Moss-Bowpitt D R

Captains

Pedder J A

Lieutenants

Preston D A
Sawyer D K

2nd Lieutenants

ØWebb E A

NOTTINGHAM HIGH SCHOOL

Lieutenant Colonels

Wood G L

Lieutenants

Cleverley M T
Neville W H

2nd Lieutenants

Clarke R J

OAKHAM SCHOOL

Lieutenant Colonels

Gregory R C

Captains

Morgan D J

Lieutenants

Rochester M B
Smith R B

OLD SWINFORD HOSPITAL SCHOOL

Lieutenant Colonels

Ison K R

Majors

Milner R

Captains

Krukowski Z L

Lieutenants

Day R E
Dewar D

2nd Lieutenants

Hudson S J

ORATORY SCHOOL

Majors

Gillham A E
Womersley R B

Captains

Harris J C

2nd Lieutenants

Ibbetson-Price W C R
Robinson S C

OSWESTRY COLLEGE

Lieutenant Colonels

Pinner R T

Captains

Wapshott P D

Lieutenants

Woollam P J

OSWESTRY SCHOOL

Majors

Foster I C C

Captains

Evanson R G

Lieutenants

Hollywell A J
Leonard R M

OUNDLE SCHOOL

Majors

Worthington I R A

Captains

Dew D W
Moynehan C

Lieutenants

Cunnington J T M
Towers P L

2nd Lieutenants

Crookes J P
Frobisher H
Newman R B
Nunn A M
Sharp D

PANGBOURNE COLLEGE

Lieutenants

Horner J R

PERSE SCHOOL

Captains

Dunkley D G

Lieutenants

Baker D H J
Pinhey J L G

2nd Lieutenants

Vodden H B G

PETER SYMONDS' COLLEGE

Lieutenant Colonels

Clarkson R C

2nd Lieutenants

ØForcey E E
Sault S J

PIERREPONT SCHOOL

Majors

Morgan J G

Captains

Huber M F
Melbourne A J

Lieutenants

Wickson T J

2nd Lieutenants

James N K

PLYMOUTH COLLEGE

Lieutenant Colonels

Parker P M

Majors

Forsyth T McD

Lieutenants

Elliott R

2nd Lieutenants

Gatherer C D M
Owen J P

PLYMPTON GRAMMAR SCHOOL

Captains

Williams A G

Lieutenants

Dunton D J

2nd Lieutenants

ØStimpson J M

POCKLINGTON SCHOOL

Lieutenant Colonels

Whilesmith D G

Lieutenants

Hawkes E J
Milne M G
Parsons D J
Thompson G M

CITY OF PORTSMOUTH BOYS SCHOOL

Captains

Walker J

Lieutenants

Pitt J D
Robson P T
Smout P R

PORTSMOUTH GRAMMAR SCHOOL

Majors

Hunt J C A
Penn B W

Lieutenants

ØGiles C
Priestley D M
Taylor W M

PRESENTATION COLLEGE

Captains

Moran T S

2nd Lieutenants

Murphy M

PRINCE HENRY'S HIGH SCHOOL

Captains

Byrd C C

PRIOR PARK COLLEGE

Captains

Symonds C W

PRIORY SCHOOL

Captains

Grimster R

Lieutenants

Trwoga C D

QUEEN ELIZABETH'S GRAMMAR SCHOOL, ASHBOURNE

Captains

Greenwood J B
Howe N L

2nd Lieutenants

ØBenn S A
Brown I D

QUEEN MARY'S (THE VYNE SCHOOL), BASINGSTOKE

Lieutenant Colonels

Townend C M

Captains

Harding S W

Lieutenants

Barnes D

QUEEN MARY'S GRAMMAR SCHOOL, WALSALL

Captains

Anderson J S

Lieutenants

Fudge I S
Gabbott J L

QUEEN VICTORIA SCHOOL, DUNBLANE

Majors

Hankinson J D

Captains

Deeley J

Lieutenants

Garden D
Watson G M

2nd Lieutenants

Carroll G D M

RADLEY COLLEGE

Majors

Pollard R

2nd Lieutenants

Bird J F
Wakley N V

RATCLIFFE COLLEGE

Majors

Friendship C G

Captains

Beaver J A

READ SCHOOL

Lieutenant Colonels

Green I R P

Captains

Staves J

Lieutenants

Cleveland P L

READING SCHOOL

Captains

Shaw G C

2nd Lieutenants

Morland T C I
Toone N R

READING BLUE COAT SCHOOL

Majors

Imeson J S

Captains

Haynes K A
Sheen M J

Lieutenants

Brown J P

REED'S SCHOOL

Lieutenants

Hamilton D H

REIGATE GRAMMAR SCHOOL

Majors

Gardiner J

Lieutenants

Crabtree S H A

2nd Lieutenants

Stephens P G

REPTON SCHOOL

Majors

Carrington C R
Scott T D H

Captains

Atwood R A S
Cox A A
Wimbush M R H

Lieutenants

Drew B V
Gould A E
Muir J R

ROBERT GORDON'S COLLEGE

Majors

Dow J G

Lieutenants

Simms B B

2nd Lieutenants

Cowie K S
Hopps A L

ROSSALL SCHOOL

Majors

Caulfield B I
Felton S A

Captains

Scales M G

Lieutenants

Bryans C
Clapp R J
Cooke R M D
Smiles M

ROYAL SCHOOL, ARMAGH

Majors

McCahon W E

Captains

Walker D G

Lieutenants

Furlong G
Martin N W K

2nd Lieutenants

Maxwell R T

ROYAL BELFAST ACADEMICAL INSTITUTION

Majors

Farnan M G *MBE TD*

Captains

Stevenson H H
Weir D J

Lieutenants

øFarnan P J *TD*
Todd B J

ROYAL GRAMMAR SCHOOL, GUILDFORD

Lieutenant Colonels

Crathorne J F

Captains

Bell F J
Jones D H B

Lieutenants

Weaver R

2nd Lieutenants

Badham E J
Beer S R
Woolcott D J

ROYAL GRAMMAR SCHOOL, HIGH WYCOMBE

Lieutenant Colonels

Cooper F N

Captains

Davies M M
Hollingworth R G

Lieutenants

Boreham A
Grundy S J
Meyer I R
Stubbs D J

ROYAL GRAMMAR SCHOOL, LANCASTER

Captains

Hickman A

2nd Lieutenants

Potter G S
Workman C

ROYAL GRAMMAR SCHOOL, NEWCASTLE

Captains

Griffiths M A

Lieutenants

Barlow M R
Goldsborough I
Moore J C S

ROYAL HOSPITAL SCHOOL

Majors

Horne A A

ROYAL RUSSELL SCHOOL

Majors

Tomlin M F

Captains

Green P W

Lieutenants

Balaam R D
Thompson E A L

ROYAL WOLVERHAMPTON SCHOOL

Majors

Duchart R N *TD*
Pope D M

Lieutenants

Beckett G W
Padden J C
Rowland E L

RUGBY SCHOOL

Majors

Elvins B S
Toole M R

Captains

Hughes-D'Aeth W J
Ray R D R

Lieutenants

Burton C A
John P D
McMenemey J D S

2nd Lieutenants

Dewey P W

RUTHIN SCHOOL

Lieutenant Colonels

Cloke S

Captains

Miln R Q A

Lieutenants

Johnson J

RUTLISH SCHOOL

Captains

Blackabey P D
Rendell G G

ST ALBANS SCHOOL

Lieutenant Colonels

Pryke G E *OBE TD*

Captains

Billingham D

Lieutenants

Woodsmith N A

ST ALOYSIUS COLLEGE

Lieutenants

Dennehy T P

ST BARTHOLOMEW'S SCHOOL

Majors

Patrick A J

Captains

Beale R J
Stratford B E

Lieutenants

Hart M C
øMoss I F

ST BEES SCHOOL

Lieutenant Colonels

Francis A

Captains

Markbride L
Rice T A P

Lieutenants

Davies D W
Payne A C

2nd Lieutenants

ØRae I M E

ST BENEDICT'S SCHOOL

Lieutenant Colonels

Baker R

Captains

Pearce M D

Lieutenants

Doyle-Smith P M
Potts I M

ST BRENDAN'S COLLEGE

Captains

Ruszala D S J

Lieutenants

Wall T

ST DUNSTAN'S COLLEGE

Lieutenant Colonels

Savage M P

Majors

Pickering D J

Captains

Davis P F

Lieutenants

Austin R
Burgess I P

ST EDMUND'S COLLEGE

Captains

Latham K

2nd Lieutenants

Drew A A

ST EDMUND'S SCHOOL

Majors

Hawkins S R

Captains

Hawkins G N

Lieutenants

Askwith R J
Barnard C D

ST EDWARD'S SCHOOL

Lieutenant Colonels

McPartlin J J

Majors

Anderson R A L

Captains

Bond R A D
Mallalieu P

Lieutenants

Blackett H W
Drake-Brockman D

ST GEORGE'S SCHOOL

Captains

Rapsey F R G

2nd Lieutenants

Jamieson M B
Sinclair J

ST IGNATIUS COLLEGE

Lieutenant Colonels

Knight A E W

Majors

East G A R

Captains

Edwards H J

ST JOHN'S SCHOOL

Majors

Noble P C

Lieutenants

Gale A B
King A P

2nd Lieutenants

Seale B F T

ST LAWRENCE COLLEGE

Lieutenant Colonels

Garden R A

Captains

Fletcher D E

Lieutenants

Gill E B

2nd Lieutenants

ØFerber B

ST MARY'S COLLEGE

Captains

Askew A D

Lieutenants

McMahon W J

2nd Lieutenants

Batterton I P
Doyle J
Mawer R

ST PETER'S HIGH SCHOOL

Lieutenant Colonels

Forey M F

Captains

Hayward D W

2nd Lieutenants

ØForey J M
ØOgden L R

ST PETER'S SCHOOL

Captains

Tooms H A

Lieutenants

Stephen P J

2nd Lieutenants

Mason S

SANDBACH SCHOOL

Captains

Ayres R J

Lieutenants

Stacey M J

2nd Lieutenants

Munro A A

SCARBOROUGH COLLEGE

Majors

Rowe K W

Lieutenants

ØPepper M
ØRowe G A
Sharp A D

SEAFORD COLLEGE

Lieutenant Colonels

Dobinson E A

Captains

Snowden P O M
Woodcock K R

2nd Lieutenants

Oakes R J H
Phelan B D
Putnam A J

SEDBERGH SCHOOL

Majors

Moore R W
Whittaker P

Captains

Horsfall M J

Lieutenants

Fraser R H
Knowles P J N
Light J V
Scarratt C W H

SEVENOAKS SCHOOL

Captains

Spear M R

Lieutenants

Cunningham C W A
Ford P

2nd Lieutenants

Hill P T

SHERBORNE SCHOOL

Lieutenant Colonels

Riley J P

Majors

Mitchell-Innes C W

Captains

Hope M E

SHIPLAKE COLLEGE

Lieutenant Colonels

Lee R M

Captains

Morris T S
Partridge D S

Lieutenants

Webb P J F

2nd Lieutenants

Barclay A F
Cassells G

SHREWSBURY SCHOOL

Majors

Caney S S *MBE*

Captains

Cox P T C
Field R E W
Martin S W

Lieutenants

Furniss J H
Storey B
Twells M

2nd Lieutenants

Gladwin J M

SIR ROGER MANWOOD'S SCHOOL

Majors

Harlow R S

Captains

Pashley H T

Lieutenants

Dean P G
Denton A R

2nd Lieutenants

Setchell T J

SKINNERS' SCHOOL

Majors

Fitzwater R W

Captains

Holding A J
Taylor M F

Lieutenants

Fowling J M
McGowan J R
Wallace J D *MBE*

2nd Lieutenants

Mardle R D

SOLIHULL SCHOOL

Majors

Miller D R

Captains

Griffiths P J
Melling R J
Rudge M J
Skippings S E

Lieutenants

Flood R N
Keylock B J

STAMFORD SCHOOL

Majors

Woolf G W

Captains

Barton M R

Lieutenants

Froggett G

2nd Lieutenants

Chew J L
Earl G T
Hargreaves P D
Marshall J G

STONEYHURST COLLEGE

Majors

Cobb J

Captains

Fairburn J M

Lieutenants

Jenkins M F
Scarisbrick E

STOWE SCHOOL

Majors

Smith M J

Captains

James D W
Mullineux C D

Lieutenants

Collins S O

STRATHALLAN SCHOOL

Captains

Dutton A L K

Lieutenants

Court C N

SUTTON MANOR HIGH SCHOOL

Majors

Wall J H

SUTTON VALENCE SCHOOL

Majors

Parkinson C F G *TD*

Captains

Sabine R M

Lieutenants

Moore D H
Shaw C R G
Smith K M

TAUNTON SCHOOL

Majors

Miller D D

Lieutenants

Hill T J
Snow T N

2nd Lieutenants

Pugh S E

TONBRIDGE SCHOOL

Majors

Briggs D M
Turner E M S

Captains

Cazalet F W G

TRENT COLLEGE

Captains

Baynes C J

TRINITY COLLEGE, GLENALMOND

Majors

Lord R N A

Captains

Bassett J D
Comins D
Given H M H

Lieutenants

Allnutt M
Carpenter J R
Shephard P M

2nd Lieutenants

Reid A J

UPPINGHAM SCHOOL

Majors

Boston R A S

Captains

Boston E J R
Rudman J P

Lieutenants

Cannings P W
Pattinson S J
Rust R C

VICTORIA COLLEGE

Majors

Stockton R L

Lieutenants

Gilson A

WARMINSTER SCHOOL

Captains

Miller B J

Lieutenants

Burgess R G
Reed G
ØSharpe G

WARWICK SCHOOL

Lieutenant Colonels

Hughes A H

Captains

Collis H E

Lieutenants

Bannerman J P C

WELBECK COLLEGE

Majors

Dean A J

2nd Lieutenants

Cunliffe M S

WELLINGBOROUGH SCHOOL

Lieutenants

Ashworth A E
Elbourne N J
ØKing M E K

WELLINGTON COLLEGE

Majors

Tinniswood M C
Walker R J W

Captains

Adcroft H J
Auger R C
Bawden M W

Lieutenants

Stewart A J

WELLINGTON SCHOOL

Captains

Lungley D R
Salt A

Lieutenants

ØBrace J M
Pearce P M
Stephens R E W

2nd Lieutenants

Rixon T P

WELLS CATHEDRAL SCHOOL

Majors

Green G R

Captains

Johnson P

Lieutenants

Millard A P

2nd Lieutenants

ØHopkins S A

WEST BUCKLAND SCHOOL

Captains

Crowl C F

Lieutenants

Clark D A
Downward M
Reilly J D M
Squire J W

WHITGIFT SCHOOL

Majors

Gibson P L

Captains

Brownrigg P A
Reddy A

Lieutenants

Lewis D L
Trevis P S
Williams D R

2nd Lieutenants

Halls A D

WILLIAM ELLIS SCHOOL

Captains

Mitchell I G

2nd Lieutenants

Campbell-Drew R J

WILLIAM HULME'S GRAMMAR SCHOOL

Majors

Chudleigh J F

Captains

Fisher D M

Lieutenants

Grange H V
Moss G B
Simkin A

WILLIAM PARKER SCHOOL

Majors

Bruce A J *TD*■■

2nd Lieutenants

Venner C R

WILSON'S SCHOOL

Lieutenant Colonels

Daynes K B

Captains

Lyons D C

Lieutenants

Jeffreys A P
Parker J D
Wellman D

WINCHESTER COLLEGE

Lieutenant Colonels

Somerset R F

Majors

Massen R J
Tanter B J A

Captains

Osmand V

Lieutenants

Brook G A
Brooks J S
Durran J H
Spanier S G
Tombling P R
Wallis M D

WOODBRIDGE SCHOOL

Captains

Gwyther I W

Lieutenants

Beaven D R
Green N

WORCESTER ROYAL GRAMMAR SCHOOL

Captains

Clough D R
Fretwell J E

Lieutenants

Moss D

WORKSOP COLLEGE

Majors

Biddulph B C
Brown G P

Captains

Driver J A S

Lieutenants

Farmer G T
Jordan S

WREKIN COLLEGE

Captains

Nurse D
Savage A
Swayne D A

2nd Lieutenants

Berry P J
Swayne D A
Yates-Ward R H

WYCLIFFE COLLEGE

Majors

Thomas W P

Captains

Evans D C

Lieutenants

Gordon A J H

WYMONDHAM COLLEGE

Captains

Hill A C

Lieutenants

Shelton K S

EDINBURGH SCHOOL, MUNSTER

Majors

Moore E G L
Scott A J

Lieutenants

øClare P M

PRINCE RUPERT SCHOOL, RINTELN

Majors

Middleton M A

Lieutenants

Smith F

CORNWALL SCHOOL, DORTMUND

2nd Lieutenants

øHall J E
Sholl C N

ARMY CADET FORCE

Colonel in Chief....................................Field Marshal *HRH The Prince* Philip *Duke of* Edinburgh *KG KT OM GBE QSO*

Cadet Commandant Scotland............Brig D D G Hardie *TD DL*

ANGUS AND DUNDEE BN

County Cadet Commandant

Col I S Taylor *TD*

Cadet Executive Officer

Maj R Boylen

Lieutenant Colonels

Traynor E *MM*

Majors

Cassidy A H
Diplexcito J E
Gibson D L
Robertson S G

Captains

Bissett A B
Bruce J
Falconer R
Gilbert J G
Grant G *MBE MM*
Gray B
Henderson L M
Lindsay D
Wallace A J

Lieutenants

Anderson D H
Dorman J
Dunn S
Durajczyk I
Hutton W
Leggatt I R S
Little R C
Murphy G P
Nicoll J E
Russell C A

2nd Lieutenants

Bell J K
McGrath P F

ANTRIM AND BELFAST

County Cadet Commandant

Col Baird G H *OBE TD*

Cadet Executive Officer

Lt Col G B Matthews

Lieutenant Colonels

Corbett J G

Majors

Howard P J
Lavery J S
Parkes R J
Trebbett R G

Captains

Adjey H C
Blair R T
Pennington W F
Pepper M A
Perry M
Rosbotham D B
Smyth J G
Williamson H

Lieutenants

Adjey C D
Baskin C A
Blair W P
Crockett H B
Entwistle J
Graham J A
Gregg W M
Hill C A
Houston W
Howard D J
Killen D E
Linton D R
McConnell L W
McMorran A
McMurry L D
Patterson J S
Tannahill J D

2nd Lieutenants

Ayton R A
Graham R S
McGough M G
Moore P A
Sampson K J

THE ARGYLL AND SUTHERLAND HIGHLANDERS BN

County Cadet Commandant

Col R A David *TD*

Cadet Executive Officer

Maj N B M Crawford

Lieutenant Colonels

Gibson J Y
Kerr P D

Majors

Clark B H
Gallacher J R
Love J
Smith A G
Spence H B M
Spowage A F

Captains

Bingham D H
Brooks A B
Campbell J B
Christie J S
Clark M
Coleman G W
Coleman J S
Donoughue A B
Harton J
King E
Nicol J
Turnbull N
Walker O G
Warren B G

Lieutenants

Brown I M
Burgess J
øCameron M
Cresswell R
Donachie I
øEadie M A
Ellis L S
Fraser J M
øGillies M I M
Gillies J
Houston D
Howe L
Igoe J P
Kerr P D
Kerr G B
Livingstone W T
Milne L
O'Shea J
Rice J M
Soudan D M
øStewart I
Wilson R D

2nd Lieutenants

Bruce J H
øClark A B
øHoulihan V M
Kettrick M
Martin C J
McDonald J
McDonald D
McMahon C D
McNee A M K
Murphy H F
Setchfield P R
Smith K E
øSpence C W

ARMAGH AND DOWN

County Cadet Commandant

Col R E Dale *OBE TD*

County Executive Officer

Maj Sadlier R F *OBE TD*

Lieutenant Colonels

Gibson J A B *MBE*

Majors

Quinn T
Smyth S D
Wilson J A V

Captains

Apsley A T
Bateson H E
Cooper H H
Donnan C D
Jones T R
McElroy R
Rea T J
Wallace C J
Watt T D

Lieutenants

Allen R J
Armstrong W R A
Barker W K
Berry W I
Black R
Budding M
Casey B P G
Duke W T
Faulkner R
ØHalligan L
Hollinger T
Lemon J H
Lowe M
McQuoid J A
Nelson J A
Norman J R
Ramsey D W
Steele T
Stevenson N H
Street M T

2nd Lieutenants

McCulla D N
McInnes I A B
ØTurkington E R
ØWilson M E

AVON

County Cadet Commandant

Col F J J Bartlett

Cadet Executive Officer

Maj J D P Cowell

Lieutenant Colonels

Coleman R E *JP*

Majors

Faulkner H M
Pocock M J *JP*
Shapcott L M
Thomson B R
Wright B J

Captains

Beauchamp J A
Bees M F
Blundell J M
Evans R E
Gill M G
Oaten D J
Pruett M J
Rodgers W C
Scott M J
Selby M
Stickings P T

Lieutenants

Bailey G J
Cake C C E
Chapman C R
Cole P R
Cook S
Doble R G
Dyke V W C
John-Lewis M P
Joyner A R D
Strong M J

2nd Lieutenants

Bryant S
Evans J S
Fitt R G
Spooner A G

AYR AND RENFREW BN

County Cadet Commandant

Col R T Kellie *TD*

Cadet Executive Officer

Maj A M Smith

Lieutenant Colonels

Williamson H *MBE*

Majors

Dawes W J
Donnell R H
Gallacher J
Jagielko O R
Kennedy H T

Captains

Black J
Docherty J McS
Kerr S S
McAllister J
McBride C
McLay H D
Reid P

Lieutenants

Barclay W B
ØBrown D M
ØElder I
Grady E
Heron W
Lee E D
Lynch N
McCrae W
McFarlane G B
Monaghan J A
Montgomery R R
Nesbit I
Robertson K
Shaw W S
Simpson P McA
Thomson K T
Young W

2nd Lieutenants

Chan C C W
Coughlan J M
Holt F G
Johnstone W
Maclean D
ØSmart E D

BEDFORDSHIRE

County Cadet Commandant

Col L J Rose *DL*

Cadet Executive Officer

Maj N R Treasure *DL*

Majors

Bruckshaw J T
Holmes R D
Wilson K P
Worrall A G

Captains

Crowdy A H
Johnson R W
King C M
Mackay J P
Mansell A C
Sumner E N
Turnbull J

Lieutenants

Allen B K
Austin A F
Barden M G
Blackwood D
Clark C W
Cordery R W
Edgar N *MBE*
Mack J F
McGrath S V
O'Donnell J L
Roberts C J
Robinson N P
Terry P A

2nd Lieutenants

Fitzpatrick I G
Milnthorpe V A

ROYAL COUNTY OF BERKSHIRE

County Cadet Commandant

Col J W Isaacs *MBE TD*

Cadet Executive Officer

Maj P H Bond *TD*

Majors

Alway G M
Jefferies B D
Luke J A
O'Connell T R

Captains

Jeanes P A
Maidment T J
Pudwell T M
Rogers A R
Rogers W
Sale G
Simmonds R E
Taylor R D
West M G

Lieutenants

Corbett A
Harris J M C
Lockley D J
Stott J M
Tearle B C

2nd Lieutenants

Bryden-Brook S M N
Carmichael J
ØRogers M

BLACK WATCH BN

County Cadet Commandant

Col J F Rankin *TD*

Cadet Executive Officer

Maj K M Cooper

Majors

Cuthbert S
Ferrier G
Hart D J
Macpherson W J S
Mason K J A

Captains

Campbell J D
Forbes T A
Macdonald C
Robertson J R
Young J W

Lieutenants

ØBell L
Gourlay D
Johnson A R
ØMason E A
O'Neill T J
Pover D B
Robertson D Y G

2nd Lieutenants

Burnet C S
Cockwell R L
Sorbie S C
Taylor S

BUCKINGHAMSHIRE

County Cadet Commandant

Col A Crawforth

Cadet Executive Officer

Maj F A Ross

Majors

Hickman R
Robins M J
Weatherhead J A S *TD*

Captains

Carr M J
Grierson C K M
Hunt J T
Slade B M
Smith C V
Wallen R J
Williams L J

Lieutenants

Bayliss A G
Clements J M
Hunt C T
McGregor M M
Purslow M J
Scales J A
Sharpe L S
Stocker A J
Trumper J W

2nd Lieutenants

Brook M
Ford B A
Hoye J P
Roberts C J

CAMBRIDGESHIRE

County Cadet Commandant

Lt Col D E Latchford *TD*

Cadet Executive Officer

Haslam D R *TD*▪▪▪

Majors

Bailey D G
Bristow D H
Elsden C M
Jarvis M A
Norman A C
Starling K J

Captains

Anstee P D
English I L
Flood D G H
Forsdyke B W
Gynn W O
Herod S
Hunter P A
Overy T B
Seddon W T R
ØThompson S E
Veal M R
Waterfall A
Williams J W

Lieutenants

Badcock W C
Beales F J
Bliss R G
Capstaff J W
Cox T W
Craven S E
Crouch A W
Elson N L
Eve E J
Knight M
Knight J
Lawes F J
Longmuir T M
McLoone A Y S
Merry P B
Mittins F W
ØNelson J H
Nicholls R W
ØRoberts S
Tomes D P
Waldman C R
Watson J W
Wood M R

2nd Lieutenants

Brooke A C
Driscoll R J
ØPalmer H M
Reeves D
ØWelsh M

CHESHIRE

County Cadet Commandant

Col J M O'R Bassett *MBE*

Cadet Executive Officer

Maj S K D Lyng

Lieutenant Colonels

French D A *TD*

Majors

Bavister D B
Millington J H
Rowlands H E
Willocks J A

Captains

Allen G W
Darlington N D
Dawbarn M G
Evans P J
Gornall J*MM*
ØJardine V
Molyneux P E
Rathbone J W
Roberts D B H
Taylor K
Tuggey N H

Lieutenants

Booth J D
Brown M M
Butler P
Davies P R
Farrington K J
Hughes F W
Jardine K D
Kenyon H M
Moores G T
Robinson O D
Thomas D L
Ward N

2nd Lieutenants

Barnes D W

Barton G J
Bonehill K H
Brentnall D J
Disley M
Hall T L
Harris A S
Hatton P
Jones K
Littler P G
Muir A S
Robertson I S
Stewart A M
Wallace W I

CLEVELAND

County Cadet Commandant

Lt Col K W Jackson *MBE TD*

Cadet Executive Officer

Maj B C Dane *MBE*

Majors

Brown B
Kitching D
Smith T R *TD*
Smith J W

Captains

Alexander J T
Allinson C W
Bailey W T
Gaunt C D
Goldsbrough K
Gotts R F
Hassan J H
Osborne F E
Peberdy S B C
Raffan J J

Lieutenants

Alexander M J
Baume G
Boyes R
Bunn S
Good R C
Hakin D B
Hills R E
Lewis E D
Murray A A
Rayner J G
Reynolds D
Street K
Twinn M J
Woodfine C
Young B E

2nd Lieutenants

Barraclough A C
Baxter M D
Haley R A
Hyde P D
O'Neill T M
Sexton D M
Turner B J

CLWYD

County Cadet Commandant

Lt Col P Eyton-Jones *TD*

Cadet Executive Officer

Maj E G Hughes *MBE*

Majors

Evans D R
Jones W T
Moore A L G

Captains

Davies K W F
Livett C R J
Mason E R *DCM*
Mullis M C
Smythe B
Williams D A

Lieutenants

Brotherton G H D
Edwards R D
Pearson P
Shepley R

2nd Lieutenants

Glynn J J

CORNWALL

County Cadet Commandant

Col R W Potts *TD JP*

Cadet Executive Officer

Maj J G Brewer

Majors

Blenkinsop T D
Mitchell G C
Walkey P A
Whitmore R G

Captains

Chappell M J
Fee M J D
Irwin P F
Magor V L
Martin R C
Richardson P J *TD*
Smith R H
Steed A I

Lieutenants

Chandler C S
Clark R C
Collings B
Griffett H
Rickard D C
Rowe T
Scarrett D J
Wilkes D C

2nd Lieutenants

Penn R E
Power A C
Ward M A
Wenmoth C K

CUMBRIA

County Cadet Commandant

Col E W Messenger *TD*

Cadet Executive Officer

Maj F M H Faulder

Lieutenant Colonels

Crack G R *MBE*

Majors

Chandler M
Harrison G S
Lockhart T

Captains

Bell H J
Bennett J C
Brownlie G J
Gardiner C L
Hutton F
Johnson A
Rae B I
Roberts P
Wilson J

Lieutenants

Ashton M R
Beavan J B
Blackburn C J
Brown W
Burns J H
Camlin B
Casey G A P
Gibbons M N
Graham K
McManus R
Parker A G
Todd C A S
Wadsworth C
Watson D W
Wilson R F

2nd Lieutenants

Denby R
Ingram D G
Morgan D R
Oates T R
Wilkinson P M

DERBYSHIRE CADET BN (WFR)

County Cadet Commandant

Col K Hobbs

Cadet Executive Officer

Maj W G B Shiels

Lieutenant Colonels

Goodbody P J

Majors

Boyd D
Heap R N
Kay J D

Rowe N J

Captains

Bell W R
Blair I G
Cheetham M S
Cooper J L
Freeman J B
Long D R
McCormick K W
Millward H V
Nelson R F
Osborne C
Parr K J
Wilson G
Wilson J S
Wilson M R

Lieutenants

Brittle A
Brown R E
Cawley D P
Crookston W J
Crowther R W
Cumberlidge A
Derbyshire A E
Dinsdale R
Grace M F B
Hall D M
Hill P
Kirk A J
Marsden D S
Paulucci T A
Poolewood J M
Richardson I C
Saxton J D
Spencer A A
Whitworth C O

2nd Lieutenants

ØPorter A M

DEVON

County Cadet Commandant

Col P D Baldry *TD*

Cadet Executive Officer

Maj T C S Knox

Lieutenant Colonels

Casey B D
Knivett A V *OBE*

Majors

Curl I J
Embury D J
Ley A J
Reason J D
Turney P E

Captains

Barrett J R
Bayly H B
Bennington L R
Blencowe L J
Buller V
Cox E W
Davis G
Finney J L R
Merchant P A J
Molloy E C
Morse R J
Payne N W
Solway A P *MBE*
Sylvester F L
Tidball J C
Trude R S
Wiles C T *MBE*

Lieutenants

Allen B J E
Boulton T A
Dafforn S J
Denton A
Duke H V
Ellis D B
Emond G R
Gigg D B
ØGoodman H
Hamlyn P J
Harris R L W
Harvey D J M
Harvey A R
Horswell M
Kelley P R A
Lillicrap D T
Loram R L
Lucas W C
McCullock J A P *BEM*
Miles B
Morgan G H
Mullett B H
Nalder F H *MBE TD*
Ogborne A C
ØPortlock M J
ØRoberts C J
Simons R C
Trobridge J W
Turner D A
West I A
Wherry B

2nd Lieutenants

Brain D
Chapman P
Dart R H
Grant-Roy M D
Howells D T
ØMcCarthy A
ØMcDonald M P
Morris T G F
ØPayne J M
ØRoberts M
Starkey O C
ØWilliams D R
Wilsher J R

DORSET

County Cadet Commandant

Lt Col B A Catchpole

Cadet Executive Officer

Maj R J Goodman

Lieutenant Colonels

Buckby T B

Majors

Brown P J C
Fox B I
Hamblin M D
Vine T M

Captains

Amos E
Battey J A
Cann N H
Knight M J
Main P E
Pearce D
Redhead D
Taylor N J

Lieutenants

Barlow D J
Caswell N J
Cowley R C
Dunford R E
Elton A A
Folley E
McIntosh R A
Polley P
Pope K M
Reed M R
Robberts S E
Saunders R A
Woodward R A J

2nd Lieutenants

Ankers R O
Davies G J
ØMarsland L C
Smith K

DURHAM AND SOUTH TYNE

County Cadet Commandant

Col M J F Sheffield *TD DL*

Cadet Executive Officer

Maj J D Davidson

Lieutenant Colonels

Walton R

Majors

Craig A D
Davis J E
Ellwood R
Makepeace A W

Captains

Brown J E
Bujko H *BEM*
Campbell W J
Dixon A
Herbert A
Houghton G H
Johnson C M
Marshall L
McElhone P
Mitchinson A C
O'Brien R
Pearce J R
Pearce M
Richardson E W
Shield J G
Walden D

Lieutenants

Adair G
Anderson J S B
Crook V
Joyce M
Tearney C
Watson R W
Wright J G

2nd Lieutenants

Chaganis L A
Leadbitter E G
Luke D C S
Reeves J J
Thompson P
Tibbett A

DYFED

County Cadet Commandant

Col T G Walters

Cadet Executive Officer

Maj D F Edge *MC*

Lieutenant Colonels

Joyce D H J

Majors

Burton K J
Evans J E R
Glover V J E
Snook T G

Captains

Coombes B
øDavies-Jenkins S C A
Glover T G
Jenkins W L
Jones T O
Rees L
Richards K
Smith A J
Thomas T S
Wallace W S

Lieutenants

Bradford B A
Brierley R S
Evans D R
James M A I
Jones H G
Sharman D S

2nd Lieutenants

Batsford J R

ESSEX

County Cadet Commandant

Col E T Boddye *MBE TD*

Cadet Executive Officer

Maj T D Vassar

Lieutenant Colonels

Mullis D G *MBE JP*

Majors

Ainger B
Branigan A T
Calton R M N
Eade F G
Farren K C *MBE*

Captains

Bardell M J
Bowyer M
Boyce A H
Christian P A
Dickson J M
Fitzgerald D W
Harrod L C
Harrod C F
McAuley W J A *BEM*
Nichols J M
Street C W
Welland J E
Womack P
Young M D

Lieutenants

Ager M C
Ashby R W
Atkins R J
Brooker K R
Carmichael T
Cass G
Chapman A A
Collins P J
Daniell M W
Davis M K
Donovan J M
Fisher M J
Fisher A A
Hughes A V
Inkersole A T
Jaklinski G
Low B J
Mulye J E
Simmons B R
Slater P A
Smith R J G
Tandy S J
Witham A A

2nd Lieutenants

Bishop L J
Jones D R
Pritchard G
Ray D J
Smith A E
Sutcliffe J H
Towers A C
Webber C
Wright M A
Yarker V J

GLAMORGAN

County Cadet Commandant

Col B J Watkins *TD DL*

Cadet Executive Officer

Maj W G Gulley

Lieutenant Colonels

Coombes E J *MBE*
Hughes H
Prior T L

Majors

Baker D G
Banford G
Jeffery D A H
Jenkins J H B *BEM*
Knight D W
Pike R C *TD*
Roblin R
Trow A
Welsh R J

Captains

Birch M O
Bunce K E
Cartlidge D J
Cooper J G
Davies D R
Davies J B
Davies W J
Dean C E
Griffiths W E *TD*
Harris R E
Haslam A W G
Jeffreys K E
Jones D J F
Jones C T
Lemon R V
Rees W H
Veness C J G
Wilcock A J
Williams D J
Wills R S H
Woodham J H

Lieutenants

Adams R J
Bignell C J
Brelsford B R V
Button C G
Dagley G A
Davies E M
Hayman J E
Howell I H
Hunt S C
John M
John R
Jones T
Kaged J A
Martin G L
Price R H
Quirin F G
Saunders G G
Tasker D A
Toms B C W
Wardle P M
Wrona V G

2nd Lieutenants

Davies R P
Davies M C
Facey J J
Hopkins A E
Job D D
Jones B J A
Jones T H
McBratney B J
Morgan F D
Powis D C
Warren D T
Williams C

GLASGOW AND LANARKSHIRE BN

County Cadet Commandant

Col D A Wighton *MBE TD*

Cadet Executive Officer

Maj D C Baxter

Lieutenant Colonels

Ramsay J *MBE*

Majors

Copeland G W
Lawrence W P
McLatchie G
Neil P K

Captains

Bryce C R
Cowan W *MBE*
Kerrigan J
McKendry P
Reade A N
Simpson D

Lieutenants

Bissett A J
ØCattell J
Dempster J
Feggans J
Jankauskas D
ØKay S
Lamb G C
Maciver A
McCluskey D
McIntosh S J
Portwood M A
Rafferty P
Speirs J J
Stephen C
Watt A T K

2nd Lieutenants

ØDonaghey L W
Hudson P J
Robertson J
Thomson E D

1 CDT BN GLOUCESTERSHIRE REGT

County Cadet Commandant

Col R D O'Neill

Cadet Executive Officer

Maj L A Ramsden *MBE*

Majors

Andrews L M
Langley A P J
Noller W H
Readstone D W

Captains

Bennett M E
Cannaby M
Cook M L
Coombes F D
Cork J H
James M

Lieutenants

Brace M S
Calder D
Fowler E T
Gibbins D C
Hatfield R S
ØMitchell S C
Rowe M L
Savage T B

2nd Lieutenants

ØRowe D J

THE GORDON HIGHLANDERS BN

County Cadet Commandant

Lt Col R D Buchan *TD*

Cadet Executive Officer

Maj J D Beeton

Lieutenant Colonels

Sim C

Majors

Gillies D
Henderson A G
Leith J D M
Reid D McC

Captains

Gardner W
Gordon W C
Gray J A
Mackenzie I R S
McIntosh G M
Stien E V
Williamson J

Lieutenants

Beattie E T
Ewan K
Ferguson D
ØGordon H M E
Mackie K W
McMillan D W
Rae L M
Rennie E
Thow R G
Treasurer J W McD

2nd Lieutenants

Champion C R

GREATER LONDON (CITY OF LONDON & NE SECTOR)

County Cadet Commandant

Col F Gilfedder *MBE TD*

Cadet Executive Officer

Maj S A Masson *BEM*

Lieutenant Colonels

Campbell G

Majors

Anderson G S
Baker L M
Mundy R M

Captains

Emmett R E
Ettinghausen S L
Hollier R J
Jones P
Kirk A J
Lightwood K S
Naqvi R H .
Pearson P D
Waller R J

Lieutenants

Badruddin P
Corney P A
Corr F C
ØHorton L J J
Huddart N
Johnson J J
Leader D K
Stanford G F

2nd Lieutenants

Bassnett R B
Campbell N D
Ensor P
Healy D P
King R G
Mills D C
O'Donnell J P
Walker-Hebborn A
Weber J
White E L

GREATER LONDON (MIDDLESEX & NW SECTOR)

County Cadet Commandant

Col J K Evans

Cadet Executive Officer

Maj R G Ford

Lieutenant Colonels

Price F W *MBE TD*

Majors

Canning G W
Cox F M F
Denison A I
Ford A V
Perkins G H
Pinnock A G

Captains

Ash R J
Coleiro J M
Connolly T P
Craddock A
Foster W W
Hart A V
Jones R G
McManus A G
Menday S R
Reeve C F
Thorn R C M
Turner S B
Wilkinson J

Lieutenants

Barber B S
Bell D F
Clift C H
Cooper G K
Davey A J
Howell J A R
Johnson P
Joyce P J F
Livingstone S P
Lovelock M L
Marriner D F
Mitchell R A
Perrin I R
Pollard P J
Riley D I V
Rout D A
Western C D

2nd Lieutenants

Beaumont P R
Butlin C J
Collett R L
Farrier P G
Fry R E
Heathcote R W
Keeling J B N
Scannell J A

GREATER LONDON (SE SECTOR)

County Cadet Commandant

Col D P Robinson *OBE TD*

Cadet Executive Officer

Maj M P D Eastap

Lieutenant Colonels

Hill J E *TD*

Majors

Hobbs R E
Kingaby J E
Langford D A
Marsh G D

Captains

Bourner S H F
Brock W L
Cook S S
Goddard K D
Hollis J K
Mummery W K J
Simmons S
Smalley E
ØTresadern B A

Lieutenants

Ashmore G J
Blackwood J G
Cassidy S C D
Cast R C
Daniels B R
Dawson E W
Dyer R N
Gault W
ØHodgson E D
Holmes M A
Hutchins B J
Martin R J
Mills W C
Monteith G J
Philpot D L
Rayment J A
ØRose J D
Seabrook R J

2nd Lieutenants

Clarke R C
Dunn S B
Newington G A
Smith J A

GREATER LONDON (SW SECTOR)

County Cadet Commandant

Lt Col I K Russell *MBE TD*

Cadet Executive Officer

Maj R L Cooke *MBE*

Lieutenant Colonels

Reardon R J *JP*

Majors

Bale J R
Benton N H
Gold C A

Captains

Buckley M J
Davenport B P
Dobson C P
Hood K I
Joannou B
Jones P B
Leech D
McNeil J D
Roebuck R P P
Smith M J
Thompson R J
Tibble M E
Todhunter M J

Lieutenants

Andrew N M
Blishen M A
Cartwright M J B
Duke C
Hibbard M
Hughes R
Hutchins C M
Smith D A
Smith R B
Tunesi *of Liongam* J J
Wallder J P
Watt E C
Weston B H
Whittingham P M

2nd Lieutenants

Casey J
ØForbes Y
Hamilton J
Joannou J
Pickard S M
Regan P F
Roberts D
Sokolowski E B A

GREATER MANCHESTER

County Cadet Commandant

Col J R Murley *TD JP*

Cadet Executive Officer

Maj F Kirk

Lieutenant Colonels

Vail I

Majors

Carling R
Farrell B
Lindop A
McIntyre T *JP*
Newman M
Sheard M

Captains

Allen P
Ballard K
Barnes K
Bohills C J
ØBrees D M
Brotherton M J
Foster J A
Hughes J H W
Jones F W
Joyce A
Lloyd L A
Meadow M W
Ratchford D A A
Robins D J
Slattery B N
Taggart J
Warr P
Woolfenden E A

Lieutenants

Atherton P
Basford A H
Cunliffe N J
Edis K A
Flitcroft S E
Frith J T
Gawthorpe B
Hobbs J M
Hosler N W
Marshall A
McNulty A
Meakin P
Morgan M B
ØMotteram G H
Motteram E B
Quayle D J
Shaw T J B
Spencer K
Sutherland H A

Truslove S

2nd Lieutenants

Bolton C J
Chandler J A
Day B
Lester H R
McGuinness A
McMillen P T J
O'Sullivan R
Robinson M J

GWENT

County Cadet Commandant

Col T U Buckthought *TD DL*

Cadet Executive Officer

Maj M J Ryan

Lieutenant Colonels

Mead P J

Majors

Bennett C
Syred R

Captains

Beese W H
Bennett B
Clarkson R H
Clifford C
Fulton-Forrest K P
John R B

Lieutenants

Bangsund W J
Blewett S D
Campbell D N
Gwynn G E
King A L
Morgan G J
Palmer R
Pickering F
Tucker D A

2nd Lieutenants

McGill J
Meadowcroft M J
Thomas P G

GWYNEDD

County Cadet Commandant

Lt Col P Williams-Jones *TD*

Cadet Executive Officer

Maj J E Jones

Majors

Hunt S B
Jones R C
Owen G G
Pretious D P
Squire T J

Captains

Bentley A
Binfield N E
Brown P G
Rowlands J A
Scotney G R
Slaymaker G H W
Williams A Y

Lieutenants

Gibson J T A
Harris K
Head J
Lewis E L
Macarthur D M
Millership B C
Owen J H G
Parry A W
Williams R K *MBE*

2nd Lieutenants

Jones A P
Meaby D A
Thomas D R

HAMPSHIRE AND THE ISLE OF WIGHT

County Cadet Commandant

Col D W F Taylor

Cadet Executive Officer

Lt Col E P Murphy *OBE*

Lieutenant Colonels

Canipel G A
Edmead P F W

Majors

Barber C S
Currie P W
Hockney I C
Sherwell G T
Smith J
Snell A W
Tinson A R
Waddington J

Captains

Adams B W
Akers W H
Allen M J
Andrews I P
Barfield R A
Beck A A C
Bennett G L
Bone D K
Cloke J
Edwards J A
Fuller T E
Gissing R G
Godwin H E
Hempstead J S
Herridge P J
Hogg T T
Monk J T
Moody C
Niblett E W A
Pearce J L
Smith M D
Stockley J D
Trown A M
Watson W A H
Winter W T *MM*

Lieutenants

Adams D C
Aslett C G
Barnes P M L
Bateman P G
Bezant G R A
Brooks C B
Brown J P
Byrne P
Cattle P
Cripps L
Davies G J
Davis R T
Edwards D F
Fielding E
Fisher K C V
Goulson R F
Grundy R J
Hamlet T J
Hatcher M E
Hooper P W
Hudson R J
King S I
Lewcock G D
Mars G T
Martell J K
McLaren S D
Milton G J C
Parker J A
Russell M J
Snell P J
Stout P
Taylor N E B
Vella P
Whitmore R J
Wilkinson E
Woods C J

2nd Lieutenants

Brooks P R
Colleypriest A V
Cooke M E
Garman G T
Grist J H
Hadnett R G
Henwood E C
Hurley W
ØMarjoram V G
Muddiman S A
Murphy P B
O'Brien J S J
Smith I W
Sobey R J
Ward J B

HEREFORD AND WORCESTER

County Cadet Commandant

Col R G Purvis *TD*

Cadet Executive Officer

Maj M J Baker *MBE MM*

Lieutenant Colonels

Evans D

Majors

Bull A F

Hencher M J
Prewitt R
Somner B J
Stock D V

Captains

Atkinson S
Barnett W J H
Bousfield J E
Firth-Clark J J *TD*
Gaskell V A
Graham P
Maltby G G
Slater R W J
Thorne A D
Tilt D

Lieutenants

Boughey A J M
Davies D A
Dyke J W
Evans G T
Gallivan R A
Knight P
Murray A V
Piercy-Buck F S F
Russell K
Stainforth G T W
Tucker M
Warner R F

2nd Lieutenants

Barrington D E
Birch B J
Harding M K
Harris C E
Maine D F
Sword R M

HERTFORDSHIRE

County Cadet Commandant

Col R D Upton *OBE*

Cadet Executive Officer

Maj D West

Lieutenant Colonels

Cockman K R

Majors

Allen J M
Mann R B
Wilson A S G

Captains

Annan R J
Cowling E A J
Dymock A E
Furse A J
Gray M R
Hodges M G L
Macleod I D
O'Connor W J P *TD*
Ross E C W
Varney D W
Weir K J

Lieutenants

Beecham R E A
Botten T A
Eales R
Fassum J D
Ferguson I G
Fisher R H
Isaac E E
Kirby W
Lammiman A J
Lycett-King I R
øLycett-King C A
Smith B B
Tutthill I E
White S C

2nd Lieutenants

Burnett K J P
Cater D M
Murrell A F
øSmith S D
Stewart P A
Walker W D
Youles J H

HUMBERSIDE

County Cadet Commandant

Lt Col P R Horspool *TD*

Cadet Executive Officer

Maj A A Duncan

Majors

Christian M F
Evans T B A
Hughes A B
Larder D A
Telfer D
Tradewell R P
Wilson R

Captains

Bell R G
Blythe W G
Britchford G
Curnow S G
Desforges G F *BEM*
Diamond W K
Fuller D I
Godfrey N W
Jacklin R B
Jackson M C
Jones E C
Lever J V
Morris G K
Smith D S
Stark B
Tasker T G
Taylor N
Turner S D
Usher T L
Wilkinson N S

Lieutenants

Adams R
Ashton D S
Barron A G
Bartram J E
Bennett J M
Booker R L
Boot D
Broadley C T
Danby T E
Desforges M
Fisher A
Fox J
Galloway D P
Godfrey S G
Gribben G J
Holdsworth A W J
Holloway P L
Hooton J
Hudson B
Kemp G E
Locking A
Mair K G
McBlain S
Metcalfe J R
Millett G
Mitchell D
Newlove F R
Parker C
Peka P B
Sanderson D
Tucker R H
Wharam T
Willingham M

2nd Lieutenants

Barrass A J
Bartram R E
Carter G
Charlton A G
Cooper A D
Cooper R
Cruddas M J
Dawson P
Dunbar J M
Haslam J I M
Hastings P T
Hodgson M
Johnson V A
Lynch P
Mawer J A
Oxtoby C C
Robson G K
Scaum P C
Smith J R
Stark G B

ISLE OF MAN

County Cadet Commandant

Maj E P Clague-Quine

Cadet Executive Officer

Capt Oates R

Captains

Buttell F B

2nd Lieutenants

Charnley K

KENT

County Cadet Commandant

Col C N Mearns *OBE TD*

Cadet Executive Officer

Maj A B O'Hagan

Lieutenant Colonels

Philpin C H G

Riordan J C

Majors

Bellingham C M
Fletcher C V G
Martin D T
Stewart I H
Street-Williams M S
Todd P L A
Whitehead D J

Captains

Barden A R
Cairns E J *MBE*
Clay C C
Jones K H
Jones W R
Longbottom P J
Neville L
Riley R G
Spicer E G
Twomey T P
Walton J H
Wood P A
Woodhams D M J

Lieutenants

Ashman R D
Baker M R
Brisley C A
Burgess K
Burke W
Duffield B M
Gatter K A
Grundy B F
Halford R H
Hatcher B
Hughes P R
Jupp C
Lowdon K
McNeil J
Ostle-Hawkins E J S
Palmer B L
Pankhurst J A
Riley C M
Thompson P W
Thwaites R P
Whybrow D W

2nd Lieutenants

Bloor K J
Harman I D
ØHatcher J L H
ØMcGain F M
Taylor M W

KINGS OWN SCOTTISH BORDERERS BN

County Cadet Commandant

Lt Col W Thyne *TD*

Cadet Executive Officer

Maj A J C Hewat

Lieutenant Colonels

Keeton G E

Majors

Aitken I
Chisholm T C
Dalzell D
Fraser W J
McLean S C
Scott H R

Captains

Campbell E I
Cliff-McCulloch D G
Craig A
Deamer J D
Hume A G
Parker B P

Lieutenants

Carmichael C J
ØHolliday L J
Kirk J
McCallion G S T
Pearson J
Reade R F
Ridgway G E
Spence T
Swan T D
Thomson I J J

2nd Lieutenants

ØSwan M

LANCASHIRE

County Cadet Commandant

Col D McNamara

Cadet Executive Officer

Maj W G Thomas

Lieutenant Colonels

Davidson E W

Majors

Dickinson W J E
Garvey A
Hadwen F
Myers J

Captains

Allton J M
Burrows P
Eskdale J R
Freer G
Gaught P S
Gorton J A
Gray M
Houldsworth R A
Lambert S A
Lewis D A
Mann D
McGonagle J
Thomas L
Todd D
Wallis M C

Lieutenants

Charleson S A
Davies J A
Day J
Eardley J R
Foulds G
Lambson P F
McKenzie J H
Reed I
Sibson J M
Stewart D J
Taylor R R

2nd Lieutenants

Bampton S R
Clarkson K J
Clegg L C
Finch S J P
Hancock C
Lee S S
Longden M J
Moss D C
Parsons H
Peel G T
Smith J A
Tierney J W F

LEICESTERSHIRE AND NORTHAMPTONSHIRE

County Cadet Commandant

Lt Col J M K Weir *TD DL*

Cadet Executive Officer

Maj D M Andrews

Lieutenant Colonels

Beard H K
Lawson C J

Majors

Hollins A R
Holmes M D
Keers I R
Kemp L J
Powell F T
Smith B W

Captains

Betts A D
Bott R T
Collier P G
Davies S
Desborough C S
Elphinstone N H W
Graves B
Hunter M D
Maclachlan I D
Mullen S
Nurcombe J A
Thompson D T
Young D R J

Lieutenants

Baines T N
Castille P P
Collier S G
Deeley D H
Elbourne N J
Lockwood H
Milner L R
O'Connor B P
Poulton J S
Seal R D
Shooter B
Smith A M
Taylor G McL
Walker D C G
Whitlock R W
Wilson K

Wykes R

2nd Lieutenants

Hill M J
øMarsters C
Pendergast M
Walker D

LINCOLNSHIRE

County Cadet Commandant

Col M H Best *TD*

Cadet Executive Officer

Maj I H Grant

Lieutenant Colonels

Hunter J R *TD*

Majors

Baillie E M
Bain R W
Dickinson R A
Meadows C
Sendall D R

Captains

Dovey B
Downes B R
Griffiths K
Johnson S J
Ogg R M
Richmond T E
Rodgers J A
Smaller S A
Williams E
Willoughby S H

Lieutenants

Graves B
Hunter T
Oldfield P G
Swan C A
Vardy N E
Wells R J
Wilson D J

2nd Lieutenants

Dovey P
øHindle G E
Ivens A P C
Julian M A
Taylor N
Whitla E R

LOTHIAN BN

County Cadet Commandant

Col S W McBain

Cadet Executive Officer

Maj R A Ross

Lieutenant Colonels

Gordon E F

Majors

Bunyan S A *TD*
Dinnie G S *MBE*
Gilmour W
Owens C McK
Thomson B J

Captains

Crombie A
Jackson G
Law R
øMcKirdy C A

Lieutenants

Cook R H
Macphee R H
McCoach A
Orr A M
Peddie A
Tully D M

2nd Lieutenants

Armstrong S J
Burns R
Dougherty A D
McGhee T H O
McNeice A R
Mitchell G H T
Stevens W
Tilley W H T
Wright J

MERSEYSIDE

County Cadet Commandant

Lt Col G E Jones *MBE TD JP*

Cadet Executive Officer

Maj G J Corbett *JP*

Majors

Abel C W
Connolly C E
Cotton R R
Farrington T J D
O'Callaghan R *MBE*

Captains

Brandon A J
Bretherton K
Brooks G
Burns C H
Cottrell C E
Crompton W
Doyle J A
øDoyle D F
Doyle A
George B S
Griffiths C H
Marten G C W
McGough R S
Owens F R
Parry R D
Rochford J J
Sinclair R S
Strong G S *BEM*
Sullivan K
Towler R
Trollope C F A
Waller S N

Lieutenants

Black J G
Currie K
Ferris D R C
Fitzgerald T J
Fletcher K N
Graff R E
Hilton R
Mulvany A G
Phillips F J
Wareing P J

2nd Lieutenants

Allford G J
Blair R F
Davies D J
øHall F L
Heaney S D
Hunt T S
Jackson D W
McKenzie T P
øPowell P S

NORFOLK

County Cadet Commandant

Lt Col N M L Barne

Cadet Executive Officer

Maj J Hall *MBE*

Majors

Baldry J D
Fitt D F
Menezes J D
Mizen M R
Page T J

Captains

Allen P E
Doughty J F
Gidney J L T
Green M M
Hardy G S
Hewett P W
Housego J H
Keywood J R
Mason G
Newson G R
Pratt G W
Pratt W G E
Roberts A G P
Todd R S

Lieutenants

Ames R R
Amys P B
Bartram D
Borrer A G
Clarke G A
Coutts G
Dye B L
Firth D
Freeman R W
Hedges D B
Manship K J
Pillar R C
Sheppard P J
Sprules S W
Turner O A
Ward S J
Waters C P

Wilkinson C G

2nd Lieutenants

Coles C C
Hack R R
Hewitt N J
Hoggett N S
Holloway R E
Lambert R O
Lucas S
Mills J E
Wells J R
øWells L S D
Wilkin P H

NORTHUMBRIA

County Cadet Commandant

Col R W Mordue *TD*

Cadet Executive Officer

Maj G L Morrice

Lieutenant Colonels

Mackenzie J R *TD*

Majors

Bowles V C D
Chandler T
Gerrish M H
Spears A R
Wilson J B

Captains

Anderson J W
Brodie T J
Collis P
Goodinson R
Hall J W
Huggan R O
Mitchell D J
Rowe W
Smith D A
Spencer J J
Sunley D
Thompson T A
Thompson G

Lieutenants

Andrews P
Bell D G
Brownlee C J
Dickinson A
Fargus J C
Finlayson B W
Grey M
James R
Kent G
Lafferty J
Lawson K
Mitchell K
Pirie G H
Rogan P J
Ryder A
Smith P H
Southern B
Storey D L
White B M

2nd Lieutenants

Brown P H
Burnett A J
Crompton G
Lambert A D
Lawrence G R
McNichol P
Morrice K J
Price D G

NOTTINGHAMSHIRE

County Cadet Commandant

Lt Col R Merryweather *TD*

Cadet Executive Officer

Maj J S Baty

Lieutenant Colonels

Walker J P

Majors

Berry R E
Greaves S
Wharmby P
Wilds T

Captains

Ashburner C E
Bacon R
Barraclough S M
Booth E G
Chadburn D M
Fox J F
Garratt W E
Hirons M E
Hubbard M J
Locke T C
McCarthy D J
Ostler-Glenn J C

Lieutenants

Baker J M
Butt D W *BEM*
Downing G L
Flynn R A
Graham K
Leivers J H
Lowe M G R
Meakin G E
Mellors R J
Miller G W
Mills P A
Munroe J M
Rabjohn A D
Rippon N C
Silver A G
Sims M J
Smith A
White A J

2nd Lieutenants

Atherton N D
Harvey T R
Newsham D A
Pike P R W
Wright R W

ORKNEY INDEPENDENT CADET BTY LOVAT SCOUTS

County Cadet Commandant

Maj A H Yates

2nd Lieutenants

Ralph J G
Ross E A
Sinclair J G
øWalters M E

OXFORDSHIRE

County Cadet Commandant

Lt Col C R Hill

Cadet Executive Officer

Maj I A Milne

Lieutenant Colonels

McGill G R

Majors

Cousins B N
Hargreaves B
McAnaney F J
Venn P W
Vince M

Captains

Allen D J
Ansley L J
Campion T A
Cossins D J
Grafton C
Heritage J R
Stark J W *MBE*
Whawell H
Winstanley L

Lieutenants

Bowes R M B
Butler B R
Cox S P
Hill K S J
Jones W D
Keely C J
McGill A G
Morton D C
Nicholls P E
Osborne G D
Pointon J
Smith T J
Walker P J T
Wearing W O

2nd Lieutenants

Bond R A D
Hordle R I
Lloyd J P
Webb R E
Wiltshire C R

POWYS

County Cadet Commandant

Col K W Battson *OBE*

Cadet Executive Officer

Maj K B M Jones *JP*

Majors

Flexen P M J *ERD*
Pugh D H
Rowlands L R
Watson R G

Captains

Colclough J
Cook D F L
Elliott B D
Evans W B
Lewis R P
Williams K H

Lieutenants

Davies G W
Flaherty G
Ghani G
Hall P J
Heighway R
Kavanagh W
Saunders D J
Walling N K

2nd Lieutenants

Price M C J
Simkiss W E

QUEEN'S OWN HIGHLANDERS BN

County Cadet Commandant

Col J G Aird *TD*

Cadet Executive Officer

Maj A Henderson

Majors

Borrie J P
Durrand A G D
Macleod A
Sutherland A
Wood R G

Captains

Cowell P B
Durrans B
Gibbard G E
Harvey B
Macbean M
Maclean K F
Maclellan I B
Morrison A W
Murdoch G
Young J E

Lieutenants

Bain R G
Blackley B
Clark J H
Hutcheon J S
Jack A J
Macaskill J
Mackenzie C S
Macleod N
Sharp G
Swan D
Williams A J
Wilson A H

2nd Lieutenants

Macdonald M
Maclean K G
McIntyre D A

1 CADET BN THE ROYAL IRISH RANGERS

County Cadet Commandant

Lt Col J T Brewster

Cadet Executive Officer

Maj J A Glenn

Majors

Bogle W J
Hadden E S
Moore S A

Captains

Clyde A H
Dickson W
Evans J G
Logue R
Marshall T J A
McCleery D G
Moore A J L
Peacocke R A F
Quigley W A
White R J

Lieutenants

Coughlin A R
Elliott E G
ØMorrison R
Robinson T W C
Sheppard S

2nd Lieutenants

Annesley T W P
Carruthers S H
Mitchell G S
Robinson P C

SHETLAND INDEPENDENT CADET BTY

County Cadet Commandant

Maj J J Nicolson *BEM*

Captains

Robinson J C

2nd Lieutenants

Murray S G

SHROPSHIRE

County Cadet Commandant

Col C A R Lockhart

Cadet Executive Officer

Maj R G Woodfield

Majors

Aston T P *MBE*
Kingston P F
Maher J C

Captains

Cookson R
Emery J J
McClellan B F
Spencer D E
Watkins M J
Webb J P
Whittle F

Lieutenants

Barnard A D
Bassett M A
Bishop D A
Cowell W S
Hale B R
Kinsey A N
Mark R T
Power D M
Riggs D R
Semple E A
Shaw A A C
Smythe P G C
Steed W
Tonge R
Yiangou A

2nd Lieutenants

Budryk K M
Cowan D B
ØCowell E M
Goodwin S J
Jones M A
Trussler R H
Turner R

SOMERSET

County Cadet Commandant

Col D N Lowe *OBE*

Cadet Executive Officer

Maj S C Thompson

Lieutenant Colonels

Holroyd A B

Majors

Binns T
Gale W F
Morgan R W
Smith A S G

Captains

Benneyworth N J A
ØD'Souza L M
Sawyer M J
Southwell R L
Stacey J W G
Stead G
ØThompson F J

Woodrow I R

Lieutenants

Adams D L
Barnett-Jones A R
Barry-Tait J S
Broom P D
Brown D H
Davidson A J
Dawson R
Dowling R J
Johnson J H P
Jones N I
Oaten R
ØPreston C M M
Ragan R
Richardson P M
Thorne P R

2nd Lieutenants

ØBenneyworth J R
Crease T N
Farrant M D

STAFFORDSHIRE AND WEST MIDLAND NORTH SECTOR

County Cadet Commandant

Col K R Smith *TD*

Cadet Executive Officer

Maj D H M Rumsey

Lieutenant Colonels

Carter E D
Jones A G

Majors

Buckle A T G
Edge E
Hall G W *TD*
Perkins J D
Roberts G T
Stoddard R W
Tew B J

Captains

Bartlam P
Bowditch R G
Coxon G J
Eccles W G
Fisher K E
Hill D J
Leslie P A
Nott B G
Oldfield T G
Palmer L
Proctor T
Pyke H J
Sandham E

Lieutenants

Banks C A
Cockayne A H
Howells M J
Hughes D C
Hughes E
Hutton R F
Jones S P
Keates D J
Porter A W
Pyke B J
Thomasson E
Williams M J
Wilshaw P
Yates P F

2nd Lieutenants

Arnold A B
Emery B W
Hatherley T G
Jackson B T
Pace S
Redden D K
Simcox J
Washington P
Wood L H

SUFFOLK

County Cadet Commandant

Col A Munro *TD*

Cadet Executive Officer

Maj J Leslie

Lieutenant Colonels

Woolrich H F

Majors

Askew J D
Burrell-Saward C P
Pugsley C R J *TD*
Smye M L

Captains

Aldred R W
Bryant A D P
Emmerson B
Golby J E
Goldson A P
Jarvis R C
Southgate D A
Sutor M D
Symonds J A

Lieutenants

Askew E
Catt J H
Gay E C A
Ives K A
Jerome D R
King M A
Kossowski K W
Lawn B A
Leech A K
Murrow J L
Nelson J D
Price M G
Richardson A P
ØRinger J E
ØRussell-Roberts E M
Shipley D J

2nd Lieutenants

Dorrell M R
Laws B
Steel S J

SURREY

County Cadet Commandant

Col P Tween

Cadet Executive Officer

Maj R P M Oldfield

Lieutenant Colonels

Wilson C H

Majors

Cameron A J
May W L
O'Callaghan K M

Captains

Booth M J
Budd S V
Cloudsdale J R
Cox D K G
Fay F J
Jones D R
Mair F J M
Smith J W
Talbot D N

Lieutenants

Bowen I J C
Davison R S
Gould B J
Hancock D R
Hughes P R
McCauliffe M A
Musk R B
Pezet J E
Pierce-Jones M
Taylor J B R
Trafford N D
Watkins K H
Young A D

2nd Lieutenants

Blowers A M
Evans M G
ØFenton-O'Creevy L D
Groves A R
McHugh J A
Risby G A
Watkins J T
Wright P J

SUSSEX

County Cadet Commandant

Col P E Morrison *MBE*

Cadet Executive Officer

Maj P H Ridlington

Lieutenant Colonels

Crump W A

Majors

McCullough J C
McMahon A A
Moorton R

Walker R

Captains

Blackwell D J
Crowle M K
Fisher A G
Ford R C
Greenwood F H N
Newton R D
Rowles P W
Somes D
Soulsby K E G

Lieutenants

Deeprose W A M
Llewellyn M F
Perry M
Rusbridger D J
Welch A W J

2nd Lieutenants

Collett D P
Dodds R G
Earle B D
Lemon M E S
Manchee A E
Page R E C
Pearce R M
Pettitt E B
Rockall A

WARWICKSHIRE AND WEST MIDLAND SOUTH SECTOR

County Cadet Commandant

Lt Col J H Haywood *TD*

Cadet Executive Officer

Maj J W Bowyer

Lieutenant Colonels

Burgum J

Majors

Dale L R
Humphreys J C B *TD*
Kirby R
Montgomery N
Smith N J
Wormell R W

Captains

Burnell M
Cooper P R C
Davies P J
Hall R T
Hill D A
Holmes R I
Leonard B A
Lonnon B L
McKerlie A
Nock J D
Shaw T A
Snape A J

Lieutenants

Bannister P J
Bounds R W
Brant P R A
Cook R A
Cooke R T
Dexter M A
Hudson G K
Jemmett T M
Kavanagh P J
Moreton D K
Mytton E J
Patrick N G
Perfit B A
Robinson K P
Torri A J
Walford A W
Winckles D
Wood R E H

2nd Lieutenants

Ball S A
Clegg G M
Cockayne A A J
Cooper R G
Earl P J
Hunt K W
Jordan S P
Markham M J
Robertson I D
Sarling N W
Saunders P L
Seeley C J
Skillen B G J
Stuart N P
Whittard R K
Williams M A

WILTSHIRE

County Cadet Commandant

Col B R Hobbs *OBE*

Cadet Executive Officer

Maj P M Baxter

Lieutenant Colonels

Lynch T

Majors

Carter P R
Gall A C
Hinder M A F
Phillips J

Captains

Edmeads A C
Graham R
Griffin D T
Griffin K A
Griffin M P
Kelly N J
Mayo S R
Mellin D J
Nield T
Parsley H S
Radford I D

Lieutenants

Brennan E J
Carlile R W
Davis K W
Hibbs T E H
Loftus A C
Nicholls J R
Simpkins M J

2nd Lieutenants

Fenner K D
Manton S A
Marsh J D

YORKSHIRE

County Cadet Commandant

Col A C Roberts *MBE TD DL JP*

Cadet Executive Officers

Maj M P C Bray
Maj R W Gordon

Lieutenant Colonels

Addyman R *TD*
Cresswell G P
Garner D
Roberts P F T
Rowlinson A F

Majors

Barnes G
Bennett D L
Brian K
Burke W
Clark B
Cook J W C *JP*
Crowther P
Johnson B
Kemp A
Matthews J D
Moore C H *JP*
Weightman W A
Wood R A

Captains

Agar J
Alexander G
Bateson G W
Batty J K
Bonds T
Brown R S A
Cole P R
Delany K W
Garfitt A E
Hebden J W
Hennessy H
Hewson M E
Hofmann R
Holling D
Jarvis C M
Key C
Key D J
Kirk M A
Lindley R B
Lyons D
Markham J
Marren S A
Payne N
Reid J W
Render M D
Scrivens T
øSharp A D
Shaw H
Stott T B
Sykes B
Trigg J W
Turnbull A
Wilkes D A

Lieutenants

Allwood R J
Ashforth J M
Bestington D
Birkenshaw J B
Black R G
Brian M J
Bruntlett B W
Byrom D
Carter M J
Cartwright G M
Catch P
Duncan L F
Firth K G
Foster P A
Griffiths T
Grimshaw J B
Horton M J
King S P
Knight C B
Lawrance J M G
Lillystone D J
Malton P A
Martin P
McBride G W
McKenna D N
Morris D W
Perry A
Ridley S
Roughton K
Scrivens H
Sivell D S
Skelton J
Spencer S J
Stead R P
Turner N J S
Vatish S L
Walker M G
Wootton M J

2nd Lieutenants

Banner J S
Benn D
Coe S H
Cooper K
Cowan A J
ØGransbury N J
Hammond J P
Heap P R
Hillam F A
Himsworth M L
Hooks A
Houghton T P
Moran J C
Thiede C
ØWhitehead M L
ØWood B L

TERRITORIAL AUXILIARY & VOLUNTEER RESERVE ASSOCIATIONS

(Arranged alphabetically)

Note—In some cases in these lists the rank shown against officers' names is honorary.

COUNCIL OF TERRITORIAL AUXILIARY & VOLUNTEER RESERVE ASSOCIATIONS

(Centre Block, Duke of York's HQ, Kings Road, Chelsea, London, SW3 4SG)
(*Tel No:* 01-730 6122/3/4)

Patron .... Maj Gen *Lord* Michael Fitzalan Howard *GCVO CB CBE MC DL* ret pay
President .... Col *The Rt Hon Visct* Ridley *TD*
Chairman .... Lt Gen *Sir* Peter Hudson *KCB CBE DL* ret pay *(Lieutenant HM Tower of London)*
Vice-Chairmen .... Col M B Haycock *CBE TD DL*
Col G S P Carden *CBE TD DL*
Commodore R C Hastie *CBE RD DL* RNR
Maj Gen J F Mottram *CB LVO OBE*
Air Vice Marshal W J Herrington *CB*
Secretary .... Maj Gen M Matthews *CB* ret pay
Deputy Secretary .... Brig T R Birkett *OBE* ret pay

Note—Each Territorial Auxiliary & Volunteer Reserve Association is represented on this Council by its President, Vice Presidents, Chairman, Vice Chairmen and Secretary.

EAST ANGLIA

President

Sir Joshua Rowley *Bt (HM Lord Lieutenant Suffolk)*

Vice Presidents

Lt Col H C Hanbury *LVO MC JP* ret pay *(HM Lord Lieutenant Bedford)*
T J A Coleman *JP (HM Lord Lieutenant Norfolk)*
Admiral *Sir* Andrew Lewis *KCB JP (HM Lord Lieutenant Essex)*
M G A Bevan *(HM Lord Lieutenant Cambridge)*
S A Bowes Lyon *(HM Lord Lieutenant Hertford)*

Chairman

Maj J R Horrell *CBE TD DL*

Vice Chairmen

Cdr R M N Green *RD* RNR
Col J P Davey *TD DL*
Air Cdre M J E Swiney *OBE*
Col K R Fitzgerald *TD DL*
Col B E M Prophet *TD DL*
Brig J R Rigby ret pay
Maj R A Shervington *TD*
Col T C B Swayne *TD DL*
Col A I S Makin *TD*

Secretary

Col W Pakenham-Walsh *DL* ret pay

"Springfield Tyrells", 250 Springfield Road, Chelmsford, Essex, CM2 6BU
Tel No.: 0245 354262

EASTERN WESSEX

President

Capt *Sir* Ashley Ponsonby *Bt MC (HM Lord Lieutenant Oxford)*

Vice Presidents

Col *The Hon* G W N Palmer *OBE TD JP (HM Lord Lieutenant Berks)*
Lt Col *Sir* James Scott *Bt* ret pay *(HM Lord Lieutenant Hampshire)*
Comdr *The Hon* J T Fremantle RN ret *(HM Lord Lieutenant Buckinghamshire)*
Capt *The Lord* Digby *JP (HM Lord Lieutenant Dorset)*
The Rt Hon The Lord Mottistone *(HM Lord Lieutenant Isle of Wight)*

Chairman

Col T L May *TD DL*

Vice Chairmen

Maj *Sir* Philip Duncombe *Bt DL*
Air Cdre J W Frost *CBE DFC DL*
Col R J Sage *TD*
Col W H F Stevens *OBE ADC*
Col J W G Pirie *DL*
Sir David Black *Bt*

Secretary

Maj Gen J A Ward-Booth *OBE* ret pay

Headquarters Offices, 30, Carlton Place, Southampton SO1 2DX
Tel No.: 0703 228661

EAST MIDLAND

President

Col P Hilton *MC JP (HM Lord Lieutenant Derby)*

Vice Presidents

Col R A St G Martin *OBE JP* ret pay *(HM Lord Lieutenant Leics)*
J L Lowther *CBE (HM Lord Lieutenant Northants)*
Sir Gordon Hobday *(HM Lord Lieutenant Notts)*
Col H N Nevile *(HM Lord Lieutenant Lincs)*

Chairman

Brig C E Wilkinson *CBE TD*

Vice Chairmen

Air Vice Marshal W E Colahan *CB CBE DFC*
Col R A Gill *TD JP DL*
Col W J Gleadell *TD*
Col A H Hawksworth *TD ADC*
Maj H J C Loveday *TD DL*

Secretary

Col S H Clark *OBE JP DL* ret pay

*6,Clinton Terrace, Derby Road,
Nottingham NG7 1LZ*
Tel No.: 0602 476508

GREATER LONDON

President

Field Marshal *Sir* Edwin Bramall *GCB OBE MC (HM Lord Lieutenant Greater London)*

Chairman

Col G S P Carden *CBE TD DL*

Vice Chairmen

Col G D Spratt *TD*
Lt Col J M Hanscombe *MBE DL*
Air Cdre J F Langer *CBE AFC DL*
Capt G K Beattie *CBE RD DL*
Col J M Craig *TD DL*

Secretary

Brig P C Bowser *CBE* ret pay

*Duke of York's Headquarters, Chelsea,
London SW3 4RY*
Tel No.: 01-730 8131

HIGHLAND

President

Visct Arbuthnott *CBE DSC*

Vice Presidents

Lt Cdr L R D Mackintosh of Mackintosh *OBE*
The Lord Provost of The City of Aberdeen
Maj *The Earl of* Dalhousie *KT GCVO GBE MC (Ensign Queen's Body Guard for Scotland)*
Maj *The Lord* Maclean of Duart & Morvern *KT GCVO KBE PC (Lieutenant Queen's Body Guard for Scotland)*
Col T R Gordon-Duff *MC*
The Rt Hon The Visct Thurso of Ulbster *JP*
The Earl of Mar & Kellie *JP*
The Lord Provost of The City of Dundee
Capt I M Tennant *(Ensign Queen's Body Guard for Scotland)*
Col R A A S Macrae *MBE* ret pay
Col A M Gilmour *OBE MC* ret pay
Capt M M Shearer *JP*
The Rt Hon The Earl of Leven & Melville
Sir Maitland Mackie *CBE JP*
Vice Admiral *Sir* John Hayes *KCB OBE*
Brig A S Pearson *CB DSO*▪▪▪ *OBE MC TD*
Col *Sir* John Gilmour *Bt DSO TD JP (Capt Queen's Body Guard for Scotland)*
Lord Granville of Callernish
Col J Stirling *TD*
Maj D H Butter *MC JP (Brig Queen's Body Guard for Scotland)*

Chairman

Col J Stirling *TD*

Vice Chairmen

Col A M Flett *TD*
Maj M A Wedgwood *TD*
Col N V R Simpson *OBE TD*
Air Marshal *Sir* Peter Bairsto *KBE CB AFC*
Col N M Sharp *MBE TD*

Secretary

Col L E Hudson *OBE*

*"Seathwood", 365, Perth Road,
Dundee DD2 1LX*
Tel No.: 0382 68283/4

NORTH WEST OF ENGLAND & THE ISLE OF MAN

President

Sir William Downward *KT JP (HM Lord Lieutenant Greater Manchester)*

Vice Presidents

Col *The Rt Hon The Visct* Leverhulme *TD (HM Lord Lieutenant Cheshire)*
Col S Towneley *JP (HM Lord Lieutenant Lancs)*
Wg Cdr K M Stoddart *AE (HM Lord Lieutenant Merseyside)*
Sir Charles Graham *Bt (HM Lord Lieutenant Cumbria)*
Maj Gen *His Excellency* L A W New *CB CBE (Lieutenant Governor Isle of Man)*

Chairman

Col F J K Williams *TD DL*

Vice Chairmen

Maj G C Rylands *OBE TD JP DL*
Maj R R Craik *OBE TD JP DL*
Wg Cdr A R Keys *OBE DFC*
Col P M Poole *TD JP DL*
Col J B Timmins *OBE TD DL*

Secretary

Brig D L Ormerod *CBE DL* ret pay

Alexandra Court, 28, Alexandra Drive, Liverpool L17 8YE
Tel No.: 051-727 4552

LOWLANDS

President

Lt Col W B Swan *CBE TD JP*

Vice Presidents

The Lord Provost of the City of Edinburgh
The Lord Provost of the City of Glasgow
Commodore *Sir* John Clerk of Penicuik *Bt CBE VRD* RNR *(Brig Queen's Body Guard for Scotland)*
Col *The Lord* Clydesmuir *KT CB MBE TD JP (Capt Queen's Body Guard for Scotland)*
Maj *The Earl of* Wemyss & March *KT JP (Lieut Queen's Body Guard for Scotland)*
The Rt Hon The Earl of Morton
Lt Cdr *The Duke of* Buccleuch and Queensbury *KT VRD* RNR *(Capt Queen's Body Guard for Scotland)*
Lt Col A M Sprot of Haystoun *MC JP* ret pay
Maj J D Makgill Crichton Maitland
Maj H J Brewis
Lt Col A J Jardine Paterson *OBE JP*
Maj *The Rt Hon The Lord* Sinclair *MVO*
Col B M Knox *MC TD*

Chairman

Col C H K Corsar *OBE TD JP DL*

Vice Chairmen

Air Marshal *Sir* Richard Wakeford *KCB LVO OBE AFC*
Lt Col W Bruce *TD*
Col H E Lang *OBE TD*
Commodore J W Wightman *CBE* RNR
Col G J L Coltart *TD*

Secretary

Col D G B Saunders ret pay

75, Berkeley Street, Glasgow G3 7EA
Tel No.: 041-221 2273/5

NORTHERN IRELAND

President

Col M W McCorkell *OBE TD*

Vice Presidents

Capt R A F Dobbs *JP*
Col W N Brann *OBE ERD*
Lt Col J Hamilton-Stubber
Dowager Duchess of Westminster
Capt F M A Torrens-Spence *DSO DSC AFC JP*
Sir Robin Kinahan *KBE ERD JP*
Maj J T Eaton *TD*

Chairman

Maj J F Leslie *TD JP DL*

Vice Chairmen

Col R B Morton *TD*
Maj A H G Gibbon *GM JP DL*
Lt Col M R H Scott *MBE* ret pay
Col M E W Nicholl *TD*
Col W F Gillespie *TD JP DL*
Cdr K Cochrane *RD DL*
Maj W B S Buchanan *MBE TD*
Col W A Eakins *CBE TD*
Lt Col J M Steele *MBE TD* TA

Secretary

Lt Col J Hassett ret pay

NORTH OF ENGLAND

President

Col *The Lord* Gisborough *JP (HM Lord Lieutenant Cleveland)*

Vice Presidents

Col *The Lord* Barnard *TD (HM Lord Lieutenant Durham)*
Col *The Visct* Ridley *TD (HM Lord Lieutenant Northumberland)*
Col *Sir* Ralph Carr-Ellison *TD (HM Lord Lieutenant Tyne & Wear)*

Chairman

Col R M Stewart *OBE TD DL*

Vice Chairmen

Col J E Ingham *OBE TD*
Col R Scott *MBE TD JP DL*
G T Orde *TD JP*
Cdre A L C Wilkinson *CBE RD* RNR

Secretary

Brig D H Hodge *DL* ret pay

53, Old Elvet,
Durham DH1 3JJ
Tel No.: 0385 47202

SOUTH EAST

President

Col R Leigh-Pemberton *JP (HM Lord Lieutenant Kent)*

Vice Presidents

Lt Col *The Marquess of* Abergaveny *KG OBE (HM Lord Lieutenant East Sussex)*
R E Thornton *OBE JP (HM Lord Lieutenant Surrey)*
Her Grace Lavinia *Duchess of* Norfolk *CBE (HM Lord Lieutenant West Sussex)*

Chairman

Col R R St J Barkshire *TD JP*

Vice Chairmen

Col J B Ogilvie *OBE TD DL*
M J Calvert *JP DL*
Col A C Dexter *OBE*
Cdre B K Perrin *CBE VRD* RNR

Secretary

Col G O Mullins *DL* ret pay

Sandling Place, Chatham Road,
Maidstone, Kent ME14 2NJ
Tel No.: 0622 52253/4

WALES

President

Col R Hanbury-Tenison *JP (HM Lord Lieutenant Gwent)*

Vice Presidents

Marquess of Anglesey *(HM Lord Lieutenant Gwynedd)*
D C Mansell-Lewis *JP (HM Lord Lieutenant Dyfed)*
Col J L Corbett-Winder *OBE MC JP* ret pay *(HM Lord Lieutenant Powys)*
D G Badham *MBE JP (HM Lord Lieutenant Mid Glamorgan)*
Mrs S E Williams *MBE JP (HM Lord Lieutenant South Glamorgan)*
Col J V Williams *DSO OBE (HM Lord Lieutenant West Glamorgan)*
Sir William Gladstone *Bt (HM Lord Lieutenant Clwyd)*

Chairman

Col W P Howells *OBE TD DL*

Vice Chairmen

Lt Col H B Singer *TD DL*
Air Comdre T H Blackham *OBE DFC DL*
Cdre R C Hastie *CBE RD*▪ *DL* RNR
Col B T John *CBE TD ADC*
Gp Capt D H M Chandler *OBE*
Brig G J Curl *CBE* ret pay

Secretary

Brig R E L Jenkins *CBE* ret pay

Centre Block, Maindy Barracks,
Cardiff CF4 3YE
Tel No.: 0222 20251/2/3 (Cardiff Mil Ext 205)

WESTERN WESSEX

President

Lt Col G W F Luttrell *MC JP (HM Lord Lieutenant Somerset)*

Vice Presidents

Col *Sir* John Wills *Bt TD JP (HM Lord Lieutenant Avon)*
Lt Col *The Earl of* Morley *JP* ret pay *(HM Lord Lieutenant Devon)*
Visct Falmouth *JP (HM Lord Lieutenant Cornwall)*
Col M St J V Gibbs *CB DSO TD JP (HM Lord Lieutenant Gloucestershire)*
Col *Sir* Hugh Brassey *KCVO OBE MC (HM Lord Lieutenant Wiltshire)*

Chairman

Col M S Lee-Brown *OBE TD DL*

Vice Chairmen

Col R A Warner *TD*
Lt Col K C R Gibson *TD DL*
Wg Cdr E W Willey
Lt Col J G Peel *TD JP*
Col P D Baldry *TD*
Col D Lowsley-Williams *TD JP DL*
Col K D Brown *OBE TD ADC DL*
Capt E M Marks *RD*
Col J A C Uniacke

Secretary

Brig J G Starling *CBE MC DL* ret pay

2, Beaufort Road, Clifton, Bristol BS8 2JS
Tel No.: 0272 734045

WEST MIDLAND

President

The Rt Hon The Earl of Aylesford *JP (HM Lord Lieutenant West Midland)*

Vice Presidents

Sir Arthur Bryan *JP (HM Lord Lieutenant Staffs)*
C M T Smith-Ryland *JP (HM Lord Lieutenant Warwickshire)*
J R S Dugdale *(HM Lord Lieutenant Shropshire)*
Capt T R Dunne *(HM Lord Lieutenant Hereford & Worcester)*

Chairman

Col M B Haycock *CBE TD DL*

Vice Chairmen

Col A Fender *TD DL*
Gp Capt G H Burgess *CBE* RAF ret
Col R D Crawford-Clarke *MBE TD DL*
Capt R G Purchase *MBE VRD▪▪ ADC DL* RNR
Col C J Baines *CBE MC TD DL*
Col A B Griffiths *TD DL*

Secretary

Lt Col P A Winter *OBE* ret pay

Tennal Grange, Tennal Road, Harborne, Birmingham, B32 2HX
Tel No.: 021-427 5221

YORKSHIRE & HUMBERSIDE

President

R A Bethell *(HM Lord Lieutenant Humberside)*

Vice Presidents

Col *The Marquis of* Normanby *KG CBE (HM Lord Lieutenant North Yorkshire)*
Maj *The Lord* Ingrow *OBE TD JP (HM Lord Lieutenant West Yorkshire)*
Lt Col J H Neill *CBE TD JP (HM Lord Lieutenant South Yorkshire)*

Chairman

Col I G Norton *TD JP DL*

Vice Chairmen

Cdr M W Tong *RD* RNR
Maj Gen D E Isles *CB OBE* ret pay
Lt Col C A Gillett *TD DL*
Gp Capt E W Cropper

Secretary

Brig C D H Wilson ret pay

20, St George's Place York YO2 2DS
Tel No.: 0904 23081

COMBINED CADET FORCE ASSOCIATION

1, Cheltenham Terrace, London, SW3 4RR (*Tel No:* 01-730 9733)

President..Gen *Sir* Hugh Beach *GBE KCB MC* ret pay
(Vice Lord Lieutenant Greater London)

Vice Presidents

RN..Vice Admiral R R Squires
Army ....Gen *Sir* Anthony Read *GCB CBE DSO MC* ret pay
Maj Gen M S Hancock *CB MBE* ret pay
RAF...Air Vice Marshal G C Lamb *CB CBE AFC*

Chairman ....Maj Gen P C Shapland *CB MBE* ret pay
Vice Chairman..Lt Col R F Somerset
Hon Treasurer..Lt Col B T Jones *VRD*
Secretary..Brig D M Pontifex *CBE* ret pay

ARMY CADET FORCE ASSOCIATION

1, Cheltenham Terrace, London, SW3 4RR (*Tel No:* 01-730 9733)

Patron ....THE QUEEN

President..Gen *Sir* Anthony Read *GCB CBE DSO MC* ret pay
Chairman ....Lt Gen *Sir* David Scott-Barrett *KBE MC* ret pay
Vice Chairman.......................................Maj Gen D J St M Tabor *CB MC* ret pay
Hon Treasurer..Col J H Nunnerley *TD*
General Secretary..................................Brig D M Pontifex *CBE* ret pay
Asst Gen Secretary ....Maj A V Ford ret pay

INDEX

B

520073 Butterworth C M 150
514839 Butterworth E 142
484983 Butterworth F A 250
514927 Butterworth J K 336
430253 Butterworth P J 220
514765 Butterworth P J 116
511002 Butterworth P M 239
507263 Button C G 388
483867 Buxey M J 250
520445 Buxton A 273
492209 Buxton C J 114
501095 Buxton D A 116
516569 Buxton R A 219
511113 Buzzard P J 371
520577 Bye D P 285
471215 Bye P L 333
476777 Byers A 343
512401 Byers M 247
509495 Byers P R 259
514323 Byfield S D E 275
480259 Byles A P 250
493381 Byott W G J 245
457024 Byrd C C 377
472503 Byrd T 250
503774 Byrne D R 238
519446 Byrne G 322
496291 Byrne I B 233
443689 Byrne J C H S 186
499947 Byrne J P 141
520090 Byrne J S 322
501150 Byrne L K 139
503667 Byrne P 391
483511 Byrne R J 254
518303 Byrne T C 240
518565 Byrne T P 218
504368 Byrne V J 308
505894 Byrne W P J 262
473903 Byrom C E 312
510857 Byrom D 399
508819 Bywater J J 259

C

438114 Carden G S P 401
509989 Cable G L 359
485682 Cable P J 204
505428 Cable P J 235
522721 Cabrelli P 316
Cachia J 49
511335 Caddick C A 287
507885 Caddick-Adams A P 300
510834 Cade S J 246
499677 Cade T J 113
Cadman D 23
484984 Cadman F W 280
521366 Cadman M 314
439961 Cadogan H M E 200
518871 Cadogan M K 241
516837 Cadogan R H 358
499495 Cadwallader D K B 358
508654 Caen A J 354
495693 Cafe M C 338
509496 Cahill F J 259
507418 Caiger J G 122
489501 Cain A 272
521385 Cain P A 346
520279 Cain P 142
516087 Cain T D 183
488308 Cairns A J 308
485683 Cairns D P C 237
433580 Cairns E J 393
521226 Cairns R 309
499136 Cairns W 188
502945 Cake C C E 384
510289 Calascione J P B 122
490236 Calbreath J A 258
522481 Calcott C P S 247
447695 Calcutt L G 39, 135
475113 Calder A J K 176
506497 Calder D 389
501845 Calder H C 262
467232 Calder I M 341
468244 Calder K D 354
493229 Calder R P 336
511582 Calder R 264
516036 Calder-Smith J D 124
510290 Calderwood C 123
468874 Calderwood R J A 257
493692 Caldwell D R 251
520096 Caldwell P J 344
511826 Caldwell R B 123
519643 Caldwell S J 239
488535 Caldwell-Nichols C J 308
519644 Caleb N R N 142
498955 Caley S R 184
409532 Caley W J C 374
520272 Callaghan K 349
516860 Callaghan M I 284
505455 Callaghan N 253
510291 Callaghan S J 139
400816 Callan M 249
503627 Callan P G M 251
522074 Callan R R 255
486783 Callander J H 102
496000 Callander R 301
475018 Callow C G 243
473336 Callum D M 243
505939 Callun M P 262
473493 Calton R M N 388
480261 Calver J R O 271
456853 Calvert F A 319
Calvert M J 403
497386 Cameron A G H 122
511003 Cameron A H M 123
496870 Cameron A J D 244
476700 Cameron A J 397
513715 Cameron A St J E 131
522174 Cameron A 350
439963 Cameron B 128

484212 Cameron D C B 355
489329 Cameron D J 304
489502 Cameron E C 267
439964 Cameron E D 153, 161
500808 Cameron E G 297
521996 Cameron F T 334
516210 Cameron G I F 320
512936 Cameron H C D 157
492922 Cameron H R 258
516306 Cameron H 157
475115 Cameron I 264
523539 Cameron J C 311
496600 Cameron J E 356
512583 Cameron J E 172
478431 Cameron J J 338
Cameron Prof J M 65
474891 Cameron J N H 353
453448 Cameron J P 163
459219 Cameron K S 258
501372 Cameron M 344
517356 Cameron M 383
479187 Cameron N E A G 147
515760 Cameron N W 123
463902 Cameron P S G 336
516571 Cameron R B 254
472504 Cameron R N 120
503588 Cameron R N 235
491417 Cameron S J S 258
521731 Cameron W M 360
516366 Cameron-Mowat I 142
443411 Camilleri P F J 249
515383 Camlin B 386
506252 Camp J P 324
519822 Camp M C 309
516572 Camp T J 122
514766 Campbell A H E 113
496685 Campbell The Hon A J C 164
479188 Campbell A M 258
520608 Campbell A M 125
501890 Campbell A P W 166
519645 Campbell A 255
522237 Campbell A 309
513648 Campbell B A 355
493275 Campbell C A 166
509910 Campbell C M 359
357612 Campbell C P 126
470882 Campbell D A 307
493374 Campbell D A 245
518692 Campbell D A 345
485685 Campbell D J 220
508652 Campbell D J 350
493833 Campbell D L 342
Campbell D M 23
501461 Campbell D N 391
475465 Campbell E I 393
498549 Campbell E J 356
496999 Campbell E M 359
508509 Campbell E W 349
472983 Campbell Ellen B 307
504435 Campbell F B 141
471216 Campbell G B L 126
443412 Campbell G B 156
512471 Campbell G D 284
456060 Campbell G 389
495143 Campbell I D S 121
485885 Campbell I M 311
499595 Campbell I S 238
500948 Campbell J A M B 316
477741 Campbell J A 258
496272 Campbell J B 383
490487 Campbell J C 258
519990 Campbell J C 125
481054 Campbell J D 385
508820 Campbell J D 102
505940 Campbell J F R 164
458677 Campbell J M 327
496871 Campbell J M 128
510975 Campbell J M 276
487023 Campbell J S 307

515868 Collins R J 272
515094 Collins R M D 140
478120 Collins R M L 280
505222 Collins R M 116
522785 Collins R W M 309
518086 Collins S M C 125
517099 Collins S O 380
484234 Collins T A 335
513997 Collins T T C 188
472096 Collins W J N 354
514156 Collins W L 366
501571 Collinson C J 277
501572 Collinson G T 238
518041 Collinson S F 357
485698 Collis A C 250
480269 Collis A J N 110
503003 Collis A N 353
509140 Collis B W 124
476725 Collis H E 381
497274 Collis J S 302
516172 Collis M F 310
496561 Collis P 395
513829 Collison D V 368
496353 Collyer D F M 137
490163 Collyer M N 264
448936 Colman M F H 136
427628 Colman R C 369
509112 Colmer H E 286
485124 Colohan M D 342
496092 Colquhoun E S 338
494185 Colquhoun N R 370
507038 Colquhoun R K 275
471226 Colson J D 119
462517 Colston B E 236
403419 Coltart G J L 402
520240 Coltman C 133
478572 Coltman S A 137
491426 Colton J H E 298
498889 Colvill A J 364
506198 Colville A 345
495151 Colville R M L 299
517150 Colvin A P 246
464333 Colvin C A 236
521038 Colyer P J 373
503785 Combe R S 158
514108 Comben M 124
503006 Comins D 381
Commey R B 46
496627 Common W A 156
504442 Complin M R 139
515496 Comport C A 305
505386 Comport C E 305
513685 Compson G M 164
518877 Compston J A 140
513046 Compsty I B 275
521845 Compton F S 133
519361 Compton J R E 125
493025 Comyn C L 107
521804 Conaghan A P 315
500107 Concannon B P 124
472512 Conder R S 266
505223 Condie I A J 139
493077 Condie W T 221
513860 Condliffe M I 260
520933 Condon J J 218
473543 Condon J P B 187
433083 Conibear P K 39, 266
521164 Conibere M P 358
522789 Conlen M 314
486618 Conlin H L 364
488408 Conlon C P 138
516578 Conn N M M 131
520868 Conn U M E 284
471230 Conn W P 220
517171 Connaughton A M 364
470043 Connaughton R M 236
510835 Connell B C 246
478444 Connell J D 315
511007 Connell S L 240
459235 Connell T W P 266
520613 Connell W J G 123
499647 Connelly J P 253
451212 Connelly S V 174
461398 Conner G R 174
476406 Conners J J B 317
497667 Connew R A 305
511613 Connolly B 345
487671 Connolly C E 394
472338 Connolly D P 341
520614 Connolly E S 94
493226 Connolly P G 113
521014 Connolly P J 188
477162 Connolly T P 390
491427 Connon D L 165
509087 Connor C S 220
509502 Connor F J 139
519485 Connor H E 141
515588 Connor R C 329
512907 Connor T 149
488570 Conran D W M 138
512334 Conroy K 353
480886 Conroy M D 243
498880 Conroy T J 339
506290 Conroy W F 318
475122 Constable C J 237
505178 Constable J C 305
517897 Constant R A M 218
512876 Constantine C A 355
517258 Constantine D L 105
473914 Constantine M R I 171
524014 Convery C E 358
510575 Conway A L 319
505008 Conway D L 331
506992 Conway D R 218
520927 Conway M D 282
508124 Conway P A 284
521103 Conway S 365
488264 Conway-Hyde R H 250
415359 Coode D C 311
493232 Coogan J S V St R 243
523489 Cook A D 309
518696 Cook A S 247
386518 Cook A T 82
522838 Cook B C 134
468969 Cook C P 119
510299 Cook D E 230, 239
504202 Cook D F L 396
519647 Cook D H I 199
512585 Cook D J 174
471232 Cook D W 137
512269 Cook E G 254
509860 Cook E J 254
522483 Cook E J 247
521528 Cook G R N 134
497292 Cook G R 261
504143 Cook G T 240
471681 Cook J A 266
514109 Cook J A 357
494131 Cook J C D 235
522958 Cook J D 346
461650 Cook J F G 71, 249
489509 Cook J R B 138
498917 Cook J R 210
515888 Cook J V 132
507615 Cook J W C 398
479195 Cook K M 174
502942 Cook M L 389
508307 Cook M S O 327
470860 Cook M T 227
482705 Cook P C 171
517815 Cook P D 133
417997 Cook P J 342
477746 Cook P W 127, 228
476346 Cook R A M 349
503049 Cook R A 398
461399 Cook R F L 136
517062 Cook R H 394
486905 Cook R V 330
485618 Cook R 124
487993 Cook S C 308
498957 Cook S G 211
498254 Cook S K 122
505815 Cook S S 390
517668 Cook S 384
509166 Cook T K A 122
512586 Cook T R 364
488788 Cook W O 121
518235 Cook W 113
515955 Cooke A G A 108
522462 Cooke A G 350
495327 Cooke B J 129
513861 Cooke C E A 108
481672 Cooke C P 249
495852 Cooke D J A 122
495152 Cooke D J 259
420802 Cooke D L 120
439975 Cooke Sir David 236
510895 Cooke L A 270
519583 Cooke M E 391
491428 Cooke N D 121
484235 Cooke N J H 335
499598 Cooke N P 280
445823 Cooke P N 227
517746 Cooke R A 262
476486 Cooke R J H 128
510788 Cooke R J S 372
466491 Cooke R L 390
443653 Cooke R M D 377
513441 Cooke R T 398
522839 Cooke S 134
506590 Cookes H N 305
512883 Cooksley A 269
438366 Cookson E P T 120
503250 Cookson R 396
522353 Coole D 254
471686 Coombe D H 243
489894 Coombe N S 116
509229 Coombe P A 245
493266 Coombe T B J 116
499503 Coombes B 388
357289 Coombes E J 388
482071 Coombes F D 389
463618 Coombes J D 111
439976 Coombes J S 236
516930 Coombes R W 268
521805 Coombes W A G 340
507572 Coombs G R 251
482509 Coombs J T H 113
471614 Coombs M E C 102
512095 Coombs M J 124
472922 Coombs R J 235
507769 Cooney E A 105
505029 Cooper A B 141
519149 Cooper A C 374
523668 Cooper A D 392
501453 Cooper A G 124
520101 Cooper A J 247
520615 Cooper B P R 123
468970 Cooper B R 257
477747 Cooper C E 196
515421 Cooper C J 339
514235 Cooper C M 309
510300 Cooper D A 221
496133 Cooper D I S 326
516579 Cooper D O 117
451063 Cooper D W 62, 236
434111 Cooper F N 378
502108 Cooper G I 148
494956 Cooper G K 390
490490 Cooper G M 186
482167 Cooper G R 276
357063 Cooper Sir George 126, 228
490946 Cooper H H 384
473916 Cooper J A 127
519210 Cooper J A 288
503489 Cooper J D W 130
496128 Cooper J G 388
501886 Cooper J L 387
522985 Cooper J L 345

500767 Curran E A M 356
481756 Curran L D 257
468053 Curran M V 283
487474 Currie A P N 120
372473 Currie D S 311
514135 Currie D T 255
498403 Currie F 343
423959 Currie J C M 341
519091 Currie K 394
480581 Currie P W 391
504911 Currie R W 107
517964 Currie S F 287
334644 Currie W T 373
469349 Currier I B 350
523082 Curry M 358
504443 Curry N R 259
509299 Curry P C 259
522147 Curry P D 360
506737 Curry V J 287
516404 Curry-Peace F 347
459472 Curtin J P 67, 264
459238 Curtis A G H 173
506584 Curtis A G 340
520937 Curtis A J 174
511172 Curtis F G 308
463461 Curtis J M 327
516410 Curtis J P 287
480063 Curtis K E 249
521801 Curtis K J 372
513816 Curtis M E 255
503397 Curtis R A W 253
512403 Curtis T J M 134
522358 Curtis W G 110
511970 Curwen L 284
501578 Cusack D J 112
490965 Cushen J I 283
519080 Cushnir J H M 103
506295 Cussons P B 135
448946 Cutchey M C J 250
510013 Cuthbert A C 107
137599 Cuthbert E W 311
510305 Cuthbert M J 298
493027 Cuthbert R C T 138
496947 Cuthbert S 385
503793 Cuthbert-Brown M 264
508363 Cuthbertson I R 124
515713 Cuthbertson J G 133
472521 Cuthbertson-Smith D M 334
523025 Cutting E M 203
506160 Cytrynbaum S R 284
517655 Czaykowski A A P 348

D

475130 D'Alton A A M 120
484836 D'Alton A C 321
397861 D'Ambrumenil A Y 120
491140 D'Ambrumenil N J 93
523866 D'Anger P J 134
487828 d'Apice J N C 121
507193 d'Apice M H R 190
468613 d'Apice P A J 120
475132 D'Arcy-Irvine C K A 266
510854 D'Inverno I J 359
506692 D'Inverno J G 315
470056 D'Oyly C J 93
506234 D'Souza L M 357, 396
518846 D'Souza P J A 255
516371 Dabell A W 209
Dabo Bakari B 50
505499 Daborn K R 270
497913 Dadds E M 244
505213 Dade R 252
484578 Dadswell R H 237
Dady J W 39
486991 Dafforn S J 387
520023 Dagg E R 248
518326 Dagley G A 388
510099 Dahl N V 359
508989 Dailly J R 235
453644 Daintry G M 364
520620 Dainty A W 131
504354 Dainty A 268
518379 Daisley A 315
513867 Dakin J W 139
506267 Dakin K J 100
515961 Dakin N J 277
395016 Dakin R J B 337
479679 Dakin S A 359
515042 Dakin V T 100
512536 Dalal A 344
522553 Dalbahadur Gurung 228
513558 Dalbahadur Pun 223
517663 Dalbahadur Rai 226
508598 Dalbahadur Rana 223
505715 Dalbahadur Sunwar 225
512897 Dalby A H B 318
521806 Dalby A J 360
508557 Dalby C R 345
488063 Dalby K 174
484834 Dalby-Welsh T 250
521421 Dale A J 260
505231 Dale I C 259
501158 Dale J E 253
441719 Dale K W 311
473588 Dale L R 398
518094 Dale P S 199
458537 Dale R E 383
517879 Dales K J 278
521880 Daley V L 337
518881 Dalgliesh J D A 94
063322 Dalhousie The Earl of 8, 401
Daljit Singh 88
489514 Dallas G McG 156
484835 Dalley M J 251
515894 Dallimore M S 284
485707 Dallow J R 189
416408 Dally P A 3, 136
508275 Dalman Golay 225
508361 Dalrymple D J 123
513308 Dalrymple The Viscount 148
Dalrymple-Hamilton N E F 8
492841 Dalrymple-Hamilton N J F 301
445832 Daly B P 126
520621 Daly D C 109
400521 Daly D J 82
515962 Daly J H 232
515002 Daly J J 124
522359 Daly J P K 114
521559 Daly K L 288
504857 Daly M A 332
458529 Daly M H 243
463243 Daly M 283
419500 Daly P J 341
521049 Daly P M R 114
495853 Daly P W N 356
497906 Daly S E 283
476495 Daly T M A 211
508456 Daly U M 359
483888 Dalzel-Job I E 147
491828 Dalzell D 393
514070 Dalziel S P C 355
Damah D C 46
510236 Damant W N 135
519008 Damarbahadur Gurung 226
509039 Damberbahadur Shrestha 224
487893 Dana D K 272
501404 Danbahadur Burathoki 223
484615 Danby K G 138
507993 Danby P J 122
519000 Danby T E 392
500813 Danchev A 272
522558 Dand D G 322
507808 Dando J A 287
504296 Dando R A 356
478543 Dane B C 386
502159 Danells R L 140
506435 Dangerfield K R 268
430280 Daniel J R A 29, 173
517652 Daniel J W H 152
501343 Daniel N A 305
462668 Daniel P E B 236
505704 Daniel P J 141
505233 Daniel P M 130, 228
521903 Daniel R J A 219
494871 Daniel T M 343
496686 Daniell A H 296
467547 Daniell F A F 127
495807 Daniell I M 129
487268 Daniell J A 218
507209 Daniell L R 274
516748 Daniell M W 388
463331 Daniell P J 119
471615 Daniell S R 107
511501 Daniell W H 100
474793 Daniels B R 390
284757 Daniels R A 311
510642 Danilewicz C J 325
451223 Dann K G F 120
491436 Dannatt F R 186
508827 Danvers C H D 109
496356 Daplyn T J 215
523756 Darby J M 360
508918 Darby P 344
477751 Darby R G 257
496984 Darbyshire P J 321
508163 Darcy J J C 333
504601 Darcy L M 345
512096 Dare L 123
513868 Dare R A 125
501532 Darell C H D 109
522776 Darke G A 328
514980 Darley T R 185
511435 Darling A P 339
512590 Darling P J A 112
430855 Darlington J 115
499121 Darlington N D 385
496254 Darlington N E 320
500862 Darlow K I 267
430281 Darmody M J 119
491437 Darnell C I 158
501579 Darnley R A 164
522070 Darragh E 345

510819 English J H 370
501473 English J R S 300
509467 English R M 322
520177 English S N 241
473940 English T H 266
512599 English W P O 114
513819 Englishby C J 308
506127 Englishby C 273
522019 Englishby V L 345
506432 Ennis L J 123
515410 Ensor C H 284
513312 Ensor J A 260
523919 Ensor P 389
523118 Enticknap D 233
470061 Entwisle I J 266
506375 Entwistle J 383
487484 Enzer P J 128
519199 Epplestone C A 285
352560 Errington Sir Geoffrey 182
503962 Errington-Weddle B A 254
Ershad H M 51
489519 Erskine Crum D V 147
516676 Erskine E 309
505390 Erskine G D 355
509435 Erskine J G 345
522841 Erskine J H 134
503803 Erskine J M K 161
488333 Escott J J 302
502308 Esgate H J 267
489444 Eskdale J R 393
492342 Eskell C L 313
488427 Eskell S 128
476986 Esmonde-White J L P 271
514202 Espey S D 326
468992 Esson F J M 60, 232
487749 Esson J A 313
496744 Esson R 312
461415 Estcourt E J 119
477758 Estcourt R M 59, 215
517542 Etches S J 305
508579 Etheridge B J 239
470062 Etheridge R C 137
463199 Etheridge S P 328
518102 Etherington J B 199
512448 Etherington J 105
517579 Etherington J 247
518621 Etherington M R 221
523288 Etherington R C A 365
515967 Etherington S D 176
502101 Etherton D J 313
514385 Etherton R P 141
501823 Ettinghausen S L 389
477759 Eustace D W 215
475999 Eustace J W H 243
519662 Eustace R A 209
500353 Eustace R J 210
522954 Eva R F 263
522295 Evans A E 358
499601 Evans A G 254
483897 Evans A H B 145
515095 Evans A L 369
495162 Evans A T 138
488241 Evans B J 310
518986 Evans B R 133
510128 Evans B 357
507705 Evans C A 357
497412 Evans C J A 166
521752 Evans C J 133
518103 Evans C M 260
Evans C R 77
473941 Evans C R 206
Evans Sir David 79
495878 Evans D C 382
510836 Evans D G R 247
502013 Evans D H C 343
495463 Evans D J 270
513433 Evans D M 273
468920 Evans D R 386
482353 Evans D R 388
517823 Evans D R 125
520960 Evans D R 152
461240 Evans D S 317
500880 Evans D W 308
462187 Evans D 391
465596 Evans D 321
509887 Evans E R 329
519013 Evans F E 360
498084 Evans G B 330
502309 Evans G J L 268
501740 Evans G L 151
516363 Evans G N 218
461416 Evans G R A 104
516591 Evans G St J 134
516073 Evans G T 392
457687 Evans G W 318
522119 Evans H R 328
521620 Evans H S 174
516686 Evans H 332
451233 Evans I D 119
505832 Evans I D 246
445847 Evans J A M 61, 92
491803 Evans J A 372
419054 Evans J D 341
502360 Evans J D 368
515826 Evans J E F 245
462241 Evans J E R 388
420391 Evans J G 3, 307
497841 Evans J G 396
433104 Evans J J 249
472118 Evans J K 389
363911 Evans J M 337
500608 Evans J M 283
Evans Mr J N G 66
522218 Evans J P 328
483628 Evans J R 331
500138 Evans J S 350
522046 Evans J S 384
515415 Evans J 364
439340 Evans K G C 304
519663 Evans K L 140
485117 Evans K R G 310
513039 Evans L R 345
468076 Evans M A 350
481766 Evans M A 127
496127 Evans M D 116
515401 Evans M D 313
500352 Evans M G 252
523301 Evans M G 397
426873 Evans M J 3, 34, 115
497611 Evans M R 267
475147 Evans N F 120
497730 Evans N R H 184
488428 Evans P A D 238
443434 Evans P B 25, 236
518622 Evans P C W 265
503804 Evans P H M 262
501178 Evans P J 385
520635 Evans P R M 142
508564 Evans P R 132
Evans R 82
495030 Evans R D 330
497122 Evans R E 384
489520 Evans R J 138
493706 Evans R J 264
419035 Evans R N 242
501591 Evans R O N 139
496268 Evans R R B 334
504355 Evans R 268
457160 Evans S F E 266
509173 Evans S J 130
520222 Evans S K 285
516915 Evans S 140
488893 Evans T B A 392
501472 Evans T M 300
511527 Evans T P 215
512754 Evans V E 357
461417 Evans W A 105
506451 Evans W B 396
516291 Evans W F 314
491696 Evans W G O 121
514884 Evans W G 205
502616 Evans W J 198
523101 Evans Y B 284
515686 Evanson A 287
498257 Evanson G W 264
503015 Evanson R G 376
476504 Evanson-Goddard L M 338
522654 Evason P C 334
517600 Eve E J 385
499697 Eve J A 273
520636 Eve R R T 125
513879 Evelegh E J 219
494416 Eveleigh T H 258
515968 Everard J R 114
505044 Everard N C 108
495618 Everard R A S 295
491959 Everest R C 245
511011 Everett C J 165
520067 Everett C J 285
487832 Everett C R B 276
507863 Everett M E 314
490861 Everett M J 330
438042 Everett P 311
517266 Everett S P 106
499044 Everett T J 141
514399 Everett T P 125
453470 Everett-Heath E J 27, 232
483898 Everingham P J 237
523663 Everist H M 144
522367 Everitt A C 276
513313 Evers T J M 252
420115 Eversfield J C 312
501592 Everson P F 277
521399 Everton M W 240
518769 Eveson J A 358
496357 Evetts J M I 298
482723 Evetts R 237
521621 Evetts S N 276
Evraire R J 86
501355 Ewan A E 286
519342 Ewan K 389
521494 Ewart C D 326
521003 Ewart I C 345
493536 Ewart J V 251
489522 Ewart J 171
502416 Ewbank J K 138
504452 Ewell A A 139
478916 Ewen R 307
491147 Ewence M W 121
465755 Ewens M 249
479220 Ewer G A 237
493537 Ewers T J 250
463420 Ewing C A 63, 119
499698 Ewing D S 139
513260 Ewing G 352
443435 Ewing J D 307
513403 Ewing N J 287
518366 Exley S H 285
479221 Exon H J P 137
454369 Exton J B 353
476505 Eydes P W 158
519457 Eyre G R 305
507437 Eyre M D 262
489729 Eyre R S 307
460040 Eyres R C 225
465294 Eyton-Jones P 386

F

G

514567 Garlick R W 198
521772 Garman G T 391
489654 Garman P F 227
520197 Garner A 345
518891 Garner C G 134
494754 Garner D 398
517188 Garner G K 353
519458 Garner G K 358
516822 Garner K E 285
501799 Garner P G 215
517761 Garner S A 262
521891 Garner S E 357
451109 Garner T H 237
523121 Garnett C H E 95
461654 Garnett J C M 36, 202
502424 Garnett J W 116
519366 Garnett N A 287
479896 Garnett R A F 243
445863 Garnett R D 29, 126
452428 Garnett R M F 325
508748 Garrad C S 324
515562 Garratt C R 330
522526 Garratt G W 254
515978 Garratt J P J 174
403461 Garratt J R 313
505046 Garratt M J 258
502550 Garratt W E 395
497753 Garraway C H B 282
519037 Garrett B 346
453737 Garrett C J 64, 242
337960 Garrett H E M L 21, 126
478841 Garrett K 353
518892 Garrett N D 94
480301 Garrett R J M 215
511016 Garrett S C 172
497421 Garrick R S 238
514384 Garrity C R C 124
483907 Garrod F J 138
514478 Garrod M E 254
488675 Garrow I A 261
520468 Garrow N J 200
473400 Garside F J 307
468632 Garton C T 136
519315 Garton C W 172
510031 Garton-Jones W N 105
516934 Gartside C 268
513317 Gartside M J 240
508839 Garven J 157
482070 Garvey A 393
507372 Garway-Templeman C M 357
430299 Garway-Templeman P D 137
489161 Garwood J 339
491459 Gascoigne P E C 147
522842 Gascoine R J 276
518792 Gash A S 116
494504 Gash R H 220
479230 Gaskell J J 182
485727 Gaskell N P 215
504326 Gaskell V A 392
517410 Gaskin P H 176
504068 Gaskin W J 251
501825 Gatehouse D 343
514568 Gatehouse J P W 144
498537 Gater-Smith H 233
486572 Gates H S 222
480302 Gates R A 100
502425 Gatfield T S K 210
512409 Gather R E 103
521192 Gatherer C D M 376
501735 Gatt D W 337
513585 Gatter K A 393
508926 Gatward R F 261
501273 Gauci C A 243
510732 Gaught P S 393
521626 Gaukroger P A 233
515593 Gault D F 248
521810 Gault M T H 306
509801 Gault W 390
497205 Gaunt A N 355
499184 Gaunt C D 386
495058 Gaunt J 132
520645 Gaunt M J 260
424328 Gaussen S C C 151
521486 Gautam R 345
469000 Gauvain A de P 198
523261 Gavin J J 309
521563 Gavin J 288
500237 Gavin M 316
521868 Gaw A A 278
501092 Gaw D A 274
521154 Gawler W E 318
519174 Gawthorpe B 390
509973 Gay A L 207
469857 Gay D S 119
511197 Gay E C A 397
519498 Gay N S 330
505389 Gay P A 308
482731 Gay P H 225
493712 Gaye J D 196
514569 Gayler A 134
480304 Gaynor A E 324
517272 Gaze J P C 146
494237 Geake J H 313
518893 Geal A 233
480804 Geal C 266
506260 Geany J P 132
497422 Geary P J 121
501203 Gebbie J D 315
503473 Geddes G 372
508649 Geddes J F 313
477508 Geddes N 312
488270 Geddie G K 250
506845 Gedge P F 262
516983 Gee A G 252
503401 Gee H M 331
490179 Gee M J 349
514188 Geear G D 371
507338 Geere R G 309
493134 Gelder G W 279
520646 Geller J S 241
518701 Gemmell I M 247
480023 Genever C B 339
515004 Gent D C 123
481999 Gent R M J 271
508842 Gent S M 116
505454 Geoghegan J 131
445473 George A F 293
485083 George A G 274
493853 George B S 394
512320 George B W 262
487726 George D B 368
516156 George D 334
517798 George E M 183
496986 George M W 336
479231 George N 120
482732 George P I D 187
490101 George P V B 327
477208 George R D 243
521878 Georgiakakis N S 368
497562 Geraghty P A 221
471262 Gerdes G S 250
491119 Gerhard B F 132
520469 Germain P S 185
522322 Gerrard T R 322
470765 Gerrish M H 395
489527 Gershon N D G 267
489528 Gethin R J St L 238
483909 Gething R J 189
440010 Getley J C 128
517212 Gettins J R 203
516802 Ghani G 396
522667 Ghansah E 355
519195 Ghattas B F A 246
416335 Ghika J N 341
504631 Ghillyer T W K 113
495272 Ghosh A K 342
518022 Ghosh D 246
518382 Giannini C F 359
487494 Gibb A H 138
518894 Gibb C I F 154
522823 Gibb D M 273
463341 Gibb F F 154
519667 Gibb I J 113
478970 Gibb J D 338
516318 Gibb J E 132
510320 Gibb W M P 224
332962 Gibbard G E 396
486552 Gibbens R A 260
497423 Gibbins D A 122
517361 Gibbins D C 340, 389
484852 Gibbins J B 121
Gibbon A H G 403
492272 Gibbon F J 120
493713 Gibbon J H 121
509177 Gibbons D A H 252
462792 Gibbons G E 271
385061 Gibbons J R P 342
505387 Gibbons J 355
515385 Gibbons M N 386
499969 Gibbs A R 343
515512 Gibbs A 319
507837 Gibbs C W 235
354509 Gibbs D E 338
476197 Gibbs D 330
505969 Gibbs G K 130
502426 Gibbs I D H 158
508708 Gibbs J R M 116
Gibbs M St J V 404
518895 Gibbs P J 150
114083 Gibbs Sir Roland 6, 91
464706 Gibby J B 271
500060 Gibson A E 305
489529 Gibson A F 251
506846 Gibson A J G 164
493714 Gibson A M 232
520361 Gibson A M 255
522910 Gibson A M 285
502331 Gibson A 312
515479 Gibson A 364
508448 Gibson B G 305
523864 Gibson D A 267
507726 Gibson D L 383
472074 Gibson E M 317
503986 Gibson E 343
514490 Gibson F J 287
514890 Gibson G C 273
508935 Gibson G E 318
511457 Gibson G M 286
517043 Gibson G M 316
500671 Gibson I M 356
521627 Gibson I P 260
468898 Gibson J A B 384
521401 Gibson J A 240
507320 Gibson J T A 391
395829 Gibson J Y 383
Gibson K C R 404
484853 Gibson M F 154
504456 Gibson M R M 165
515680 Gibson M R 262
520254 Gibson M W 209
513753 Gibson N D 142
484854 Gibson P A J 110
Gibson P E 85
475158 Gibson P H 257
481557 Gibson P L 382
503816 Gibson P M 154
506373 Gibson P 318
520647 Gibson R A 241
502975 Gibson R D 130
473950 Gibson R J 127
Gibson Mr R M 65
419815 Gibson R M 342
513595 Gibson S D 130
514570 Gibson T R S 125
513642 Gibson W D J 132
487495 Gick A P 232
509156 Giddings D M 278
507894 Giddins G E B 299

H

500744 Hill D A 398
505270 Hill D A 185
484520 Hill D J 397
498711 Hill D J 261
516429 Hill D 288
515855 Hill G C 328
440028 Hill G M 127
474165 Hill G 276
514742 Hill J A 259
510025 Hill J C 192
443796 Hill J D 342
443820 Hill J E 390
521107 Hill K A L 360
505912 Hill K S J 395
509309 Hill M A 122
520244 Hill M C 347
508679 Hill M E 268
522172 Hill M J 394
494428 Hill M K 277
515072 Hill M P B 218
470086 Hill M S 250
479509 Hill M 336
502440 Hill N L 107
517992 Hill P A 313
521906 Hill P C W 148
506780 Hill P J 260
511975 Hill P J 246
473967 Hill P M R 127
463353 Hill P M 126
520499 Hill P T 380
505690 Hill P 387
489538 Hill R A L 116
500895 Hill R A 280
502441 Hill R D 132
488442 Hill R G L 138
518123 Hill R J 188
510922 Hill R N 313
496580 Hill R V 312
470858 Hill S A S 220
515564 Hill S G 329
519350 Hill S J 241
514824 Hill S M 357
515480 Hill S T 319
492428 Hill S 304
510539 Hill T J 381
516870 Hillam F A 399
508021 Hillan E C A 253
469250 Hillard D H 307
508508 Hillier C 254
489093 Hillier D A 268
512620 Hillis C W 157
513330 Hillkirk C J 186
505662 Hillman D A 317
484874 Hills D H 156
517606 Hills D J 278
459606 Hills J E B 300
456897 Hills J W 371
514494 Hills J 339
521988 Hills N J 125
476543 Hills R A 127
493095 Hills R E 313, 386
426521 Hills R F 136
440030 Hills W G 120
504677 Hillyer C G 135
520663 Hilton A C 131
479751 Hilton A W 272
492676 Hilton D G 352
523647 Hilton D L 358
478678 Hilton G 244
509310 Hilton J C 122
506351 Hilton J J 343
505694 Hilton P J 322
085503 Hilton P 401
522946 Hilton R J 263
506947 Hilton R S 305
501960 Hilton R 394
523797 Himal Rai 226
506172 Himraj Gurung 227
521545 Himsworth M L 399
482959 Hinchcliffe P J 339
517544 Hinchcliffe R A 324
509389 Hinchliff C E 253
522129 Hinchliffe R G 133
467723 Hincks A D 184
508117 Hincks G W 262
451263 Hincks J M 137
505829 Hind H E 262
521907 Hind J E 172
514238 Hind J R 370
484353 Hind R S 370
519683 Hinde M G 186
487508 Hinde P N 215
440499 Hinder M A F 398
522173 Hindle G E 394
439889 Hindle M O 354
497829 Hindle W J 343
513444 Hindley R J W 232
520311 Hindmarsh S V 287
481464 Hinds G A 359
493096 Hinds H 356
508701 Hinds L W 314
522947 Hinds P A 263
490306 Hindshaw J M 359
Hindson Dr T C 66
297575 Hine F A C 242
485746 Hine N A 198
Hine Sir Patrick 13, 15
490519 Hine R N 116
448980 Hiney T B F 235
500274 Hingston P J 146
430327 Hinings A M 62, 189
521643 Hinsley C J 140
499216 Hinson L P 313
516378 Hinton G P P G 124
482757 Hinton J P R 120
495528 Hinton N J H 222
486131 Hinton R C 240
473968 Hipkin G W M 176
499339 Hipkin L J 342
519564 Hirabahadur Chhetri 223
514929 Hirani A 344
524550 Hirasing Rana 223
494429 Hird C W 238
518044 Hird M 357
511777 Hirons M E 395
511027 Hirst A M 252
521258 Hirst G 263
510593 Hirst M I 357
480329 Hirst P T 280
512621 Hirst P 133
514265 Hiscock E 358
522607 Hiscock J E 275
443470 Hiscock P 171
517695 Hiscoke B R 248
514011 Hiskett M W 174
495349 Hislop G F 156
476732 Hislop R L 182
514506 Hitchcock D J 202
508794 Hitchcock D 337
507459 Hitchcock I G 130
487836 Hitchcock P R 171
476545 Hitchcott M 257
511136 Hitchen M S 284
496581 Hitchings D G 350
Hitchings G A 44
514281 Hives B 245
520664 Hix D P 140
516247 Hixson N P 270
520540 Ho D R 364
504016 Hoad N A 244
506215 Hoad P J 357
522709 Hoal W J 233
507460 Hoare J A 295
482758 Hoare J D 237
482085 Hoare P R A R 336
475171 Hoare R H G 107
515475 Hobbins C S W 284
499239 Hobbs A M T 283
519916 Hobbs A 212
393173 Hobbs B R 398
519520 Hobbs C M 247
508190 Hobbs E F 144
504278 Hobbs G W 132
521798 Hobbs J H 273
518437 Hobbs J L 319
448013 Hobbs J M 307
513483 Hobbs J M 390
390119 Hobbs K 386
447271 Hobbs M F 92
500506 Hobbs N J 244
509180 Hobbs P V 165
497153 Hobbs R E 390
515773 Hobbs R J D 124
Hobday Sir Gordon 401
516379 Hobday M E 252
484875 Hobden D J 121
337882 Hobden S C L 311
518000 Hobley R A 309
506204 Hobson R B 239
Hockaday Sir Arthur 85
514574 Hockedy M E 198
515774 Hockenhull J R 277
512505 Hocking E S 141
Hockney B H 86
492906 Hockney I C 391
520030 Hockram P J 248
513892 Hodder C H 252
510250 Hodder S P 130
511334 Hoddinott A J 300
484622 Hoddinott T G 128
505980 Hodge B M 190
437087 Hodge D H 403
517381 Hodge M J 305
455031 Hodge M S 250
481798 Hodgens D A 250
467488 Hodges A K 343
495529 Hodges C O 182
518348 Hodges H 346
480330 Hodges J A 264
521644 Hodges J M 140
517791 Hodges J R 114
486202 Hodges M G L 392
475172 Hodges M G 119
515544 Hodges N P 334
462460 Hodges P J 278
493729 Hodges R E L 182
451264 Hodges R J 180
511028 Hodges S D 139
501942 Hodgetts T G 186
517580 Hodgetts T J 247
506774 Hodgins S A 284
481799 Hodgkinson C R 244
516833 Hodgkinson P 334
483800 Hodgkiss B J 257
514197 Hodgkiss P A 142
518124 Hodgson A 255
481800 Hodgson B B 220
506082 Hodgson B H 246
510439 Hodgson C W 308
512728 Hodgson E D 390
499265 Hodgson G J 293
493846 Hodgson G W 308
521645 Hodgson I B 123
473969 Hodgson I F B P 115
493434 Hodgson J C 330
493730 Hodgson K 176
520426 Hodgson M 392
504891 Hodgson P H 180
519887 Hodgson P MacG 334
179933 Hodgson P 5
514096 Hodkinson D J 370
485747 Hodkinson G A 121
521850 Hodkinson R A J 278
504387 Hodson A D F 300
513190 Hodson C A J 246
499720 Hodson J D T 331
467577 Hodson K M 111
493037 Hodson M G R 238
507211 Hodson M J T 132
496310 Hodson R M R 215

I

J

K

473608 Kennedy P N B 301
511603 Kennedy P W 112
507473 Kennedy P 221
518676 Kennedy S A 185
519522 Kennedy S J 247
Kennedy T M 4
459282 Kennedy W C A 136
515639 Kennedy W R 305
510942 Kennedy Y L 357
484029 Kennedy-Smith G M 128
499541 Kennerley P D 299
512946 Kennett A C P 221
504881 Kennett A S 356
493044 Kennett A W J 220
520085 Kennett M 263
470537 Kennett P H 257
511507 Kenney M J S 107
495541 Kenney-Herbert H C 298
511607 Kennington R 305
506310 Kennison M D H 328
475925 Kennon H W O 371
437098 Kenny Sir Brian 91, 107, 269
489728 Kenny T A J 240
514307 Kenny T J W 247
518300 Kent A E 241
522194 Kent A S H 365
520105 Kent A W 247
514382 Kent B L 370
501878 Kent D J 135
494301 Kent E D 260
516493 Kent G 395
503181 Kent H N 328
499214 Kent I S A 330
494657 Kent R H 293
511425 Kent W P 141
461909 Kent-Jones T D 332
505284 Kent-Payne V R 184
476559 Kenway A C 211
520223 Kenwell B P 326
507852 Kenworthy J M 284
509854 Kenwright J F 253
499922 Kenyon A D 157
471841 Kenyon A R T 342
488454 Kenyon C F R 121
518137 Kenyon D F H 142
515170 Kenyon H M 385
430353 Kenyon N O 257
517190 Kenyon S E 247
501380 Keogh J P 245
517465 Keogh L B 177
518515 Keogh T W 313
508206 Keough T J 180
461460 Ker R I L 59, 161
514149 Kerce J A 282
513902 Kerford M S 332
492959 Kerley M 251
485894 Kerly B L E 272
497198 Kermack J A 308
518138 Kernohan D A 123
522278 Keron R W 320
497449 Kerr A B 129
496844 Kerr A N 298
492417 Kerr A 283
519129 Kerr A 235
502897 Kerr C N 165
521139 Kerr D A 133
519028 Kerr D F 294
491485 Kerr D J 251
492050 Kerr D 312
522288 Kerr E J 285
508588 Kerr G B 383
474955 Kerr G D 342
488455 Kerr G L 121
522282 Kerr G M 314
521169 Kerr G R 345
481804 Kerr G 119
471293 Kerr H H 127
521056 Kerr H R 125
467587 Kerr I E 137
520675 Kerr J A 159
Kerr J B 16
490901 Kerr J G 277
516829 Kerr J M 334
495356 Kerr J S 251
500006 Kerr M 284
504298 Kerr M 356
437617 Kerr P D 383
503039 Kerr P D 383
518227 Kerr R B McL 347
395470 Kerr S S 384
497348 Kerr W D A 132
497243 Kerridge B S 353
518312 Kerridge D H 133
483803 Kerridge M R 267
509959 Kerrigan J 389
510252 Kerrigan K A 133
484254 Kerruish G P 202
521654 Kerry-Williams C P 125
514013 Kershaw G B 276
486679 Kershaw G C 128
494495 Kershaw R J 220
501623 Kershaw-Naylor J P 130
514922 Kerslake J G 305
499830 Kerslake W B 272
479166 Kersley Baker D R 120
502271 Kersting A W 96
477491 Kessel L J 274
502447 Ketley P A 220
512067 Kett C J C 177
500279 Kett R E 278
522880 Kettrick M 383
477791 Keun M I 115
484255 Kevans G L 237
521655 Keville P M 216
481947 Kewley J W 323
471528 Key B S 317
499148 Key C 398
500785 Key D J 398
518139 Key G J F 240
506681 Keyes N P L 171
512374 Keylock B J 380
511239 Keymer D 261
Keys A R 402
440061 Keyte J V 218
522230 Keyte M K 306
501136 Keywood J R 394
509970 Khagendrabahadur Limbu 225
523059 Khan A M 246
515602 Khan K M 247
507350 Khan M M 348
Khanga M M 49
491355 Kharkabahadur Gurung 223
512287 Kharkabahadur Limbu 228
504240 Kharkajang Gurung 228
518833 Kharkaman Gurung 224
522550 Kharkaparsad Limbu 227
513526 Kharkasing Pun 223
511127 Khembahadur Thapa 223
511421 Khilbahadur Thapa 223
519357 Khimpratap Mall 229
524148 Khusiman Gurung 224
494842 Kibbey S J 244
508722 Kidd A G 246
522468 Kidd B C 285
523035 Kidd P J 116
498070 Kiddie K W 174
501824 Kiddle D R 372
477677 Kidley R J 356
462572 Kidner R H 119
501801 Kidner S J 138
506863 Kidwell T G 122
489048 Kiehne N P 356
518409 Kift L M J 357
517995 Kightley E J 132
510677 Kikerpuu L 357
499408 Kilbride D 253
497450 Kilburn G A 191
491379 Kilburn P W 267
496651 Kilgour G 122
521964 Killacky C 340
517227 Killen D E 383
424010 Killick J E 3, 16, 118
492351 Killick R W 129
521534 Killip J Q 131
508858 Kilmister J C St J 202
494438 Kilpatrick R I 238
512947 Kilpatrick S P B 171
521303 Kiltie A E 346
507053 Kilvert-Jones T D 200
484998 Kimber A T B 138
487355 Kimber B A 140
513242 Kimber D P 132
488773 Kimberley D R 144
506285 Kimberley E C 208
484256 Kime D C H 250
491639 Kimpton G H 131
255822 Kinahan O J 266
Kinahan Sir Robin 403
469036 Kincaid J W M 119
496457 Kinch D 336
509264 Kinchin C G J 343
483951 King A A 258
520676 King A C 174
523790 King A D 358
517905 King A F 260
512261 King A L 391
515060 King A P 379
519776 King A P 320
504620 King A R 313
522577 King C A S 233
511622 King C D 287
485385 King C M 283
500088 King C M 384
505285 King C R 139
512631 King C 130
479274 King D E 257
515922 King E J 288
503038 King E 383
470382 King H R 115
520677 King I P 233
488456 King J C L 186
522938 King J E 360
518841 King J H 364
517086 King J P 142
522394 King J V 265
509965 King L J 322
518838 King M A 397
523882 King M A 134
514239 King M E K 381
511679 King M J 318
522228 King M J 306
493742 King M P 196
520314 King M S 288
479275 King M T 250
471294 King N A 215
489232 King P D 338
506864 King P J 211
518140 King P R 255
451278 King P W 176
504473 King P 139
522628 King R G F 306
519910 King R G 389
479037 King R V 310
513676 King S A 345
518141 King S D T 117
505561 King S G 364
King S H 48
490180 King S H S 121
488339 King S I 391
490253 King S J 283
505286 King S J 252
515812 King S P 399
503658 King S R C 130
493253 King T W 366
513196 King W J M 254
508859 King W N 364

L

518144 Lavan D M 185
504476 Lavender C M 204
487285 Lavender C P 222
496769 Lavender D J 308
440069 Lavender D P J 137
504743 Laverick F 140
493165 Laverick R 338
515872 Laverick S H 284
490029 Lavery E R 336
469675 Lavery J S 383
520143 Lavery K S 314
487531 Lavies P R W 129
457506 Lavine M J 345, 348
497456 Law A R 251
512895 Law A W 375
510798 Law I G 133
520836 Law I M 306
512195 Law J A 287
399361 Law K 337
510339 Law L R 259
510340 Law M C 133
518554 Law M J 262
485265 Law N J 233
499619 Law The Hon R E H 146
500132 Law R 394
479788 Law S 137
523810 Lawes B D 293
516339 Lawes F J 385
501051 Lawes R J 233
522984 Lawes S L 358
507055 Lawford H R 122
500047 Lawless P 333
512331 Lawless P 232
514808 Lawn B A 397
522398 Lawrance C M 205
513170 Lawrance J M G 399
509534 Lawrance R H 252
471301 Lawrence A F 237
491011 Lawrence C J D 364
502450 Lawrence C R 141
492961 Lawrence C 232
453513 Lawrence D H 266
509997 Lawrence F E 272
521754 Lawrence F 254
518844 Lawrence G J 254
521656 Lawrence G J 252
463165 Lawrence G P 119
522115 Lawrence G R 395
499227 Lawrence G S 366
487532 Lawrence I G 258
523886 Lawrence I G 142
520825 Lawrence J A 360
517906 Lawrence J C 222
504765 Lawrence J E 367
512881 Lawrence K G 331
513582 Lawrence L S 311
420102 Lawrence P A 342
507476 Lawrence P J 297
510654 Lawrence R C 330
506787 Lawrence R N 327
487364 Lawrence S 253
477030 Lawrence W P 389
482770 Lawrence-Brown D D J 182
498614 Lawrenson G W 244
505022 Lawrie E 148
522167 Lawrie G M 315
511709 Lawrie I M 240
479282 Lawrie J W S 147
501214 Lawry B 261
518839 Laws B 397
487354 Laws I McO 354
Laws Dr J W 65
510906 Laws W A 186
514457 Lawson A G W 278
517290 Lawson A J 197
468388 Lawson B R 128
491614 Lawson C J 393
504946 Lawson D A L 122
491486 Lawson D J 138
489551 Lawson D N 238
496886 Lawson I D 116
494202 Lawson J L 286
495102 Lawson K G 272
512053 Lawson K 395
514351 Lawson M C 273
506640 Lawson M M 238
488460 Lawson M P 171
407943 Lawson N G P 340
494098 Lawson N L 353
501502 Lawson P J 109
485768 Lawson P 121
484895 Lawson R J 250
Lawson R M 25
393195 Lawson Sir Richard 91
515038 Lawson W 141
495440 Lawson-Cruttenden A T 299
501831 Lawson-Lee R G 327
523002 Lawson-Smith N 294
505292 Lawton C P 277
479283 Lawton K J A 104
457202 Lawton R A 250
520680 Lawton S P W 241
511509 Lay J B 260
511986 Lay J D 233
511866 Laybourne J E 208
506866 Laycock M J 186
513619 Laycock P A 325
489153 Layden P J 317
513434 Layhe R E 262
506437 Layton L 268
513388 Le Blanc D A J 125
452434 Le Blanc-Smith W A 104
496315 Le Brun C G 184
505682 Le Cheminant D J 239
516058 Le Fevre G R 277
494566 Le Gallais C L 138
518453 Le-Galloudec L B 208
490006 le Gassick W A 286
512635 Le Gresley E M 123
507477 Le Grys B J 130
485769 Le Hardy C A 110
443496 Le Maitre G H 161
469281 Le Mare J S 372
516402 Le Mare R E 372
465795 Le Masurier M C 75, 276
489649 Le Mesurier R T 243
503858 Le Moignan J 335
473998 Le Quesne J E 74, 257
505993 Le Sueur M R 254
515660 Le Tiec L N 262
489986 Le-Var M W 260
511043 Le-Var R W 252
514363 Lea A O 349
518501 Lea C 285
476430 Lea F H 135
511342 Lea N 337
437100 Lea R 171
490799 Lea T E 312
518461 Leach A J 247
501632 Leach G R 139
512782 Leach G W 272
508327 Leach M J 124
501503 Leach R C 104
498902 Leach T B 131
514814 Leach U I 346
522775 Leach V R 328
471960 Leach W H 243
495544 Leadbetter N A 258
524224 Leadbitter E G 388
509693 Leader D K 389
522811 Leader M J A 329
522241 Leader R C V 358
510342 Leadsom J H 188
506867 Leadsom S S 174
517056 Leaf G E J 112
491002 Leakey A D 116
Lean J B 28
455047 Leaning J M C 120
477402 Lear P M 267
512364 Lear R B 254
433171 Learmont J H 39, 92
508208 Learmont M 135
Leary J D 30
473996 Leask A de C L 147
503517 Leasor S N M 114
Leaver Sir Christopher 338
513692 Lebeter B M 286
512634 Lebeter J 240
496504 Lechmere J M C 313
509242 Leckey M A 330
458019 Leddy P P 242
500965 Ledger A W 106
465792 Ledger M E 30, 119
500966 Ledger S W 110
Ledlie J K 16
523051 Ledwards M V 142
478594 Lee B C A 293
522854 Lee B H 239
512211 Lee C A 308
478808 Lee C H W 274
426937 Lee C J 3, 36, 202
485914 Lee C J 308
513697 Lee C L 287
511042 Lee C N D 252
522135 Lee Chuen Bun 289
509281 Lee D B 353
503600 Lee D J 311
473296 Lee D W 274
512929 Lee E D 384
493953 Lee E 319
509063 Lee F R 142
516428 Lee G R 357
365210 Lee H K 329
520972 Lee H T 183
462657 Lee J B 237
463227 Lee J S 39, 271
491598 Lee J S 370
501633 Lee J T 122
491665 Lee J W 350
Lee J 13, 14
Lee Prof J 66
507330 Lee M C 284
440073 Lee M R 151
506868 Lee N J 240
397961 Lee P H 256
507865 Lee P 245
420874 Lee R G 29, 182
431505 Lee R M 380
520476 Lee R M 123
487533 Lee R T 326
481811 Lee S M A 137
518633 Lee S N 202
523481 Lee S S 393
510990 Lee S 350
522234 Lee S 360
522658 Lee S 285
494082 Lee T W R 266
Lee-Brown M S 404
500929 Lee-Cann I R 343
508558 Lee-Cann J A 357
509068 Lee-Wood R S 273
517291 Leece S R 252
485887 Leech A C 312
514526 Leech A K 397
521260 Leech A R 263
511267 Leech D 390
Leech J G 42
508356 Leeder J 339
499521 Leeder R L 261
509536 Leedham D A 259
508050 Leedham S C 328
518495 Leeming A S 216
504477 Leeming C F 122
499739 Leeming J M A 218
485915 Lees A J 266
494662 Lees A W 232
434899 Lees B M 29, 215

455048 Lees C A 28, 227
503190 Lees C J 300
464314 Lees L A 243
484896 Lees R J 206
500423 Lees T 339
499090 Lees-Jones D R 370
H10412 Leese S 374
469042 Leeson A H 237
506293 Leeson P J 344
496003 Lefeaux J M 311
459117 Lefever P S H 29, 119
465793 Lefroy N J 187
445247 Legg M D 171
412614 Legg P F 232
499987 Legg P H 366
488808 Legg R A E 158
521870 Leggat P M R 278
512826 Leggatt I R S 383
523087 Legge F V 358
Legge J M 14
499740 Legge K G 165
Legge M J 17
484587 Legrove M 280
515730 Lehmann C S T 191
508783 Leicester F G 350
510109 Leigh D L 300
505294 Leigh D M 220
509935 Leigh E L 124
465794 Leigh M R O 104
485770 Leigh P G 258
514263 Leigh P R 344
515622 Leigh P S 353
489195 Leigh R C 264
507478 Leigh S A 139
520843 Leigh W T 324
519523 Leigh-Howarth M 247
362190 Leigh-Pemberton R 299, 403
Leighs T G 3
493395 Leighton B V 315
517623 Leighton J 93
509537 Leighton P J 186
457201 Leighton R H 119
493429 Leighton R 267
499095 Leitch A 141
495635 Leitch R A 244
477358 Leith J D M 389
490474 Leith-Macgregor I M 283
487099 Leivers J H 395
Lekhanya T 50
522593 Lemay J J J 130
511581 Lemon J H 384
486059 Lemon J M 313
498174 Lemon J R 116
482197 Lemon M D 257
521036 Lemon M E S 398
498963 Lemon M J A S J 122
500217 Lemon R V 388
506155 Lemon W J 305
506869 Lenanton J P 313
503859 Lendrum R C D 95
503564 Lenihan T P 235
513101 Lennox A J 357
475679 Lennox R N 250
518536 Lennox-Warburton A C 316
469043 Lenton B P 237
502047 Lentz M J 253
499542 Leonard A J 318
456798 Leonard B A 398
496847 Leonard C N 318
443096 Leonard J N 187
516893 Leonard M D P 130
512352 Leonard R A 132
512720 Leonard R M 376
Leong Dr J C Y 66
520025 Lequelenec A C 248
500043 Lerpiniere L A W 319
455601 Lervy W K 274
489552 Lerwill A T D 215

476565 Lerwill M G 104
495195 Lesinski G F 143
450060 Leslie G J B 342
473617 Leslie J F 403
491488 Leslie J 232
497094 Leslie J 397
520086 Leslie K J 263
507318 Leslie P A 397
492015 Leslie R B 326
Lessard G H 41
519934 Lessing-Turner G H S 285
518734 Lester C 287
521767 Lester H R 391
482899 Lester R M S 128
459287 Letchworth R C 119
494150 Letford P A 337
519967 Letori G A 141
521081 Lettin G D 183
487143 Lettington E D 274
200120 Leuchars P R 83
516859 Leung Hing Chuen 289
496015 Levack I D 343
490391 Levack W D M 277
Leven & Melville Rt Hon The Earl of 401
517292 Levene G A 255
Levene P K 13, 17
504183 Lever A 282
Lever D E 61
503407 Lever J V 392
510879 Lever J 282
Leverhulme Rt Hon The Visct 402
519111 Levett-Scrivener M J 131
509538 Levey S R 110
512636 Levine J L J 144
512009 Leviseur N T 313
516098 Lewcock G D 391
500610 Lewer A H J 278
501863 Lewer J A 314
520457 Lewin I 346
480741 Lewin J H 119
483957 Lewin R A 128
500691 Lewing A C 268
495545 Lewington M H 251
463091 Lewins M J 272
Lewis Sir Andrew 400
517837 Lewis A J 239
506649 Lewis B C M 151
489061 Lewis B P 328
455637 Lewis B R 342
508498 Lewis C J M 287
496317 Lewis C J 259
514584 Lewis C M R 142
498795 Lewis D A 304
507286 Lewis D A 393
473190 Lewis D B 347
512714 Lewis D J M 346
457205 Lewis D L 115
459793 Lewis D L 382
449703 Lewis D R P 151
491666 Lewis D W 307
503124 Lewis D 130
446182 Lewis E A 236
516708 Lewis E D 386
505505 Lewis E L 391
522962 Lewis E V 358
516009 Lewis H V 241
494771 Lewis J C 371
510343 Lewis J D 130
480352 Lewis J E C 237
515331 Lewis J W 241
502956 Lewis J 278
Lewis K J 44
505424 Lewis M B L 356
483959 Lewis M H L 200
495546 Lewis N A E 116
498216 Lewis N D 322
504089 Lewis N J 346

484897 Lewis N P C 215
519911 Lewis N R 273
479442 Lewis O M 137
512333 Lewis P E 373
494876 Lewis P J 272
503519 Lewis P J 297
511867 Lewis P M 191
522399 Lewis P R 252
447340 Lewis The Hon P H 108
501879 Lewis P 123
505695 Lewis R D 282
519690 Lewis R G 134
491489 Lewis R N A 227
497725 Lewis R P 396
501634 Lewis R T A 238
514920 Lewis R 221
418316 Lewis S D B 115
513907 Lewis S P P 203
523682 Lewis S P 358
491164 Lewis S R 129
522296 Lewis S 358
485771 Lewis T A J 225
511044 Lewis T G D 164
491490 Lewis T K 220
Lewis Mr T L T 65
507481 Lewis T P 106
502998 Lewis-Cooper C 272
497630 Lewis-Taylor C D 286
514421 Lewis-Taylor G M 142
472782 Lewthwaite C J 64, 242
494170 Lewthwaite D W 121
470434 Ley A J 387
515332 Ley C I 93
515333 Leyden L E 123
505994 Leyland G R 139
500374 Leyland P J L 182
509127 Li J H S 345
519848 Li Nai Chung 289
511045 Libbey R W 239
426939 Licence B E 127
504651 Lidbetter R S J 305
514218 Liddell D 254
518406 Liddell J C R 345
517497 Liddell R A 309
515163 Liddell-Grainger I R P 319
504478 Liddicoat M R H 122
484258 Lidster W G 137
489336 Lidstone I R 140
490699 Liggat R 284
502891 Light J V 380
514585 Light T D 182
506986 Lightbody R K 359
507482 Lightfoot A D 116
501207 Lightfoot C N 141
507483 Lightfoot P L 130
523764 Lightfoot S T 358
494389 Lightwood K S 389
513800 Lilbahadur Gurung 229
507154 Lile G 141
501635 Liles I R 174
419003 Lill J A 324
509443 Lill T R 253
501303 Lilley C H 253
507940 Lilley D A 359
483960 Lilley G D 237
477999 Lilley J M 338
501636 Lilley M R 238
496522 Lilleyman P 128
511354 Lillicrap D T 387
467591 Lillies J C 327
516616 Lillingston-Price M M 225
494623 Lillington R E F 254
510174 Lillystone D F 254
515158 Lillystone D J 399
502541 Lillywhite B 279
486287 Lillywhite L P 243
509185 Limb D M 221
504228 Limb R M 141

512930 Lynch N 384
490213 Lynch P M 121
483306 Lynch P 243
521763 Lynch P 392
488282 Lynch T J 318
429562 Lynch T 398
502455 Lynch-Staunton C H C 215
507692 Lyne A R B 273
498381 Lyne A 245
501052 Lyne-Pirkis C J A 122
519118 Lynett A M 337
492029 Lyng A S 331
487185 Lyng S K D 385
462088 Lynham R G 349
516834 Lynn A F 332
508718 Lynn A 141
503261 Lynn C 245
310149 Lynn G 337
460368 Lynott M B 283
498231 Lyon A J 244
463581 Lyon A R 257
495196 Lyon D G 121
488991 Lyon Dean C W 243
506462 Lyon G T 339
288788 Lyon R 81, 118
504812 Lyon S R 116
480793 Lyons A W 250
523526 Lyons A W 248
504170 Lyons D C 382
512892 Lyons D 398
500055 Lyons E J 135
511357 Lyons P L 279
470105 Lyons T M 120
502456 Lys G D 224
521811 Lythgoe W J 314
467594 Lytle S W St J 232
520746 Lyttle W D J 326

M

449007 Mabbett E W 73, 256
508942 Mabin D C 246
503204 Mabon A 372
494316 Macadam J F 235
519543 Macadie J J 355
498749 MacAllister A R 268
518317 Macallister N J 124
519385 MacAlpine-Downie C R 334
506608 Macandrews T J J 308
508949 Macaree T 279
479528 MacArthur C A 350
514809 Macarthur D M 391
495365 MacArthur I W 238
471646 MacArthur R I M 128
487535 Macartney T M 237
498397 Macaskill I A M 343
498401 Macaskill J 396
508212 Macaulay D G 139
481817 Macaulay N P H 120
505453 Macbean M 396
422398 Macbeth A C 237
517990 MacBeth C J 284
451283 MacCallum J A 163
515245 Maccariello E J G 318
519562 Maccariello M A 364
484999 MacCarthy-Morrogh J T D 187
455053 MacColl D J S 249
484591 MacCulloch P H 141
512638 Macdonald A A H 164
509542 Macdonald A A S 161
479539 Macdonald A G 338
487536 Macdonald A J L 180
500969 Macdonald A R 208
514847 MacDonald A S 357
488740 Macdonald C 385
517445 MacDonald D A 269
449341 MacDonald E J 75, 280
518057 Macdonald Evans V J 268
485775 Macdonald G 128
495366 Macdonald H L A 100
Macdonald Dr H R F 83
513912 Macdonald H S 134
523007 Macdonald I D 333
513267 Macdonald I L 334
499744 MacDonald I R 259
506872 MacDonald I R 122
519333 Macdonald I 104
523942 Macdonald J C 268
457210 Macdonald J D 236
499745 Macdonald J F 176
516524 MacDonald J W 337
513793 Macdonald J 141
MacDonald K C 17
510969 Macdonald M A 164
518037 MacDonald M I 287
502093 MacDonald M M 283
517134 Macdonald M 315
522650 Macdonald M 396
420887 Macdonald Milner D C 151
513723 Macdonald Milner T C 151
521659 Macdonald R I 117
491668 Macdonald R J M 243
469050 MacDonald R O 257
485776 Macdonald R 128
522467 Macdonald S A F 285
519164 MacDonald W G L 347
496108 Macdonald W J 123
486336 MacDonald W R 109
MacDonald W W 65
521488 Macdonald-Holland J 285

488624 MacDougall D J 349
481282 MacDougall G D 250
518635 Macdowell C N 209
495550 Macduff-Duncan S C 162
Mace J A 44
498723 Mace T K C 233
510636 MacEachen W R J 275
523133 Macewan A C B 149
498818 MacEwan L N A 253
508213 Macey P J 174
485591 Macey S D 36
502229 MacFarlane A E 305
517223 MacFarlane A 351
485208 Macfarlane D S 237
MacFarlane G 41
479481 Macfarlane G C 280
510674 Macfarlane G L 373
488603 Macfarlane G R 308
502902 Macfarlane I C 238
426942 Macfarlane I P 120
492963 Macfarlane J A 138
499746 Macfarlane J H 206
474813 MacFarlane J M 69, 271
520963 Macfarlane J Mc C 148
520373 Macfarlane N 117
489087 Macfarlane P T 235
486959 Macfarlane S F 354
507282 MacFarlane S M 135
513667 MacGillivray A C W 313
514838 MacGillivray M R 166
515338 Macgillivray R A B 159
511510 MacGinnis G R W 130
508868 MacGregor of MacGregor M G C 148
517719 MacGregor R C A 309
421593 Macgregor-Oakford R B 34, 214, 215
493746 Macgregor-Smith D N 166
433184 MacHeath R A 312
521660 Machin A J 131
478968 Machin J 283
437111 Machin L G 322
506403 Machin R E 328
514327 Machindrabahadur Rai 227
523134 Maciejewski J C W 218
522139 Macilwaine J H 360
Macinnes I G A 43
488926 MacIntosh E 271
477982 MacIntosh K C 342
487791 Macintosh V 356
505522 Macintyre A K 317
516767 Macintyre B H 241
406352 MacIntyre D J 312
480773 MacIntyre P D 154
516105 Maciver A 389
511973 Maciver D K 244
514174 Mack J F 384
495198 Mackain-Bremner C M F 215
501642 Mackain-Bremner J N D 104
502457 Mackaness J R St D 108
513345 Mackay A D 159
479415 Mackay A I 271
495055 Mackay A S 316
483087 Mackay B G 243
523249 Mackay C A 358
490360 Mackay D G 220
487405 Mackay D J 334
520682 Mackay D J 125
499102 MacKay D M 253
517293 Mackay E A C R 260
500377 Mackay H E 220
491807 Mackay H 337
440088 Mackay I 3, 156
497304 Mackay J P 384
465956 Mackay J W 310

518375 McKee J H 359
509316 McKee J K 313
508009 McKeegan R D 252
494809 McKeen R 315
498362 McKeever W B 339
489152 McKelvey R S J H 336
503056 McKen G 316
518280 McKend I G 239
522408 McKendrick E A 157
506512 McKendry P 389
509363 McKenna D N 399
506313 McKenna K G 309
505080 McKenna M F 337
510352 McKenna P A 259
517618 McKenna P G 273
487044 McKenna R G 124
495311 McKenzie J H 393
524082 McKenzie T P 394
494180 McKenzie Johnston R A 114
500328 McKeown D F 313
480880 McKeown J H 127
520815 McKeown R A M 364
476574 McKeown R D 120
492016 McKeown W J 326
507099 McKerlie A 398
512713 McKibbin A 357
515640 McKibbin R 305
516439 McKie B J 93
518933 McKie W H 167
518231 McKillop J A 326
492967 McKinlay M J 138
480360 McKinley S D G 218
522677 McKinnel N H P 336
511333 McKinnell J 271
504484 McKinnell R W 161
514213 McKinney H J 368
522099 McKinney W J 371
516217 McKinnon A J 346
451285 McKinnon I A 250
517139 McKinnon J S 346
517007 McKirdy C A 394
487543 McKitrick R A S S 121
500735 McKnight W 245
509936 McLachlan I H 123
519956 McLachlan W K 233
485210 McLaren D E G 121
472931 McLaren E H 342
440086 McLaren R M 163
519319 McLaren R W 140
513187 McLaren S D 391
466250 McLatchie G 389
469052 McLaughlan I W 147
493871 McLaughlin E 124
494479 McLay D 312
503197 McLay H D 384
483970 McLean A A J 128
522723 McLean A J 309
McLean D B G 44
479291 McLean D J 137
488634 McLean G G 355
504485 McLean G W 146
521669 McLean H D A 216
487136 McLean I S 304
517094 McLean J 334
516084 McLean M 344
430373 McLean R D W 210
489198 McLean R W K 158
478477 McLean S C 393
502465 McLean S C 264
McLean Dr T P 77
516883 McLean V F P 149
521983 McLellan J H 346
483971 McLelland P D 171
477998 McLeman L 307
515807 McLennan I D 346
489918 McLennan J R 128
515261 McLennan R M 340
522856 McLeod A B 241
518389 McLeod A R 154
516018 McLeod C G A 172
471305 McLeod D N K 120
519827 McLeod G 317
474861 McLeod H N G 332
469053 McLeod I 220
516458 McLeod L 358
523026 McLeod R J 148
517688 McLernon W B 332
516340 McLoone A Y S 385
512967 McLoughlin F C 141
510946 McLoughlin J 357
516541 McLoughlin P J 141
523822 McLoughlin T J 141
498610 McLucas W J 107
481824 McLuckie D S 138
486001 McMahon A A 397
496968 McMahon B O 287
522885 McMahon C D 383
516317 McMahon E G 322
483972 McMahon J B J 258
511151 McMahon J P 141
476733 McMahon K 271
498799 McMahon M D 313
508481 McMahon M J 273
510353 McMahon M J 239
500285 McMahon P 238
513175 McMahon S A 318
519334 McMahon T 103
483973 McMahon W A 232
490762 McMahon W D J 308
516325 McMahon W J 379
483974 McManamon D G 258
495368 McManners J H 121
510176 McManners P J 130
480853 McManus A G 390
443503 McManus D L 257
476968 McManus M J 271
491226 McManus R 386
520248 McMeechan D G 155
496047 McMeeken G D 327
504172 McMeekin D C 155
467595 McMeekin G B 60, 232
519285 McMeekin J 125
477148 McMenemey J D S 378
522457 McMenigall A S 157
512106 McMillan B P A 124
464291 McMillan C R 243
513222 McMillan C S 346
506574 McMillan D W 389
522542 McMillan D W 365
516901 McMillan E J 284
478753 McMillan I 338
505070 McMillan J M 245
510649 McMillan S R 328
472577 McMillen C P 266
522746 McMillen P T J 391
498550 McMillen P 356
516895 McMinn T A W 240
507356 McMorran A 383
501451 McMorris W C 313
503329 McMullen A B 141
478599 McMullen J J 277
516180 McMullen T M 278
480172 McMullin J A 337
071814 McMurdo A W 311
508872 McMurdo D J 259
McMurray D B 81
481519 McMurry L D 383
418328 McMurtrie D H 62, 215
519697 McMurtrie T D 215
483975 McNab I D 258
481952 McNab J G 350
512381 McNair D R 326
488602 McNair I J 307
516310 McNair R W L 240
517033 McNally B F 346
507752 McNally J W 161
489563 McNally N J 251
470484 McNamara D 393
496321 McNamara G M 129
518249 McNamara J A 318
470880 McNaught L W 119
479464 McNaught P J 276
489154 McNaught R M G 312
522992 McNaughton A D 350
McNaughton D M 41
458464 McNaughton J 235
481069 McNaughton P 321
522884 McNee A M K 383
475197 McNee A S 120
522101 McNeice A R 394
510431 McNeice F M 357
484912 McNeil A 222
502466 McNeil C P 328
522184 McNeil D R 317
489564 McNeil I H 145
523132 McNeil I N 260
377668 McNeil J D 390
507826 McNeil J 393
516019 McNeilis A J 192
506001 McNeill G J 139
521391 McNeill M L 358
486553 McNeill R J F 317
505305 McNeill W I 267
493574 McNeilly B J 245
519282 McNeish S G 279
524462 McNichol P 395
495990 McNicoll I D G 321
502903 McNinch H H 259
519176 McNulty A 390
509551 McNulty P J 276
513657 McPartlan C W 357
456729 McPartlin J J 379
515214 McPeake G W C 340
511794 McPeake J J 246
522632 McPhee M J 255
496322 McPherson A M 259
515007 McPherson I 124
507942 McPherson J S 64, 244
412272 McPherson N F W 337
519524 McPherson R J E 247
483807 McQueen P D P 232
513158 McQuilton K C 262
501729 McQuoid J A 384
440087 McQuoid R F P 119
497779 McRae J R 316
510881 McRae K R 141
497664 McRobbie I W B 338
475198 McSheehy E P V 202
509071 McSherry I R 188
509937 McSherry T E 123
520076 McSweeney D J 345
489919 McSwiney B A 102
508519 McVeigh A D J 141
520008 McVeigh J E 358
518026 McVicar I H 354
488559 McVicker W B J 304
509350 McVitie A 221
483976 McVittie M R 166
505871 McWhinnie L P 356
498604 McWilliams V F 272
521584 Meaby D A 391
510355 Meacher G J 135
502788 Meachin B A 141
477201 Mead D A 338
500131 Mead D J 235
499991 Mead G J 261
468564 Mead P J 391
518638 Mead W 255
439635 Meaden E A A 283
437117 Meadmore J R C 266
506058 Meadow M W 390
522771 Meadowcroft M J 391
486224 Meadows C 394
489064 Meads J A 330
521525 Meads R G 320
490716 Meager P 235
469057 Meagher A G P 257
507137 Meakin G E 395
477435 Meakin G 137

N

O

P

515537 Pickard P W 350
520874 Pickard R C 285
476303 Pickard R L W 274
522053 Pickard S M 390
522197 Picken A K 340
478044 Pickering D J 379
518758 Pickering F 391
511329 Pickering J 308
520569 Pickering K 279
521967 Pickersgill J 319
499581 Pickersgill T 325
489579 Pickford A J 258
504051 Pickford R 239
509090 Pickles C P 359
487565 Pickles C S 128
508097 Pickles D M 305
514955 Pickles K M 273
495804 Pickles R 307
511449 Pickles S 132
523139 Picknell A D J 140
501934 Pickup B 334
471329 Pickup C J 232
451310 Pickup E 137
513183 Pickup G 240
510760 Pickup M E C 328
502628 Pickworth D G 261
433213 Picton I R 120
466055 Pidcock F 335
506919 Pidgeon G J 149
514313 Pidgeon N R 216
475926 Pierce-Jones M 397
516075 Piercy-Buck F S F 392
507687 Piers M G E 287
504963 Pierson H T K 107
518945 Piggins J D 188
H10480 Piggott S 373
Pighills C D 81
477816 Pigott A D 127
433672 Pike C J 227
520581 Pike G F 285
504826 Pike G W D 318
472599 Pike H W R 59, 220
512963 Pike J J 264
461487 Pike M A 250
492189 Pike M F E 347
509366 Pike P R W 395
410744 Pike R C 388
440132 Pike W R W 176
516114 Pilcher R L 275
508453 Pilcher R 274
486725 Pilkington A J 128
517218 Pilkington M T A 318
507786 Pillar K J 235
495691 Pillar R C 394
Pillar Sir William 38
484734 Pillay J N A 283
496772 Pilleau M D 107
487924 Pilley D V 229, 272
517446 Pilling A M 269
488747 Pimble P V 283
497201 Pinchen G J 327
488301 Pincher S 253
505332 Pincott M E 139
484930 Pinder D N 184
484340 Pinder G A 124
485631 Pinder K 262
Pindling The Rt Hon Sir Lynden 51
517386 Pine J N 117
488213 Pinel J A 129
426215 Pinhey J L G 376
454145 Pinion A J 119
489117 Pinkerton J W D 312
476790 Pinner R T 376
511512 Pinney G R 114
451713 Pinnock A G 389
515652 Piper B R 309
446297 Piper G E 276
505382 Piper J W 313
510586 Piper M E 246
496853 Piper P G 121
514732 Piper R A 130
512254 Piper T L 262
513682 Pippen B I B 300
Pirie Sir Gordon 80
515498 Pirie G H 395
Pirie J W G 400
514901 Pirthibahadur Gurung 229
520170 Piskorowskyj A 285
484643 Pitcher G E T 350
508334 Pitcher T S 245
494955 Pitchers A J 191
502924 Pitchforth E R 254
510721 Pitman G D 207
470277 Pitt A W H 300
505569 Pitt B J G 284
503559 Pitt J D 376
460177 Pitt J K 22, 70, 236
476014 Pitt J R M 120
504695 Pitt J 339
520221 Pitt P A 285
462252 Pitt P C C 342
509047 Pittaway P 260
488214 Pittendreigh D W 272
519712 Pittman A J 101
Pitts A P 24
492709 Plant I M 128
504122 Planterose R M 298
376103 Plaskett F J 82, 236
507516 Plastow J I S 218
474035 Platt A G 257
482437 Platt H S 4, 341
483064 Platt J R 135
512214 Platt N B 334
505117 Platt P J 330
479324 Platt R D 258
497293 Platt W H 261
508228 Platts A C 130
515554 Platts B W 344
511677 Platts G 140
516414 Platts K E 287
503046 Platts T 322
455556 Playfair H G L 368
490547 Pleasants D J 238
519570 Plenderleith R 133
519976 Plews R L 309
440133 Plommer G L 128
520983 Plowman J M 285
423092 Plowman J R 371
513515 Plowman S J F 318
493772 Plowright C J 238
495646 Plowright N R 238
520063 Plumb J 263
504804 Plumb L J 139
489581 Plummer B P 200
503898 Plummer C J 122
262914 Plummer L H 118
520147 Plummer P M 263
493469 Pockley T G 371
468845 Pocklington M 304
451311 Pocock J I 100
513930 Pocock M C 125
492239 Pocock M D A 296
493145 Pocock M J 384
499920 Pocock P A 245
519496 Pocock R E 349
474036 Podevin D C 137
488090 Podmore A J 324
511569 Poe A D 333
465820 Poett S E N H 215
516470 Poffley M A 262
521134 Poffley M W 255
507184 Pointet D A J 122
520233 Pointing W J 216
481405 Pointon J 395
507805 Pointon T 345
509567 Polden A J 122
520506 Polglase A P 300
507517 Polin J C 116
Polkey Mr C E 66
494694 Poll D C 349
493626 Pollak T E 334
446685 Pollard A J G 59, 176
481381 Pollard A W 250
377902 Pollard C B 126
519354 Pollard G A 310
508885 Pollard J C D G 176
515558 Pollard P J 390
492164 Pollard R 377
509321 Polley N G T 111
512385 Polley P 387
505764 Polley R D S 112
521263 Pollin R S 263
518731 Pollington D L 287
476615 Pollock C D C 266
497489 Pollock D J M 235
497490 Pollock J H O'H 149
507777 Pollock J 279
494181 Pollock The Hon R C S 299
507025 Pollock T 337
468205 Pollock W G 266
487930 Pomeroy M J 337
522417 Pomroy G A 239
480377 Ponikowski M A 237
Ponnamperuma M T W 46
Ponsonby Sir Ashley 400
522163 Ponsonby N L 317
501411 Ponsonby R C 300
518534 Ponsonby W J C 364
232590 Pontifex D M 405
505333 Ponting K T 240
497861 Ponting R A 267
476616 Pook R J 196
505334 Pool M G 268
487758 Pool N W 338
522032 Pool R C A 142
495966 Poole A 235
514464 Poole B 262
523042 Poole C A 252
509830 Poole D J T 142
507980 Poole D N J 339
500432 Poole J R 366
521871 Poole M A 278
495451 Poole P A H 129
Poole P M 402
485806 Poole P M 238
474740 Poole S J 274
486795 Poole-Warren J A 218
517476 Poolewood J M 387
516190 Pooley C A 285
519713 Pooley J D 108
514386 Poots I 372
493078 Pope A C 129
504403 Pope A J 344
507518 Pope C M 130
488564 Pope D M 378
Pope Dr G G 77
459309 Pope J J B 340
516637 Pope K A 159
509700 Pope K M 387
518175 Pope M C 255
494453 Pope M D M 121
513735 Pope N A W 139
502966 Pope N S 238
522418 Pope N 134
437567 Pope R J 293
499516 Pope S M 355
498284 Pope T F 244
362368 Popham C J 126
504716 Pople K R 232
514617 Pople P V 140
519220 Popp E S M 106
489283 Poppleton A J 138
491182 Poraj-Wilczynski J J P 220
511479 Porat A P 350
Porritt Lord 65

506573 Porritt A J 141
432072 Porteous W R 304
519954 Porter A J 124
520135 Porter A M 387
513638 Porter A W 397
440134 Porter B D 73, 256
440135 Porter D J 249
511408 Porter D L 287
491515 Porter J K R 174
519009 Porter K C 134
486726 Porter N S 184
437141 Porter R J M 120
510368 Porter R J M 200
495678 Porter S E 305
507599 Porter S L 176
518946 Porter S S 255
522735 Porter S W 285
471653 Porter T L M 200
445946 Porter-Wright J 220
512777 Portlock M J 387
484931 Portman M B 112
461227 Portman S H 250
503196 Portwood M A 389
508995 Posnett A 313
489582 Postance A J 251
492308 Postgate K G 258
500210 Postill J P S 324
520009 Postlethwaite W T 346
484004 Potter A C L 184
453542 Potter A J 257
491516 Potter A M F 188
493344 Potter B J 325
465337 Potter B 237
508886 Potter C M 125
516792 Potter D 324
498185 Potter G R A 105
522927 Potter G S 378
503900 Potter J A H 122
501459 Potter J D 305
486727 Potter J L 296
503145 Potter J P F 122
512818 Potter J R 355
509149 Potter J 156
517221 Potter K G 218
502183 Potter M N 375
487566 Potter R N 147
515679 Potter S J 313
490217 Potter S M J 106
511995 Potter W R 326
512776 Pottle B C 358
460421 Potton A E 338
519574 Potts C W 174
467614 Potts D H 120
501678 Potts D R 122
511288 Potts G A 235
520317 Potts G A 288
486951 Potts I M 379
511513 Potts J N 130
514619 Potts K M 165
505336 Potts M F 350
488254 Potts R E 274
383559 Potts R W 386
477480 Potts R W 274
523792 Potts S J 358
516904 Potts S W 319
493773 Poucher M S 190
513469 Poulten C M 284
518947 Poulter P A 125
520582 Poulton E H 285
516107 Poulton J S 393
511798 Pounder R 247
500845 Pountain M N 122
514097 Pountney A H 369
516494 Pover D B 385
512283 Pover J 262
503321 Povey A 353
492843 Pow R A 338
506017 Powe J J 116
484005 Powell A J W 109
491721 Powell A R 258
517313 Powell A T 260
519260 Powell A 177
521297 Powell C C 340
445947 Powell C K 136
516443 Powell C R 262
522125 Powell D J 306
521281 Powell D S 365
507519 Powell D W 139
515811 Powell D 262
482809 Powell E M 58, 137
489844 Powell F T 393
494455 Powell G L 264
500615 Powell G 141
500584 Powell J L 261
499215 Powell J M N 202
495864 Powell J M 356
510369 Powell J N 203
513932 Powell J R J 172
481842 Powell J S W 186
508533 Powell J W 357
515890 Powell J 124
486281 Powell M G 267
494367 Powell M J 262
523095 Powell M J 263
523778 Powell P S 394
469188 Powell R F 151
474409 Powell R J 250
433573 Powell S B 120
499142 Powell T B D'E 272
485807 Powell T S 276
397742 Powell W 364
465821 Powell-Jones E D 225
520423 Power A C 386
490591 Power A J 275
510564 Power C 273
478401 Power D J 342
516205 Power D M 396
490748 Power J C 334
472600 Power J F B 266
522419 Power J 260
504260 Power R A 246
493560 Power T M T 176
465055 Powers N 342
521267 Powers N 263
500695 Powis D C 388
520211 Powis J 358
523453 Powles B 221
403654 Pownall J L 113
497595 Pownall-Gray H D 297
464344 Powney R T 228, 272
494456 Powrie C P T 244
486728 Powrie I G C 121
501679 Powrie R A D 166
507520 Powrie R D G 124
497859 Poynter D G 220
518176 Poynter N G 131
497596 Poyntz C H N 202
499109 Poyntz J D P 239
519388 Poyzer J L 357
515138 Poznansky J B 275
524232 Prabin Gurung 223
498186 Prain J F 129
499331 Pratapsing Limbu 225
521067 Pratchek N D S 276
522543 Pratelli N J 365
506769 Prati C G A 316
513765 Pratley M S 287
503901 Pratley P A 139
451313 Pratt A D 27, 119
489082 Pratt B D 235
519965 Pratt B J 116
515782 Pratt D M 139, 229
497161 Pratt G W 394
519714 Pratt J C R 150
517604 Pratt J C 146
427339 Pratt R W 250
519804 Pratt S J 285
512231 Pratt S 286
499144 Pratt W G E 394
491517 Pratten J N 171
522609 Preece J M R 275
479977 Preece M D G 121
500208 Preece M L 319
516512 Preece R M H 260
474332 Preece R 257
499798 Preedy R E 121
498542 Prees J V 140
472601 Preiss W J 127
522972 Prem Rai 226
Premadasa R 46
519251 Prembahadur Gurung 223
522035 Premser Lama 224
470132 Prendergast J H V 115
472602 Prendergast N H D 128
488202 Prentice K H N 121
518046 Prentice M V G 227
510646 Prentice P C 316
474037 Prentis P M 232
511628 Prescott D W 174
496372 Prescott J B C 176
521684 Presland M W 152
522584 Presland P J 233
519096 Preston A D 260
414095 Preston A W 366
469080 Preston B D S 119
516099 Preston C M M 397
497627 Preston D A 375
475217 Preston G E 115
514621 Preston J C 191
514258 Preston J 354
501680 Preston K N 238
508768 Preston L 207
505137 Preston M D 273
521828 Preston M H 345
443540 Preston R St C 214, 215
482022 Preston R T 271
518177 Preston S D 192
514259 Preston S 275
488823 Prestwich C T S 112
437302 Prestwood J 308
506704 Pretious D P 391
499005 Pretsell I A 274
496110 Prewer A L R 123
487851 Prewer E R 135
500685 Prewitt R 392
499557 Price A C R 308
503205 Price A H 235
509322 Price A N 225
476619 Price A R 108
520875 Price B A 246
498188 Price B S 238
512111 Price B S 364
483815 Price C E 165
481258 Price C K 104
514951 Price C P 282
502700 Price D A 328
510663 Price D E 254
524465 Price D G 395
433530 Price E C V 342
475599 Price F W 326, 389
Price G A 23
517628 Price G C 124
502908 Price G J F 129
517526 Price H E 345
513199 Price I W 239
493300 Price J A J 333
513933 Price J C E 233
453946 Price J L 342
515096 Price J L 369
455080 Price J N 28, 120
455081 Price J R 120
504127 Price J R 235
511238 Price J R 340
Price J S B 15
485808 Price K A 121
519424 Price M C J 396
504543 Price M G 397
472603 Price M W T 301
512187 Price N J 130
506100 Price R C 317

Q

R

450317 Russell M C J 283
505344 Russell M H F 238
514365 Russell M J 391
516791 Russell M J 270
499034 Russell M S 277
482203 Russell M 283
483545 Russell N F 171
511241 Russell P A 122
522142 Russell P D 365
469844 Russell P F 198
512379 Russell P M 272
514826 Russell P M 358
494780 Russell P R 267
492355 Russell P S 220
503917 Russell R G 188
502910 Russell R P 208
522126 Russell R T 309
504500 Russell S J 264
485946 Russell W H 115
522994 Russell-Floyd R S 351
485821 Russell-Jones P J 128
517912 Russell-Parsons D J C 144
499981 Russell-Roberts E M 397
500297 Rust D J 267
488482 Rust M J 238
506730 Rust R C 381
521492 Rust T J 351
506348 Ruszala D S J 379
496062 Rutherford A C 188
521235 Rutherford C 285
520782 Rutherford D F 268
489594 Rutherford D M 267
513427 Rutherford I C 346
495760 Rutherford J 355
452743 Rutherford P L 283
522633 Rutherford P M 235
485822 Rutherford R F 138
468476 Rutherford W G 353
504501 Rutherford-Jones D J 112
485938 Rutherford-Young N R 317

490720 Rutledge A A 356
495453 Rutledge M J 108
523067 Rutter D J 134
518593 Rutter G E 370
504502 Rutter J W 232
482823 Rutter-Jerome M S 119
510089 Rutterford B D 116
518650 Ruxton S J 134
470454 Ryall M R 235
516235 Ryall R P 369
500600 Ryan A 339
469474 Ryan D C 327
411796 Ryan D E 21, 92
520706 Ryan D F 125
523629 Ryan E A 358
498355 Ryan I 326
484496 Ryan J M 243
511403 Ryan J M 284
522793 Ryan J M 270
511987 Ryan J N 233
487574 Ryan K M 176
501280 Ryan M J 391
506494 Ryan M J 339
507987 Ryan M J 345
458830 Ryan P F 349
523683 Ryan P G 345
509217 Ryan R K 333
443552 Rycroft D G F 127
512847 Ryde T C K 281
509013 Ryder A 395
497502 Ryder D J 267
510827 Ryder D 287
523916 Ryder D 254
518372 Ryder E N 302
461493 Ryding K 58, 137
518232 Rye P R 287
497181 Rylance R C 268
Rylands G C 402
501320 Rylands H J J 305
504971 Rylands J M C 211
511286 Ryles J A 278
463025 Rymer D J T 336
497503 Rynn N J 186

S

495405 Sabine R M 381
510378 Saddleton P R 252
522803 Sadkowski D 263
522572 Sadler J F 306
515064 Sadler J W 240
522509 Sadler P J 247
519758 Sadler R S 246
513430 Sadler S N S 305
440505 Sadlier R F 383
524226 Saeed A 348
426997 Safford G C 31, 118
520816 Sagan C Z 364
522979 Sage B G 318
507167 Sage J W 133
478804 Sage R J 311, 400
514949 Saggar S N 244
520534 Sahi S P 246
453727 Sainsbury J D 304
521691 Saker I R M 110
506962 Saksena V K 343
507762 Sale G 385
507859 Sale M J 375
484939 Sale R A 215
507534 Sale R P A 151
481861 Sales J B 271
521747 Sales R W 133
517317 Salisbury C S 260
498192 Salisbury N J N 166
443097 Salisbury N S 343
442410 Salisbury P A 119
447367 Sallitt T W B 311
520396 Sallitt W T B 134
515190 Salloway P C 305
510497 Salmon A J 309
509903 Salmon D A 368
509922 Salmon F 276
486736 Salmon J A B 171
507813 Salmon J A 287
509396 Salmon J B 246
403675 Salmon N H 313
513612 Salmon P F E 293
455391 Salmon R E A 334
475741 Salmon R W 348
518952 Salmons A N E 254
499998 Salt A 381
Salter A 29
477041 Salter A J D 318
500122 Salter A T J 336
522028 Salter R C 365
437161 Salusbury-Trelawny J W 145
516642 Salvoni R C P 142
523044 Salwey R P 219
505416 Samaratunga K A 343
483546 Sambell E H 137
Sami Khan 87
504842 Samler C H 105
500863 Samphier M 268
498088 Sample C J 301
489595 Sample M W 112
486876 Sampson A J 367
522045 Sampson K J 383
493562 Sampson R C B 93
445962 Sampson R K 119
512010 Sampson W S 313
495286 Samson P J 286
502709 Samuel P D 344
493427 Samuel R R 336
Samuelson P H 83
516116 San M G 275
461494 Sandars H M 106
Sanday J N 51
501057 Sandbach C P L 104
511463 Sanders A J 359
523485 Sanders D G 285
494592 Sanders D J 338

487588 Stewart R A 198
499880 Stewart R C 129
450258 Stewart R F 27, 236
Stewart R I 86
477841 Stewart R J M 120
503935 Stewart R J N 130
490935 Stewart R L 267
410998 Stewart R M 312, 403
522440 Stewart S A 134
483553 Stewart S M P 100
518544 Stewart T L 263
495001 Stewart T 339
519215 Stewart T 286
483095 Stewart W T A 337
517334 Stewart W 132
335387 Stewart-Cox A G E 118, 304
467590 Stewart-Liddon R J 364
502316 Stewart-Smith G 267
521915 Stewart-Wilson A J O 219
403692 Stewart Wilson B A 3
503536 Stibbe G G E 93
437174 Stibbon J J 16, 92, 266, 276
519731 Stichbury J D 165
501261 Stickings P T 384
506579 Stien E V 389
523255 Stiles H C 314
493357 Stiling G W 353
455626 Still N M 34, 114
521574 Stimpson J M 376
521843 Stimpson R F 133
521268 Stinchcombe D J 263
485839 Stirk W J Q 232
517049 Stirling H A C 334
490560 Stirling J B 171
410797 Stirling J 401
500507 Stirling R W 244
495587 Stirling T 238
519218 Stirling W 317
517322 Stisted C D 148
489606 Stiven N S 121
523142 Stobie A M M 154
469461 Stobie D M M 250
502040 Stobo A J 313
505727 Stock C B W 122
478875 Stock D G 243
485415 Stock D V 392
508464 Stock G 276
446813 Stockbridge A C 235
480830 Stockdale D R 338
497525 Stockdale M R G 139
514649 Stockdale P T 240
498042 Stockdale W J 298
503373 Stocker A J 385
519846 Stocker A J 285
507771 Stocker B G 302
465839 Stocker S R A 202
505140 Stockill J A 272
496640 Stockley A E 270
467456 Stockley J D 391
509074 Stockley P J 233
511659 Stockport S M 284
468070 Stocks A G H 318
522317 Stocks J R 360
516828 Stocks R D 230, 240
505085 Stockton R L 381
465879 Stoddard R W 397
483829 Stoddart C 120
Stoddart K M 402
493155 Stoddart T McK 140
411145 Stoddart-Seller J S 337
512321 Stoker A E 262
507683 Stoker T H 248
440172 Stokes J T 127
480409 Stokes R G 137
514444 Stokes S P 132
481267 Stokes T O G 121
522441 Stokes T 124
486748 Stokoe J D 137
467634 Stone A C P 118
484271 Stone A T J 251
517162 Stone C M 247
484035 Stone D J A 211
513189 Stone D J 284
496795 Stone G A 261
517704 Stone H 248
520006 Stone J M 345
509580 Stone J P F 122
498694 Stone M J 191
511784 Stone M J 246
520138 Stone P J 337
461965 Stone P P D 176
479411 Stone P R 304
423135 Stone R H 372
467457 Stone R J 338
505356 Stone R Q J 122
516415 Stone S E 287
522982 Stonebridge J M 322
520461 Stonebridge P A 345
517527 Stoneham C M 358
479358 Stoneham F T 267
520510 Stonehouse S A 360
523540 Stoner R F 311
507636 Stones C D 284
428601 Stones N 249
496378 Stones W R 121
500638 Stonestreet B F 338
483109 Stoney I M 305
484655 Stooksbury K I 373
510390 Stopford J R H 149
437176 Stopford S R A 23, 92
507305 Stopforth B 329
508729 Storey B 380
497524 Storey C A 251
492669 Storey C B 272
488237 Storey D L 395
507579 Storey E F 288
514650 Storey G E 254
509924 Storey J P 262
483352 Storey J W 350
503020 Storey J 356
503660 Storey K 349
500069 Storey L G H 141
510425 Storey M A 262
517917 Storey N J 166
516262 Storey P J 372
494049 Storey R J 349
501292 Storey T N 146
492831 Storie-Pugh P A D 318
464981 Stormer A E W 236
498695 Stormonth Darling A J 102
486749 Stormonth R J 121
508623 Storr J A 316
471358 Storr J F 137
513759 Storr J P 183
515787 Storrie A J S 196
482290 Storrie I S 283
504680 Storrie R S 340
512044 Storton J 357
484272 Story P C T 128
523817 Stothard C A 125
514036 Stott C D 262
472628 Stott H 119
516700 Stott J M 385
469102 Stott M W 127
485220 Stott R W 276
499353 Stott T B 398
514175 Stout P 391
504512 Stovell R J 124
481878 Stow A J 128
522149 Stow D H 334
500304 Stow R J S 298
516478 Stowell G H 374
512255 Strachan B G 262
522871 Strachan D J 174
521031 Strachan I B 314
521702 Strachan J L 157
518362 Strachan N A 318
474471 Strachan N 343
489722 Strachan R 342
523193 Strachan S G 337
493377 Strain I MacK 244
498944 Straker M A 112
519730 Straker S C 112
519382 Strange F 346
503019 Strange J 356
508074 Strange S R 345
424481 Strange T E L 237
511910 Strangways R G 188
503440 Stratford B E 378
455104 Strathern F A 119
474908 Straton T D 353
519010 Stratta A M 221
511519 Stratton J B W 123
471360 Stratton M 220
483100 Stratton P J 300
511520 Stratton-Christensen M J J E 95
513951 Strawbridge D L 131
507541 Strawbridge R F 139
469103 Streatfield C M 237
450461 Streatfield D L 22, 70, 135
369843 Streatfield T S C 118
489987 Street C W 388
518012 Street K L 284
522469 Street K M 285
511105 Street K 386
492985 Street M J 121
515863 Street M T 384
481879 Street N J 120
445980 Street R D 338
503327 Street-Williams M S 393
476646 Streeten J D R 127
515050 Streeter I 240
516513 Streeter-Smith G H 247
520492 Stremes J T 123
489607 Stretch M K 138
522983 Stretton J C 318
498978 Stretton J H 239
478645 Strevens R E 356
521703 Strickland A J 135
Strickland Dr B 82
515671 Strickland J D 284
483554 Strickland S W L 180
520493 Stringer A J 140
489016 Stringer A 268
497936 Stringer C 307
484157 Stringer D A 311
510391 Stringer M 130
506898 Stringer P J 277
468458 Stringer R J 280
486750 Strivens V G 138
495384 Strong B 116
513785 Strong C C 106
501063 Strong C 190
404904 Strong D S 349
472629 Strong D 137
Strong E D T 21, 76
494463 Strong G I M 267
505135 Strong G S 394
486752 Strong I M G 138
504028 Strong J A R 130
493411 Strong J W F 339
521112 Strong K J 365
504215 Strong M J 384
455105 Strong M R 257
519460 Strong P W 346
475655 Strong W E 119, 361
510728 Strongman I M 328
434846 Stroud A F 257
510981 Strowbridge N F 244
485840 Strudley D 108
481880 Strudwick M J 154
513040 Strutt A F 345
509581 Strutt D G 172
510059 Stuart A R 125

U

V

W

X

Y

Z

SUBJECT INDEX

LLOYD'S PATRIOTIC FUND

LLOYD'S BUILDING, LIME STREET
LONDON, EC3M 7HA

ESTABLISHED 1803

Chairman—DAVID BECK, Esq., M.C.

This Fund is administered by Trustees under a scheme approved by the Charity Commissioners.

The Trustees grant financial aid to such Officers and Men of the Royal Navy, the Army and Royal Marines, or their Widows, Orphans or Dependent Relatives, as, in the opinion of the Trustees, are in need of such aid, having special regard to long and meritorious service, and to suffering and losses arising therefrom.

This fund also nominates children of such Officers and Men to Army and Navy Schools.

Applications and enquiries should be addressed to the Secretary.

CHARITY OF WILLIAM KINLOCH

(Administered by the Scottish Hospital of the Foundation of King Charles II, otherwise known as the Royal Scottish Corporation)

Candidates for the benefits of the Charity must be Scotsmen or women who have served in the Navy, Army or Air Force who are in need and deserving. Preference will be given to those who have been maimed or wounded in the service of their country. Help is given by way of a weekly allowance. Application must be made in the first place in writing to the Secretary of The Royal Scottish Corporation, 37 King Street, Covent Garden, London WC2E 8JS. (Telephone 01-240 3718). Every applicant must state his or her name, address, age and occupation, and the date of his or her entry into the Navy or Army or Air Force and the date and cause of his or her discharge therefrom, and must produce evidence of his or her qualification for the appointment.

ST. ANDREWS' SCOTTISH SOLDIERS CLUB FUND

(Administered by the Scottish Hospital of the Foundation of King Charles II, otherwise known as the Royal Scottish Corporation)

The Trustees grant financial aid to:

(a) Scottish Soldiers serving in the Aldershot Garrison under the Command of the Commander in Chief United Kingdom Land Forces
(b) Scottish Soldiers serving elsewhere under the said command
(c) Serving and former Scottish Soldiers and their families and dependants in any part of the world

who are in conditions of need, hardship or distress. Application in writing to The Secretary, Royal Scottish Corporation, 37 King Street, Covent Garden, London, WC2E 8JS. (Telephone: 01-240 3718).

The Duke of York's Royal Military School, Dover

President: Major General H.R.H. THE DUKE OF KENT,
K.G., G.C.M.G., G.C.V.O., A.D.C.

Her Majesty's Commissioners:
Chairman: THE PAYMASTER-GENERAL
and 12 others

1. The School is an independent boarding grammar school which provides an education up to GCE Advanced and Scholarship level for the sons of officers and non-commissioned officers, who have served for a minimum of four years on a regular engagement. It is situated in 165 acres of downland two miles east of Dover. The 470 boys, aged 11 to 18, are comfortably provided for in every respect and enjoy a very high standard of academic, sporting and social facilities. The aim is to fit young men for University, the Services, the professions, commerce and industry.

2. A boy can be registered for admission when he is eight years old, but is not admitted to the School until he is eleven. He normally enters at the beginning of the School year, in September, and must be registered by 1 November in the year previous to admission. Each boy is subjected to educational, general and medical tests to assess his suitability for admission. Selection of boys for admission rests with Her Majesty's Commissioners. Preference is given to certain compassionate categories and such cases constitute about 10% of the normal intake. The remaining places are awarded on the basis of academic performance and potential, and parent's service.

3. Further information, including details of the very moderate costs, will be given on application to the Headmaster at the School.

Queen Victoria School
DUNBLANE

FOR THE SONS OF SCOTTISH SAILORS, SOLDIERS AND AIRMEN

Patron: **H.R.H. THE DUKE OF EDINBURGH, K.G., K.T., O.M., G.B.E.**

HM COMMISSIONERS

President:
The Secretary of State for Scotland

Vice-President:
The GOC HQ Scotland

and 17 others

The School provides boarding school education for the sons of Scottish Sailors, Soldiers and Airmen of the Regular Forces. The sons of officers are not eligible unless their fathers have had at least four years' service in the ranks. Boys may be registered for entry at the age of seven and are normally admitted to the Primary School at the age of 10 or 11. Applications must reach the School by 31 December so that they may be considered for admission the following September. Eligible candidates and at least one parent will be interviewed by the Selection Board at the School in February when practicable. In all cases candidates will be required to sit an educational test either at the School or at their current school.

The School is organised in Primary and Secondary departments in accordance with the requirements of the Scottish Education Department. Boys leave the School at various ages between sixteen and eighteen, according to their academic ability and choice of career. Boys who are academically qualified are prepared for Ordinary and Higher grades of the SCE or University Entry. Every encouragement is given to boys who wish to enter the Services but no pressure is put on them to do so.

For further information write to: The Commandant, Queen Victoria School, Dunblane, Perthshire, FK15 0JY.

ROYAL SCHOOL
FOR DAUGHTERS OF OFFICERS OF THE ARMY

Lansdown, Bath

INSTITUTED 1864

Chairman: Lt. General Sir Peter Hudson, K.C.B., C.B.E.

EXTRACTS FROM RULES, ETC.

The Daughters of Officers who hold, or have held, permanent commissions in Her Majesty's Regular Army, or in the Royal Marines, are eligible for admission. Girls are admitted between the ages of 10 and 14 years. They may be registered from birth.

Boarding fees are £1,320 per term. Reductions are considered, by the Governors, for daughters of widows of army officers.

Day pupil fees are £790 per term.

Details of the above and any further information can be obtained from the Bursar, 'Gatehouse', Charlcombe Lane, Lansdown, Bath.

THE SIR OSWALD STOLL FOUNDATION
446 FULHAM ROAD, LONDON SW6 1DT

Telephone: 01-385 2110

The Foundation consists of a block of 138 flats where disabled ex-service men, Merchant Navy, Police, Fire, Postal and Municipal ex-employees, who are in need of medical treatment or nursing care may live with their families in flats which are self-contained and designed for disabled occupiers.

Admission is to a LICENCE Agreement Occupancy and a weekly maintenance payment, not exceeding the estimated "Fair Rent" assessment is charged.

At present, the Foundation, which is Registered as an Almshouse Charity with the Housing Corporation, is engaged on an extensive scheme for the Rehabilitation/Redevelopment of the premises. It is likely to be some time before any new admissions can be considered, but any enquiries should be addressed to the *Housing Manager* at the above address.

ALEXANDRA HOUSE

(Royal United Services Short Stay Residence for Service Children)

6-8 Berthon Road, Bull Point, St. Budeaux, Plymouth PL5 1EX
Telephone: Plymouth 365203

Patron: H.R.H. Princess Alexandra, the Hon. Mrs. Angus Ogilvy, G.C.V.O.

President: The Flag Officer, Plymouth

The Foundation (formerly based at Newquay) has since 1839 looked after children of all ranks in the Armed Services. Its short stay home is now established in a modern house to meet the immediate temporary need that arises when a family crisis occurs, such as injury to the father serving abroad, sudden departure of the mother to join him, and lack of relatives or friends to care for the children. The problem is met AT ONCE, at any hour of day or night, and the children are cared for, placed in schools and by arrangement given whatever special instruction, treatment or maintenance they need for up to 3 months, while family affairs are settled.

The House is run as a family home, not as an Institution, and the Mother-in-charge has long experience in child care. It is supported by voluntary contributions and by a modest scale of payments by the parents. Financial help can sometimes be given or lent by the Foundation.

Urgent and emergency inquiries should be made by telephone as above. Routine correspondence should be addressed to the Comptroller, Alexandra Foundation.

Grants, covenants, donations and legacies are especially valuable to the Foundation as a Charity under current law, and an outline of the tax advantages to the donor or his estate may be obtained from the Comptroller by interested parties.

ARMY OFFICERS' DEPENDANTS' FUND

President: The Adjutant General

The Army Officers' Dependants' Fund is a scheme under which a sum of money is provided for the immediate needs of a dependant beneficiary or beneficiaries of subscribers who die whilst members of the Fund — irrespective of cause or place of death.

Membership of the Fund is open to all single male and female officers who are not eligible for membership of the Army Officers' Widows' Fund. The subscription is £3 per annum for single serving officers, and £6 per annum for single Retired Officers retaining their Regular Army Commission and employed in an appointment normally reserved for serving or retired officers of the Regular Army. The benefit is currently £1,800 taxfree.

Full details are contained in current AGAI's or can be obtained from:

The Secretary AODF
Room 7179
Ministry of Defence, Main Building,
Whitehall, LONDON SW1A 2HB

Telephone: 01-218 7536/6893

THE EX-SERVICES MENTAL WELFARE SOCIETY

The Ex-Services Mental Welfare Society, which has been established for over 60 years, is the only voluntary organisation which exists to assist men and women who have become mentally disabled due to service in the Armed Forces or the Merchant Navy.

They have two treatment centres where patients are cared for in the first instance under qualified staff and an assessment is made of their ability to take their place in Society.

The Society's Welfare Officers visit people in their own homes and, where required, assistance is given. Visits are also paid to about 11,000 ex-Servicemen in Mental Hospitals.

The Society has a Veterans Home for the more elderly to pass their latter days in peace, and a hostel for the homeless who are unable to take their place in the community.

The people who seek the Society's help are not only victims of the two World Wars, but also of the many continuing campaigns since, which with their guerilla tactics and street fighting, are equally likely to be the cause of mental breakdown and damage.

This work, which is unique, requires about £500,000 a year by voluntary contributions, and too often those who are serving (or have served) in the Armed Forces do not know of the Society's existence. Many who might benefit by its work are therefore missed and, equally, some who would like to contribute have no chance to do so.

Enquiries about the Society's work, or offers of help should be made to the General Secretary, Ex-Services Mental Welfare Society, Broadway House, The Broadway, Wimbledon, SW19 1RL.